DATA AND COMPUTER NETWORK COMMUNICATION

SECOND EDITION

DATA AND COMPUTER NETWORK COMMUNICATION

SECOND EDITION

By

PROF. SHASHI BANZAL

Ex Faculty Member

Deptt. of Computer Science

P.M.B. Gujarati Science College, Indore, M.P.

UNIVERSITY SCIENCE PRESS

(An Imprint of Laxmi Publications Pvt. Ltd.)

BANGALORE • CHENNAI • COCHIN • GUWAHATI • HYDERABAD

JALANDHAR • KOLKATA • LUCKNOW • MUMBAI • RANCHI • NEW DELHI

INDIA • USA • GHANA • KENYA

DATA AND COMPUTER NETWORK COMMUNICATION

Printed and bound in India
Typeset at ABRO Enterprises
First Edition: 2007; Second Edition: 2015
ISBN 978-81-318-0139-0

Published in India by

UNIVERSITY SCIENCE PRESS
(An Imprint of Laxmi Publications Pvt.Ltd.)
113, GOLDEN HOUSE, DARYAGANJ,
NEW DELHI - 110002, INDIA
Telephone : 91-11-4353 2500, 4353 2501
Fax : 91-11-2325 2572, 4353 2528
www.laxmipublications.com info@laxmipublications.com

Branches

✆	Bangalore	080-26 75 69 30	
✆	Chennai	044-24 34 47 26,	24 35 95 07
✆	Cochin	0484-237 70 04,	405 13 03
✆	Guwahati	0361-254 36 69,	251 38 81
✆	Hyderabad	040-27 55 53 83,	27 55 53 93
✆	Jalandhar	0181-222 12 72	
✆	Kolkata	033-22 27 43 84	
✆	Lucknow	0522-220 99 16	
✆	Mumbai	022-24 91 54 15,	24 92 78 69
✆	Ranchi	0651-220 44 64	

C—
Printed at: Repro Knowledgecast Limited, Thane

PREFACE TO THE SECOND EDITION

This book is a complete guide to data and computer network communication. The book covers all networking layers in detail. First it places emphasis on the physical layer, which has been the high growth area of hardware and computer networking and communication.

Also at top layer, indeed, many of the recent revolutions in computer networking including the Web, audio and video streaming and content distribution have taken place at the application layer. In preparation of first edition of this book, we believed that the application layer would remain the highest "growth area" in the field, both in terms of research and actual deployment. The intervening years have unquestionably shown this to be true. An early emphasis on the application layer issues differ from the approaches taken in most other texts, which have only a small (or non-existent) amount of material on network applications, their requirements, application layer paradigms (*e.g.,* clients/server) and the application programming interfaces.

Second, our experience as instructors has been that teaching networking applications near the beginning of the course is a powerful motivational tool. Students are thrilled to learn about how networking applications work-applications such as e-mail and the web, which most students use on a daily basis. Once a student understands the applications, the student can then understand the network services needed to support these applications. The student can then, in turn, examine the various ways in which such services might be provided and implemented in the upper layers. Covering applications early thus provides motivation for the remainder of the text.

Third, the bottom-up approach enables instructors to introduce network hardware development at an early stage. Students not only see how popular applications and protocols work, but also learn how easy it is to create their own network applications and application-level protocols. Other introductory computer networking texts do not cover application development and socket programming. Thus, with the bottom-up approach, students get early exposure to the notions of hardware programming interfaces (APIs), service models, and protocols-important concepts that resurface in all of the subsequent layers.

The part-by-part description of the book follows; it is divided into five parts. Part 1 describes the introduction to data and computer network communication, explores data communication and focuses on computer network as part of an effective strategy to solve that problem. This part contains two chapters. Part 2 describes the physical layer structure and it covers six chapters. Part 3 describes the data link layer structure and it contains three chapters. Part 4 describes the medium access control layer, it contains two chapters. Part 5 describes the local area network, it contains ten chapters. Part 6 describes all about network layer right from its working and routing. Part 7 describes flow and congestion control. Part 8 describes transport layer and contains one chapter on the topic. The last Part 9 contains one last chapter describing all protocols which are used at presentation and application layer.

The book contains a large number of examples, exercises and figures, which should enhance its suitability for class room instructions some of the exercises are theoretical and practical in nature and supplement substantially the main text.

—AUTHOR

PREFACE TO THE FIRST EDITION

Unlike the other computer networking texts, this text is organized in a bottom-up manner—that is, it begins at the physical layer and works its way down towards the application layer. The bottom-up approach has several important benefits. First, it places emphasis on the physical layer, which has been the high "growth area" of hardware and computer networking and communication. Also at top layer, indeed, many of the recent revolutions in computer networking—including the Web, audio and video streaming and content distribution—have taken place at the application layer. In preparing the first edition of this book, we believed that the application layer would remain the highest growth area in the field, both in terms of research and actual deployment. The intervening years have unquestionably shown this to be true! An early emphasis on application layer issues differs from the approaches taken in most other texts, which have only a small (or nonexistent) amount of material on network applications, their requirements, application layer paradigms (*e.g.*, client/server), and the application programming interfaces. Second, our experience as instructors has been that teaching networking applications near the beginning of the course is a powerful motivational tool. Students are thrilled to learn about how networking applications work—application such as e-mail and the Web, which most students use on a daily basis. Once a student understands the applications, the student can then understand the network services needed to support these applications. The student can then, in turn, examine the various ways in which such services might be provided and implemented in the upper layers. Covering applications early thus provides motivation for the remainder of the text.

Third, the bottom-up approach enables instructors to introduce network hardware development at an early stage. Students not only see how popular applications and protocols work, but also learn how easy it is to create their own network applications and application-level protocols. Other introductory computer networking texts do not cover application development and socket programming. Thus, with the bottom-up approach, students get early exposure to the notions of hardware programming interfaces (APIs), service models, and protocols—important concepts that resurface in all of the subsequent layers.

The Part-by-Part description of the book follows, it is divided into five parts:

Part 1, The part describes the Introduction to Data and Computer Network Communication, explores data communication and focuses on computer network as part of an effective strategy to solve that problem. The part contains two chapters:

Chapter 1, This chapter focuses on.

Chapter 2, This chapter describes about.

Part 2, The part describes the Physical layer structure and it covers six chapters:

Chapter 3, This chapter explain about data transmission signals.

Chapter 4, This chapter describe about multiplexing techniques and switching.

Chapter 5, This chapter focuses on all transmission medias in details.

Chapter 6, This chapter describe about telephone networks.

Chapter 7, This chapter explain about cable modem and television.

Chapter 8, This chapter focuses on high speed network access such as SONET.

Part 3, The part describes the data link layer structure and it contains three chapters:

Chapter 9, This chapter describe about data link layer.

Chapter 10, This chapter focuses on error control, detection and correction.

Chapter 11, This chapter explain all about data link layer protocol.

Part 4, The part describes the Medium access control layer, it contains two chapters:

Chapter 12, This chapter describe about channels.

Chapter 13, This chapter focuses on medium access control layer.

Part 5, The part describes the local area network, it contains ten chapters:

Chapter 14, This chapter explain about local area network.

Chapter 15, This chapter describe about token ring.

Chapter 16, This chapter focuses on blue-tooth.

Chapter 17, This chapter explain about virtual local area network.

Chapter 18, This chapter focuses on wireless transmission and satellite communication.

Chapter 19, This chapter describe about frame relay.

Chapter 20, This chapter explain about ATM.

Chapter 21, This chapter focuses on FDDI.

Chapter 22, This chapter describe about switched multi-megabit data service.

Chapter 23, This chapter focuses on ISDN.

Part 6, The part describes all about network layer right from its working and routing:

Chapter 24, This chapter describe about network layer.

Chapter 25, This chapter explain about inter-networking.

Chapter 26, This chapter focuses on basics of routing.

Part 7, The part describes flow and congestion control:

Chapter 27, This chapter explain about flow and congestion control.

Chapter 28, This chapter describe about bridge, hub, repeater and gateway.

Part 8, The part describes transport layer:

Chapter 29, This chapter describe about transport layer.

Part 9, The part describes all protocols which are used at presentation and application layer:

Chapter 30, This chapter focuses on presentation and application layer.

The book contains a large number of examples and exercises, which should enhance its suitability for classroom instructions. Some of the exercises are theoretical in nature and supplement substantially the main text.

—AUTHOR

ACKNOWLEDGEMENTS

There are a number of individuals who have helped us with the contents of this book. Specifically, I thank Shri Vivek Banzal (DGM) for enormous support during writing this book.

We are grateful to all our former teaching assistants who helped us in developing exercises, assignments and systems. There have been a number of friends and colleagues whose comments have led to improvements in the text. We are also truly indebted to the anonymous outside for their detailed comments and constructive criticism, which were extremely useful.

We are grateful to our editors, for their enthusiastic support of this project. The production team at Laxmi Publications Pvt. Ltd. has been great.

Finally, we would like to warmly thank my parents, husband and both kids for providing advice, encouragement and support at various stages of the preparation of this book. We also thank them for reminding us that there are things in life beyond writing books. In end, we thank to all staff of Laxmi Publications Pvt. Ltd. for essential support throughout the arduous process of getting the book into print.

—AUTHOR

CONTENTS

PART 2 : PHYSICAL LAYER

PART 3 : DATA LINK LAYER

PART 4 : THE MEDIA ACCESS CONTROL SUBLAYER (MAC)

PART 5 : LOCAL AREA NETWORK (LAN)

PART 6 : NETWORK LAYER

PART 7 : FLOW AND CONGESTION CONTROL

PART 1

Computer Communication and Network Basics

1 OVERVIEW OF COMPUTER COMMUNICATION AND NETWORKING

Today, computer is available in many offices and homes and therefore, there is a need to share data and programs among various computers with the advancement of data communication facilities.

The communication between computers has increased and thus it has extended the power of computer beyond the computer room. Now, a user sitting at one place can communicate computers of any remote sites through communication channel.

COMMUNICATION SYSTEM AND NETWORKING

Nowadays, we are fully absorbed by the information age and spending more time communicating and gathering information through the Internet, it has become necessary to have a working knowledge of the technology behind the scenes. We are faced with terms like baud rate, modems, cellular phones, TCP/IP, ATM, ISDN etc., and trying to make decision about our communications needs involving the systems that these terms apply to. In order to develop a useful working and understanding of this technology requires us to have a good understanding of the basic and background technology and fundamentals of data communications.

Basic Elements of Communication System

For any communication system to be useful, three main parts are essential. They are:

1. Sending end (Source)
2. Transmission channel (Transmission channel)
3. Receiving end (Receiver)

These parts are shown in figure 1.1. Without these parts we can not do communication.

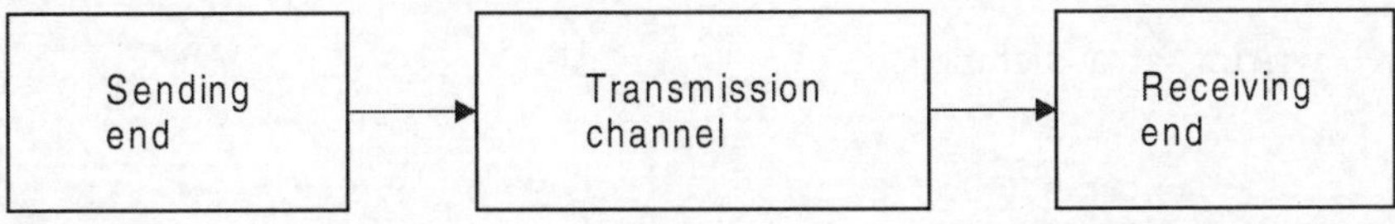

Figure 1.1 *Basic Parts of a Communication System.*

Speech is the simplest communication man uses, yet it contains all three main parts. When a person speaks (message generation or sending end), his thoughts are converted to movement which operate vocal cords. The thoughts are in turn converted to pressure variations in the air. These variations travel outwards (as a signal) through moving air (transmission channel) and they end up reaching the listener (receiving end). A more generalized view of a communication system is shown in figure 1.2.

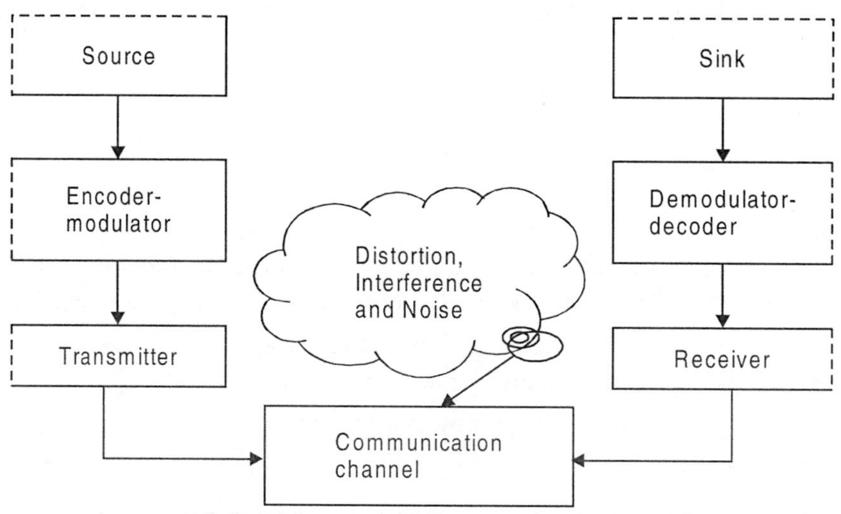

Figure 1.2 *Elements of a Communication System.*

The urgent need to send information quickly over long distances led to telecommunications. Communication over long distances is no longer a problem, people can communicate instantly in time using modern telephone networks. These telecommunication networks have made it possible for people to communicate among themselves and when appropriately modified they can facilitate communication between people and electronic machines (*e.g.*, computer).

The words "tele", "phon", and "graph" are derived from Greek.

Tele—means 'at a distance'

Phon—means sound or speech

Graph—means writing or drawing.

Therefore, telecommunication means communication at a distance. This can be done through wires called transmission lines or through atmosphere by a radio link. Other examples include :

Telephone—speaking at a distance

Television—seeing at a distance

Telegraph—writing at a distance.

NEED FOR COMPUTER NETWORK

If your business has more than one computer, chances are you could benefit from networking them. A Local Area Network (LAN) connects your company's computers, allowing them to share and exchange a variety of information. While one computer can be useful on its own, several networked computers can be much more useful.

Here are some of the ways a computer network can help your business:

- **File sharing:** Have you ever needed to access a file stored on another computer? A network makes it easy for everyone to access the same file and prevents a people from accidentally creating different versions. There is no need to carry a floppy disk.
- **Printer sharing:** If you use a computer, then there are also chances of use of printer. With a network, several computers can share the same printer and take print-outs. Although you might need a more expensive printer to handle the added work-loads, it's still cheaper to use a network printer than to connect a separate printer to every computer in your office.
- **Communicate and collaborate:** It's hard for people to work together if no one knows what anyone else is doing. A network allows employees to share files, view other people's work and exchange ideas more efficiently and easily. In a larger office, you can use email and instant messaging tools to communicate quickly and to store messages for future reference.
- **Get organized:** A variety of network scheduling software is available that makes it possible to arrange meetings without constantly checking everyone's schedules. This software usually includes other helpful features, such as shared address books and to-do lists.
- **Get online:** If you have several computers but just one phone line, a network makes using the internet much easier. Several computers can share one modem to use the same internet connection. Or you can even install a dedicated high-speed internet connection (such as a cable modem or DSL) for your network.
- **Save your data:** Nowadays, its very important to backup and update your computer data regularly. A network makes it easier to back up all of your company's data on one set of tapes, CDs or other backup systems.

  Of course this isn't a complete list—once you have a network, you'll probably find many other uses for it. And once you get used to the benefits of a network, you'll never look at your computer the same way again.

EVOLUTION OF NETWORK

In the past, networks intended to be designed specifically to carry voice, video, or data signals.

The design of voice, video, or data networks differed because of fundamental differences between voice, video, and data signals, *e.g.*, voice is analog, data is digital in nature.

The telephone network was the first and is by far the largest network supporting wired telephones, fax machines, cellular phones, cordless phones, answering machines, and modems for data transmission over the phone network.

The TV network uses a combination of coaxial cable, satellite links, and electromagnetic propagation through air to transmit video (including voice) signals.

The data network uses a variety of transmission media, including the voice and TV networks, to transmit data in the form of digital signals.

Today, voice and video are becoming increasingly digitized (digital phones, high resolution digital TV) and are increasingly transmitted by data networks.

Ultimately all voice, video, and data will be digital and will be transmitted by digital (data) networks. The reason is that it is far more cost effective to build, operate and manage networks that use digital rather than analog signals. (*e.g.*, if the telephone network were built today, it would be an all digital network). Future data networks will interconnect multimedia devices capable of handling voice, video, and data.

Evolution of Computer Network

Computer networking started to evolve in the early and mid 1960's with the advent of timesharing.

By 1970 timesharing machines supported networks of local and remote terminals.

These early networks supported timesharing and remote batch processing.

In the latter part of the 1970's, computer to computer network connections were used for load sharing and data interchange (*e.g.*, early electronic funds transfer).

In the late 1970's and early 1980's, ARPA (Advanced Research Projects Agency) started to test networks for peer-to-peer computer communication and terminal support on a national scale.

By the mid 1980's this network became available to the universities and NSF (National Science Foundation) started funding university connectivity.

Early applications of these networks included electronic mail, downloading large data sets (ftp) and remote access to computers (telnet).

By the early 1990's, there were several million workstations connected to the Internet and usage was growing very rapidly.

By the mid 1990's, the Internet was proven reliable technology and began to be commercialized. Companies such as CompuServe and America online began to provide a number of services using the Internet, including providing Internet connectivity to personal computers in people's homes.

Today, about 20 million workstations are connected to the commodity Internet and usage continues to increase, resulting in congestion at peak times of the day over many parts of the network.

The increasing network congestion reduced the value of the Internet for new applications such as web-based distance education and low latency, high bandwidth connection to and among supercomputers. These applications require support for QoS (Quality of Service) not available on the current Internet. *e.g.,* bandwidth reservation

Low variance in latency to prevent jerkiness in video transmission. Consequently, leading research institutions are leading the development of Internet 2, a new high bandwidth network strictly for universities to avoid congestion due to commercial traffic and one that supports QoS functions required by multimedia and other applications.

FUNCTIONS OF DATA NETWORKS

In general, the vast majority of today's networks are store and forward networks in that stored data is forwarded from its source to its destination in a series of hops when it is convenient to do so.

While the store and forward technique has several disadvantages (*e.g.,* it is difficult to transmit voice because the transmission delays are highly variable), it has the advantage that results in more affordable networks and it allows errors to be detected and corrected through retransmission.

The store and forward concept makes it convenient for networks to be used for:

- Exchanging electronic mail
- Reading and posting to electronic bulletin boards
- Accessing files and information anywhere in the network (e.g., library and web services)
- Accessing unique hardware and software resources
- Sharing of information (workgroup collaboration)

Such applications provide users with access to needed information and resources when they are needed from wherever there is telephone or some other means of network access. This is changing how we play, work, communicate, teach, learn, and conduct business. They provide both new opportunities and new challenges.These challenges will slow the deployment of networks to a rush from what would otherwise be a stampede.

NETWORK CHALLENGES

Due to address space shortage, IP addresses are limited to 2**32 and efforts are underway to increase this to 2**128. Enterprises cannot use all 2**24 addresses allowed by a class a license.

Class C addresses are more effective but they increase the size of routing tables in routers, reducing the efficiency of packet forwarding. Decentralized control allows the network to easily scale. It also threatens to turn it into anarchy where reliable service is not guaranteed. Security is also an issue. It also means there is no uniform way to do usage accounting, which is required to guarantee quality of service for emerging applications (*e.g.,* multimedia).

Multimedia (voice, video, and data) applications need real-time performance guarantees such as a certain minimum bandwidth or bounded latency with small variance (jitter+). These

Quality of Service (QoS) performance parameters are not well supported with the current Internet technologies.

QoS requires signaling to inform all routers in the path about the quality of service parameters for each class of traffic. New traffic streams must be allowed or denied entry to the network depending upon the current traffic streams and their QoS parameters. This is difficult to accomplish under decentralized network control.

IMPORTANCE OF NETWORK

Key technology of 20th century is information gathering, processing, and distribution.

World wide telephone networks were constructed. Radio and television networks have reached every corner of the world. Communications satellites have been launched. In the past 20 years very powerful affordable standalone computers have been interconnected to form computer networks. These computer networks are changing the way we teach, learn, do business, and communicate with each other.

NETWORKING BASICS

A network is a group of computers, printers, and other devices that are connected together with cables. Information travels over the cables, allowing network users to exchange documents & data with each other, print to the same printers, and generally share any hardware or software that is connected to the network. Each computer, printer, or other peripheral device that is connected to the network is called a node. Networks can have tens, thousands, or even millions of nodes or computers. Like most things, networks are assembled according to certain rules. Cabling, for example, has to be a certain length; each cabling strand can only support a certain amount of network traffic, etc. The rules that govern how a network is set up are called its topology. The most popular topology in use today is called Ethernet, which consists of computers and peripherals cabled together in specific ways. Ethernet is relatively inexpensive, easy to set up and use, and very, very fast.

Ethernet networks are categorized by how fast they can move information. Speed is expressed in megabits per second (or Mbps), where one "bit" is equal to 1/8th of a character, letter, or number. There are currently two Ethernet speed categories. Standard Ethernet operates at a fast 10Mbps, which is quick enough for most networking tasks. Fast Ethernet, by contrast, races along at a blistering 100Mbps, making it ideal for desktop video, multimedia, and other speed-hungry applications. The new technology behind fast Ethernet, which was introduced in the beginning of 1995, is not readily compatible with standard Ethernet. Making the two "talk" with each other requires special equipment and some knowledge of Internet working. If you're building your first network, decide whether to go with standard or fast Ethernet before you begin shopping around for network hardware and software. Unless you plan on using video, multimedia, or heavy graphics software, plan on using standard Ethernet.

CABLING BASICS

In network, cabling is very important.

The two most popular types of network cabling are twisted-pair (also known as 10BaseT) and thin coax (also known as 10Base2). 10BaseT cabling looks like ordinary telephone wire, except that it has 8 wires inside instead of 4. Thin coax looks like the copper coaxial cabling that's often used to connect a VCR to a TV set.

Thin coax and 10BaseT can both be used exclusively or together, depending on the type of network that you're putting together. Small networks, for example, may want to use 10BaseT cabling by it, because it's inexpensive, flexible, and ideal for going short distances. Larger networks (usually with 10 or more computers) may use a thin coax backbone with small clusters of 10BaseT cabling that branch off from it at regular intervals.

DATA COMMUNICATION AND COMPUTER NETWORK

Today, computer is available in many offices, factories and homes and therefore, there is a need to share data and programs among various computers with the advancement of data communication facilities. The communication between computers has increased and thus it has extended the power of computer beyond the computer room. Now a user sitting at one place can communicate computers of any remote sites through communication channel.

Data Communication

Data Communications is the transfer of data or information between a source and a receiver. The source transmits the data and the receiver receives it. The actual generation of the information is not part of data communications nor is the resulting action of the information at the receiver. Data Communication is interested in the transfer of data, the method of transfer and the preservation of the data during the transfer process.

In local area networks, we are interested in "connectivity", connecting computers together to share resources. Even though the computers can have different disk operating systems, languages, cabling and locations, they still can communicate to one another and share resources.

The purpose of data communications is to provide the rules and regulations that allow computers with different disk operating systems, languages, cabling and locations to share resources. The rules and regulations are called protocols and standards in data communications.

We all are acquainted with some sorts of communication in our day to day life. For communication of information and messages we use telephone and postal communication systems. Similarly, data and information from one computer system can be transmitted to other systems across geographical areas. Thus, data transmission is the movement of information using some standard methods. These methods include electrical signals carried along a conductor, optical signals along an optical fibers and electromagnetic areas.

Suppose a manager has to write several letters to various clients. First he has to use his PC and word processing package to prepare his letter. If the PC is connected to the entire client's PCs through network, he can send the letters to all the clients within minutes. Thus, irrespective of geographical areas, if PCs are connected through communication channel, the data and information, computer files and any other program can be transmitted to other computer systems within seconds. The modern form of communication like e-mail and Internet is possible only because of computer networking.

The distance over which data moves within a computer may vary from a few thousandths of an inch, as is the case within a single IC chip, to as much as several feet along the backplane of the main circuit board. Over such small distances, digital data may be transmitted as direct, two-level electrical signals over simple copper conductors. Except for the fastest computers, circuit designers are not very concerned about the shape of the conductor or the analog characteristics of signal transmission.

Frequently, however, data must be sent beyond the local circuitry that constitutes a computer. In many cases, the distances involved may be enormous. Unfortunately, as the distance between the source of a message and its destination increases, accurate transmission becomes increasingly difficult. This results from the electrical distortion of signals traveling through long conductors, and from noise added to the signal as it propagates through a transmission medium. Although some precautions must be taken for data exchange within a computer, the biggest problems occur when data is transferred to devices outside the computer's circuitry. In this case, distortion and noise can become so severe that information is lost.

Data communications concerns the transmission of digital messages to devices external to the message source. "External" devices are generally thought of as being independently powered circuitry that exists beyond the chassis of a computer or other digital message source. As a rule, the maximum permissible transmission rate of a message is directly proportional to signal power and inversely proportional to channel noise. It is the aim of any communications system to provide the highest possible transmission rate at the lowest possible power and with the least possible noise.

Criteria of Data Communication Network

The major criteria that a data communication network must meet are:

1. Performance
2. Consistency
3. Reliability
4. Recovery
5. Security

1. Performance

Performance is defined as the rate of transference of error-free data. It is measured by the response time. Response time is the elapsed time between the end of an inquiry and the beginning of a response, *e.g.*, requesting a file transfer and starting the file transfer. Factors that affect response time are:

Number of Users: The more users are on a network, the slower the network will run.

Transmission Speed: The speed that the data will be transmitted at measured in bits per second (bps).

Media Type: The type of physical connection used to connect nodes together.

Hardware Type: Slow computers such as XT, or fast ones such as Pentiums.

Software Program: How well is the network operating system (NOS) written.

2. Consistency

Consistency is the predictability of response time and accuracy of data.

Users prefer to have consistent response times; they develop a feel for normal operating conditions. For example, if the "normal" response time is 3 seconds for printing to a network printer but a response time of over 30 seconds occurs, we know that there is a problem in the system.

Accuracy of data determines if the network is reliable! If a system loses data, then the users will not have confidence in the information and will often not use the system.

3. Reliability

Reliability is the measure of how often a network is usable. MTBF (Mean Time between Failures) is a measure of the average time a component is expected to operate between failures, and is normally provided by the manufacturer. A network failure can be caused by a problem with the hardware, the data carrying medium, or the network operating system.

4. Recovery

Recovery is the network's ability to return to a prescribed level of operation after a network failure. This level is where the amount of lost data is non-existent or at a minimum. Recovery is based on having backup files.

5. Security

Security is the protection of hardware, software and data from unauthorized access. Restricted physical access to computers, password protection, limiting user privileges and data encryption are common security methods. Anti-virus monitoring programs to defend against computer viruses are also a security measure.

Basic Components of Communication

Three basic components are required for communication. Followings are basic components of the communication:

- **Source:** The transmitter of data. Examples are: Terminals, Computers, Mainframes
- **Medium:** The communications stream through which the data is being transmitted. Examples are: Cabling, Microwave, Fiber optics, Radio Frequencies (RF), Infrared Wireless.
- **Receiver:** The receiver of the data transmitted. Examples are: Printers, Terminals, Mainframes, Computers.

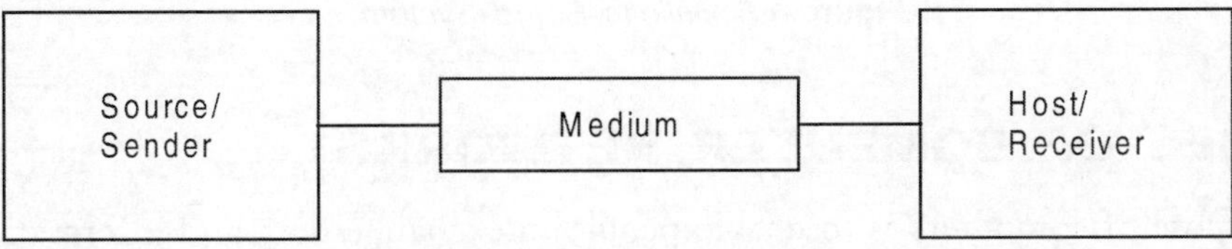

Figure 1.3 *Basic Components.*

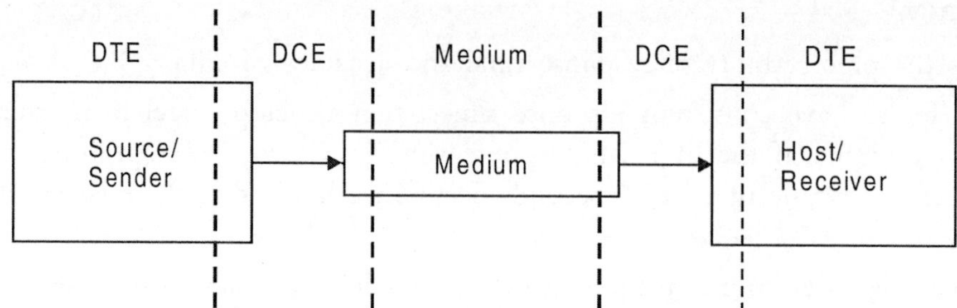

Figure 1.4 *Source Medium Receiver.*

- **DCE:** The interface between the source and the medium, and the medium and the receiver are called the DCE (Data Communication Equipment) and are a physical piece of equipment.
- **DTE:** Data terminal equipment is the telecommunications name given to the source and receiver's equipment.

An example of this would be your PC dialing into a BBS (Bulletin Board System):

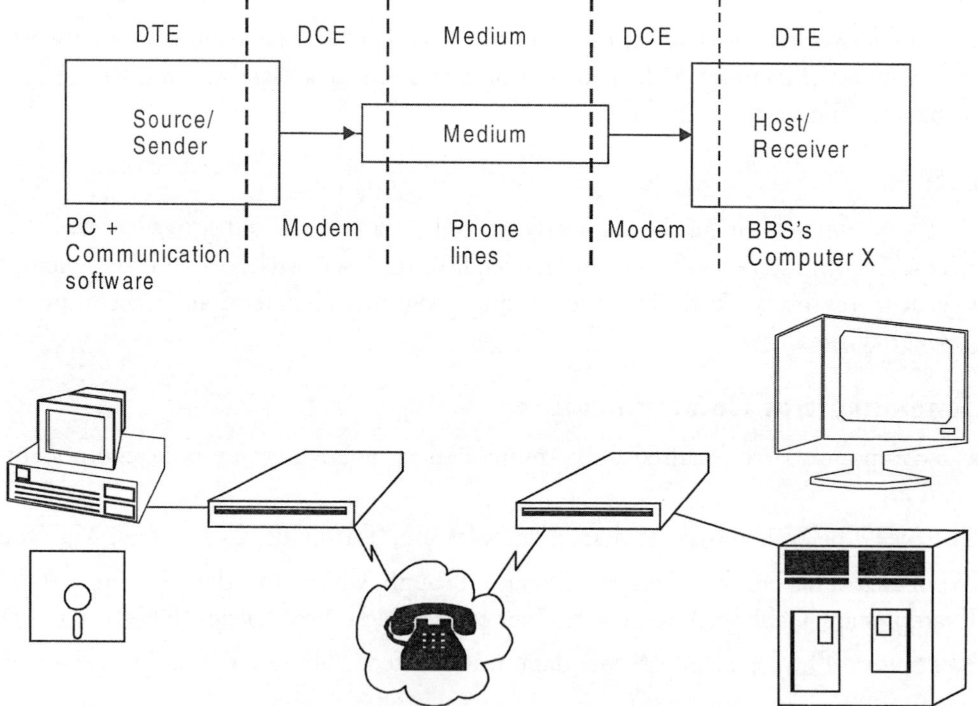

Figure 1.5 *Bulletin Board System.*

MAIN USES OF COMPUTER NETWORKS

The main purpose of computers is to enable people to exchange data and information. This can take the form of electronic mail (e-mail) or Intra and Extranets. It is the use of these resources that can decide whether a computer network is an asset or a problem for the operators.

On the most basic level computer networks are great to share resources, such as printers and storage space. On the most advanced level computer networks can carry video data for remote video conferencing for example.

Business Use

In the business context computer networks can be a real asset. This includes storage and retrieval of information, reducing the need for paper traffic and record keeping in paper format, as well as rationalizing the time that staff spends producing correspondence and accounts. The big danger is that the real purpose of a computer network is not fully assessed resulting in an installation and maintenance plan that is not adequate for its use.

In addition, if the installation of a new computer network is not fully supported by the staff, then the network itself is may not be taken full advantage of, and record keeping becomes a mixture between digital and paper based records.

In a business context the following uses are typical. They are listed in ascending order of complexity:

- Share resources such as printer.
- Share data on a central server, where all data is collected.
- Communicate via e-mail.
- Exchange information via an internal network.
- Allow all staff access to the Internet.

Use the network and the Internet to allow staff access to business data from anywhere in the world.

Integrate the whole business operation into a networked operation, including sales activity, stock holding, quotations, ordering raw materials, control the production process, process invoices, process all the accounts, analyze business performance, quality control.

Each stage introduces an extra layer of complexity to the operation and an extra level of staff expertise and acceptance. In addition to the sheer network installation each level of functionality is combined with a suite of software that needs to be configured once and kept running subsequently. One example of how complicated things become on the simplest level is access and sharing of data. A detailed plan and assessment of who should have access to what kind of data, and who can change and delete data needs to be drawn up and implemented. From a technical point of view this is very simple, from an organizational point of view this may be a serious difficulty.

With the adoption of a new procedure within the business and the learning of the new processes by the staff, the network becomes ever more mission critical. This means, that if a problem occurs, the operation of the business could be seriously disrupted. To avoid major losses, for example, consider the introduction and purchase of adequate data backup procedures.

And this also means that careful planning is required to make sure that the necessary maintenance of the system is always kept up. Usually the cost of the system and ongoing maintenance is offset by the productivity gains of the improved operation of the business.

It is strongly advisable to make a full assessment of the cost and benefits that the introduction of the new procedure entails and to argue the introduction of a new process in terms of a strict business case.

Very often such undertakings fail because of a communication gap between the technical personnel and engineers who carry out the installation, and the management and staff of the company that takes such a new system on.

Overall, especially in small to medium sized businesses, the strict assessment of cost and benefit is not carried leading to serious problems.

There is also the tendency to overcomplicate the procedure in software terms. Software can in theory do anything you like (as long as it is an algorithmic process), but different off-the-shelf packages may not interact with each other very well. It is impossible to foresee problems of this kind without the detailed input by experienced engineers.

Scientific Use

Within science, computer networks were used very early on to share resources and exchange data. This goes back to the beginnings of the Internet, and in fact, the Internet as we know it today was created within a scientific laboratory.

It is standard procedure to use networks to share data and use remote computers to carry out large computations. This includes the use of supercomputers in various locations. As an example consider the use of a supercomputer located in Norway by researchers in the UK. To the operator the physical distance is immaterial. Data nowadays can be transferred very quickly from remote computers.

In addition to the "outsourcing" of computing power, the old system of using one powerful machine within a department to carry out large computations, and many small hosts for the creation of reports is very common.

Research is underway to examine the way in which networked computers can be used for the parallel processing of large computations. The ultimate aim is to produce a system that would use all the resources available on a computer network (and even the Internet) as a computing resource.

The use of computers connected via a network for parallel computations is a non-trivial problem. Many researchers are developing procedures for data transfer and data handling, as well as the adaptation of algorithms for given tasks to parallel processing.

Parallel computations are also carried out by large machines that contain more than one processor. There are two types:

- Processor with local memory
- Processors with shared memory

  Conceptually the difference between parallel computers and computers on a network is very small. Both exchange data, both have separate memory per processor.

  Here, we now need to make a distinction between processor and computer:

- A computer is the combination of a processor, memory and peripheral devices.
- A processor is an integrated circuit chip in which the processing is takes place. Without peripheral devices a processor cannot work.

For scientific use it is inconceivable nowadays not to be using a computer network. Interestingly, each laboratory has a technician who is dedicated to the maintenance of the computer network and the safeguarding of data through regular backups. Businesses ought to take notice of this.

COMMUNICATIONS AND DATA TRANSMISSION MODES

Serial and Parallel Communication Modes

In addition to the different models of communications, there are several methods in which data can be transmitted between source and destination nodes. So, there are two types of communication modes,

1. Serial communications
2. Parallel communications.

Most digital messages are vastly longer than just a few bits. Because it is neither practical nor economic to transfer all bits of a long message simultaneously, the message is broken into smaller parts and transmitted sequentially. Bit-serial transmission conveys a message one bit at a time through a channel. Each bit represents a part of the message. The individual bits are then reassembled at the destination to compose the message. In general, one channel will pass only one bit at a time. Thus, bit-serial transmission is necessary in data communications if only a single channel is available. Bit-serial transmission is normally just called serial transmission and is the chosen communications method in many computer peripherals. Byte-serial transmission conveys eight bits at a time through eight parallel channels. Although the raw transfer rate is eight times faster than in bit-serial transmission, eight channels are needed, and the cost may be as much as eight times higher to transmit the message. When distances are short, it may nonetheless be both feasible and economic to use parallel channels in return for high data rates. The popular centronics printer interface is a case where byte-serial transmission is used. As another example, it is common practice to use a 16-bit-wide data bus to transfer data between a microprocessor and memory chips; this provides the equivalent of 16 parallel channels. On the other hand, when communicating with a timesharing system over a modem, only a single channel is available, and bit-serial transmission is required. This figure illustrates these ideas:

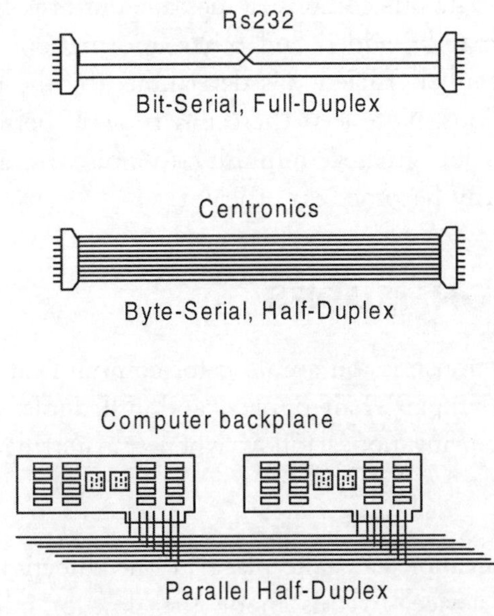

Figure 1.6 *Communication Modes.*

The baud rate refers to the signaling rate at which data is sent through a channel and is measured in electrical transitions per second. In the EIA232 serial interface standard, one signal transition, at most, occurs per bit, and the baud rate and bit rate are identical. In this case, a rate of 9600 baud corresponds to a transfer of 9,600 data bits per second with a bit period of 104 microseconds (1/9600 sec.). If two electrical transitions were required for each bit, as is the case in non-return-to-zero coding, then at a rate of 9600 baud, only 4800 bits per second could be conveyed. The channel efficiency is the number of bits of useful information passed through the channel per second. It does not include framing, formatting, and error detecting bits that may be added to the information bits before a message is transmitted, and will always be less than one.

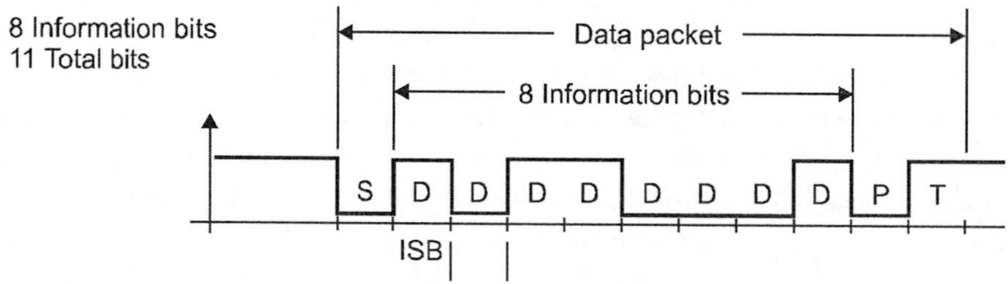

Figure 1.7 *Baud Rate.*

The data rate of a channel is often specified by its bit rate (often thought erroneously to be the same as baud rate). However, an equivalent measure channel capacity is bandwidth. In general, the maximum data rate a channel can support is directly proportional to the channel's bandwidth and inversely proportional to the channel's noise level.

A communications protocol is an agreed-upon convention that defines the order and meaning of bits in a serial transmission. It may also specify a procedure for exchanging messages. A protocol will define how many data bits compose a message unit, the framing and formatting bits, any error-detecting bits that may be added and other information that governs control of the communications hardware. Channel efficiency is determined by the protocol design rather than by digital hardware considerations. Note that there is a tradeoff between channel efficiency and reliability—protocols that provide greater immunity to noise by adding error-detecting and correcting codes must necessarily become less efficient.

DATA TRANSMISSION MODES

Three different modes of data transmission are used for communication purposes, each responds to a specific type of circuit: simplex, half-duplex, and full-duplex. These modes specify the protocols that sending and receiving nodes follow when transferring data.

1. Simplex

In simplex mode the communication can take place in one direction. The receiver receives the signal from the transmitting device. In this mode the flow of information is unidirectional. Hence, it is rarely used for data communication.

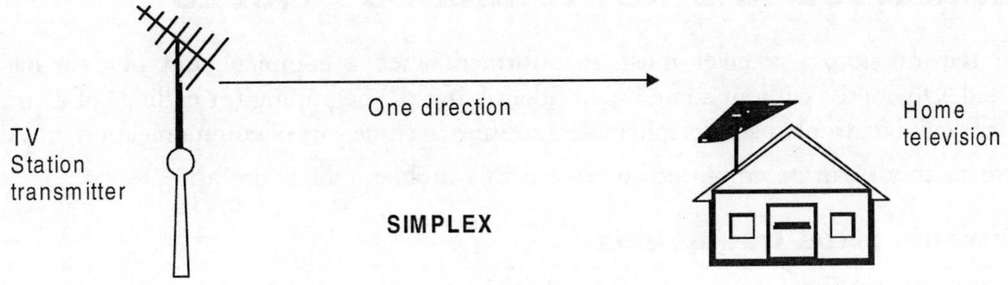

Figure 1.8

2. Half-Duplex

In half-duplex mode the communication channel is used in both directions, but only in one direction at a time. Thus, a half-duplex line can alternately send and receive data.

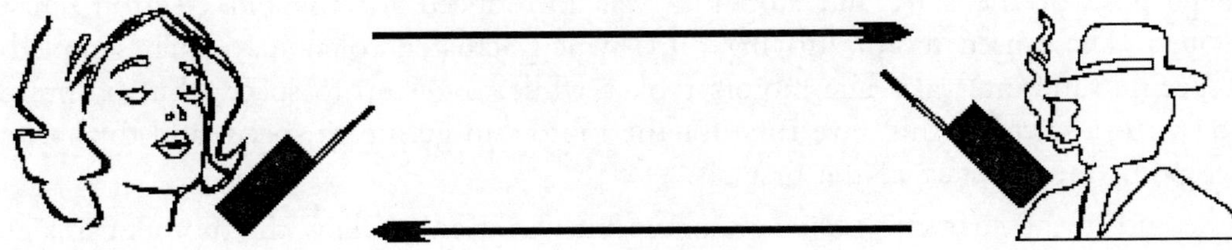

Figure 1.9

3. Full-Duplex

In full-duplex the communication channel is used in both directions at the same time. Use of full-duplex line improves the efficiency as the line turn-around time required in half-duplex arrangement is eliminated. Example of this mode of transmission is the telephone line.

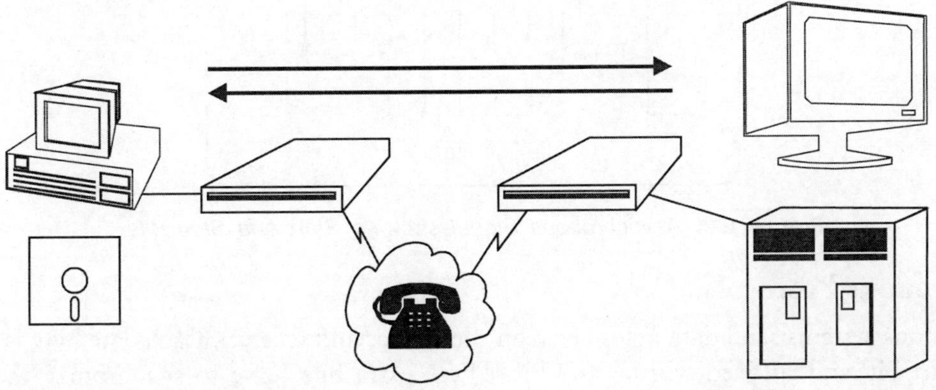

Figure 1.10

SYNCHRONOUS AND ASYNCHRONOUS MODES

In serial transmission, a receiver must be informed when a complete unit of data has been transmitted. Obviously, without some way of identifying the beginning (or ending) of a character, the transmitted data would be indecipherable, resulting in some sort of communication breakdown.

Two methods can be employed to resolve this problem. They are as:

Asynchronous Serial Transmission

We can synchronize the sending and receiving nodes so that the receiving node always knows when a new character is being sent or we can insert within the bit stream special "start" and "stop" bits. This technique is called asynchronous communication.

Because no signal lines are used to convey clock (timing) information, this method group's data together into a sequence of bits (five-eight), then prefixes them with a start bit and a stop bit.

The purpose of the start and stop bits was introduced for the old electromechanical teletypewriters. These used motors driving cams which actuated solenoids which sampled the signal at specific time intervals. The motors took a while to get up to speed, thus by prefixing the first bit with a start bit, this gave time for the motors to get up to speed, and thus acted as a reference point for the start of the first bit.

At the end of the character sequence, a stop bit was used to allow the motors/cams etc to get back to normal, in addition, it was also need to fill in time in case the character was an end of line, when the teletypewriter would need to go to the beginning of a new-line. Without the stop character, the machine could not complete this before the next character arrived.

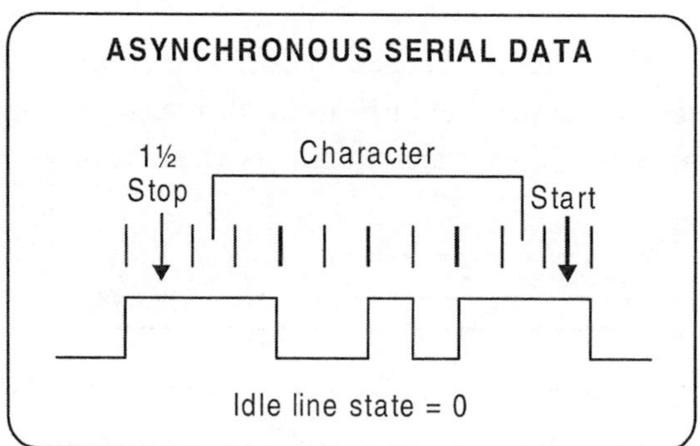

Figure 1.11 *Asynchronous Signal showing Start and Stop Bits.*

Asynchronous Protocols

Asynchronous systems send data bytes between the sender and receiver. Each data byte is preceded with a start bit, and suffixed with a stop bit. These extra bits serve to synchronize the receiver with the sender.

Transmission of these extra bits (2 per byte) reduce data throughput. Synchronization is achieved for each character only. When the sender has no data to transmit, the line is idle and the sender and receiver are not in synchronization. Asynchronous protocols are suited for low speed data communications.

Synchronous Serial Transmission

In synchronous transmission, the line idle state is changed to a known character sequence (7E), which is used to synchronize the receiver to the sender. The start and stop bits are removed, and each character is combined with others into a data packet. The data packet is prefixed with a header field, and suffixed with a trailer field which includes a checksum value (used by the receiver to check for errors in sending).

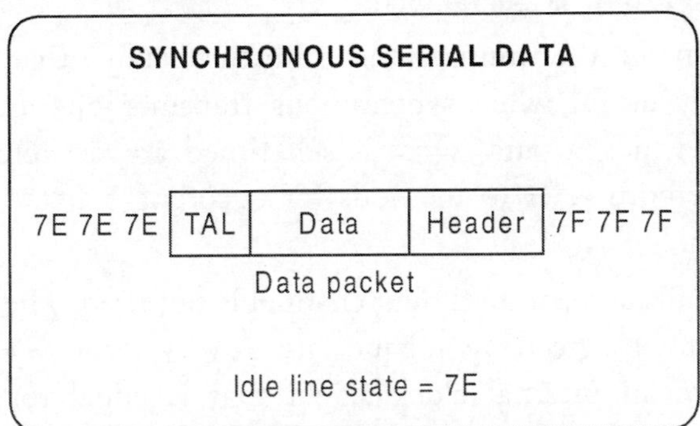

Figure 1.12 *Synchronous Data.*

The header field is used to convey address information (sender and receiver), packet type and control data. The data field contains the users data (if it can't fit in a single packet, then use multiple packets and number them) or control data. Generally, it has a fixed size. The tail field contains checksum information which the receiver uses to check whether the packet was corrupted during transmission.

Synchronous Protocols

Synchronous protocols involve sending timing information along with the data bytes, so that the receiver can remain in synchronization with the sender. When the sender has no data to transmit, the sender transmits idle flags (a sequence of alternating 0's and 1's) to maintain sender/receiver synchronization. Data bytes are packaged into small chunks called packets, with address fields being added at the front (header) and checksums at the rear of the packet. There are two main types of synchronous protocols used today, character orientated (bi-sync) and bit orientated (hdlc).

Asynchronous Vs. Synchronous Transmission

Serialized data is not generally sent at a uniform rate through a channel. Instead, there is usually a burst of regularly spaced binary data bits followed by a pause, after which the data flow resumes. Packets of binary data are sent in this manner, possibly with variable-length pauses between packets, until the message has been fully transmitted. In order for the receiving end to know the proper moment to read individual binary bits from the channel, it must know exactly when a packet begins and how much time elapses between bits. When this timing information is known, the receiver is said to be synchronized with the transmitter, and accurate data transfer becomes possible. Failure to remain synchronized throughout a transmission will cause data to be corrupted or lost.

Two basic techniques are employed to ensure correct synchronization. In synchronous systems, separate channels are used to transmit data and timing information. The timing channel transmits clock pulses to the receiver. Upon receipt of a clock pulse, the receiver reads the data channel and latches the bit value found on the channel at that moment. The data channel is not read again until the next clock pulse arrives. Because the transmitter originates both the data and the timing pulses, the receiver will read the data channel only when told to do so by the transmitter (via the clock pulse), and synchronization is guaranteed.

Techniques exist to merge the timing signal with the data so that only a single channel is required. This is especially useful when synchronous transmissions are to be sent through a modem. Two methods in which a data signal is self-timed are nonreturn-to-zero and biphase Manchester coding. These both refer to methods for encoding a data stream into an electrical waveform for transmission.

In asynchronous systems, a separate timing channel is not used. The transmitter and receiver must be preset in advance to an agreed-upon baud rate. A very accurate local oscillator within the receiver will then generate an internal clock signal that is equal to the transmitters within

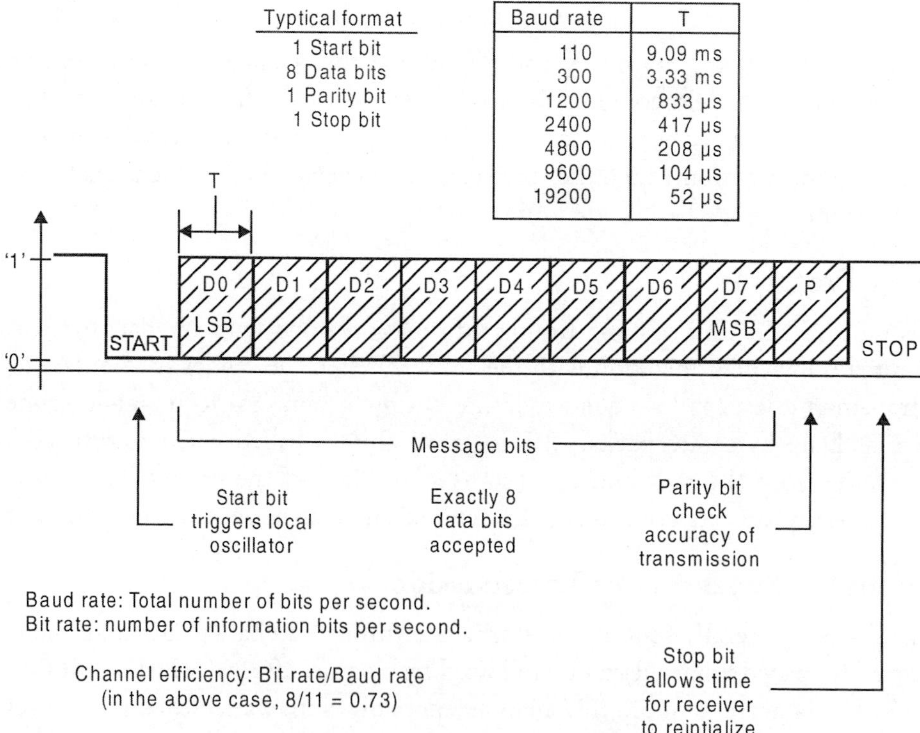

Figure 1.13 *Asynchronous Systems.*

a fraction of a percent. For the most common serial protocol, data is sent in small packets of 10 or 11 bits, eight of which constitute message information. When the channel is idle, the signal voltage corresponds to a continuous logic '1'. A data packet always begins with a logic '0' (the start bit) to signal the receiver that a transmission is starting. The start bit triggers an internal timer in the receiver that generates the needed clock pulses. Following the start bit, eight bits of message data are sent bit by bit at the agreed upon baud rate. The packet is concluded with a parity bit and stop bit. One complete packet is illustrated as in figure 1.13.

The packet length is short in asynchronous systems to minimize the risk that the local oscillators in the receiver and transmitter will drift apart. When high-quality crystal oscillators are used, synchronization can be guaranteed over an 11-bit period. Every time a new packet is sent, the start bit resets the synchronization, so the pause between packets can be arbitrarily long. Note that the EIA232 standard defines electrical, timing, and mechanical characteristics of a serial interface. However, it does not include the asynchronous serial protocol shown in the previous figure, or the ASCII alphabet.

Digital and Analog Transmission

Data is transmitted from one point to another point by means of electrical signals that may be in digital and analog form. So one should know the fundamental difference between analog and digital signals. In analog signal the transmission power varies over a continuous range with respect to sound, light and radio waves. On the other hand, a digital signal may assume only discrete set of values within a given range. Examples are computer and computer related equipment. Analog signal is measured in volts and its frequency in hertz (Hz). A digital signal is a sequence of voltage represented in binary form. When digital data are to be sent over an analog form the digital signal must be converted to analog form. So, the technique by which a digital signal is converted to analog form is known as modulation. And the reverse process, that is the conversion of analog signal to its digital form, is known as demodulation. The device, which converts digital signal into analog, and the reverse, is known as modem.

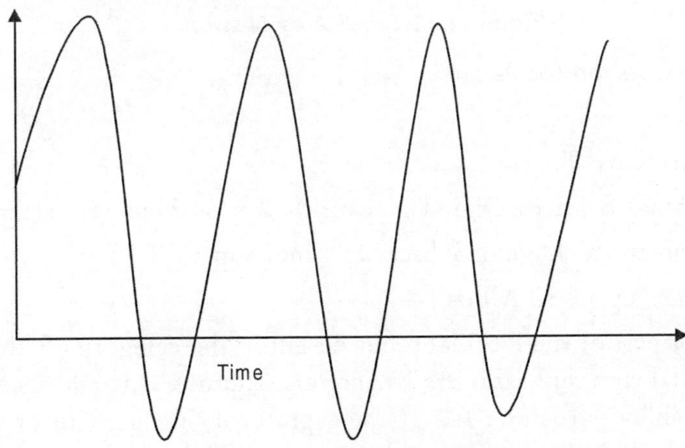

Figure 1.14 *Analog Signal.*

CLASSIFYING NETWORK BY AREA

Communication networks are usually defined by their size and complexity. Here, we can distinguish four main types:

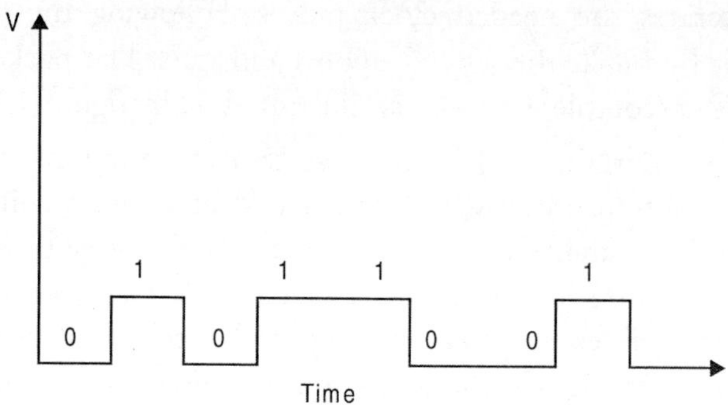

Figure 1.15 *Digital Signal.*

1. Small Area Network (SAN)

The small area network is often called "the last mile" and it refers to the last mile of analog phone line that goes from the Central Office (CO) to your house.

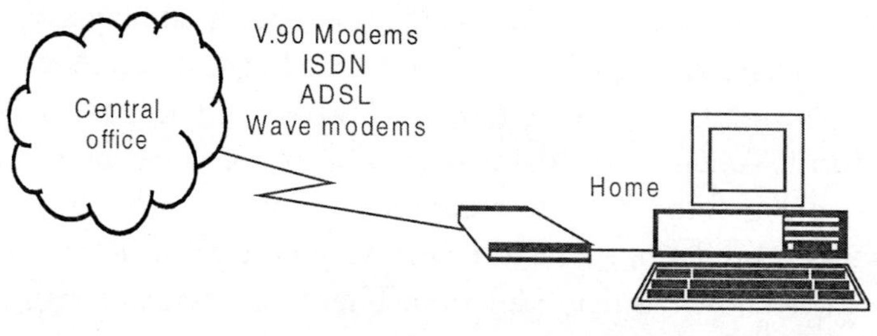

Figure 1.16 *Small Area Network.*

Typical small area network protocols are:

- Voice lines
- Modem connections 56 kbps
- ISDN (Integrated Services Digital Network) 2 × 64 kbps digital lines
- ADSL (Asymmetrical Digital Subscriber Line) up to 8 Mbps
- Cable Modems up to 30 Mbps

Cable modems are not part of the local loop but do fall in the category of "the last mile" or how to get high speed digital communication to the premise (home). It would incredibly expensive to replace the existing cabling structure. All of these protocols are used to overcome the existing cabling limitations in the local loop and provide high speed digital data transmission. The existing cabling was designed for voice communications and not digital.

2. Local Area Network (LAN)

These networks connect computer equipment and other terminals distributed in a localized area, *e.g.*, a university campus, factory, office. The connection is usually a cable or fiber, and the extent of the cable defines the LAN (Local Area Networks).

A network is any collection of independent computers that communicate with one another over a shared network medium. LANs are networks usually confined to a geographic area, such as a single building or a college campus. LANs can be small, linking as few as three computers, but often link hundreds of computers used by thousands of people. The development of standard networking protocols and media has resulted in worldwide proliferation of LANs throughout business and educational organizations.

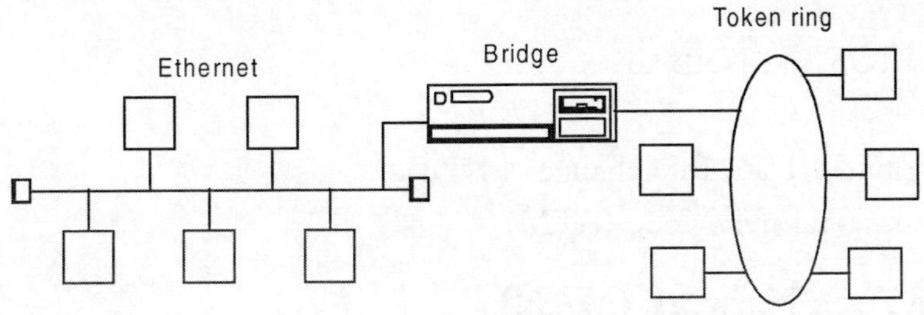

Figure 1.17 *Local Area Network.*

The components used by LANs can be divided into cabling standards, hardware and protocols.

★ Examples of cabling standards used on LANs are:
- Cat 3, 4 and 5 cables
- IBM type 19 cabling standards
- EIA568A and 568B
- Ethernet cabling standards: IEEE 802.3 (10Base5), IEEE 802.3a (10Base2), IEEE 802.3i (10BaseT)
- Unshielded Twisted Pair (UTP)
- Shielded Twisted Pair (STP)
- Connectors: RJ45, RJ11, hermaphroditic connectors, RS232, DB25, BNC, TEE

★ Examples of hardware devices are:
- Network Interface Cards NICs
- Repeaters
- Ethernet hubs or multiport repeaters
- Token ring MultiStation Access Units (MSAUs), Control Access Units (CAUs) and Lobe Access Modules (LAMs)
- Bridges
- Brouters
- Routers
- Gateways
- Print servers
- File servers
- Switches

★ Examples of LAN protocols are:

- Ethernet frame types: Ethernet_II, Ethernet_SNAP, Ethernet_802.2, Ethernet_802.3
- Media Access Control layer (MAC layer)
- Token ring: IBM and IEEE 802.5
- Logical Link Control Layer (LLC) IEEE 802.2
- TCP/IP
- SMB, NetBIOS and NetBeui
- IPX/SPX
- Fiber Distributed Data Interchange (FDDI)
- Asynchronous Transfer Mode (ATM)

3. Metropolitan Area Network (MAN)

Metropolitan Area Networks (MANs) are used to interconnect LANs that are spread around, say, a town or city. This kind of network is a high speed network using optical fiber connections.

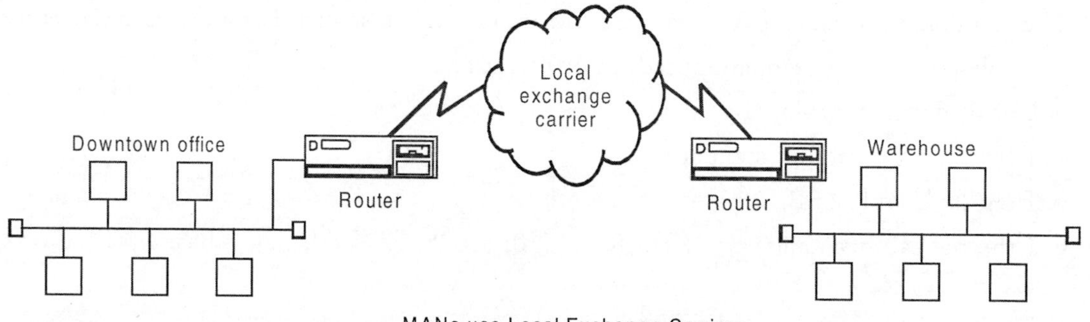

Figure 1.18 *Metropolitan Area Networks.*

The main criteria for a MAN are that the connection between LANs is through a local exchange carrier (the local phone company). The protocols that are used for MANs are quite different from LANs except for ATM which can be used for both under certain conditions.

★ Examples of MAN protocols are:

- RS232, V35
- X.25 (56kbps), PADs
- Frame relay (up to 45 Mbps), FRADs
- Asynchronous Transfer Mode (ATM)
- ISDN (Integrated Services Digital Network) PRI and BRI
- Dedicated T1 lines (1.544 Mbps) and fractional T1
- T3 (45 Mbps) and OC3 lines (155 Mbps)
- ADSL (Asymmetrical Digital Subscriber Line) up to 8 Mbps
- xDSL (many different types of Digital Subscriber Lines).

4. Wide Area Network (WAN)

These networks connect computers and other terminals over large distances. They often require multiple communication connections, including microwave radio links and satellite.

Often a network is located in multiple physical places. Wide area networking combines multiple LANs that are geographically separate. This is accomplished by connecting the different

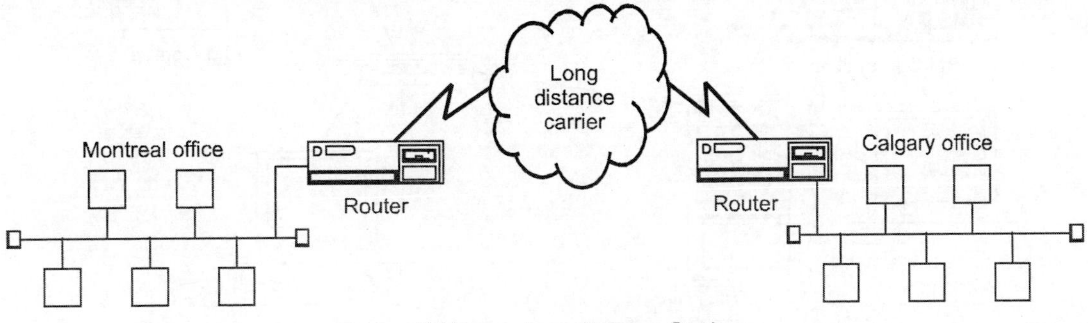

Figure 1.19 *Wide Area Network.*

LANs using services such as dedicated leased phone lines, dial-up phone lines (both synchronous and asynchronous), satellite links, and data packet carrier services. Wide area networking can be as simple as a modem and remote access server for employees to dial into, or it can be as complex as hundreds of branch offices globally linked using special routing protocols and filters to minimize the expense of sending data sent over vast distances.

The main difference between a MAN and a WAN is that the WAN uses long distance carriers. Otherwise the same protocols and equipment are used as a MAN.

CLASSIFYING THE NETWORK BY TOPOLOGY

A network topology describes the configuration of a network (how the network components are connected together). There are *five* main topologies.

1. Star

The star topology uses a central hub through which all components are connected. In a computer network, the central hub is the host computer, and at the end of each connection is a terminal.

A star network uses a significant amount of cable, each terminal is wired back to the central hub, even if two terminals are side by side several hundred meters away from the host. All routing decisions are made by the central hub, and all other workstations can be simple.

An advantage of the star topology is failure in one of the terminals does not affect any other terminal, however; failure of the central hub affects all terminals.

This type of topology is frequently used to connect terminals to a large time-sharing host computer.

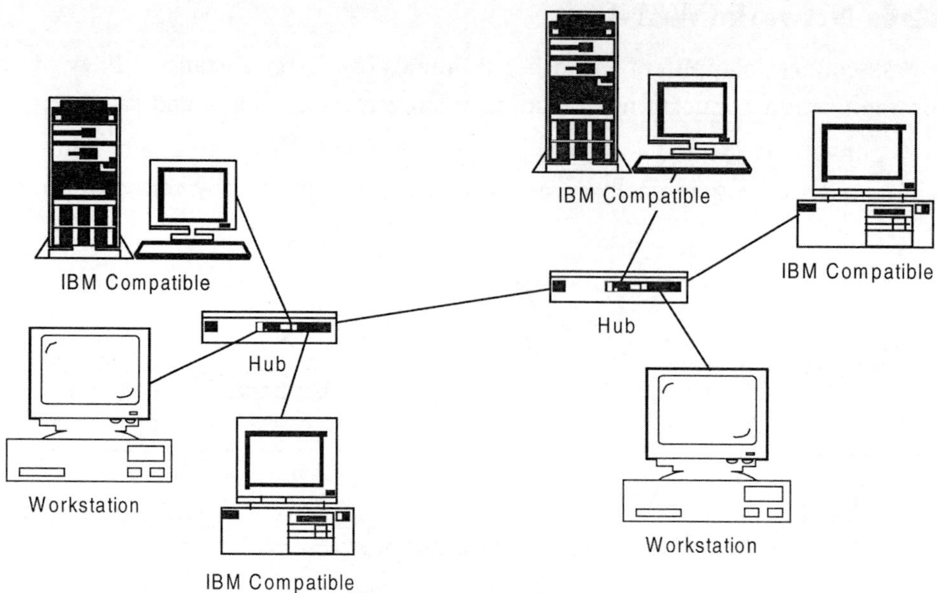

Figure 1.20 *Star Topology.*

2. Ring

The ring topology connects workstations in a closed loop. Each terminal is connected to two other terminals (the next and the previous), with the last terminal being connected to the first. Data is transmitted around the ring in one direction only; each station passing on the data to the next station till it reaches its destination.

Faulty workstations can be isolated from the ring. When the workstation is powered on, it connects itself into the ring. When power is off, it disconnects itself from the ring and allows the information to bypass the workstation.

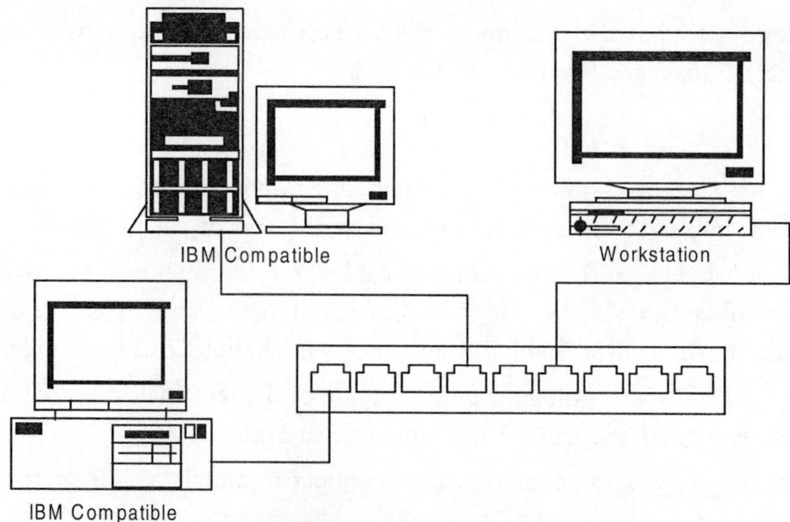

Figure 1.21 *Ring Topology.*

Information travels around the ring from one workstation to the next. Each packet of data sent on the ring is prefixed by the address of the station to which it is being sent to. When a packet of data arrives, the workstation checks to see if the packet address is the same as its own. If it is, it grabs the data in the packet. If the packet does not belong to it, it sends the packet to the next workstation in the ring.

Ring systems use 4 pair cables (separate send/receive). The common implementation of this topology is token ring. A break in the ring causes the entire network to fail. Individual workstations can be isolated from the ring.

3. Bus

The bus topology connects workstations using a single cable. Each workstation is connected to the next workstation in a point to point fashion. All workstations connect to the same cable.

If one workstation goes faulty, all workstations are affected. Workstations share the same cable for the sending and receiving of information. The cabling costs of bus systems are the least of all the different topologies. Each end of the cable is terminated using a special terminator.

The common implementation of this topology is Ethernet. A message transmitted by one workstation is heard by all the other workstations.

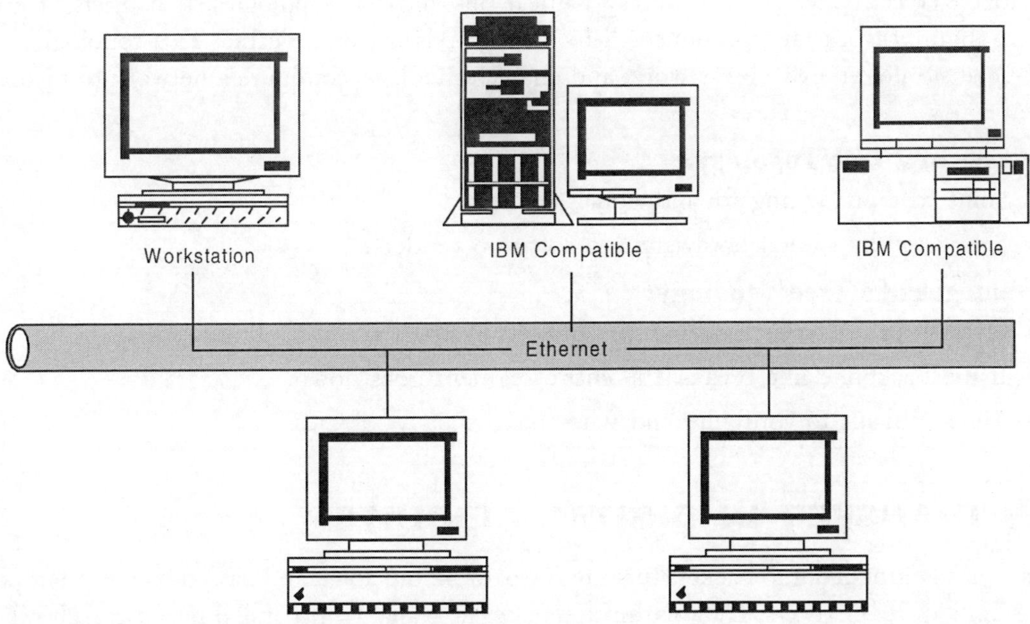

Figure 1.22 *Bus Topology.*

4. Mesh

The mesh topology connects all computers to each other. The cable requirements are high, but there are redundant paths built in. Any failure of one computer allows all others to continue, as they have alternative paths to other computers.

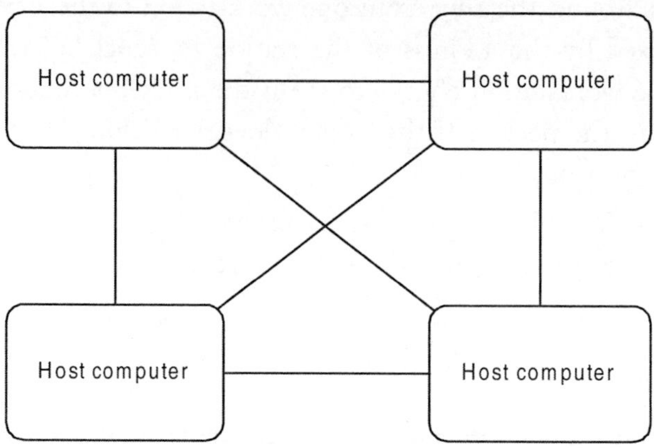

Figure 1.23 *Mesh Topology.*

Mesh topologies are used in critical connection of host computers (typically telephone exchanges). Alternate paths allow each computer to balance the load to other computer systems in the network by using more than one of the connection paths available.

5. Tree

A tree topology combines characteristics of linear bus and star topologies. It consists of groups of star-configured workstations connected to a linear bus backbone cable. Tree topologies allow for the expansion of an existing network, and enable schools to configure a network to meet their needs.

Advantages of a Tree Topology:

- Point-to-point wiring for individual segments.
- Supported by several hardware and software venders.

Disadvantages of a Tree Topology:

- Overall length of each segment is limited by the type of cabling used.
- If the backbone line breaks, the entire segment goes down.
- More difficult to configure and wire than other topologies.

DATA TRANSFER IN DIGITAL CIRCUITS

Data is typically grouped into packets that are 8, 16, or 32 bits long, and passed between temporary holding units called registers. Data within a register is available in parallel because each bit exits the register on a separate conductor. To transfer data from one register to another, the output conductors of one register are switched onto a channel of parallel wires referred to as a bus. The input conductors of another register, which is also connected to the bus, capture the information.

Following a data transaction, the content of the source register is reproduced in the destination register. It is important to note that after any digital data transfer, the source and destination registers are equal; the source register is not erased when the data is sent.

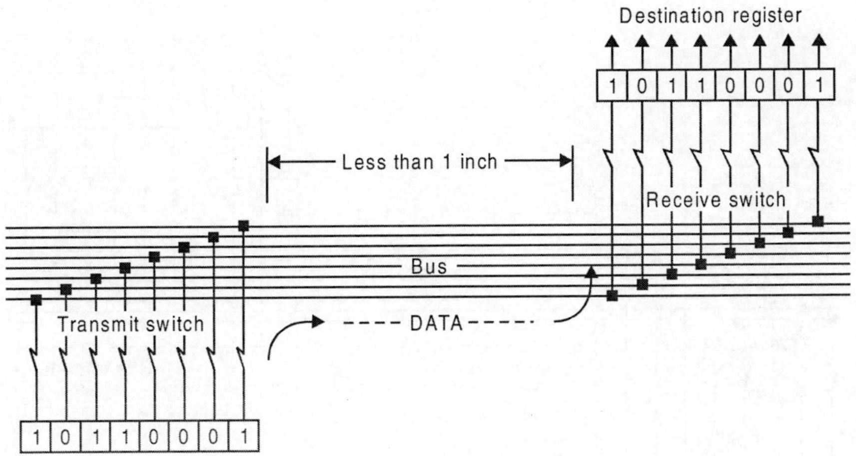

Figure 1.24 *Digital Data Transfer.*

The transmit and receive switches shown above are electronic and operate in response to commands from a central control unit. It is possible that two or more destination registers will be switched on to receive data from a single source. However, only one source may transmit data onto the bus at any time. If multiple sources were to attempt transmission simultaneously, an electrical conflict would occur when bits of opposite value are driven onto a single bus conductor. Such a condition is referred to as a bus contention. Not only will a bus contention result in the loss of information, but it also may damage the electronic circuitry. As long as all registers in a system are linked to one central control unit, bus contentions should never occur if the circuit has been designed properly. Note that the data buses within a typical microprocessor are fundamentally half-duplex channels.

Transmission Over Short Distances (<2 Feet)

Whenever the source and destination registers are part of an integrated circuit (within a microprocessor chip, for example), they are extremely close (thousandths of an inch). Consequently, the bus signals are at very low power levels, may traverse a distance in very little time, and are not very susceptible to external noise and distortion. This is the ideal environment for digital communications. However, it is not yet possible to integrate all the necessary circuitry for a computer (*i.e.*, CPU, memory, disk control, video and display drivers, etc.) on a single chip. When data is sent off-chip to another integrated circuit, the bus signals must be amplified and conductors extended out of the chip through external pins. Amplifiers may be added to the source register.

Bus signals that exit microprocessor chips and other VLSI circuitry are electrically capable of traversing about one foot of conductor on a printed circuit board, or less if many devices are connected to it. Special buffer circuits may be added to boost the bus signals sufficiently for transmission over several additional feet of conductor length, or for distribution to many other chips such as memory chips.

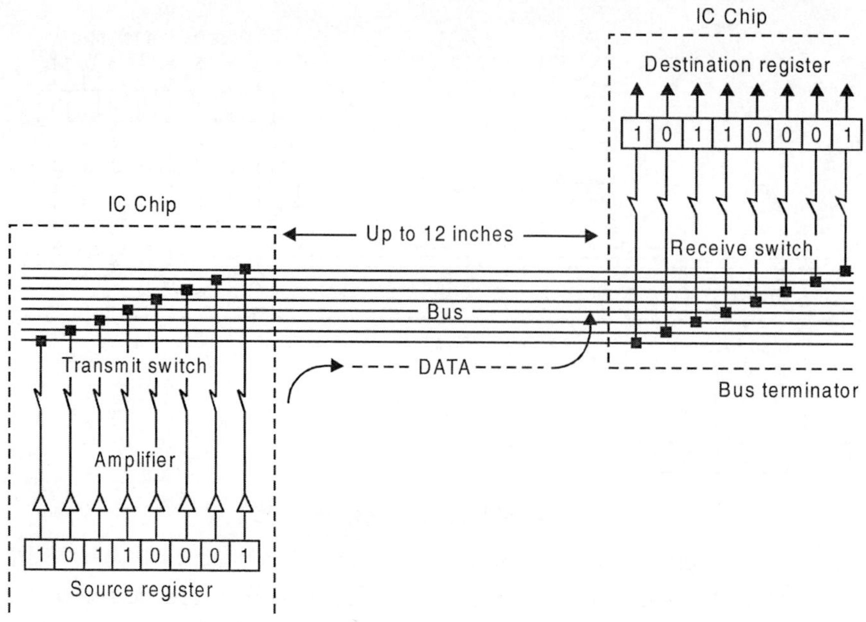

Figure 1.25 *Transmission over Short Distances (<2 feet).*

Transmission Over Medium Distances (<20 Feet)

Computer peripherals such as a printer or scanner generally includes mechanisms that cannot be situated within the computer itself. Our first thought might be just to extend the computer's internal buses with a cable of sufficient length to reach the peripheral. Doing so, however, would expose all bus transactions to external noise and distortion even though only a very small percentage of these transactions concern the distant peripheral to which the bus is connected.

If a peripheral can be located within 20 feet of the computer, however, relatively simple electronics may be added to make data transfer through a cable efficient and reliable. To accomplish this, a bus interface circuit is installed in the computer:

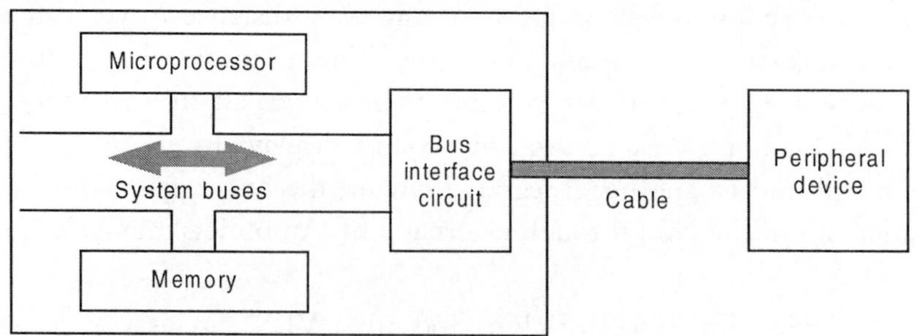

Figure 1.26 *Transmission Over Medium Distances (<20 feet).*

It consists of a holding register for peripheral data, timing and formatting circuitry for external data transmission, and signal amplifiers to boost the signal sufficiently for transmission through a cable. When communication with the peripheral is necessary, data is first deposited in the holding register by the microprocessor. This data will then be reformatted, sent with error-detecting codes, and transmitted at a relatively slow rate by digital hardware in the bus interface circuit. In addition, the signal power is greatly boosted before transmission through the cable. These steps ensure that the data will not be corrupted by noise or distortion during its passage through the cable. In addition, because only data destined for the peripheral is sent, the party-line transactions taking place on the computer's buses are not unnecessarily exposed to noise.

Data sent in this manner may be transmitted in byte-serial format if the cable has eight parallel channels (at least 10 conductors for half-duplex operation), or in bit-serial format if only a single channel is available.

Transmission Over Long Distances (<4000 Feet)

When relatively long distances are involved in reaching a peripheral device, driver circuits must be inserted after the bus interface unit to compensate for the electrical effects of long cables.

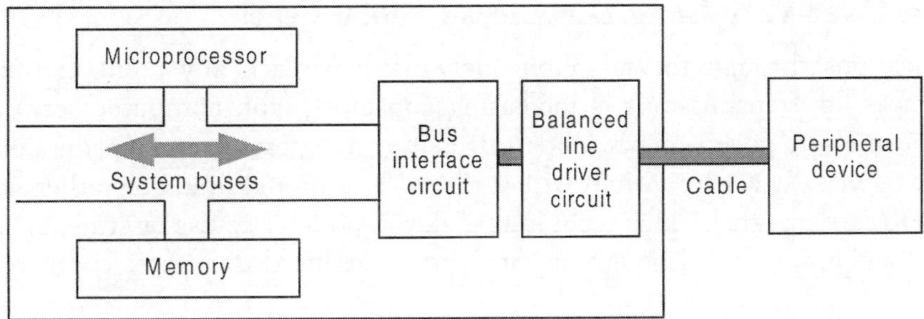

Figure 1.27 *Transmission Over Long Distances (<4000 feet).*

This is the only change needed if a single peripheral is used. However, if many peripherals are connected, or if other computer stations are to be linked, a Local Area Network (LAN) is required, and it becomes necessary to drastically change both the electrical drivers and the protocol to send messages through the cable. Because multiconductor cable is expensive, bit-serial transmission is almost always used when the distance exceeds 20 feet.

In either a simple extension cable or a LAN, a balanced electrical system is used for transmitting digital data through the channel. This type of system involves at least two wires per channel, neither of which is a ground. Note that a common ground return cannot be shared by multiple channels in the same cable as would be possible in an unbalanced system.

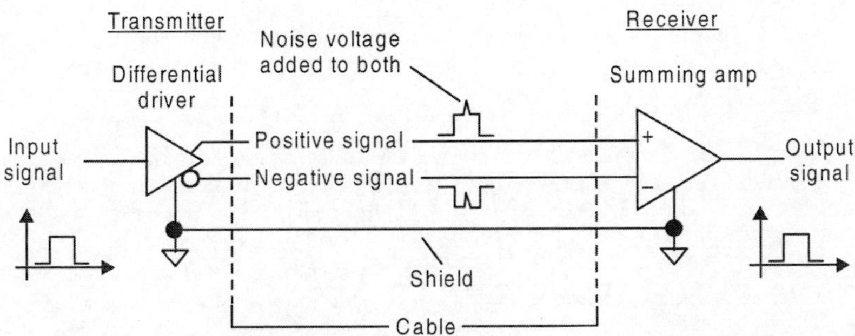

Figure 1.28 *Summing Amplifier.*

The basic idea behind a balanced circuit is that a digital signal is sent on two wires simultaneously, one wire expressing a positive voltage image of the signal and the other a negative voltage image. When both wires reach the destination, the signals are subtracted by a summing amplifier, producing a signal swing of twice the value found on either incoming line. If the cable is exposed to radiate electrical noise, a small voltage of the same polarity is added to both wires in the cable. When the signals are subtracted by the summing amplifier, the noise cancels and the signal emerges from the cable without noise.

A great deal of technology has been developed for LAN systems to minimize the amount of cable required and maximize the throughput. The costs of a LAN have been concentrated in the electrical interface card that would be installed in PCs or peripherals to drive the cable, and in the communications software, not in the cable itself (whose cost has been minimized). Thus, the cost and complexity of a LAN are not particularly affected by the distance between stations.

Transmission Over Very Long Distances (>4000 Feet)

Data communications through the telephone network can reach any point in the world. The volume of overseas fax transmissions is increasing constantly, and computer networks that link thousands of businesses, governments, and universities are pervasive. Transmissions over such distances are not generally accomplished with a direct-wire digital link, but rather with digitally-modulated analog carrier signals. This technique makes it possible to use existing analog telephone voice channels for digital data, although at considerably reduced data rates compared to a direct digital link.

Transmission of data from your personal computer (PC) to a timesharing service over phone lines requires that data signals be converted to audible tones by a modem. An audio sine wave carrier is used, and, depending on the baud rate and protocol, will encode data by varying the frequency, phase, or amplitude of the carrier. The receiver's modem accepts the modulated sine wave and extracts the digital data from it. Several modulation techniques typically used in encoding digital data for analog transmission are shown below.

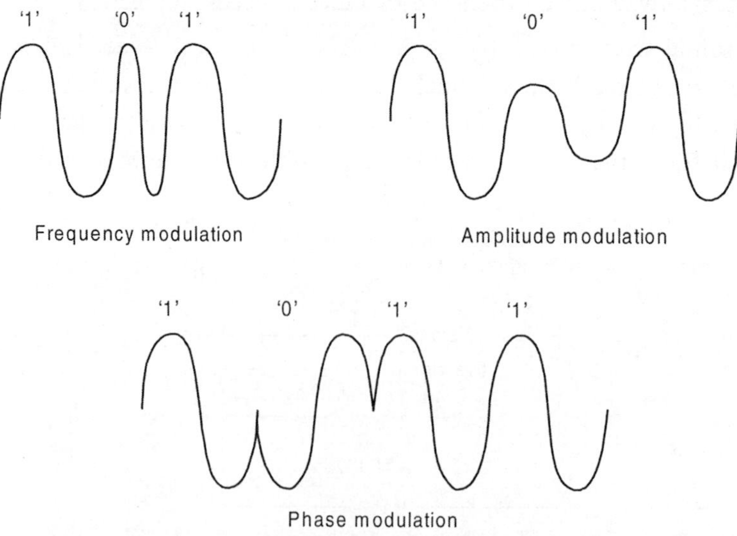

Figure 1.29 *Encoding Digital Data for Analog Transmission.*

Similar techniques may be used in digital storage devices such as hard disk drives to encode data for storage using an analog medium.

NETWORK FACILITIES

This section describes some common network facilities and connections. They are as:

1. Point to Point Circuits

Point to point topologies are simplest and most straight forward.

Point to point circuits are sometimes called two-point circuits , and are used where the remote terminal has sufficient data to warrant using a dedicated single connection to the host computer. The star network is as being point to point.

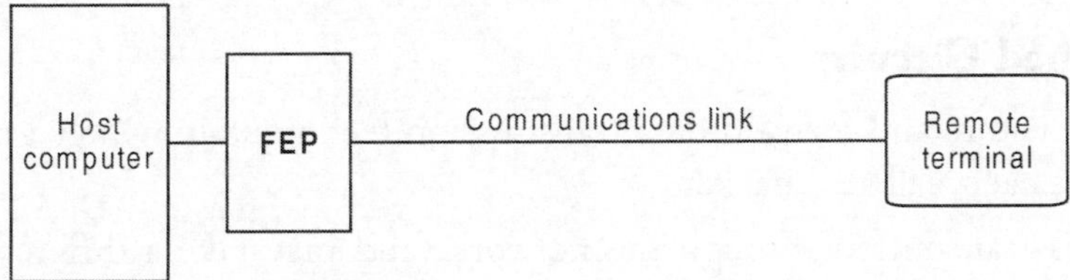

Figure 1.30 *Point to Point Circuit.*

2. Multidrop/Multipoint Circuits

Multiple devices are attached to a common connection. This allows a number of devices to share an expensive line. Only one device can use the line at any one time, and the line is often managed using polling. Frame relay is the most common technology to implement this scheme, and it is typically a WAN technology. All the remote points are connected to a single frame relay switch or router port, and communication between sites is managed by that central point.

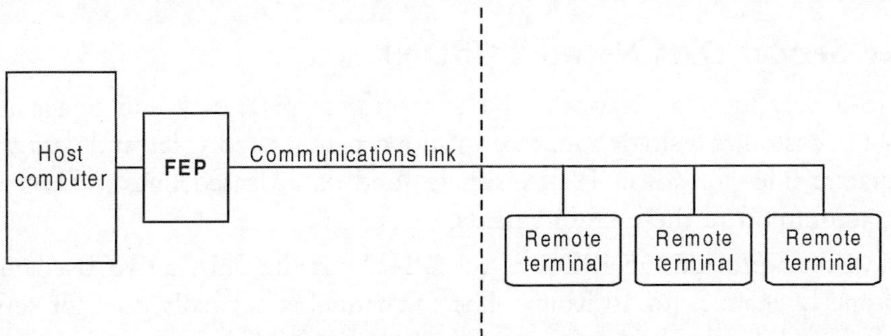

Figure 1.31 *Multi-drop Circuits.*

3. Switched Circuits

Switched circuits are offered by all public communications carriers. Dial-up telephone circuits are an example of switched circuits. Connections are made via a central switching center, which connects the two circuits together (like terminal and host computer).

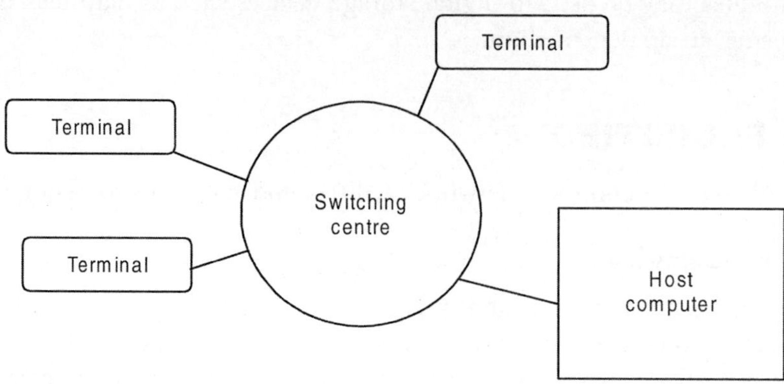

Figure 1.32 *Switched Circuits.*

4. Packet Switched Circuits

Packet switching is a store and forward data transmission technique in which a message is broken up into small parts, each called a packet.

Each packet is transmitted through the network (and may take a different route from the previously sent packet), independent of other transmitted packets. They are reassembled at the destination end into the original message. The facility which converts a message into packets, and reassembles packets into messages is called a Packet Assembly/Disassembly (PAD) facility.

Charges are related to either time, the number of packets transmitted, or a combination of both. Distance charges are relatively non-existent.

Packet switching is very reliable, and public communications carriers offer packet switching as an alternative to other forms of connections (like leased lines for example). There is a high degree of error detection and control built into the packet switching protocol used to transfer packets from point to point in a network.

5. Integrated Service Data Network (ISDN)

ISDN refers to a new form of network which integrates voice, data and image in a digitized form. It offers the customer a single interface to support integrated voice and data traffic. Rather than using separate lines for voice (PABX system) and data (leased lines), ISDN uses a single digital line to accommodate these requirements.

The basic circuit provided in ISDN is the 2B+D circuit. This is two B channels (each of 64 Kbits) and one D channel (of 16 Kbits). The D channel is normally used for supervisory and signaling purposes, whilst the B circuits are used for voice and data.

6. Local Area Network

A LAN is a group of microcomputers or other workstation devices located in the same general area and connected by a common cable. The characteristics of LAN's are:

- Physically limited<2 Km
- High bandwidth>1 MHz

- Inexpensive cable media
- Data and hardware sharing amongst users owned by the user.

A LAN is used to share resources amongst a group of individuals or company employees. These resources are typically files, application software, printers, computing power, modems, and fax machines

7. Wide Area Network

A wide area network is similar to a LAN, but geographically spread over a wider area. The different segments of the WAN are interconnected by communication links (high speed serial, X.25 etc). In fact, a WAN often comprises a number of interconnected LAN's at various sites.

The characteristics of a WAN are:

- Geographically expansive.
- Large number of computers and multiple host machines.
- Sophisticated support devices like routers and gateways for interconnecting the various segments.

TYPES OF NETWORK ACCESS

A LAN connects resources together so they can be shared by users. In today's terms, this often means linking PC's together. As discussed earlier, the PC's can be linked together using a bus, ring or star topology.

Each PC is equipped with a network interface card, which fits into an available expansion slot. Appropriate driver software provides an interface between the PC operating system and the network interface card. Once the network software is loaded, access to provide to other machines on the network. There are three main types of network access provided.

1. Peer to Peer Services

Each PC in the network can directly communicate and share resources with any other machine in the network. Examples of this are:

- Lantastic
- LAN Manager
- Windows for workgroups
- Windows NT
- OS/2
- UNIX

Software programs are executed either locally, or on the peer computer. A user can take advantage of a faster computer by specifying that the program run on the faster machine, rather than their own.

2. File Server Services

A number of machines are designated as HOST servers. Users login to the host machines and access files and application software stored on them. Users have no access to other non host machines. Examples of this are NOVELL NETWARE (Also LAN Manager, Windows NT, and LANtastic). This software is executed on the user's machine. The file server only provides file access; the file is downloaded from the file server into the workstation, where it is then executed.

3. Client/Server Services

This is used extensively in database applications, where a front end software program sends commands to a server for execution, with the results being displayed on the user's machine. It utilizes the high speed of the server machine to do number crunching and complex operations.

The major problems associated with using networks are:

- User training
- Support (user and system)
- Configuration

Table 1.1 Comparison of LAN and WAN Characteristics

Characteristic	*LAN*	*WAN*
geographical size	0 – 2 Km	1 – 100 Km
number of nodes	1 – 200	1 – 500
data rate	1 – 100 Mbps	1 – 100 Mbps
error rate	<10 – 9	<10 – 6
delays	1 – 100 ms	100 ms – 100 s
routing	simple	sophisticated
linkage	bridges/repeaters	gateways/routers

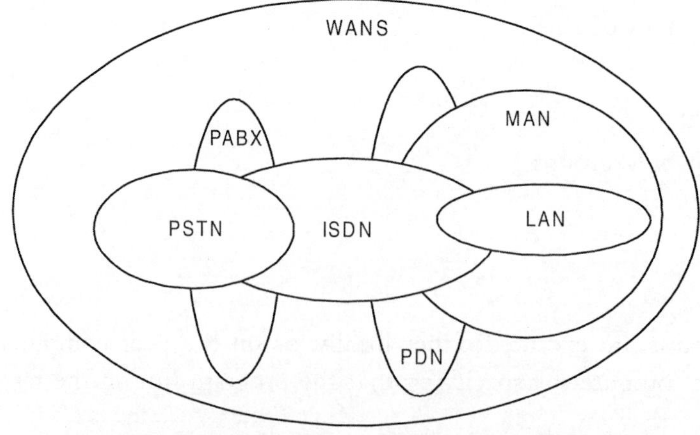

Figure 1.33 *Relationship between Network Architectures.*

SUB-NETWORK (SUBNET)

A sub-network is a portion of a network, or a network that is part of a larger Internet work. This term is also a rather subjective one; sub networks can in fact be rather large when they are part of a network that is very large. The abbreviated term "subnet" can refer generically to a sub-network.

THE INTERNET, INTRANETS AND EXTRANETS

In fact, the Internet is not just a large internet work, but substantially more. The Internet is defined not just as the computers that are connected to each other around the world, but as the set of services and features that it offers. More than that, the Internet defines a specific way of doing things, of sharing information and resources between people and companies. And though it might be a bit melodramatic to say so, to many people the Internet is a way of life. As Internet use and popularity exploded in the 1990s, many people realized that the techniques and technologies used on the Internet would be useful if applied to internal company networks as well. The term Intranet was coined to refer to an internal network that functioned like a "private Internet". It comes from the prefix "intra", which means "within". Of course, "inter" is the opposite of "intra", so this makes some people think that an "intranet" is the opposite of an "Internet". In fact, most intranets are Internet works as well.

As if that weren't bad enough from a jargon standpoint, the buzzword then decided to take matters a step further. If an intranet is "extended" to allow access to it not only strictly from within the organization, but also by people or groups outside the main company, this is sometimes called an extranet. "Extra" of course, is a prefix that means "outside" or "beyond".

So, an extranet is a type of internal, private Internet that isn't entirely internal. An extranet is an extended intranet, which is really a type of Internet that works like the Internet. An extranet isn't public and open to all—it is controlled by a private organization. At the same time, it isn't entirely private either.

As you can see, the lines between the Internet, intranets and extranets were pretty blurry from the start, and the concepts are rapidly blending into a diffuse mass of gray, as the whole computing world becomes more tightly integrated. For example, even if you have an entirely private intranet, you will want to connect it to the Internet to communicate with the "outside world" and to allow access to Internet resources. And an extranet may be implemented, in part, through the public Internet infrastructure, using technologies such as Virtual Private Networking (VPN).

The key that binds all of these concepts together is that they all use "Internet technologies", a term that is it somewhat vague. This usually refers to the use of the TCP/IP protocol suite, which is the defining technology of the Internet, as well as the set of services that are available on the Internet.

The bottom line is that being told that a company has an "intranet" or an "extranet"—as opposed to a plain old boring "network"—doesn't tell you much at all. It is best not to rely on the slogans and instead look at the underlying characteristics of the network or Internet work itself. Furthermore, when designing such a network, focus on using the technologies and protocols that make sense.

REVIEW QUESTIONS

1. What do you understand by computer network ?
2. Write short note on evolution of computer.
3. What are the different functions of data network ?
4. What are the different network components of communication ?
5. What are the main uses of computer network ?
6. Write different modes of communication.
7. What are the differences of asynchronous and synchronous transmissions ?
8. What are differences between Internet, intranets and extranets ?
9. Define the difference between a LAN and MAN.
10. Specify the amount of territory covered by each of the following network types: LAN, MAN, CAN, WAN, GAN.
11. What are the three main types of network topologies ?
12. Encode the following uni-polar data stream into a differential Manchester-encoded data stream.
13. What is the purpose of a Network Interface Card (NIC) ?
14. What are the NIC's specification tasks ?
15. Which IEEE standard addresses metropolitan area networks ?
16. What are slots used for ?
17. What is an intranet? How does it differ from the Internet ?
18. What functions does an extranet provide ?
19. The original three network types were LAN, MAN, and WAN. Describe how they differ from one another.
20. What is a topology ?
21. List the basic network topologies.
22. Define bus topology.
23. Draw a hybrid topology with a star backbone and three ring networks.
24. Draw a hybrid topology with a ring backbone and two bus networks.
25. Draw a hybrid topology with a bus backbone connecting two ring backbones. Each ring backbone connects three star networks.
26. Find three standards defined by ISO.
27. Give two instances of how networks are a part of our life today.
28. Assume six devices are arranged in a mesh topology. How many cables are needed? How many ports are needed for each device ?

2

NETWORK MODELS

Before discussing network models, we will see network architecture which is a formal, logical structure that defines how network devices and software interact and function. It defines communication protocols message formats, and standards required for interoperability. New hardware or software products created within a specific architecture are generally compatible with other products create within the same architecture. Network architectures are designed by standards organizations and manufacturers.

For example, IBM designed the Systems Network Architecture (SNA), Digital Equipment Corporation designed the Digital Network Architecture (DNA), and the International Organization for Standardization (ISO) designed the Open System Interconnect (OSI) architecture.

There are several network models such as:

- The internet layered protocol
- The TCP/IP 4 layered protocol
- The Microsoft networking protocol

But ISO Network model is unique which is described below.

INTRODUCING THE ISO OSI REFERENCE MODEL

Nearly all digital network descriptions start with the OSI (Open Systems Interconnect) model (Figure 2.1). It explains the various "layers" of network technology. To the casual user, this model is a little abstract, but there is not a better way to begin to understand what is going on.

Sometimes it helps to understand each layer by examining the technology it represents. The application layer is the most intuitive because it is what the user sees. It represents the problem that the user wants the system to solve. Internet browsers and e-mail programs are good examples. They allow the user to input and read data while connected between a client PC and a server somewhere on the Internet. In an industrial application, a program on a Programmable Logic Controller (PLC) might control a smart valve.

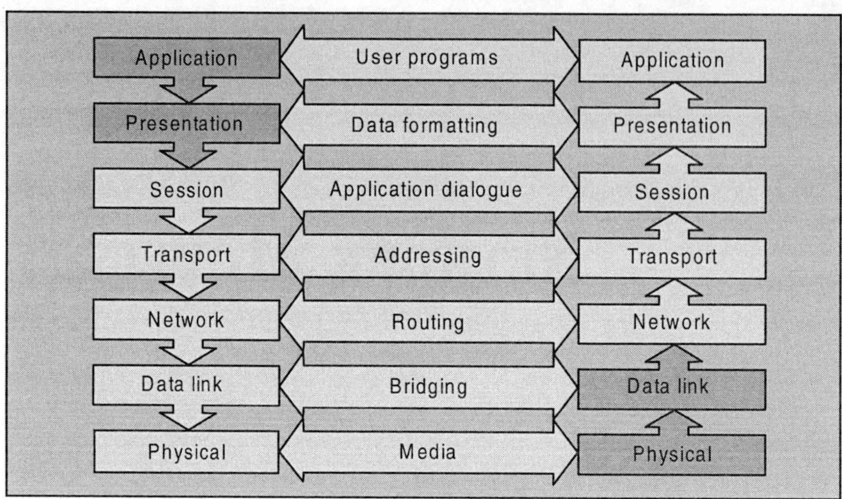

Figure 2.1 *The Seven Layer OSI Network Model.*

The presentation layer performs formatting on the data going to and from the application. This layer performs such services such as encryption, compression, and conversion of data from one form to another. For example, an application (one layer up) might send a time stamp formatted in 12-hour time: 01 : 30 : 48 p.m. A more universal representation is 13 : 30 : 48, in 24-hour time, which can be accepted or presented at the next node's application in the form that it needs. One advantage to presentation services is that they help eliminate overhead, or embedded services, in application programs.

The session layer establishes the connection between applications. It also enforces dialogue rules, which specify the order and speed of data transfer between a sender and a receiver. For example, the session layer would control the flow of data between an application and a printer with a fixed buffer, to avoid buffer overflows. In the time stamp example, once the data is presented in 24-hour time format, an identifier and length indicator are appended to the data string.

The transport layer is essentially an interface between the processor and the outside world. It generates addresses for session entities and ensures all blocks or packets of data have been sent or received. In the time stamp example, an address for each session entity (sender and receiver) and checksum are appended to the block generated by the session layer.

The network layer performs accounting, addressing, and routing functions on messages received from the transport layer. If the message is lengthy, this layer will break it up and sequence it over the network. This layer also uses a network routing table to find the next node on the way to the destination address. In the time stamp example, a node address and sequence number are appended to the message received from the session layer.

The data link layer establishes and controls the physical path of communication from one node to the next, with error detection. This layer performs Media Access Control (MAC) to decide which node can use the media and when. The rules used to perform these functions also are known as protocols. Ethernet and token ring contention are examples of protocols. In the time stamp example, a header and trailer are appended to the message received from the transport layer for flagging the beginning and end of the frame, type of frame (control or data), checksum, and other functions.

The physical layer is perhaps the most conspicuous layer from a cost point of view. It is relatively easy to understand the labor and material costs of pulling cables, along with a physical infrastructure (conduits, raceways, and duct banks) for maintaining cable integrity. This layer does not add anything to the message frame. It simply converts the digital message received from the data link layer into a string of ones and zeroes represented by a signal on the media. One example is RS-485, where a binary 1 is represented by a mark, or off state, and a binary 0 is represented by a space, or on state. A mark is a negative voltage between terminals on the generator, while a space is a positive voltage on those terminals.

OPEN SYSTEMS INTERCONNECTION (OSI) ARCHITECTURE

A number of bodies have attempted to define standards to cover all aspects of computer communications, including LANs. Many standards have been established by default. Though they were developed as products, Ethernet and token ring networks have been adopted as international standards by such bodies as the Institute of Electrical and Electronic Engineers (IEEE) and the International Standards Organization (ISO).

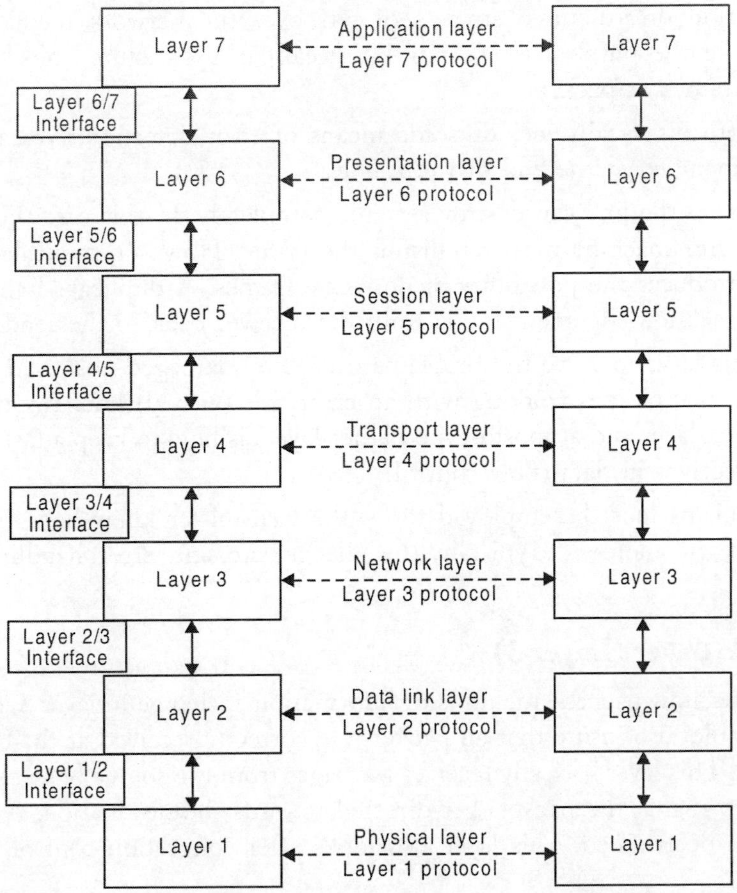

Figure 2.2 *OSI Seven Layer.*

OSI refers to communications between computer systems which are enabled to exchange information freely irrespective of type and manufacturer by virtue of their mutual adherence to a set of standards.

1. The Physical Layer (Layer 1)

The physical layer is the first or the lowest layer in the OSI model. This layer is concerned with transmitting raw bits of data over a communication channel. The design issues have to do with making sure that when one side sends a 1 bit, it is received by the other side as a 1, not a 0 bit. Other points which concern this layer include:

- How many microseconds a bit occupies ?
- Whether transmission may proceed simultaneously in both directions ?
- How the initial connection is established ?
- How it is torn down when both sides are finished ?
- How many pins the network connector has and what each pin is used for ?

2. The Data Link Layer (Layer 2)

The data link layer provides the node-to-node packet delivery service. Its function includes transmission/reception of structured streams of bits over the network media. It provides the facility to sub-divide the physical layer's raw bit stream into structured blocks of information commonly called frames or packets.

Data link protocols usually include some means of error detection, typically based upon a simple checksum included at the end of the frame.

A noise burst on the line can destroy a frame completely. In this case the data link layer's software on the source machine must retransmit the frame. However, multiple transmissions of the same frame introduces the possibility of duplicate frames. A duplicate frame could be sent, for example, if the acknowledgement frame from the receiver back to the sender was destroyed.

It is up to this layer to solve the problems caused by damaged, lost, and duplicate frames so that layer 3 can assume it is working with an error-free (virtual) line. Another problem that arises at the data link layer and at most of the higher layers is how to keep a fast transmitter from drowning a slow receiver in data (flow control).

Some mechanisms must be employed to let the transmitter know how much buffer space the receiver has at the moment. Typically, this mechanism and error handling are integrated together.

3. The Network Layer (Layer 3)

This unit determines how packets, the units of information exchange in layer 3, are routed within the network. It should also insure that all packets are correctly received at their destinations and in the proper order. This layer basically receives messages from the source host, converts them into packets, and sees to it that the packets get directed towards the destination. A key design issue is how the route is determined. This layer also looks after congestion control.

4. The Transport Layer (Layer 4)

This layer provides for the transparent transfer of data, *e.g.*, files between systems which might organize their data somewhat differently. It relieves the transport user from any concern about how in detail data transfers may be affected and optimises the available communications resources. This layer can be viewed as a bridge between the communication oriented lower three layers and the application oriented upper three layers.

5. The Session Layer (Layer 5)

This layer supports the establishment, control and termination of dialogues between application processes. It facilitates full duplex operation and maintains continuity of session connections. It also supports synchronization between user's equipment and generally manages the data exchanges for the applications task.

6. The Presentation Layer (Layer 6)

The presentation layer is concerned with the syntax and semantics of the information transmitted. A typical example of a presentation service is encoding data in a standard agreed-upon way. Most user programs do not exchange random binary bit strings. They exchange things such as people's names, dates, amount of money, and invoices. These items are represented as character strings, integers, floating point numbers, and data structures composed of several simpler items.

Different computers have different codes for representing character strings (*e.g.*, ASCII and ABCDIC), integers (*e.g.*, one's complement and two's complement), and so on. In order to make it possible for computers with different representations to communicate, the data structures to be exchanged can be defined in an abstract way, along with a standard encoding to be used 'on the wire'.

The job of managing these abstract data structures and converting from the representation used inside the computer to the network standard representation is handled by the presentation layer. The presentation layer is also concerned with other aspects of information representation. For example, data compression can be used here to reduce the number of bits that have to be transmitted and cryptography is frequently required for privacy and authentication.

Services provided by the presentation layer include:

(*a*) Data Representation

Different computers have different internal representations for data. All the large IBM mainframes use EBCDIC as the character code, whereas practically all other computers use ASCII. Some computers also represent integers in one's complement and other in two's complement. To solve this problem, a conversion will have to be made and this is carried out by the presentation layer.

(*b*) Data Compression

The organizations that operate computer networks frequently expect to be paid for their efforts. In nearly all cases, the cost of using a network depends on the amount of data sent. It is clear that the more bytes sent, the more it costs, so the final bill can be reduced by compressing the data before sending them. Data compression has been studied in many context for years. It is widely used to save space in memory, on disk, and on magnetic tape.

(c) Network Security and Privacy

Back in the early years when corporations and universities had a single computer centre, achieving security was easy. All the organization had to do was station a guard at the door to the computer room. The guard made sure that no one removed any tapes, disks, or card from the room unless explicitly authorized to do so.

With the advent of networking the situation has changed radically. No one can manually police the millions of bits of data that daily move between the computers in a network. Moreover, organizations have no way of being sure that their data are not secretly copied by wiretap or other means on the way to their proper destination. Clearly, some kind of encryption is needed to make the data unintelligible to all but their intended recipient. Protecting data from prying eyes is not the only security issue in networking. One can imagine at least four security services:

★ Protecting data from being read by unauthorized persons preventing unauthorized persons from inserting or deleting messages, verifying the sender of each message

★ Making it possible for users to send signed documents electronically. Encryption can be used to achieve all these goals.

7. The Application Layer (Layer 7)

The application layer holds the user (also known as application) programs that do the actual work for which the computers were purchased. These programs make use of the services offered by the presentation layer for their communication needs. However, certain applications, such as file transfer, are so common that standards have been developed for them to eliminate the need for each company to develop its own, and to make sure that everyone uses the same protocols.

The transfer and remote file access are two of the most common applications in any computer network. People who are working together on a project commonly need to share files. One approach is to have a machine where the original of each file is held, and have copies transferred to other machines as needed. Another approach is to have each file 'live' on the machine where it was created (or where it is maintained), and have users on other machines ask for copies when they need them.

Another situation in which file transfer is used is at a university that has many diskless workstations spread around campus along with one or more machines with large disks. Students can log into any workstation and access their files over the network. In an alternative design, the workstations can be equipped with small disks, allowing students to download their files to their workstations at the start of each terminal session and upload them back to the main machine when they are done. This arrangement means that a student can log into any workstation on campus (or perhaps even at the dorm), not just the one specific workstation where his/her files are. Remote file access (as in the case diskless workstations) is similar to file transfer, except that only pieces of files are read or written, rather than entire files. The techniques used for file transfer and remote file access are similar.

In contrast to the session and presentation layers, on which there has been very little work done outside of OSI, there has been a great deal of research about file transfer done at universities and in industry. Many file servers have been built and experimented with.

The key idea behind most modern file servers is that of a virtual file store, an abstract file server, either free-standing or running as a process on a timeshared computer. The virtual file store presents a standardized interface to its clients, and provides a set of standardized operations that the clients can execute. Transfers to and from the virtual file store use standardized protocols. If the real file server has a different internal structure than that of the virtual file store, it will need some application layer software to hide the truth from the clients and make only the virtual file store interface visible. By standardizing on a particular virtual file store interface, as OSI has done, it is possible for application programs to access and transfer remote files without knowing all the details of numerous incompatible file servers.

Physical Layer Options

There are a number of implementations of the physical layer. Network devices allow a wide range of connectivity options. Some networks are well defined using the OSI model, where cables, bridges, routers, servers, modems, and PCs are easily identified. Sometimes only a few devices are linked together in some kind of proprietary network, or where the network services are bundled in a black-box fashion with the device.

The most common serial data exchange interfaces are RS-232, RS-422, and RS-485 for connecting two or more devices together. All three interfaces use Data Terminal Equipment (DTE) and Data Communication Equipment (DCE) terminology (Figure 2.3). The DTE is the component that wants to communicate with another component somewhere else, such as a PC communicating with another PC. The DCE is the component actually doing the communicating, or, performing the functions of the generator and receiver discussed in the standards. A modem is a common example of a DCE.

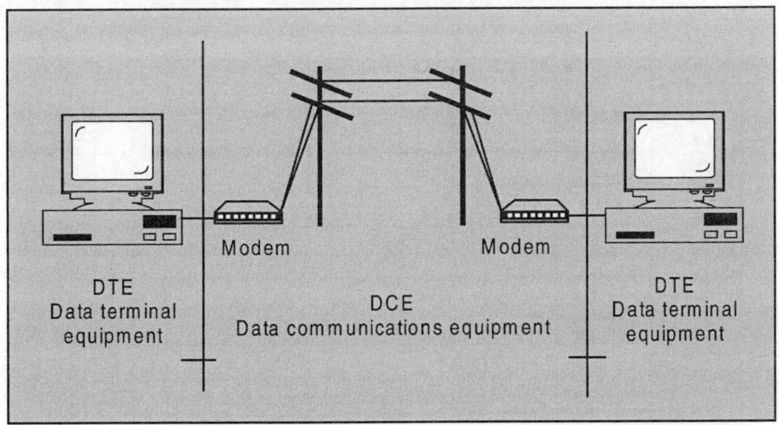

Figure 2.3 *Serial Data Transmission.*

The interfaces between DTE and DCE can be categorized by mechanical, electrical, functional, and procedural aspects. Mechanical specifications define types of connectors and numbers of pins. Electrical specifications define line voltages and waveforms, as well as failure modes and effects. Functional specifications include timing, data, control and signal grounds, and which pin(s) the functions are to use. The procedural interface specifies how signals are exchanged.

RS-485 is another serial data transmission method. Officially, it is EIA 485, or "standard for electrical characteristics of generators and receivers for use in balanced digital multipoint systems" by the Electronics Industry Association (EIA). This standard defines a method for generating ones and zeroes as voltage pulses. Remember, for all the data handling, framing, packeting, routing and addressing performed by the upper layers, it still comes down to pushing ones and zeroes over some physical media.

What is important to know about RS-485 is that it allows multiple receivers and generators, and it specifies cable characteristics in terms of signaling speeds and lengths. A typical cable is a shielded twisted copper pair, which is adequate for the typical signaling rate of 10 million bits per second (Mbps). This standard only defines the electrical characteristics of the waveforms. Note that RS-485 does not specify any media control functions-that is strictly up to the device connected to the generator (usually a chip). RS-485 is generally good for cable lengths up to 2,000 feet.

One example of a simple serial network might be a series of recorders connected over an RS-485 link to a PC that receives data acquired by each recorder. The manufacturer sells a plug-in card that installs in each recorder, with wiring instructions. Each network card is daisy-chained to the others over a series of shielded twisted pair cables that ultimately terminate on a network interface card in the PC. There is no real need to know and understand the network layers in this arrangement, except to understand the limitations on RS-485 (distance, shielding, data rate, etc.).

By title, the RS-422 standard is TIA/EIA 422 B, "electrical characteristics of balanced voltage digital interface circuits" by the telecommunications industry association (in association with the EIA). It is similar to RS-485; the main differences being the rise times and voltage

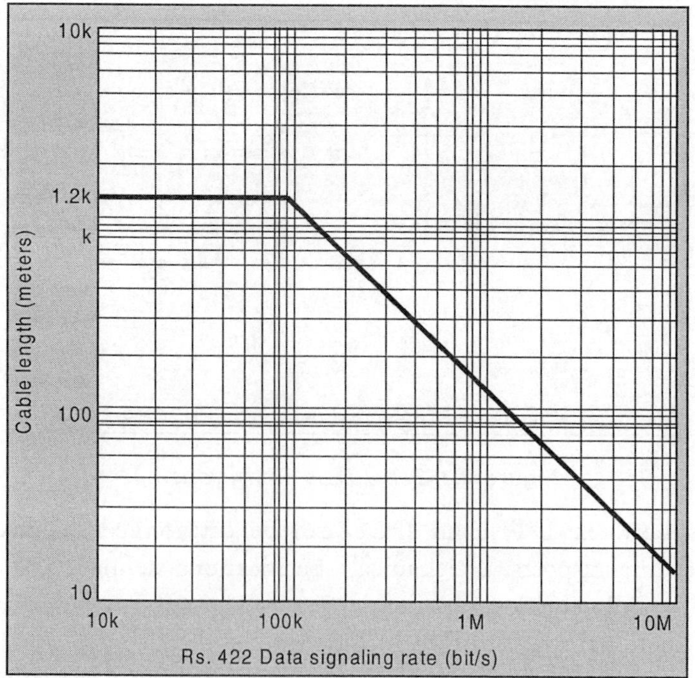

Figure 2.4 *Graph of Data Signaling Rate.*

characteristics of the waveform. RS-422 generally allows cable lengths up to 1.2 kilometers at up to 100 thousand bits per second (kbps). At 10 million bps (Mbps), cable lengths are limited to around 10 meters (Figure 2.4). In the presence of cable imbalance or high common mode noise levels, cable lengths may be further reduced in order to maintain a desired signaling rate.

INTERACTION BETWEEN OSI MODEL LAYERS

A given layer in the OSI model generally communicates with three other OSI layers: the layer directly above it, the layer directly below it, and its peer layer in other networked computer systems. The data link layer in system A, for example, communicates with the network layer of system A, the physical layer of system A, and the data link layer in system B. Figure 2.5 illustrates this example.

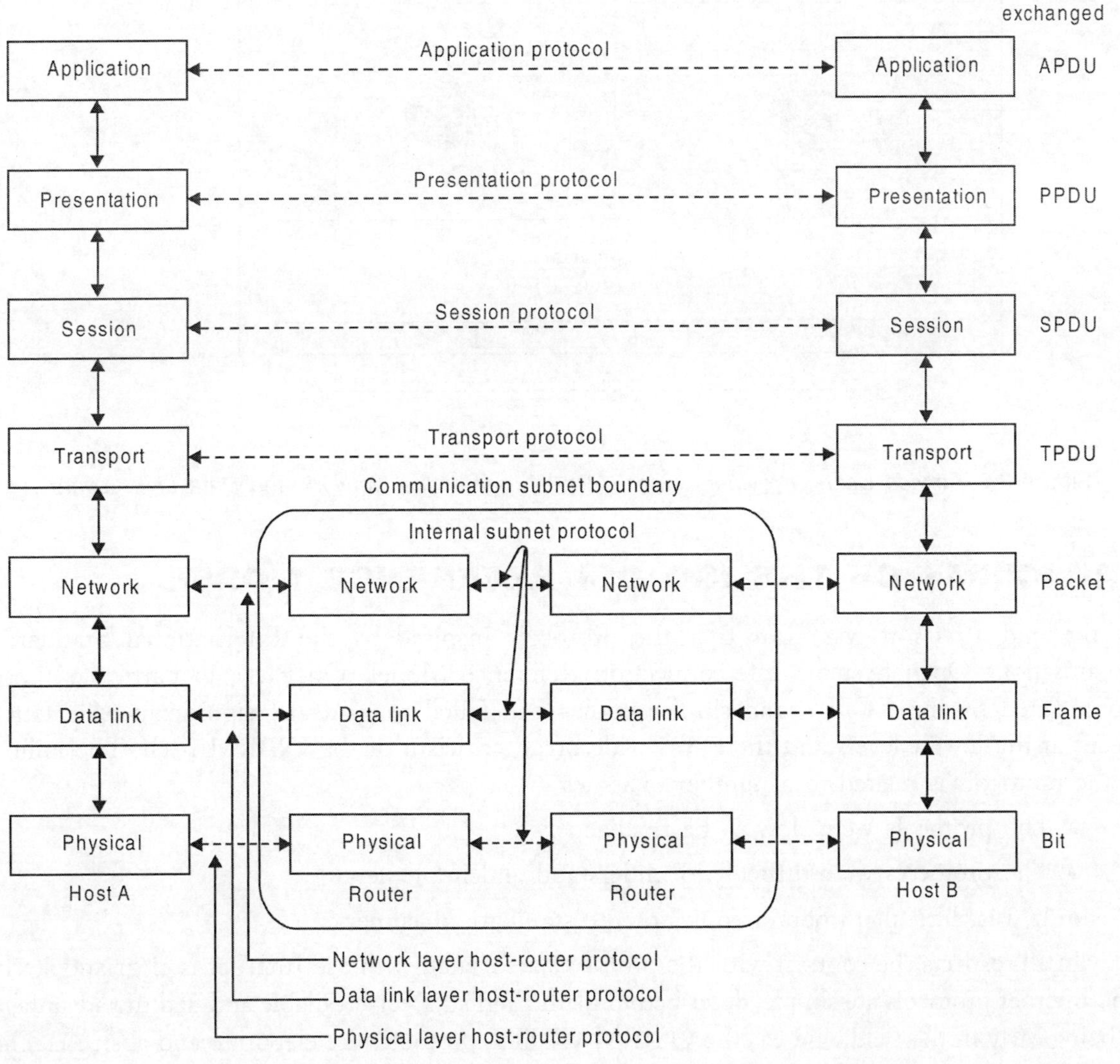

Figure 2.5 *OSI Model Layers Communicate with other Layers.*

OSI Layer Services

One OSI layer communicates with another layer to make use of the services provided by the second layer. The services provided by adjacent layers help a given OSI layer communicate with its peer layer in other computer systems. Three basic elements are involved in layer services: the service user, the service provider, and the Service Access Point (SAP).

In this context, the service user is the OSI layer that requests services from an adjacent OSI layer. The service provider is the OSI layer that provides services to service users. OSI layers can provide services to multiple service users. The SAP is a conceptual location at which one OSI layer can request the services of another OSI layer.

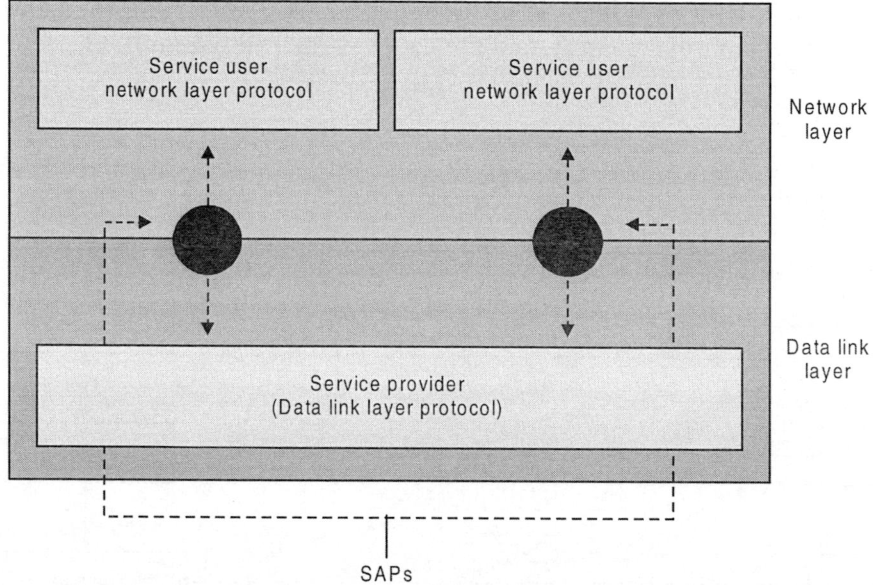

Figure 2.6 *Service Users, Providers, and SAPs Interact at the Network and Data Link Layers.*

CRITICISMS OF THE ISO OSI REFERENCE MODEL

By the mid 1990's it was clear that the protocols inspired by the International Standards Organisations Open Systems Interconnection Reference Model (OSIRM), in particular those promulgated by the CCITT and similar bodies had failed to gain any significant acceptance except at the lowest levels and there was widespread criticism of the OSIRM itself. The failure of the protocols is related to a number of issues.

- The protocols were slow to be finalized
- The protocols were difficult to understand and implement
- It was difficult to obtain copies of the standards documents

In all respects the contrast with the protocols associated with the Internet is clear and stark. The Internet protocols are simple, described in plain English, freely available and had the advantage of being early in the field whereas the OSIRM/CCITT protocols are elaborate and abstruse. The Internet protocols were developed in response to a direct and immediate need. The Internet protocols were developed in the context of computer networking rather than the highly regulated world of the national telecommunication bodies who were heavily involved in the OSIRM protocol developments.

Even so it could be and has been suggested that the OSIRM based protocols could or would eventually replace the original Internet protocols as the OSIRM based protocols became better understood and the consequences of the informal design of the Internet protocols became clearer. It now seems most unlikely that this will happen. This is, of course, partly due to the complete market dominance of the Internet protocols and related products but there are also fundamental problems with the OSIRM.

The OSIRM prescribes how entities at the various levels should interact with each other and entities at other levels. Level N entities must exchange data using services provided by level N-1 entities. Another was of saying this is that level N-1 entities must be involved in every data transfer between level N entities. Level N-1 entities provide their service by exchanging data units which contain level N-1 control information and data from level N entities. Level N control information is passed to the remote side as level N-1 data.

The reference model further specifies seven levels (or layers). This seven layer model has been reproduced in practically every text on communications, unfortunately the chosen levels bear little relation to the practicalities of communications protocol implementation and null layers and sub-layers are common.

The Internet protocols fit in a much less rigidly defined framework with no formally defined layers but hierarchical use of "lower" protocols by "higher" protocols being common. To those familiar with the formal framework of the OSIRM the Internet protocols seem "ad hoc" and pragmatic, as indeed they are. It is a matter of observation that the OSIRM community has not produced anything like the world wide web or the usenet. On a more technical front the less prescriptive Internet protocols allow the use of a variety protocol methods that do not fit into the OSIRM scheme of things.

The use of escape characters within a data stream to allow control information to be included within the data stream to which it refers. This technique is adopted by the telnet protocol. The use of separate control and data connections at the same level (*i.e.*, using the same lower level service). This technique allows for different qualities of service for the control and data connections. This method is used by the Internet FTP . Lower level control information can be used for higher level functions. For example a low level link closure can imply closure at higher levels without need for explicit closure at the higher levels.

An entity may use the services of several lower level (or even similar level) entities during a liaison. The use of DNS is a good example of this kind of thing. A high level entity may by-pass intermediate levels requesting direct explicit encapsulation at the lower levels. This techniques is proposed for the real time extensions to IPng and may also be useful to allow high level access to facilities such as multicasting and broadcasting.

The OSIRM can be further criticised for inadequate support for the concept of interconnected networks and the various management functions such as name service. Interconnected networks imply that entities on two networks that are not directly connected can still communicate even though the networks may be quite different. This has always been fundamental for the Internet community. Such Internet protocols seem to fit between level 3 and level 4 of the OSIRM. They rely on network services to transport data from one part of a network to another (*i.e.,* from one gateway to another) but they are used by end-to-end protocols such as TCP which belong at level 4 of the OSIRM.

Management services simply do not seem to fit very well into the hierarchical model. The simplest examples of management services are various name servers (such as DNS), connectivity tests (such as PING) and more general network management protocols (such as SNMP). Such things can be seen either as services in their own right or as facilities to be used by other services.

The Internet protocols place a much stronger emphasis on connectionless services. The basic Internet protocol is connectionless.

EXAMPLE OF OSI COMMUNICATION

A typical OSI communications scenario can now be sketched. Assume that one end system (local computer) has a client program which requires the services of a remote server program located at a remote computer connected by a communications network. A simplified diagram is shown in figure 2.7. This shows the peer-to-peer communication.

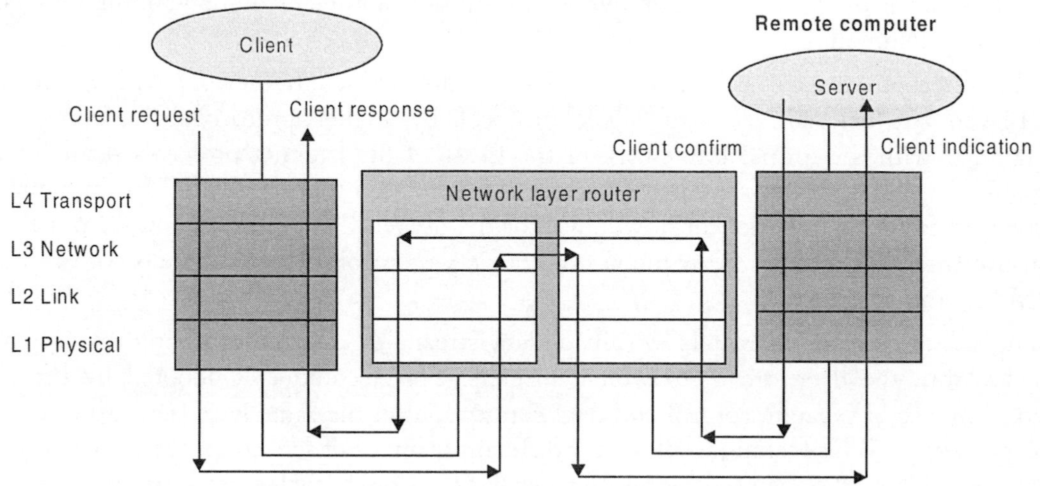

Figure 2.7 *Client/Server Interaction Across a Packet Data Network.*

The diagram provides only a very simplified view of what happens. In fact, a number of primitives are required to perform even such simple communication. The text below performs a detailed analysis of the primitives and PDUs which are exchanged.

The user executes the client program and attempts to send one piece of data to the server (for example,. a request to lookup the address corresponding to a name). The actual data need not be of concern here. Before the client may send the data, it must first establish a connection to the application layer (*i.e.,* communications software library) on the local computer.

The client program uses an A-Associate request function call to start the communication session. Once the application layer has initialized, it contacts the presentation layer, sending a

P-Connect request primitive. This establishes the format of the data to be used and the data formats which are to be supported by the system A on the network. This information is sent to the session layer as an SDU with a S-Connect request primitive. The session layer allocates a session identifier, and selects appropriate protocol options to support the services requested by the application layer. The session layer also identifies the intended recipient of the communication (*i.e.,* the remote computer).

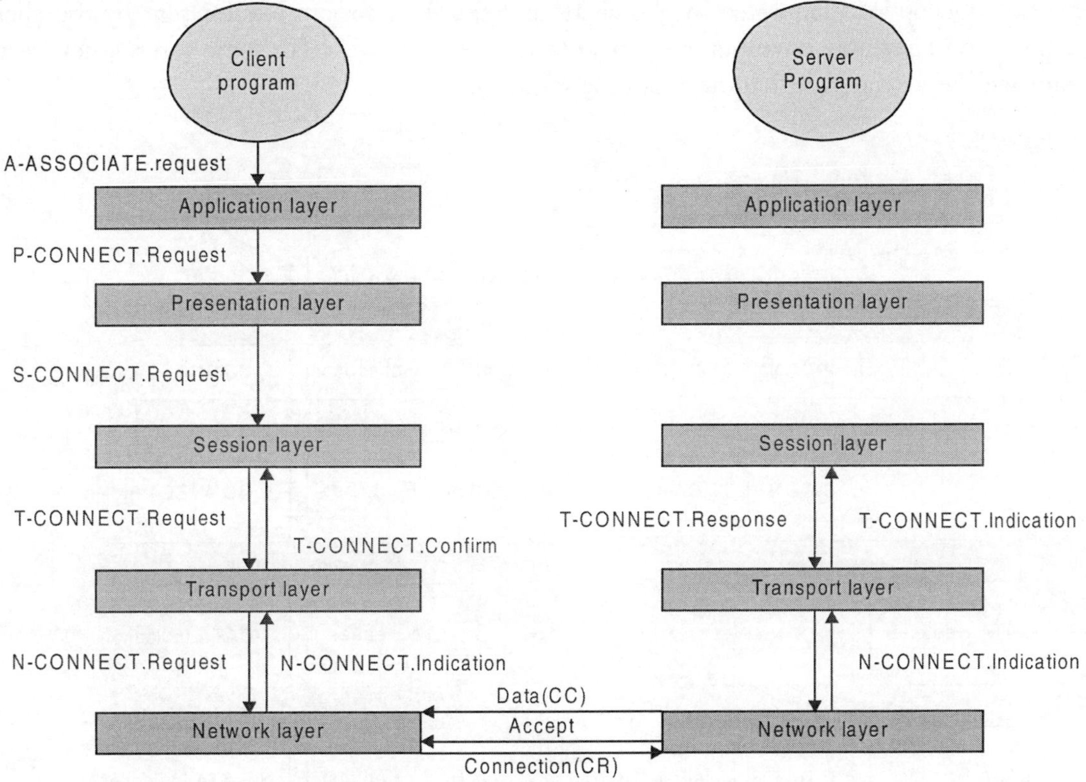

Figure 2.8 *Establishment of a Connection between Client and Server (part 1).*

The session layer proceeds to request a transport layer connection to the remote system using a T-Connect request. At this stage, the session layer may choose to not send the S-Connect SDU, and instead to wait to see whether the transport connection request succeeds. The transport request identifies the remote service required (*i.e.,* the port identifier for the server) and the type of transport protocol to be used. The basic types of transport service are reliable and best-effort.

At this stage the transport layer requests the network layer to establish a connection to the remote system. The network layer service will normally have established a link layer connection (and a physical layer connection) to the nearest intermediate system. In this case however, we assume that all the layers must be connected.

Finally, the network layer connect packet is sent using the link layer service to the remote system. The system responds by invoking the requested transport layer, and establishing a transport layer connection. If the remote system is able, it will then confirm the establishment of the transport connection, and pass the confirmation back to the local client computer. At this time the two systems have a communications path using the transport layer service.

The transport layer may then use this service to request a connection to the server process on the remote computer. It does this by forwarding the original session layer SDU (which it had previously stored in the session layer of the local computer) as a transport layer packet. This passes across the network layer service, and at the remote system is passed to the session layer protocol.

The received SDU identifies the session ID and the application process with which the client wishes to communicate. The presentation layer is sent a S-Connect indication, containing the presentation options requested by the client and the A-Associate request sent by the client. The application layer now attempts to connect to the server process. (In some cases, a new server program will be activated to handle this new request).

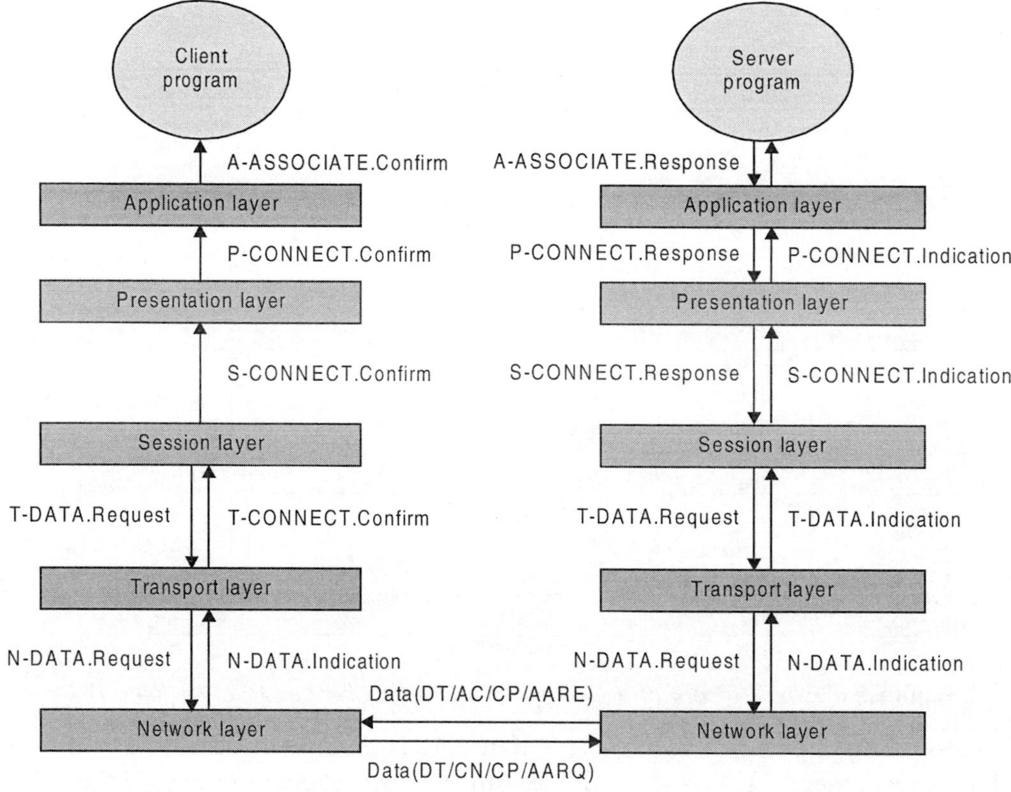

Figure 2.9 *Establishment of a Connection between Client and Server (part 2).*

Once this has succeeded a response is generated, carrying the final details of the connection. This information is passed as an A-Associate response primitive to the application layer. At each layer additional PCI is added by the remote system, and finally an N-Data primitive is sent across the network layer service. At the receiver each layer verifies the information it receives, and confirms the successful connection. The application layer send an A-Associate confirm message to the client process which is then ready to transmit data.

Transmission of data is accomplished similarly. The client application sends a data request primitive, along with the data, to the application layer, which adds its header and passes a data request primitive and data unit to the presentation layer. This process continues, with addition of appropriate headers, until it reaches the data link layer, which adds its header and passes the individual bits to the physical layer for transmission. The bits are received at the remote physical layer, and passed to the remote system data link layer. When the data link layer recognizes the end of the data unit, it strips off the header and sends the remaining PDU to the network layer (by including it in a data indication primitive).

Data indication primitives, with reduced data units, cascade up the layers until the application data reaches server application. Client application only learns of successful receipt if the server application returns an acknowledgement (in this case, possibly with the requested data). The acknowledgement returns across the network. The "association" has now been made and data may be sent across the network between the client and server.

THE TCP/IP REFERENCE MODEL

The TCP/IP reference model is the network model used in the current Internet architecture. It has its origins back in the 1960's with the grandfather of the Internet, the ARPANET. This was a research network sponsored by the department of defense in the United States. The following were seen as major design goals:

- Ability to connect multiple networks together seamlessly
- Ability for connections to remain intact as long as the source and destination machines were functioning
- To be built on flexible architecture

The reference model was named after two of its main protocols, TCP (Transmission Control Protocol) and IP (Internet Protocol).

They choose to build a packet-switched network based on a connectionless Internet work layer.

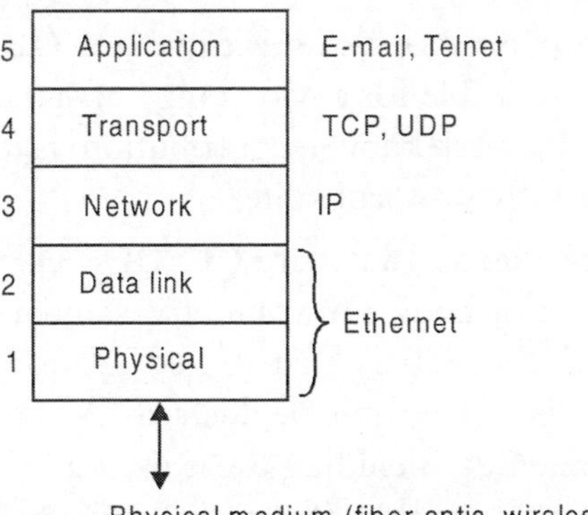

Figure 2.10 *TCP/IP Network Protocol.*

A detailed description of the reference model is beyond the scope of this document and project. The basic idea of the networking system is to allow one application on a host computer to talk to another application on a different host computer.

The application forms its request, then passes the packet down to the lower layers, which add their own control information, either a header or a footer, onto the packet. Finally the packet reaches the physical layer and is transmitted through the cable onto the destination host. The packet then travels up through the different layers, with each layer reading, deciphering, and removing the header or footer that was attached by its counterpart on the originating computer. Finally the packet arrives at the application it was destined for. Even though technically each layer communicates with the layer above or below it, the process can be viewed as one layer talking to its partner on the host, as figure shows.

Communication Standards

De jure (meaning "from the low") standards are ratified by an international body such as International Standards Organization (ISO), CCITT, IEEE. De facto (meaning "from the fact") standards become standards because every decides they are a good idea.

Example: IBM's System Network Architecture (SNA), which defines how computers and devices communicate together. DOS 3.1 and Novell's NetWare, all of these have become de facto standards because they hold important positions in the market.

STANDARDS ORGANIZATIONS

A wide variety of organizations contribute to Internetworking standards by providing forums for discussion, turning informal discussion into formal specifications, and proliferating specifications after they are standardized.

Most standards organizations create formal standards by using specific processes: organizing ideas, discussing the approach, developing draft standards, voting on all or certain aspects of the standards, and then formally releasing the completed standard to the public.

Some of the best-known standards organizations that contribute to Internetworking standards include these:

1. **International Organization for Standardization (ISO).** ISO is an international standards organization responsible for a wide range of standards, including many that are relevant to networking. Its best-known contribution is the development of the OSI reference model and the OSI protocol suite.
2. **American National Standards Institute (ANSI).** ANSI, which is also a member of the ISO, is the coordinating body for voluntary standards groups within the United States. ANSI developed the Fiber Distributed Data Interface (FDDI) and other communications standards. Electronic Industries Association (EIA)—EIA specifies electrical transmission standards, including those used in networking. The EIA developed the widely used EIA/TIA-232 standard (formerly known as RS-232). Institute of Electrical and Electronic Engineers (IEEE)—IEEE is a professional organization that defines networking and other standards. The IEEE developed the widely used LAN standards IEEE 802.3 and IEEE 802.5.
3. **International Telecommunication Union Telecommunication Standardization Sector (ITU-T).** Formerly called the Committee for International Telegraph and Telephone (CCITT), ITU-T is now an international organization that develops communication standards. The ITU-T developed X.25 and other communications standards.

4. **Internet Activities Board (IAB).** IAB is a group of internet work researchers who discuss issues pertinent to the Internet and set Internet policies through decisions and task forces. The IAB designates some Request for Comments (RFC) documents as Internet standards, including Transmission Control Protocol/Internet Protocol (TCP/IP) and the Simple Network Management Protocol (SNMP).

IEEE HISTORY

The IEEE and its predecessors, the AIEE (American Institute of Electrical Engineers) and the IRE (Institute of Radio Engineers), date to 1884.

From its earliest origins, the IEEE has advanced the theory and application of electro technology and allied sciences, served as a catalyst for technological innovation and supported the needs of its members through a wide variety of programs and services. The last quarter of the nineteenth century was marked by a tremendous growth in electrical technology. By the early 1880s, telegraph wires crisscrossed the United States. Europe and America were connected by underwater cable.

This growth in the technology and the planning for an international electrical exhibition to be held by the Franklin Institute in Philadelphia prompted twenty-five of America's most prominent electrical engineers, including Thomas Edison, Elihu Thomson and Edwin Houston, to issue a call for the formation of a society to promote their burgeoning discipline. On 13 May 1884, the AIEE was born in New York and quickly gained recognition as a representative for American electrical engineers.

AIEE—Wire Communications, Light and Power

From the beginning, the major interests of the AIEE was wire communications and light and power systems.

An early and active participant in the development of electrical industry standards, the institute laid the foundations for all work on electrical standards done in the United States. During its first three decades, the AIEE confronted and resolved such internal concerns as locating permanent headquarters for the organization providing mechanisms for contact with a far-flung membership and with students, and fostering new technical interests through committees that were established to meet the challenge of increasing specialization.

By 1912, however, the interests and needs of those specializing in the expanding field of radio could no longer be satisfied by periodic technical committee meetings in their local areas.

The IRE—Wireless Communications

Two largely local organizations—the Society of wireless and telegraph engineers and the wireless institute—merged to form an international society for scientists and engineers involved in the development of wireless communications—the institute of radio engineers. Many of the original members of the IRE were members of the AIEE and both organizations continued to have members in common until they merged to form the IEEE in 1963. The structural development and general activities of the IRE were similar to those of the AIEE.

Specialized segments were gathered into professional groups under a central governing body. Geographical units and student branches were formed. Meetings and publications facilitated the creation of an extensive literature and the exchange of knowledge. Membership grades were established. Standards development became a major effort.

The nature of radio technology meant that the interests of the IRE went beyond national boundaries. Therefore, the new organization sought and attracted members from many countries and eventually established units in several areas throughout the world. From the beginning the 'Proceedings of the IRE' regularly published papers from authors outside the United States. In the 1930's, electronics became part of the vocabulary of electrical engineering. Electronics engineers tended to become members of the IRE, but the applications of electron tube technology became so extensive that the technical boundaries differentiating the IRE and the AIEE became difficult to distinguish.

AIEE, IRE MERGE TO FORM IEEE

In 1961, the leadership of both the IRE and the AIEE resolved to seek an end to these difficulties through consolidation. The next year a merger plan was formulated and approved and became effective on 1 January 1963.

IEEE Ethernet Standards

Here is the listing of some IEEE standards.

- IEEE 802.1
- 802.1D (1993) MAC Layer Bridges(ISO 10038)
- 802.1p Quality of Service and Multicast Support
- 802.1Q VLAN processing
- 802.1G Remote Bridges
- List of most useful Supplements to the IEEE 802 Standards:
- 802.3 (1985) Base Standard (10B5)
- 802.3a (1992) 10B2 Ethernet over thin coaxial cable
- 802.3b (1985) Broadband Ethernet (using coaxial TV cable, now seldom used)
- 802.3c (1985) Improved definition of a Repeater 802.3d (1987) Definition of Ethernet for Fiber (10BFOIRL) (now seldom used)
- 802.3e (1987) 1Base5 or StarLAN (now seldom used)
- 802.3h (1991) Layer Management
- 802.3i (1990) 10BaseT, Ethernet over CAT-5 Unshielded Twisted Pair(UTP)
- 802.3j (1993) defines Ethernet over Fiber (10BF)
- 802.3p/q (1993) Definition of Managed Objects
- 802.3u (1995) Definition of Fast Ethernet (100BTX, 100BT4, 100BFX)
- 802.3x (1998) Definition of Full Duplex Operation in a switched LAN

- 802.3y (1998) Definition of Fast Ethernet (100BT2 over low quality UTP)
- 802.3z Definition of Gigabit Ethernet (over Fiber)
- 802.3aa Definition of Gigabit Ethernet Maintenance
- 802.3ab Definition of Gigabit Ethernet (over UTP CAT-5)
- 802.3ac Definition of Ethernet VLANs
- 802.3ad Definition of Ethernet VLAN Trunking

INTRODUCTION TO TCP/IP PROTOCOL ARCHITECTURE

TCP/IP protocols map to a four-layer conceptual model known as the *DARPA model*, named after the U.S. government agency that initially developed TCP/IP. The four layers of the DARPA model are: Application, transport, Internet, and network interface. Each layer in the DARPA model corresponds to one or more layers of the seven-layer Open Systems Interconnection (OSI) model. Figure 2.11 shows the TCP/IP protocol architecture.

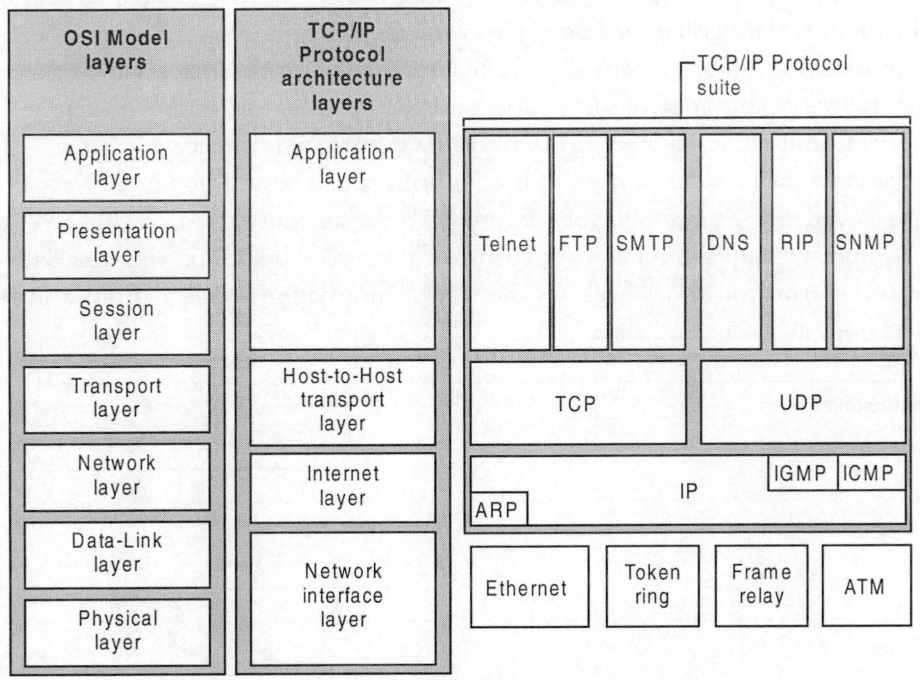

Figure 2.11 *TCP/IP Protocol Architecture.*

While there is no universal agreement about how to describe TCP/IP with a layered model, it is generally viewed as being composed of fewer layers than the seven used in the OSI model. Most descriptions of TCP/IP define three to five functional levels in the protocol architecture. The four-level model illustrated in figure 2.12 is based on the three layers (application, host-to-host, and network access) shown in the DOD protocol model, with the addition of a separate Internet layer. This model provides a reasonable pictorial representation of the layers in the TCP/IP protocol hierarchy.

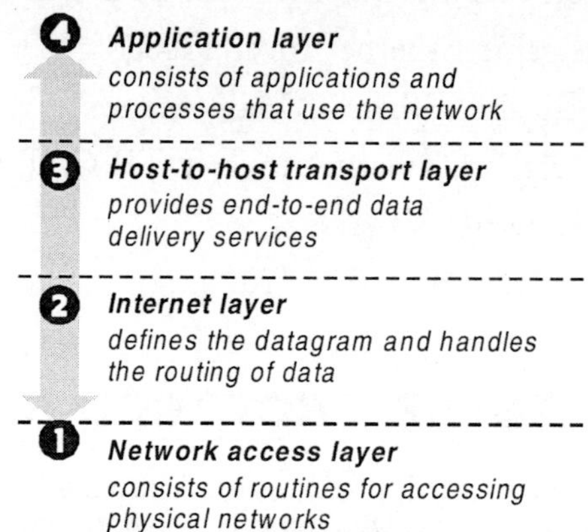

Figure 2.12 *Layers in the TCP/IP Protocol Architecture.*

As in the OSI model, data is passed down the stack when it is being sent to the network, and up the stack when it is being received from the network. The four-layered structure of TCP/IP is seen in the way data is handled as it passes down the protocol stack from the application layer to the underlying physical network. Each layer in the stack adds control information to ensure proper delivery. This control information is called a *header* because it is placed in front of the data to be transmitted. Each layer treats all of the information it receives from the layer above as data and places its own header in front of that information. The addition of delivery information at every layer is called *encapsulation.* (See figure 2.13 for an illustration of this.) When data is received, the opposite happens. Each layer strips off its header before passing the data on to the layer above. As information flows back up the stack, information received from a lower layer is interpreted as both a header and data.

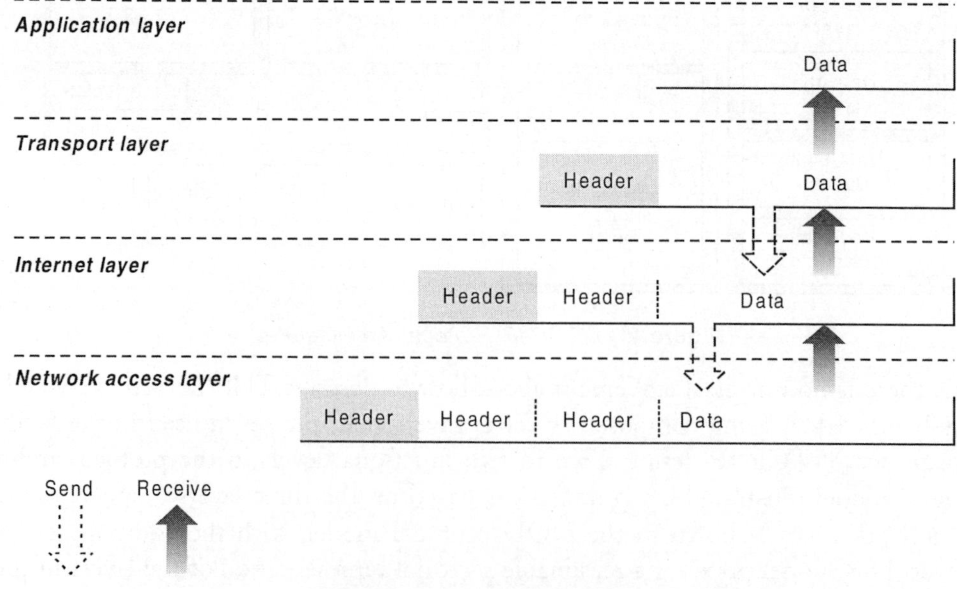

Figure 2.13 *Data Encapsulation.*

Each layer has its own independent data structures. Conceptually, a layer is unaware of the data structures used by the layers above and below it. In reality, the data structures of a layer are designed to be compatible with the structures used by the surrounding layers for the sake of more efficient data transmission. Still, each layer has its own data structure and its own terminology to describe that structure.

Figure 2.14 shows the terms used by different layers of TCP/IP to refer to the data being transmitted. Applications using TCP refer to data as a *stream*, while applications using the User Datagram Protocol (UDP) refer to data as a *message*. TCP calls data a *segment*, and UDP calls its data structure a *packet*. The Internet layer views all data as blocks called *data-grams*. TCP/IP uses many different types of underlying networks, each of which may have a different terminology for the data it transmits. Most networks refer to transmitted data as *packets* or *frames*. In figure we show a network that transmits pieces of data it calls *frames*.

Let's look more closely at the function of each layer, working our way up from the network access layer to the application layer.

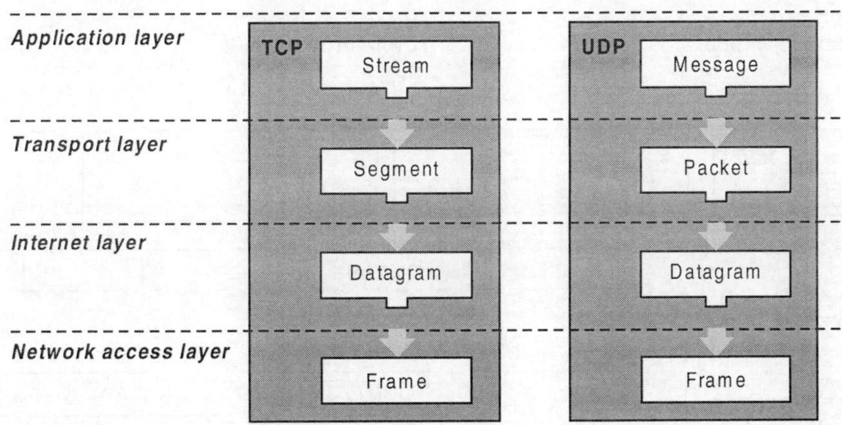

Figure 2.14 *Data Structures.*

NETWORK PROTOCOLS AND STANDARDS

Network operating systems provide access to network resources for user processes, but much more is needed to realize the goal of interoperability between processes running on separate systems. Interoperability means that distinct processes, each running on its own processor, co-operate in accomplishing some goal. They co-operate by exchanging information, by notifying each other as various tasks are completed, by requesting services from and granting services to each other. The processes run in separate and perhaps very different operating environments; they are related only in the co-operation. Their co-operative operation depends on a common understanding of how their interaction will proceed. They must agree on the format and the meaning of messages exchanged, and under what conditions the exchange will take place. The agreement about what messages will be sent and expected, under what conditions, in what format, and with what meaning is called a protocol.

For example, suppose we want to have the ability to send a message from one station in a network to another, have the receiving station confirms that the message arrived and then display the message on the screen. Sending the message is not sufficient; even if we are sure the message will be received by the destination machine. What is needed is an agreement, a protocol, that says.

I will send you a message with a header containing my identification and yours and the letters C and D. I understand that when you receive the message, you will know that C means confirm and D means display. I expect that when you receive the message, you will send me a message with a header containing your identification and mine and message body containing the letters ok. You will also display my message on your screen.

To complete the protocol specification, we include the reciprocal agreement: Furthermore, I agree to respond to a message from you, containing my identification and yours and the letters C and D, in the same way that you respond to my message.

Simple protocol operating between two stations on a network and allowing each to display a message on the other's screen lets call this protocol ConfirmAndDisplay. Now suppose two other stations in the network, or in a different network, use a protocol called AcknowledgeAndShow.

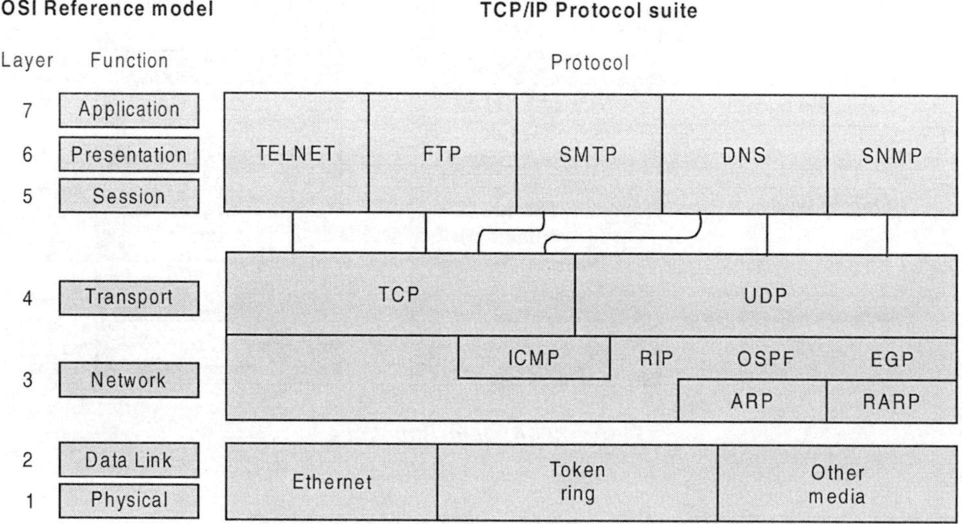

Figure 2.15 *Shows this Simple Protocol in Operation.*

AcknowledgeAndShow works exactly the same as ConfirmAndDisplay, except that in the message transmission, the letter S is used instead of C and D. (The S indicates that the message is to be shown on the screen. An acknowledgement of receipt of the message is always expected and not explicitly requested in the message.) If stations named Mars and Venus use the protocol ConfirmAndDisplay only and stations Neptune and Uranus, in the same network, use the protocol AcknowledgeAndShow only, then Mars and Neptune cannot display messages on each other's screens.

Why would such a situation arise and what can be done about it? The situation may have arisen because the idea of the mutual screen write by separate computers occurred to more than one person and each implemented it on the computers he or she wanted it on. Neither was aware of or even interested in the other's existence. Only later did someone recognize a reason to have the same facility on all the systems. There are four potential solutions to the problem:

Drop one protocol entirely and use the other on all the systems. This is the obvious solution and seems reasonable at first glance. Unfortunately, it turns out that each protocol has spread beyond its initial use and is deeply imbedded in a number of applications. If the protocol is discontinued, all the applications that use it will have to be identified and modified to use the replacement. Neither side is willing to be the one to go to that trouble. Further, each side is convinced that its own approach is better and does not wish to give up the perceived advantages.

Drop both protocols and develop a new one that all stations use. The new protocol would be carefully designed after thorough study and would address all the situations in which such a protocol might be useful. Since the new protocol would be installed in a very large collection of systems, not just the original Mars, Venus, Neptune, and Uranus, each of these systems would gain access to many other partners in using the protocol.

Each station runs both protocols, using the correct one for each communication. This is very practical for a simple case of two competing, similar protocols. However, if there are many other versions of this protocol, the burden on each system to keep all of them is substantial.

Keep the original protocol in each set of stations and also adapt the new global protocol to extend the range of stations each can work with. Mars and Venus will still use ConfirmAndDisplay when they work together because each knows the other will work correctly with that protocol and each has a number of application programs that include ConfirmAndDisplay. To display a message on Neptune's screen, Mars will use the new global protocol.

This very small example illustrates the current condition in network protocols. There are many reasons why a number of different protocols exist for accomplishing similar goals. Some of the differences result from requirements that demand specific features that are not consistent with other requirements. Others grew out of historic events and have become deeply ingrained in the products and practices of the industry. The various stations on a network come from different manufacturers, each with a long history of its own way of working. Allowing processes to interoperate, machines to communicate with each other and to co-operate to share a common transmission medium requires another kind of co-operation—the development of standards. The standards define protocols independent of individual manufacturers and applications.

Joining incompatible independent systems by agreeing to some common principles is not a new activity. In the 19th century, a railroad built for one region had a different width of track from a railroad in another region. As long as the regions remained separate, and the equipment was manufactured specifically for use in one region, the differences were immaterial. However, when the use of the railroads expanded, and the ability to travel and ship goods over long distances was recognized, the problem illustrated in figure 2.16 had to be solved. The solution was an agreement to build railroad equipment according to a common or standard specification. Notice that agreeing on a standard gauge track did not allow trains to travel between narrow and wide gauge tracks. The original tracks and trains could still be used for transportation within the region; but when travel between regions occurred, only standard gauge track and trains built to run on it would do.

The incompatible personal computer systems initially built by IBM and Apple provide another example. A lot of development effort is expended in preparing programs to run in these different environments.

The situation is similar with the developing network standards. Older proprietary protocols can still be used between the systems that implement them. However, to interoperate with other systems, the global standards must be observed. As a result, more than one set of protocols may exist in many systems. As more and more systems adopt the global standards there will be less reason to use the older, more restricted, protocols. However, because of the investment in the current systems and the number of applications that depend on them, these older protocols will continue to be important for some time.

COMMUNICATIONS PROTOCOLS

A communications protocol defines the rules for sending blocks of data (each known as a Protocol Data Unit (PDU)) from one node in a network to another node. Protocols are normally defined in a layered manner and provide all or part of the services specified by a layer of the OSI reference model. A protocol specification defines the operation of the protocol and may also suggest how the protocol should be implemented. It consists of three parts:

1. Definition of Protocol Control Information (PCI) format which forms the PDU header.
2. Definition of procedures for transmitting and receiving PDUs.
3. Definition of services provided by the Protocol Data Layers.

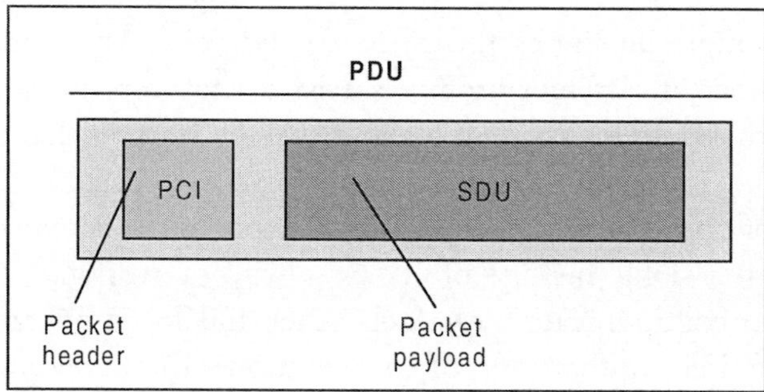

Figure 2.16 *A Protocol Data Unit.*

A PROTOCOL DATA UNIT

The PDUs exchanged have two parts: a header (also known as the protocol control information (PCI)) and a payload (also known as a service data unit (SDU)). The protocol does not define or constrain the data carried in the payload part. It does specify the format of the PCI, defining the fields which are present and the way in which the patterns of bits are to be interpreted.

A protocol also defines the procedures which determine how the PDU will be processed at the transmit and receive nodes. The procedures specify the valid values for the PCI fields, and the action be taken upon reception of each PCI value (usually based on stored control information). Examples of procedures which are implemented in protocols include:

- error recovery (*e.g.*, the check point procedure, the go-back-n procedure)
- flow control
- segmentation
- service access point selection
- connection management

The documents which define a protocol procedures are usually large and are seldom concrete (*i.e.*, they may not be directly translated to executable programs). They typically define the actions to be taken when a particular condition is detected, but not how the condition is to be detected. It has been said that "Part of what makes a protocol mature is good implementation guidelines and folklore". The success of the TCP/IP protocol suite is largely due to the "industrial strength" code available in freely distributed reference implementations.

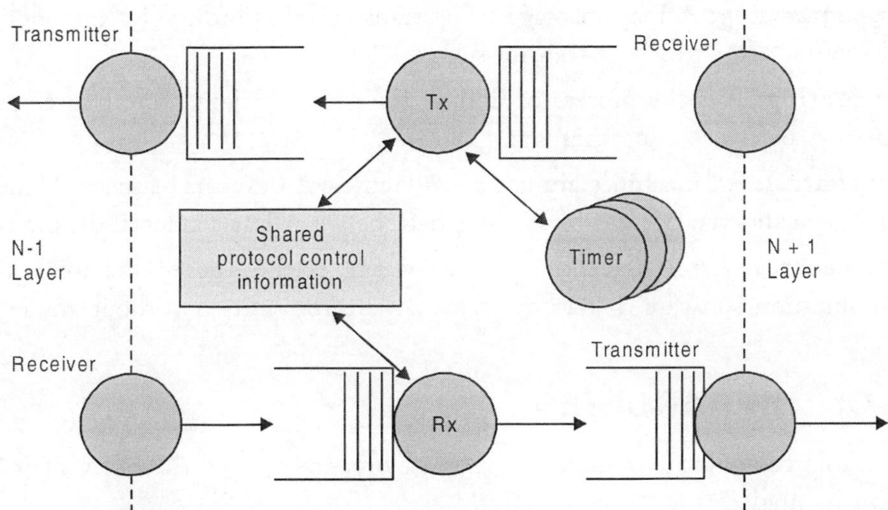

Figure 2.17 *A Protocol Implemented by Several Processes (represented by circles) Communicating Using Queues of PDUs.*

A protocol implemented by several processes (represented by circles) communicating using queues of PDUs, a shared information area (shown as a rectangle) and function calls between the processes (represented by arrows).

Protocols are usually implemented by writing a number of programs (processes) which communicate with one another through queues and by function calls. One or more timers are also usually required to ensure correct operation of the protocol. To start and stop timers, a protocol normally uses an interface to the computer's operating system. This interface is also used to request new (empty) buffers for received PDUs (or PDUs created by the layer) and to release buffers which are no longer needed by the protocol.

Protocols are generally described using a layered architecture known as the OSI reference model. Which abstracts the details of the protocol and allows a simple description of the service provided by the protocol to the protocol layer above and the service required by protocol layer from the layer below?

Examples of protocols include:

- Data link layer—HDLC, MAC, ARP
- Network layer—IP, ICMP
- Transport layer—UDP, TCP

You may be wondering how do the computers send and receive data across communication links. The answer is data communication software. It is this software that enables us to communicate with other systems. The data communication software instructs computer systems and devices as to how exactly data is to be transferred from one place to another. The procedure of data transformation in the form of software is commonly called protocol.

The data transmission software or protocols perform the following functions for the efficient and error free transmission of data.

- **Data sequencing:** A long message to be transmitted is broken into smaller packets of fixed size for error free data transmission.
- **Data routing:** It is the process of finding the most efficient route between source and destination before sending the data.
- **Flow control:** All machines are not equally efficient in terms of speed. Hence the flow control regulates the process of sending data between fast sender and slow receiver.
- **Error control:** Error detecting and recovering is the one of the main function of communication software. It ensures that data are transmitted without any error.

PROTOCOL HIERARCHIES

To reduce the design complexity of networks, they are organized as a series of layers or levels, each one built upon its predecessor.

The purpose of each layer is to offer certain services to the higher layers. Layer n with one machine carries on a conversation with layer n with another machine. The rules and conventions used in this conversation are collectively known as the layer n protocol.

Network Protocol Levels

You should be aware of the fact, that when talking about networking you will hear the word "protocol" all the time. This is because protocols are sets of standards that define all operations within a network. They define how various operations are to be performed. They may even define how devices outside the network can interact with the network. Protocols define everything from basic networking data structures, to higher level application programs. They define various services and utility programs. Protocols operate at many layers of the network models described below. There are protocols considered to be transport protocols such as TCP and UDP. Other protocols work at the network layer of the OSI network model shown below, and some protocols work at several of the network layers.

RFCs

Protocols are outlined in Request for Comments (RFCs). At the end of this document is a list of protocols and associated RFC numbers protocols. Although RFCs define protocols not all RFCs define protocols but may define other requirements for the internet such as RFC 1543 which provides information about the preparation of RFCs. The following RFCs are very central to the TCP/IP protocol.

RFC 1122—Defines host requirements of the TCP/IP suite of protocols covering the link, network (IP), and transport (TCP, UDP) layers.

RFC 1123—The companion RFC to 1122 covering requirements for internet hosts at the application layer.

RFC 1812—Defines requirements for internet gateways which are IPv4 routers.

REVIEW QUESTIONS

1. Write complete note on ISO OSI reference model.
2. Write short description on all seven layers.
3. What are the differences of TCP/IP and OSI model ?
4. What are the different standard organizations ?
5. Draw TCP/IP protocol architecture.

❑❑❑

PART 2

PHYSICAL LAYER

3

DATA TRANSMISSION SIGNALS

INTRODUCTION TO TRANSMISSION

Today's world of telecommunications is quickly changing from telephone based services into a global network of all digital services. Telephone service has been one of the primary methods of communications in the twentieth century. Although the telephone network was designed to transmit voice signals, pressure from other technologies forced it to be adapted to handle data transmission, facsimile and video.

When computers began sending data electronically the telephone network provided the logical framework for the connections between systems. The telephone network was ideal for computer communications because telephone service provided connections into most businesses and homes. The only problem with the telephone network was converting the non-voice signals so that they could be carried on voice circuits.

Since computers communicated in a digital format and the telephone network was analog, the transmitted signals had to be converted by devices called modems. Technology has now shown it is easier to create a network for digital transmission and convert the voice signals to move them. In actual usage voice, data and video can all be digitized and moved through the same network.

The main challenge seen today is the majority of the existing public telephone network is set up to carry voice signals. We are also seeing a growth in communications requirements due to new services like videoconferencing and local area networks. These new services require transmission speeds ranging from 100 kilobits per second up to a megabit or more.

Modern transmission technology came to the rescue by showing that it is easier and more cost effective to build a network that transmits digital signals. All we have to do is convert everything to digital prior to putting it into the network for transmission. In actual usage, the computers already use digital information, and only the voice and video need to be digitized. For the past twenty years telephone companies around the world have been installing new transmission equipment in their internal networks to carry all signals in digital format. Now, they are extending the digital signals all of the way into businesses and homes by converting the telephone networks from "telephone service" to "digital service." These new networks will provide you with end to end connections of binary or digital bit streams at various speeds. You will then select and use the bit stream at the proper speed to encode your voice, video or data information on the circuit. In essence the telephone companies will become "digital companies" providing a service called Integrated Services Digital Network (ISDN). The purpose of this training course is to provide an introduction to digital transmission techniques and systems. The course is divided into five parts that take you from the basic concepts of the digital network through to the customer interface and use of the network.

SIGNAL

A signal is any physical phenomenon that can be modelled as a function from time or position to some scalar or vector valued domain that can be real or complex valued.

Signal Characterization

Communications is the process of transmitting meaningful signals from one location to another. Signals have several classifications and properties.

- **Signal Classifications**
  * Deterministic signals
  * Random signals
  * Energy signals
  * Power signals
- **Signal Properties**
  * Time averages
  * Auto correlation
  * Bandwidth

DATA TRANSMISSION SIGNALS

The information carrying signals are divided into two broad classes;

- Analog
- Digital

Analog Signals

Analog signals are continuous electrical signals that vary in time as shown in figure 3.1 . Most of the time, the variations follow that of the non-electric (original) signal. Therefore, the two are analogous hence the name analog.

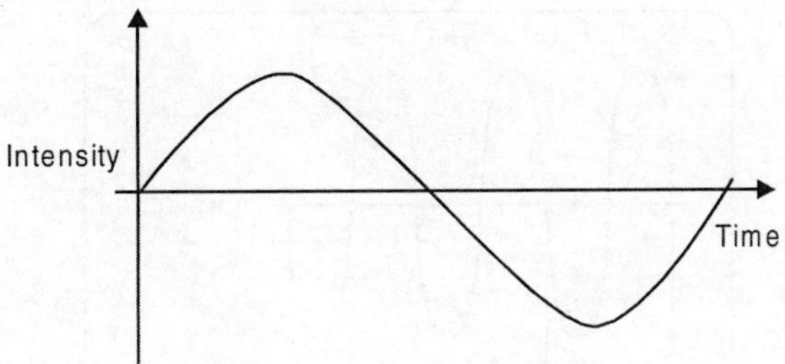

Figure 3.1 *Analog Signal.*

Not all analog signals vary as smoothly as the waveform shown in figure 3.2. Analog signals represent some physical quantity and they are a 'model' of the real quantity.

Example:

Telephone voice signal is analog. The intensity of the voice causes electric current variations. At the receiving end, the signal is reproduced in the same proportion. Hence the electric current is a 'model' but not one's voice since it is an electrical representation or analog of one's voice.

Analog signals are what we encounter every day of our life. Speech is an analog signal, and varies in amplitude (volume) and frequency (pitch). The main characteristics of analog signals are:

Amplitude

This is the strength of the signal. It can be expressed a number of different ways (as volts, decibels). The higher the amplitude, the stronger (louder) the signal.

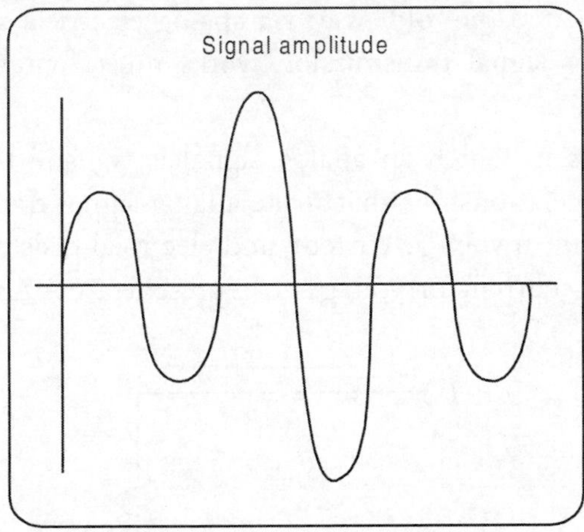

Figure 3.2 *Signal Amplitude.*

Frequency

This is the rate of change the signal undergoes every second, expressed in Hertz (Hz), or cycles per second. A 30Hz signal changes thirty times a second. In speech, we refer to it as the number of vibrations per second, as the air that we expel out of our mouth pushes the surrounding air at a specific rate.

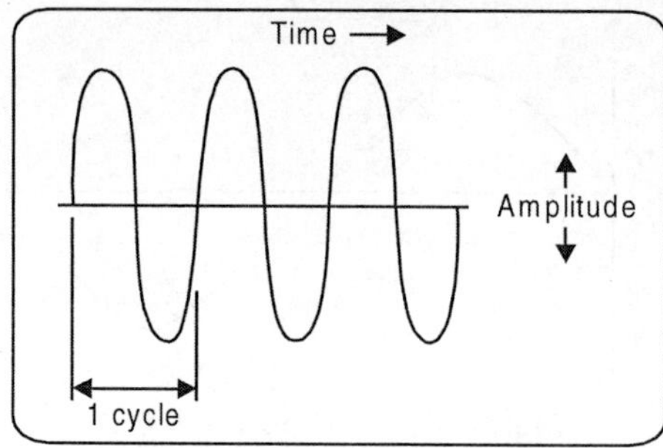

Figure 3.3 *Signal Frequency.*

One cycle is defined as a point on the wave to the next identical point. The numbers of cycles there are per second determine the frequency of the signal.

Analog Transmission

Using analog transmission techniques, such as those found on the existing telephone networks has presented a problem as newer services are brought into the network. This section will explore some of those problems and contrast them to the advantages of providing digital services.

Analog Signal Transmission

Although the microprocessor and digital network technologies have fundamentally reinvented the ways in which today's data acquisition systems handle data, much laboratory and manufacturing information is still communicated the "old" way, via analog electrical signals. And a fundamental understanding of how analog signal transmission works must first begin with a discussion of electrical basics.

To understand the ways in which an analog signal is transmitted over a circuit, it is first important to understand the relationships that make analog signal transmission possible. It is the fundamental relationship between voltage, current, and electrical resistance (Figure 3.4) that allow either a continuously varying current or voltage to represent a continuous process variable.

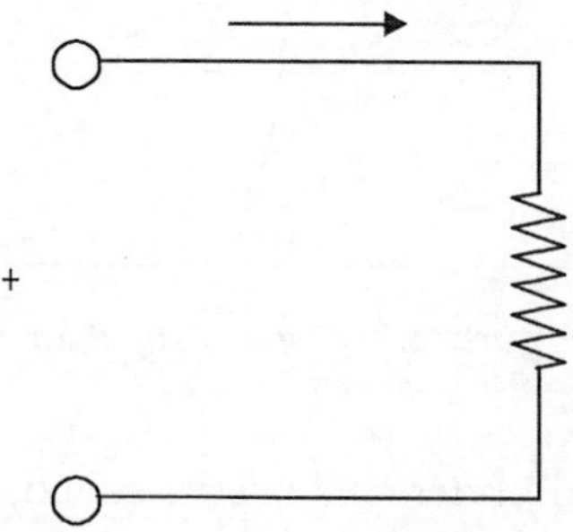

Figure 3.4 *A Basic Electric Circuit.*

While charge flow is electric current, voltage is the work done in moving a unit of charge (1 coulomb) from one point to another. The unit of voltage is often called the potential difference, or the volt (V). The International System of Units (SI) unit for electrical flow is the ampere (A), defined as one coulomb per second (c/s).

A signal source of voltage, V, will cause a current, I, to flow through a resistor of resistance, R. Ohm's law, which was formulated by the German physicist George Simon Ohm (1787–1854), defines the relation:

$$V = IR$$

While most single-channel analog signal transmissions use direct current (DC) variations in current or voltage to represent a data value, frequency variations of an alternating current (AC) also can be used to communicate information. In the early 19th century, Jean Baptiste Joseph Fourier, a French mathematician and physicist, discovered that AC signals could be defined in terms of sine waves. A sine wave is described by three quantities: amplitude, period, and frequency. The amplitude is the peak value of the wave in either the positive or negative direction, the period is the time it takes to complete one cycle of the wave, and the frequency is the number of complete cycles per unit of time (the reciprocal of the period).

To begin, we must understand that for most of its first one hundred years the worldwide telephone network was concerned with only carrying voices. This meant that the network was built to connect telephones across the world and carry a voice between two points. Although the network architecture worked well for voice transmission, the newer services like computer data, facsimile and video transmission have been constrained by the analog voice network design.

Looking at figure 3.5, we can see how the existing telephone network is used to provide a variety of office communications. This drawing shows one key problem with the telephone network. Each of the various lines for telephone or data communications requires a separate line or circuit. The telephone systems have tie-lines and trunks to the outside world, computers use high speed analog or digital circuits and video systems use high speed or broadband circuits. Each type of circuit has its own problems related to installation, support and maintenance. In many cases the telephone companies had different service organizations to handle each service creating confusion for the customers.

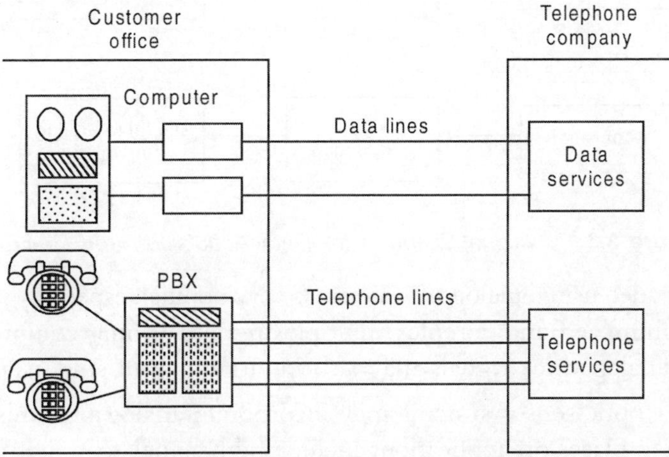

Figure 3.5 *Analog Telephone Services.*

Telephone companies also found problems with voice quality as it was transmitted across long distances. Analog transmission and amplification had limits, since noise was usually amplified along with the voice signal. This meant there was a limit to how many times an analog signal could be amplified and still be recognized.

Analog transmission systems were also difficult to test and service. Usually, the telephone company technicians had to take an analog transmission system out of service before doing any testing or maintenance.

In addition to the analog transmission problems, telephone companies were faced with increased pressure from customers for more services and greater bandwidths. Growth in telephone usage in the 1950's and 1960's also added to the telephone companies requirements to provide more voice circuits globally.

Analog I/O Functionality

Today, digital computers and other microprocessor-based devices have replaced analog recording and display technologies in all but the simplest data acquisition applications. And while computers have had an undeniably positive impact on the practice of data acquisition, they speak only a binary language of ones and zeroes. Manufacturing processes and natural phenomena, however, are still by their very nature analog. That is, natural processes tend to vary smoothly over time, not discontinuously changing states from black to white, from on to off.

To be meaningfully recorded or manipulated by a computer then, analog measurements such as pressure, temperature, flow rate, and position must be translated into digital representations. Inherently digital events, too, such as the tripping of a motor or a pulse generated by a positive displacement flow meter, must be made interpretable as a Transistor-to-Transistor Logic (TTL) level changes in voltage. Hence, the origination and ongoing development of input/output (I/O) systems (Figure 3.6) for converting analog and digital information about real-world processes and events into the language of computers.

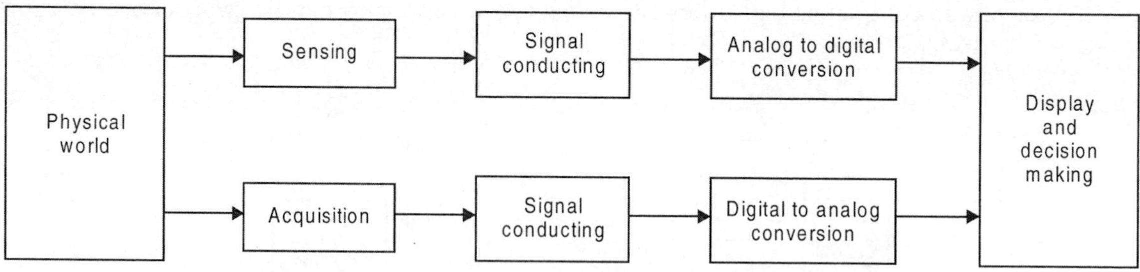

Figure 3.6 *Functional Diagram for Data Acquisition and Control.*

Transmission of video using analog techniques is very popular, especially for shorter distances, where costs can be minimized and complex multiplexing and timing equipment is unnecessary. The transmission of analog voice signals may also be attractive in small short-haul systems.

In addition, fiber optic sensor systems may incorporate analog transmission. Requirements that analog transmission places on applications include high signal-to-noise ratio and high source linearity. While analog transmission can be attractive for short-haul or medium-haul systems, it is unattractive for long-haul systems where digital techniques provide better performance.

Digital Signals

Digital signals are non-continuous, they change in individual steps. They consist of pulses or digits with discrete levels or values. The value of each pulse is constant, but there is an abrupt change from one digit to the next. Digital signals have two amplitude levels called nodes. The value of which are specified as one of two possibilities such as 1 or 0, high or low, true or false and so on. In reality, the values are anywhere within specific ranges and we define values within a given range.

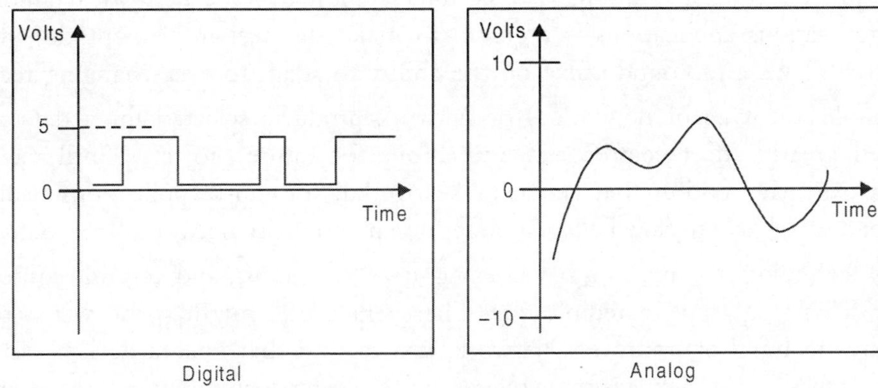

Figure 3.7 *Digital Signal.*

Digital signals are the language of modern day computers. Digital signals normally comprise only two states. These are expressed as ON or OFF, 1 or 0 respectively. The following diagram shows a digital signal.

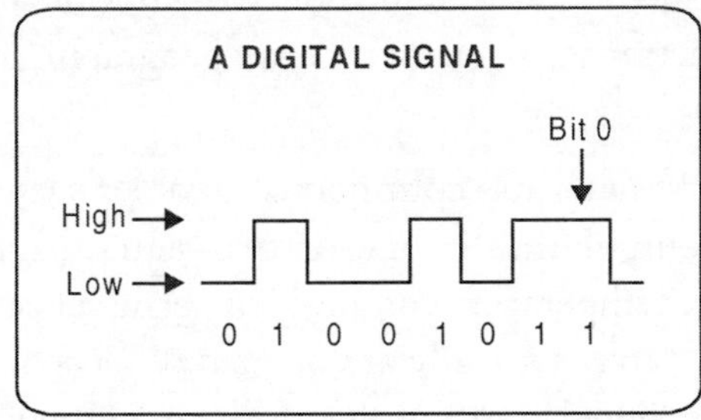

Figure 3.8 *Digital Signal Showing Two States, 0 and 1.*

Digital Transmission

In the early 1960's the telephone companies began using a new form of transmission called "digital." This system allowed them to accept standard analog voice signals and convert them to digital signals for transmission across their long distance and toll networks. This service was called T-Carrier in the North America and E-Carrier in Europe (or sometimes just "digital transmission systems").

Digital transmission offers an advantage with regard to the acceptable signal-to-noise ratio (SNR) at the optical receiver. Digital communication systems can tolerate large amounts of signal loss and dispersion without impairing the ability of the receiver to distinguish a binary 1 from a binary 0. Digital signalling also reduces the effects that optical source nonlinearities and temperature have on system performance. Source nonlinearities and temperature variations can severally affect analog transmission. Digital transmission provides superior performance in most complex systems (Such as LANs) and long-haul communication systems. In short-haul systems, the cost and complexity of analog-to-digital and digital-to-analog conversion equipment, in some cases, outweigh the benefits of digital transmission.

Digital Signal Transmission

Industrial networks that transmit data using digital signals often are an integral part of a data acquisition or process control solution. A basic understanding of the network technologies that are available for various applications is required to make the best implementation decisions—decisions that can have a profound effect on the ability to adapt to ever-changing technologies.

For example, the type of network(s) or network products selected for a data acquisition application can greatly affect cost/benefit evaluations for future projects. Until recently, fiber optics was an expensive option that seemed like overkill for most applications. But with the information load now likely to flow between nodes on an enterprise network, fiber looks attractive.

Network technologies come in a bewildering array of options, and certain segments of this technology are changing at an incredible rate. The average user might spend weeks researching the various ways to build or improve a network, just to find that once a decision is made and products are purchased, the next wave of bigger, better, faster technology is now available.

A well-designed, integrated solution to data transmission will yield a competitive advantage to any industrial enterprise. Users in all aspects of a business should be able to obtain plant and business data from any physical node, local or remote. "gluing" pieces of new and/or existing networks together is becoming more feasible with the use of bridging, routing, and media conversion technologies that link local area, wide area, and industrial networks together. And with Internet and wireless technologies, data transmission over large geographic areas is increasingly feasible.

Digital I/O Functionality

In contrast to analog transducers that sense continuous variables such as pressure and temperature, many transducers provide an output that is one of two states: high or low, open or closed. A pressure might be too high or a temperature too low, triggering closure of a switch. Outputs, too, are not strictly analog-solenoid valves typically are opened or closed, many pumps and heaters are simply turned on or off. Pulse signals are another form of digital I/O, with one rotation of a turbine flow meter or tachometer corresponding to a single, countable event. Digital I/O also can be used for parallel communications among plug-in expansion cards, and to generate clock and other timing signals.

Already in the binary language of computers, these types of digital, or discrete, inputs and outputs (I/O) are much easier for microprocessor-based data acquisition systems to deal with than analog signals. Similar to analog-to-digital converters used for analog I/O, digital I/O is designed to deal directly with Transistor-to-Transistor Logic (TTL) level voltage changes. TTL typically sets the low voltage level between 0 and 0.8 V and the high voltage level between 2.0 and 5.0 V. Voltage levels between 0.8 and 2.0 V are not allowed. A voltage change, then, from the high range to the low range (or vice versa) represents a digital change of state from high to low, on to off, etc.

And because acquiring an analog signal is more complex than acquiring a digital one, analog I/O channels also are more expensive. Hence, if digital I/O is adequate, do not bother with analog.

This system was a great advantage for telephone companies because it reduced their transmission and maintenance costs. The disadvantage was that it did not extend directly to the customer's office. Up until the 1980's the telephone company still accepted and switched the majority of telephone circuits using analog techniques. The only benefit the customer received from this arrangement was better quality sound on long distance telephone calls.

There was also an anomaly since great efforts were being made to build modems that translated computer digital signals to analog signals for transmission across telephone circuits. So while companies were paying money for modems which translated computer digital signals into analog transmission, the telephone company was transporting that analog signal on a digital network. Taking the digital signal and converting it into analog and then converting that analog signal into a digital transmission format were a very inefficient way to transmit information. In fact the modems had upper speed limits of 19,200 bits per second, while the signal was actually being carried on a 64,000 bit per second digital carrier.

In the 1980's the telephone companies began extending the digital service to the customer allowing them to do their own analog to digital conversion. By moving the digital conversion into the customer's office, the telephone company can provide one type of link and the customer can differentiate the various services. This means that the customer can have one link into the telephone company and the telephone company has one "easy to maintain" network.

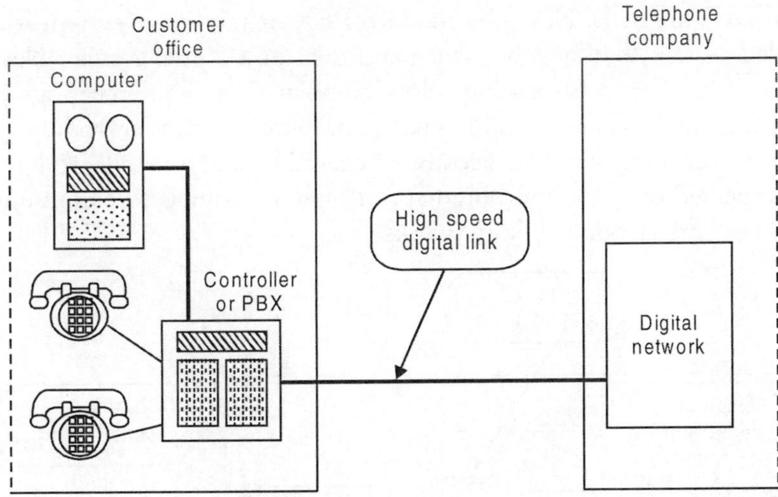

Figure 3.9 *Digital Services.*

As shown in figure 3.9, the use of digital services allows the one link to provide all of the voice and data connections. As digital networks evolve, everything can be connected to a common communications link. First, the computer systems are connected to the PBX or some other type of digital communications controller. This PBX or controller can then be connected to one or more high speed digital circuits which go into the telephone company. Whether the incoming transmission is voice, data, video or images it will be translated into common digital format and moved through a common digital network worldwide.

It's easy to understand that if we convert everything to digital it makes communications easier because we only need one type of circuit for all of our communications. You should understand though that through the use of all digital communications both the telephone company and the end user are winners.

The payback for the telephone companies is a massive reduction in maintenance costs. Digital communications networks are easier to test and maintain because there is only one type of signal. Also digital transmission systems can detect failures and switch to back-up systems automatically. This payback of lower maintenance costs can be a greater incentive to the telephone companies than the customer requirements for digital services.

For end users or customers, the use of fully digital communications can reduce circuit costs by fifty percent or more. Also the use of digital circuits improves quality and reliability of voice and data communications.

The world's telephone companies are responding to the economic, competitive and customer pressures to install networks that are fully digital. Eventually this will mean that the ability to provide telephone connections, data transmission, video links or other services will be done by the customer at their site through a common digital controller. The organization that we know today as the telephone company or PTT will become only a "digital company" providing one of the new services like ISDN (Integrated Services Digital Network) or ATM (Asynchronous Transfer Mode).

The Future of Digital Communications

Within today's office the use of communications has advanced far beyond the simple telephone on a desk. The revolution begins with personal computers on desks tied together on a local area network as shown in figure 3.10. Next, the modern PBX or telephone system is a sophisticated, computer controlled system that switches voice and data in a digital format. Next, new uses for digital technologies like videoconferencing allow companies to hold meetings between offices across the globe. And finally there are still central computer systems providing support for core applications such as accounts payable, accounts receivable and payroll. Today, most of these systems can be connected over common high speed digital channels to communicate with other systems worldwide on private or public networks.

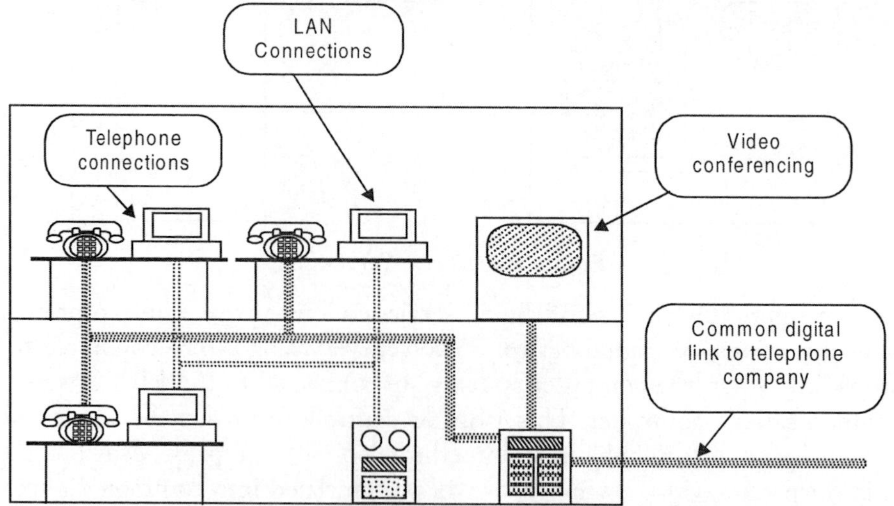

Figure 3.10 *Modern Office Communications.*

In reality though the use of digital communications is not that prolific and as a result we will still see two types of switching systems and networks supported for many years as shown in figure 3.11. The older network will continue to provide common telephone services to areas that still use the older equipment. The new all digital networks will support the switching and transmission of digital signals along with modern digital telephones and other services. Both networks will allow telephone calls and certain other existing services to cross between them and maintain compatibility.

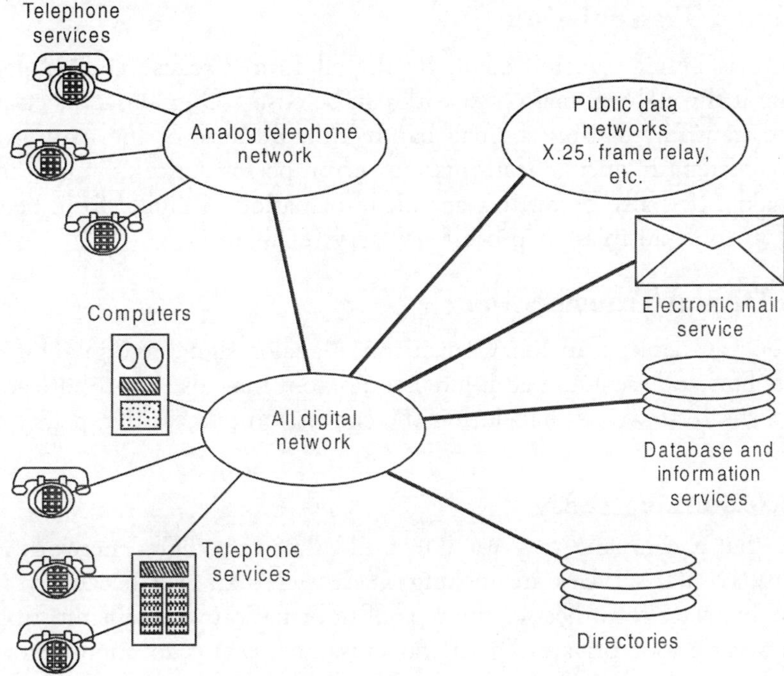

Figure 3.11 *The Future Networks.*

Although there will be bridging to support telephone calls and other common service between the two networks, some of the newer services will only be available to all digital users.

Again looking figure 3.11, the new all digital networks will be simply providing digital bandwidth. Therefore in order to compete the telephone companies will have to provide access to other services in order to maintain their market shares. Rather than using separate lines to connect to these information services, you could simply connect through the digital company and receive the charges as a part of your regular telephone billing. The types of services customers will see through the future all digital networks include:

Access to existing and future data networks. This would include the existing packet switched networks (X.25, etc.) and the future public data networks (frame relay, etc.). Global electronic mail services providing access to services like the Internet and gateways to the mail services of other providers.

Databases and Other Online Information Services

Access to worldwide directories providing information on how to navigate through the future digital world to find businesses, people and information services. Remember that any of these services will be as easy as dialing a telephone call. Most of the digital circuits in use today are available either as special services from the telephone company or provided through private networks of microwave, fiber optic or satellite links. The concept of a single common digital public network has been emerging over the past ten years under the "Integrated Services Digital Network" or the acronym ISDN. ISDN is not a theory but, is actually available and in use in several industrialized countries including Japan, Singapore, France, the United States and Great Britain to name a few.

Advantages Digital Transmission

Digital information is better transmitted in its digital form because converting the signal to analog and sending it through an analog network can be costly. Digital data is easily compressed; therefore it can be transmitted using a small bandwidth. Because of the nature of devices used to boost the signal strength during transmission, error performance is much improved when compared with analog. It is also better to transmit information in digital form because computer components used in the transmission process are very reliable.

Disadvantages Digital Transmission

Information is widely available as analog. Conversion of analog signal to digital bit stream requires special equipment. This adds cost and additional equipment may also contribute additional points of failure. Another disadvantage is that during the conversion process the quality of the signal is negatively affected.

Private Digital Networking Today

It is also possible that a company may want to build a private digital network and bypass the telephone company. Digital services are making this easier than ever because you only need to meet one common interface regardless of the type of information you transmit. In today's market, the end user has a variety of private digital transmission systems to choose from as shown in figure 3.12.

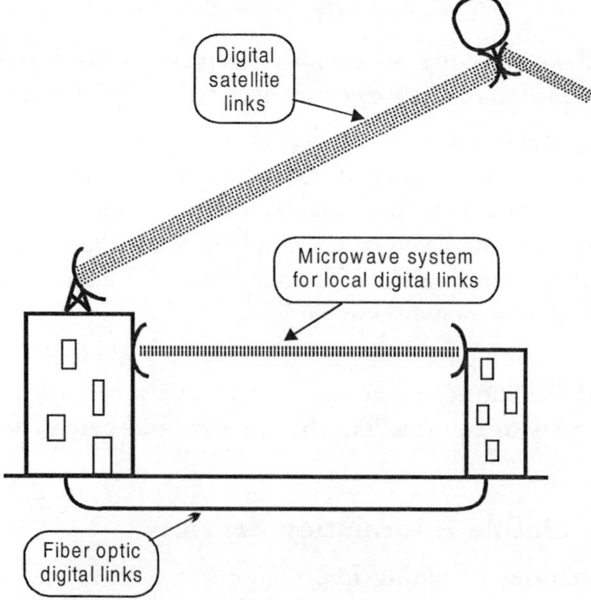

Figure 3.12 *Private Digital Link Options.*

Options for private digital networks today include:

- Satellite earth stations that can provide both national and international links directly between customer sites (bypassing the local telephone company connections).
- Microwave radio systems that can provide links of up to fifty miles. In some cases, customers have even used microwave systems to provide back-up or emergency links into their local telephone company.
- Fiber optic cables that can provide digital services linking local or remote buildings. Private networks can also be built around dedicated services purchased from telephone companies.

ANALOG SIGNAL TYPES

Most data acquisition signals can be described as analog, digital or pulse. While analog signals typically vary smoothly and continuously over time, digital signals are present at discrete points in time in figure 3.13. In most control applications, analog signals range continuously over a specified current or voltage range, such as 4–20 mA dc or 0 to 5 V dc. While digital signals are essentially on/off (the pump is on or off, the bottle is there or isn't), analog signals represent continuously variable entities such as temperatures, pressures, or flow rates. Because computer-based controllers and systems understand only discrete on/off information, conversion of analog signals to digital representations is necessary.

Transduction is the process of changing energy from one form into another. Hence, a transducer is a device that converts physical energy into an electrical voltage or current signal for transmission. There are many different forms of analog electrical transducers. Common transducers include load cells for measuring strain via resistance, and thermocouples and resistance temperature detectors (RTDs) for measuring temperature via voltage and resistance measurement, respectively. Transmission channels may be wires or coaxial cables.

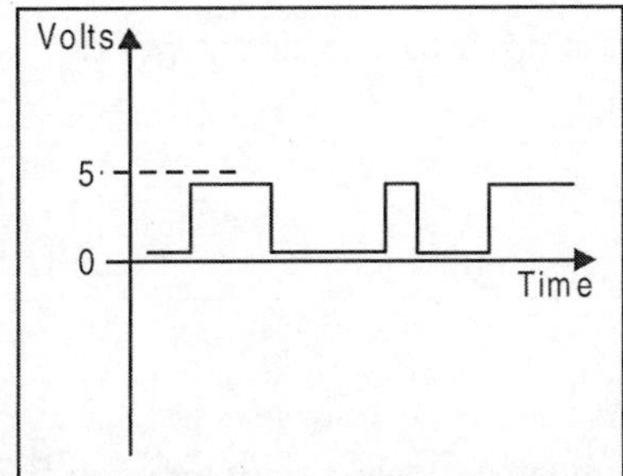

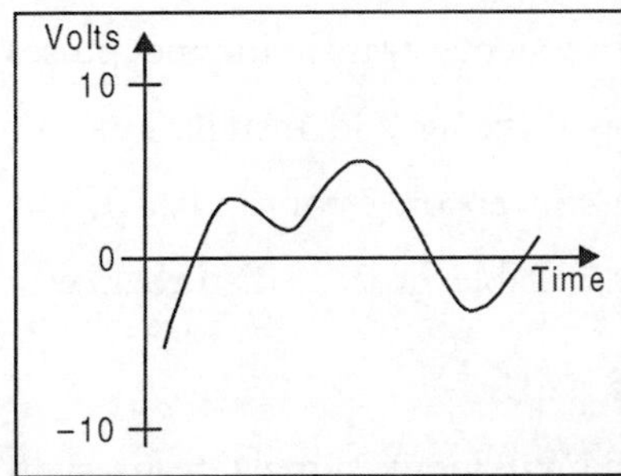

Figure 3.13 *Digital and Analog Signal Representations.*

For noise-resistant transmission over significant distances, the raw transducer signal is often converted to a 4–20 mA signal by a two-wire, loop-powered transmitter. The bottom value of a process variable's range, for example, a temperature, is typically designated as 4 mA, making it easy to distinguish transmitter failure (0 mA) from a valid signal. If the current source is of good quality, current loops tend to be less sensitive to noise pickup by electromagnetic interference than voltage-based signals.

Noise and Grounding

In transmitting analog signals across a process plant or factory floor, one of the most critical requirements is the protection of data integrity. However, when a data acquisition system is transmitting low level analog signals over wires, some signal degradation is unavoidable and will occur due to noise and electrical interference. Noise and signal degradation are two basic problems in analog signal transmission.

Noise is defined as any unwanted electrical or magnetic phenomena that corrupt a message signal. Noise can be categorized into two broad categories based on the source-internal noise and external noise. While internal noise is generated by components associated with the signal itself, external noise results when natural or man-made electrical or magnetic phenomena influence the signal as it is being transmitted. Noise limits the ability to correctly identify the sent message and therefore limits information transfer. Some of the sources of internal and external noise include:

1. Electromagnetic interference (EMI).
2. Radio-frequency interference (RFI).
3. Leakage paths at the input terminals.
4. Turbulent signals from other instruments.
5. Electrical charge pickup from power sources.
6. Switching of high-current loads in nearby wiring.
7. Self-heating due to resistance changes.
8. Arcs.
9. Lightning bolts.
10. Electrical motors.
11. High-frequency transients and pulses passing into the equipment.
12. Improper wiring and installation.
13. Signal conversion error, and
14. Uncontrollable process disturbances.

Digital Inputs

Many types of digital input signals from switch closures relay contacts, or TTL-compatible interfaces can be read directly by digital I/O cards (Figure 3.14). Other types of inputs may require some signal conditioning, most likely to reduce higher-level voltage changes to TTL levels. A variety of signal conditioning modules are available to provide isolation and other digital conditioning functions.

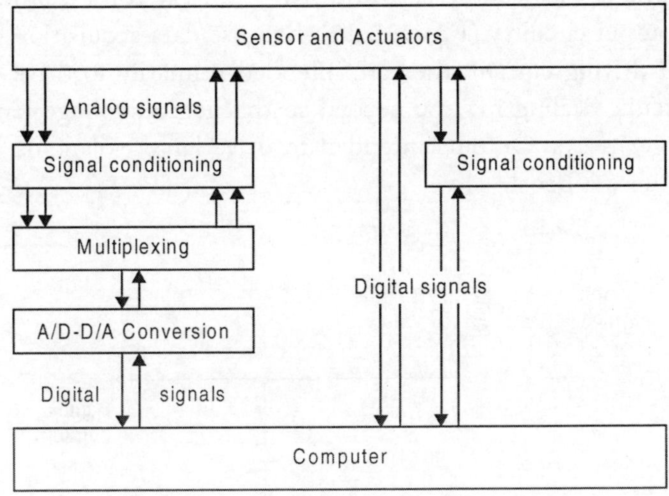

Figure 3.14 *Signal Processing Requirement.*

For Digital and Analog Signals

The most common type of digital input is the contact closure (Figure 3.15). Essentially a sensor or switch of some type closes or opens a set of contacts in accordance with some process change. An applied electrical signal then determines whether the circuit is open or closed. Current flows if the circuit is closed, registering a "1" in a transistor at the computer interface. Conversely, an open circuit retains a high voltage (and no current), registering a "0" at the transistor.

Another type of digital input useful in data acquisition applications is the hardware trigger. This allows an external event—a high reactor temperature, perhaps, or a low tank level-to control data collection. If during routine operation data is only being acquired for archival storage on a once-per-second basis, a hardware trigger can be used to boost the data acquisition rate during an upset until normal conditions are restored.

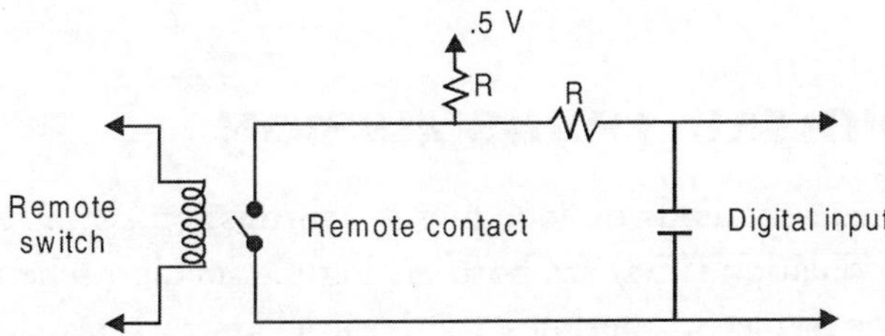

Figure 3.15 *Digital Input Applied to a Contact Closure.*

Digital Outputs

At its simplest, a digital output provides a means of turning something on or off. Applications range from driving a relay to turning on an indicator lamp to transmitting data to another computer. For latching outputs, a "1" typically causes the associated switch or relay to latch, while a "0" causes the switch to unlatch. Devices can be turned on or off, depending on whether the external contacts are normally open or normally closed.

Standard TTL level signals can be used to drive 5-V relay coils; a protective diode is used to protect the digital output circuitry (Figure 3.16). Because data acquisition boards can typically supply only 24 mA of driving current, they are intended primarily to drive other logic circuits, not final control elements. Scaling may be needed so that logical voltage levels are sufficient to cause switching in larger relays. Outputs intended to drive larger solenoids, contactors, motors, or alarms also may require a boost.

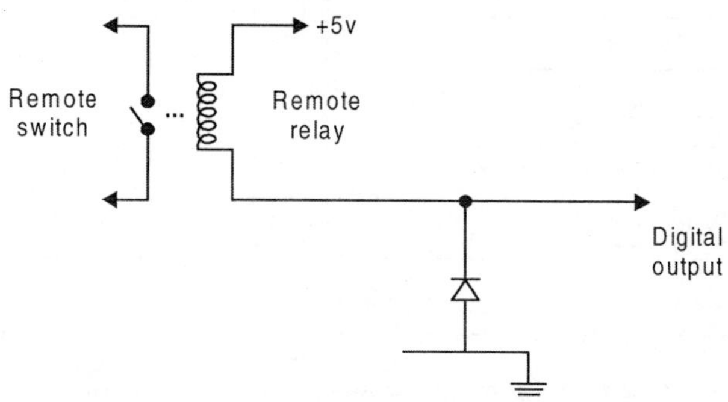

Figure 3.16 *Digital Output Applied to a Relay.*

Pulse I/O

A somewhat separate class of digital I/O is pulse inputs and outputs, which typically is associated with frequency, counting, or totalization applications. Pulse inputs might be used to count the rotations of a turbine flow meter; pulse outputs might be used to drive a stepping motor.

Pulse inputs are handled in much the same way as digital logic inputs, but the output of the sensing circuit is normally connected to a counter rather than a specific bit position in the input register. Successive pulses increment or decrement the counter. Add an elapsed time measure and a frequency or pulse rate can readily be determined. Similar to an analog-to-digital converter, a counter is characterized by its number of bits—an N-bit counter can accumulate up to 2N discrete events. Thus, a 16-bit counter can count to 216 = 65,536.

ANALOG VS. DIGITAL TRANSMISSION

There are three predominant methods of encoding a transmission signal. Amplitude modulation (AM) and Frequency Modulation (FM) are both analog modulation schemes. The third method is digital modulation. The Table 3.1 outlines the basic characteristics of the three modulation schemes.

AM, FM and digital modulation are described in detail in other sections of this web site. One key difference between analog and digital transmission involves the bandwidth, or transmission capacity required for both schemes. Analog signals require much less bandwidth, only about 4.5 MHz with a 143.2 Mb/s data rate. For the average NTSC video signal. By comparison, some digital video transmission standards require as much as 74.25 MHz with a data rate of 1485 Mb/s. Advances in single-mode optical fiber make these higher rates more accessible for longer distances. Copper coax fails to perform at these data rates.

Table 3.1 Comparison of AM, FM and Digital Encoding Techniques

Parameter	*AM*	*FM*	*Digital*
Signal-to-noise ratio	Low-to-moderate	Moderate-high	High
Performance vs. Attenuation	Sensitive	Tolerant	Invarian
Transmitter cost	Moderate-high	Moderate	High
Receiver cost Receiver gain adjustment	Moderate Often required	Moderate-high Not required	High Not required
Installation	Adjustments requires	No adjustments	No adjustments
		Required	Required
Multichannel capabilities	Require high linearity	Fewer channels	Good
	Optics		
Performance over time	Moderate	Excellent	Excellent
Environmental factors	Moderate	Excellent	Excellent

Another difference between analog and digital transmission deals with the hardware's ability to recover the transmitted signal. Analog modulation, which is continuously variable by nature, can often require adjustment at the receiver end in order to reconstruct the transmitted signal. Digital transmission, however, because it uses only 1's and 0's to encode the signal, offers a simpler means of reconstructing the signal. Both types of modulation can incorporate error detecting and error correcting information to the transmitted signal. However, the latest trend in signal transmission is Forward Error Correcting (FEC). This scheme, which uses binary numbers, is suited to digital transmission. Extra bits of information are incorporated into the digital signal, allowing any transmission errors to be corrected at the receive end.

A third important difference relates to the cost of analog transmission links compared to digital transmission links. Because the circuitry required for digital transmission is more complex, the cost is often much higher. In short distance applications, analog modulation will almost always be the most cost-effective system to specify. However, today's demand for high speed Internet, video on demand, videoconferencing , and "pushed" data directly to our home computers requires moderate to long-distance transmission systems to specify digital equipment. And as is the case with any form of technology, greater demand will lead to mass production, inevitably driving the cost of digital systems down. However, it will always be true that the decision to specify one type of modulation over the other involves the same system design considerations.

Signal Conversion

Conversion is the changing of a signal from one class type to the other. Analog signals are readily available. With this in mind, we can safely say the natural world is analog in nature. The modern world of computers is digital and because we live in this modern world, everything around us appears to be going digital, hence the need for conversion. Conversion from digital-to-analog and analog-to-digital is achieved with the assistance of a device called a modem.

Without the use of a modem, it would be impossible to accomplish computer communication across analog circuits. A modem enables us to send digital information across an analog circuit.

Resolution and Aliasing

Most sensors for measuring temperature, pressure, and other continuous variables provide a continuously varying electrical output to represent the magnitude of the variable in question. To make this signal interpretable by a microprocessor, it must be converted from a smooth continuous value to a discrete, digital number as in figure 3.17.

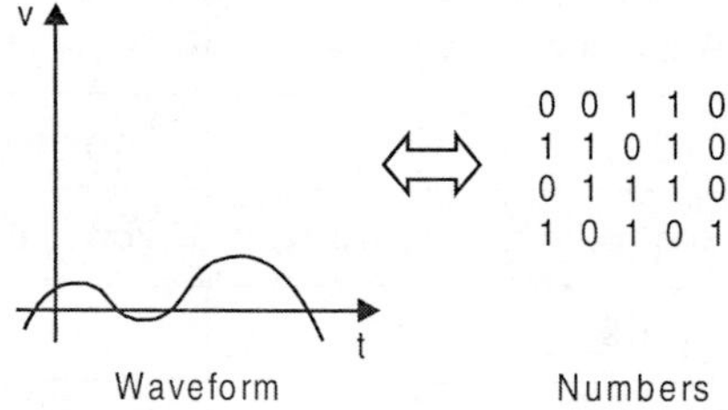

Figure 3.17 *The Analog-to-Digital Interface.*

This Analog-to-Digital (A/D) conversion process poses two primary challenges: one of quantization and one of sampling in time as in figure 3.18. Quantization refers to the uncertainty introduced upon conversion of an analog voltage to a digital number. Measurement transducers or transmitters typically provide continuously varying signals between 0–10 V dc, ±5 V dc, 0–100 mV dc, or 4–20 mA dc. Thermocouples and resistance temperature devices (RTDs) are other common low voltage inputs.

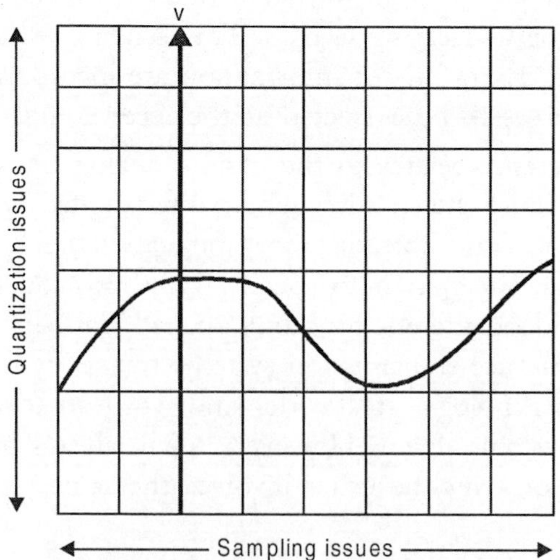

Figure 3.18 *A/D Conversion Compromises.*

When this analog value is represented as a digital number, however, this essentially continuous resolution is limited to discrete steps. This resolution of an A/D conversion often is stated in terms of bits-the more bits the finer the resolution. The number of bits determines the number of divisions into which a full-scale input range can be divided to approximate an analog input voltage. For example, 8-bit resolution of a 0-10 V input signal means that the range is divided into 28 = 256 steps. This yields a step, or interval, size of 10 V/256 = 0.039 V. Thus, a 10-V input is equal to the digital number 255 and a 0-V input corresponds to 0. Each 0.039-V change in the input is indicated by adding or subtracting 1 from the previous number. (For example, 9.961 V is digitally represented by 254.)

Digital data acquisition systems not only quantize data in terms of magnitude; time, too, is parceled into discrete intervals as in figure 3.18. In general, there is no information about the behavior of the process between data points gathered. Special precautions, then, must be taken to ensure no meaningful data is lost and interpolation between recorded points remains a valid assumption.

The Nyquist theorem defines the necessary relationship between the highest frequency contained in a signal and the minimum required sampling speed. Nyquist stated that the sample rate must be at least twice the highest frequency component contained within the input signal. So, to sample a 1-Hz sine wave, the sample rate should be at least 2 Hz. But a rate of 8-16 Hz would be much better for resolving the true shape of the wave.

The primary implications of ignoring the Nyquist criterion include not only missing high frequency information but of introducing aliasing; if the sample rate is not fast enough, the presence of totally nonexistent frequencies may be indicated as in figure 3.19. It is aliasing that makes a helicopter's rotors or a car's wheels appear to turn slowly backwards when seen in a movie. Low-pass or anti-aliasing filters can be used to limit the measured waveform's frequency spectrum so that no detectable component equals or exceeds half of the sampling rate.

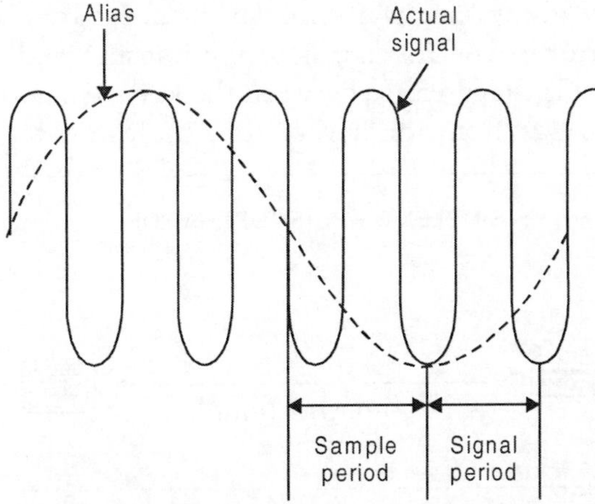

Figure 3.19 *Aliasing Due to Slow Sample Rate.*

Designing or specifying a device for A/D conversion consists of a series of trade-offs. As will be amply demonstrated in the next section, more resolution (more bits) means more accurate conversion but more expensive hardware. Similarly, slower sample rates mean cheaper A/D conversion, but the Nyquist criterion must still be satisfied.

NETWORKS

A network is a circuit made up of elements which work together to support the transfer of information.

Analog Networks

These networks were used for decades until around 1980. Traffic was principally speech with low speed data. The composition of an end to end long distance circuit included signaling, multiplex, cable or radio line and transmission equipment. Accumulation of noise with circuit length and special conditioning needed for traffic are some of the disadvantages of analog circuits.

Digital Networks

Communication is going digital and a lot of these networks are been used to replace what started off as analog. Digital networks offer superior quality service for voice traffic. High speed data are now possible because of these networks. High capacity of channels was introduced with digital systems using fiber optics.

Digital networks comprise of computer network elements, therefore, they can be managed easily and effectively. They can also be easily upgraded.

DATA TRANSMISSION CIRCUITS

Here the three main types of transmission circuits, simplex, half duplex and full duplex are described.

- **Simplex**

Data in a simplex channel is always one way. Simplex channels are not often used because it is not possible to send back error or control signals to the transmit end. An example of a simplex channel in a computer system is the interface between the keyboard and the computer, in that key codes need only be sent one way from the keyboard to the computer system.

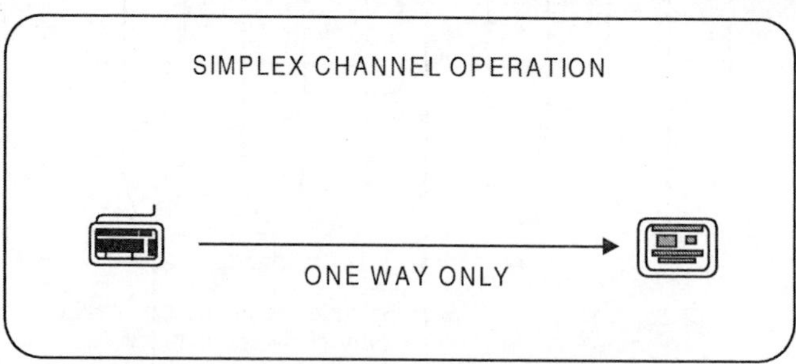

Figure 3.20 *Simplex (one-way) Channel.*

- **Half-Duplex**

A half-duplex channel can send and receive, but not at the same time. It's like a one-lane bridge where two way traffic must give way in order to cross. Only one end transmits at a time, the other end receives.

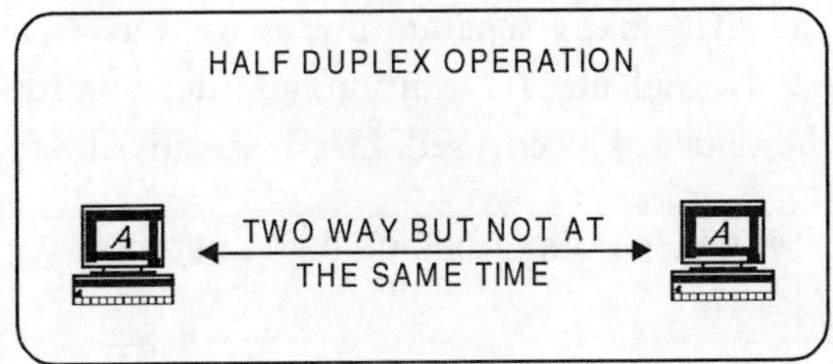

Figure 3.21 *Half-Duplex Channel.*

• Full-Duplex

Data can travel in both directions simultaneously. There is no need to switch from transmit to receive mode like in half-duplex. It's like a two lane bridge on a two-lane highway.

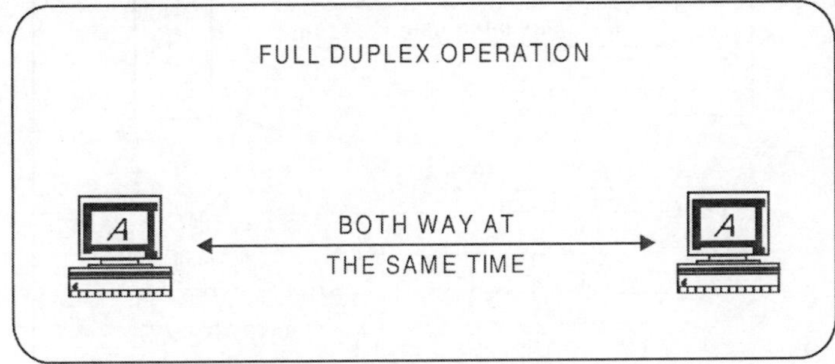

Figure 3.22 *Full-Duplex Channel.*

PARALLEL AND SERIAL DATA

Data may be transmitted between two points in two different ways. Let's consider sending 8 bits of digital data (1 byte).

• Parallel

Each bit uses a separate wire. The organization looks likes,

PARALLEL DATA TRANSMISSION

bit0 —— bit0
bit1 —— bit1
bit2 —— bit2
bit3 —— bit3
bit4 —— bit4
bit5 —— bit5
bit6 —— bit6
bit7 —— bit7

SENDER MEDIA RECEIVER

Figure 3.23 *Parallel Interface.*

To transfer data on a parallel link, a separate line is used as a clock signal. This serves to inform the receiver when data is available. In addition, another line may be used by the receiver to inform the sender that the data has been used, and it's ready for the next data.

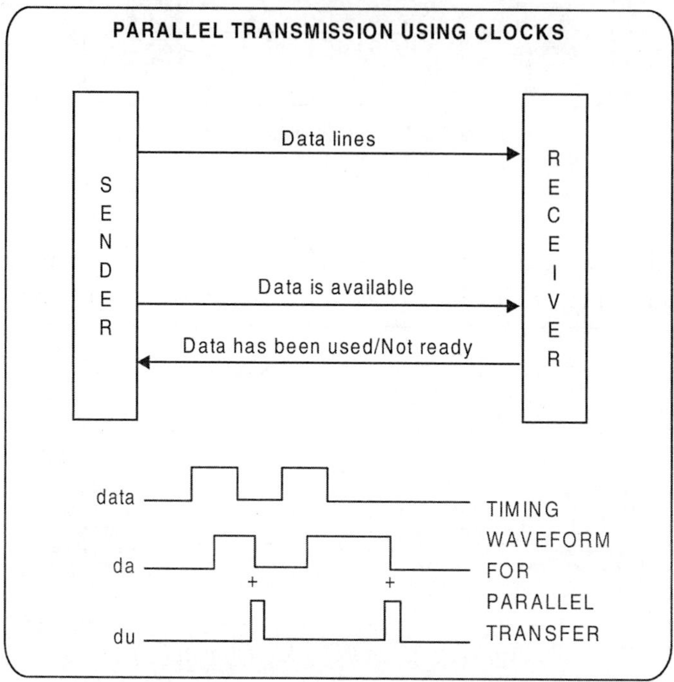

Figure 3.24 *Parallel Interface Timing.*

• Serial

Each bit is sent over a single wire, one after the another. The organization looks like,

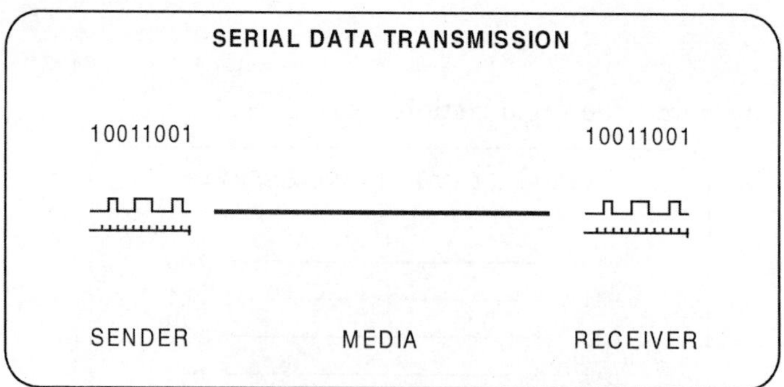

Figure 3.25 *Serial Interface.*

No signal lines are used to convey clock (timing information). There are two ways in which timing information is encoded with the signal so that the sender and receiver are synchronized (working on the same data at the same time). If no clock information was sent, the receiver would misinterpret the arriving data (due to bits being lost, going too slow).

Parallel transmission is obviously faster, in that all bits are sent at the same time, whereas serial transmission is slower, because only one bit can be sent at a time. Parallel transmission is very costly for anything except short links.

A/D CONVERSION

Continuous electrical signals are converted to the digital language of computers using analog-to-digital (A/D) converters. An A/D converter may be housed on a PC board with associated circuitry or in a variety of remote or networked configurations. In addition to the converter itself, sample-and-hold circuits, an amplifier, a multiplexer, timing and synchronization circuits, and signal conditioning elements also may be on board as shown in figure 3.26. The logic circuits necessary to control the transfer of data to computer memory or to an internal register also are needed.

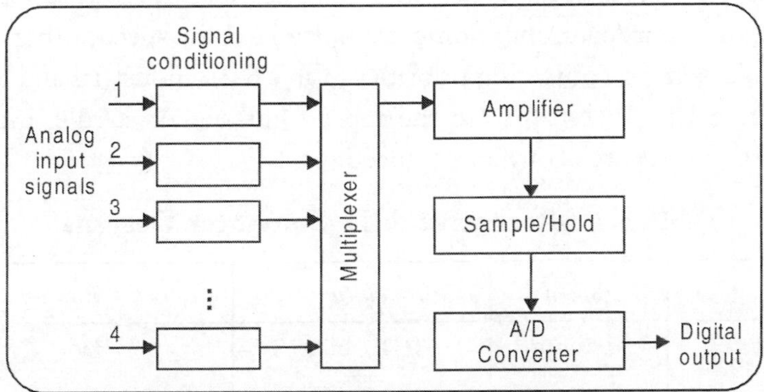

Figure 3.26 *Analog Input Flow Diagram.*

When determining what type of A/D converter should be used in a given application, performance should be closely matched to the requirements of the analog input transducer(s) in question. Accuracy, signal frequency content, maximum signal level, and dynamic range all should be considered.

Central to the performance of an A/D converter is its resolution, often expressed in bits. An A/D converter essentially divides the analog input range into 2N bins, where N is the number of bits. In other words, resolution is a measure of the number of levels used to represent the analog input range and determines the converter's sensitivity to a change in analog input. Amplification of the signal, or input gain, can be used to increase the apparent sensitivity if the signal's expected maximum range is less than the input range of the A/D converter. Because higher resolution A/D converters cost more, it is especially important to not buy more resolution than you need-if you have 1% accurate (1 in 100) temperature transducers, a 16-bit (1 in 65,536) A/D converter is probably more resolution than you need.

Absolute accuracy of the A/D conversion is a function of the reference voltage stability (the known voltage to which the unknown voltage is compared) as well as the comparator performance. Overall, it is of limited use to know the accuracy of the A/D converter itself. Accuracy of the system, together with associated multiplexer, amplifier, and other circuitry is typically more meaningful.

The other primary A/D converter performance parameter that must be considered is speed-throughput for a multi-channel device. Overall, system speed depends on the conversion time, acquisition time, transfer time, and the number of channels being served by the system: Acquisition is the time needed by the front-end analog circuitry to acquire a signal. Also called aperture time, it is the time for which the converter must see the analog voltage in order to complete a conversion. Conversion is the time needed to produce a digital value corresponding to the analog value. Transfer is the time needed to send the digital value to the host computer's memory. Throughput, then, equals the number of channels being served divided by the time required to do all three functions.

A/D Converter Options

While all analog-to-digital converters are classified by their resolution or number of bits, how the A/D circuitry achieves this resolution varies from device to device. There are four primary types of A/D converters used for industrial and laboratory applications-successive approximation, flash/parallel, integrating, and ramp/counting. Some are optimized for speed, others for economy, and others for a compromise among competing priorities (Table 3.2). Industrial and lab data acquisition tasks typically require 12 to 16 bits-12 are the most common. As a rule, increasing resolution results in higher costs and slower conversion speed.

Table 3.2 Alternative A/D Converter Designs

Design	*Speed*	*Resolution*	*Noise Immunity*	*Cost*
Successive approximation	Medium	10–16 bits	Poor	Low
Integrating	Slow	12–18 bits	Good	Low
Ramp/counting	Slow	14–24 bits	Good	Medium
Flash/parallel	Fast	4–8 bits	None	High

Successive Approximation

The most common A/D converter design used for general industrial and laboratory applications is successive approximation as in figure 3.27. This design offers an effective compromise among resolution, speed, and cost. In this type of design, an internal digital-to-analog (D/A) converter and a single comparator-essentially a circuit that determines which of two voltages is higher-are used to narrow in on the unknown voltage by turning bits in the D/A converter on until the voltages match to within the least significant bit. Raw sampling speed for successive approximation converters is in the 50 kHz to 1 MHz range.

To achieve higher sampling speeds, a redundancy technique allows a fast initial approximate conversion, followed by a correction step that adjust the least significant bit after allowing sufficient settling time. The conversion is therefore completed faster at the expense of additional hardware. Redundancy is useful when both high speed and high resolution are desirable.

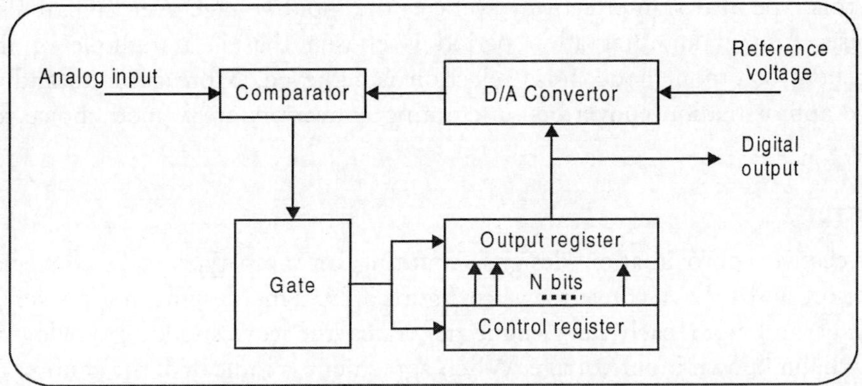

Figure 3.27 *A/D Conversion by Successive Approximation.*

Flash/Parallel

When higher speed operation is required, parallel, or flash-type A/D conversion is called for. This design uses multiple comparators in parallel to process samples at more than 100 MHz with 8 to 12-bit resolution. Conversion is accomplished by a string of comparators with appropriate references operating in parallel as in figure 3.28.

The downside of this design is the large number of relatively expensive comparators that are required-for example; a 12-bit converter requires 4,095 comparators.

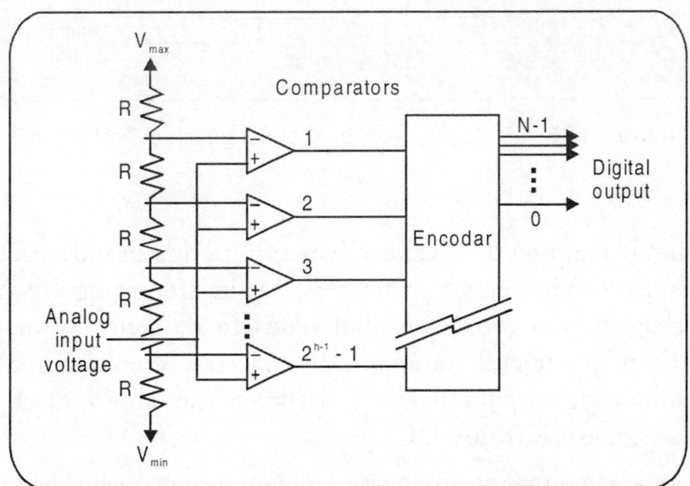

Figure 3.28 *A/D Conversion by Flash/Parallel Technique.*

Integrating

This type of A/D converter integrates an unknown input voltage for a specific period of time, and then integrates it back down to zero. This time is compared to the amount of time taken to perform a similar integration on a known reference voltage. The relative times required and the known reference voltage then yields the unknown input voltage. Integrating converters with 12 to 18-bit resolution are available, at raw sampling rates of 10–500 kHz.

Because this type of design effectively averages the input voltage over time, it also smoothes out signal noise. And, if an integration period is chosen that is a multiple of the AC line frequency, excellent common mode noise rejection is achieved. More accurate and more linear than successive approximation converters, integrating converters are a good choice for low-level voltage signals.

Ramp/Counter

Similar to successive approximation designs, counting or ramp-type A/D converters use one comparator circuit and a D/A converter as in figure 3.29. This design progressively increments a digital counter and with each new count generates the corresponding analog voltage and compares it to the unknown input voltage. When agreement is indicated, the counter contains the digital equivalent of the unknown signal.

A variation on the counter method is the ramp method, which substitutes an operational amplifier or other analog ramping circuit for the D/A converter. This technique is somewhat faster.

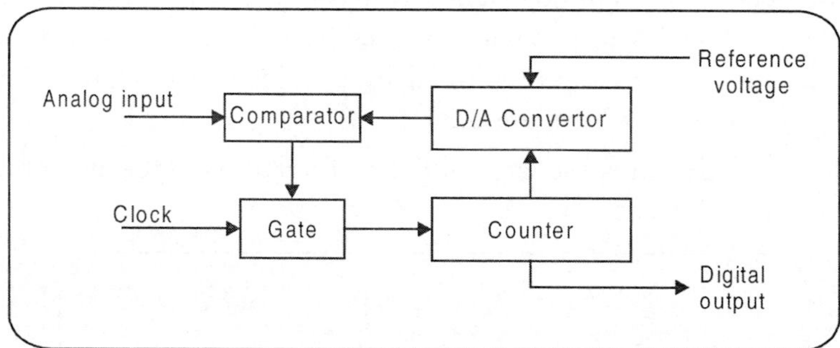

Figure 3.29 *A/D Conversion by Counting/Ramp Technique.*

D/A Conversion

Analog outputs commonly are used to operate valves and motors in industrial environments and to generate inputs for electronic devices under test. Digital-to-analog (D/A) conversion is in many ways the converse of A/D conversion, but tends to be generally more straightforward. Similar to analog input configurations, a common D/A converter often is shared among multiplexed output signals. Standard analog output ranges are essentially the same as analog inputs: ±5 V DC, ±10 V DC, 0–10 V DC, and 4–20 mA DC.

Essentially, the logic circuitry for an analog voltage output uses a digital word or series of bits, to drop in (or drop out, depending on whether the bit is 1 or 0) a series of resistors from a circuit driven by a reference voltage. This ladder of resistors can be made of either weighted value resistors or an R-2R network using only two resistor values-one if placed in series as in figure 3.30. While operation of the weighted-value network is more intuitively obvious, the R-2R scheme is more practical. Because only one resistor value need be used, it is easier to match the temperature coefficients of an R-2R ladder than a weighted network, resulting in more accurate outputs. Plus, for high resolution outputs, very high resistor values are needed in the weighted-resistor approach.

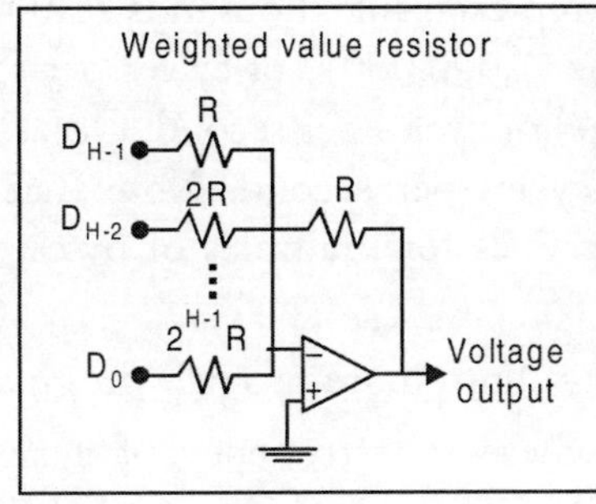

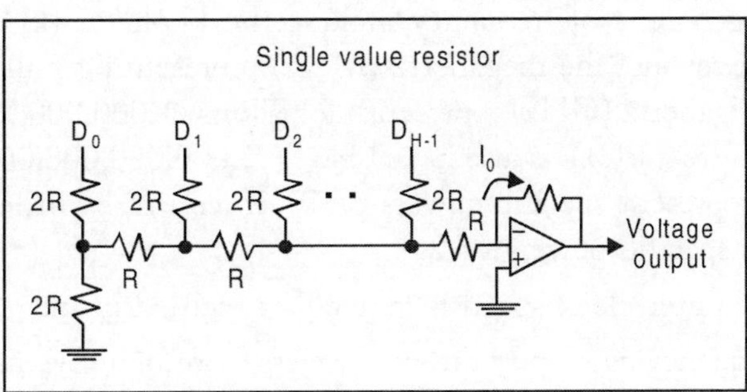

Figure 3.30 *Weighted Value & Single Value Resistor Networks for D/A Conversion.*

Key specifications of an analog output include: Settling time: Period required for a D/A converter to respond to a full-scale set point change.

Linearity: This refers to the device's ability to accurately divide the reference voltage into evenly sized increments.

Range: The reference voltage sets the limit on the output voltage achievable.

Because most unconditioned analog outputs are limited to 5 mA of current, amplifiers and signal conditioners often are needed to drive a final control element. A low-pass filter may also be used to smooth out the discrete steps in output.

BANDWIDTH

Bandwidth has a general meaning of how much information can be carried in a given time period (usually a second) over a wired or wireless communications link. For example, a link with a broad bandwidth—that is, a broadband link—is one that may be able to carry enough information to sustain the succession of images in a video presentation.

More technically, bandwidth is the width of the range of frequencies that an electronic signal occupies on a given transmission medium. Any digital or analog signal has a bandwidth.

In digital systems, bandwidth is expressed as bits (of data) per second (bps). Thus, a modem that works at 57,600 bps has twice the bandwidth of a modem that works at 28,800 bps. In analog systems, bandwidth is expressed in terms of the difference between the highest-frequency signal component and the lowest-frequency signal component. The frequency of an analog signal is measured in the number of cycles of change per second, or hertz. A typical voice signal has a bandwidth of approximately three kilohertz (3 kHz); an analog television (TV) broadcast video signal has a bandwidth of six megahertz (6 MHz)—some 2,000 times as wide as the voice signal.

It should be remembered that a real communications path usually consists of a succession of links, each with its own bandwidth. If one of these is much slower than the rest, it is said to be a bandwidth bottleneck.

FREQUENCY

For an oscillating or varying current, frequency is the number of complete cycles per second in alternating current direction. The standard unit of frequency is the hertz, abbreviated Hz. If a current completes one cycle per second, then the frequency is 1 Hz; 60 cycles per second equals 60 Hz (the standard alternating-current utility frequency in some countries).

Larger units of frequency include the kilohertz (kHz) representing thousands (1,000's) of cycles per second, the megahertz (MHz) representing millions (1,000,000's) of cycles per second, and the gigahertz (GHz) representing billions (1,000,000,000's) of cycles per second. Occasionally the terahertz (THz) is used; 1 THz = 1,000,000,000,000 cycles per second. Note that these prefixes represent specific powers of 10, in contrast to the prefixes for multiples of bytes, which represent specific powers of 2.

Computer clock speed is generally specified in megahertz and, more recently, in gigahertz.

Frequency is important in wireless communications, where the frequency of a signal is mathematically related to the wavelength. If f is the frequency of an electromagnetic field in free space as measured in megahertz, and w is the wavelength as measured in meters, then

$$w = 300/f$$

And conversely

$$f = 300/w$$

SIGNAL

1. In electronics, a signal is an electric current or electromagnetic field used to convey data from one place to another. The simplest form of signal is a direct current (DC) that is switched on and off; this is the principle by which the early telegraph worked. More complex signals consist of an alternating-current (AC) or electromagnetic carrier that contains one or more data streams.

   Data is superimposed on a carrier current or wave by means of a process called modulation. Signal modulation can be done in either of two main ways: analog and digital. In recent years, digital modulation has been getting more common, while analog modulation methods have been used less and less. There are still plenty of analog signals around, however, and they will probably never become totally extinct.

   Except for DC signals such as telegraph and base band, all signal carriers have a definable frequency or frequencies. Signals also have a property called wavelength, which is inversely proportional to the frequency.
2. In some information technology contexts, a signal are simply "that which is sent or received," thus including both the carrier and the data together.
3. In telephony, a signal is special data that is used to set up or control communication.

CARRIER

1. In information technology, a carrier (or carrier signal) is a transmitted electromagnetic pulse or wave at a steady base frequency of alternation on which information can be imposed by increasing signal strength, varying the base frequency, varying the wave phase, or other means. This variation is called modulation. With the advent of laser transmission over optical fiber media, a carrier can also be a laser-generated light beam on which information is imposed.

Types of analog modulation of a carrier include Amplitude Modulation (AM), Frequency Modulation (FM), and phase modulation. Types of digital modulation include varieties of Pulse Code Modulation (PCM), including Pulse Amplitude Modulation (PAM), Pulse Duration Modulation (PDM), and Pulse Position Modulation (PPM).

Carrier detect (see modem lights) is a control signal between a modem and a computer that indicates that the modem detects a "live" carrier that can be used for sending and receiving information.

2. In the telecommunications industry, a carrier is a telephone or other company that sells or rents telecommunication transmission services. A Local Exchange Carrier (LEC) is a local phone company and an Inter-Exchange Carrier (IEC or IXC) carries long-distance calls.

Digital T Carriers

As technology improved the speed at which electronic circuits could dependably operate, the need to increase the rate at which data is transferred also increased. To respond to the need for interconnecting computers and database facilities, the telephone company turned to supplying lines for carrying data in digital form. As well as supplying the lines, the telephone company also established the limitations for their use. The basic designation for these lines is T carriers and they begin with basic T1 carrier specified for the bell system voice network.

T1 carriers are digital, leased twisted –pair lines, operating as 4 – wire trunk lines, designed to handle 24 PCM voice grade channels operating at a maximum data rate of 64 kbps each. Thus, the t1 line requires a bandwidth large enough to handle 1.544 mbps (24.64 kbps). T1 lines are designed to interconnect stations that are up to 80 kilometers (km) apart, using regenerative repeaters every 1.6 km. The last repeater placed before the nearest switch station is to be no more than 0.8 km from that station. These repeaters reshape the digital data that has been distorted due to attenuation or pulse spreading caused by effects on the signals of the signals of the propagation delays inherent in the reactive nature of the cabling.

Each channel is sent, using time division multiplexing of eight bits per channel at a time. Since 24 channels are sent at once, a total of 8.24 bits, or 192 data bits, are sent per transmission period. An additional frame boundary bit (like a start/stop bit) increases the total to 193 bits per frame (transmission). Dividing the total data rate by the total number of bits per frame yields a frame rate of 8,000 frames per second.

T-Carriers Lines

T-carrier lines are high-speed dedicated digital lines that can be leased from telephone companies. This creates an always open, always available line between you and whomever you choose to connect to when you establish the service. T-carrier lines can support both voice and data transmissions and are often used to create point-to-point private networks. Because they are a dedicated link, they can be a costly WAN option. Four types of T-carrier lines are available:

- T1 T1 lines offer transmission speeds of 1.544Mbps, and they can create point-to-point dedicated digital communication paths. T1 lines have commonly been used for connecting LANs.

- T2 T2 leased lines offer transmission speeds of 6.312Mbps. They accomplish this by using 96 64Kbps B channels.
- T3 T3 lines offer transmission speeds of up to 44.736Mbps, using 672 64Kbps B channels.
- T4 T4 lines offer impressive transmission speeds of up to 274.176Mbps by using 4,032 64Kbps B channels.

Of these T-carrier lines, the ones commonly associated with networks.

It is important to point out that T-carrier is the designation to the technology used in the United States and Canada. In Europe, they are referred to as E-carriers and in Japan, J-carriers. Table 3.3 shows the T/E/J carriers.

Table 3.3 Comparing T/E/J Carriers

Name	*Transmission Speed*
T-1	1.544Mbps
T-1C	3.152Mbps
T-2	6.312Mbps
T-3	44.736Mbps
T-4	274.176Mbps
J-0	64Kbps
J-1	1.544Mbps
J-1C	3.152Mbps
J-2	6.312Mbps
J-3	32.064 Mbps
J-3C	97.728Mbps
J-4	397.200Mbps
E-0	64Kbps
E-1	2.048Mbps
E-2	8.448Mbps
E-3	34.368Mbps
E-4	139.264Mbps
E-5	565.148Mbps

Multi-Carrier Modulation

Multi-Carrier Modulation (MCM) is a method of transmitting data by splitting it into several components, and sending each of these components over separate carrier signals. The individual carriers have narrow bandwidth, but the composite signal can have broad bandwidth.

The advantages of MCM include relative immunity to fading caused by transmission over more than one path at a time (multi-path fading), less susceptibility than single-carrier systems to interference caused by impulse noise, and enhanced immunity to inter-symbol interference. Limitations include difficulty in synchronizing the carriers under marginal conditions, and a relatively strict requirement that amplification be linear.

MCM was first used in analog military communications in the 1950s. Recently, MCM has attracted attention as a means of enhancing the bandwidth of digital communications over media with physical limitations. The scheme is used in some audio broadcast services. The technology lends itself to digital television, and is used as a method of obtaining high data speeds in Asymmetric Digital Subscriber Line (ADSL) systems. MCM is also used in Wireless Local Area Networks (WLANs).

SAMPLING THEOREM

A technique for sending analog information on digital carriers involve translating voice or other analog signals into a train of pulses, which are, in turn, coded into digital format.

The digital data is then transmitted and the process reversed at the receiving end. In effect, this process combines sampling with Analog to Digital Conversion (ADC) and Digital to Analog Conversion (DAC). An advantage gained by this method is in the reduction of noise effects usually inherent in analog transmissions.

The process of digitizing an analog signal starts by dividing the original the original signal into uniformly spaced pulses or samples. The amplitudes of the sample pulses rise and fall with amplitude of the original signal. Specifically, this part of the process is a form of Pulse Amplitude Modulation (PAM) since the original signal is being separated into individual pulse (or samples), each of which has different amplitude based on the amplitude of the original signal. At the receive end, these samples are used to reconstruct the original signal. The more frequently the samples are taken, the more accurate is the reconstructed waveform.

QUANTIZATION

Quantization is the process of approximating sample levels into their closest fixed value. The values are pre-selected and since they are fixed, they are easy to encode. The quantized waveform experiences either quantum changes in amplitude or no change in amplitude. Given a signal, f(s), with peak voltage points of VH and v1, the size, s, of a quantum step is determined by the relationship:

$$S = (vh - v1)/n$$

Where n is the number of steps or levels between VH and v1.

The quantized waveform appears similar to a sample-and-hold approximation of the same f(s) as shown in figure 3.31. The difference is that the normal sample-and-hold result has voltage levels equivalent to the voltage level of f(s) at the point the sample is taken.

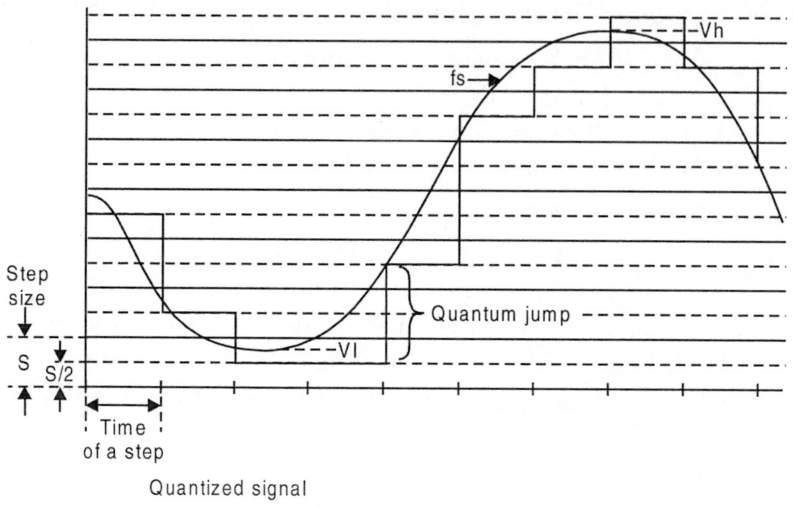

Figure 3.31 *Quantized Signal.*

The difference between the sample-and-hold and the quantized results is called the quantization error or quantization noise. Essentially, the process of sampling and quantizing a signal is a form of Pulse Amplitude Modulation (PAM), where the samples produce pulses of varying amplitudes. The coding of a quantized signal is as shown in figure 3.32. When these amplitudes are restricted to discrete quantized values, they can be assigned specific binary codes using a method called pulse coded modulation.

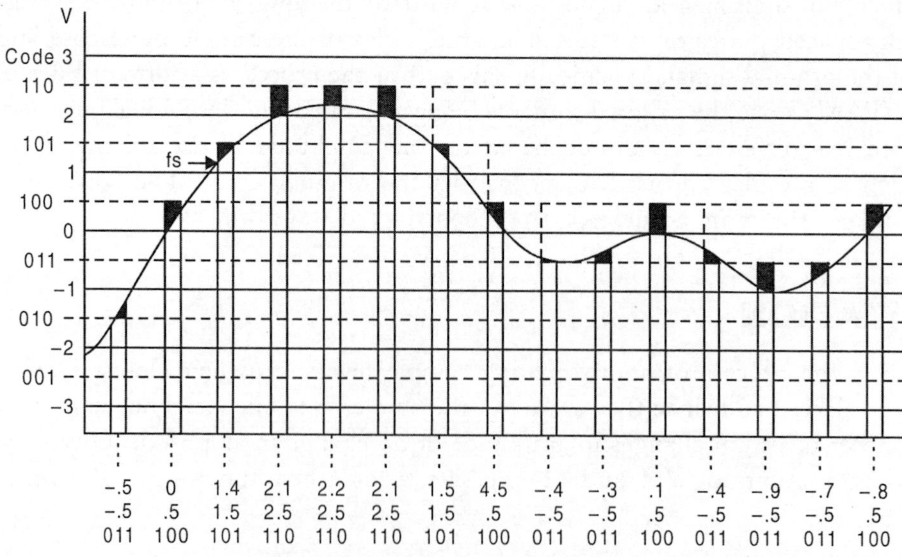

Figure 3.32 *Coding a Quantized Signal.*

MODEM

A modem (modulator/demodulator) is connected between a computer and a telephone network. It connects computers by a telephone line. This device converts a digital signal from one computer into an audio signal (tones) suitable for transmission over a telephone line. The tones can then be passed as normal analog speech. At the receiving end, the tones are converted back to the digital before being applied to another computer. A modem is one device that makes it possible for us to surf the Internet, to 'chat' with our friend and send them text based messages called electronic mail or E-mail for short.

The fact that computers can processes information in digital form has had a deep effect on the modern world of communication and information processing.

CODECS

Codecs (coder/decoder) make the reverse process to that of a modem. It enables us to send analog information across a digital circuit. In short we can say it helps us to achieve analog-to-digital and digital-to-analog conversion. A CODECS is a device designed to convert analog signals, such as voice communications into PCM-compressed samples to be sent onto digital carriers and to reverse the process, replicating the original analog signal, at the receiver. The term CODECS is an acronym for coder/decoder signifying the pulse coding/decoding functions of the device. Originally, CODECS functions were managed by several separate devices, each performing the tasks necessary for PCM communication. These functions are sampling, quantizing, analog-to-digital and digital-to-analog conversions, filtering, and companding. Today, all of these functions are available on a single CODECS IC chip like intel's 2913.

The 2913 codec operates in one of two modes—fixed data rate or variable data rate. In the fixed data rate modes, the chip is capable of operating with one of three fixed-clock frequencies: T1's 1.544 MHz, ITU's 2.048 MHz, and also 1.536 MHz. In the variable data rate, the clock frequency can be set anywhere from 64 kHz to 4.096 MHz . The 2913 allows selection of either m-law or a-law for the companding function.

MODULATION AND DEMODULATION

Signals consist of two components—the information signal and the carrier signal. The transmission of any signal over some communication medium usually involves modulation of a carrier. Prior to their transmission the information signal and the carrier signal are combined and the process of combining these two signals is called modulation.

Example of Modulation

I am sitting at the back of a big spacious hall. I see my friend at the front. I have information which I want to pass to my friend. Assuming for any reason I cannot get close to my friend. I write the information I want to pass to my friend on a piece of paper and wrap the paper around a pen (*carrier*) and throw (*transmit*) the two (*information and carrier*) to my friend. The information will reach her.

The high frequency wave which carries the information through a medium is called the carrier. The information is superimposed onto the *'carrier wave'* by modulation. Therefore the carrier provides a means of transferring information at high frequency. Before modulation the carrier does not contain any *'intelligence'* and it only serves to carry information. Once the information is extracted from the carrier at the receiving end, the carrier becomes redundant, the carrier is a single frequency generally represented as:

A (t) = A sin (Ft + ö)

A = the amplitude

Ft = Frequency

ö = Phase

Modulating the carrier means changing something in the equation above. *Only three things can be changed as shown above: amplitude, frequency or phase reference.* This leads to one class of analog modulation.

- Changing A leads to amplitude modulation
- Changing F leads to frequency modulation
- Changing ö leads to phase modulation.

Before being modulated by an information signal, the carrier signal has a single Frequency and steady Amplitude. After modulation the carrier will have varying amplitude or frequency. There are various types of modulation and the following three will be covered in this class:

- Amplitude Modulation (AM)
- Frequency Modulation (FM)
- Phase Modulation (PM)

Figure 3.33 shows a modulator. The modulator output is shown drawn both in time spectrum and frequency spectrum. If we look carefully at the frequency spectrum we can see that there are two new frequencies which were not present at the beginning. These are the side frequencies we talked about when dealing with frequency division multiplexing. Fc + fm is the upper sideband and Fc − fm is the lower sideband, *i.e.,* the relationship between modulation and frequency division multiplexing.

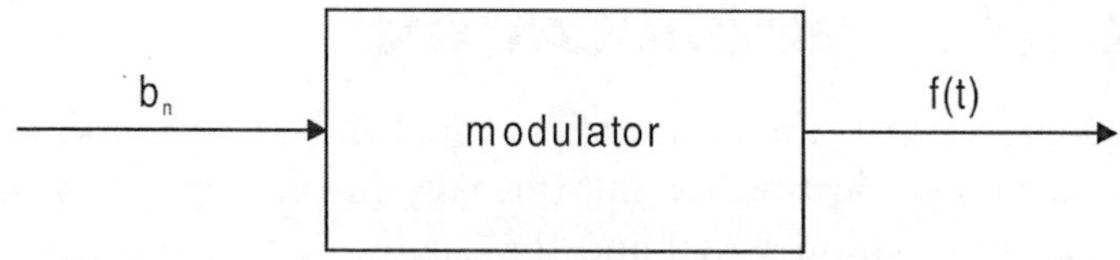

Figure 3.33 *Modulator.*

MODULATION

Modulation is the addition of information (or the signal) to an electronic or optical signal carrier. Modulation can be applied to direct current (mainly by turning it on and off), to alternating current, and to optical signals. One can think of blanket waving as a form of modulation used in smoke signal transmission (the carrier being a steady stream of smoke).

Morse code, invented for telegraphy and still used in amateur radio, uses a binary (two-state) digital code similar to the code used by modern computers. For most of radio and telecommunication today, the carrier is Alternating Current (AC) in a given range of frequencies. Common modulation methods include:

1. Amplitude Modulation (AM), in which the voltage applied to the carrier is varied over time.
2. Frequency Modulation (FM), in which the frequency of the carrier waveform is varied in small but meaningful amounts.
3. Phase Modulation (PM), in which the natural flow of the alternating current waveform is delayed temporarily.

These are sometimes known as continuous wave modulation methods to distinguish them from Pulse Code Modulation (PCM), which is used to encode both digital and analog information in a binary way. Radio and television broadcast stations typically use AM or FM. Most two-way radios use FM, although some employ a mode known as Single Sideband (SSB).

More complex forms of modulation are Phase Shift Keying (PSK) and Quadrature Amplitude Modulation (QAM). Optical signals are modulated by applying an electromagnetic current to vary the intensity of a laser beam.

1. digital data, digital signal:
   - NRZ
   - Multilevel binary
   - Biphase
   - Modulation rate
   - Scrambling technique
2. digital data, analog signal
3. analog data, digital signal
4. analog data, analog signal

• Amplitude Shift Key Modulation

In this method the amplitude of the carrier assumes one of the two amplitudes dependent on the logic states of the input bit stream. A typical output waveform of an ASK modulator is shown in figure 3.34. The frequency components are the USB and LSB with a residual carrier frequency. The low amplitude carrier is allowed to be transmitted to ensure that at the receiver the logic 1 and logic 0 conditions can be recognized uniquely.

• Frequency Shift Key Modulation

In this method the frequency of the carrier is changed to two different frequencies depending on the logic state of the input bit stream. The typical output waveform of an FSK is shown in figure 3.35. Notice that logic high causes the centre frequency to increase to a maximum and a logic low causes the centre frequency to decrease to a minimum.

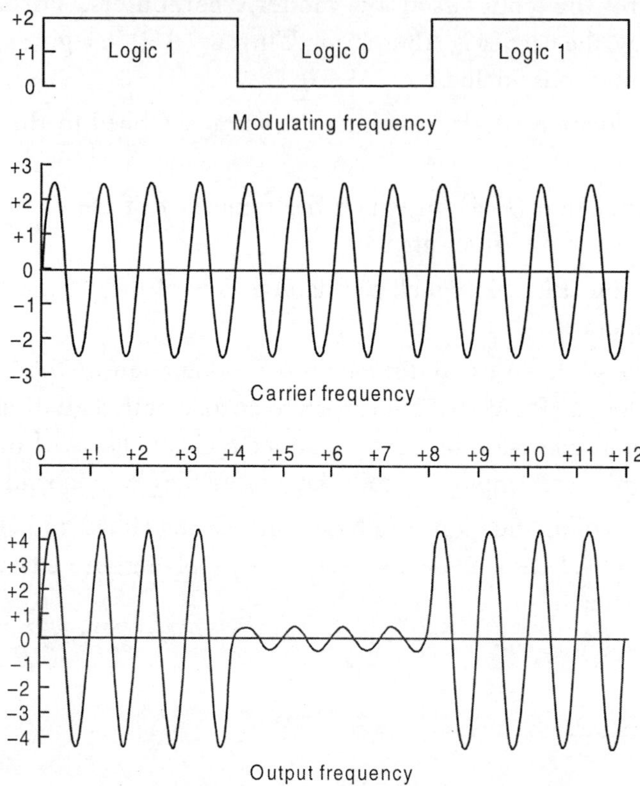

Figure 3.34 *Amplitude Shift Key Modulation.*

• Phase Shift Key Modulation

With this method the phase of the carrier changes between different phases determined by the logic states of the input bit stream.

There are several different types of *Phase Shift Key* (PSK) modulators.

1. Two-Phase (2 PSK)
2. Four-Phase (4 PSK)
3. Eight-Phase (8 PSK)
4. Sixteen-Phase (16 PSK)
5. Sixteen-Quadrature Amplitude (16 QAM).

The 16 QAM is a composite modulator consisting of amplitude modulation and phase modulation. The 2 PSK, 4 PSK, 8 PSK and 16 PSK modulators are generally referred to as Binary Phase Shift Key (BPSK) modulators and the QAM modulators are referred to as *Quadrature Phase Shift Key* (QPSK) modulators.

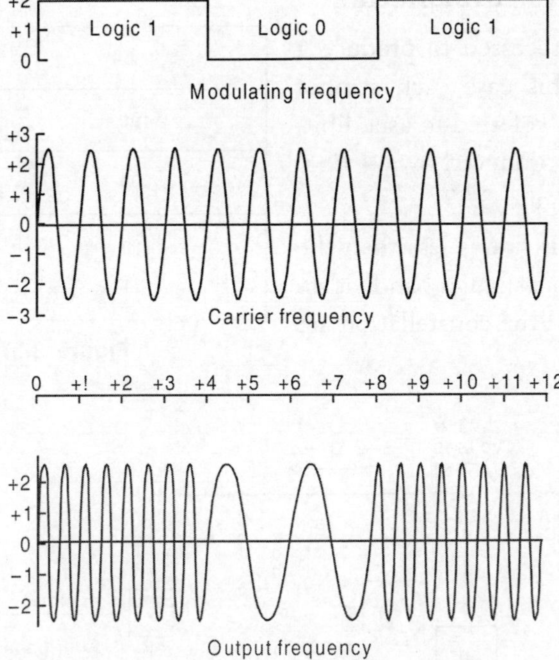

Figure 3.35 *Frequency Shift Key Modulation.*

• Two-Phase Shift Key Modulation

In this modulator the carrier assumes one of two phases. Logic 1 produces no phase change and logic 0 produces a 180° phase change. The output waveform for this modulator is shown in figure 3.36.

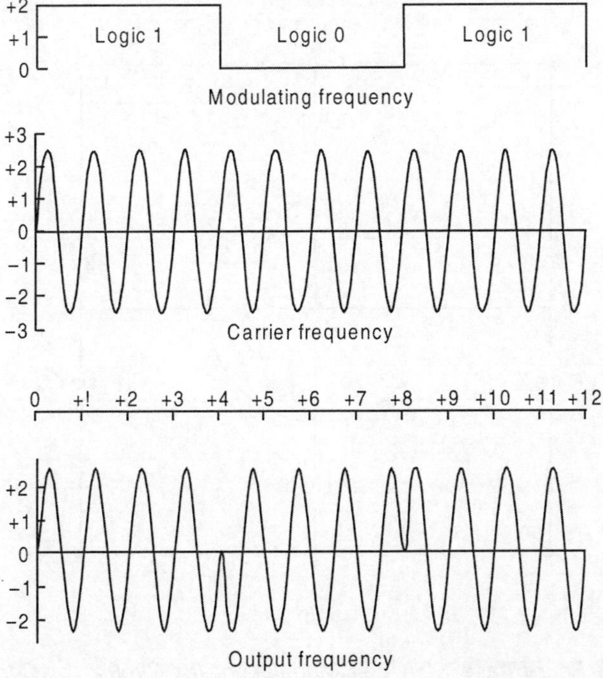

Figure 3.36 *Phase Shift Key Modulation.*

• Four-Phase Shift Key Modulation

With 4 PSK, 2 bits are processed to produce a single phase change. In this case each symbol consists of 2 bits, which are referred to as a dibit. The actual phases that are produced by a 4 PSK modulator are shown in figure 3.37.

Because the output bit rate is less than the input bit rate, this results in a smaller bandwidth. A typical 4 PSK circuit and the constellation are shown in figure 3.38.

Dibit	Phase Change
00	+225°/–135°
01	+135°/–225°
10 11	315°/–45° –45°/–315°

Figure 3.37 *PSK Table.*

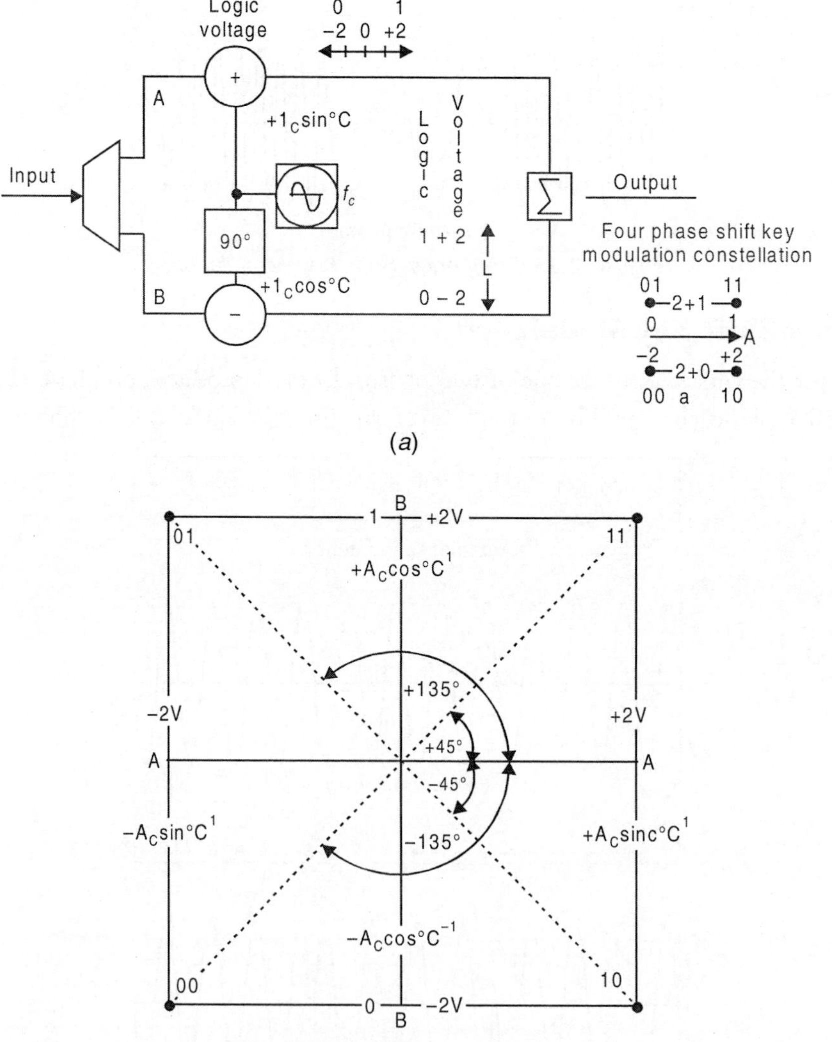

Figure 3.38 *Four-Phase Shift Key Modulation: (a) Circuit; (b) Constellation.*

PULSE CODE MODULATION

PCM (Pulse Code Modulation) is a digital scheme for transmitting analog data. The signals in PCM are binary; that is, there are only two possible states, represented by logic 1 (high) and logic 0 (low). This is true no matter how complex the analog waveform happens to be. Using PCM, it is possible to digitize all forms of analog data, including full-motion video, voices, music, telemetry, and Virtual Reality (VR).

To obtain PCM from an analog waveform at the source (transmitter end) of a communications circuit, the analog signal amplitude is sampled (measured) at regular time intervals. The sampling rate, or number of samples per second, is several times the maximum frequency of the analog waveform in cycles per second or hertz. The instantaneous amplitude of the analog signal at each sampling is rounded off to the nearest of several specific, predetermined levels. This process is called quantization. The number of levels is always a power of 2 – for example, 8, 16, 32, or 64. These numbers can be represented by three, four, five, or six binary digits (bits) respectively. The output of a pulse code modulator is thus a series of binary numbers, each represented by some power of 2 bits.

At the destination (receiver end) of the communications circuit, a pulse code demodulator converts the binary numbers back into pulses having the same quantum levels as those in the modulator. These pulses are further processed to restore the original analog waveform.

Differential Pulse Code Modulation

Differential Pulse Code Modulation (DPCM): Pulse-code modulation in which an analog signal is sampled and the difference between the actual value of each sample and its predicted value, derived from the previous sample or samples, is quantized and converted, by encoding, to a digital signal. There are several variations of differential pulse-code modulation.

The quantization in the section quantizing a signal requires not a priori knowledge about the transmitted signal. In practice, you can often make educated guesses about the present signal based on past signal transmissions. Using such educated guesses to help quantize a signal is known as predictive quantization. The most common predictive quantization method is Differential Pulse Code Modulation (DPCM).

Delta Modulation

Delta Modulation (DM): Analog-to-digital signal conversion in which (a) the analog signal is approximated with a series of segments, (b) each segment of the approximated signal is compared to the original analog wave to determine the increase or decrease in relative amplitude, (c) the decision process for establishing the state of successive bits is determined by this comparison, and (d) only the change of information is sent, *i.e.,* only an increase or decrease of the signal amplitude from the previous sample is sent whereas a no-change condition causes the modulated signal to remain at the same 0 or 1 state of the previous sample.

Information on Delta Modulation

Delta modulation can be considered to be an incremental Pulse-Code Modulation (PCM) system where, rather than transmitting the absolute amplitude at each sampling, only the changes in signal amplitude from sampling instant to sampling instant are transmitted. This provides a simpler system and requires less information to be transmitted. The range of signal amplitudes is divided into a similar number of quantization levels as in pulse-code modulation systems. However, at each sampling, the presence or absence of only one transmitted pulse contains the information. The delta-modulation code is therefore a one-element code in which a '1' is transmitted if the sampled signal at any sampling instant is greater than the immediately previous sampling instant. A '0' is transmitted if the sampled signal is lower. The step size is called delta (the Greek letter) and hence the name delta modulation.

- analog data, analog signal

Amplitude Modulation (AM)

In Amplitude Modulation (AM), the information signal is mixed with the carrier signal in such a way as to cause the amplitude of the carrier to vary at the frequency of the information signal.

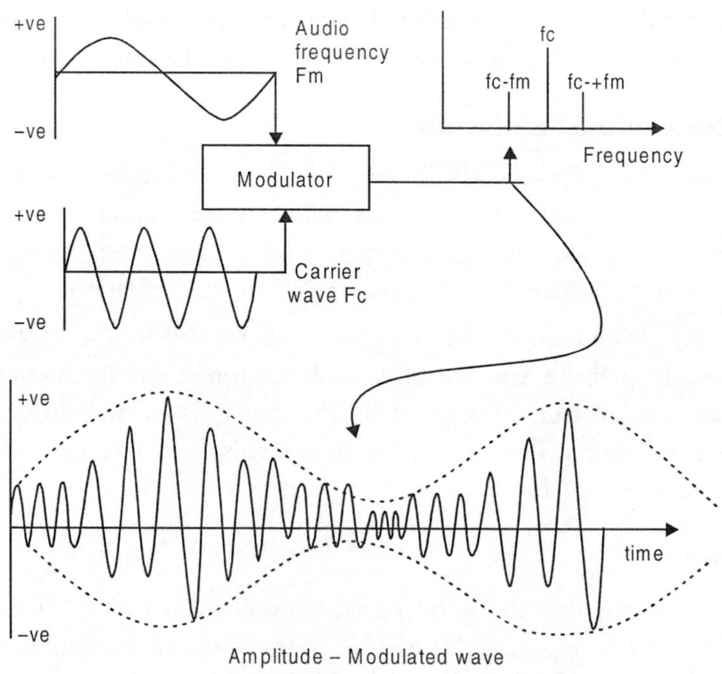

Figure 3.39 *Amplitude Modulation.*

Amplitude Modulation (AM) uses the same scheme as AM radio. This simple technique often requires very low-cost hardware. Two basic types of AM techniques include base band and RF carrier. In a base band system, the input signal directly modulates the strength of the transmitter output, in this case light. In the RF carrier AM technique, a carrier, with a frequency much higher than the encoded information, varies according to the amplitude of the information being encoded. In a fiber optic system, the magnitude of the voltage input signal directly translates into a corresponding light intensity.

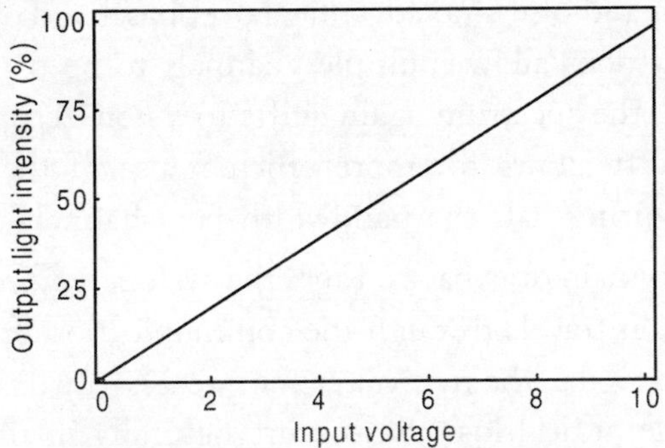

Figure 3.40 *AM System Operation.*

In order to use AM transmission over optical fiber, there must be compensation for optical link loss budget. This problem may be solved two ways: by taking advantage of some special property of the input waveform (for video, the sync pulse is an invariant that can be used to distinguish optical loss from signal level variation) or using a technique that allows the signal level to be interpreted independently from optical loss. To accomplish this, one could send a pilot tone at a high frequency that is above or below the frequency of the information being encoded.

Three techniques for AM video transmission include base band AM, RF carrier AM, and vestigial-sideband AM. Studying the corresponding frequency spectra of these modulation schemes, illustrated in figure 3.41, allows for a clearer understanding of their differences. Simple base band AM occupies the region from DC to about 5 MHz and requires the least bandwidth

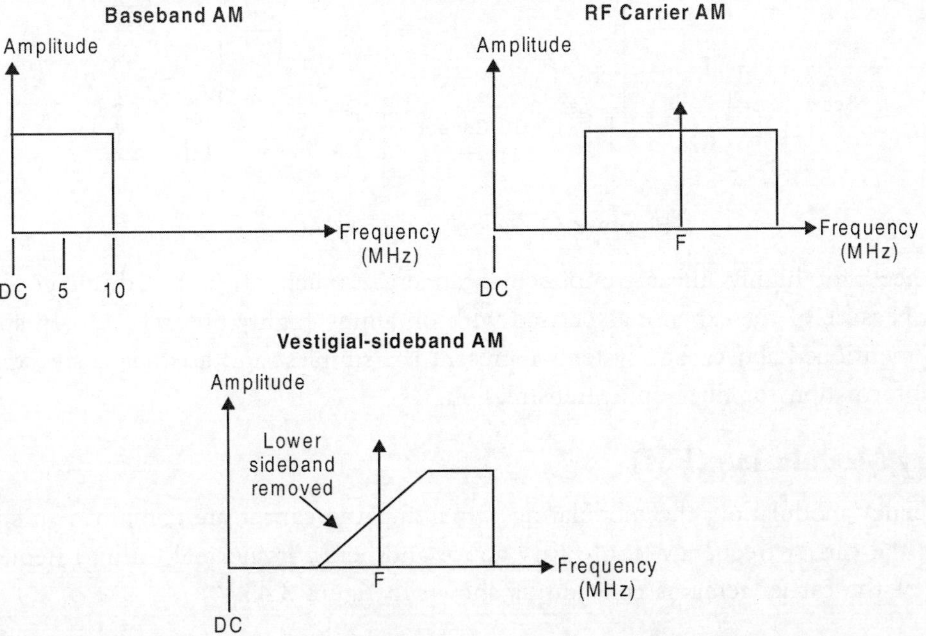

Figure 3.41 *Frequency Spectra of Three AM Transmission Techniques.*

(assuming we are talking about uncompressed digital encoding techniques). The RF carrier modulation spectrum is similar; it has been shifted to a non-zero frequency (F). This approach requires additional bandwidth and offers no advantage over baseband operation in a single channel per fiber system. However, it does allow multiple channels to be combined onto a single fiber. With vestigial-sideband AM, the spectrum again shifts to a non-zero frequency (F), and filtering removes the lower sideband. It allows for more efficient use of the spectrum as compared to straight RF carrier AM, requiring half the bandwidth per channel.

AM modulation has two main drawbacks. First, the system requires highly linear components to prevent signal distortion as it travels through the communication link. Second, because varying the light intensity encodes the signal, the receiver cannot necessarily differentiate between intended signal level variations and the optical loss that occurs naturally in the fiber itself. For instance, providing a 100% maximum signal into the optical transmitter with 10 dB of optical loss between the transmitter and receiver, the receiver would indicate that the signal level is 10%. The receiver cannot readily distinguish between changes in signal level and changes in optical loss due to the fiber. Automatic gain control can compensate for these losses in an AM link. One approach uses a sophisticated circuit that analyzes the input waveform and sets the sync pulse level to the required 40 IRE units. Figure 3.42 illustrates this.

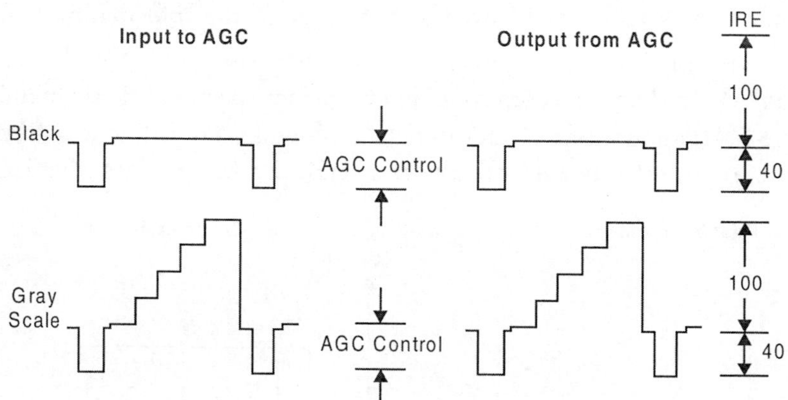

Figure 3.42 *Sync Pulse Level AGC.*

The need for highly linear components can erase much of AM's advantage over other techniques because of the expense associated with obtaining highly linear LEDs. In spite of the difficulties mentioned above, AM systems represent the simplest and least expensive approach to encoding information for fiber optic transmission.

Frequency Modulation (FM)

With frequency modulation, the modulating signal and the carrier are combined in such a way that causes the carrier frequency (fc) to vary above and below its normal (idling) frequency. The amplitude of the carrier remains constant as shown in figure 3.43.

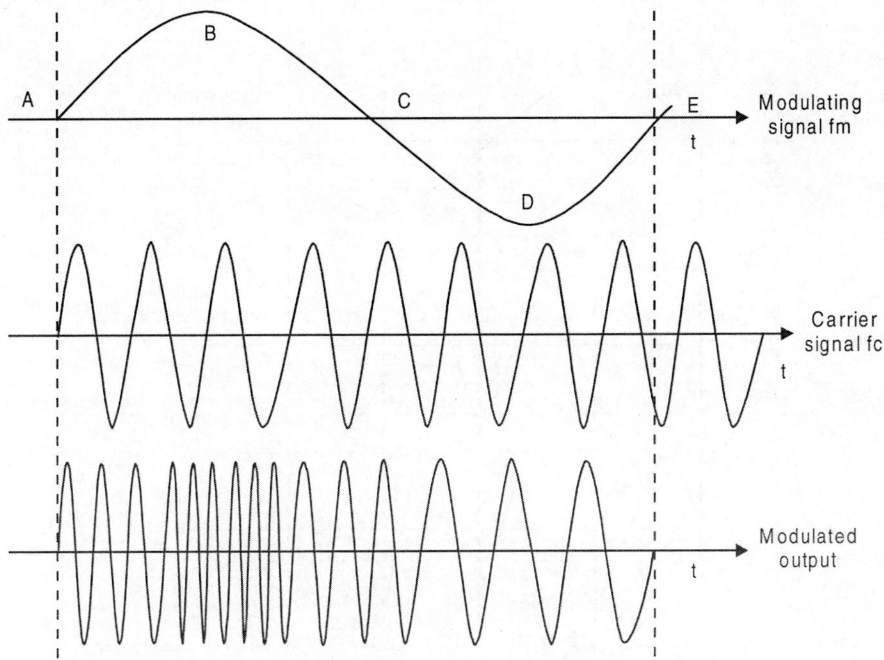

Figure 3.43 *Frequency Modulation.*

As the voltage of the modulating signal increases in the positive direction from A to B, the frequency of the carrier is increased in proportion to the modulating voltage. As the voltage reduces from B to C, the frequency of the carrier decreases until it is back to the original value at C. The modulating voltage increases in the negative direction from C to; hence the carrier frequency decreases to a minimum value at D. It will start increasing again from D to E until it reaches its original value again. Thus in one cycle, the frequency has gone up and down (*i.e.,* above and below the idling frequency) as mentioned earlier.

Throughout this process the amplitude of the carrier is not affected. The carrier frequency change above and below that of the unmodulated condition is proportional to sign and amplitude of the modulating signal.

Phase or Angle Modulation (PM or Indirect FM)

Phase modulation is a type of frequency modulation. Here, the amount of the carrier frequency shift is proportional to both the amplitude and frequency of the modulating signal.

The phase of the carrier is changed by the change in amplitude of the modulating signal as shown in figure 3.44.

The modulated carrier wave is lagging the carrier wave when the modulating frequency is positive. This can be clearly seen if we concentrate on the peak amplitude along line AB (previous slide). When the modulating frequency is negative, the modulated carrier wave is leading the carrier wave. This can be seen clearly by looking at the peak amplitude along line CD (previous slide).

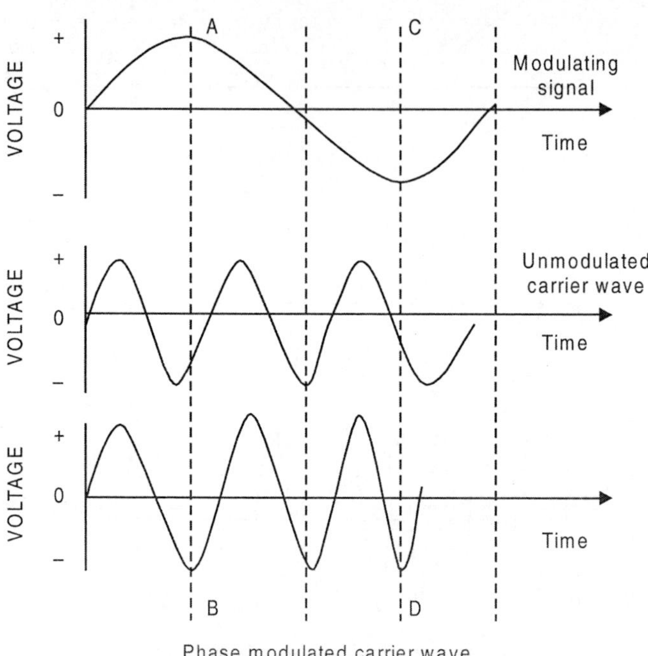

Figure 3.44 *Phase Modulation.*

RS232C INTERFACE

Several interface standards have been formulated to interconnect any one of the many modems also known as data sets of installation and environmental shifts during its lifetime. An additional strength member and an outer jacket surround the inner jacket to bring the overall cable size to between 0.1 and 0.15 millimeters in diameter.

A fiber-optic cable is very small in diameter, which accounts for its lightweight. Thousands of these fiber cables can be bundled together and packed into a tough sheathing. This provides for the ruggedness required when laying miles and miles of fiber cables. This is done to protect against breaks in the cable under normal usage. Attempting to repair a break in a fiber optic bundle by "splicing" cables together is much too expensive. Each cable would have to be accurately aligned in the splice so that the light from or other Data Communications Equipment (DTC) systems made today.

One of the more popular and widely used standards is EIA's RS232C. This standard designates the physical connector type used, the electrical characteristics, and functions of the signals applied to the lines of the interconnect cabling between the terminal and modem. The RS232character standard has been incorporated by numerous standards agencies into their suites of protocols and specifications.

RS232C FUNCTIONS

Serial data is sent out on the transmit data (TX data) line, BA. The RS232C standard specifications require that the output voltage level of a driving amplifier for mark (logic 1) data lie between −5 and −15 volts and for space (logic 0) data lies between +5 and +15 volts. Terminating circuits receiver serial data on the receive serial data on the receive data (rx data) line, bb, which recognizes a mark (logic 1) level as a voltage of at least −3 volt and a space (logic 0) level of at least +3 volts providing for a 2 volt noise immunity between sending and receiving data. Thus, the data lines operate using negative logic since logic 1 is more negative than logic 0.

For all control lines, the voltage levels have the same values as the data lines, but the logic type is positive logic. An "on" condition uses positive voltages while an "off" condition is indicated by negative voltage values. The main control signals used to establish a data link is:

1. RTS (request-to-send)—sent by the UART to the modem, this signal begins the process by which a data link is established. The modem, after a short delay, responds by asserting its CTS (clear-to-send). The purpose of these local handshake signals is to establish a communications link between the modem and the UART. The delay between RTS and CTS allows the modem circuits to come on and settle before data can be sent to it by the UART.

CD (carrier detect), dad (data carrier detect) or RLSD (receiver line signal detect)—when a modem detects a RTS input from the UART, one of its responses is to start sending a mark logic 1 tone onto the telephone line. On the receiving side, when a modem detects the presence of the mark tone on the telephone line, it responds by asserting the CD signal as a remote handshake signal. The UART detects an active CD and interprets it to mean that a remote station is connected online and the data link is completed.

DTR (data terminal ready) from DTE and DSR (data set ready) from the modem these lines are used to inform the two main units (DTE and modem) in the data link that they are electrically ready to establish a data link. In some systems, these signals are connected directly to positive voltage sources. In this case, they only indicate that the RS232character cables firmly connected between the two units. Other systems generate an active DTR when the DTE is up and running (actually I a ready state). Modems in this type of system assert DSR shortly after the modem is powered and operating, again, essentially saying that it is "ready".

Common signal return—This line establishes a common signal reference point between the modem and DTE.

RI (ring indicator)—This line is asserted by modern capable of detecting an incoming telephone ring signal. These modems are equipped to automatically answer the call. A DTE connected to an auto-answering modem responds to the RI signal by asserting its beginning the process required to establish the data link.

The remaining lines are used for secondary channel signaling and for timing control for modems requiring data stream synchronization. A signal quality detector line cg is an available for DCE's that have the electrical means for error detection incorporated into them.

Secondary channel data rates are much lower than the data channel. Their primary use is for control signal information. Frequently, they are configured to send acknowledgement or control data in the opposite direction from the data channel. When they are configured this way, the secondary channel is referred to as a back channel.

RS449 INTERFACE STANDARD

The RS449 standard contains most of the signal lines and electrical specifications outlines in the RS232c. It specifies two connectors, one with 37 pins for the main data channel and one containing 9 pins for secondary channel signaling. The increased number of pins is used to accommodate the added functions. A number of pins shares the same function to assist in reducing line capacitance. This allows for data transfer rates up to 2 mbps over cables that can reach a maximum of 200 feet in length. The RS449 pin assignment and connector are as shown in respectively.

New functions include control indications for local and remote loop-back test function. Local loop-back (ll) indicates the system is in the local loop—back test mode. Data placed on the transmit data line is looped back through the modem onto the receiver data line to the DTE. This mode is used to test the modem functions. Since data is not placed onto the medium, the test is restricted to the local equipment at a station. In contrast, the remote loop-back test mode, checks the telephone system connections and lines as well as the modem at both stations. The data sent by a station is looped back through the remote modem onto the telephone lines back to the sending station. The remote DTE is not included in this test mode. A third control line, test control line, test mode TM signals the DTE that the modem is in one or the other test mode. A similar type of control signal, the data mode (dm) indicates that the modem is in a normal data transfer mode. This last control line replaces the DSR function of the RS232character standard.

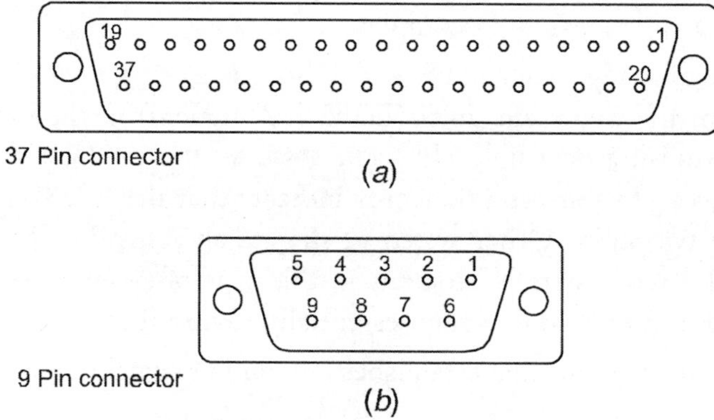

Figure 3.45 *RS449 Pin Connector.*

RS422 AND RS423 INTERFACE STANDARDS

The RS232C and RS449 specifications detail requirements for interfacing DTE and DCE equipment. Two individual circuits used for transferring serial data. They are the RS422 for balanced circuits and RS423 for unbalanced circuits. Balanced networks generate two outputs that are the complements of one another. The voltage (or power) of each output (v1 and v2) can be measured in relation to a common reference point. However, the full output is generally measured differentially between both outputs (v3).

The output of an unbalanced circuit is taken from a single output with reference to a common return such as ground. Balanced networks are used to assist in the elimination of noise experienced on the lines between the generator and receiver units. Unlike the desired outputs, noise on one output is approximately identical to the noise from the other output. The potential difference between the noise levels is negligible. This reduction in noise power is called common-mode rejection and results in less noise presented to the receiver from the generator.

The RS422 and RS423 specifications set requirements for balanced and unbalanced digital interface circuits. Another area specified by RS422 is the length of the cable between the generator and receiver. As with the RS232C standard, RS422 specifies the capacitance per foot as the limiting factor to a cable's length rather than attempting to specify actual lengths.

RS449 Pin Assignment

37-Pin Connector (Main Channel)

PIN NO.	RS232	CIRCUIT	NAME	DIRECTION
1			Shield	Common
2	CI	IS	Signal Rate Indicator	From DCE
3			Not Used	
4, 22	TD	SD	Send Data	From DTE
5, 23	DB	ST	Send Timing	From DCE
6, 24	RD	RD	Receive Data	From DCE
7, 25	RTS	RS	Request-to-Send	From DTE
8, 26	DD	RT	Receive Timing	From DCE
9, 27	CTS	CS	Clear-toSend	From DCE
10		LL	Local Loop-Back	From DTE
11, 29	DSR	DM	DataMode	From DCE
12, 30	DTR	TR	Terminal Ready	From DTE
13, 31	RLSD	RR	Receiver Ready	From DCE
14		RI	Remote Loop-Back	From DTE
15	RI	IC	Incoming Call	From DCE
16	CH	SF	Select Frequency	From DTE
		SR	Signaling Rate Selector	
17, 35	DA	TT	Terminal Timing	From DTE
19	SG	SG	Signal Ground	Common
20		RC	Receive Common	From DTE
23	CG	SQ	Signal Quality	From DCE
28		IS	Terminal in Servgice	From DTE
32		SS	Select Standby	From DTE
34		NS	New Signal	From DTE
36		SB	Standby Indicator	From DCE
37		SC	Send Common	From DCE

9-Pin Connector (S—Secondary Channel)				
1			Shield	Common
2	SCF	SRR	Receive Ready	From DCE
3	SBA	SSD	Send Data	From DTE
4	SBB	SRD	Receive Data	From DCE
5	SG	SG	Signal Ground	Common
6		RC	Receive Common	From DCE
7	SCA	SRS	Request-to-Send	From DTE
8	SCB	SCS	Clear-to-Send	From DCE
9		SC	Send Common	From DCE

Figure 3.46 *RS449 Pin-assignment.*

REVIEW QUESTIONS

1. What are the different transmission signals ?
2. What are the advantages and disadvantages of analog and digital signals ?
3. What are the difference between analog and digital signals ?
4. Write successive approximation method of A/D conversion.
5. Write short notes on bandwidth and frequency.
6. What are digital T carriers ?
7. Why do we use sampling theorem ?
8. What are modulation and de-modulation, explain ?
9. What are the different types of modulations ?
10. Why is full-duplex Frequency Shift Keying (FSK) an example of Frequency Division Multiplexing (FDM) ?
11. How are FDM groups created ?
12. How are multiple channels sent on a single line using TDM ?
13. What is meant by Pulse Amplitude Modulation (PAM) ?
14. What is the Nyquist sampling rate when sampling a signal whose highest frequency is **1630** Hz and lowest frequency is **250** Hz ?
15. What is quantizing error ?
16. What happens to quantized samples in a PCM system ?
17. Give four characteristics of a T**1** carrier.
18. What is a CODEC and how does it differ from a modem ?
19. What is the basic idea behind delta modulation ?
20. Explain the two modes for transmitting binary data across a link.
21. What are the advantages and disadvantages of parallel transmission ?

22. Compare the two methods of serial transmission. Discuss the advantages and disadvantages of each.
23. What is digital-to-analog modulation ?
24. What is analog-to-analog modulation ?
25. Why is frequency modulation superior to amplitude modulation ?
26. What is the advantage of QAM over ASK or PSK ?
27. What are the methods that convert a digital signal to an analog signal ?
28. What is the difference between bit rate and baud rate ? Give an example where both are the same. Give an example where they are different.
29. What is modulation ?
30. What is the purpose of a carrier signal in modulation ?
31. How is baud rate related to transmission bandwidth in ASK ?
32. How is baud rate related to transmission bandwidth in FSK ?
33. How is baud rate related to transmission bandwidth in PSK ?
34. How is baud rate related to transmission bandwidth in QAM ?
35. How is QAM related to ASK and PSK ?
36. What is the function of a modulator ? What is the function of a demodulator ?
37. What does the term modem stand for ?
38. Explain the asymmetry of 56 k modems.
39. Why are modems needed for telephone communications ?
40. Compare the FM bandwidth with the AM bandwidth in terms of the modulating signal.
41. What are the three major multiplexing techniques ?
42. How does FDM combine multiple signals into one ?
43. What is the purpose of a guard band ?
44. How does TDM combine multiple signals into one ?
45. How are T lines related to DS service ?
46. How can T lines be used for analog transmission ?
47. What is inverse multiplexing ?
48. Which error-detection method is used most frequently with asynchronous data streams ?
49. How many errors can parity reliably detect in a single character ?
50. What is one drawback when using parity for error detection ?
51. How many hamming bits are used for the message in question **7** ?
52. Why is full-duplex Frequency Shift Keying (FSK) an example of Frequency Division Multiplexing (FDM) ?
53. How are FDM groups created ?
54. How are multiple channels sent on a single line using TDM ?
55. What is meant by Pulse Amplitude Modulation (PAM) ?
56. What are the functions of RS449 interface standard ?
57. What are the voltage levels for RS232C data on the transmit line ?
58. What is the benefit of using RS422 balanced interface circuits ?

59. What are the main functions of a modem in a low-speed data communications system ?

60. What is the common data rate for V34 modems ?

61. What is the common data rate for V90 modems ?

62. What is one modulation technique used with V90 modem ?

63. Which tone is initially used to cause Carrier-Detect (CD) line to be asserted by a modem ? What logic level does that tone represent ?

64. Describe the three characteristics of a sine wave.

65. Contrast an analog signal with a digital signal.

66. Name three types of transmission impairment.

67. What do you understand by transmission impairments ? Discuss the major transmission impairments. *(IV BCA (4.1)–DCCN)*

68. Differentiate between the following pairs:

(*i*) Periodic signal—Aperiodic signal

(*ii*) Digital signal—Analog signal

(*iii*) Time domain—Frequency domain

(*iv*) Half duplex—Full duplex. *(IV BCA (4.1) – DCCN)*

69. Explain about RS232C interface. *(IV BCA (4.1) – DCCN)*

70. Explain amplitude modulation and frequency modulation with suitable diagram. *(IV BCA (4.1) – DCCN)*

4 MULTIPLEXING AND SWITCHING

MULTIPLEXING BASICS

Multiplexing is a process in which multiple data channels are combined into a single data or physical channel at the source. Multiplexing can be implemented at any of the OSI layers. Conversely, de-multiplexing is the process of separating multiplexed data channels at the destination. One example of multiplexing is when data from multiple applications is multiplexed into a single lower-layer data packet.

Another example of multiplexing is when data from multiple devices is combined into a single physical channel (using a device called a multiplexer).

A multiplexer is a physical layer device that combines multiple data streams into one or more output channels at the source. Multiplexers de-multiplex the channels into multiple data streams at the remote end and thus maximize the use of the bandwidth of the physical medium by enabling it to be shared by multiple traffic sources.

Some methods used for multiplexing data are Time-Division Multiplexing (TDM), Asynchronous Time-Division Multiplexing (ATDM), Frequency-Division Multiplexing (FDM), and statistical multiplexing.

In TDM, information from each data channel is allocated bandwidth based on pre-assigned time slots, regardless of whether there is data to transmit. In ATDM, information from data channels is allocated bandwidth as needed by using dynamically assigned time slots. In FDM, information from each data channel is allocated bandwidth based on the signal frequency of the traffic. In statistical multiplexing, bandwidth is dynamically allocated to any data channels that have information to transmit.

MULTIPLEXING

Multiplexing is sending multiple signals or streams of information on a carrier at the same time in the form of a single, complex signal and then recovering the separate signals at the receiving end as shown in figure 4.1 (*a*). In analog transmission, signals are commonly multiplexed using

Frequency-Division Multiplexing (FDM), in which the carrier bandwidth is divided into sub-channels of different frequency widths, each carrying a signal at the same time in parallel. In digital transmission, signals are commonly multiplexed using Time-Division Multiplexing (TDM), in which the multiple signals are carried over the same channel in alternating time slots. In some optical fiber networks, multiple signals are carried together as separate wavelengths of light in a multiplexed signal using Dense Wavelength Division Multiplexing (DWDM). The categorization of multiplexing is shown in figure 4.1 (*b*).

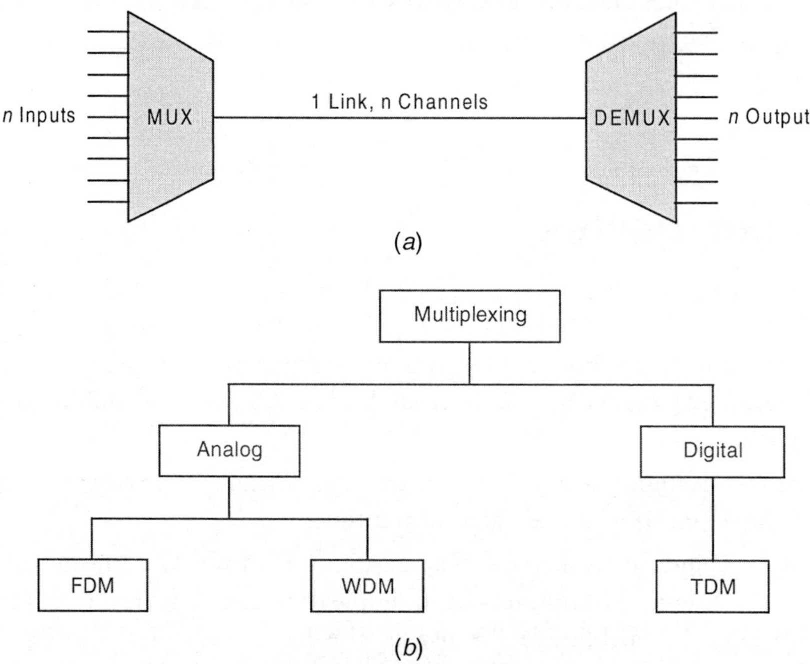

Figure 4.1 *Multiplexing.*

INVERSE MULTIPLEXER

An **inverse multiplexer** (often abbreviated to "inverse mux" or "imux") allows a data stream to be broken into multiple lower data rate communications links. An inverse multiplexer differs from a demultiplexer in that each of the low rate links coming from it is related to the other ones and they all work together to carry the same data. By contrast, the output streams from a demultiplexer may each be completely independent from each other and the demultiplexer does not have to understand them in any way. Note that this is the opposite of a multiplexer which creates one high speed link from multiple low speed ones.

MULTIPLEXING METHODS

One way to increase the capacity of data transmission is to multiplex numerous channels into a single transmission channel, using a multiplexer (MUX) . This has the advantage of requiring of multiplexing is that there is a requirement for either additional time or bandwidth to achieve the multiplexing. There are four basic techniques used for multiplexing:

1. Time-Division Multiplexing (TDM)
2. Frequency Division Multiplexing (FDM)
3. Wavelength Division Multiplexing (WDM)
4. Statistical Time Division Multiplexing

• Time-Division Multiplexing

Time-Division Multiplexing (TDM) is a method of putting multiple data streams in a single signal by separating the signal into many segments, each having a very short duration. Each individual data stream is reassembled at the receiving end based on the timing. Using the point-to-point conventional means of transferring data on a base band system , sending three messages of varying lengths is accomplished a message is transmitted first, followed, in time, by second message, and then third message. This is a simple and straight forward process.

The circuit that combines signals at the source (transmitting) end of a communications link is known as a multiplexer. It accepts the input from each individual end user, breaks each signal into segments, and assigns the segments to the composite signal in a rotating, repeating sequence. The composite signal thus contains data from multiple senders. At the other end of the long-distance cable, the individual signals are separated out by means of a circuit called a de-multiplexer, and routed to the proper end users. A two-way communications circuit requires a multiplexer/de-multiplexer at each end of the long-distance, high-bandwidth cable.

If many signals must be sent along a single long-distance line, careful engineering is required to ensure that the system will perform properly. An asset of TDM is its flexibility. The scheme allows for variation in the number of signals being sent along the line, and constantly adjusts the time intervals to make optimum use of the available bandwidth. The Internet is a classic example of a communications network in which the volume of traffic can change drastically from hour to hour. In some systems, a different scheme, known as Frequency-Division Multiplexing (FDM), is preferred. The TDM system is illustrated as in figure 4.2.

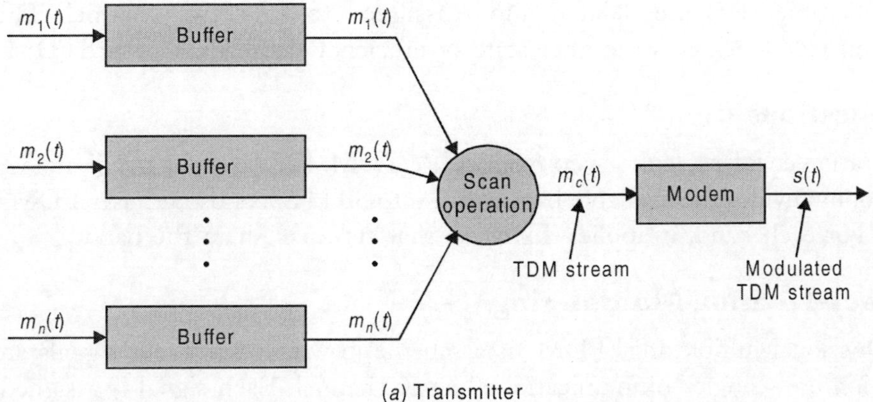

(*a*) Transmitter

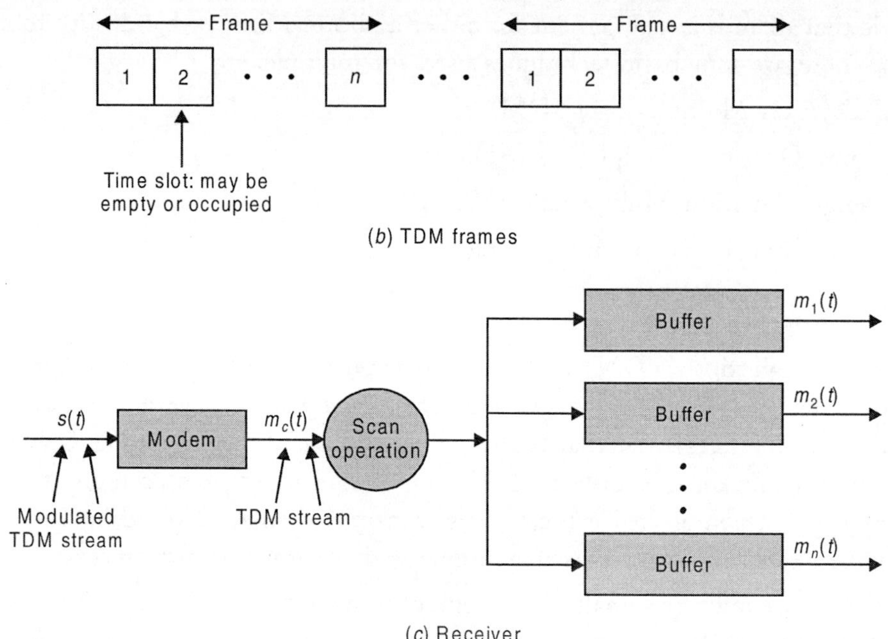

Figure 4.2 *TDM System.*

TDM Methods

Two basic types of TDM are in use today, synchronous TDM (STDM) and asynchronous TDM (ATDM), also known as statistical TDM (STATDM) or Stat MUX. STDM systems assign time slots of equal length to all packets regardless if whether or not anything is to be sent by each station with an assigned time slot. STDM systems are comparatively easy to implement once the applications software allocates the time slots. Stat MUX networks assign time slots only when they are to be used and deletes them when they are idle. The total time used for a stat MUX frame varies with the amount of traffic currently being handled.

Stat MUX systems are most suitable for these high-density, high–traffic applications. A constant flow of messages are assigned time slot and interleaved as each channel on the send side becomes active and requires communications with another channel. If a channel does not have any traffic, its time slots are deleted and reassigned to an active channel. This way, the interconnecting media achieves a higher state of efficiency usage than with STDM systems.

TDM Applications

Second-generation cellular telephone companies use TDM. For example, the digital version of the cellular telephony divides the available bandwidth into 30 kHz bands and uses FDM to combine these bands. For each band, it applies TDM so that six users share the band.

• Frequency-Division Multiplexing

Frequency-Division Multiplexing (FDM) is a scheme in which numerous signals are combined for transmission on a single communications line or channel. Each signal is assigned a different frequency (sub-channel) within the main channel.

A typical analog Internet connection via a twisted pair telephone line requires approximately three kilohertz (3 kHz) of bandwidth for accurate and reliable data transfer. Twisted-pair lines are common in households and small businesses. But major telephone cables, operating between large businesses, government agencies, and municipalities, are capable of much larger bandwidths.

Suppose a long-distance cable is available with a bandwidth allotment of three megahertz (3 MHz). This is 3,000 kHz, so in theory, it is possible to place 1,000 signals, each 3 kHz wide, into the long-distance channel. The circuit that does this is known as a multiplexer. It accepts the input from each individual end user, and generates a signal on a different frequency for each of the inputs. This results in a high-bandwidth, complex signal containing data from all the end users. At the other end of the long-distance cable, the individual signals are separated out by means of a circuit called a de-multiplexer, and routed to the proper end users. A two-way communications circuit requires a multiplexer/de-multiplexer at each end of the long-distance, high-bandwidth cable.

When FDM is used in a communications network, each input signal is sent and received at maximum speed at all times. This is its chief asset. However, if many signals must be sent along a single long-distance line, the necessary bandwidth is large, and careful engineering is required to ensure that the system will perform properly. In some systems, a different scheme, known as time-division multiplexing, is used instead.

In its simplest form, FDM is represented by a Frequency Shift Key (FSK) modem. Here two frequencies were used to represent a one and a zero. In a full-duplex system, four sets of frequencies occupied the line with a maximum of two signals on the line at any one time. In effect, the bandwidth of the telephone line was shared by each of the signal frequencies. This example falls short, since it deals with single channel of communication and does not involve any form of true multiplexing. It does, however, as shown in figure 4.3 frequency allocating the transmit frequency bands within the bandwidth.

FDM applies itself to the increased usage of a network's capacity by utilizing as much available frequency bandwidth as is allocated to the system. Applications of FDM include fiber optic links, microwave, and satellite communications that have bandwidths in the megahertz and gigahertz ranges.

Applications of FDM

A very known and common application of FDM is AM and FM radio broadcasting. Radio uses the air as the transmission medium. A special band, from 530 to 1700 kHz, is assigned to AM radio. All radio stations need to share this band. Another common use of FDM is in television broadcasting. Each TV channel has its own bandwidth of 6 MHz.

The concept corresponding to frequency division multiplexing in the optical domain is known as wavelength division multiplexing. In optical communications, FDM is referred to as Wavelength-Division Multiplexing (WDM).

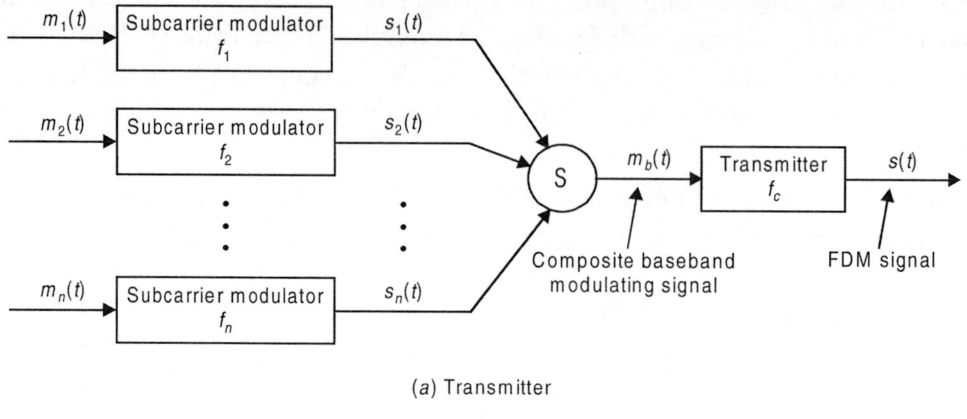

(*a*) Transmitter

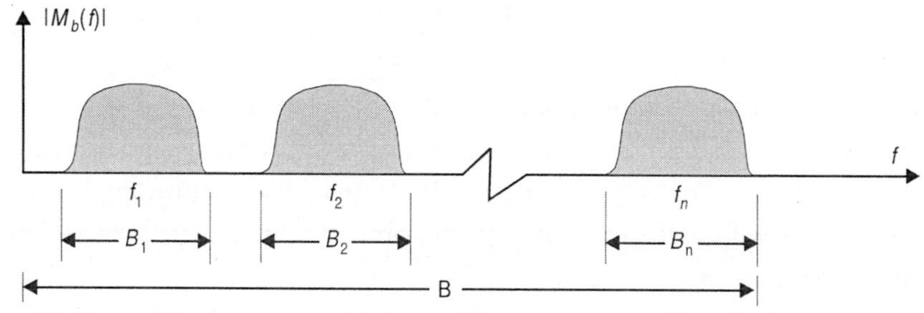

(*b*) Spectrum of composite baseband modulating signal

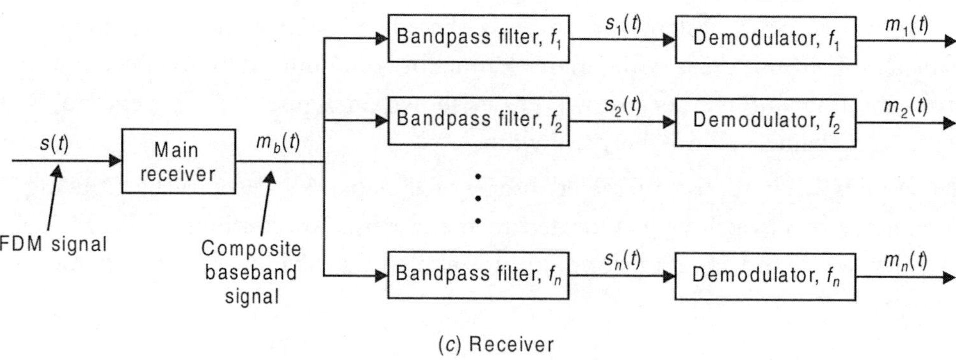

(*c*) Receiver

Figure 4.3 *FDM System.*

• Wavelength Division Multiplexing

Until the late 1980s, optical fiber communications was mainly confined to transmitting a single optical channel. Because fiber attenuation was involved, this channel required periodic regeneration, which included detection, electronic processing, and optical retransmission. Such regeneration causes a high-speed optoelectronic bottleneck and can handle only a single wavelength. After the new generation amplifiers were developed, it enabled us to accomplish high-speed repeaterless single-channel transmission. We can think of single ~Gbps channel as a single high-speed lane in a highway in which the cars are packets of optical data and the highway is the optical fiber. However, the ~25 THz optical fiber can accommodate much more bandwidth than the traffic from a single lane. To increase the system capacity we can transmit several different independent wavelengths simultaneously down a fiber to fully utilize this enormous fiber bandwidth. Therefore, the intent was to develop a multiple-lane highway, with each lane representing data travelling on a different wavelength. Thus, a WDM system enables the fiber to carry more throughput. By using wavelength-selective devices, independent signal routing also can be accomplished.

Basic Operation

As explained before, WDM enables the utilization of a significant portion of the available fiber bandwidth by allowing many independent signals to be transmitted simultaneously on one fiber, with each signal located at a different wavelength. Routing and detection of these signals can be accomplished independently, with the wavelength determining the communication path by acting as the signature address of the origin, destination or routing. Components are therefore required that are wavelength selective, allowing for the transmission, recovery, or routing of specific wavelengths.

In a simple WDM system figure, each laser must emit light at a different wavelength, with all the lasers. Light multiplexed together onto a single optical fiber. After being transmitted through a high-bandwidth optical fiber, the combined optical signals must be demultiplexed at the receiving end by distributing the total optical power to each output port and then requiring that each receiver selectively recover only one wavelength by using a tunable optical filter. Each laser is modulated at a given speed, and the total aggregate capacity being transmitted along the high-bandwidth fiber is the sum total of the bit rates of the individual lasers. An example of the system capacity enhancement is the situation in which ten 2.5 Gbps signals can be transmitted on one fiber, producing a system capacity of 25 Gbps. This wavelength-parallelism circumvents the problem of typical optoelectronic devices, which do not have bandwidths exceeding a few gigahertz unless they are exotic and expensive. The speed requirements for the individual optoelectronic components are, therefore, relaxed, even though a significant amount of total fiber bandwidth is still being utilized.

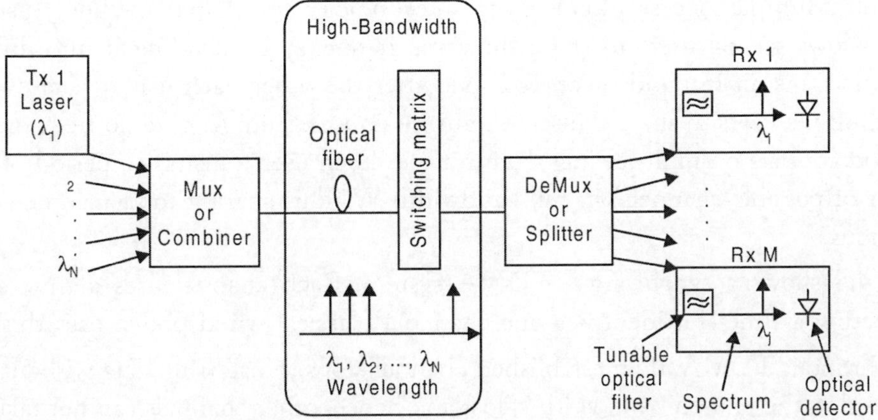

Figure 4.4 *Diagram of a Simple WDM System.*

• Statistical Time Division Multiplexing

Statistical time division multiplexing uses intelligent devices capable of identifying when a terminal is idle. They allocate time only to lines when required. This means that more lines can be connected to a transmission medium as this device statistically compensates for normal idle time in data communication line.

A TDM where slots are allocated on demand. Unlike synchronous TDM, empty slots are never sent. All sources connected to a multiplexer are not always transmitting. Stat TDM exploits this property by allowing the sum of the maximum data rates of each source to exceed the outgoing data rate. However, since almost always all the sources are never transmitting at their maximum rate, the instantaneous sum of their data rates is within the capacity of the multiplexer line. If there are n source and k slots per fame in the outgoing frame then k < n. During each scan of the input, only up to k buffers are read. Statistical TDM—Issues in synchronous TDM every slot is allocated to one source, so the demux knows where to output each slot. With statistical TDM however, each slot could contain arbitrary source data, hence addressing information is required for each slot. This is an overhead that was not present in synchronous TDM. If the sources maintain average data rate, stat TDM will work fine, however during peak periods, there might not be enough slots so the input will have to buffer data till slots become available. This causes a buffering requirement at sender, however more importantly the subsequent backlog due to buffering causes an delay in sending of data. So the backlog/delay of frames is directly related to the output capacity of the line.

MEDIA SHARING TECHNIQUES

Media sharing occurs when two communication channels use the same media. This section presents how some communication channels can use the same media link without architecture considerations. There are three main techniques, they are as:

• Time Division Multiple Access (TDMA)

Time Division Multiple Access (TDMA) is a technology for shared medium (usually radio) networks. It allows several users to share the same frequency by dividing it into different time slots. The users transmit in rapid succession, one after the other, each using there own timeslot. This allows multiple users to share the same transmission medium (*e.g.*, radio frequency). So, this simple method consists on multiplexing data in time. Each user transmits a period of time equal to 1/(number of possible channels) in full bandwidth W. This sharing mode can be synchronous or asynchronous.

Figure 4.5 shows a synchronous TDMA system. Each channel uses a time slot each T periods. Selecting a time slot identifies one channel. Classical wired phone uses this technique.

In synchronous TDMA, if an established channel stops transferring data without freeing the assigned time slot, the unused bandwidth is lost and hence, other channels can not take advantage of this. This technique has evolved to asynchronous TDMA to avoid this problem.

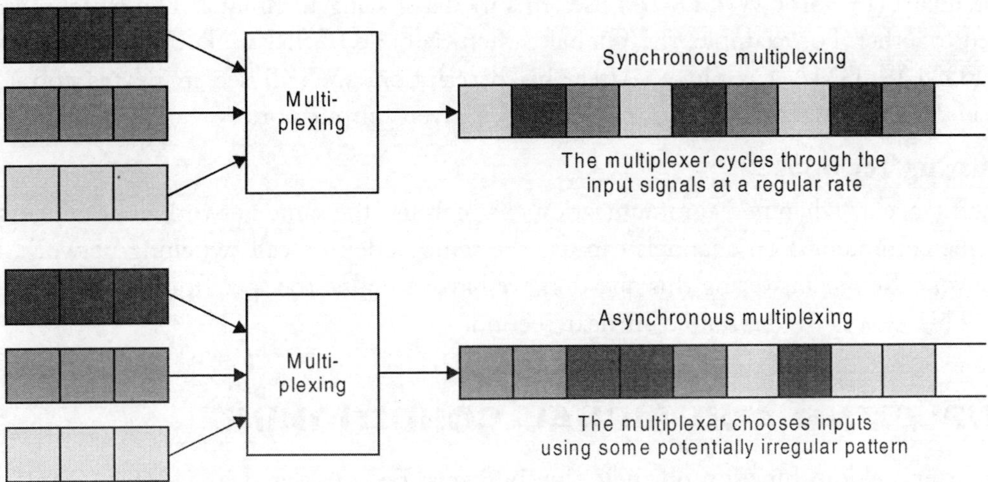

Figure 4.5 *Synchronous and Asynchronous TDMA Diagram.*

Figure 4.5 shows an asynchronous TDMA system. Each channel uses a time slot when the user needs to transfer data and when a time slot is unused. The header of each time slot data stream identifies the channel identification. ATM networks use this technique.

These two techniques are used to connect users. Providing broadcast channels in TDMA can not be done easily. Frequency division multiple access technique avoids this problem. Next section presents this sharing mode.

• Frequency Division Multiple Access (FDMA)

Frequency division multiple access (FDMA) is the oldest and most important of the three main ways for multiple radio transmitters to share the radio spectrum. This sharing method consists on giving to each channel a piece of available bandwidth.

Each user transmits over a constant bandwidth equal to W/(number of possible channels). Filtering with a bandwidth equal to 'W' = W/(number of possible channels) the whole W bandwidth spectrum selects one channel. TV and radio broadcasters use this media sharing technique.

Another method has been developed based on the frequency dimension. This method called code division multiple access uses an encoding-decoding system used, initially, for military communications. Today consumer market applications also use this technique. In the next section this method is discussed in detail.

• Code Division Multiple Access (CDMA)

Code Division Multiple Access (CDMA) is a form of spread spectrum which is sent by multiple transmitters to the same receiver on the same frequency channel at the same time without harmful interference.

Each user transmits using the full bandwidth. Demodulating the whole W band (as given in FDMA) using a given identification code selects one channel out of the others. Next mobile phones standard (IS-95 or W-CDMA) uses this media sharing technique. These techniques can be merged together. For example, the Global System Mobile (GSM = Natel D) phone standard uses an FDMA-TDMA technique. After this description, we will see in next section how a network node routes data from an input port to a given output port.

Node Sharing Technique

Node sharing occurs when two communication channels use the same network node. The question is how some communication channels can use the same node in a cell switching network, *i.e.*, an ATM network. Before answering this question, we have to define the specification of the switching function. This concept is presented in next section.

MULTIPLEXING AND SIGNAL CONDITIONING

A/D converters seldom function on their own but must be considered in a systems context with associated circuitry for signal conditioning, multiplexing, amplification, and other functions. Every application will dictate a unique mix of add-ons that may be implemented in a variety of physical configurations-on a PC I/O board, inside a remote transmitter, or at a local termination panel.

Multiplexing. In many industrial and laboratory applications, multiple analog signals must be converted to digital form. And if speed is not the limiting factor, a single A/D converter often is shared among multiple input channels via a switching mechanism called a multiplexer. This is commonly done because of the relatively high cost of converters. Multiplexers also allow amplification and other signal conditioning circuitry to be time-shared among multiple channels. Software or auxiliary hardware controls the switch selection.

Sample-and-hold. It is important to acknowledge that a multiplexer does reduce the frequency with which data points are acquired, and that the Nyquist sample-rate criterion still must be observed. During a typical data acquisition process, individual channels are read in turn sequentially. This is called standard, or distributed, sampling. A reading of all channels is called a scan. Because each channel is acquired and converted at a slightly different time, however, a skew in sample time is created between data points.

MULTIPLEXED CHANNELS

If time synchronization among inputs is important, some data acquisition cards offer burst mode operation or simultaneous sample-and-hold circuitry. Burst mode, or pseudo-simultaneous sampling, acquires each channel at the maximum rate of the board, then waits a user-specified amount of time before sampling again.

True simultaneous sample-and-hold systems can sample all channels within a few nanoseconds of each other, eliminating phase and time discontinuities for all but the fastest processes. Essentially, a switched capacitor on each channel tracks the corresponding input signal. Before starting the A/D conversion process, all switches are opened simultaneously, leaving the last instantaneous values on the capacitors.

Because A/D converters work best on signals in the 1-10 V range, low voltage signals may need to be amplified before conversion-either individually or after multiplexing on a shared circuit. Conversely, high voltage signals may need to be attenuated.

Amplifiers also can boost an A/D converter's resolution of low-level signals. For example, a 12-bit A/D converter with a gain of 4 can digitize a signal with the same resolution as a 14-bit converter with a gain of 1. It's important to note, however, that fixed-gain amplifiers, which essentially multiply all signals proportionately, increase sensitivity to low voltage signals but do not extend the converter's dynamic range.

Programmable Gain Amplifiers (PGAs), on the other hand, can be configured to automatically increase the gain as the signal level drops, effectively increasing the system's dynamic range. A PGA with three gain levels set three orders of magnitude apart can make a 12-bit converter behave more like an 18-bit converter. This function does, however, slow down the sample rate.

From a systems perspective, amplifier performance should be on par with that of the A/D converter itself-gain accuracy should be specified as a low percentage of the total gain. Amplifier noise and offset error also should be low. Other conditioning functions: Other A/D signal conditioning functions required will vary widely from application to application.

In practical telecommunication systems, a nominal channel allocation of 0–4 kHz is assumed to allow for finite cut-off filters. Hence the 4kHz channel spacing in F.D.M. assemblies. The frequency shifting process (also called *frequency translation*) of the information signal produces two new frequency bands. One is called the *Upper Sideband* (USB) and the other *Lower Sideband* (LSB). Both are referred to as *side frequencies.*

In practical systems, complex multiplexing formats are encountered. For example, the Table 4.1 shows an FDM structure for telephony which is recommended by the *Consultative Committee of the International Telecommunications Union* (CCITT). CCITT is an international advisory body. The structure allows telephone calls to be combined in blocks of appropriate sizes for transmission through a national or international telephone network.

Table 4.1 CCITT FDM Hierarchy

Channel	1 channel (4 kHz)
Group	12 channels (48 kHz)
Super group (5 groups)	60 channels (240 kHz)
Master gruop (5 groups)	300 channels (1.2 MHz)
Super master group (3 groups)	900 channels (3.6 MHz)

The frequency assignments set forth by CCITT, which is based in Geneva, Switzerland, makes sure that systems using these in various countries are compatible.

We can now take a look at the basic group (known as the standard telephone group-12 channel) and see how the information signals are combined into a composite signal for transmission over a single communication channel. It is also worth mentioning at this point that the CCITT recommends that all multichannel systems should be based on two alternative 12 channel group (*i.e.,* one group should utilize the USB and the other should use the LSB).

We will take a look at an example of a 12 channel multiplex system utilizing the lower sideband. LSB BPF is a band pass filter which will allow only the lower sidebands to pass through to the transmission line.

Synchronization

Synchronization is the coordination of occurrences to operate in unison with respect to time. This process can be a premeditated arrangement set forth on a parallel time scape, or it can be an observable coincidence in eventuality. In terms of digital logic and data transfer, a synchronous object requires a clock signal.

Systems operating with all their parts in synchrony are said to be *synchronous* or *in sync.* Some systems may be only approximately synchronized, or plesiochronous. For some applications relative offsets between events need to be determined, for others only the order of the event is important.

Interleaving

The transmission of pulses from two or more digital sources in time-division sequence over a single path. Bit padding is the addition of one or more extra bits to a transmission or storage unit to make it conform to a standard size. Some sources identify bit padding as a type of bit stuffing.

Timeslots

Time Division Multiple access (TDMA) allows several users to share the same frequency by dividing it into different *timeslots.* The users transmit in rapid succession, one after the other, each using their own timeslot.

MODULATION AND MULTIPLEXING

Modulation is a technique whereby an analogue signal can be changed (modulated) so as to carry information or a message.

Communication can be achieved simply by sending a signal directly over a wire link. Such a simple method has several disadvantages. One of them is that: only one conversation can be carried out at a time. This means that between the number of pairs of individuals who wish to communicate and the number of lines provided, there has to be a one to one correspondence. A subscriber has his own link to the exchange and a connection to any other line on the exchange. This can be done for shorter distances and a small population.

It is impractical and unnecessary to do so (*i.e.*, provide as many links as there are subscribers) for long distances and a large population. This is where the concept of multiplexing comes into play.

MODULATION STANDARDS

There are many standards for modulation. Some terms are defined below:

- **Bell 103 & 212A:** These are old standards. Bell 103 transmits at 300 bps at 1 bit per baud. Bell 212A was the next step up, capable of two bits per baud. It was capable of 1200 bps of 600 baud. Each used a different type of modulation.

- **V.21:** Uses mainly outside the U.S., it was a sort of international standard. It is not compatible with Bell protocols, and is only capable of 300 bps.
- **V.22:** Shares the features of V.21, but was capable of 1200 bps. Later, the V.22bis protocol was used. It was used both in the U.S. and outside, and ran at 4 bits per baud for a total of 2400 bps.
- **V.23:** Used mainly in Europe, this allowed the modem to send and receive data at the same time, although it could send data only at 75 bps. This standard was developed to lower the cost of modems. A 1200 bps modem was very expensive at the time.
- **V.29:** A half-duplex standard, meaning one-way. It works at 9600 bps. The standard is not laid out well for modems, therefore isn't much used. The protocol is most often used for fax machines.
- **V.32:** This standard began to get users into the ballpark we are all in now. It was a full-duplex standard and operated at 9600 bps, with a 2400 baud rate. It incorporates error-correcting and negotiation. The error-correcting allowed V.32 to work well over phone line noise.
- **V.32bis:** This is one step up from V.32. It transmitted 6 bits per baud, allowing throughputs of 14,400 bps. It also allowed fallback onto regular V.32 if the phone line was impaired. Many still use this modem standard primarily.
- **V.32fast:** Better known as the 28,800 bps modem.
- **V.34:** The latest real modem standard. It provides a reliable 28,800 bps connection. With upgrades to the ROM BIOS on the modem, the standard is often used for 33,600 bps transmissions.
- **V.90:** is the latest and fastest ITU-ratified "V." specification, offering a top dialup rate of 56 kbps.

REVIEW QUESTIONS

1. Discuss the basic of multiplexing.
2. What are the different methods of multiplexing ?
3. What do you understand by multiplexing and modulation ?
4. Discuss different switching methods.
5. Which switching technique is also known as store-and-foreward ?
6. Contrast message and packet switching.
7. What is multiplexing ? Explain the various categories of multiplexing used in data communication. *(IV–BCA(4.1)–DCCN)*
8. Explain about RS232C interface. *(IV–BCA (4.1)–DCCN)*
9. Explain the Pulse Code Modulation (PCM) technique of encoding. *(IV–BCA(4.1)–DCCN)*
10. Explain amplitude modulation and frequency modulation with suitable diagram. *(IV–BCA(4.1)–DCCN)*

❑❑❑

5

TRANSMISSION MEDIA

Cable is the medium through which information usually moves from one network device to another. There are several types of cable which are commonly used with LANS. In some cases, a network will utilize only one type of cable, other networks will use a variety of cable types. The type of cable chosen for a network is related to the network's topology, protocol, and size. Understanding the characteristics of different types of cable and how they relate to other aspects of a network is necessary for the development of a successful network.

The *physical* layer provides for physical connectivity between networked devices. Transmission and receipt of data from the physical media (copper wire, fiber, radio frequencies, barbed wire, string etc.) is managed at this layer.

The *physical* layer receives data from the data link layer, and transmits it to the wire. The *physical* layer controls the electrical and mechanical functions related to the transmission and receipt of a communications signal. It also manages the encoding and decoding of data contained within the modulated signal.

Note that for two devices to communicate, they must be connected to the same type of physical medium (wiring). 802.3 Ethernet to 802.3 Ethernet, FDDI to FDDI, serial to serial etc. Two end stations using different protocols can only communicate through a multi-protocol bridge or a router.

The physical layer is responsible for two jobs:

1. Communication with the data link layer above it.
2. Fragmentation of data into frames
3. Reassembly of frames into data link protocol data units.
4. Transmission and receipt of data.

It should be noted that in most modern network interface adaptors, the *physical* and data link functions are performed by the adaptor.

The physical layer is the hardware level of the protocol model that is concerned with electronic signals. Physical layer protocols send and receive data in the form of packets. A packet contains a source address, the transmission itself, and a destination address.

TCP/IP supports a number of physical layer protocols, including Ethernet. Ethernet is an example of a packet-switching network; its communications channels are occupied only for the duration of the transmission of a packet. On the other hand, the telephone network is an example of a circuit-switching network.

The physical layer (layer 1) of the OSI reference model serializes the frame (*i.e.,* converts it to a series of bits) and sends it across a communications circuit (*i.e.,* cable) to the destination (or an intermediate) system. There are a number of types of circuit/cable (sometimes also called "media") that may be used, these include:

1. Open wire circuits
2. Twisted pair cables
3. Coaxial cables
4. Fiber optics cable
5. Signaling of bits

The physical layer defines the representation of each bit as a voltage, current, phase, or frequency. Four basic schemes are used:

1. RZ, Return to Zero (Pulse signaling)
2. NRZ (non return to zero transmission)
3. Manchester encoding (Edge/phase signaling)

In NRZ transmission, each data bit is represented by a level. A high level may represent a logic 1, where as a low level may represent a logic 0. The term is derived from the earlier transmission technique of sending pulses to represent bits (called Return to Zero, RZ) in which a logic 1 is represented by a pulse and a logic 0 by the absence of a pulse. (AMI and HDB3 are techniques derived from RZ). Manchester encoding uses a still different scheme where a logic 1 is represented by a transition in a particular direction (usually a rising edge) in the centre of each bit. A transition in the opposite direction (downward in this case) is used to represent a logic 0.

TIMING OF BITS

At the receiver, the remote system reassembles the series of bits to form a frame and forwards the frame for processing by the link layer. A clock (timing signal) is needed to identify the boundaries between the bits (in practice it is preferable to identify the centre of the bit—since this usually indicates the point of maximum signal power). There are two systems used to providing timing:

1. Asynchronous communication (independent transmit & receive clocks)
2. Simple interface (limited data rate < 19.2 kbps)

TRANSMISSION MEDIA

There are two basic categories of transmission media:

- Guided media
  - Open wire
  - Twisted pair
  - Coaxial cable
  - Optical fiber
- Unguided Media
  - Wireless
    - Radiowaves
    - Microwave
    - Infrared
  - Satellite

1. Guided Media

Guided transmission media uses a cabling system that guides the data signals along a specific path. The data signals are bound by the cabling system. Guided media is also known as bound media. "Cabling" is meant in a generic sense, and is not meant to be interpreted as copper wire cabling only. There four basic types of guided media:

(*i*) Open wire (*ii*) Twisted pair

(*iii*) Coaxial cable (*iv*) Optical fiber

(*i*) *Open Wire.* Open Wire is traditionally used to describe the electrical wire strung along power poles. There is a single wire strung between poles. No shielding or protection from noise interference is used. We are going to extend the traditional definition of open wire to include any data signal path without shielding or protection from noise interference. This can include multi-conductor cables or single wires. This media is susceptible to a large degree of noise and interference and consequently not acceptable for data transmission except for short distances under 20 ft.

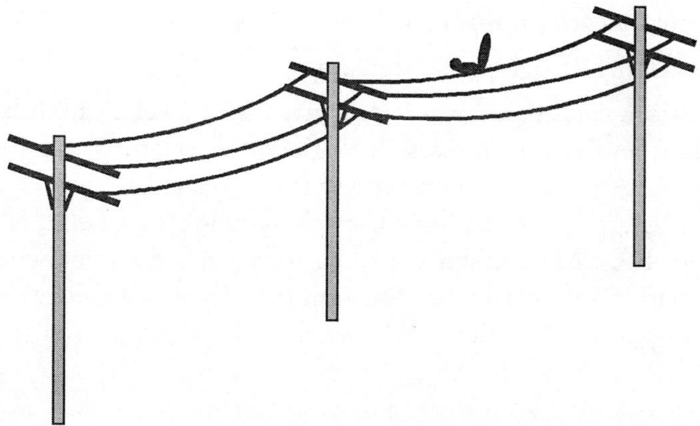

Figure 5.1 *Open Wire.*

(*ii*) *Twisted Pair.* The wires in twisted pair cabling are twisted together in pairs. Each pair would consist of a wire used for the +ve data signal and a wire used for the -ve data signal. Any noise that appears on 1 wire of the pair would occur on the other wire. Because the wires are opposite polarities, they are 180 degrees out of phase (180 degrees—phasor definition of opposite polarity). When the noise appears on both wires, it cancels or nulls itself out at the receiving end. Twisted pair cables are most effectively used in systems that use a balanced line method of transmission: polar line coding (Manchester encoding) as opposed to uni-polar line coding (TTL logic).

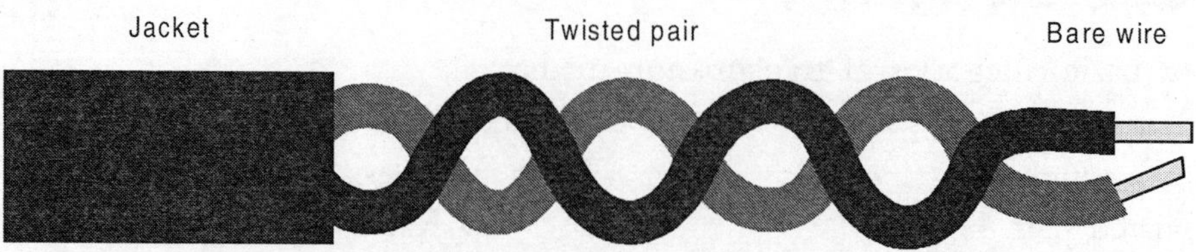

Figure 5.2 *Unshielded Twisted Pair.*

The degree of reduction in noise interference is determined specifically by the number of turns per foot. Increasing the number of turns per foot reduces the noise interference. To further improve noise rejection, a foil or wire braid shield is woven around the twisted pairs. This "shield" can be woven around individual pairs or around a multi-pair conductor (several pairs).

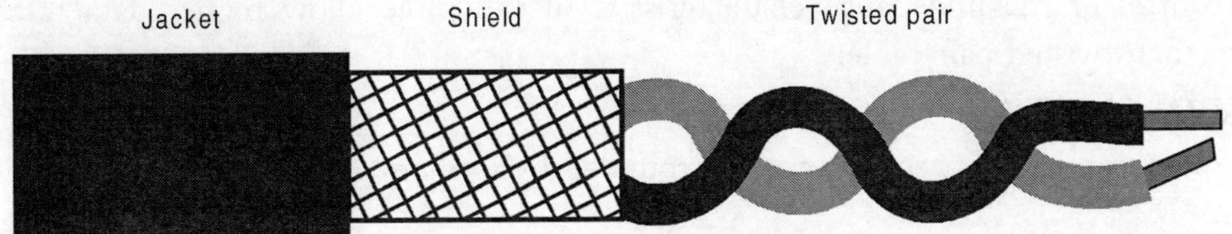

Figure 5.3 *Shielded Twisted Pair.*

Cables with a shield are called Shielded Twisted Pair and commonly abbreviated STP. Cables without a shield are called Unshielded Twisted Pair or UTP. Twisting the wires together results in a characteristic impedance for the cable. A typical impedance for UTP is 100 ohm for Ethernet 10BaseT cable.

UTP or Unshielded Twisted Pair cable is used on Ethernet 10BaseT and can also be used with token ring. It uses the RJ line of connectors (RJ45, RJ11, etc.) STP or Shielded Twisted Pair is used with the traditional token ring cabling or ICS-IBM cabling system. It requires a custom connector. IBM STP (Shielded Twisted Pair) has a characteristic impedance of 150 ohms.

(iii) Coaxial Cable. Coaxial cable was invented in 1929 and first used commercially in 1941. AT and T established its first cross-continental coaxial transmission system in 1940. Depending on the carrier technology used and other factors, twisted pair copper wire and optical fiber are alternatives to coaxial cable.

Coaxial cable is the kind of copper cable used by cable TV companies between the community antenna and user homes and businesses. Coaxial cable is sometimes used by telephone companies from their central office to the telephone poles near users. It is also widely installed for use in business and corporation Ethernet and other types of local area network. Coaxial cable is called "coaxial" because it includes one physical channel that carries the signal surrounded (after a layer of insulation) by another concentric physical channel, both running along the same axis. The outer channel serves as a ground. Many of these cables or pairs of coaxial tubes can be placed in a single outer sheathing and, with repeaters, can carry information for a great distance.

Coaxial cable consists of 2 conductors. The inner conductor is held inside an insulator with the other conductor woven around it providing a shield. An insulating protective coating called a jacket covers the outer conductor.

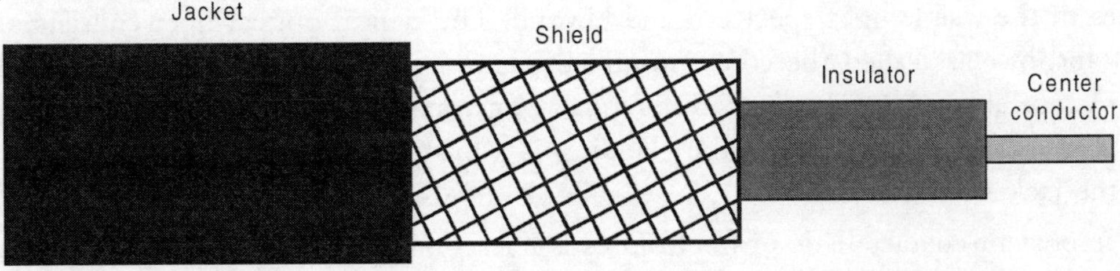

Figure 5.4 *Coax Cable.*

The outer shield protects the inner conductor from outside electrical signals. The distance between the outer conductor (shield) and inner conductor plus the type of material used for insulating the inner conductor determine the cable properties or impedance. Typical impedances for coaxial cables are 75 ohms for cable TV, 50 ohms for Ethernet thinnet and thicknet. The excellent control of the impedance characteristics of the cable allow higher data rates to be transferred than twisted pair cable.

Baseband Coaxial Cable

The medium consists of a copper core surrounded by insulating material and a braided outer conductor.

- The term base-band indicate it is for digital transmission.
- Physical connection consists of a metal pin touching the copper core. There are two possible ways.
  - — Use of a T connector. This is often used with thin Ethernet cable.
  - — Use of a vampire tap in which a metal pin is inserted into the core. A cliper-type of device is used to hold the connection. This is often used with thick Ethernet cable.
- Data rates of a few 10 s of Mbps to a couple of Gbps are possible.

Broadband Coaxial Cable

A similar type of cable, but the bandwidth is wider than 4 kHz. (In computer networking world, any network using analog transmission is considered as broadband).

- Typical bandwidth of 300 MHz.
- Operate at distances up to 100 km.
- Use analog signal.
- Often the traffic is one-way.
- Requires amplifiers to boost signal strength.
- Cable TV uses this technology, so the infra-structure is already there.

Two types of systems have emerged.

— Dual cable systems use two cables, one for each direction.

— Mid-split systems use one cable, but the frequency is divided such that one portion of the frequency is used in one direction, the second is used for the other direction.

(*iv*) *Optical Fiber.* Optical fiber consists of thin glass fibers that can carry information at frequencies in the visible light spectrum and beyond. The typical optical fiber consists of a very narrow strand of glass called the core. Around the core is a concentric layer of glass called the cladding. A typical core diameter is 62.5 microns (1 micron = 10^{-6} meters). Typically cladding has a diameter of 125 microns. Coating the cladding is a protective coating consisting of plastic, it is called the jacket.

An important characteristic of fiber optics is refraction. Refraction is the characteristic of a material to either pass or reflect light. When light passes through a medium, it "bends" as it passes from one medium to the other. An example of this is when we look into a pond of water.

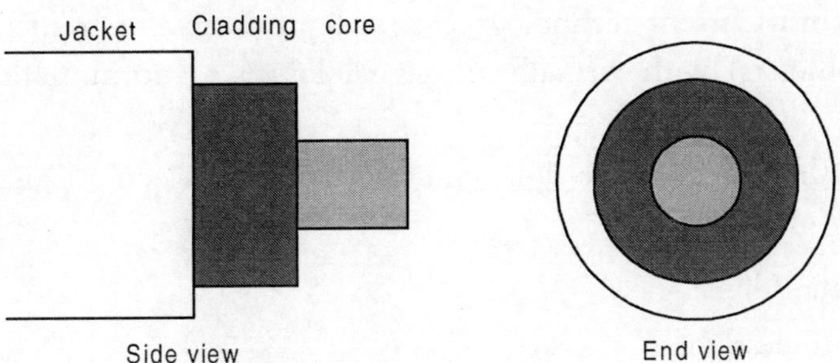

Figure 5.5 *Optical Fiber.*

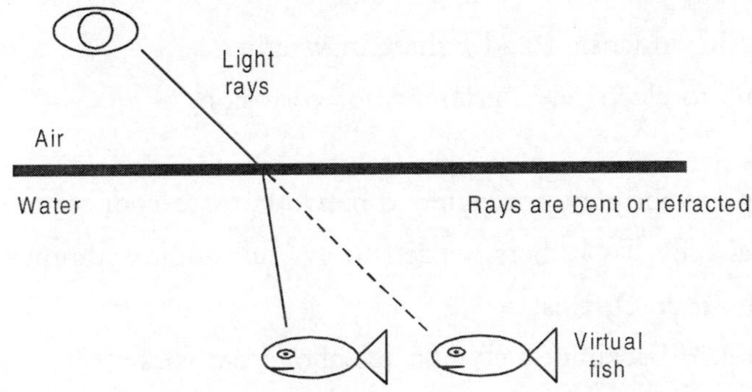

Figure 5.6 *Characteristic of Fiber Optics.*

If the angle of incidence is small, the light rays are reflected and do not pass into the water. If the angle of incident is great, light passes through the media but is bent or refracted.

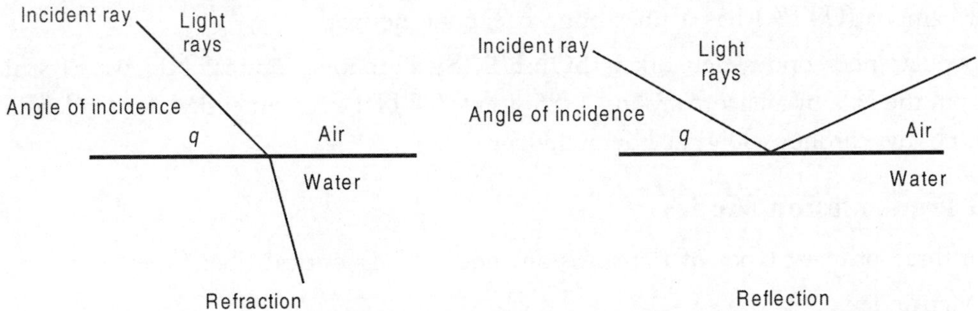

Figure 5.7 *Angle of Incidence.*

Optical fibers work on the principle that the core refracts the light and the cladding reflects the light. The core refracts the light and guides the light along its path. The cladding reflects any light back into the core and stops light from escaping through it.

In fiber optic technology, lights are used to transmit signals instead of electronics. At a fixed rate, the presence of the light means 1, the absence 0, for example.

Three components are required.

1. **Light source:** Typically a Light Emitting Diode (LED), or laser diode.

2. **Fiber medium:** Current technology carries light pulses for tremendous distance (*e.g.*, 100s of kilometers) with virtually no signal loss (*i.e.*, no amplifiers or repeaters are needed).
3. **Detector:** Which detects the light and converts it to electric signals.

Advantages:

1. High data rate, Gbps.
2. Low error rate, less than
3. Difficult to tap onto the network, so better security. In wire connection, it is difficult to know if somebody has a tap on it. In fiber, tapping is much more difficult.
4. Much thinner in dimension and lighter in weight.
5. Not susceptible to electrical interference or corrosion.

Disadvantages:

1. Difficult to tap (to add new computer to network, or to connect to a different network)
2. One way signal only. Two fibers needed to get full duplex communication.

Applications of Fiber Optics:

- Long-haul trunks—backbone network, telephone network
- Metropolitan trunks—without repeaters (average 8 miles in length)
- Rural exchanges trunks—link towns and villages
- Local loops—direct from central exchange to a subscriber
- Local area network—100 Mbps ring networks.

Our campus (UTPA) has a fiber optic backbone network.

A popular fiber optics network is SONET (Synchronous Optical NETwork) which was developed in the U.S. by Bellcore around 1985. Later CCITT recommended its standard in 1989, called SDH (Synchronous Digital Hierarchy).

Optical Transmission Modes

There are three primary types of transmission modes using optical fiber. They are:

1. Step index
2. Graded index
3. Single mode

1. *Step Index Mode.* Step index has a large core, so the light rays tend to bounce around inside the core, reflecting off the cladding. This causes some rays to take a longer or shorter path through the core. Some take the direct path with hardly any reflections while others bounce back and forth taking a longer path. The result is that the light rays arrive at the receiver at different times. The signal becomes longer than the original signal. LED light sources are used. Typical core : 62.5 microns.

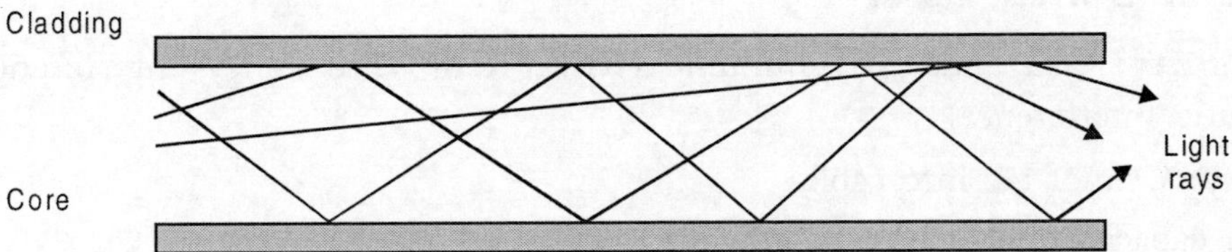

Figure 5.8 *Step Index Mode.*

2. *Graded Index Mode.* Graded index has a gradual change in the core's refractive index. This causes the light rays to be gradually bent back into the core path. This is represented by a curved reflective path in the attached drawing. The result is a better receive signal than with step index. LED light sources are used. Typical core: 62.5 microns.

   Both step index and graded index allow more than one light source to be used (different colors simultaneously), so multiple channels of data can be run at the same time!
3. *Single Mode.* Single mode has separate distinct refractive indexes for the cladding and core. The light ray passes through the core with relatively few reflections off the cladding. Single mode is used for a single source of light (one color) operation. It requires a laser and the core is very small : 9 microns.

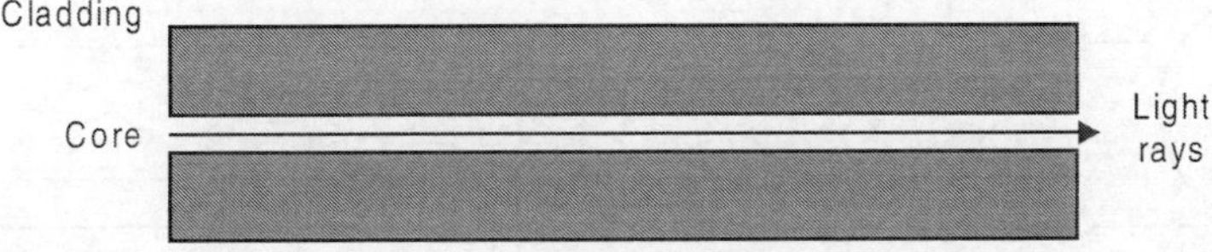

Figure 5.9 *Cladding.*

Comparison of Optical Fibers

We don't use frequency to talk about speed any more, we use wavelengths instead. The wavelength of light sources is measured in nanometers or 1 billionth of a meter.

Indoor cable specifications:

- LED (Light Emitting Diode) light source
- 3.5 dB/Km attenuation (loses 3.5 dB of signal per kilometer)
- 850 nM—wavelength of light source
- Typically 62.5/125 (core dia/cladding dia)
- Multimode—can run many light sources.

Outdoor cable specifications:

- Laser light source
- 1 dB/Km attenuation (loses 1 dB of signal per kilometer)
- 1170 nM—wavelength of light source
- Mono-mode (single mode)

Advantages of Optical Fiber

Noise immunity: RFI and EMI immune (RFI—Radio Frequency Interference, EMI—Electromagnetic Interference)

Security: Cannot tap into cable.

- Large capacity due to BW (bandwidth)
- No corrosion
- Longer distances than copper wire
- Smaller and lighter than copper wire
- Faster transmission rate

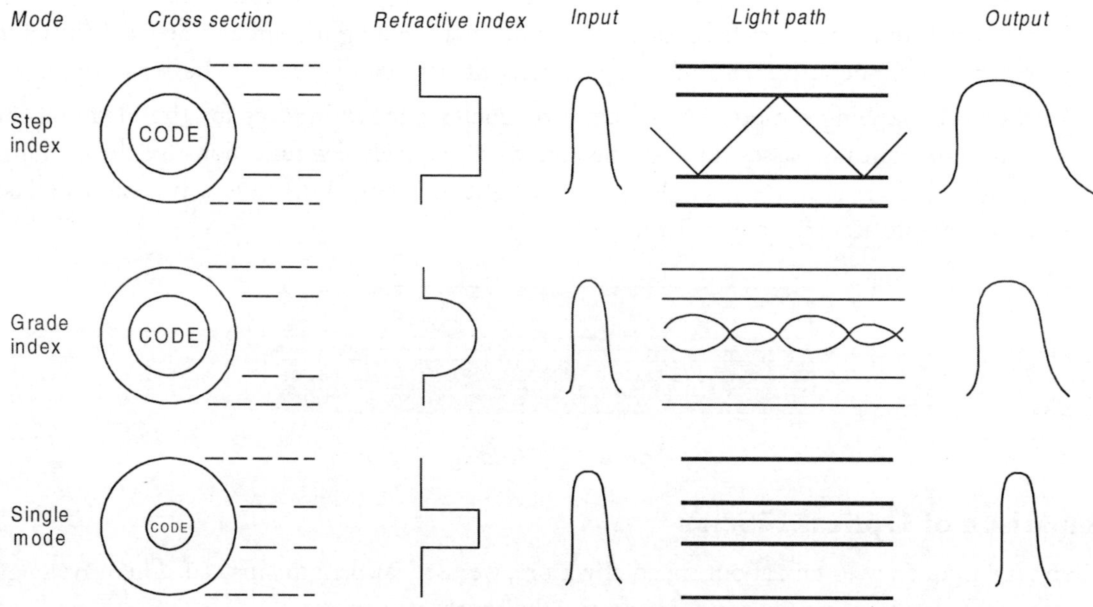

Figure 5.10 *Comparison of Optical Fibers.*

Disadvantages of Optical Fiber

- Physical vibration will show up as signal noise
- Limited physical arc of cable. Bend it too much and it will break
- Difficult to splice

The cost of optical fiber is a trade-off between capacity and cost. At higher transmission capacity, it is cheaper than copper. At lower transmission capacity, it is more expensive.

Media Versus Bandwidth

The following table 5.1 compares the usable bandwidth of the different guided transmission media.

Table 5.1 Bandwidths of Transmission Media

Cable Type	*Bandwidth*
Open cable	0 – 5 MHz
Twisted pair	0 – 100 MHz
Coaxial cable	0 – 600 MHz
Optical fiber	0 – 1 GHz

HISTORY OF FIBER OPTIC TECHNOLOGY

People have used light to transmit information for hundreds of years. However, it was not until the 1960s, with the invention of the laser, that widespread interest in optical (light) systems for data communications began. The invention of the laser prompted researchers to study the potential of fiber optics for data communications, sensing, and other applications. Laser systems could send a much larger amount of data than telephone, microwave, and other electrical systems. The first experiment with the laser involved letting the laser beam transmit freely through the air. Researchers also conducted experiments letting the laser beam transmit through different types of waveguides. Glass fibers, gas-filled pipes, and tubes with focusing lenses are examples of optical waveguides. Glass fibers soon became the preferred medium for fiber optic research.

Initially, the very large losses in the optical fibers prevented coaxial cables from being replaced. Loss is the decrease in the amount of light reaching the end of the fiber. Early fibers had losses around 1,000 dB/km making them impractical for communications use. In 1969, several scientists concluded that impurities in the fiber material caused the signal loss in optical fibers. The basic fiber material did not prevent the light signal from reaching the end of the fiber. These researchers believed it was possible to reduce the losses in optical fibers by removing the impurities. By removing the impurities, construction of low-loss optical fibers was possible.

There are two basic types of optical fibers, multimode fibers and single mode fibers. In 1970, corning glass works made a multimode fiber with losses under 20 dB/km.

This same company, in 1972, made a high silica-core multimode optical fiber with 4 dB/km minimum attenuation (loss). Currently, multimode fibers can have losses as low as 0.5 dB/km at wavelengths around 1300 nm. Single mode fibers are available with losses lower than 0.25 dB/km at wavelengths around 1500 nm.

Advantages and Disadvantages of Fiber Optics

Fiber optic systems have many attractive features that are superior to electrical systems. These include improved system performance, immunity to electrical noise, signal security, and improved safety and electrical isolation.

Other advantages include reduced size and weight, environmental protection, and overall system economy. Here, details are given of the main advantages of fiber optic systems.

Advantages of Fiber Optics

- System performance
- Greatly increased bandwidth and capacity
- Lower signal attenuation (loss)
- Immunity to electrical noise
- Immune to noise (electromagnetic interference [EMI] and radio-frequency interference [RFI]).
- No crosstalk
- Lower bit error rates
- Signal security
- Difficult to tap
- Nonconductive (does not radiate signals) electrical isolation
- No common ground required
- Freedom from short circuit and sparks
- Size and weight
- Reduced size and weight cables
- Environmental protection
- Resistant to radiation and corrosion
- Resistant to temperature variations
- Improved ruggedness and flexibility
- Less restrictive in harsh environments
- Overall system economy
- Low per-channel cost
- Lower installation cost

PARTS OF A FIBER OPTIC LINK

Fiber optic transmission uses the same basic elements as copper-based transmission systems: A transmitter, a receiver, and a medium by which the signal is passed from one to the other, in this case, optical fiber. Figure 5.11 illustrates these elements.

The transmitter uses an electrical interface to encode the use information through AM, FM or digital modulation. A laser diode or an LED do the encoding to allow an optical output of 850 nm, 1310 nm, or 1550 nm (typically).

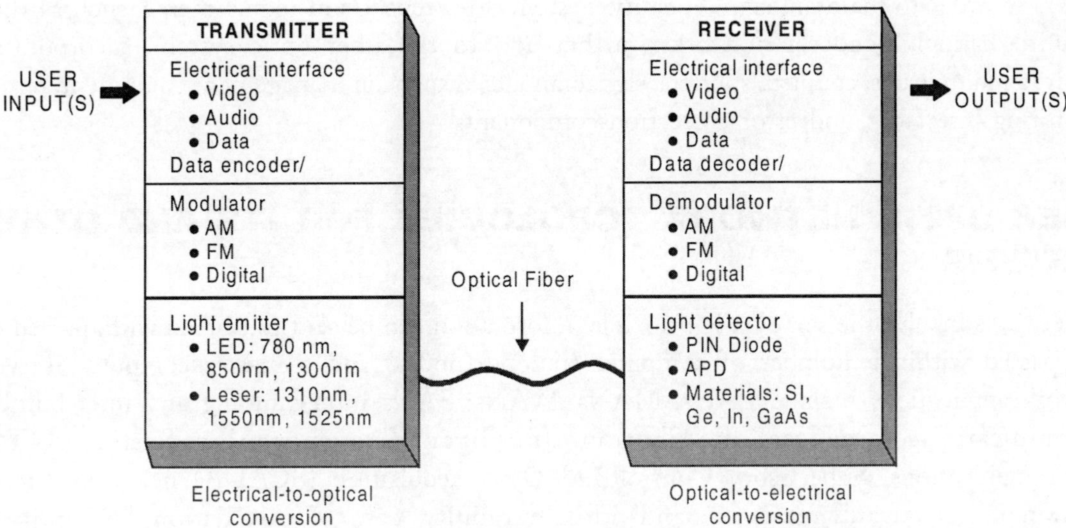

Figure 5.11 *Elements of a Fiber Optic Link.*

The optical fiber connects the transmitter and the receiver. This fiber may be either single-mode or multimode. The fiber consists of three main regions, as illustrated in (figure 5.12). The core, the center of the fiber, actually carries the light. The cladding surround the core in a glass with a different refractive index than the core, allowing the light to be confined in the fiber core. A coating or buffer, typically plastic, provides strength and protection to the optical fiber.

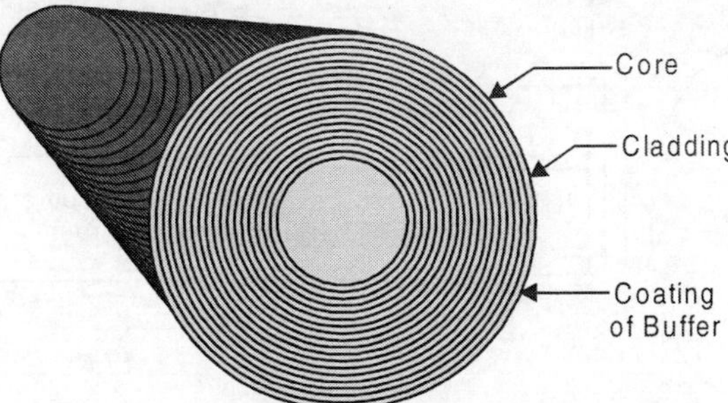

Figure 5.12 *Cross-section of an Optical Fiber.*

The receiver uses either a PIN photodiode or an ADP to receive the optical signal and convert it back into an electrical signal. A data demodulator converts the data back into its original electrical form. These elements comprise the simplest link, but other elements may also appear in a fiber optic transmission system.

For example, the addition of WDM components allows two separate signals to be joined into a composite signal for transmission, and then can be separated into their original signals at the receive end. Other wavelength-division multiplexing techniques allow up to eight signals (CWDM) or more (DWDM) to be combined onto a single fiber.

Long distance fiber optic transmission leads to further system complexity. Many long-haul transmission systems require signal regenerators, signal repeaters, or optical amplifier such as

EDFAs in order to maintain signal quality. System drop/repeat/add requirements, such as those in multi-channel broadcast networks, further add to the fiber optic system, incorporating add-drop multiplexers, couplers/splitters, signal fanouts, dispersion management equipment, remote monitoring interfaces, and error-correction components.

FIBER OPTIC NETWORK TOPOLOGIES FOR ITS AND OTHER SYSTEMS

All networks involve the same basic principle: information can be sent to, shared with, passed on, or bypassed within a number of computer stations (nodes) and a master computer (server). Network applications include LANs, MANs, WANs, SANs intra-building and inter-building communications, broadcast distribution, Intelligent Transportation Systems (ITS), telecommunications, Supervisory Control and Data Acquisition (SCADA) networks, etc. In addition to its advantages (*i.e.*, bandwidth, durability, ease of installation, immunity to EMI/RFI and harsh environmental conditions, long-term economies, etc.), optical fiber better accommodates today's increasingly complex network architectures than copper alternatives. Figure 5.13 illustrates the interconnection between these types of networks.

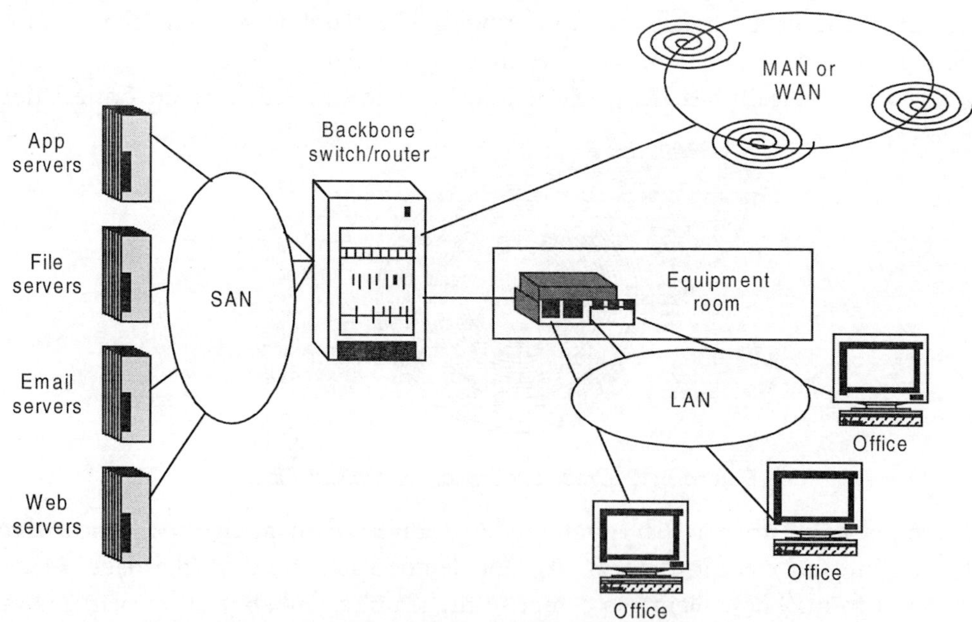

Figure 5.13 *Interconnections between Different Network Types.*

Networks can be configured in a number of topologies. These include a bus, with or without a backbone, a star network, a ring network, which can be redundant and/or self-healing, or some combination of these. Each topology has its strengths and weaknesses, and some network types work better for one application while another application would use a different network type. Local, metropolitan, or wide area networks generally use a combination, or "mesh" topology.

BUS NETWORK

A bus network topology, also called a daisy-chain topology has each computer directly connected on a main communication line. One end has a controller, and the other end has a terminator. Any computer that wants to talk to the main computer must wait its turn for access to the transmission line. In a straight network topology, only one computer can communicate at a time. When a computer uses the network, the information is sent to the controller, which then sends the information down the line of computers until it reaches the terminating computer. Each computer in the line receives the same information. Figure 5.14 illustrates a bus network topology.

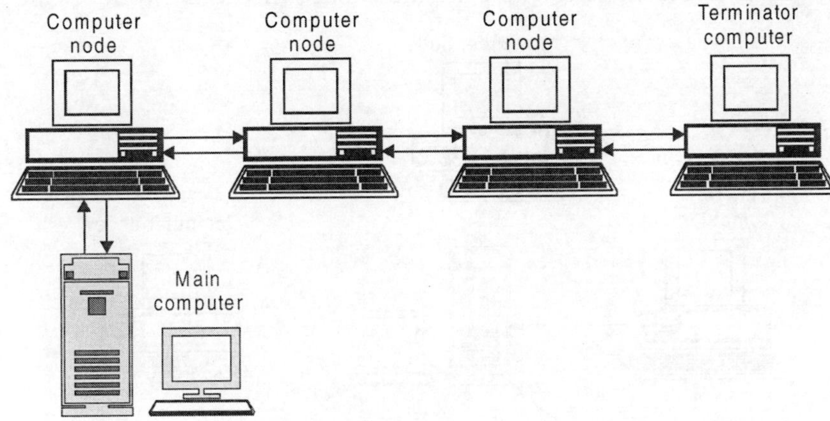

Figure 5.14 *Bus Network Topology.*

A bus network with a backbone operates in the same fashion, but each computer has an individual connection to the network. A bus network with a backbone offers greater reliability than a simple bus topology. In a simple bus, if one computer in the network goes down, the network is broken. A backbone adds reliability in that the loss of one computer does not disrupt the entire network. Figure 5.15 illustrates this topology with a backbone.

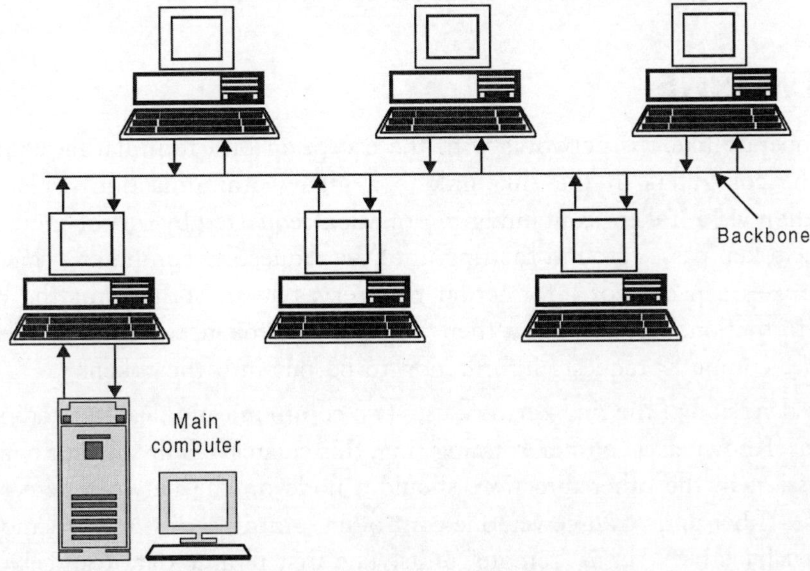

Figure 5.15 *Bus Network with Backbone.*

STAR NETWORKS

Star networks incorporate multi-port star couplers in to achieve the topology. Once again, a main controlling computer or computer server interconnects with all the other computers in the network. As with the bus topology with a backbone, the failure of one computer node does not cause a failure in the network. Figure 5.16 illustrates a star network topology.

Both the bus and the star network topologies use a central computer that controls the system inputs and outputs. Also called a server, this computer has external connections, to the Internet for example, as well as connections to the computer nodes in the network.

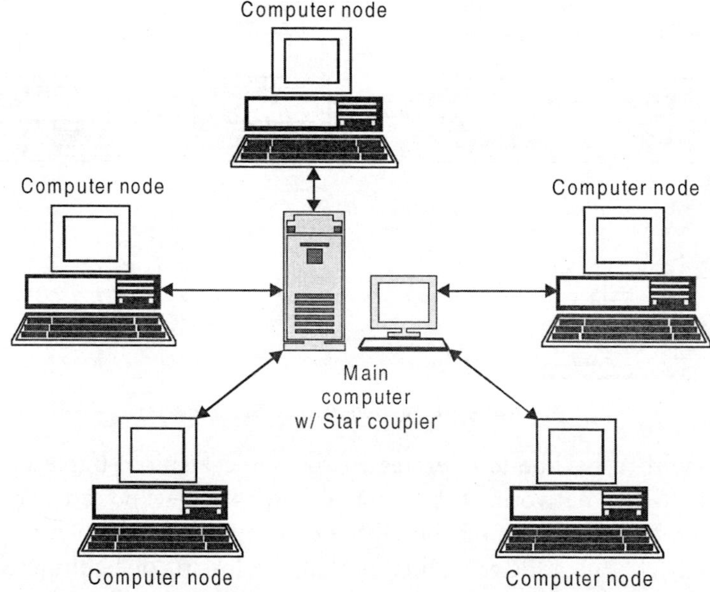

Figure 5.16 *Star Network Topology.*

RING NETWORKS

Ring networks operate like bus networks with the exception of a terminating computer. In this configuration, the computers in the ring link to a main communication cable. The network receives information via a "token" containing information requested by one or more computers on the network. The token passes around the ring until the requesting computer(s) have received the data. The token uses a packet of information that serves as an address for the computer that requested the information. The computer then "empties" the token, which continues to travel the ring until another computer requests information to be put into the token.

An advanced version of the ring network uses two communication cables sending information in both directions. Known as a counter-rotating ring, this creates a fault tolerant network that will redirect transmission in the other direction, should a node on the network detect a disruption. This network uses fiber optic transceiver, one controlling unit in set in "master" mode along with several nodes that have been set as "remote" units. The first remote data transceiver receives the transmission from the master unit and retransmits it to the next remote unit as well as transmitting it back to the master unit. An interruption in the signal line on the first ring is bypassed via the second ring, allowing the network to maintain integrity.

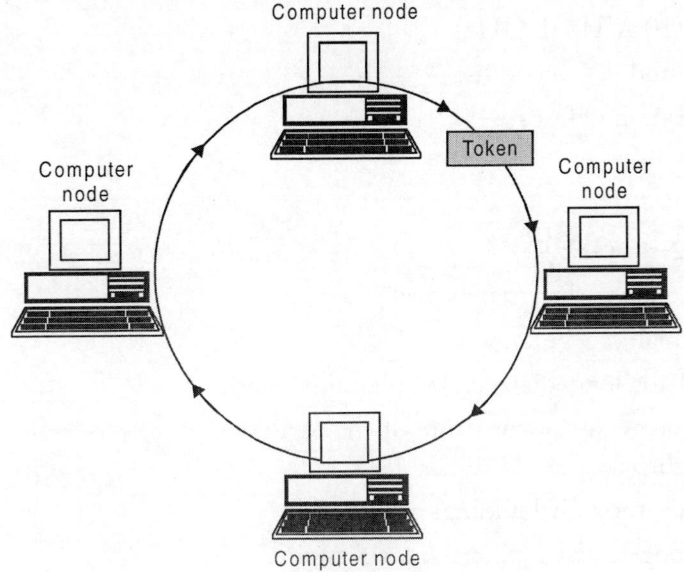

Figure 5.17 *Token Ring Network Topology.*

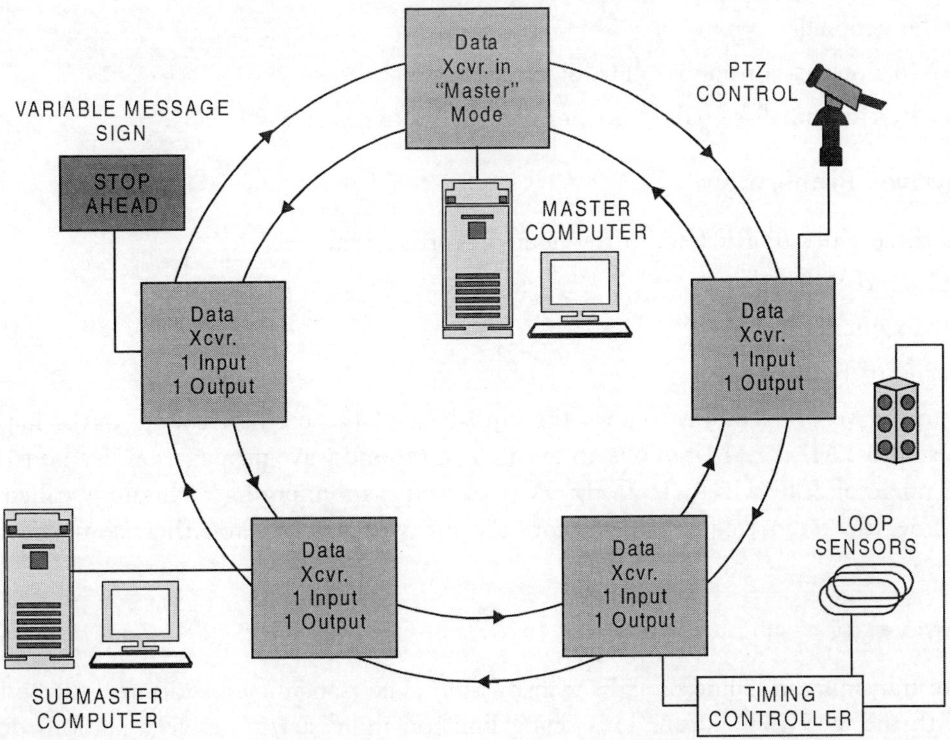

Figure 5.18 *Self-healing Ring Topology.*

2. Unguided Media

Unguided transmission media is data signals that flow through the air. They are not guided or bound to a channel to follow. They are classified by the type of wave propagation as given below:

- **Radiowaves** (30 MHz–1 GHz)
  - ★ Like radio and TV broadcast
  - ★ Can penetrate buildings
  - ★ Travel long distances
  - ★ Omnidirectional
- **Microwave** (2–40 GHz)
  - ★ Higher frequency than radiowaves
  - ★ Unidirectional–can be aimed
  - ★ Long used for long–distance telephone network
  - ★ Do not bend with the curvature of the earth, so tall towers and repeaters are needed (line-of-sight)
  - ★ Do not pass through buildings well
  - ★ Used for long-haul telephone transmission.
- **Infrared**
  - ★ Higher frequency than microwave
  - ★ Directional
  - ★ Do not pass through solid objects
  - ★ Used for small signal–room network or indoor wireless LANs.

• Radiowaves Propagation

There are three types of RF (Radio frequency) propagation:

- Ground Wave
- Ionospheric
- Line of Sight (LOS)

Ground wave propagation follows the curvature of the earth. Ground waves have carrier frequencies upto 2 MHz . AM radio is an example of ground wave propagation. Radio frequencies are in the range of 300 kHz to 10 GHz. We are seeing an emerging technology called wireless LANs. Some use radio frequencies to connect the workstations together, some use infrared technologies.

• Microwave

Microwave transmission is line of sight transmission. The transmitting station must be in visible contact with the receiving station. This sets a limit on the distance between stations depending on the local geography. Typically the line of sight due to the earth's curvature is only 50 km to the horizon. Repeater stations must be placed so that data signal can hop, skip and jump across the country.

Mircowaves operate of high operating frequencies of 3 to 10 GHz. This allows them to carry large quantities of data due to their large bandwidth.

• Infrared Transmission

Infrared communication is now common as a means of wireless communication between devices. It will not penetrate buildings and therefore is secure.

Used for very short line of sight transmission, remote car locking systems, wireless security alarms, remote TV channel changes etc.

It utilises a wide frequency band, 2 to 40 GHz but is susceptible to attenuation and interferences. Attenuation can rise markedly in poor atmospheric conditions, *e.g.* rain but adversely affects the higher end of the frequency band which is only used for short distance transmission. Natural noise severally affects transmission frequencies below 2 GHz.

REVIEW QUESTIONS

1. Name the two major categories of transmission media.
2. How do guided media differ from unguided media ?
3. What are the three major classes of guided media ?
4. What is the form of the signal in twisted-pair cable and coaxial cable ? How does this differ from the signal in fiber-optic cable ?
5. Give a use for each class of guided media.
6. What is the major advantage of shielded twisted-pair over unshielded twisted-pair cable ?
7. What is the significance of the twisting in twisted-pair cable ?
8. Why is coaxial cable superior to twisted-pair cable ?
9. What are the disadvantages of optical fiber as a transmission medium ?
10. Write short history of fiber optic technology.
11. What are the different topologies ?
12. Explain the various unguided media used in data communication.

❑❑❑

6 TELECOMMUNICATION

INTRODUCTION

Telecommunication is the technique of transmitting a message, from one point or place to another with the typical additional attribute of being bi-directional. In practice it also recognizes that something may be lost in the process; hence the term 'telecommunication' covers all forms of distance communication, including radio, telegraphy, television, telephony data communication and computer networking.

The elements of a telecommunication system are a transmitter, a medium (line) and possibly a channel imposed upon the medium, and receiver. The transmitter is a device that transforms or encodes the message into a physical phenomenon; the signal. The transmission medium, by its physical nature, is likely to modify or degrade the signal on its path from the transmitter to the receiver. The receiver has a decoding mechanism capable of recovering the message within certain limits of signal degradation. In some cases, the final "receiver" is the human eye and/or ear (or in some extreme cases other sense organs) and the recovery of the message is done by the brain.

Telecommunication can be point-to-point, point-to-multipoint or broadcasting, which is a particular form of point-to-multipoint that goes only from the transmitter to the receivers. The art of the telecommunications engineer is to analyse the physical properties of the line or transmission media, and the statistical properties of the message in order to design the most effective encoding and decoding mechanisms.

When systems are designed to communicate through human sense organs (mainly vision and hearing), physiological and psychological characteristics of human perception will be taken into account. This has important economic implications and engineers will research what defects may be tolerated in the signal yet not affect the viewing or hearing experience too badly.

EXAMPLES OF HUMAN (TELE) COMMUNICATIONS

In a simplistic example, take a normal conversation between you and a friend. The message is the sentence, your mind decides to communicate to your friend. The transmitter is the language areas in your brain, the motor cortex, your vocal cords, the larynx, and your mouth that produce those sounds called speech. The signal is the sound waves that can be identified as speech. The channel is the air carrying those sound waves, and all the acoustic properties of the space you are in: echoes, ambient noise, reverberation. Between you and your friend (the receiver), may be other technologies that do or do not introduce their own distortions of the original vocal signal (*e.g.*, telephone, HAM radio, IP phone, etc.) The penultimate receiver is your friend's ear, the auditory nerve, the language areas in your friend's brain that will make the difference between your voice and the sound of a car passing by, and decode your speech into, hopefully, the same sentence.

The car passing by is an example of an important property of the channel called noise. Another important aspect of the channel is called the bandwidth, and you would become very aware of the effects of a limited bandwidth if you were now talking to your friend on a telephone or a walkie-talkie.

TELEPHONE NETWORK

The telephone system has been developed over many years and has gone through many incremental evolutionary steps. The traditional service of the telephone network has been for voice communication and only recently the network has been used to support the high amount of data transfer we are currently experiencing. For cost effective voice communications it has been identified that the humans can communicate at frequencies between 300 Hz to 3500 Hz. Though we can hear and speak at higher and lower frequencies, voice communications between 300 Hz and 3500 Hz are clear and efficient for the telephone network to transmit and receive. A voice channel goes from 0 Hz to 4000 Hz and was developed to avoid any overlapping to any other adjacent voice channels.

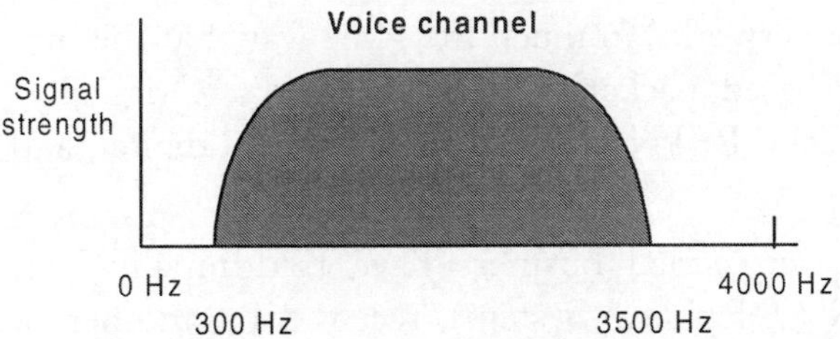

Figure 6.1 *Telephone Voice Channel.*

Through the telephone network development it has been discovered that it is more efficient to transmit a voice channel in a digital form. In a digital form the voice channel can be routed to its destination with very low noise, higher reliability and more cost effectiveness. To do this the voice channel is converted to digital by an Analog to Digital Converter (A/D converter or ADC) at the central office. The Central Office (CO) is the location in your area that the 2-Wires that come from your house called tip and ring are terminated. Once the voice channel has been digitized it is transmitted over the network to the CO of the number you called. At this remote CO the voice channel is reconstructed back into an analog form so that remote person can understand it. This transformation back to analog is done by a digital to analog converter also know as a D/A converter or DAC.

One important point to know is that the A/D converter samples the voice channel at twice the frequency of the voice channel; that is at 8 kHz. The reason the sampling is done at twice the original signals frequency is due to a law called the Nyquist rate, which states to digitize a waveform and have enough information to reconvert it back to the an analog waveform one must sample the original waveform at no less than twice the frequency of the original waveform. Also each sample is identified by 8 unique bits that represent 256 different states. 8 bits sampled 8000 times a second is equal to 64 kbps.

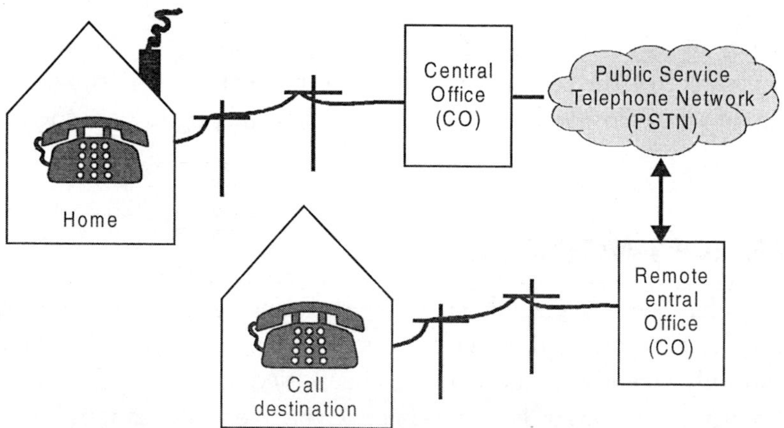

Figure 6.2 *The Traditional Communication Process.*

PUBLIC SWITCHED TELEPHONE NETWORK

The Public Switched Telephone Network (PSTN) is the concatenation of the world's public circuit switched telephone networks, in much the same way that the internet is the concatenation of the world's public IP-based packet-switched networks. Originally a network of fixed-line analog telephone systems, the PSTN is now almost entirely digital, and now includes mobile as well as fixed telephones.

Homeworking and very small business have traditionally been supported by modem connection to the PSTN (Telephone System), received by another modem at the other end. Requires digital signals to be converted to analogue and then back to the digital at the receiver.

Today's modems can handle a maximum transmission rate of 56 Kbps using complex compression techniques but upload transmission rates can be much less. The actual amount of information transferred is much less than the theoretical maximum.

The PSTN is largely governed by technical standards created by the ITU-T, and uses E.163/ E.164 addresses (known more commonly as telephone numbers) for addressing.

The basic digital circuit in the PSTN is a 64-kilobit-per-second channel, originally designed by Bell labs, called a "DS0" or digital signal 0. To carry a typical phone call from a calling party to a called party, the audio sound is digitized at an 8 kHz sample rate using 8-bit pulse code modulation.

The DS0's are the basic granularity at which switching takes place in a telephone exchange. DS0's are also known as time-slots because they are multiplexed together in a time-division fashion. Multiple DS0's are multiplexed together on higher capacity circuits, such that 24 DS0's make a DS1 signal, which when carried on copper is the well-known, T-carrier system, T1 (the European equivalent is an E1, containing 32–64 kbit/s channels). In modern networks, this multiplexing is moved as close to the end user as possible, usually into cabinets at the roadside in residential areas, or into large business premises.

The time-slots are conveyed from the initial multiplexer to the exchange over a set of equipment collectively known as the access network. The access network and inter-exchange transport of the PSTN use Synchronous Optical Transmission (SONET and SDH) technology, although some parts still use the older PDH technology.

Within the access network, there are a number of reference points defined. Most of these are of interest mainly to ISDN but one—the V reference point—is of more general interest. This is the reference point between a primary multiplexer and an exchange. The protocols at this reference point were standardised in ETSI areas as the V5 interface.

Only the very oldest and most backward parts of the telephone network still use analog technology for anything other than the last mile loop to the end user, and in recent years digital services have been increasing rolled out to end users using services such as DSL and ISDN.

Advantages

There are following advantages of PSTN.

- Cheap equipment
- Uses ordinary telephone connection
- Local call charges for internet connection.

Disadvantages

There are following disadvantages of PSTN.

- Low bandwidth for multimedia
- Ties up the telephone line
- Need an ISP to connect to the Internet.

ARCHITECTURE AND CONTEXT

In the 1970s the telecommunications industry conceived that digital services would follow much the same pattern as voice services, and conceived a vision of end-to-end circuit switched services, known as the Broadband Integrated Services Digital Network (B-ISDN). The B-ISDN vision has been overtaken by the disruptive technology of the Internet.

Many observers believe that the long term future of the PSTN is to be just one application of the Internet—however, the Internet has some way to go before this transition can be made. The quality of service guarantee is one aspect that needs to be improved on in the voice over IP technology.

There are a number of large private telephone networks which are not linked to the PSTN, usually for military purposes. There are also private networks run by large companies which are linked to the PSTN only through limited gateways, like a large PABX system.

IMPORTANCE OF NETWORK IN TELEPHONES

Telephones and networking work hand in hand. The telecommunications industry has been gradually integrating with the computer industry and the computer industry has been gradually integrating with the telecommunications industry. The common goal is to join distantly located local area networks into Metropolitan and Wide Area Networks (MANs and WANs).

VOICE CHANNELS

When we think of telecommunications, the first thing that comes to mind is telephone systems and the phone at home. Talking to someone on the phone uses voice channels.

We use voice channels for modem communications to connect to BBSs (Bulletin Board Services) or to connect to the Internet. We also use voice channels to connect LANs using remote access. Due to the bandwidth limits on voice channels, the data transfer rate is relatively slow.

Typical voice channel communication rates are: 300, 1200, 2400, 9600, 14.4 k, 19.2 k, 28.8 k, 33.6 k and 56 kbps (bits per second).

Voice Channel Constraints

Due to the limited Bandwidth (BW) of the voice channel (0–4 kHz), we are limited to the amount of data that we can pass through the voice channel. The Nyquist Theorem addresses this limitation.

DATA CHANNELS

Data channels are dedicated lines for communicating digitized voice and data. At the end of 1996, there was a major milestone when more data was communicated in North America's telecommunications system than voice.

Data channels are special communications channels provided by "common carriers" such as Telus, Sprint, Bell Canada, AT and T, etc. for transferring digital data. Data channels are also called "leased lines". They are "directly" connected: you don't have to dial a connection number. The connections are up and running 24 hours per day. They appear to work as if there were a wire running directly between the source and the destination. Typical transfer rates for data channels are: 56 k, 128 k, 1.544 M, 2.08 M, 45 M and 155 Mbps.

Common carriers charge for data connections by:

1. The amount of data transferred (megabytes per month)
2. The transfer rate (bits per second)
3. The amount of use (time per month)

ADSL—ASYMMETRICAL DIGITAL SUBSCRIBER LINE

Asymmetrical Digital Subscriber Line (ADSL) uses the existing analog local loop lines for digital data transfer (to and from the home). It is asymmetrical because the upstream transfer rate is slower than the downstream data rate. This means that the data transfer from the premise (home) to the CO is a different rate than the data transfer from the CO to the home.

The data transfer rate is adaptive. This means that, depending on the condition of the local loop lines, ADSL will automatically compensate (*i.e.,* find the fastest transfer rate possible). The range for upstream data transfer is from 64 kbps to 768 kbps. The range for downstream data transfers is from 1.5 Mbps to 8 Mbps. The reasoning for the asymmetrical transfer rate is that most users will be surfing the Internet; upstream requests tend to be small web page addresses. The downstream data consists of downloads of large graphic intensive web pages. Small upstream requests, larger downstream response.

The data transfer rate depends on the distance from the central office, the quality of the line, and the wire gauge. If the distance from the central office is 15,000 to 18,000 ft, then the maximum transfer rate is 1.5 Mbps. If the distance is 9,000 ft or less, the maximum transfer rate is 8 Mbps.

ADSL Standards

At the time of this writing, there are 3 competing standards for ADSL (shown below):

1. Carrierless phase modulation ADSL
2. Splitterless ADSL
3. Discrete multitone ADSL

Carrierless Phase Modulation (CAP) ADSL is a modulation technique similar to quadrature amplitude modulation. It provides echo cancellation, and overlaps upstream and downstream signals.

Splitterless ADSL (also called ADSL Lite, G.Lite, PnP ADSL, Universal ADSL) has a lower transmitting rate, and is easier to implement.

DMT—Discrete multi-tone is an ANSI T1.413 standard that uses a broadband modem (covering the 4 kHz to 2.2 MHz range). It has 256 channels of 4 kHz: each channel is assigned 15 bits of data to transfer. In addition, each channel is checked for signal quality, and bits are assigned accordingly. A poor responding channel may have less bits assigned, or none at all. DMT adjusts for the local loop line conditions, and attempts to make the fastest transfer rate possible.

ADSL OSI Model

ADSL is a physical layer protocol that covers the transmission of data and cabling requirements.

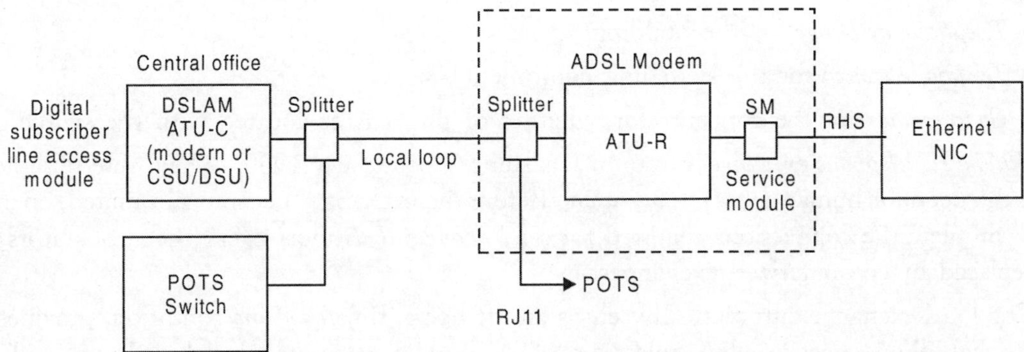

Figure 6.3 *ADSL Premise Equipment.*

ADSL shares the bandwidth of the local loop with the existing phone system. It does not require modification to the central office switch. Instead, a splitter combines the ADSL information with the POTS switch's analog information. At the central office end, the ADSL signal is sent to the Digital Subscriber Line Access Module (DSLAM), and then to a communication server.

At the premise end, another splitter separates the ADSL information from the analog information. An ADSL modem, called an ATU-R device, decodes the ADSL information, and sends it to the Service Module (SM). The service module translates it to Ethernet. In plain network terms, ADSL comes in and an Ethernet signal goes out for connection to a network interface card.

ADSL Advantages:

1. No expensive modification is required to CO switch.
2. Simple splitter splits ADSL signal from the existing analog line.
3. High bandwidth is available.
4. The POTS works regardless of ADS.
5. ADSL has competitive pricing versus other technologies.

ADSL Disadvantages:

1. The transfer rate depends on distance from the central office.
2. The presence of bridged taps and load coils on the local loop affect the transfer rate.
3. ADSL must be installed to test if it will work.
4. 25% of existing local loops will not work with ADSL.
5. There is an 18,000 ft distance limit from the central office.
6. There can be a bottleneck at the communication server (at the central office).

DIGITAL SWITCH

In U.S. and military telecommunication, a *digital switch* is a switch that performs time-division-multiplexed switching of digitized signals. All switches built since the 1970s are digital, so for practical purposes this is a distinction without a difference.

- *Telephone exchange* for the building
- *Telephone switch* for the switching equipment
- *Concentrator* for the concentrator, whether or not it is co-located with the switch

Automatic telephone exchanges came into existence in the early 1900s. They were designed to replace the need for human *telephone operators*. Before the exchanges became automated, operators had to complete the connections required for a *telephone call*. Almost everywhere, operators have been replaced by computerized exchanges.

The local exchange automatically senses an off hook (tip) *telephone* condition, provides dial tone to that phone, receives the pulses or DTMF tones generated by the phone, and then completes a connection to the called phone within the same exchange or to another distant exchange.

The exchange then maintains the connection until a party hangs up, and the connection is disconnected. Additional features, such as billing equipment, may also be incorporated into the exchange. Early exchanges used motors, shaft drives, rotating switches and relays. Some types of automatic exchanges were stronger, all relay, X-Y, panel and crossbar.

A *telephone switch* is the brains of an exchange. It is a device for routing calls from one *telephone* to another, generally as part of the public switched telephone network. They work by connecting two or more digital virtual circuits together, according to a dialed *telephone number*. Calls are setup between switches using the ISUP protocol, or one of its variants.

Digital switches encode the speech going on, in extremely minute time slices—many per second. At each time slice, a digital representation of the tone is made. The digits are then sent to the receiving end of the line, where the reverse process occurs, to produce the sound for the receiving phone. In other words, when you use a telephone, you are generally having your voice "encoded" and then reconstructed for the person on the other end. Your voice is very slightly delayed in the process (probably by only a small fraction of one second)—it is not "live", it is reconstructed—delayed only minutely.

Individual local loop telephone lines are connected to a remote concentrator. In many cases, the concentrator is co-located in the same building as the switch. The interface between concentrators and telephone switches has been standardised by ETSI as the V5 protocol.

Some telephone switches do not have concentrators directly connected to them, but rather are used to connect calls between other telephone switches. Usually a complex machine (or series of them) in a central exchange building, these are referred to as "carrier-level" switches or tandems.

Some telephone exchange buildings in small towns now house only remote switches, and are homed "parent" switch, usually several kilometres away. The remote switch is dependent on the parent switch for routing and number plan information. Unlike a digital loop carrier, a remote switch can route calls between local phones itself, without using trunks to the parent switch.

Telephone switches are usually owned and operated by a telephone service provider or "carrier" and located in their premises, but sometimes individual businesses or private commercial buildings will house their own switch, called a PBX, or Private Branch Exchange.

The Switch's Place in the System

Telephone switches are a small part of a large network. The majority of work and expense of the phone system is the wiring outside the central office, or the "outside plant".

Some companies use "pair gain" devices to provide telephone service to subscribers. These devices are used to provide service where existing copper facilities have been exhausted or by sitting in a neighborhood, can reduce the length of copper pairs, enabling digital services such as ISDN or DSL. Pair gain or Digital Loop Carriers (DLCs) are located outside the central office, usually in a large neighborhood distance from the CO.

DLCs are often referred to as Subscriber Loop Carriers (SLCs). Early SLC systems (SLC-1) used an analog carrier for transport between the remote site and the central office. Later systems (SLC-96, SLC-5) and other vendors' DLC products contain line cards that convert the analog signal to a digital signal (usually PCM). This digital signal can then be transported over copper, fiber, or other transport medium to the central office. Other components include ringing generators to provide ringing current and battery backups.

DLCs can be configured as universal (UDLCs) or integrated (IDLCS). Universal DLCs have two terminals, a Central Office Terminal (COT) and a Remote Terminal (RT), that function similarly. Both terminals interface with analog signals, convert to digital signals, and transport to the other side where the reverse is performed. Sometimes, the transport is handled by separate equipment. In an Integrated DLC, the COT is eliminated. Instead, the RT is connected digitally to equipment in the telephone switch. This reduces the total amount of equipment required. Switches are used in both local central offices and in long distance centers.

Switch Design

Long distance switches may use a slower, more efficient switch-allocation algorithm than central offices, because they have near 100% utilization of their input and output channels. Central offices have more than 90% of their channel capacity unused.

While traditionally, telephone switches connected physical circuits (*e.g.*, wire pairs), modern telephone switches use a combination of space—and time-division switching. In other words, each voice channel is represented by a time slot (say 1 or 2) on a physical wire pair (A or B). In order to connect two voice channels (say A1 and B2) together, the telephone switch interchanges the information between A1 and B2. It switches both the time slot and physical connection. To do this, it exchanges data between the time slots and connections 8000 times per second, under control of digital logic that cycles through electronic lists of the current connections. Using both types of switching makes a modern switch far smaller than either a space or time switch could be by itself.

The structure of a switch is an odd number of layers of smaller, simpler subswitches, interconnected by a web of wires that goes from each subswitch, to a set of the next layer of subswitches. In most designs, a physical (space) switching layer will alternate with a time switching layer. The layers are symmetric, because every call is symmetric (there's a connection in both directions). A space-division sub-switch uses digital multiplexers controlled by a cyclic memory. This takes physical space for the wiring.

A time-division sub-switch reads a complete cycle of time slots into a memory, and then writes it out in a different order, also under control of a cyclic computer memory. This causes some delay in the signal.

Switch Control Algorithms

The scarce resources in a telephone switch are the connections between layers of sub-switches. The control logic has to allocate these connections. The connections consist of both time slots and wires. The first thing to try is to search for a sub-switch that contains the needed in and out connections. There are two design paths to go if this simple search fails.

Fully-connected mesh network is one way to have enough switching fabric to assure that the pair-wise allocation will always succeed by building a fully-connected mesh network .This is the method usually used in central office switches, which have low utilization of their resources.

Topological Sort

Another way is to have a minimal switching fabric that still can theoretically make all the connections, and reorganize the switch's connections when a new connection won't fit.

If a sub-switch with the needed pair of connections can't be found, a pair of sub-switches will still have the necessary in and out, because there has to be at least the same number of connections between each layer of the switch, or else the switch will not be able to complete a full set of connections.

The pair of sub-switches' connections can be reorganized with a clever algorithm called a topological sort, so that all the existing connections continue, though they might migrate between the two different sub-switches. This is the method usually used in long distance switches, which have high utilization of their switching fabric.

A topological sort picks two sub-switches. One has a needed input connection. The other has a needed output connection. The connections of both sub-switches are placed in a list that also includes the desired new connection.

In the list, the basic trick is to trace connections. Starting from some input or output, the computer traces a connection to an output, then traces the other connection at that output to an input, and so forth, until it comes to an end. Each time it traces from input to output, the connection is placed in one sub-switch, and removed from the list. When it traces from output to input, the connection is placed in the other sub-switch and removed from the list. To complete correctly, tracing must begin with single connection inputs and outputs, and only then trace double-ended inputs and outputs, which might form loops.

Fault Tolerance

Composite switches are inherently fault-tolerant. If a sub-switch fails, the controlling computer can sense it during a periodic test. The computer marks all the connections to the sub-switch as "in use". This prevents new calls, and does not interrupt old calls that remain working. As calls are ended, the sub-switch then becomes unused. Some time later, a technician can replace the circuit board. The next test succeeds, the connections to the repaired sub-switch are marked "not in use", and the switch returns to full operation.

To prevent frustration with unsensed failures, all the connections between layers in the switch are allocated using first-in-first-out lists. That way, when a disgusted customer hangs up and redials, they will get a different set of connections and sub-switches. A last-in-first-out allocation of connections might cause a continuing string of very frustrating failures.

TELEPHONE STRUCTURE

The telephone network consists of your phone at home that is connected (by the local loop) to the central office. The central office is in turn connected to a hierarchical phone network. Worldwide, there are over 300 million (300,000,000) telephones—98% of them interconnected.

POTS—Plain Old Telephone Set

The POTS, or Plain Old Telephone Set, consists of these 5 sections:

1. Ringer unit
2. Hook switch
3. Dialer unit
4. Hybrid/Speech network
5. Hand set

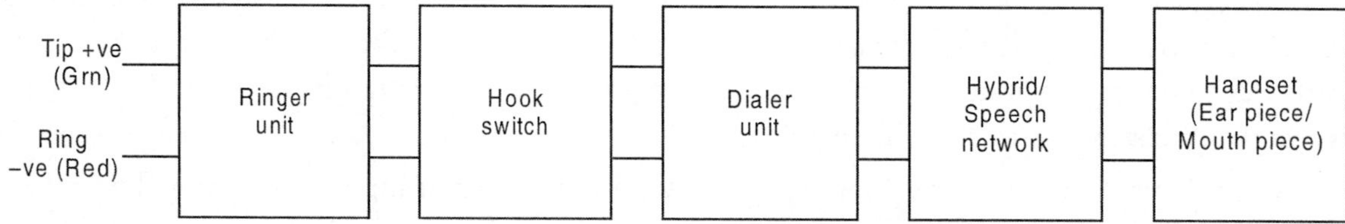

Figure 6.4 *Plain Old Telephone Set.*

The connection to the CO (Central Office) comprises only 2 wires: Tip and Ring. This connection is called the "local loop."

The Tip is +ve and colored green. The ring is -ve and colored red. If you look at a phone jack in your house, you will see that it is wired for 4 wires: Red, green, black and yellow. However, black and yellow are not normally used.

The black and yellow wires can be used for a second telephone line or they can be used for running a network physical layer protocol called Phonenet (by Farralon). Phonenet uses the black and yellow for network communications. It is for use with Appletalk, and is a replacement for Localtalk. It runs at the Localtalk speed of 230 Kbps, reasonable for small networks.

1. Ringer Unit

The ringer is a device that alerts you to an incoming call, it interprets the ringing voltage from the central office. Originally, the ringer was a electromagnetic bell. Today, though, most ringers are electronic devices.

The central office sends the following:

(*i*) 90 to 120 VAC ringing voltage

(*ii*) Frequency of 20 Hz

(*iii*) Cadence for North America is 2 sec ON or 4 sec Off

2. Hook Switch

The hook switch is activated by lifting the handset off of the cradle. The position of the hook switch determines whether the telephone is waiting for a call, or is actively using the line. The off-hook position informs the network of a request for use. The on-hook position releases the use of the network.

3. Dialer Unit

There are two types of dialer units: Rotary and touch tone. Rotary is the old "put your finger in the hole and spin" type. The rotary dial operates by toggling the hook switch on and off.

Touch tone is the modern method where 2 frequencies per push button are sent. Touch tone is a trade name; the correct name is DTMF (Dual Tone Multi Frequency).

4. Hybrid/Speech Network

The Hybrid/Speech Network performs these functions:

(*i*) It converts the Tx/Rx 4 wires from the handset to the 2 wires for the local loop.

(*ii*) It interfaces the signals from the dialer unit to the telephone line.

(*iii*) It provides auto line compensation for line length to keep the volume constant.

5. Handset

The Handset contains transducers that convert mechanical energy into electrical energy. The microphone converts speech into electrical energy while the diaphragm (or speaker) converts electrical signals into audible signals.

FUNCTIONS OF A TELEPHONE SET

There are following functions of a telephone set:

1. Request use of network from the CO (Central Office).
2. Inform you of the network status: Dial-tone, ringing, busy, fast busy (Talk Mail).
3. Informs CO of desired number.
4. Informs you when a call is incoming (phone rings).
5. Releases use of network when call is complete (hang-up).
6. Transmit speech on network and receives speech from distant caller.
7. Adjust power levels and compensates for line length.

LOCAL LOOPS

The local loop is the connection between the central office and the home or business. Two wires (1 pair) are run into every home. The pair does not go directly to the central office. Instead, it goes to those big green boxes—that you see on the street corners—called "Serving Area Interfaces" (SIA) . Large multi-conductor bundles of wires then go from there to the central office.

CENTRAL OFFICE

The central office provides the following functions:

It supplies the battery voltage for the telephone system. The on-hook voltage is 48 VDC +/– 2V. The off-hook voltage is – 6.5 VDC.

It supplies the ringing generator – 90 to 120 VAC, 20 Hz, 2 sec on/4 sec off

It supplies the busy signal (480 + 620 Hz, 0.5 sec on/0.5 sec off), dial tone (350 + 440 Hz) and fast busy (480 + 620 Hz, 0.2 sec on/ 0.3 sec off).

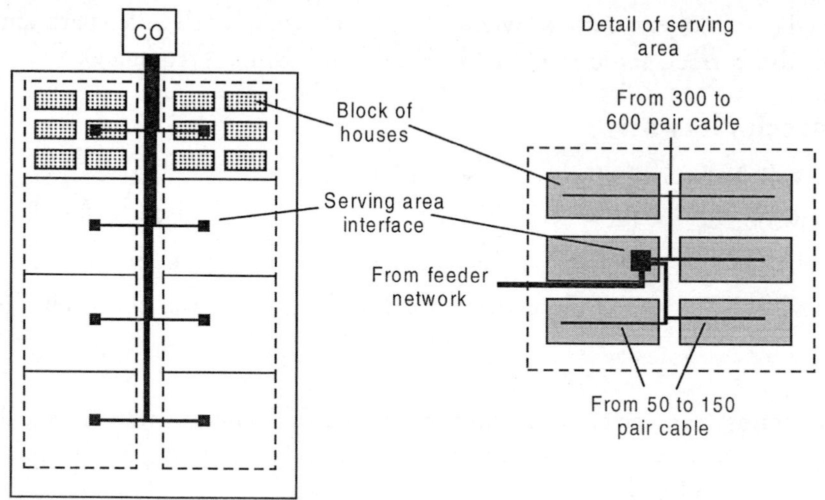

Figure 6.5 *Central Office.*

It has the digital switching gear that determines if the number is an interoffice call (local) or an intra-office call (Toll—long distance).

HIERARCHICAL PHONE NETWORKS

The PSTN (Public Switch Telephone Network) is divided into a hierarchical network. Here are the 5 classes of switching centers in North America:

Class Center	*Abbreviation*	*Symbol*	*Examples*	
1	Regional center	RC	□	2 in Canada: West-ReginaEast-Montreal
2	Sectional center	SC	△	Calgary serves Alberta
3	Primary center	PC	○	Edmonton
4	Toll center	TC	⊖	Drumheller
4b	Toll point	TP	⊖	Rainbow lake
5	Central office (Local loop)	CO	●	284-xxxx

In the following example:

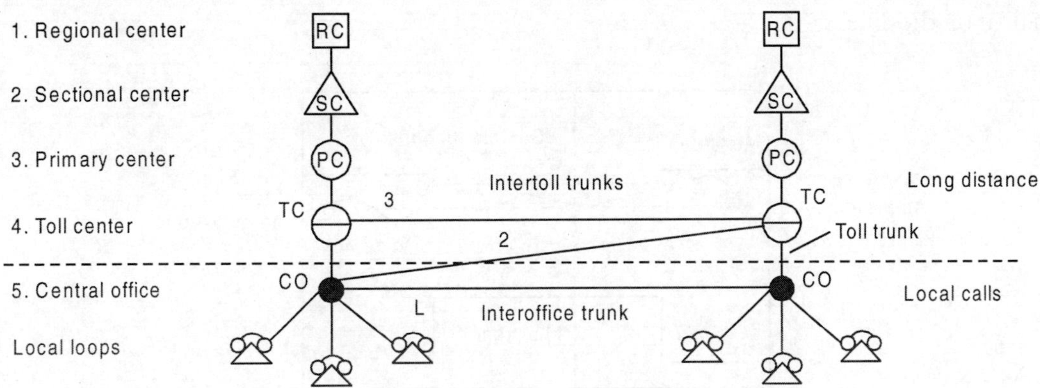

Figure 6.6 *Hierarchical Phone Networks.*

The Hierarchical portion is seen as follows:

Trunk	Long distance telephone cable
Tool Trunk	Connects CO (Central Office) to TC (Toll Center)
Inter Tool Trunk	Everything above TC (Toll Center) and TC to TC
Inter Office Trunk	Between CO (Central Office)
Intra Office Trunk	Call between 2 subscribers within the same CO (284–7079 to 284–8181).

CALL ROUTING

Call routing is determined by network engineering and physical location. When all lines are idle, the call routing selects the preferred route. If the preferred route is busy, then the call is routed to the second choice. Because the second choice is routed through one toll center, the charge for the call is greater than the preferred route. The third choice is used when the second choice is busy. The third choice goes through 2 toll centers, and is the most expensive route.

A central office can have up to 10,000 subscribers (for example, 284–0000 to 284–9999). Most have 4,000 to 5,000 subscribers. The central office bases the loading requirements on roughly 10% of the phones that will be in use at any one time. However, the use of Internet dialup access has drastically changed this statistic.

TELEPHONE LINE CHARACTERISTICS

Telephone lines are not perfect devices due to their analog nature. The quality of the telephone line determines the rate that modulated data can be transferred. Good noise-free lines allow faster transfer rates (such as 14.4 kbps) while poor quality lines require the data transfer rate to be stepped down to 9600 bps or less. Phone lines have several measurable characteristics that determine the quality of the line.

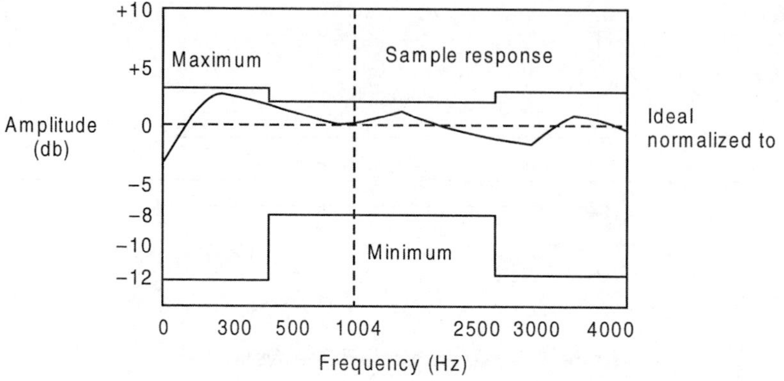

Figure 6.7 *Attenuation Distortion.*

- Attenuation distortion
- Propagation delay
- Envelope delay distortion

Attenuation distortion is the change in amplitude of the transmitted signal over the voice band: it is the frequency response curve of the voice band.

ATTENUATION VERSUS FREQUENCY

To measure attenuation distortion, the phone line has a test frequency. This frequency is transmitted from 0 – 4 kHz into the line at a standard amplitude of 0 db. The loss of signal—or attenuation—is measured at the receiving end, and compared to a standard reference frequency of 1004 Hz.

Decibel (db) is a relative unit of measure. It is a log unit and a +3 db gain will indicate an amplitude of 2x the reference. It is a logarithmic ratio between input voltage and output voltage, calculated by the following formula:

$$\text{db} = 10 \times \log (\text{Vout}/\text{Vin})$$

The resulting information is graphed on an attenuation vs. frequency chart. Attenuation is a loss of signal amplitude (the receive signal is a smaller amplitude than the transmitted signal). It is indicated by a positive db. It's also possible to have a signal appear at the receiving end, with a larger amplitude than when it started (this is indicated by negative db).

Attenuation occurs because the signal has to pass through many pieces of electronic equipment and transmission media. Some can amplify the signal (make it a larger amplitude) and some may attenuate the signal (make it smaller).

There are maximum and minimum acceptable limits for the attenuation distortion that is on phone lines. The basic channel conditioning is as follows:

Frequency Range	*Loss (db)*
500–2500	−2 to +8
300–3000	−3 to +12

The above loss is a range of acceptable values for the frequency range. In the Basic channelling conditioning, it is acceptable to have a loss in signal—in the frequency range of 500–2500 Hz—of "8 db loss to −2 db loss" (referenced to the amplitude at 1 kHz). Note that this is shown as −8 db and +2 db (see the graph).

A +3 db attenuation is equal to −3 db in signal amplitude and a +8 db attenuation equates to −8 db in signal amplitude.

PROPAGATION DELAY

Signals transmitted down a phone line will take a finite time to reach the end of the line. The delay from the time the signal was transmitted to the time it was received is called propagation delay. If the propagation delay was the exact same across the frequency range, then there would be no problem. This would imply that all frequencies from 300 to 3000 Hz have the same amount of delay in reaching their destination over the phone line. They would arrive at the destination at the same time, but delayed by a small amount of propagation delay.

For example, this delay is heard when talking on long distance telephones. In this instance, we have to wait a little longer before we speak (to ensure that the other person hasn't already started to talk). Actually, all phone lines have propagation delay.

Figure 6.8 *Propagation Delay.*

If the propagation delay is long enough, the modem or communications package may time-out and close the connection. In other words, it may think that the receive end has shut off.

ENVELOPE DELAY DISTORTION

If the propagation delay changes with frequency, we would then have the condition where the lower frequencies—such as 300 Hz—may arrive earlier or later than the higher frequencies—such as 3000 Hz. For voice communication, this would probably not be noticeable. However, for data communication using modems, this could affect the phase of the carrier or the modulation technique that's used to encode the data.

When the propagation delay varies across the frequency range, we call this envelope delay distortion. We measure propagation delay in microseconds (μs), and the reference is from the worst case to the best case.

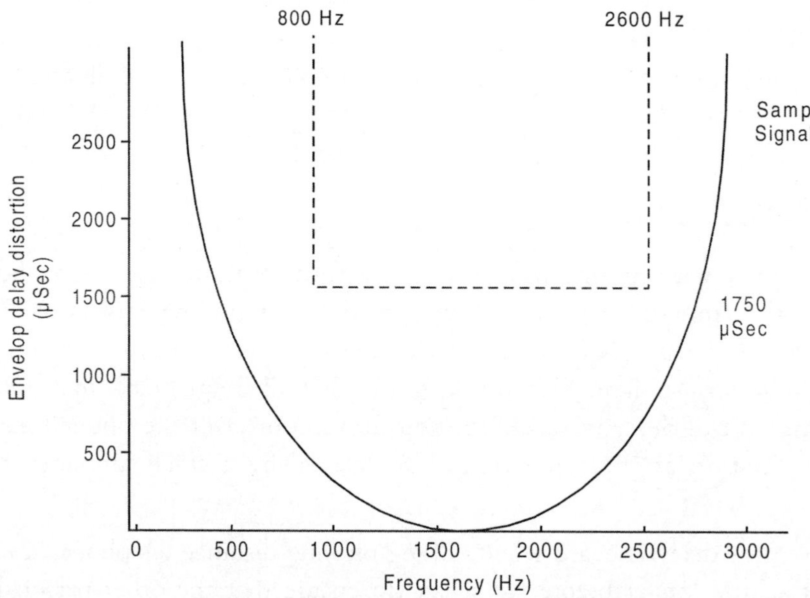

Figure 6.9 *Envelope Delay Distortion.*

LINE IMPAIRMENTS

Line impairments are faults in the line that occur due to either improper line terminations or equipment out of specifications. These cannot be conditioned out, but can be measured to determine the amount of the impairment.

Crosstalk

Crosstalk is when one line induces a signal into another line. In voice communications, we often hear this as another conversation going on in the background. In digital communication, this can cause severe disruption of the data transfer. Cross talk can be caused by the overlapping of bands in a multiplexed system, or by poor shielding of cables running close to one another. There are no specific communications standards that are applied to the measurement of crosstalk.

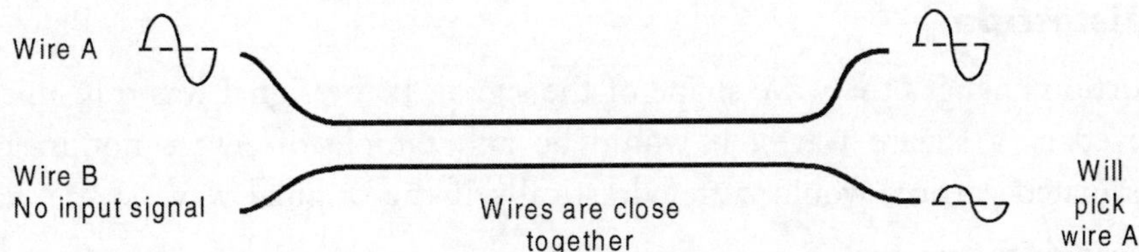

Figure 6.10 *Cross-talk.*

Echo or Signal Return

All media have a preferred termination condition for perfect transfer of signal power. The signal arriving at the end of a transmission line should be fully absorbed, otherwise it will be reflected back down the line to the sender (and appear as an echo). Echo suppressors are often fitted to transmission lines to reduce this effect.

Figure 6.11 *Echo or Signal Return.*

Usually during data transmission, these suppressors must be disabled or they will prevent return communication in full duplex mode. Echo suppressors are disabled on the phone line if they hear carrier for 400 ms or more. If the carrier is absent for 100 ms, the echo suppressor is re-enabled.

Echo cancellers are currently used in modems to replicate the echo path response. These cancellers then combine the results to eliminate the echo (thus, no signal interruption is necessary).

Frequency Shift

Frequency shift is the difference between the transmitted frequency and the received frequency. This is caused by the lack of synchronization of the carrier oscillators.

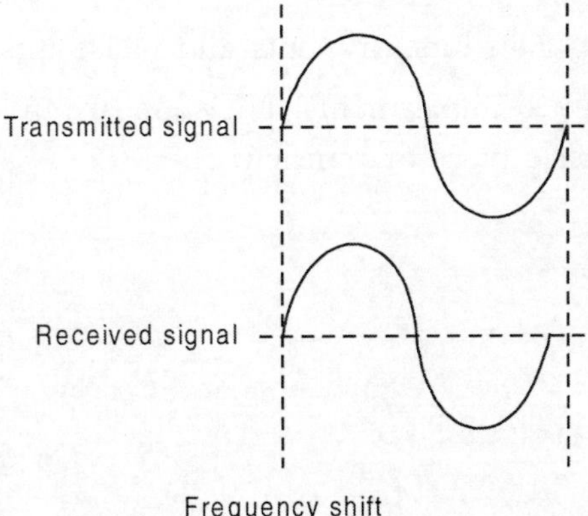

Figure 6.12 *Frequency Shift.*

Nonlinear Distortion

Nonlinear distortion changes the wave shape of the signal. If the signal was transmitted as a sine wave (and arrived as a square wave), it would be an example of severe nonlinear distortion. Amplitude modulated carriers would suffer drastically if the original wave shape was distorted.

- Nonlinear distortion

JITTER: AMPLITUDE AND PHASE

Here are the two types of jitter:

- Amplitude jitter
- Phase jitter

Amplitude jitter is the small constantly changing swing in the amplitude of a signal. It is principally caused by power supply noise (60 Hz) and ringing tone (20 Hz) on the signal.

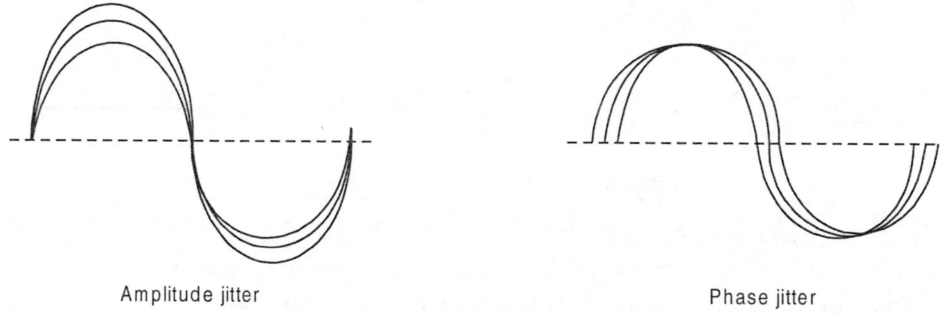

Figure 6.13 *Amplitude Jitter and Phase Jitter.*

Phase jitter is the small constantly changing swing in the phase of a signal. It may result in the pulses moving into time slots that are allocated to other data pulses when used with time domain multiplexing.

Telephone company standards call for no more than 10 degrees between 20 and 300 Hz and no more than 15 degrees between 4 and 20 Hz.

Transients: Impulse noise, gain hits, dropouts and phase hits.

Transients are irregular-timed impairments. They appear randomly, and are very difficult to troubleshoot. There are four basic types of transients.

1. Impulse noise
2. Gain hits
3. Dropouts
4. Phase hits

1. Impulse Noise

Impulse noise is a sharp and quick spike on the signal that can come from many sources: electromagnetic interference, lightning, sudden power switching, electromechanical switching, etc.. These appear on the telephone line as clicks and pops: they're not a problem for voice communication, but can appear as a loss of data (or even as wrong data bits) during data transfers. Impulse noise has a duration of less than 1 ms and their effect is dissipated within 4 ms.

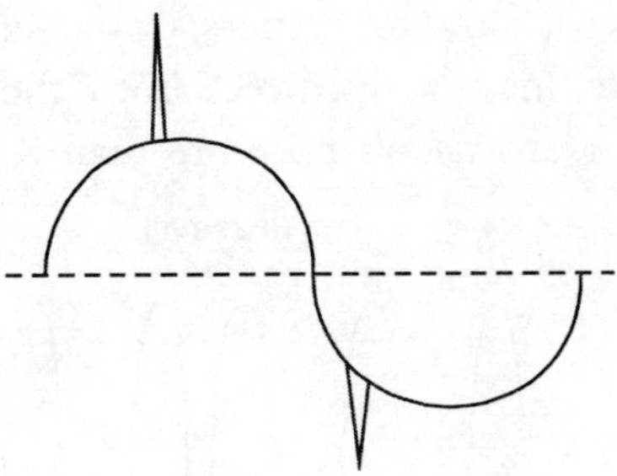

Figure 6.14 *Impulse Noise.*

2. Gain Hits

Gain hits are sudden increases in amplitude that last more than 4 ms. Telephone company standards allow for no more than 8 gain hits in any 15 minute interval. A gain hit would be heard on a voice conversation as if the volume were turned up for just an instance. Amplitude modulated carriers are particularly sensitive to gain hits.

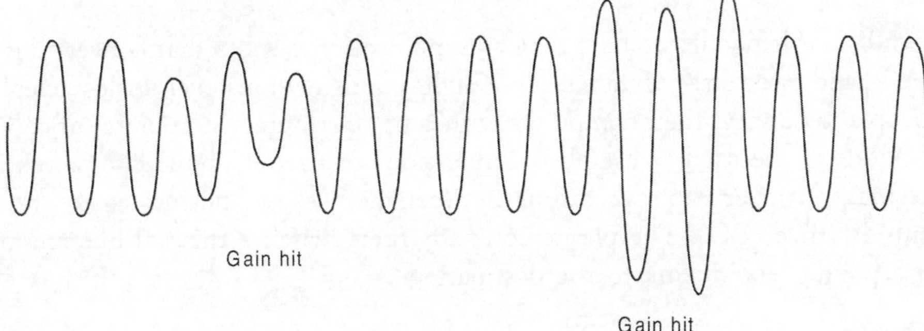

Figure 6.15 *Gain Hits.*

3. Dropouts

Dropouts are sudden losses of signal amplitude that are greater than 12 db, and last longer than 4 m sec. They cause more errors than any other type of transients. Telephone company standards allow no more than 1 dropout for every 30 minute interval. Dropouts can be heard on a voice conversation (similar to call waiting), where the line goes dead for a 1/2 second. This is a sufficient loss of signal for some digital transfer protocols (such as SLIP), where the connection is lost and would then have to be re-established.

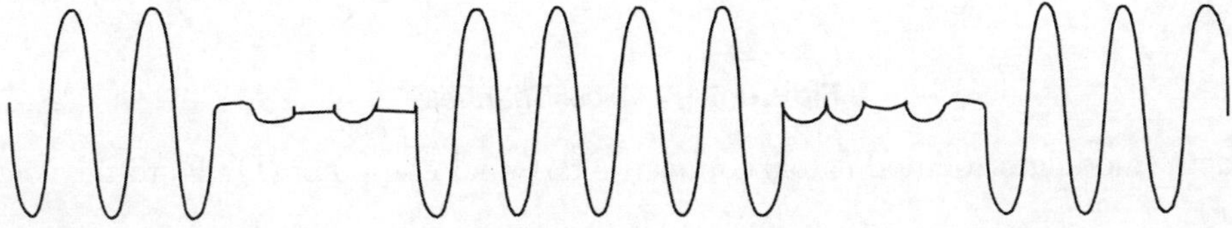

Figure 6.16 *Dropouts.*

4. Phase Hits

Phase hits are either a sudden—and large—change in the received signal phase (20 degrees), or a frequency that lasts longer than 4 m sec. Phase hits generally occur when switching between telcos, common carriers, or transmitters. FSK and PSK are particularly sensitive to phase hits. The data may be incorrect until the out-of-phase condition is rectified. The telephone company standard allows no more than 8 phase hits in any 15 minute period.

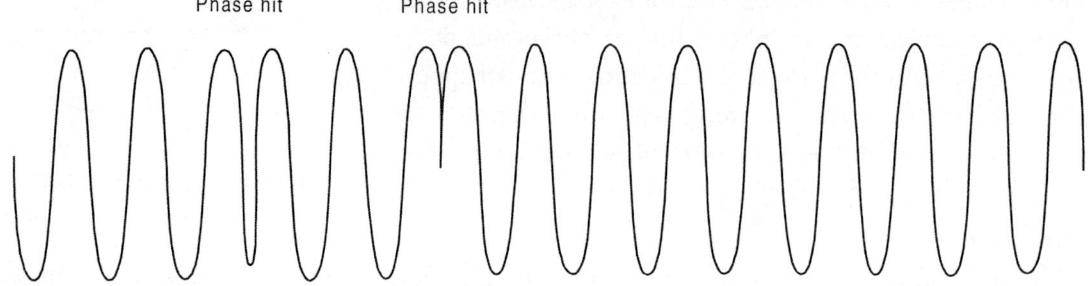

Figure 6.17 *Phase Hits.*

MODEMS

Modems (modulators/demodulators) are data communication devices that convert digital signals to analog signals, and vice versa. Modems allow digital transmissions over analog telephone lines. They allow people to connect their computers with other computers, corporate office LANs, and the Internet. Modems are used to establish connections of the telephone company's local loop, which is the analog copper cable that runs between homes and businesses to the telephone company Central Office (CO). The phone company then switches the call like any other voice call to create a point-to-point link to the destination.

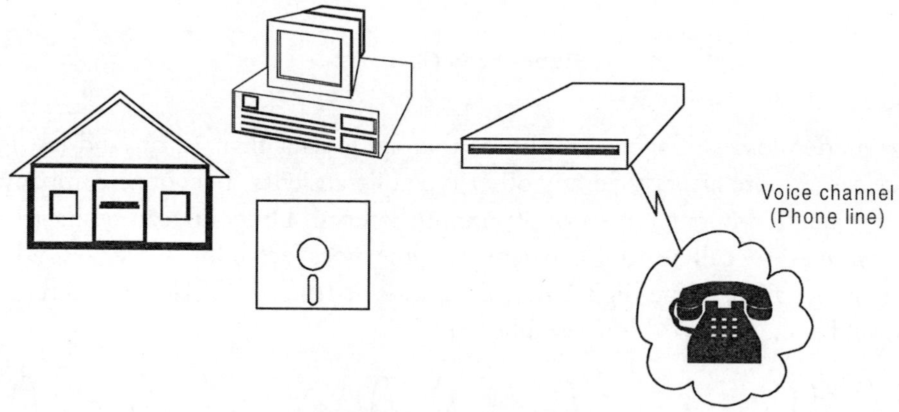

Figure 6.18 *Voice Channel.*

A modem (modulator/demodulator) connects a terminal/computer (DTE) to the voice channel (dial-up line).

Modems are devices which allow digital data signals to be transmitted across an analogue link. Modem stands for modulator/demodulator. A modem changes the digital signal to an analogue frequency, and sends this tone across the analogue link. At the other end, another modem receives the signal and converts it back to digital.

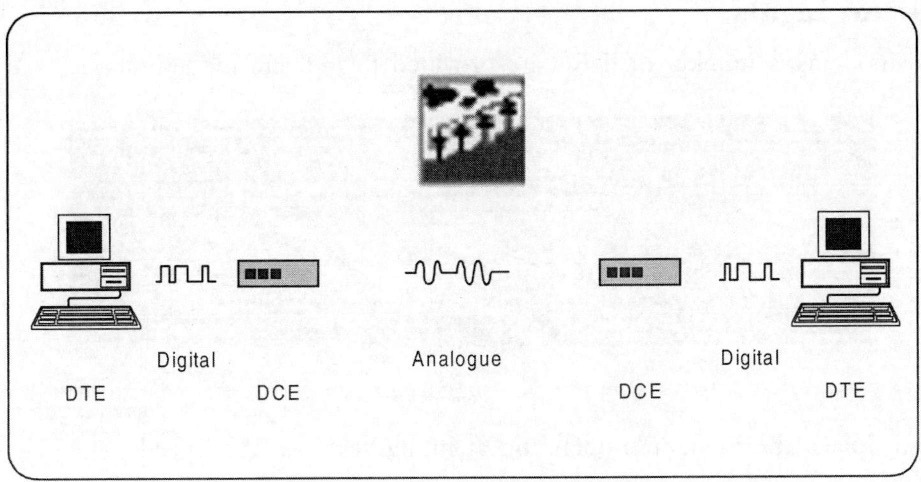

Figure 6.19 *Modems in a network.*

Modem Commands

Modems can receive and act on commands from the computer terminal. Commands begin with the symbol AT and are terminated with a carriage return. The range of commands is called the AT command set. Depending upon how the modem is configured (whether to echo results of commands), the modem will return the symbol OK in response to a command request if it is performed.

The AT Command Set

Hayes corporation developed a smart modem which accepted AT type commands. This is now a widely accepted standard. The following is a brief list of the AT command set.

- ATA Answer call
- ATA/Repeat last command
- ATC Turn modems carrier signal ON (ATC1) or OFF (ATC0)
- ATD Dial a telephone number (ATDT255-0789)
- ATE Enable (ATE1) or disable (ATE0) the echo of characters to the screen
- ATH Hang up the phone (ATH0) or pick up the phone (ATH1)
- ATM Turn on modem speaker (ATM1) or turn off speaker (ATM0)
- ATO Place modem on-line
- ATP Pulse dial
- ATS Set values in modem 'S' registers
- ATT Touch tone dial
- ATZ Reset the modem

Modem Status Lights

On external modems, a number of lights are provided to indicate modem status.

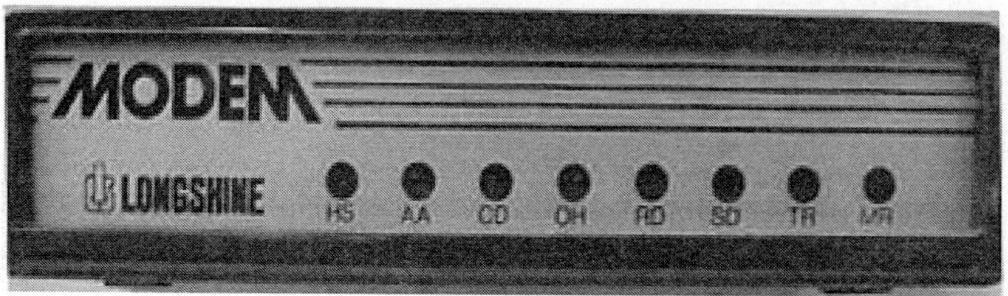

- HS

  High Speed: the modem is operating at its highest available speed
- AA

  Auto Answer: the model will automatically answer incoming calls
- CD

  Carrier Detect: means it has detected a carrier signal from a remote computer
- OH

  Off Hook: lights when the modem takes control of the phone line
- MR

  Modem Ready: the modem is turned on and is ready
- RD

  Receive Data: flickers to indicate incoming data
- SD

  Send Data: flickers to indicate data is being transmitted

Basic Definition of Modem

The modem (DCE—Data Communication Equipment) is connected between the terminal/computer (DTE—Data Terminal Equipment) and the phone line (voice channel). A modem converts the DTE (Data Terminal Equipment) digital signal to an analog signal that the voice channel can use.

A modem is connected to the terminal/computer's RS-232 serial port (25 pin male D connector) and the outgoing phone line with an RJ11 cable connector (the same as on a telephone extension cord). Male connectors have pins, female connectors have sockets.

Digital Connection

The connection between the modem and terminal/computer is a digital connection. A basic connection consists of a Transmit Data (TXD) line, a Receive Data (RXD) line and many hardware handshaking control lines.

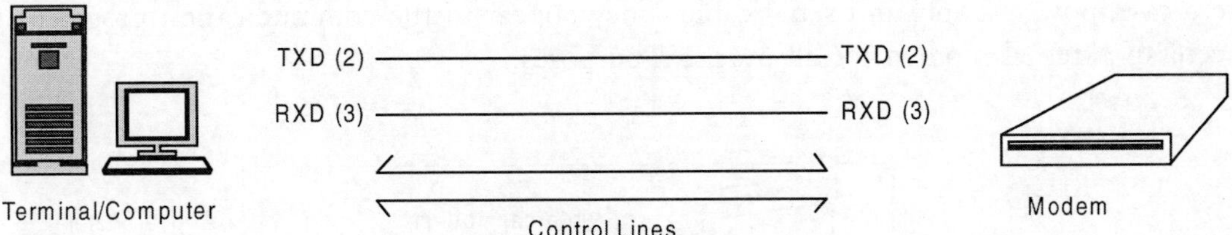

Figure 6.20 *Digital Connection.*

The control lines determine whose turn it is to talk (modem or terminal), if the terminal/computer is turned on, if the modem is turned on, if there is a connection to another modem, etc.

Analog Connection

The connection between the modem and the outside world (the phone line) is an analog connection. The voice channel has a bandwidth of 0–4 kHz but only 300–3400 Hz is usable for data communications.

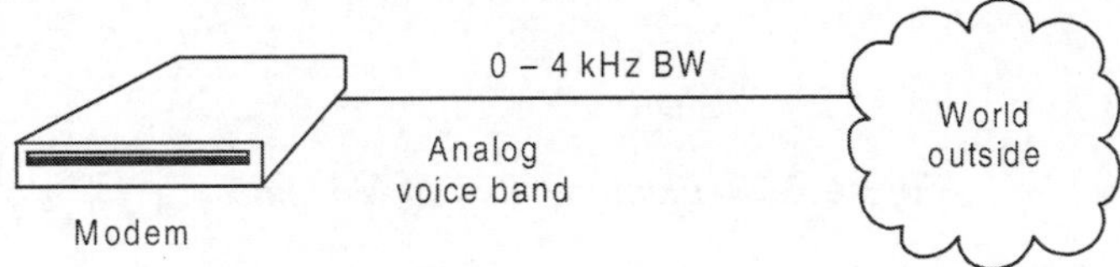

Figure 6.21 *Analog Connection.*

The modem converts digital information into tones (frequencies) for transmitting through the phone lines. The tones are in the 300–3400 Hz voice band.

External/Internal Modems

There are 2 basic physical types of modems: Internal and External modems. External modems sit next to the computer and connect to the serial port using a straight-through serial cable.

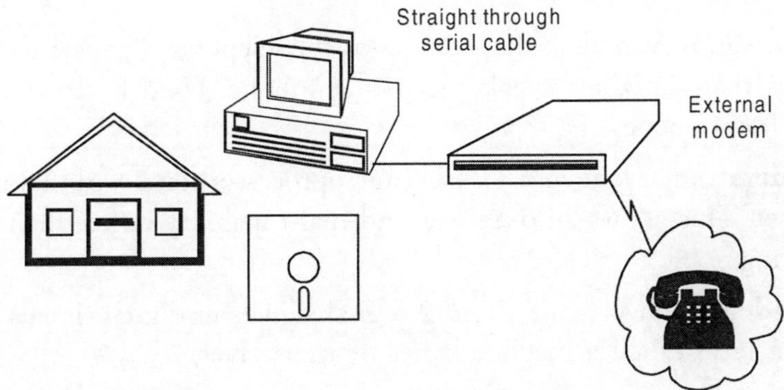

Figure 6.22 *External/Internal Modems.*

An internal modems is a plug-in circuit board that sits inside the computer. It incorporates the serial port on-board. They are less expensive than external modems because they do not require a case, power supply and serial cable. They appear to the communication programs as if they were an external modem for all practical purposes.

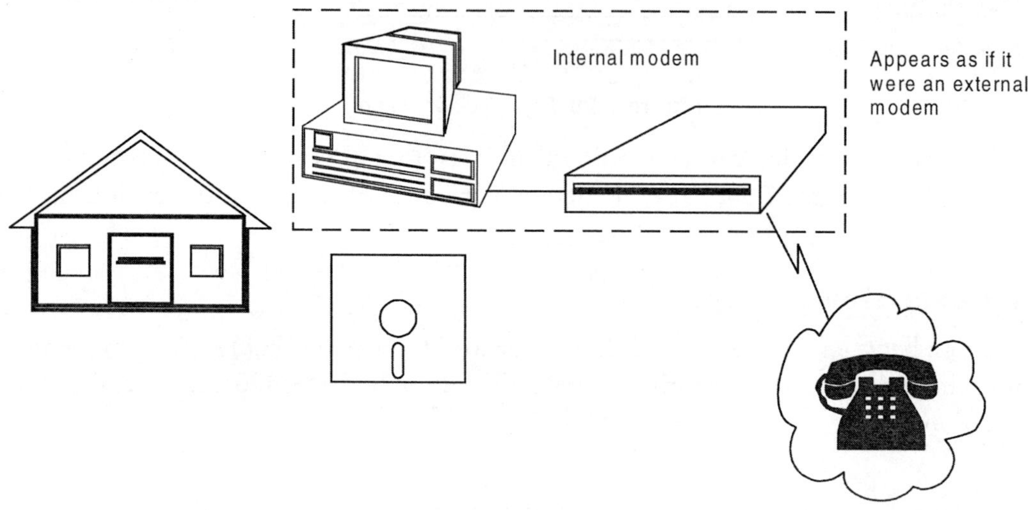

Figure 6.23 *External/Internal Modems.*

Modem Types

There are many types of modems, the most common of which are:

- **Optical modem:** Uses optical fiber cable instead of wire. The modem converts the digital signal to pulses of light to be transmitted over optical lines (more commonly called a media adapter or transceiver).
- **Short haul modem:** A modem used to transmit data over 20 miles or less. Modems we use at home or to connect computers together among different offices in the same building are short haul modems.
- **Acoustic modem:** A modem that couples to the telephone handset with what looks like suction cups that contain a speaker and microphone. Used by traveling salespeople to connect to hotel phones.
- **Smart modem:** A modem with a CPU (microprocessor) on board that uses the hayes AT command set. This allows auto-answer and dial capability rather than manually dialing and answering.
- **Digital modem:** Converts the RS-232 digital signals to digital signals more suitable for transmission (also called a media adapter or transceiver).
- **V.32 modem:** A milestone modem that uses a 2400 baud modem with 4 bit encoding. This results in a 9600 bps (bits per second) transfer rate.

Baud is the speed at which the analog data is changing on the voice channel and bps is the speed at which the decoded digital data is being transferred.

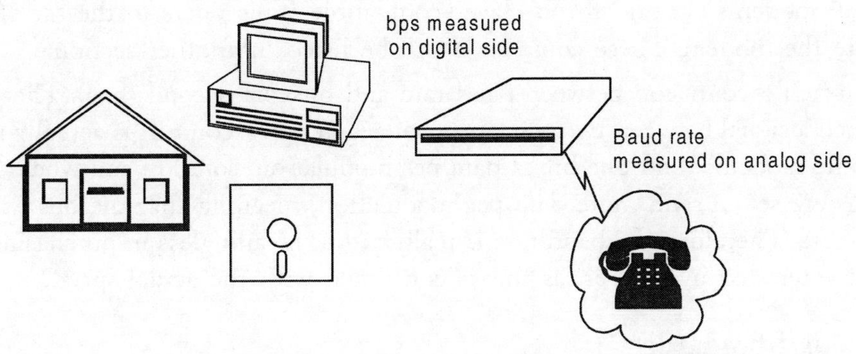

Figure 6.24 *Baud Rate and bps.*

Features of Modems

- **Speed:** The speed at which the modem can send data in bps (bits per second). Typical modem speeds are: 300, 600, 1200, 2400, 4800, 9600, 14.4K, 19.2K, 28.8K bps.
- **Auto Dial/Re-dial:** Smart modems can dial the phone number and auto re-dial if a busy signal is received.
- **Auto answer:** Most modems have ring detect capability and can automatically answer the telephone at the time of incoming call.
- **Self testing:** Newer modems have self-testing features. They can test the digital connection to the terminal/computer and the analog connection to a remote modem. They can also check the modem's internal electronics.
- **Voice over data:** Voice over data modems allow a voice conversation to take place while data is being transmitted. This requires both the source and destination modems to have this feature.
- **Synchronous or Asynchronous transmission:** Newer modems allow a choice of synchronous or asynchronous transmission of data. Normally, modem transmission is asynchronous (we send individual characters with just start and stop bits). Synchronous transmission or packet transmission is used in specific applications.

Standards to all Modems

There are many standards for modem protocols, but the field has evened out lately. A protocol is a method by which two devices, modems, agree to communicate. You can think of it as a language that is agreed on.

Bell Labs and the CCITT have both set standards for modem protocols. Bell Labs no longer sets standards, although they are still used in some locations. Most newer modems conform to the CCITT standards.

Some companies branched out and created modems using their own proprietary standard protocol. Such protocols are published broadly so that other manufacturers can create modems to work with it. Some of these proprietary standards have become popular. Most modems are designed to work with several different protocols.

Almost all modems are said to be Hayes-compatible. This refers to the set of commands used to operate the modem. These commands will be listed in another section.

There is often a confusion between baud rate and bits-per-second (bps). The baud rate is the rate at which a signal between two modems changes in one second. It is actually independent of the bps. Some modems send one bit of data per modulation, so 300 baud would be 300 bps. Other modems are set to send more data per modulation, meaning that the bps will be higher than the baud rate. Therefore, the baud rate is really rather meaningless in purchasing a modem. You should be interested in the bps, as this is concerned with the actual speed.

Modem Speeds/Standards

The following table 6.1 lists some of the ITU-T modem standards. The modulation techniques described in the table are FSK (frequency-shift keying), PSK (phase-shift keying), QAM (quadrature amplitude modulation), and TCM (trellis-coded modulation). See "modulation techniques."

Table 6.1

V.22	1,200 bits/sec, full-duplex, PSK encoding
V.22bis	2,400 bits/sec, full-duplex, QAM encoding
V.32	Asynchronous/synchronous, 4,800/9,600 bits/sec, QAM encoding
V.32bis	Asynchronous/synchronous, 14,400 bits/sec, TCM encoding
V.35	Defines high data rates over combined circuits
V.42	Defines error checking standards
V.42bis	Defines modem compression using the Lempel Ziv method
V.44	The newest data compression standard, announced with V.92 in 2000
V.34	A standard for 28 Kbits/sec using TCM encoding
V.34+	Boosts V.34 to 33.6 Kbits/sec
V.90	56 Kbits/sec download speed, assuming only one digital-to analog conversion
V.92	Improves the upload speed of the V.90 standard from 33.6 Kbits/sec to 47 Kbits/sec
V.90	56-Kbit/sec Modems

Two competing modem standards emerged in the late 1990s to take advantage of higher throughput rates that were made possible by the configuration. Note that the ISP is connected to the CO with a digital connection. This allows for a cleaner modem signal and faster rates, as explained in a moment. The two competing standards were U.S. robotics X2 and lucent/rockwell semiconductor systems K56flex. Both companies rushed to release 56K products, creating two standards and a lot of consumer confusion. 56K technology requires that ISPs also install compatible modems, so the technology advanced slowly at first because ISPs could not decide on which standard to use.

In 1998, the ITU created the V.90 standard, which is designed for connections that are digital at one end and have only one digital-to-analog conversion. V.90 harmonized the two competing X2 and K56flex proposals and has become a worldwide standard.

V.90 specifies up to 56 Kbits/sec in the downstream mode and 31.2 Kbits/sec in the upstream mode. However, it is very unlikely that anyone can reach those speeds.

The lastest modem standard is V.92, which is V.90 (56-Kbits/sec) technology with a few refinements and some new features. "V.PCM upstream" allows for upstream communication at up to 48 Kbits/sec (V.90 supported on 31.2 Kbits/sec upstream). The bit rate should be high since most people always dial the same number for Internet access. "modem on hold" allows a modem to suspend a data call and take an incoming voice call. When the data call resumes, a transmission continues where it left off. This feature benefits homes with only one line, and is a useful feature if you've ever tried to call someone that has been online for hours. "quick connect" shortens connect times by up to 50%. The modem uses stored settings from previous calls (if they can be used) rather than renegotiating during the connect phase. This feature is also useful in conjunction with "modem on hold" since it speeds up the resumption of the call.

Be aware of so-called "soft modems" (also called "Winmodems" or "controllerless modems"). These modems use your computer's processors instead of an on-board processor. They are cheap because they have fewer chips, but it's a good idea to pay a little more for a full-function modem. Some soft modems run modulation/demodulation in hardware, but run other functions such as compression, error control, and V.90 protocols in software. HSP (host signal processing) modems run everything in software and are really nothing more than plug-in telephone jacks. You're paying for software. Usually, low price is the only indicator that a modem is a soft-modem. Look at the box carefully. If it indicates that the modem only runs under windows, it's a softmodem.

Bell 103	300 bps FSK—Half duplex
Bell 113	300 bps FSK—Full duplex
Bell 202	1200 baud half duplex
Bell 212A	1200 bps DPSK (Dibit Phase Shift Keying)—V.22 compatible 300 bps FSK (Frequency Shift Keying)—NOT V.22 compatible
MNP1-3	Microcon networking protocol—Basic error detection and control of errors
MNP4	Error correction + adapts to line conditions
MNP5	Error correction + adapts to line conditions; adds compression technique to double the data transfer rate
RS-232D	Cable and connector standard
V.22	1200 bps DPSK (Dibit Phase Shift Keying) - Bell 212A compatible 600 bps PSK (Phase Shift Keying)—NOT Bell 212A compatible
V.22bis	2400 bps—International standard fall back in Europe to V.22 Fall back in America to Bell 212A
V.24	European mechanical specifications for RS-232D
V.26.	Synchronous 2400 bps modem 1200 bps DPSK full duplex

V.27	Synchronous 4800 bps DPSK modem
V.28	European electrical specifications for RS-232D
V.29	Synchronous 9600 bps QAM
V.32	9600 bps QAM
V.32bis	14.4 Kbps QAM1
V.33	14.4 Kbps Trellis coded modulation for noise immunity
V.34	28.8 Kbps modem standard
V.34bis	33.6 Kbps modem standard
V.42bis	Compression technique to roughly double the data transfer rate. Uses Automatic Repeat Request ARQ and CRC (Cyclic Redundancy Checking).
WE201	Synchronous Western Electric 2400 bps DPSK
WE208	Synchronous 4800 bps DPSK
WE209	Synchronous 9600 bps

Summary of Modem Standard

CCITT/ITU Standards

(**C**omite **C**onsultatif **I**nternational **T**elegraphique et **T**elephoneique/**I**nternational **T**elecommunications **U**nion)

Standard	*baud (Hz)*	*Bits Per Second*	*Comment*
V.22	600	1,200	The same as the Bell 212A standard but different handshaking.
V.22bis	600	2,400	(*bis stands for 'second'*)
V.32	2,400	4,800/9,600	
V.32bis	2,400	*V.32* + 7,200/12,000/ 14,400	
V32terbo	2,400	*V.32bis* + 19,000	*These two 'proposed' standards contributed*
V.FC	3,429	*V.32bis* + 28,000	*and were consolidated in the V34 standard*
V.34	3,429	*V.32bis* + 28,000/33,600	Introduced in June 94
V42/MNP4	Error correction standard		Includes the Microcom MNP4 standard
V.42bis	Compression standard		
X2 (56K)	Pushed by 3Com/U.S. Robotics		*These two 'proposed' standards contributed*
K56-Flex (56k)	Pushed by Rockwell (now conexant), Lucent		*and were consolidated in the V90 standard*

V90	*V34* + 56,000	Introduced February '99 56k Asymmetric communication Max upstream of 33.6k Max downstream of 54k Good connections only possible if within 3-1/2 miles of local exchange (NOT as the crow flies)
V92	*V34* + 56,000	Introduced January 2000 Faster Connection times Increased Compression throughput

TRANSFER RATE VS. PC BUS SPEED

The lowest XT PC can out-perform the fastest modem transfer rate. For example, an XT has an 8 bit parallel expansion bus operating at 4.77 MHz. This equates to a data transfer rate of:

8 bits × 4.77 MHz = 38.16 Mbps

Compare this to the fastest modem transfer rates of 57.6 kbps.

Before the Internet, the usual connection was for one user to dial another user, or for a user to dial into a modem at a bulletin board, place of business, or a school. In these cases, the connection is modem to modem across the PSTN. The computer's outgoing digital signal is converted to an analog signal for transmission across the copper local loop to the CO. At the CO, the analog signal is converted back to digital for transmission across its digital backbones. At the destination CO, the signal is once again converted from digital to analog and transmitted to the end user's modem, where it is converted back to digital.

In recent years, the 2400 bits per second modem that could carry e-mail has become obsolete. 14.4 Kbps and 28.8 Kbps modems were temporary landing places on the way to the much higher bandwidth devices and carriers of tomorrow. From early 1998, most new personal computers came with 56 Kbps modems. By comparison, using a digital Integrated Services digital network adapter instead of a conventional modem, the same telephone wire can now carry up to 128 Kbps. With Digital Subscriber Line (DSL) systems, now being deployed in a number of communities, bandwidth on twisted-pair can be in the megabit range.

Today, most users dial into the Internet, where they connect with other users via e-mail, collaborative applications, instant messaging, and so on. Users also connect with their home networks over the Internet by using secure VPN technology. This allows users to dial into a local number and connect to the corporate office across the Internet. The bottom half of figure 6.25 illustrates how most modem connections are made in today's Internet-connected environment. The important point of this configuration is that the ISP is connected to the telephone company's CO with a digital connection. This configuration makes high-speed 56-Kbit/sec modem technology possible.

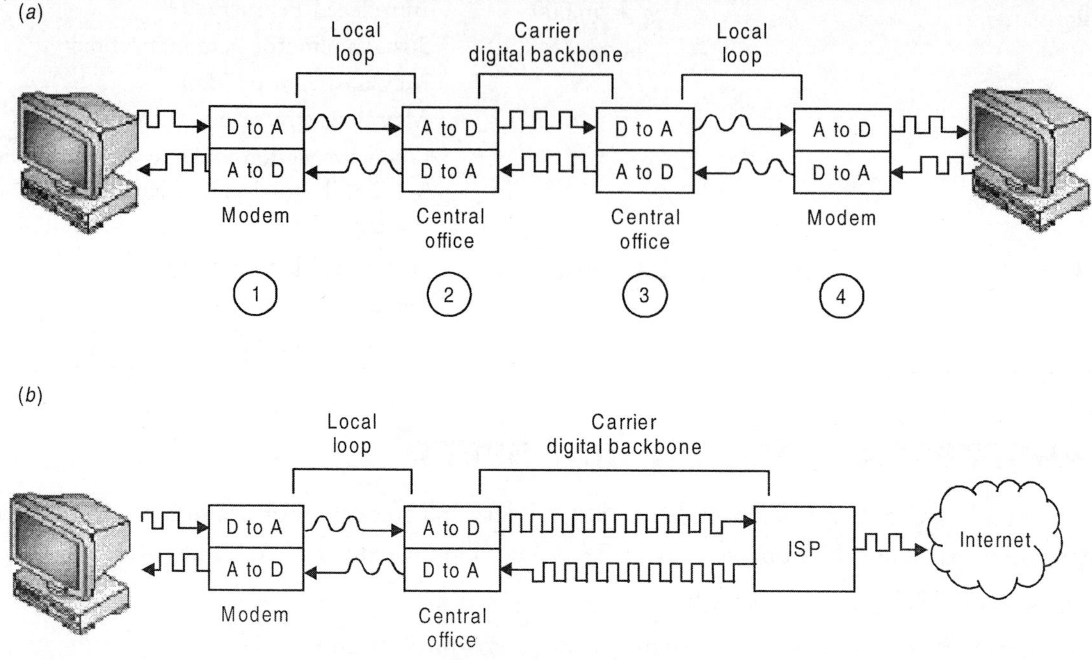

Figure 6.25 *Modem.*

There are also different types of technical modems:

Consumer voice-grade Modems: Most off-the-shelf modems are designed to allow PC users to communicate over the voice phone system. The modems employ compatible communication techniques that comply with several standards, most notably the ITU V series standards (previously called the CCITT standards).

Broadband Modems: These are modems for nontelephone system connections. A company may set up its own dedicated lines or microwave towers and use broadband modems to achieve very high data rates between those sites.

A modem puts an AC (alternating current) carrier signal on the line (in the 1,000–2,000 Hz range) and adds digital information to this signal. A modem at the receiving end then extracts the digital information from the carrier signal. Modulation and demodulation are covered more fully under "modulation techniques." Two other related topics are "error detection and correction" and "signals."

There are some restrictions in the local loop. Long ago, the telephone company established the frequency range of 300–3,300 Hz as the range for voice. The telephone switching system filters out higher frequencies to eliminate noise. Unfortunately, this filtering equipment prevents taking advantage of higher frequencies and wider bandwidth that could help boost data transmission rates. Therefore, a number of techniques, including encoding and compression, have been developed to squeeze as much digital data into the 300–3,300 Hz range as possible.

A voice-grade modem may be either an external box or an internally mounted circuit board. The PC card format is also available for portable computers. The external modem connects to a computer serial port via an RS-232 serial cable.

Carriers and service providers often have racks of modems that users dial into. These are connected to remote access servers that manage the modems and authenticate users. Modems are usually integrated into RAC (remote access concentrator) devices

Modems are asynchronous, synchronous, or both. An asynchronous transmission can be compared to the sporadic flow of cars on a highway, while a synchronous transmission can be compared to a steady stream of boxcars on a train track. In asynchronous mode, data is framed and each frame is sent independently. The receiver must be able to detect when a frame starts and ends. In asynchronous mode, a clock signal separates the beginning and end of each frame of data. Synchronous modems are generally more efficient and are typically used for dedicated links between two sites and long streaming data transfers. Most consumer modems are asynchronous.

When one modem "calls" another, the destination modem answers and a signal exchange takes place that establishes the parameters for a communication session. The negotiation process determines the maximum signaling rate available between the two modems, as well as the use of compression.

A full-duplex modem will send signals in both directions at the same time and at the same rate. Newer high-speed (56-Kbit/sec) voice-grade modems such as the V.90 series are asymmetrical, meaning that the download channel has a higher rate than the upload channel.

FSK Modems

The last functional block in a basic low-to-medium speed data link is the modulator/demodulator or modem, dataset, or DCE. It is the job of the modem to convert the serial digital data stream from a UART to a series of audio sine waves or tones. For a Frequency Shift Key (FSK) modem, one tone represents a logic one (mark) and another is used for a logic zero (space). On the receiver end, these tones are converted back to digital levels by the receiver's modem.

On the transmit side, serial data is supplied by the UART through a RS-232 character interface, on the TX data input and fed to a Voltage-Controlled Oscillator (VCO). The VCO acts as a frequency modulator by converting DC voltages into different analog sine waves. These sine waves have a different frequency for each level of DC voltage applied. Hence, a tone at one frequency is produced for a logic one's DC voltage and a second tone at a different frequency is produced for the space logic DC voltage level.

The request-to-send (RTS) input from the terminal (or UART) initiates the modem's RTS/CTS delay, which varies with each modem type and requirements. The general purpose of the delay is to give modem circuits time to turn on and stabilize before handling data from the UART. Once the delay is completed, the modem generates a Clear-to-Send (CTS) signal back to the terminal completing the local data link handshaking. An active CTS enables the voltage controlled oscillator, which, sensing idle line once from the UART, immediately outputs a mark tone on the telephone lines.

Intelligent Modems

Almost every modem does more, with appropriate software, a user can enter commands directing the modem to take certain actions such as dialing or answering the phone. Such intelligent modems have a processor to carry out functions.

Hays microcomputer products, inc., developed a modem that has become commonplace. The hayes modems are designed to respond to a set of instructions called AT commands. Using appropriate software, the user enters the letters AT followed by the command. Each command consists one or more letters followed by parameters.

Two common parameters are the D and T commands. The letter D represents dial and instructs the modem to dial the number that follows the command. The letter T indicates the modem should use tone dialing as opposed to pulse dialing. To illustrate, a user wanting the modem to dial the number 555-1483 from a touch-tone phone would enter the command ATDT5551483.

In some cases, when dialing from within an organization we must first enter 9, wait for another dial tone, and then dial the number. If it simply dials the number, before the second dial tone, it may try to connect to an operator's recorded message saying, "Your phone call cannot be completed...." We can instruct some modems to pause by including a comma (,) as part of the command. For example, if we must dial 9, wait, and then dial 555-1483, the appropriate command would be ATDT9,5551483.

The different modem commands can be entered from a PC using appropriate software. Some software also allows us to write several commands in a file. The files may be called scripts or macros; they allow the user to execute the commands on a file many times without having to type them each time. The feature is useful in cases where we frequently dial up the same line and go through the same logon procedures.

Null Modems

Sometimes, we want to allow two devices such as PCs to communicate directly, that is, with no network or DCES between them, in this case, our first reaction might be to connect their RS-232 ports with a cable and let the protocols do their job. After all, they both send and receive from the RS-232 ports. Using a simple cable, however, connects the same pins on each side. For example, the cable would connect pin 2 of each DTE. The problem is that both pins try to send over the same line. The first DTE sends data and the second receives it over line 2. Since the second DTE expects to receive data over line 3, the direct connection will not work. Similarly, since the cable connects pin 3 on each end, both expect to receive on the same circuit, but neither sends over it.

One solution to this problem is to connect the DTEs but cross some circuits. A null modem may be either a cable connecting different pins on each connector or a device that simply crosses connections using existing cables. Thus Null modem is used for connecting two PCs in the same room.

CARRIER

1. In information technology, a carrier (or carrier signal) is a transmitted electromagnetic pulse or wave at a steady base frequency of alternation on which information can be imposed by increasing signal strength, varying the base frequency, varying the wave phase, or other means. This variation is called modulation. With the advent of laser transmission over optical fiber media, a carrier can also be a laser-generated light beam on which information is imposed.

Types of analog modulation of a carrier include Amplitude Modulation (AM), Frequency Modulation (FM), and phase modulation. Types of digital modulation include varieties of Pulse Code Modulation (PCM), including Pulse Amplitude Modulation (PAM), Pulse Duration Modulation (PDM), and Pulse Position Modulation (PPM).

Carrier detect (see modem lights) is a control signal between a modem and a computer that indicates that the modem detects a "live" carrier that can be used for sending and receiving information.

2. In the telecommunications industry, a carrier is a telephone or other company that sells or rents telecommunication transmission services. A Local Exchange carrier (LEC) is a local phone company and an Inter-Exchange Carrier (IEC or IXC) carries long-distance calls.

Digital T Carriers

As technology improved the speed at which electronic circuits could dependably operate, the need to increase the rate at which data is transferred also increased. To respond to the need for interconnecting computers and database facilities, the telephone company turned to supplying lines for carrying data in digital form. As well as supplying the lines, the telephone company also established the limitations for their use. The basic designation for these lines are T carriers and they begin with basic T1 carrier specified for the bell system voice network.

T1 carriers are digital, leased twisted–pair lines, operating as 4–wire trunk lines, designed to handle 24 PCM voice grade channels operating at a maximum data rate of 64 kbps each. Thus, the t1 line requires a bandwidth large enough to handle 1.544 mbps (24.64 kbps). T1 lines are designed to interconnect stations that are up to 80 kilometers (km) apart, using regenerative repeaters every 1.6 km. The last repeater placed before the nearest switch station is to be no more than 0.8 km from that station. These repeaters reshape the digital data that has been distorted due to attenuation or pulse spreading caused by effects on the signals of the propagation delays inherent in the reactive nature of the cabling.

Each channel is sent, using time division multiplexing of eight bits per channel at a time. Since 24 channel are sent at once, a total of 8.24 bits, or 192 data bits, are sent per transmission period. An additional frame boundary bit (like a start/stop bit) increases the total to 193 bits per frame (transmission). Dividing the total data rate by the total number of bits per frame yields a frame rate of 8,000 frames per second.

Multi-Carrier Modulation

Multi-Carrier Modulation (MCM) is a method of transmitting data by splitting it into several components, and sending each of these components over separate carrier signals. The individual carriers have narrow bandwidth, but the composite signal can have broad bandwidth.

The advantages of MCM include relative immunity to fading caused by transmission over more than one path at a time (multi-path fading), less susceptibility than single-carrier systems to interference caused by impulse noise, and enhanced immunity to inter-symbol interference. Limitations include difficulty in synchronizing the carriers under marginal conditions, and a relatively strict requirement that amplification be linear.

MCM was first used in analog military communications in the 1950s. Recently, MCM has attracted attention as a means of enhancing the bandwidth of digital communications over media with physical limitations. The scheme is used in some audio broadcast services. The technology lends itself to digital television, and is used as a method of obtaining high data speeds in Asymmetric Digital Subscriber Line (ADSL) systems. MCM is also used in Wireless Local Area Networks (WLANs).

SWITCHING

We know that networks establish communication links based on either circuit or packet switching. For high-speed optical transmission, packet switching holds the promise for more efficient data transfer.

Network packet switching can be accomplished in a straightforward manner by requiring a node to optoelectronically detect and transmit each and every incoming optical data packet. As for the routing, all the switching functions can occur in the electrical domain prior to optical retransmission of the signal. Unfortunately, this approach suffers from an optoelectronic speed bottleneck. Alternatively, much research is focused toward maintaining an all-optical data path and performing the switching functions all optically with only some electronic control of the optical components. However, there are many difficulties with optical switching, for instance:

1. A redirection of an optical path is not easy since photons do not have as strong interaction with their environment as electrons do.
2. Switching has to be extremely fast due to the high speed of the incoming signal.
3. Switching nodes cannot easily tap a signal and acquire information about the channel.

Switching Network

Figure 6.26 shows a switching network. Lines are the media links. Ovals are called network nodes. Media links simply carry data from one point to other. Nodes take the incoming data and route them to an output port.

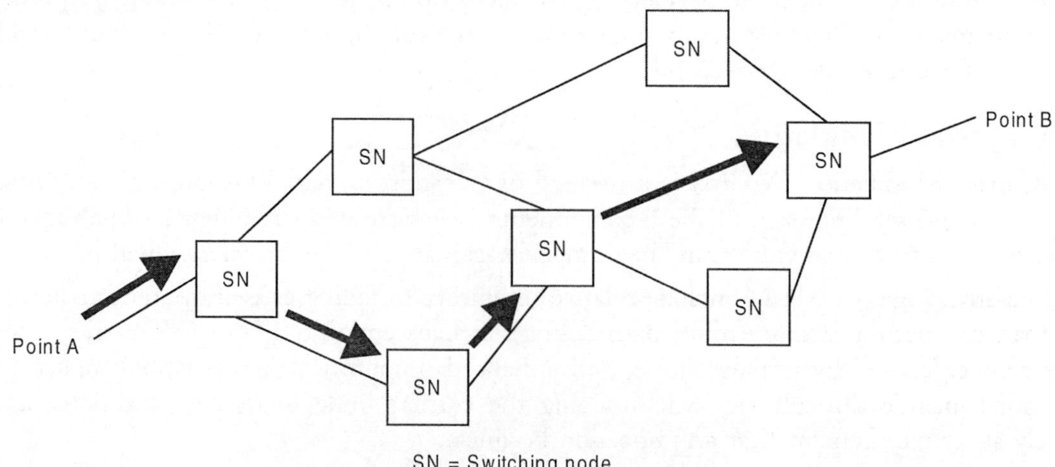

Figure 6.26 *Switching Network.*

If two different communication paths intersect through this network they have to share some resources. Two paths can share a media link or a network node.

NETWORKS

Historically, most communication systems have started with point-to-point links which directly connect together the users wishing to communicate using a dedicated communication circuits. As the distance between users increases beyond the length of the cable (*e.g.*, the length of a telegraph wire), the connection between the users was formed by a number of sections which were connected end-to-end in series to form the circuit. The connection between the users (A and D) in figure 6.27 (*i.e.*, A and D) is represented by a series of links (AB, BC, and CD) each link connects two entities known as nodes. For a point-to-point circuit, (also known as a permanent circuit) the nodes are patch panels which provide a simple connection between the two links (*i.e.*, the two transmission circuits).

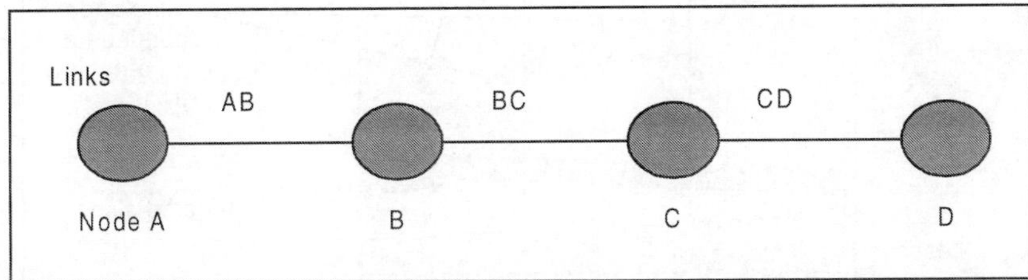

Figure 6.27 *A Connection between Two Systems A and D Formed from 3 Links.*

As the number of connected users increased, it has become infeasible to provide a circuit which connects every user to every other user, and some sharing of the transmission circuits (known as "switching") has become necessary. To accomplish this goal, the data communications network has evolved. A network is a set of nodes that are interconnected to permit the exchange of information. Three switching techniques have been proposed for building networks:

1. Circuit Switching
2. Message Switching
3. Packet Switching (Both Virtual Circuit and Datagram)

Each allows sharing communication facilities among multiple users (end systems), and each uses equipment located at the nodes (intermediate systems) to replace the patch-panels used in a point-to-point connection. Packet switching is most often used for data communication. Most networks consist of many links which allow more than one path through the network between nodes. A data communications network must be able to select an appropriate path for each required connection. A mesh of network nodes connected by links.

Any of the three approaches (circuit switching, message switching, and packet switching) could yield minimum delay in a particular situation, though situations where message switching yields minimum delay are rare. The relative performance of circuit switching and packet switching depends strongly on the speed and "cost" of establishing a connection.

1. Circuit Switching

Circuit switching is the most familiar technique used to build a communication network. It is used for ordinary telephone calls. It allows communications equipment and circuits, to be shared among users. Each user has sole access to a circuit (functionally equivalent to a pair of copper wires) during network use.

Network use is initiated by a connection phase, during which a circuit is set up between source and destination, and terminated by a disconnect phase. These phases, with associated timings, are illustrated in figure 6.28.

After a user requests a circuit, the desired destination address must be communicated to the local switching node (B). In a telephony network, this is achieved by dialing the number.

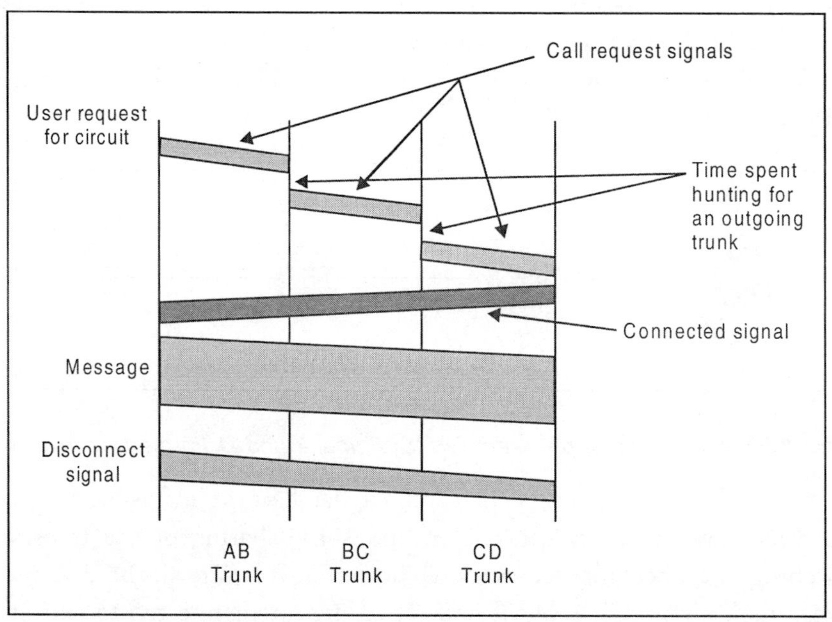

Figure 6.28 *A Circuit Switches Connection between A and D.*

Node B receives the connection request and identifies a path to the destination (D) via an intermediate node (C). This is followed by a circuit connection phase handled by the switching nodes and initiated by allocating a free circuit to C (link BC), followed by transmission of a call request signal from node B to node C. In turn, node C allocates a link (CD) and the request is then passed to node D after a similar delay.

The circuit is then established and may be used. While it is available for use, resources (*i.e.,* in the intermediate equipment at B and C) and capacity on the links between the equipment are dedicated to the use of the circuit.

After completion of the connection, a signal confirming circuit establishment (a connect signal in the diagram) is returned; this flows directly back to node A with no search delays since the circuit has been established. Transfer of the data in the message then begins. After data transfer, the circuit is disconnected; a simple disconnect phase is included after the end of the data transmission.

Delays for setting up a circuit connection can be high, especially if ordinary telephone equipment is used. Call setup time with conventional equipment is typically on the order of 5 to 25 seconds after completion of dialing. New fast circuit switching techniques can reduce delays. Trade-offs between circuit switching and other types of switching depend strongly on switching times.

2. Message Switching

Sometimes there is no need for a circuit to be established all the way from the source to the destination. Consider a connection between the users. A and D are represented by a series of links (AB, BC, and CD).

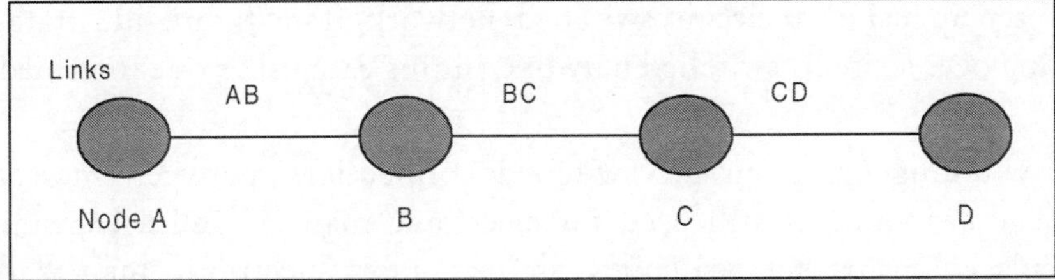

Figure 6.29 *A Connection between Two Systems A and D Formed from 3 Links.*

For instance, when a telex (or email) message is sent from A to D, it first passes over a local connection (AB). It is then passed at some later time to C (via link BC), and from there to the destination (via link CD). At each message switch, the received message is stored, and a connection is subsequently made to deliver the message to the neighboring message switch. Message switching is also known as store-and-forward switching since the messages are stored at intermediate nodes en route to their destinations.

The figure 6.30 illustrates message switching; transmission of only one message is illustrated for simplicity. As a complete message is sent from node A to node B when the link interconnecting them becomes available. Since the message may be competing with other messages for access to facilities, a queuing delay may be incurred while waiting for the link to become available. The

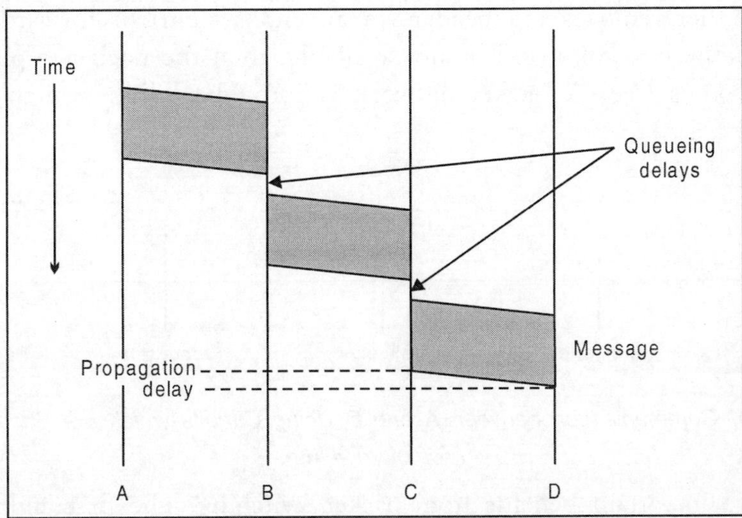

Figure 6.30 *The Use of Message Switching to Communicate between A and D.*

message is stored at B until the next link becomes available, with another queuing delay before it can be forwarded. It repeats this process until it reaches its destination.

Circuit setup delays are replaced by queueing delays. Considerable extra delay may result from storage at individual nodes. A delay for putting the message on the communications link (message length in bits divided by link speed in bps) is also incurred at each node en route. Message lengths are slightly longer than they are in circuit switching, after establishment of the circuit, since header information must be included with each message; the header includes information identifying the destination as well as other types of information.

Most message switched networks do not use dedicated point-to-point links and therefore a call must be set-up using a circuit switched network. The figure illustrates the use of message switching over a circuit switched network, in this case using one intermediate message switch.

Message switching using circuit switched connections between message switches. Although message switching is still used for electronic mail and telex transmission, it has largely been replaced by packet switching (in fact, most electronic mail is carried using message switching with the links between message switches provided by packet or circuit switched networks).

3. Packet Switching

Packet switching is similar to message switching using short messages. Any message exceeding a network-defined maximum length is broken up into shorter units, known as packets, for transmission; the packets, each with an associated header, are then transmitted individually through the network. The fundamental difference in packet communication is that the data is formed into packets with a pre-defined header format (i.e. PCI), and well-known "idle" patterns which are used to occupy the link when there is no data to be communicated.

A packet network equipment discards the "idle" patterns between packets and processes the entire packet as one piece of data. The equipment examines the packet header information (PCI) and then either removes the header (in an end system) or forwards the packet to another system. If the out-going link is not available, then the packet is placed in a queue until the link becomes free. A packet network is formed by links which connect packet network equipment.

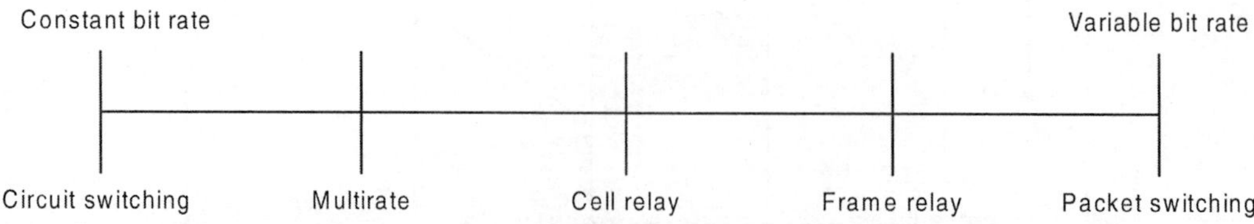

Figure 6.31 *Communication between A and D Using Circuits which are Shared Using Packet Switching.*

There are two important benefits from packet switching. The first and most important benefit is that since packets are short, the communication links between the nodes are only allocated to transferring a single message for a short period of time while transmitting each packet. Longer messages require a series of packets to be sent, but do not require the link to be dedicated between the transmission of each packet. The implication is that packets belonging to other messages may be sent between the packets of the message being sent from A to D. This provides a much fairer sharing of the resources of each of the links.

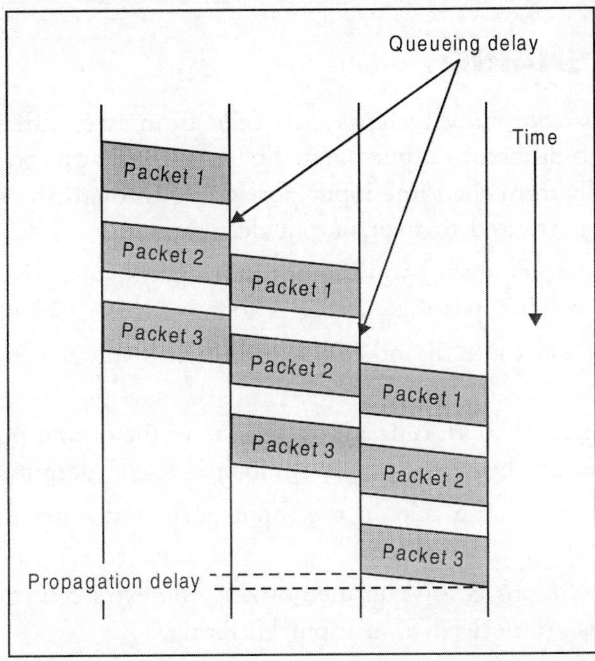

Figure 6.32 *Packet-switched Communication between Systems A and D.*

Another benefit of packet switching is known as "pipelining". Pipelining is visible in the figure above. At the time packet 1 is sent from B to C, packet 2 is sent from A to B; packet 1 is sent from C to D while packet 2 is sent from B to C, and packet 3 is sent from A to B, and so forth. This simultaneous use of communications links represents a gain in efficiency, the total delay for transmission across a packet network may be considerably less than for message switching, despite the inclusion of a header in each packet rather than in each message.

INTRODUCTION

Many characteristics of switched communication networks are directly dependent on how data is relayed over the wires. Early networks carried continuous bitstreams over physical links in a technique called circuit switching, well suited to transmit voice or real time data from a single sender to a single receiver (unicast communication). However, a physical link failure in circuit switching networks has dramatic consequences leading to the interruption of all communications using the failed link. Datagram packet switching networks like the Internet fix these drawbacks by cutting data into small chunks called *packets*. In datagram packet switching networks, two consecutive packets from the same communication are independently handled by the network. Therefore, when a link fails, packets previously sent on the failed link can be *rerouted* to avoid the failed link and communications are not interrupted. Datagram packet switching networks are said to be *resilient* to link failures because link failures are hidden to end-users. On the other hand, it is more difficult to manage end-to-end flows of data in datagram packet switching networks than in circuit switching networks due to the lack of a separate circuit for each flow.

SWITCHING SCENARIO

Some switching scenarios. Scenario 1 shows two cells from two different input ports going through the switch to two different output ports. These two cells can be simultaneously routed. Scenario 2 shows two cells from the same input port going through the switch to two different output ports. Both cells are routed to their output destinations.

Scenario 3 shows two cells from two different input ports going through the switch to the same output port. There are five possible strategies to solve this problem:

1. To drop one cell and route the other. This solution involves a data lost, hence, it is not a good approach.
2. To route simultaneously both cells and memorize in the output port the cell that has not been sent on the attached line. This technique is called output buffering.
3. To memorize the incoming cells in the input ports and route them. This technique is called input buffering.
4. The two other solutions consist on memorizing the extra cells during the routing task. These techniques are derived from input buffering.

PACKET SWITCHING VERSUS CIRCUIT SWITCHING

In a *circuit-switched* network architecture, a dedicated circuit is established between a sender and a receiver, and the signals coming from one end are transmitted to the other. This connection is maintained for as long as both parties desire, after which it is closed. The drawback is that if a large part of a conversation consists of silence, the line carrying the conversation is effectively idle for most of the time. This problem is considerably aggravated for *digital* signals, which are sent in staccato bursts rather than continuously. Since no other use can be made of a line while a call is in progress, circuit-switching inevitably suffers from a considerable waste of expensive resources.

This problem can be solved by *packet-switching*. The idea is to divide messages into message blocks or *packets* before sending them out across the network. The blocks are sent separately and rejoined into a whole when they are received at their destination. To this end, packets are put in the computer equivalent of an envelope, which contains information on the origin, the address and the sequence number. In the place of switches which merely connect and disconnect circuits, packet networks use routers-computers that read the address of a packet and pass it to another router closer to the destination. At the destination, the packets are received, reassembled in the correct order and converted back into the original message. The routers are permanently connected via high-speed lines, whose capacity is used much more economically than the links of a circuit-switched network.

MOBILE TELEPHONE SYSTEM

Mobile Phones—Technology

The mobile phone, also known as cellular phone, has become one of the most successful inventions in the 20th century. In the late 90's, mobile phones became one of the major communication devices. The first commercial mobile phone system started in 1979 in Japan. According to cellular online, the global mobile phone subscribers in 2003 are around 1.52 billion, which is about 20 percent of the current world population. This figure 6.33 showed the success of the mobile phone industries. In about 20 years' time, this technology conquered the global and became a demand for the majority of people in the world. It provided communication for people no matter anywhere and anytime.

Mobile phones were meant to be a device which enables users to have the ease on telecommunication freely wherever they want. But in the late 90's, SMS (Short Message Service), a new technology was brought out. SMS is a transmission of short text message from mobile phones to mobile phones. This became a revolution making mobile phones to develop into a device that not only allows simple voice to voice telecommunication. Mobile phone now not only

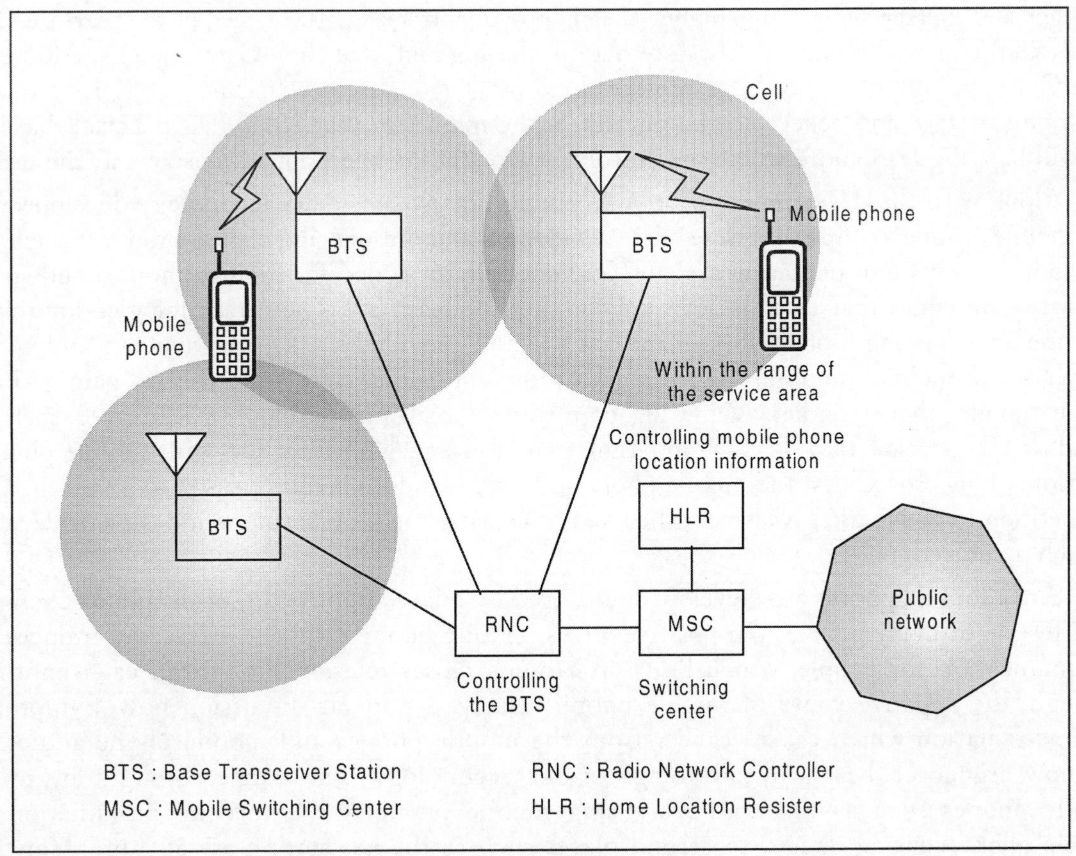

Figure 6.33 *Mobile Phone System.*

became an entertainment device (featuring functions such as camera, FM and MP3 players etc) but also allowing users to access through Internet, Personal Digital Assistant (PDA) functions and also having video conference using the latest 3G network. Someday, mobile phones might be able to replace computers.

From the early stages of analog cellular to now the latest 3G mobile phone system, the mobile phone developed rapidly in the past 20 years. Each stage of development provided a big improve to the industries. From early stages of voice to voice simple communication, to the WAP and GPRS Internet connection and now the high speed Internet connection through the Internet, it showed that mobile phones is one of the leading technology in the high technology industry. The convenience brought by this technology indeed changed the life of many people and society. Many things such as banking, gathering information such as reports or latest news, control the share market via GPRS etc are what the technology helped to improve and ease the life of people. Japan is the country which the mobile phone technology develops the fastest in the world. Before the 3G technology was launched in other countries, the Japanese had already mastered the technology.

Studies believed that a new mobile phone network system, 4G will be in the market in the nearby future. 4G, or known as the fourth generation mobile is a whole new radio access network. Stronger and clearer signals and higher speed (broadband speed, 100 times faster than the 3G connection) connection through the Internet are the highlights of the 4G technology. Although the 3G technology had only been promoted no long ago, this new technology is now under development stage and believed to be put out in the market in year 2010. It is believed that the 4G will be a big leap and a whole new revolution for the mobile phone industry and the users.

Along with the development of mobile phones, many subsidiary technology developed by the mobile phone companies were also developed and influencing other products such as Bluetooth, symbian(an operating system (OS) specially designed for mobile phones) and some software companies that designs software for the Symbian OS. These technologies improved the interactive among mobile phones and the users. It provided a much convenience and wider usage for the mobile phone users. More and more companies now are trying to gain a share in the mobile phone market. Many big companies which are developing PDA OS such as Window CE (Pocket PC), PALM and Linux are also engaging their OS with mobile phones functions. This proved that the mobile phone industry is indeed a good market to invest in. The competition in the market is also another reason causing the mobile phone industry to develop in such a short time.

Since mobile phone was developed and used by a large population of people, it changed the lifestyle of many people. On positive views, mobile phone provided a fast and immediate communication for people, which built up a much closer relationship within each another. Though, the negative views of mobile phone became a popular discussion now. Symptoms such as radiation which causes cancer from the mobile phones and mobile phone addiction are now argued to be the disadvantage of the technology. The danger brought by using mobile phones such as the unsafe of using mobile phone during driving or radiation of mobile phone causing danger to certain places such as the gas station are also problems for mobile phone users.

REVIEW QUESTIONS

1. Name three types of transmission impairment.
2. What type of lines are long distance calls carried on ?
3. What is the voice bandwidth of the telephone system ?
4. What is the purpose of a repeater on long distance lines ?
5. What is the bandwidth of the telephone system ?
6. What type of telephone line-scan can be conditioned ?
7. Can the bit rate be less than the pulse rate? Why or why not ?
8. Why is synchronization a problem in data communications ?
9. How can block coding aid in synchronization ?
10. How can block coding aid in error detection ?

❑❑❑

7

CABLE TELEVISION

The first foray into cable television appears to have taken place simultaneously in both Pennsylvania and Oregon in the late 1940s and early 1950s. At the time, the fledgling television industry provided broadcast signals only to the most populous (that is, economically advantageous) areas. For those regions that had poor TV reception either because of obstructions or long distances from signal transmitters, cable television provided a workable solution. Essentially, the early cable providers constructed large antennas on hilltops or buildings for improved TV reception, and then strung coaxial cable from the antenna to the local community. Out of this environment the acronym CATV, representing Community Antenna Television was born.

With the advent of satellite broadcasts to cable systems in the 1970s, cable operators were able to provide more channels than were available over the traditional airwaves. Because of these value added capabilities, cable television made significant inroads into markets where TV reception was already reasonably acceptable. Additional services such as specialty channels and pay-per-view have brought the cable industry to where it is today: approximately 63% of American households have cable TV, and cable service passes by about 95% of all U.S. residences.

The cable industry is less than 50 years old, and yet with such a large market penetration, is already reasonably mature. In searching for growth opportunities, the much ballyhooed National Information Infrastructure (NII) or “information superhighway” provides an opening for cable television to build upon its extensive architecture and experience to deliver the necessary features for the upcoming information age.

SYSTEM ARCHITECTURE

Traditional cable television systems can be divided into five major sections. Figure 7.1 depicts graphically the “tree and branch” architecture.

The head-end is the center of CATV activity. It is here where external signals such as satellite, microwave, and local TV station broadcasts are received from the various types of deployed antennas. Additionally, locally produced and pre-recorded programs can be introduced into the mix. Ultimately it is the head-end’s responsibility to process, combine, and assign a channel frequency to all signals destined for cable distribution.

A number of trunks, originally constructed out of large diameter coaxial cable, carry the signals from the head-end to a series of distribution points. Trunk cables share the same properties as do generic transmission lines with regard to attenuation; in order to maintain adequate signal strength over long distances, amplifiers are required at regular intervals. Much experience has shown that on average, amplifiers need to be spaced approximately 2,000 feet apart. Only a finite number may be cascaded (approximately 30-40), as each amplifier introduces additional noise and distortion to the signal. There are well known thresholds of signal distortion, above which, TV picture quality will be affected.

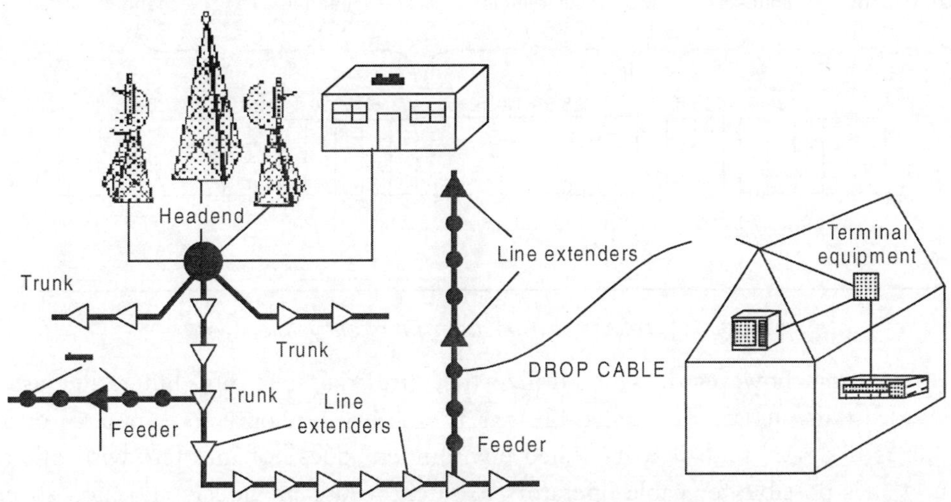

Figure 7.1 *Traditional Cable Television Architecture.*

The smaller distribution or feeder cables branch out from the trunks and are responsible for serving local neighborhoods. To avoid excessive attenuation and noise, feeder cable is also severely limited in length, since usually a maximum of two amplifiers, called line extenders, are allowed per feeder. The statement that 95% of households can be reached by cable services means that those homes are sufficiently close enough to a feeder cable.

Feeder cables are tapped at periodic locations to furnish the familiar coaxial drop cables that enter directly into the customer's premises. Drop cables too are limited in length to about 150 feet. Terminal equipment (consumer electronics) is connected to the drop cable inside the home. Among the more common devices are televisions, VCRs, set-top boxes, converters, descramblers, splitters, and cable modems.

Cable Television Advantages and Disadvantages

Compared to the telephone industry, cable television systems do have, and have had for 50 years, a truly high-bandwidth delivery system to the home. The simple reason for this fact is that television is, even by today's standards, a high-bandwidth application. During the 1940's, when broadcast standards were being set by the NTSC (National Television Systems Committee), technology and compromise dictated that each television channel be assigned a 6-MHz portion of the electromagnetic spectrum. Since that time, much has improved to increase utilization of the spectrum, but the standards still remain the same—it would be very difficult to force all consumers to replace their NTSC compliant equipment for devices based upon newer albeit better standards.

Figure 7.2 graphically represents the television spectrum allocation. The 6-MHz-wide channels were prudently assigned to avoid inter channel interference. The remaining unallocated terrestrial spectrum is dedicated to a host of other communication services.

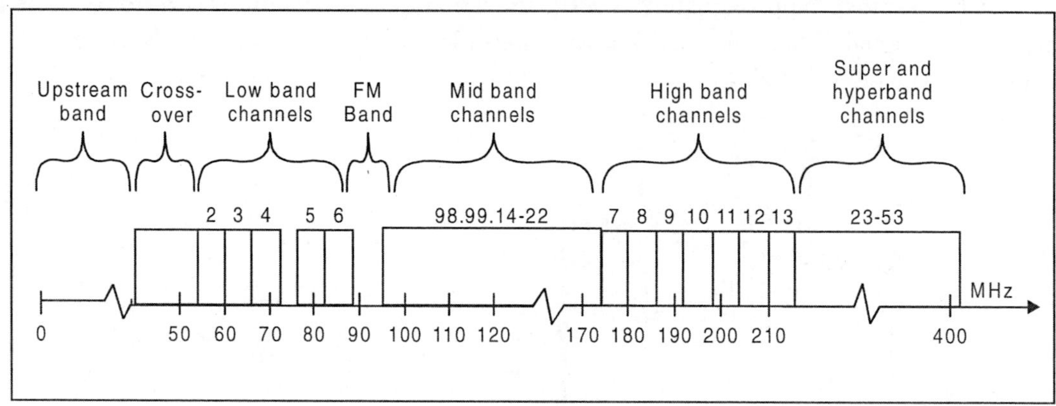

Figure 7.2 *Television Spectrum Frequency Allocation.*

Cable television, however does not utilize the terrestrial spectrum, but rather uses coaxial cable to broadcast its signals. Coaxial cable has the ability not only to "emulate" over-the-air spectrum, but is designed such that its sealed environment does not interfere with other signals. Consequently, it is possible for cable operators to safely re-use previously allocated spectrum, or to deploy multiple cables, each of which contains its own separate impervious spectra.

Regrettably, the original cable systems architecture was never really envisioned to be a general purpose two-way communications medium. Its primary goal was simply to deliver high bandwidth video signals to residences. In order to accommodate upstream communications, the existing cable plant must be upgraded.

CABLE MODEMS

A cable modem is used to connect a computer to a cable TV service that provides Internet access. Cable modems can dramatically increase the bandwidth between the user's computer and the Internet service provider, specially in the downlink (from ISP to user). Unlike analog modems that take time to dial a number. Cable modems connect to the computer via an Ethernet port, which is an always-on connection. Ethernet is a shared medium, and the individual user's speed will vary depending on how many customers are sending or receiving data on that cable segment at the same time.

The cable modem technology is a competitive technology to bridge the last mile. Cable television companies are battling head to head with the phone companies to provide high speed bandwidth to homes. The telephone companies have the digital equipment backbone (starting at the central office) but they are crippled by the existing local loop cable.

The cable television companies have the high speed bandwidth to the homes, but don't have the digital equipment backbones at the head end (the head end is where all the television signals in a cable TV line originate from). Cable modems use the existing cable TV line to provide the high speed bandwidth.

It is an asymmetrical transfer rates with the upstream data transfer rate at 2 Mbps. The downstream data transfer rate is a maximum of 30 Mbps. Most users connect the cable modem to their 10 Mbps Ethernet NIC, and don't utilize the cable modems full bandwidth. Switching to a 100 Mbps Ethernet NIC would give them full bandwidth.

The actual transfer speed depends upon the number of users that are online. The cable line is shared with the other subscribers in the local neighborhood. Most cable companies use dynamic IP addressing: each time the user connects, they are assigned a new IP address. For a fee, permanent static IP addresses can be assigned.

Most cable TV companies are placing high performance web proxy servers at the head end. These servers store the most commonly accessed web pages and files locally at the head end. The user's web browser first checks the proxy server to see if the file has been downloaded there. If it hasn't, then it goes out on the Internet to download it. The storing of the web pages and files on the local proxy server reduces the load on the communication servers (to the Internet), and gives the impression of extremely fast Internet access.

Cable Modems Standards

There are three competing standards for cable modems at the time of this writing.

1. The European standard DVB/DAVIC
2. The American standard MCNS
3. The geneva standard IEEE 802.14

Only the geneva standard guarantees the transfer rate.

Cable Modems Premise Equipment

The cable modem is connected to the existing cable TV RG59 coax line, using a standard RF connector. The output of the cable modem is a 10BaseT or 100BaseT Ethernet connection to your NIC.

Cable Modems Security Issues

Cable modems have some security issues. Users can see each other on network neighborhood (in windows). Some systems have each cable modem connection encrypted.

The assignment of IP addresses is based on the MAC address of the Ethernet card. Hackers can access the network if they know another users' MAC addresses.

Cable Modem Advantages

- Fast data transfers, up to 30 Mbps if using a 100BaseT NIC
- Competitive pricing against competing technologies
- Easy to install—home pre-wired

Cable Modem Disadvantages

- The available bandwidth depends on the number of users on the local cable TV line segment.
- There is an asymmetrical transfer rate. Upstream is slower than downstream.
- There can be a bottleneck at the communication server at the head end.

A device that has received considerable attention resulting, in part, from the upgrade of television cable delivery systems and the desire for faster bit rates for Internet connections. The cable modem is designed to interface with the analog components of a cable TV (CATV) provider. Many CATV subscribers are already familiar with the cable box that typically sits on top of a television. It is connected to a wall jack through which incoming CATV signals are transmitted. The box decodes incoming scrambled signals and sends them to the television for viewing. In many areas the box can also receive commands from a remote controller and send signal back to the cable company. This ability allows subscribers to order and watch pay-per-view movies. To some extent the cable modem is similar as in figure 7.3. Like a regular cable box, it can route TV signals to a television. However, it also has an extra output jack that can connect to a PC. In this capacity it functions much like the modems, by converting between analog and digital signals.

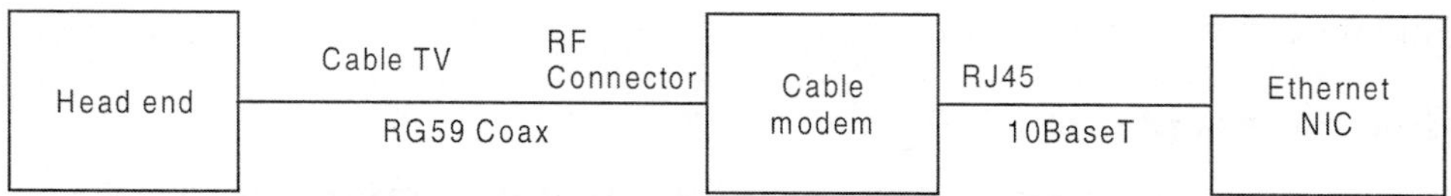

Figure 7.3 *Cable Modems Premise Equipment.*

In effect, the cable modem is designed to give us access to the Internet via the CATV signals instead of calling an Internet service provider over the telephone. There are several advantages to this setup. One is that information can be transmitted using the high-frequency signals of CATV instead of the much lower frequencies of the telephone's local loop, resulting in much higher data rates (measured in Mbps instead of Kbps). Another advantage is that we will not need to dial in to make a connection, the connection is always there. A disadvantage is that although there are vendors making cable modems, there is not yet a standard governing the transportation of data over cable television networks.

The figure 7.3 shows the basic operation of a cable modem. Typically, a cable signal coming into a home has a frequency range of up to about 750 MHz. This signal is divided into 6 MHz bands, each of which carries the signal from a particular station such as discovery, ESPN, or CNN. Tuning in a channel effectively blocks out unwanted frequencies and allows only one 6 MHz signal to pass, enabling us to view the desired station. For Internet access, the cable company maintains a connection to the Internet through a provider. Information from the Internet can then be downloaded onto a 6 MHz band somewhere between 42 MHz and 750 MHz.

At the user's end the cable modem can access downloaded information by tuning into the appropriate 6 MHz band and converting those analog signals to a digital format.

There are a number of techniques that can be used for modulating and demodulating, but two of the more popular are Quaternary Phase Shift Keying (QPSK) and Quadrature Amplitude Modulation (QAM64). Both are much more complex versions of similarly named techniques. QAM methods are typical for the high-bandwidth requirements of downloading information. Some estimates have placed downloaded data rates at up to 36 Mbps. Many PCs are not capable of receiving data that quickly, however, so more realistic rates are between 3 Mbps and 10 Mbps.

The cable modem can also transmit information in the other direction (uploading). It can take information received from a PC and modulate it into a frequency range usually between 5 MHz and 40 MHz. This is the range typically used by a two-way cable network for uploading. A problem is that signals in this range are more susceptible to electrical interference from home appliances. As a result, QPSK techniques are more common for uploading because they tend to be more robust. The drawback is that they have smaller bit rates. On the other hand uploading usually has smaller bandwidth demands. For example, sending email or commands usually requires much less data than downloading a graphic image.

DSL VS. CABLE MODEM COMPARISON

Both offer advantages to the home and small business customer. Is the cable company in your neighborhood offering a "sweet deal" on their cable modem service? May be the phone company has contacted you about their new DSL rollout? Some people live in places where neither cable modem nor DSL service is available, but many others have the choice of both.

Head to Head

Both Digital Subscriber Line (DSL) and cable modem services offer high-speed Internet access. Compared to traditional dial-up access, these two technologies open up homes and small businesses to a new realm of possibilities for network connectivity and applications. Video-on-demand, multimedia conferencing, and online gaming are just a few examples of services on the net that don't work so well at 56 kbps but can function nicely at broadband data rates.

While similar in many respects, DSL and cable modem differ in some fundamental ways. The two technologies can be compared and contrasted along these dimensions:

- Speed
- Cost
- Security
- Reliability and availability
- Usability and quality of service

Some of the differences between DSL and cable modem arise from the history of the technologies they are built upon. Others originate with differences in the approach of service providers. In fact, the speed, cost, availability, and many other elements of DSL *or* cable modem service can vary significantly depending on the provider.

In terms of theoretical peak raw performance, cable modem generally wins the speed battle over DSL. Cable technology can, in theory, achieve networking speeds of approximately 30 Mbps (using a 100 Mbps network interface card), whereas most forms of DSL cannot reach 10 Mbps. (VDSL is one variant of DSL that matches cable's performance, but it is not generally available.)

In practice, though, the speed advantage of cable over DSL is much lower than might first be apparent. Both cable modem and DSL performance vary from one minute to the next depending on the pattern of use and traffic congestion on the Internet. This means that both services will rarely—if ever, reach peak performance.

Furthermore, cable modem technology delivers *shared bandwidth* within the local neighborhood while DSL delivers *dedicated local bandwidth*. With cable, performance at any given time depends on how many cable subscribers in the neighborhood are currently actively using the network *as well as* load on the Internet generally. This "double whammy" suggests that cable modem will perform relatively slower during peak usage periods.

Keynote systems completed a benchmark test that backs up this assertion. Keynote showed that a very modest ADSL service (offering 384 kbps downstream and 128 kbps upstream) actually outperformed cable during the "peak personal hours" of 5 PM to 11 PM. While bandwidth on the net is ultimately always shared at some point, it seems that cable services remain more susceptible to the phenomenon than DSL services.

Speed Caps

Both cable and DSL service providers have commonly employed the controversial practice of bandwidth caps for their home customers. Bandwidth caps place an artificial limit on the maximum speed a customer can achieve by monitoring their current usage and throttling network packets if necessary. Service providers may have several motivations for imposing caps including the following:

1. Providers concerned about the capacity limits of their network may implement a short-term cap so that they can accommodate more customers without causing scalability problems.
2. Providers may believe that the vast majority of customers do not actually need any more bandwidth than that allowed under the cap.
3. Providers may want to create a fair-and-equal distribution of bandwidth of customers rather than allow customers closer to the central office to receive disproportionately more bandwidth.
4. Providers may be attempting to increase future profits by generating demand for "premium" classes of service—customers may be willing to pay more for a higher cap or no-cap level of performance.

DSL Speed

DSL services typically offered today typically range in performance from 128 kbps to 1.544 Mbps. It can be difficult to pin down precise speed numbers for DSL because of the many variations in equipment. DSL is also a *distance-sensitive* technology, and that complicates the performance picture even further.

The bandwidth available to a home user, for example, depends significantly on the length of cabling running from the home to the provider's facilities as well as the electrical quality of that line.

LasVegas. NET is a fairly typical regional provider of DSL service. It offers three different performance packages as follows:

Table 7.1

Package	*Downstream / Upstream Data Rate*
Standard	512 kbps/128 kbps
Premium	1.544 Mbps/384 kbps
Executive	640 kbps/640 kbps

Although it may seem limiting, asymmetric DSL services are still more commonly used than symmetric ones. Most Net users require more bandwidth for surfing the web (that involves frequent loading of web pages) than they do for sending email or web publishing (that involves transmitting data to remote locations). Therefore, an ADSL user tends to spend very little of their time limited by a 128 kbps upstream data rate. Symmetric DSL (SDSL) service can be more appealing to business customers, however, who tend to use a different mix of applications and need more bandwidth in both directions.

Cable Speed

Cable service providers usually don't quote absolute performance numbers like the DSL vendors because of the differences in dedicated versus shared bandwidth. For example, on their home page the road runner cable modem service states:

Today, cable modem retains a slight performance advantage over DSL but this advantage seems to be a short-term one. Most cable networks have not yet reached high enough subscriber levels to make the shared bandwidth issue critical. With technologies like dedicated-bandwidth VDSL, however, DSL threatens to erase cable's speed advantage even before cable services become overcrowded.

When debating the relative merits of cable modem and DSL service, network security might be the most controversial item on the comparison chart. At first glance it appears one clearly wins the security battle over the other, but does this commonly held opinion stand up to closer scrutiny?

Cable's Network Neighborhood

Cable modem service uses a shared cable line to provide service to an entire neighborhood. Essentially, all cable customers in the region belong to the same Local Area Network (LAN). Without any security measures in place, anybody in the neighborhood might technically be able to click on their windows network neighborhood icon and actually see the computer names and addresses of their neighbors on the service. If a customer enables file sharing on any drives, neighbors could even download copies of their data!

Although some cable customers encountered this problem in the past, many providers avoid this problem today by bundling security features in the cable modem hardware. In particular, basic network firewall capabilities will prevent files from being viewed or downloaded. Most cable modems today also implement the Data Over Cable Service Interface Specification (DOCSIS). DOCSIS includes support for cable network security features including authentication and packet filtering.

DSL uses dedicated rather than shared cabling, and DSL customers in a given neighborhood do not appear as nodes on a LAN. From this, many have concluded DSL service provides better security. However, this argument is at best an oversimplified one.

56K Technology

While the V.9x standards define a rate of 56 Kbits/sec, this is never met due to rate restrictions, line noise, and cable distance. Estimates are that less than 30 percent of the lines in the U.S. are clean enough to let these modems operate near top speed. The shorter the distance of the local loop, the better.

INTERNET OVER CABLE

For implementing and starting the Internet access over cable following devices are required, they are listed below:

Cable Modem

A modem designed to operate over cable TV lines. Because the coaxial cable used by cable TV provides much greater bandwidth than telephone lines, a cable modem can be used to achieve extremely fast access to the world wide web. This, combined with the fact that millions of homes are already wired for cable TV, has made the cable modem something of a holy grail for Internet and cable TV companies.

There are a number of technical difficulties, however. One is that the cable TV infrastructure is designed to broadcast TV signals in just one direction from the cable TV company to people's homes. The Internet, however, is a two-way system where data also needs to flow from the client to the server. In addition, it is still unknown whether the cable TV networks can handle the traffic that would ensue if millions of users began using the system for Internet access.

Cable Head-End

A cable television company's local facility that originates and communicates cable modem and cable TV services to its subscribers. The cable company's head-end includes the CMTS, which is essential in providing high-speed Internet access to cable subscribers.

Web TV

Originally, a general term for a whole category of products and technologies that enable you to surf the web on your TV. Most web TV products today consist of a small box that connects to your telephone line and television. It makes a connection to the Internet via your telephone service and then converts the downloaded web pages to a format that can be displayed on your TV. These products also come with a remote control device so that you can navigate through the web. More recently, the name web TV has been trademarked by microsoft.

Address

A location of data, usually in main memory or on a disk. You can think of computer memory as an array of storage boxes, each of which is one byte in length. Each box has an address (a unique number) assigned to it. By specifying a memory address, programmers can access a particular byte of data. Disks are divided into tracks and sectors, each of which has a unique address.

CABLE MODEMS

Cable modems are devices that allow high-speed access to the Internet via a cable television network. While similar in some respects to a traditional analog modem, a cable modem is significantly more powerful, capable of delivering data approximately 500 times faster.

Working of Cable Modem

Current Internet access via a 28.8, 33.6, or 56–kbps modem is referred to as voice-band modem technology. Like voice-band modems, cable modems modulate and demodulate data signals. However, cable modems incorporate more functionality suitable for today's high-speed Internet services. In a cable network, data from the network to the user is referred to as downstream, whereas data from the user to the network is referred to as upstream. From a user perspective, a cable modem is a 64/256 QAM RF receiver capable of delivering up to 30 to 40 Mbps of data in one 6-MHz cable channel. This is approximately 500 times faster than a 56–kbps modem. Data from a user to the network is sent in a flexible and programmable system under control of the head-end. The data is modulated using a QPSK/16 QAM transmitter with data rates from 320 kbps up to 10 Mbps. The upstream and downstream data rates may be flexibly configured using cable modems to match subscriber needs. For instance, a business service can be programmed to receive as well as transmit higher bandwidth. A residential user, however, may be configured to receive higher bandwidth access to the Internet while limited to low bandwidth transmission to the network.

A subscriber can continue to receive cable television service while simultaneously receiving data on cable modems to be delivered to a Personal Computer (PC) with the help of a simple one-to-two splitter (see figure 7.4). The data service offered by a cable modem may be shared by up to sixteen users in a Local Area Network (LAN) configuration.

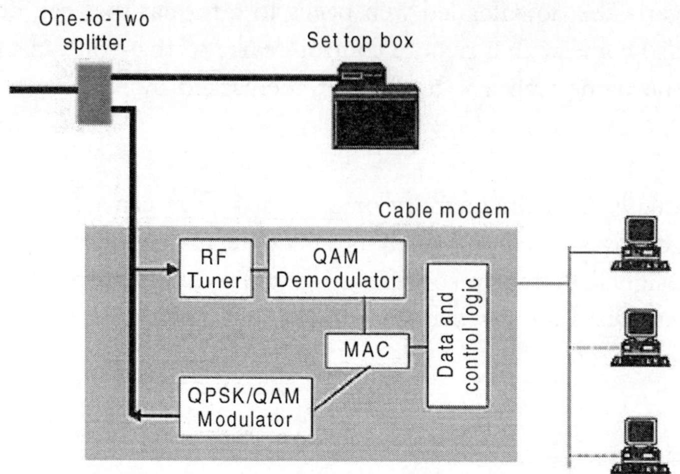

Figure 7.4 *Cable Modem at the Subscriber Location.*

Because some cable networks are suited for broadcast television services, cable modems may use either a standard telephone line or a QPSK/16 QAM modem over a two-way cable system to transmit data upstream from a user location to the network. When a telephone line is used in conjunction with a one-way broadcast network, the cable data system is referred to as a telephony return interface (TRI) system. In this mode, a satellite or wireless cable television network can also function as a data network.

At the cable headend, data from individual users is filtered by upstream demodulators (or telephone-return systems, as appropriate) for further processing by a cable modem termination system (CMTS). A CMTS is a data switching system specifically designed to route data from many cable modem users over a multiplexed network interface. Likewise, a CMTS receives data from the Internet and provides data switching necessary to route data to the cable modem users. Data from the network to a user group is sent to a 64/256 QAM modulator. The result is user data modulated into one 6-MHz channel, which is the spectrum allocated for a cable television channel such as ABC, NBC, or TBS for broadcast to all users in existence.

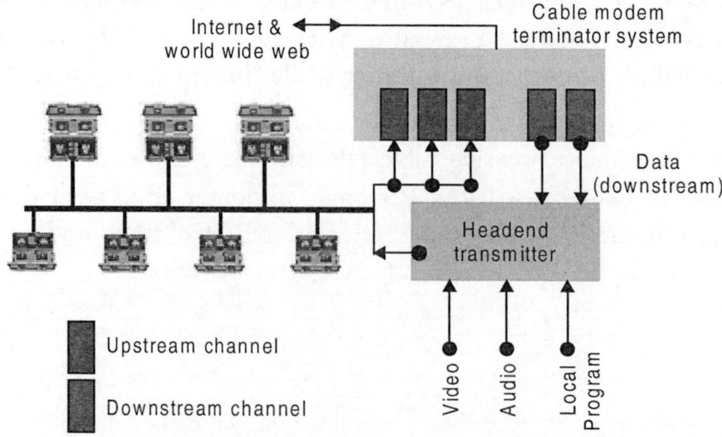

Figure 7.5 *Cable Modem Termination System and Cable Head-end Transmission.*

A cable head-end combines the downstream data channels with the video, pay-per-view, audio, and local advertiser programs that are received by television subscribers. The combined signal is then transmitted throughout the cable distribution network. At the user location, the television signal is received by a set-top box, while user data is separately received by a cable modem box and sent to a PC.

A CMTS is an important new element for support of data services that integrates upstream and downstream communication over a cable data network. The number of upstream and downstream channels in a given CMTS can be engineered based on serving area, number of users, data rates offered to each user, and available spectrum.

Another important element in the operations and day-to-day management of a cable data system is an Element Management System (EMS). An EMS is an operations system designed specifically to configure and manage a CMTS and associated cable modem subscribers. The operations tasks include provisioning, day-to-day administration, monitoring, alarms, and testing of various components of a CMTS. From a central network operations center (NOC), a single EMS can support many CMTS systems in the geographic region.

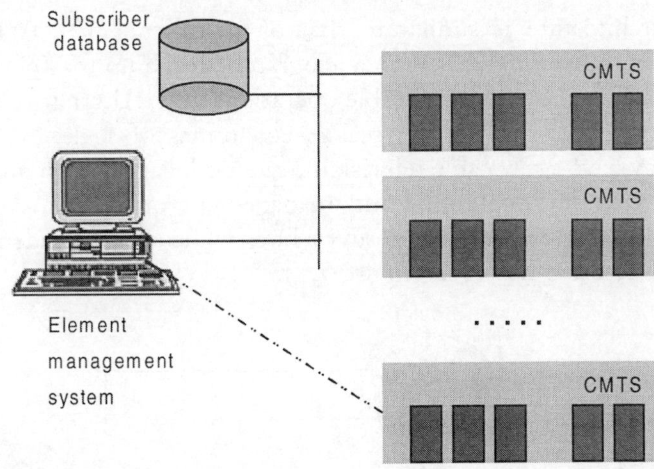

Figure 7.6 *Operations and Management of Cable Data Systems.*

Cable Data System Features

Beyond modulation and demodulation, a cable modem incorporates many features necessary to extend broadband communications to Wide Area Networks (WANs). The network layer is chosen as Internet Protocol (IP) to support the Internet and world wide web services. The data link layer is comprised of three sub-layers: logical link control sub-layer, link security sub-layer conforming to the security requirements, and Media Access Control (MAC) sub-layer suitable for cable system operations. Current cable modem systems use Ethernet frame format for data transmission over upstream and downstream data channels. Each of the downstream data channels and the associated upstream data channels on a cable network form an extended Ethernet WAN. As the number of subscribers increases, a cable operator can add more upstream and downstream data channels to support demand for additional bandwidth in the cable data network. From this perspective, growth of new cable data networks can be managed in much the same fashion as the growth of Ethernet LANs within a corporate environment.

The link security sublayer requirements are further defined in three sets of requirements: Baseline Privacy Interface (BPI), Security System Interface (SSI), and Removable Security Module interface (RSMI). BPI provides cable modem users with data privacy across the cable network by encrypting data traffic between the user's cable modem and CMTS. The operational support provided by the EMS allows a CMTS to map a cable modem identity to paying subscribers and thereby authorize subscriber access to data network services. Thus, the privacy and security requirements protect user data as well as prevent theft of cable data services.

Early discussions in the Institute of Electrical and Electronic Engineers (IEEE) 802.14 committee referred to the use of Asynchronous Transfer Mode (ATM) over cable data networks to facilitate multiple services including telephone, data, and video, all of which are supported over cable modems. Although current cable modem standards incorporate Ethernet over cable modem, extensions are provided in the standards for future support of ATM or other protocol data units. IP—telephony support over cable data networks is expected to be a new value-added service in the near term.

Cable Data Network Architecture

Cable data network architecture is similar to that of an office LAN. A CMTS provides an extended Ethernet network over a WAN with a geographic reach up to 100 miles. The cable data network may be fully managed by the local cable operations unit. Alternatively, all operations may be aggregated at a regional data center to realize economies of scale. A given geographic or metropolitan region may have a few cable television headend locations that are connected together by fiber links. The day-to-day operations and management of a cable data network may be consolidated at a single location, such as a super hub, while other headend locations may be economically managed as basic hubs (see figure 7.7).

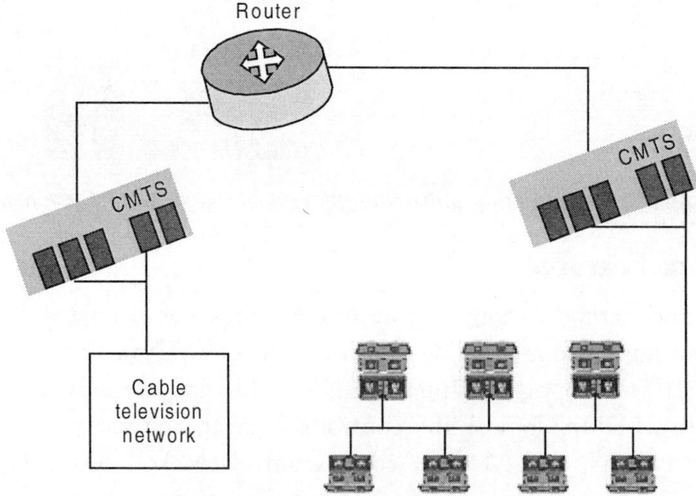

Figure 7.7 *Basic Distribution Hub.*

A basic distribution hub is a minimal data network configuration that exists within a cable television head-end. A typical head-end is equipped with satellite receivers, fiber connections to other regional head-end locations, and upstream RF receivers for pay-per-view and data services. The minimal data network configuration includes a CMTS system capable of upstream and downstream data transport and an IP router to connect to the super hub location.

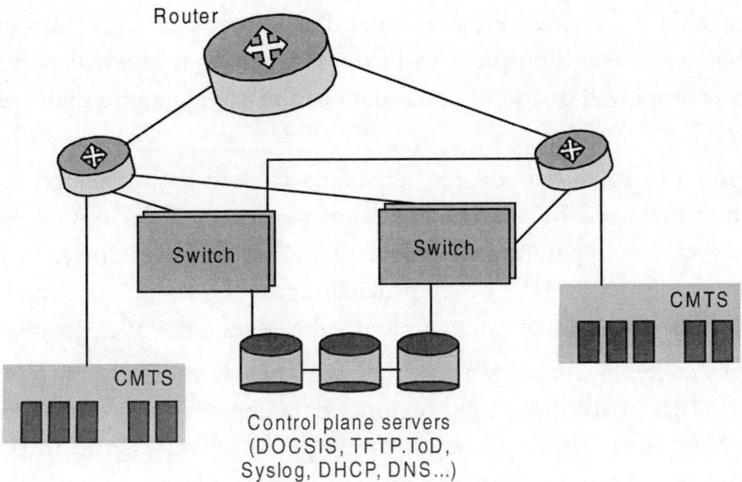

Figure 7.8 *Super Hub.*

A super hub is a cable head-end location with additional temperature-controlled facilities to house a variety of computer servers, which are necessary to run cable data networks. The servers include file transfer, user authorization and accounting, log control (syslog), IP address assignment and administration (DHCP servers), DNS servers, and data over cable service interface specifications (DOCSIS) control servers. In addition, a super hub may deploy operations support and network management systems necessary for the television as well as data network operations.

User data from basic and super hub locations is received at a regional data center for further aggregation and distribution throughout the network (see figure 7.9). A super hub supports Dynamic Host Configuration Protocol (DHCP), DNS (domain name server), and log control servers necessary for the cable data network administration. A regional data center provides connectivity to the Internet and the world wide web and contains the server farms necessary to support Internet services. These servers include e-mail, web hosting, news, chat, proxy, caching, and streaming media servers.

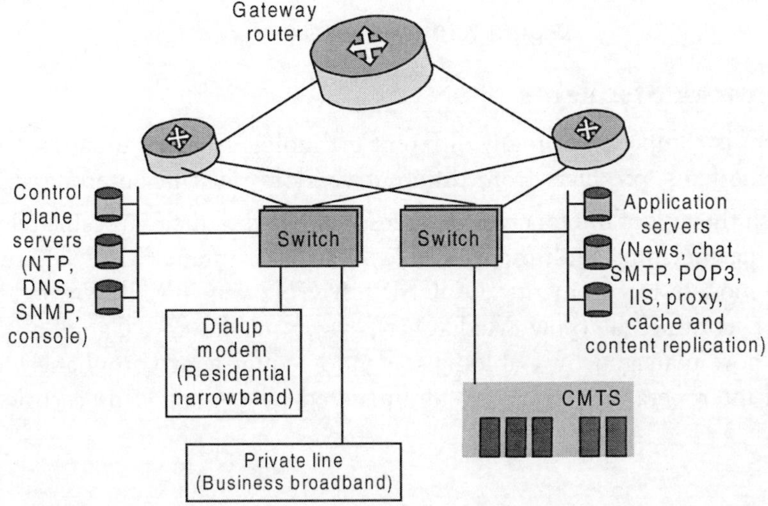

Figure 7.9 *Regional Data Center.*

In addition to cable data networks, a regional data center may also support dial-up modem services (*e.g.*, 56-kbps service) and business-to-business Internet services. A network of switching, routers, and servers is employed at the regional data center to aggregate dial-up, high-speed, and business Internet services.

A super hub and a regional data center may be co-located and managed as a single business entity. A super hub is managed by a cable television service provider (TCI), while the regional data center is managed as a separate and independent business (@home). In some regions, an existing Internet Service Provider (ISP) may provide regional data center support for many basic and super hub locations managed by independent cable data network providers.

A regional data center is connected to other regional data centers by a national backbone network (see figure 7.10). In addition, each regional data center is also connected to the Internet and world wide web services. Traffic between the regional networks, the Internet and all other regional networks is aggregated through the regional data center.

Figure 7.10 *National Network.*

Cable Data Network Standards

A cable data system is comprised of many different technologies and standards. To develop a mass market for cable modems, products from different vendors must be interoperable.

To accomplish the task of interoperable systems, the North American cable television operators formed a limited partnership, Multimedia Cable Network System (MCNS), and developed an initial set of cable modem requirements (DOCSIS). MCNS was initially formed by comcast, cox, TCI, time warner, continental (now MediaOne), rogers cable, and CableLabs. The DOCSIS requirements are now managed by CableLabs. Vendor equipment compliance to the DOCSIS requirements and interoperability tests are administered by a CableLabs certification program.

PHYSICAL LAYER

Downstream Data Channel

At the cable modem physical layer, downstream data channel is based on North American digital video specifications and includes the following features:

- 64 and 256 QAM
- 6 MHz–occupied spectrum that coexists with other signals in cable plant concatenation of reed-solomon block code and Trellis code, supports operation in a higher percentage of the North American cable plants variable length interleaving supports, both latency-sensitive and latency-insensitive data services contiguous serial bit-stream with no implied framing, Provides Complete Physical (PHY) and MAC layer decoupling

Upstream Data Channel

The upstream data channel is a shared channel featuring the following:

- QPSK and 16 QAM formats
- Multiple symbol rates
- Data rates from 320 kbps to 10 Mbps
- Flexible and programmable cable modem under control of CMTS
- Frequency agility
- Time-division multiple access
- Support of both fixed-frame and variable-length protocol data units
- Programmable reed-solomon block coding
- Programmable preambles

DIGITAL SUBSCRIBER LINE (DSL)

Digital Subscriber Line is a technology that dramatically increases the digital capacity of ordinary telephone lines (the local loops) into the home or office. DSL speeds are tied to the distance between the customer and the telco central office. DSL is geared to two types of usage. Asymmetric DSL (ADSL) is for Internet access, where fast downstream is required, but slow upstream is acceptable. Symmetric DSL (SDSL, HDSL, etc.) is designed for short haul connections that require high speed in both directions.

Unlike ISDN, which is also digital but travels through the switched telephone network, DSL provides “always-on” operation. At the telco central office, DSL traffic is aggregated in a unit called the DSL Access Multiplexor (DSLAM) and forwarded to the appropriate ISP or data network.

Although DSL only arrived in the very late 1990s, there have been more versions and alphabet soup than most any other new transmission technology. The major DSL flavors are summarized below.

ADSL

Asymmetrical Digital subscriber line (ADSL) uses the existing analog local loop lines for digital data transfer. It is asymmetrical because the upstream transfer rate is slower than the downstream data rate. That is the data transfer rate is adaptive.

Asymmetric DSL shares the same line as the telephone, because it uses higher frequencies than the voice band. However, a POTS splitter must be installed on the customer's premises to separate the line between voice and ADSL. A version of ADSL, known as G.lite, Universal ADSL, ADSL Lite and splitterless ADSL, is geared to the consumer. It eliminates the splitter and associated installation charge, but all phones on the line must plug into low-pass filters to isolate them from the higher ADSL frequencies. ADSL is available in two modulation schemes: Discrete Multitone (DMT) or Carrierless Amplitude Phase (CAP).

RADSL

Rate adaptive DSL is a version of ADSL that adjusts speeds based on signal quality. Many ADSL technologies are actually RADSL.

VDSL (also VHDSL)

Very high bit rate DSL is an asymmetric version of DSL that is used as the final drop from a fiber optic junction point to nearby customers. VDSL lets an apartment or office complex obtain high-bandwidth services using existing copper wires without having to replace the infrastructure with optical fiber. Like ADSL, VDSL can share the line with the telephone.

HDSL

High bit rate DSL is a symmetric technology, which provides the same transmission rate in both directions. HDSL is the most mature DSL, because it has been used to provide T1 transmission over existing twisted pair without the additional provisioning typically required for setting up T1 circuits such as the removal of bridged taps and the installation of repeaters. HDSL requires two cable pairs and goes up to 12,000 feet, while HDSL-2 requires only one cable pair and supports distances up to 18,000 feet. HDSL does not allow line sharing with analog phones.

SDSL

Symmetric DSL is an HDSL variation that uses only one cable pair and is offered in a wide range of speeds from 144 Kbps to 1.5 Mbps. SDSL is a rate adaptive technology, and like HDSL, SDSL cannot share lines with analog telephones.

IDSL

ISDN DSL offers a rather low speed (144 Kbps) in both directions compared to other symmetric versions, but it does provide 16 Kbps more than standard ISDN, because the 16 Kbps "D" channel is used for data rather than call setup. It also offers the longest distance of 26,000 feet. Unlike standard ISDN, IDSL does not support analog phones, and signals are not switched through the telephone network. Since IDSL uses the same 2B1Q line coding as ISDN, ISDN customers can use their existing equipment (ISDN BRI terminal adapters and routers) when connecting to IDSL.

ADSL Transmission

Using different frequencies in the line, ADSL allows data to ride over the same wires as voice conversations. The signals are combined and split apart at both sides. At the customer's site, the splitting is done either with an external device that must be installed by the telephone company, or it is built into the DSL modem.

REVIEW QUESTIONS

1. What does broadband mean ?
2. What is cable modem access ?
3. What is DSL access ?
4. How are broadband services different from traditional dial-up services ?
5. How is broadband access different from the network that is used at work ?
6. What does "broadband" mean ?
7. What is cable modem access ?
8. How are broadband service different from the network ?

❑❑❑

8 High Speed Digital Access—SONET

INTRODUCTION TO SONET

Short for *synchronous optical network,* a standard for connecting fiber optics transmission systems. SONET was proposed by Bellcore in the middle 1980s and is now an ANSI standard.

SONET defines interface standards at the physical layer of the OSI seven-layer model. The standard defines a hierarchy of interface rates that allow data streams at different rates to be multiplexed. SONET establishes Optical Carrier (OC) levels from 51.8 Mbps to 2.48 Gbps. Prior rate standards used by different countries specified rates that were not compatible for multiplexing. With the implementation of SONET, communication carriers throughout the world can interconnect their existing digital carrier and fiber optic systems.

The international equivalent of SONET, standardized by the ITU, is called SDH. The Synchronous Optical NET-work (SONET) standard for fiber optic networks was developed in the mid-1980s. It remains in widespread use today. In a nutshell, SONET allows multiple technologies and vendor products to interoperate by defining standard physical network interfaces.

The increased configuration flexibility and bandwidth availability of SONET provides significant advantages over the older telecommunications system. These advantages include the following:

- Reduction in equipment requirements and an increase in network reliability.
- Provision of overhead and payload bytes—the overhead bytes permit management of the payload bytes on an individual basis.
- Definition of a synchronous multiplexing format for carrying lower level digital signals and a synchronous structure that greatly simplifies the interface to digital switches, digital cross-connect switches, and add-drop multiplexers.
- Availability of a set of generic standards that enable products from different vendors to be connects.
- Definition of a flexible architecture capable of accommodating future applications, with a variety of transmission rates.

APPLICATIONS

SONET was originally designed for the public telephone network. In the early 1980's, the forced breakup of AT and T in the United States created numerous regional telephone companies, and these companies quickly encountered difficulties in networking with each other. Fiber optic cabling already prevailed for long distance voice traffic transmissions, but the existing networks proved unnecessarily expensive to build and difficult to extend for so-called *long haul* data and/or video traffic.

The American National Standards Institute(ANSI) successfully devised SONET as the new standard for these applications. Like Ethernet, SONET provides a "layer 1" or *interface layer* technology (also termed *physical layer* in the OSI model). As such, SONET acts a carrier of multiple higher-level application protocols. For example, Internet Protocol (IP) packets can be configured to flow over SONET.

TECHNOLOGY

SONET commonly transmits data at speeds between 155 megabits per second (Mbps) and 2.5 gigabits per second (Gbps). To build these high-bandwidth data streams, SONET *multiplexes* together channels having bandwidth as low as 64 kilobits per second (Kpbs) into *data frames* sent at fixed intervals.

Compared to Ethernet cabling that spans distances up to 100 meters (328 feet), SONET fiber typically runs much further. Even *short reach* links span up to 2 kilometers (1.2 miles); *intermediate* and *long reach* links cover dozens of kilometers.

Basic SONET Signal

SONET defines a technology for carrying many signals of different capacities through a synchronous, flexible, optical hierarchy. This is a accomplished by means of a byte-interleaved multiplexing scheme. Byte-interleaving simplifies multiplexing and offers end-to-end network management.

The first step in the SONET multiplexing process involves the generation of the lowest level or base signal. In SONET, this base is referred to as synchronous transport signal-level 1, or simply STS–1, which operates at 51.84 Mbps. Higher-level signals are integer multiples of STS–1, creating the family of STS–N signals. An STS–N signal is composed of N-byte-interleaved STS–1 signals.

SONET/SDH

SONET, which stands for synchronous optical network, is an ANSI standard for high-speed transmission of digital signals using fiber-optic technology. Officially recognized by the telecommunications industry in the late 1980's, SONET quickly gained popularity in the 1990's due to the high-speed rates, "five-nines" reliability, OAM and P, quality of service and the standardization (interoperability). An almost equivalent standard called SDH, synchronous digital hierarchy, was also established by ITU shortly after SONET to address the slightly different digital hierarchies found in Europe, Japan, and the rest of the world. For the most part, SONET and SDH are equivalent.

SONET and SDH define base rates of 51.84 Mbps (OC-1) and 155.51 Mbps (STS-1), respectively. Faster rate signals are integer multiples of the base rates and are referred to as OC-N or STS-N. Today, SONET/SDH systems are capable of providing up to 10 Gbps speeds (OC-192/STM-64). Future SONET systems will provide 40 Gbps (OC-768) and 160 Gbps (OC-3072) speeds. Aside from its application in long haul transport for the PSTN, SONET and SDH are also used in B-ISDN as the transport technology for ATM backbones networks, for transporting IP packets (Packet over SONET), digital cable, and other applications requiring high speed in wide area, metro area, and access networks.

SYNCHRONOUS OPTICAL NETWORK (SONET)

SONET is the American National Standards Institute (ANSI) standard for synchronous data transmission on optical media. The international equivalent of SONET is Synchronous Digital Hierarchy (SDH). SONET provides standards for a number of line rates up to the maximum line rate of 39.808 gigabits per second and beyond. SONET is considered to be the foundation for the physical layer of the broadband ISDN (B-ISDN). Asynchronous transfer mode runs as a layer on top of SONET as well as on top of other technologies.

The network defines optical carrier levels and their electrical equivalents, called Synchronous Transport Signals (STS) for fiber optic transmission. The first step in the process involves multiplexing multiple signals by generating the lowest level or base signal, called STS-1. Its optical carrier counterpart is called OC-1, and it transmits at 51,480 Mb/s. Other levels operate from 155 Mb/s up to 40 Gb/s. The basic network elements include the terminal multiplexer (PTE), a regenerator (as needed for long distance transmissions), an add-drop multiplexer(ADM), for use in point-to-multipoint configurations, Wideband Digital Cross-Connects (W-DCS), broadband digital cross-connects, and the digital loop carrier. Together, these elements may be used in a point-to-point, point-to-multipoint (hub), or ring network configuration. Figure 8.1 illustrates a typical hub network configuration.

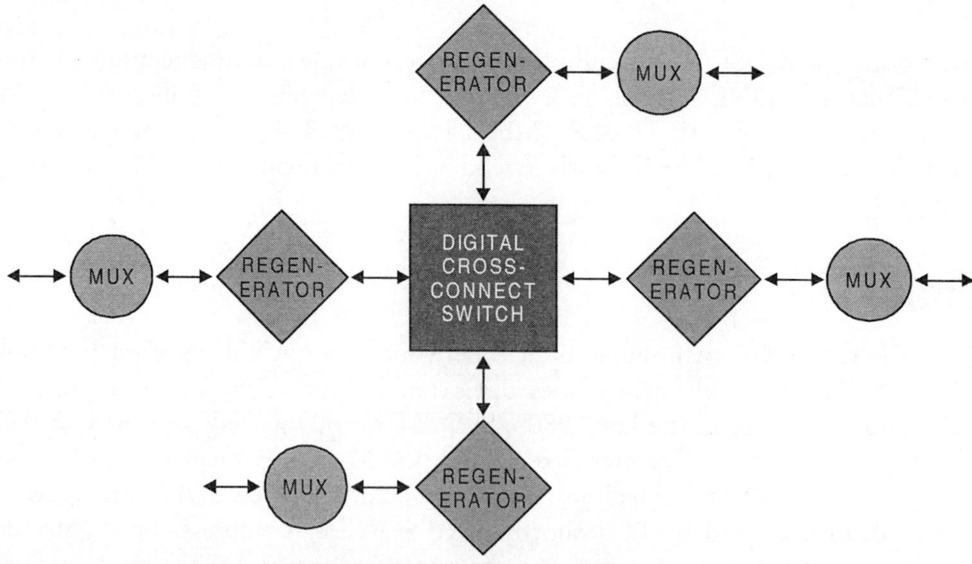

Figure 8.1 *SONET Hub Network.*

SONET provides a number of benefits over asynchronous systems. Its multiplexing technique allows simplified synchronous clocking and reduced back-to-back multiplexing, which reduces circuit complexity and cost. SONET's optical interconnections meet a number of vendor requirements. The hub configuration adds greater flexibility to the system, allowing the convergence of a number of types of network protocols, ATM, internet protocol, etc.

OVERVIEW OF SONET

In brief, SONET, defines Optical Carrier (OC) levels and electrically equivalent Synchronous Transport Signals (STSs) for the fiber-optic-based transmission hierarchy.

Before SONET, the first generations of fiber–optic systems in the public telephone network used proprietary architectures, equipment, line codes, multiplexing formats and maintenance procedures.

All networks involve the same basic principle: information can be sent to, shared with, passed on, or bypassed within a number of computer stations (nodes) and a master computer (server). In addition to various topologies for networks, a number of standards and protocols have been developed, each with their own advantages, topologies, and medium requirements.

REVIEW QUESTIONS

1. What do you understand by SONET technology?
2. What are the different applications of SONET?
3. What do you understand by SDH?

❑❑❑

PART 3

DATA LINK LAYER

9

DATA LINK LAYER

DATA LINK LAYER (DLL)

Data Link Layer (DLL) is the layer above the MAC. While MAC provides a physical stream connection between two stations connected by a network, the data link layer provides a reliable, efficient communication between stations connected by a single communication channel.

Group the physical layer bit stream into units called *frames*. Note that frames are nothing more than "packets" or "messages". By convention, we'll use the term "frames" when discussing data link layer packets. Sender checksums the frame and sends checksum together with data. The checksum enables the receiver to determine when a frame has been damaged in transit.

Receiver uses the checksum to detect any transmission errors. If an error is found, the frame is discarded. Return a *positive* or *negative* acknowledgement to the sender. A positive acknowledgement indicates the frame was received without errors, while a negative acknowledgement indicate the opposite. Flow control prevent a fast sender from overwhelming a slower receiver. For example, a supercomputer can easily generate data faster than a PC can consume it.

In general, data link layer provide service to the network layer. The network layer wants to be able to send packets to its neighbors without worrying about the details of getting it there in one piece.

The main task of the data link layer is to take a raw transmission facility and transform it into a line that appears free of transmission errors in the network layer. It accomplishes this task by having the sender break the input data up into data frames (typically a few hundred bytes), transmit the frames sequentially, and process the acknowledgement frames sent back by the receiver. Since the physical layer merely accepts and transmits a stream of bits without any regard to meaning of structure, it is up to the data link layer to create and recognize frame boundaries. This can be accomplished by attaching special bit patterns to the beginning and end of the frame. If there is a chance that these bit patterns might occur in the data, special care must be taken to avoid confusion. The data link layer should provide between adjacent nodes.

Another issue that arises in the data link layer (and most of the higher layers as well) is how to keep a fast transmitter from drowning a slow receiver in data. Some traffic regulation mechanism must be employed in order to let the transmitter know how much buffer space the receiver has at the moment. Frequently, flow regulation and error handling are integrated, for convenience.

If the line can be used to transmit data in both directions, this introduces a new complication that the data link layer software must deal with. The problem is that the acknowledgement frames for A to B traffic compete for the use of the line with data frames for the B to A traffic.

The data link layer is concerned with addressing at the physical machine level. Protocols at this layer are involved with communications controllers, their chips, and their buffers. Ethernet is supported at this layer by TCP/IP.

Two additional TCP/IP protocols, ARP and RARP, can be viewed as existing between the network and data link layers. ARP is the Ethernet address resolution protocol. It maps known IP addresses (32 bits long) to Ethernet addresses (48 bits long).

RARP is the IP reverse address resolution protocol. It maps known Ethernet addresses (48 bits long) to IP addresses (32 bits long), the reverse of ARP.

DATA LINK LAYER FUNCTIONS

The following are the key tasks performed at the data link layer:

Logical Link Control (LLC)

Logical link control refers to the functions required for the establishment and control of logical links between local devices on a network. As mentioned above, this is usually considered a DLL sublayer; it provides services to the network layer above it and hides the rest of the details of the data link layer to allow different technologies to work seamlessly with the higher layers. Most local area networking technologies use the IEEE 802.2 LLC protocol.

Media Access Control (MAC)

This refers to the procedures used by devices to control access to the network medium. Since many networks use a shared medium (such as a single network cable, or a series of cables that are electrically connected into a single virtual medium) it is necessary to have rules for managing the medium to avoid conflicts. For example, Ethernet uses the CSMA/CD method of media access control, while Token Ring uses token passing.

- **Data Framing:** The data link layer is responsible for the final encapsulation of higher-level messages into frames that are sent over the network at the physical layer.
- **Addressing:** The data link layer is the lowest layer in the OSI model that is concerned with addressing: labelling information with a particular destination location. Each device on a network has a unique number, usually called a hardware address or MAC address, that is used by the data link layer protocol to ensure that data intended for a specific machine gets to it properly.
- **Error Detection and Handling:** The data link layer handles errors that occur at the lower levels of the network stack. For example, a Cyclic Redundancy Check (CRC) field is often employed to allow the station receiving data to detect if it was received correctly.

DIVISION OF DATA LINK LAYER

The data link layer is logically divided into two sub-layers. The Media Access Control (MAC) Sub-layer and the Logical Link Control (LLC) Sub-layer.

Data Link Layer Sub-layers: Logical Link Control (LLC) and Media Access Control (MAC)

The data link layer is often conceptually divided into two sub-layers: Logical Link Control (LLC) and Media Access Control (MAC). This split is based on the architecture used in the IEEE 802 project, which is the IEEE working group responsible for creating the standards that define many networking technologies. By separating LLC and MAC functions, interoperability of different network technologies is made easier.

Logical Link Sub-layer

According to the IEEE 802 family of standards, Logical Link Control (LLC) is the upper sublayer of the OSI data link layer. The LLC is the same for the various physical media (such as Ethernet, Token ring, and WLAN). The LLC sublayer is primarily concerned with:

- Multiplexing protocols transmitted over the MAC layer (when transmitting) and demultiplexing them (when receiving).
- Providing flow and error control

The protocol used for LLC in IEEE 802 networks and in some non-IEEE 802 networks such as FDDI is specified by the IEEE 802.2 standard. Some non-IEEE 802 protocols can be thought of as being split into MAC and LLC layers. For example, while HDLC specifies both MAC functions (framing of packets) and LLC functions (protocol multiplexing, flow control, detection, and error control through a retransmission of dropped packets when indicated), some protocols such as Cisco HDLC can use HDLC-like packet framing and their own LLC protocol. An LLC header tells the data link layer what to do with a packet once a frame is received. It works like this: A host will receive a frame and look in the LLC header to find out where the packet is destined for—say, the IP protocol at the network layer or IPX. The LLC Sub-layer is responsible for synchronizing frames, error checking, and flow control.

Media Access Control Sub-layer

The MAC Sub-layer is responsible for addressing on the Local Area Network. The MAC Sub-layer is also responsible for determining when nodes on a Local Area Network are allowed to transmit. In Ethernet, this is accomplished using the CSMA/CD protocol.

SERVICE PROVIDED TO NETWORK LAYER

There are some services which data link layer provide to network layer such as:

- **Reliable Delivery**

Frames are delivered to the receiver reliably and in the same order as generated by the sender.

Actually computes and verifies the checksum (note that the MAC layer sends and receives checksums but they don't generate, nor do they check). Maintain *connection state* which keeps track of frame orders and which frames require re-transmission.

- **Best Effort**

The receiver may not return acknowledgments to the sender, so the sender has no way of knowing if a frame has been successfully delivered. When would such a service be appropriate?

When the error rate is very low and higher layer may be able to recover the errors by themselves, the data link layer doesn't have to provide the error recovery service.

In some real-time applications requiring "better never than later" semantics. Old data may be *worse* than no data. For example, when a real-time speech is delivered over the network, later arrived speech clips are worse than simply dropping off a few of them.

- **Acknowledged Delivery**

The receiver returns an acknowledgement frame to the sender indicating that a data frame was properly received. The sender keeps connection state, but may not necessarily retransmit unacknowledged frames. The receiver may receive frames out of order. The data link layer in this case just hands the received frames to the higher layer and let the higher layer decide what to do.

Typically, each frame is assigned a unique *sequence number*, which the receiver returns in an *acknowledgement frame* to indicate which frame the ACK refers to. The sender must *retransmit* unacknowledged (*e.g.*, lost or damaged) frames. One good question to ask here is: How does the receiver know that a frame is lost? (time-out usually is the mechanism used; if time-out is used, then we have to deal with duplicated frames)

- **Role of the Data Link Layer**

We have seen that the physical layer is responsible for actually transmitting bits over a transmission medium and in general a bit stream given from the higher layer is coded and modulated to do this.

Although the physical layer tries to maximize the transmission efficiency, *i.e.*, make use of the entire capacity of the transmission medium, it is possible that bits will be transmitted in error.

Furthermore, it is possible that the receiver's higher layers are not operating fast enough (*e.g.*, buffering and copying the received data to a disk file) to accommodate the rate at which the sender is sending the data. An important function of the data link layer is the establishment of reliable and efficient communication with another data link layer peer.

This is achieved by having appropriate error control and flow control algorithms. The data link layer in one machine/node collects data bits from its network layer (next higher layer), frames them and requests its physical layer to transmit to the other machine/node.

At the receiving peer, communicated bits are collected by the physical layer and passed onto its data link layer. The data link layer in the receiver extracts the data and passes the data to its network layer.

IEEE 802.2 LLC—LOGICAL LINK CONTROL LAYER

The logical link control layer resides in the upper portion of the data link layer. The LLC layer performs following functions:

- Managing the data link communication
- Link addressing
- Defining Service Access Points (SAPs)
- Sequencing

The LLC provides a way for the upper layers to deal with any type of MAC layer (*e.g.*, Ethernet—IEEE 802.3 CSMA/CD or Token ring IEEE 802.5 Token passing).

Network	Unix IP SAP: 80	IBM Netbios SAP: F0	Novell IPX SAP: E0
Data link	IEEE 802.2 Logical Link Control Layer (LLC)		
	IEEE 802.3 CSMA/CD Medium Access Control Layer		
Physical	802.3 - 10Base5	802.3a - 10Base2	802.3i - 10BaseT

Figure 9.1 *Logical Link Control Layer.*

The data field of the MAC layer frame transmits the LLC protocol data unit.

DSAP	SSAP	Control	Information
8 bits	8 bits	8/16 bits	M*8 bits

Figure 9.2 *LLC PDU Format.*

The Data Link Layer and IEEE

When we talk about Local Area Network (LAN) technology the IEEE 802 standard may be heard. This standard defines networking connections for the interface card and the physical connections, describing how they are done. The 802 standards were published by the Institute of Electrical and Electronics Engineers (IEEE). The 802.3 standard is called Ethernet, but the IEEE standards do not define the exact original true Ethernet standard that is common today. There is a great deal of confusion caused by this. There are several types of common Ethernet frames. Many network cards support more than one type.

The Ethernet standard data encapsulation method is defined by RFC 894. RFC 1042 defines the IP to link layer data encapsulation for networks using the IEEE 802 standards. The

802 standards define the two lowest levels of the seven layer network model and primarily deal with the control of access to the network media. The network media is the physical means of carrying the data such as network cable. The control of access to the media is called Media Access Control (MAC). The 802 standards are listed below:

- 802.1 — Internet working
- 802.2 — Logical Link Control *
- 802.3 — Ethernet or CSMA/CD, Carrier-Sense Multiple Access with Collision detection LAN *
- 802.4 — Token-Bus LAN *
- 802.5 — Token Ring LAN *
- 802.6 — Metropolitan Area Network (MAN)
- 802.7 — Broadband Technical Advisory Group
- 802.8 — Fiber-Optic Technical Advisory Group
- 802.9 — Integrated Voice/Data Networks
- 802.10 — Network Security
- 802.11 — Wireless Networks
- 802.12 — Demand Priority Access LAN, 100 Base VG-any LAN

*The Ones with stars should be remembered in order for network certification testing.

SERVICE ACCESS PORTS (SAPs)

SAPs are service access ports. A SAP is a port (logical link) to the network layer protocol. If we were operating a multi protocol LAN, each network layer protocol would have its own SAP. This is the method that the LLC uses to identify which protocol is talking to which other protocol. For example, Unix's TCP/IP, Novell's SPX/IPX and IBM's Netbios would all have different SAPs to identify which was which.

DSAP stands for Destination Service Access Port, and is the receiving station's logical link to the network layer protocol. SSAP stands for Source Service Access Port, and is the transmitting station's logical link to the network layer protocol.

SAPs ensure that the same network layer protocol at the source talks to the same network layer protocol at the destination (*i.e.*, TCP/IP talks to TCP/IP, Netbios talks to Netbios, and IPX/SPX talks to IPX/SPX).

TYPES OF LLC OPERATION

LLC defines these two types of operation for data communication:

Type 1: Connectionless

Type 2: Connection Oriented

Connection-Oriented and Connectionless Network Services

In general, transport protocols can be characterized as being either connection-oriented or connectionless. Connection-oriented services must first establish a connection with the desired service before passing any data. A connectionless service can send the data without any need to establish a connection first. In general, connection-oriented services provide some level of delivery guarantee, whereas connectionless services do not.

Connection-oriented service involves three phases: connection establishment, data transfer, and connection termination.

During connection establishment, the end nodes may reserve resources for the connection. The end nodes also may negotiate and establish certain criteria for the transfer, such as a window size used in TCP connections. This resource reservation is one of the things exploited in some Denial of Service (DOS) attacks. An attacking system will send many requests for establishing a connection but then will never complete the connection. The attacked computer is then left with resources allocated for many never-completed connections. Then, when an end node tries to complete an actual connection, there are not enough resources for the valid connection.

The data transfer phase occurs when the actual data is transmitted over the connection. During data transfer, most connection-oriented services will monitor for lost packets and handle resending them. The protocol is generally also responsible for putting the packets in the right sequence before passing the data up the protocol stack. When the transfer of data is complete, the end nodes terminate the connection and release resources reserved for the connection.

Connection-oriented network services have more overhead than connectionless ones. Connection-oriented services must negotiate a connection, transfer data, and tear down the connection, whereas a connectionless transfer can simply send the data without the added overhead of creating and tearing down a connection. Each has its place in internet works.

Type 1: Connectionless

Connectionless service for data communications is very similar to sending mail through the postal system (hand delivered mail): the data is sent and we hope it arrives at its destination. There is no feedback from the destination to indicate whether it arrived or not.

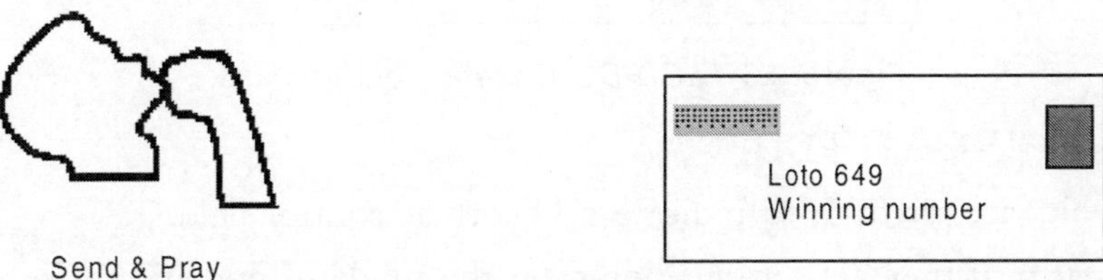

Figure 9.3 *Connectionless.*

Type 2: Connection Oriented

Connection oriented service for data communications is very similar to having a phone conversation. A connection is made and established by dialing the number, waiting for it to ring, then someone picking up the line and saying hello. This establishes the connection. During the conversation, confirmation that the other person is still there and listening (hasn't fallen asleep or died) is given by hearing things like: yeah, oh really, uh huh, etc. This is the acknowledgement of receipt of data. If the destination party did not hear something correctly, they ask to have it repeated (*i.e.*, automatic repeat request, or ARQ).

Figure 9.4 *Connection Oriented Service.*

Type 2: Connection oriented operation for the LLC layer provides these 4 services:

- Connection establishment
- Confirmation and acknowledgement that data has been received.
- Error recovery by requesting received bad data to be resent.

CLASSES OF LLC

The 2 classes of logical link control are defined below:

Class I : Type 1 operation only (connectionless) Class II: Both

Type 1 (connectionless) and Type 2 (connection-oriented) operation allowed.

LLC PDU control field formats

These are the 3 LLC PDU control field formats:

- Un-numbered (U-format PDU)
- Information transfer (I-format PDU)
- Supervisory (S-format PDU)

M M M	P/F	M M	1 1

Figure 9.5 *LLC PDU Control Field Formats.*

Un-numbered (U-format PDU)

The last 2 bits are set to 1, to indicate a U-format control field.

M—Modifier bits, they are set depending on the mode of operation: Command, response or data.

P/F—Poll/Final bit: this bit is used by the source to solicit a response from the destination. It is used by the destination to respond to a solicit from the source.

The un-numbered LLC control field is used mainly in type 1 (connectionless) operation. The PDUs are not numbered: they are sent out and hopefully arrive at their destination.

U-format PDUs can be commands, responses and data. There are only 8 bits in a U-format LLC PDU. In the U-format (Un-numbered), there are 8 commands and responses:

- UI—Un-numbered information
- DISC—Disconnect
- SABME—Set Asynchronous Balanced Mode Extended
- XID—Exchange IDs
- TEST—Test the link
- UA—Un-numbered Acknowledgement
- DM—Disconnect Mode
- FRMR—Frame Reject

Information Transfer

It is used for transferring information or data between source and destination in a type 2 (connection oriented) operation. It is the only LLC PDU allowed to transfer information in a type 2 operation.

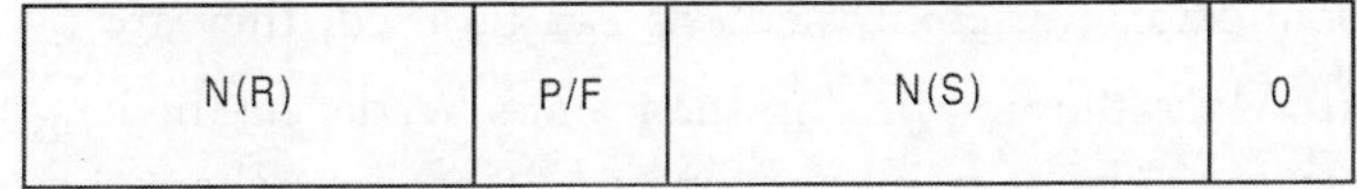

Figure 9.6 *I-Format Control Field Format.*

- The last bit is set to 0, to indicate that it is an I-format control field.
- P/F—Poll / Final bit: this bit is used by the source to solicit a response from the destination. It is used by the destination to respond to a solicit from the source.
- N(R)—PDU number received. It is used with the sliding window and for acknowledging PDUs.
- N(S)—PDU number sent. It is used with the sliding window and for acknowledging PDUs.
- The N(R) bits are commonly called "piggyback acknowledgement" because the response is acknowledged along with the transfer of data. The acknowledgement is piggybacked onto a data transfer.

In the I-format (information), there are no commands and responses, but it is typically indicated by the following:

I—Information (data transfer)

Supervisory (S-format PDU)

Supervisory (S-format) LLC control fields are used for data link supervisory control functions (handshaking). The S-format control fields are used for acknowledging I-format PDUs, requesting retransmission, and for requesting a temporary suspension of transmission (buffers full-wait).

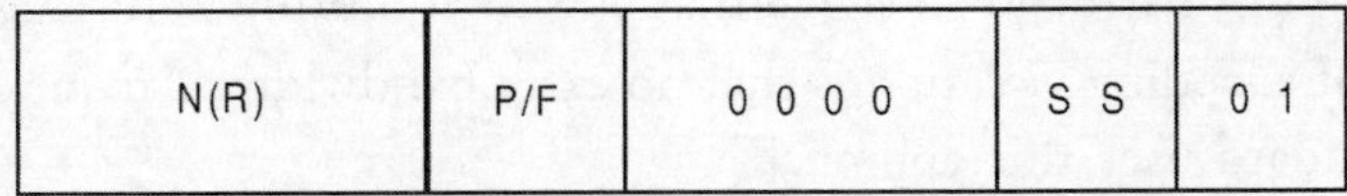

Figure 9.7 *S-Format LLC PDU Control Field.*

The last 2 bits are set to 0 1, to indicate that it is a S-format control field

S—Supervisory function bits, determines the purpose of the control field.

The four 0s in a row are reserved bits, and are always set to 0.

P/F—Poll/Final bit, this bit is used by the source to solicit a response from the destination. It is used by the destination to respond to a solicit from the source.

N(R)—PDU number received. Used with the sliding window, and for acknowledging PDUs.

In the S-format (supervisory), these are the 3 commands and responses:

RR—Receive ready (awake and ready to receive)

RNR—Receive not ready (got problems, hold off for awhile)

REJ—Reject (received a bad PDU, send the PDU with this number again)

FRAMING

The DLL translates the physical layer's raw bit stream into discrete units (messages) called *frames*. For detecting frame boundaries, different methods can be used, they are :

- **Length count:** Make the first field in the frame's header be the length of the frame. The receiver knows how big the current frame is and can determine where the next frame begins.

Disadvantage: Receiver loses synchronization when bits are damaged. Although checksum can help detecting incorrect frames, when counter becomes incorrect, how can the receiver identify where the checksum is?

- **Bit stuffing:** Use reserved pattern to indicate the start and the end of a frame. For instance, use the 4-bit sequence of 0111 to delimit consecutive frames. A frame consists of everything between two delimiters.

Problem: what if the reserved delimiter happens to appear in the frame itself ? The solution is *bit stuffing*. If the above 4-bit pattern is used as delimiter, within the frame, replace every occurrence of two consecutive 1's with 110, that is, append a zero bit after each pair of 1's in the data. This prevents 3 consecutive 1's from ever appearing in transmission. For example, data "1011101" would be transmitted over the physical layer as "10110101". When the receiver receives this data, it will convert back to "1011101".

The main disadvantage with this approach is the waste of bandwidth, as well as computing time needed to insert and remove the bit stuffing.

- **Character stuffing:** The same idea as bit-stuffing, but operates on bytes instead of bits.

Use reserved characters to indicate the start and the end of a frame. If the reserved characters happen to appear in data, use character stuffing.

Disadvantage: character is the smallest unit that can be operated on; not all architectures are byte oriented.

- **Encoding violations:** Send an signal that doesn't conform to any legal bit representation.

The advantage of encoding violation is that no extra bandwidth is required as in bit-stuffing. The IEEE 802.4 standard uses this approach.

Some systems use a combination of these techniques.

FRAMING DATA UNITS

DU's to be sent from one data link layer to another are framed into a sequence of bits before being given to the physical layer.

Some of the bits in the sequence say how many bits in total the sequence contains, *i.e.,* the frame length. Most computer network physical layers don't provide connection oriented services. In fact the computer networks were successful because they avoided connection oriented services. Framed data is inherently used for connectionless services. The entire frame is either sent for transmission or it is not.

Framed data allows "breaks" in between the transmission of the data, so that the receiver can check for errors so far in the communication and can indicate if it is ready to receive more data.

• Error Sources

No errors can occur in the ideal transmission medium. However, none of the transmission media is ideal. The signal representing the data is always subject to various error sources. As the signal propagates along the transmission media its amplitude decreases. This phenomenon is called as the signal attenuation. The signal cannot be detected if it is too weak. In addition, as the length of the medium increases the waveform also changes during the transmission. This phenomenon is called as the delay distortion. The signal cannot be recognized if it is too distorted. Furthermore, the transmission media can also be a subject to interference resulting from other cables or signals caused by electromagnetic radiation. The medium itself may also cause constant white noise. All transmission errors increase as the length of the transmission medium inreases.

• Error Bursts

In practice, data communication systems are designed so that the transmission errors are within acceptable rate. Under normal circumstances there are only few errors. However, it is possible that the signal conditions can be sometimes so weak that sometimes the signal cannot be received at all. It is also possible that sometimes the interference signal is stronger than the signal to be transmitted. Consequently, the data sent during the break is lost. The contiguous blocks of data corrupted by the error signal are called error bursts. The length and frequency of the error bursts depend on the quality of the data link which in turn depends on the transmission medium and the signal conditions. Therefore, the error detection and control should be able to handle as many errors as possible. However, the applications limit which error detection and control schemes are suitable. All applications benefit from the effeciency of the methods to be used. In addition, some applications may require short codeword length or low latency whereas some other applications might prefer extremely low error rate, for example.

• Error Detection

Error detection is a method that allows some communications errors to be detected. The data is encoded so that the encoded data contains additional redundant information about the data. The data is decoded so that the additional redundant information must match the original information. This allows some errors to be detected. Unfortunately, some error bursts may cause incorrectly received blocks which pass the error detection test. Therefore, good error detection schemes are designed so that this should occur as infrequently as possible.

Suppose we have a really bad bit of static, so a 1 turns into a 0 or vice versa. So, we can detect errors by transmitting some additional, redundant information.

Usually, we transmit a "parity" bit: this is an extra bit that is 1 if the original number has an odd number of 1s. Therefore, the transmitted bytes always have an even number of 1s. This is called "even" parity.

So, this helps in the way, if the receiver gets a byte with an odd number of 1s, there must have been an error, so we ask for a re-transmission. Thus, we can detect errors in transmission.

• Parity Checking

Parity checking is a primitive character-based error detection method. The characters are encoded so that an additional bit is added to each character. The additional bit is 0 or 1 according to the number of bits set in the character. The resulting number is either even or odd. There extra bit is set according to this result and according to which parity setting, either even or odd, is being used. If even parity is used, the extra bit is always set so that the codeword always contains an even number of bits set. In even parity, the number of bits set in the codeword is always odd. The decoding is done simply by checking the codeword and removing the extra bit. The parity checking will only detect one bit error bursts in each codeword. Parity checking has been used in character-based terminals but it is not useful for today's reliable communications. However, it is being used in memory chips to ensure correct operation.

• Block Check

Block check is a block-based error detection method. The data is divided in blocks in the encoding process. An additional block check is added to each block of data. The check is calculated from the current block. The receiver also performs the same calculation on the block and compares the calculated result with the received result. If these checks are equal the blocks are likely to be valid. Unfortunately, the problem with all block checks is that the block check is shorter than the block. Therefore, there are several different blocks that all have the same checksum. It is possible that the data is corrupted by a random error burst that modifies the block contents so that the block check in the corrupted frame also matches the corrupted data. In this case the error is not detected. Even best block checks cannot detect all error bursts but good block checks minimize this propability. However, the reliability increases as the length of the block check increases.

• Block Check Sum

The block check sum is a primitive block check sum that is the sum of all characters in the block. The result is a character that is equally long as the characters in the block. Therefore, the result is sometimes referred as the Block Check Character (BCC). Unfortunately, even a long BCC may allow relatively simple errors. In other words, it is easy to find different blocks that generate the same block check sum. Calculating check sum is certainly fast and easy but the reliability of the check sum is not adequate for today's reliable communications. However, due to its speed it is used in some applications which require that the calculation is done by the software.

• Cyclic Redundancy Check

The Cyclic Redundancy Check (CRC) is an intelligent alternative for block check sum. It is calculated by dividing the bit string of the block by a generator polynomial. The value of the cyclic redundancy check is the reminder of the calculation which is one bit shorter than the generator polynomial. This value is also sometimes referred as the Frame Check Sequence (FCS). However, the generator polynomial must be chosen carefully. CRC is a stronger check than the block check sum and it is being used in today's reliable communication. Calculating the CRC requires slighty more processing than the check sum. It can be easily implemented by using shift registers and xor-operations both in hardware and software implementations. The most common CRC is the CCITT CRC-16. The CRC is able to detect all single error bursts up to the number of bits in the CRC and most random errors. Unfortunately, the error bursts in many applications are random and the CRC can find only most of them. Therefore, a random error burst on the block might sometimes match both the original and the corrupted data. This is the case especially when CRC-16 is being used. Therefore, the number of bits in the checksum should be as high as possible or at least high enough. CRC-32 is enough for many todays applications. It has been tested that as the number of bits in the CRC increases the propability that two different blocks with the same CRC are encountered during the data transmission approaches zero. The test results show that the even CRC-48 can be enough to ensure than no two different blocks having the same CRC can be found in practice.

• Error Control

Error control is a method that can be used to recover the corrupted data whenever possible. There are two basic types of error control which are backward error control and forward error control. In backward error control, the data is encoded so that the encoded data contains additional redundant information which is used to detect the corrupted blocks of data that must be resent. On the contrary, in Forward Error Control (FEQ), the data is encoded so that it contains enough redundant information to recover from some communications errors.

This is typically achieved by adding redundant bits in each frame during its transmission. Based on all the bits in the frame (data + error check bits), the receiver may be able to detect errors in the frame.

• Backward Error Control

Using backward error correction requires a two-way communication channel. The sender divides the data in blocks encodes the data with redundant additional information that is used to detect communications errors. The receiver applies error detection and if the receiver detects errors in the incoming blocks it requests the sender to resend the block. This mechanism is also called as the Automatic Repeat Request (ARQ). The ARQ can always repair any errors it can detect but it causes a variable delay on the data transfer. The basic types of ARQ are idle RQ and continuous RQ. The backward error control is used in many data transfer protocols. In addition, in order to use data compression, the communications errors must always be corrected.

• Idle RQ

Idle RQ is a fundamental backward correction scheme used in many protocols. The data is transferred in packets by using error detection. The receiver checks the incoming packets and sends an acknowledgement (ACK) to the sender if the packet was valid. If the sender receives an acknowledgement in the specified time it sends the next packet to the receiver. Otherwise, the sender must resend the packet. Idle RQ is very simple but it is often too inefficient. It can only send data to one direction at a time. In addition, the delay on the data transfer may result in situation where only a small fraction of the capacity of the communications link is used.

• Continuous RQ

Continuous RQ is an improvement over Idle RQ when there is a delay on the data transfer. It allows several packets to be sent continuously. Therefore, the sender must use packet numbering. The receiver also receives packets continuously and sends an acknowledgement containing a packet number after receiving a valid packet. In case the sender cannot get an acknowledgement it starts resending packets in either of the two ways. In selective repeat, only each block that was corrupted is resent. Selective repeat is complex but it is useful when error are common. In go-back-n, once a corrupted block is detected, the transmission continues from the corrupted block and all blocks after the corrupted blocks are discarded. Go-back-n is less effective than selective repeat but it is also very simple and it is almost equally effective if the errors are infrequent.

• Forward Error Control

Using FEQ requires a one-directional channel only. The data is encoded to contain enough additional redundant information to recover from some communication errors. Unfortunately, the FEQ cannot recover from errors only when enough information has been successfully received. There is no way to recover from errors when this is not the case. However, the FEQ operates continuously without any interrupts and it ensures constant delay on the data transfer which is useful for real-time applications.

• Hamming Single-bit Code

Hamming single-bit is a block code in which each block is separate from each other. The input block size can be made as small as necessary. The number of bit errors to be corrected can be specified by using a adding enough redundant information in the encoding process. The minimum number of bits that differ on all possible code-words is called the Hamming distance. This yields that the error bursts shorter than the Hamming distance can be detected. Therefore, to detect communications errors, the Hamming distance of the line code must be longer than the length of the error bursts. A N-bit error requires an encoding with a Hamming distance of N+1 for detection and 2*N+1 for recovery.

• Convolutional Forward Error Correction

In block codes, each block is independent of other blocks. On the contrary, in the convolution forward error correction, the encoded data depends on both the current data and the previous data. The convolutinal encoder contains a shift register that is shifted each time a new bit is added. The length of the shift register is called as the constraint length and it contains the memory of the encoder. Each new input bit is then encoded with each bit in the shift register by using modulo-2 adders. The decoding is more difficult than the encoding. The data is decoded by using the Viterbi algorithm that tries to find the best solution for the decoding. Of course, all errors cannot be corrected but the error rate can be decreased. The convolutional error correction has an advantage of using all previous correctly received bits for error correction.

• Golay Forward Error Correction

Golay codes are block codes that allow short codewords. The perfect Golay code is an encoding that encodes 12 bits into 23 bits, denoted by (23, 12). It allows the correction of three or fewer single bit errors. The extended Golay code contains an additional parity bit which allows up to four errors to be detected. The resulting code is (24,12) which is also known as the half-rate Golay code. The decoding can be performed by using either soft or hard decisions. The soft decisions provide better error correction but require more processing. Golay codes are useful in applications that require low latency and short codeword length. Therefore, Golay codes are used in real-time applications and radio communications.

• Reed-Solomon Forward Error Correction with Interleaving

The Reed-Solomon forward error correction with interleaving is a forward error correction scheme that is intended to be used with high-quality video communications. The encoding is performed by filling a two dimensional array of 128*47 octets, that is, 128 octets in each row containing 124 octets of data and 4 octets of redundant check data. The encoding is done by filling the buffer column-wise 47 octets at a time. After this has been repeated 124 times the buffer is full and it is encoded by writing each row at a time. This encoding allows two cells to be corrected or 4 cells to be reconstructed. Two interleave buffers are required because a single buffer can only be either read or written at a time. The decoder also needs two buffers for the same reason. The decoder writes a row at a time, then performs the possible recovery and reconstruction of defective cells and reads the array column-wise. Unfortunately, the encoding and decoding both cause an additional delay on the data transfer that is equal to the transmission time of a single buffer. This type of encoding does not completely repair all error but it ensures high-quality throughput in real time.

• Error Detection Coding

The theoretical limitations of coding are placed by the results of information theory. These results are frustrating in that they offer little clue as to how the coding should be performed. Error detection coding is designed to permit the detection of errors. Once detected, the receiver may ask for a re-transmission of the erroneous bits, or it may simply inform the recipient that the transmission was corrupted. In a binary channel, error checking codes are called parity check codes.

Practical codes are normally block codes. A block code converts a fixed length of **K** data bits to a fixed length **N** codeword, where **N > K.** The rate of the code is the ratio K/N, and the redundancy of the code is 1 – (K/N). Our ability to detect errors depends on the rate. A low rate has a high detection probability, but a high redundancy.

The receiver will assign to the received codeword the pre-assigned codeword that minimises the Hamming distance between the two words. If we wish to identify any pattern of **n** or less errors, the Hamming distance between the pre-assigned codewords must be **n + 1** or greater.

A very common code is the single parity check code. This code appends to each **K** data bits an additional bit whose value is taken to make the **K + 1** word even (or odd). Such a choice is said to have even (odd) parity. With even (odd) parity, a single bit error will make the received word odd (even). The pre-assigned codewords are always even (odd), and hence are separated by a Hamming distance of 2 or more.

To see how the addition of a parity bit can improve error performance, consider the following example. A common choice of **K** is eight. Suppose the BER is $P=10^{-4}$, Then:

$$\begin{aligned} P\,\{\text{single bit error}\} &= p \\ P\,\{\text{no error in single bit}\} &= (1 - p) \\ P\,\{\text{no error in 8 bits}\} &= (1 - p)^8 \\ P\,\{\text{unseen error in 8 bits}\} &= 1 - (1 - p)^8 \\ &= 7.9 \times 10^{-4} \end{aligned}$$

Figure 9.8 *Addition of Parity Bit.*

So, the probability of a transmission with an error is $7.9*10^{-4}$. With the addition of a parity error bit we can detect any single bit error. So:

$$\begin{aligned} P\,\{\text{no error in single bit}\} &= (1 - p) \\ P\,\{\text{no error in 9 bits}\} &= (1 - p)^9 \\ P\,\{\text{single error in 9 bits}\} &= 9\,(P\,\{\text{single bit error}\}\ P\,\{\text{no error in other 8 bits}\}) \\ &= 9p\,(1 - p)^8 \\ P\,\{\text{unseen error in 9 bits}\} &= 1 - P\,\{\text{no error in 9 bits}\} - \{\text{single error in 9 bits}\} \\ &= 1 - (1 - p)^9 - 9p\,(1 - p)^8 \\ &= 3.6 \times 10^{-7} \end{aligned}$$

Figure 9.9 *Detecting Single Bit Error.*

As can be seen, the addition of a parity bit has reduced the uncorrected error rate by three orders of magnitude.

Single parity bits are common in asynchronous, character oriented transmission. Where synchronous transmission is used, additional parity symbols are added that checks not only the parity of each 8 bit *row*, but also the parity of each 8 bit *column*. The column is formed by listing each successive 8 bit word one beneath the other. This type of parity checking is called block sum checking, and it can correct any single 2 bit error in the transmitted block of rows and columns. However, there are some combinations of errors that will go undetected in such a scheme figure 9.10.

	P1	B6	B5	B4	B3	B2	B1	B0
	0	0	0	0	0	0	0	0
	1	0	1	0	1	0	0	0
	0	1	0+	0	0	1+	1	0
	0	0	1	0	0	0	0	0
	1	0	1	0	1	1	0	1
	0	1	0	0	0	0	0	0
	1	1	1+	0	0	0+	1	1
	1	0	0	0	0	0	1	1
P2	1	1	0	0	0	0	0	1

P1 is odd parity for rows

P2 is even parity for columns

Figure 9.10 *Example of Block Sum Check Showing Undetected Errors.*

Parity checking in this way provides good protection against single and multiple bit errors when the probability of the errors are independent. However, in many circumstances, errors occur in groups, or bursts. Parity checking of the kind just described then provides little protection. In these circumstances, a polynomial code is used.

The mechanism of polynomial codes is beyond the scope of this course. We shall content ourselves with a description. Polynomial codes work on each frame. Additional digits are added to the end of each frame. These digits depend on the contents of the frame. The number of added digits depends on the length of the expected error burst. Typically 16 or 32 digits are added. The computed digits are called the Frame Check Sequence (FCS) or Cyclic Redundancy Check (CRC). Before transmission, each frame is divided by a generator polynomial. The remainder of this division is added to the frame. On reception, the division is repeated. Since the remainder has been added, the result should be zero. A non-zero result indicates that an error has occurred.

A polynomial code can detect any error burst of length less than or equal to the length of the generator polynomial. The technique requires the addition of hardware to perform the division. However, with modern integrated circuitry, this hardware is now available inexpensively. CRC error checking is now quite common, and its use will increase.

• Error Checking Basics

Assume the receiver has no prior knowledge of the block transmitted to it. If the transmitter sends only bits, the receiver does not know whether any errors were introduced. Generally, the number of transmitted bits is, the act of deciding whether a received block contains errors is called error detection. Note that there is no way of always being able to detect errors in a received block. Error detection simply means that the receiver detects the fact that some errors exist in a received block. So, there is a necessity for error checking and then correcting it.

• Error-Checking

Error-checking schemes determine whether transmitted data has become corrupt or otherwise damaged while traveling from the source to the destination. Error checking is implemented at several of the OSI layers.

One common error-checking scheme is the Cyclic Redundancy Check (CRC), which detects and discards corrupted data. Error-correction functions (such as data retransmission) are left to higher-layer protocols. A CRC value is generated by a calculation that is performed at the source device. The destination device compares this value to its own calculation to determine whether errors occurred during transmission. First, the source device performs a predetermined set of calculations over the contents of the packet to be sent. Then, the source places the calculated value in the packet and sends the packet to the destination. The destination performs the same predetermined set of calculations over the contents of the packet and then compares its computed value with that contained in the packet. If the values are equal, the packet is considered valid. If the values are unequal, the packet contains errors and is discarded.

• Error Correction

The error correction capability of a code is the maximum number of errors that can occur in transmitted codewords while always remaining possible for the receiver to recover the error or the original message.

Let and be two codewords. If the received word is, and given the fact that there were two errors, you cannot determine whether the transmitted codeword is or .This only means that error correction capability is less than two. We could not decide the original codeword as the received word is exactly in between and. How do we correct errors? What is the limit on number of errors that can be corrected?

Let be the transmitted codeword and be the received word (after affected by the channel) hence, where is the error word. The effect of the error is that it increases the Hamming distance between the codeword and the received word. In error correction, we choose a most likely codeword nearest to the received word.

Error correction is possible only if the number of errors is less than half the minimum Hamming distance of the code because this will ensure that an erroneous received message will be closer the transmitted codeword than to any other codeword in the code.

With some additional mathematical tricks, we can not only detect that a bit is wrong, but which bit is wrong, which means we can correct the value. Thus, we don't even have to ask for re-transmission, we can just fix the problem and go on.

Type in a number, it will tell us the binary code to transmit. Then, take the bits and add any single-bit error we want (in other words, change any 1 to 0 or any 0 to 1). If we click on "receive", it will tell us which bit is wrong and correct it.

Here are some points to be considered about error correction, as:

- Data is sent from the sender with redundancies so that errors in the received frame can be either detected (and the frame rejected) or detected and corrected.
- A total of check bits are added to a block of data bits to generate a–bit data block for transmission from the sender to the receiver. This is referred to as a code with rate .
- The check bits are generated in a systematic fashion following some appropriate algorithm. The receiver essentially uses a similar algorithm to check for errors in the received block of bits.

- For error correction, a syndrome is generated at the receiver specifying the bits which need to be corrected. For error detection, the syndrome generated declares that there is an error somewhere in the received block of bits but does not specify the actual location of the errors.
- Typically, the overhead associated with doing error correction is high so that such codes are usually of low rate and are not very efficient.
- Error correction is typically only used in situations where the intrinsic error rate of the physical channel is poor and needs to be improved with error correction techniques.

THE CONCEPT OF PARITY

The parity of an integer can be either odd or even. An even parity is called parity 0. An odd parity is called parity 1. The parity of a certain group of bits refers to the parity of number of elements of value in the group.

The parity of first four elements is 1. The parity of the block (first 8 elements) is 0. Result: The parity of the sum of two blocks is equal to the sum of their parities.

Parity

A parity bit is a check bit added to a data block such that the number of 1 bits in the resulting codeword is even (for even parity) or odd (for odd parity).

The use of a single parity bit yields a code with a minimum Hamming distance of 2, which can thus be used for single error detection.

Parity Checking

Most error detection techniques require sending additional bits whose values depend on the data that is sent thus, if the data is changed the additional bit values no longer correspond to the new data. Probably the most common approach is parity checking, which involves counting all the 1 bits in the data and adding one more bit to make the total number of 1 bits even (even parity) or odd (odd parity) . The extra bit is called the parity bit. For example, suppose the number of 1 bits in the data is odd. By defining the parity bit as 1, the total number of 1 bits is now even. Similarly, if the number of bits in the data is already even, the parity bit is 0. The first one has four 1 bits. Therefore, its parity bit is 0. The second one has five 1 bits, so its parity bit is 1.

Character Parity

Parity is an error detection technique which is typically used on asynchronous links. It is used to verify the integrity of individual characters (or bytes) within the transmitted stream. When used, each character is protected by a single parity bit which is the logical exclusive. Two types of parity are used: even parity, where a 1-parity-bit is sent if there are an even number of 1-bits and odd which is the opposite.

CYCLIC REDUNDANCY CHECKS

As we have seen that parity checking by itself is not very reliable. However, if we combine frames into two-dimensional bit arrays and send them one column at a time, parity checking can be very reliable. A problem with this approach is that an error is not detected until after all the columns are sent. Consequently, the receiver does not know which columns are incorrect. Thus, there is no choice but to retransmit all the columns—a lot of extra work for a single error. The problem is compounded if another error occurs as the columns are being sent the second time.

So, one method is developed which determined immediately whether there was an error, this method is called Cyclic Redundancy Check (CRC). CRC is a powerful method for detecting errors in the received data is a Cyclic Redundancy Check (CRC). This is usually done by the data link protocol and calculated CRC is appended to the end of the data link layer frame. CRC is a rather unusual but clever method that does error checking via polynomial division. The method interprets each bit string as a polynomial. In general, it interprets each bit string as a polynomial. In general, it interprets the bit string

Bn-1bn-2bn-3…b2b1b0

As the polynomial

Bn-1x^n-1+bn-2x^n-2+ …+b2x^2+b1x+b0

For example, the bit string 10010101110 is interpreted as

X^10+x^7+x^5+x^3+x^2+x^1

Since each bit is either 0 or 1, we just write x^i when bit is 1 and do not write any term when bit is 0.

We outline the CRC method. We also assume all computations are done modulo 2.

Given a bit string, append several 0s to the end of it and call it b. Let b(x) be the polynomial corresponding to b.

Divide b(x) by some agreed-on polynomial g(x) (generator polynomial) and determine the remainder r(x).

Define t(x)=b(x)-r(x). Later we will show that t(x)/g(x) generates a 0 remainder and that the subtraction can be done by replacing the previously appended 0 bits with the bit string corresponding to r(x).

Transmit t, the bit string corresponding to t(x).

Let t' represent the bit stream the receiver gets and t'(x) the associated polynomial. The receiver divides t'(x) by g(x). If there is a 0 remainder the receiver concludes t=t' and no error occurred . Otherwise, the receiver an error occurred and requests a retransmission.

Bit Order

The CRC is the only field which is by convention sent most significant bit first. Thus, the first bit of the CRC–16 to be sent is the bit corresponding to X16 and the last, the bit corresponding to X1.

Use of CRC

CRC Checking is used in Telecom circuits over microwave and is used in ATM, digital signialling, Ethernet, FDDI, Token Ring and many other protocols. Computer systems performs Internet CRC checking when accessing large blocks of data from hard disks or transferring data over serial connections or network cards.

HAMMING CODES

When errors are detected there are typically two choices: resend the original frame or fix the damaged frame. The latter choice requires a method to not only detect an error but also to determine precisely which bits were affected. The simple parity checks could not do this.

Single-bit Error Correction

A method developed by R.W. Hamming involves creating special code words from data to be sent. The Hamming code requires the insertion of multiple parity bits in the bit string before sending. The parity bits check the parity in strategic locations. The idea is that if bits are altered, their positions determine a unique combination of parity checks. When a frame is sent, the receiver recalculates the parity checks. If any fail , the combination of failures tells the receiver which bits were affected. The receiver then can set the bits to their correct values. This technique is quite common for memory addressing and transferring bits from registers to RAM and back.

How a Hamming code works for the simplest case, the detection and correction of any single-bit error. Suppose that frames consist of eight bits. Label them as

M1m2m3m4m5m6m7m8.

The next step is to define parity bits for parity checks in select positions. The logical questions are how many parity checks do we use? And which positions does each one check?

In general, if n parity checks are used, there are 2^n possible combinations of failures and successes. We must associate each bit position with a unique combination to allow the receiver to analyze the parity checks and conclude where an error occurred. However, in order to account for every bit position, we need n so that 2^n is larger than the number of bits sent. We also must remember that each additional parity check requires another bit to be sent.

The relationship between n and the number of bits sent, assuming we start with an 8-bit frame. As it shows, if we use four parity checks there are 16 possible combinations of parity successes and failure.

Hamming code is a special class of linear codes. The code was discovered by a Bell Labs engineer Richard Hamming while trying fix the "bug" in his computer memories (magnetic relays). Hamming codes have many interesting mathematical properties which make them easy to define and use in practice.

- Length of the code = = , where.
- No. of information bits =.
- Minimum Hamming distance =.
- Error correcting capability: Corrects single error.

Possible dimensions of the code: etc.

If the bits of a codeword are numbered from 1 to n, parity bits are located at all power of two bit positions, with the data bits interspersed in the remaining bit positions. For example, given an 8–bit data word, a Hamming codeword would be constructed by inserting parity–checking bits in bit positions 1, 2, 4, and 8, with the data bits occupying bit positions 3, 5, 6, 7, 9, ..., 12, as follows :

$$P_1\ P_2\ D_3\ P_4\ P_5\ D_6\ D_7\ P_8\ D_9\ D_{10}\ D_{11}\ D_{12}$$

The parity bit in position K checks all bits with a 1 in bit position K of the binary representation of its bit position. To continue the 8-bit data word example :

P_1 checks bits 1, 3, 5, 7, 9, 11

P_2 checks bits 2, 3, 6, 7, 10, 11

P_4 checks bits 4, 5, 6, 7, 12

⋮

P_8 checks bits 8, 9, 10, 11, 12

This code has a minimum Hamming distance of 3, so it is capable of correcting single-bit errors. If a single-bit error occurs, the erroneous bit's position can be determined by adding together the bit positions of the parity bits that are now in error.

HUFFMAN CODING

Many computers use 8-bit bytes to represent the letters A through Z, the numbers 0-9, and various other symbols. The use of an 8-bit byte to represent a total of 256 separate ASCII symbols is an example of so-called "block" coding. In block coding, all code frames have the same length, regardless of the frequency with which any particular code frame occurs. Thus, for instance, the ASCII symbols 'e' and 'z' are both represented by 8-bit code frames, even though in common usage the letter 'e' occurs far more often than the letter 'z'. In other words, block coding takes no advantage of the actual frequency of usage of the individual characters as a means of reducing the code frame size. During the execution of a program, block coding offers great advantages in terms of speed and simplicity in fetching and manipulating symbols. However, for purposes of storage and transmission other schemes offer significant advantages.

When Morse and Vail constructed the telegraph code, they sought to minimize the time and effort required to transmit ordinary message traffic, and in doing so intentionally avoided the use of block coding. Instead, they undertook to empirically determine the relative frequency of occurrence of alphabetic symbols in written text. Thus, in Morse code the letter 'e' is represented by a code frame of length 1 (a single dot), whereas the letter 'z' is represented by a code frame of length 4 (dash-dash-dot-dot).

Unblocked codes, such as Morse code, are sometimes referred to as "compressed" codes, because they shorten or "compress" the amount of time or space required to transmit and/or store a given amount of information. An excellent example of how data compression can be performed in a systematic manner is demonstrated by Huffman codes. Huffman codes are quite easy to generate, and an overview of their characteristics and how to mechanize them is given below:

Approach

- *Non-block*—make code words as short as possible by assigning the shortest code words to those symbols with the highest probability (frequency of occurence)
- *Non-singular*—Each code symbol should be distinct from all other code symbols.
- *Uniquely Decodable*—No code symbol should be the prefix of another code symbol (known as the "prefix" property).
- *Instantaneous*—Decoding (data recovery) should be sequential with no dependence on the preceding symbol.
- *Synchronization*—The decoding may be started anywhere within the message, with synchronization occurring after only a few errors due to missed codes.
- *Redundancy*—There should be minimal redundancy in the code.

Despite the fact that these requirements may seem formidable, they are easily met by Huffman codes. The method of generating such codes is straightforward and is illustrated below using a typical Huffman encoding scheme as applied to an imaginary set of data:

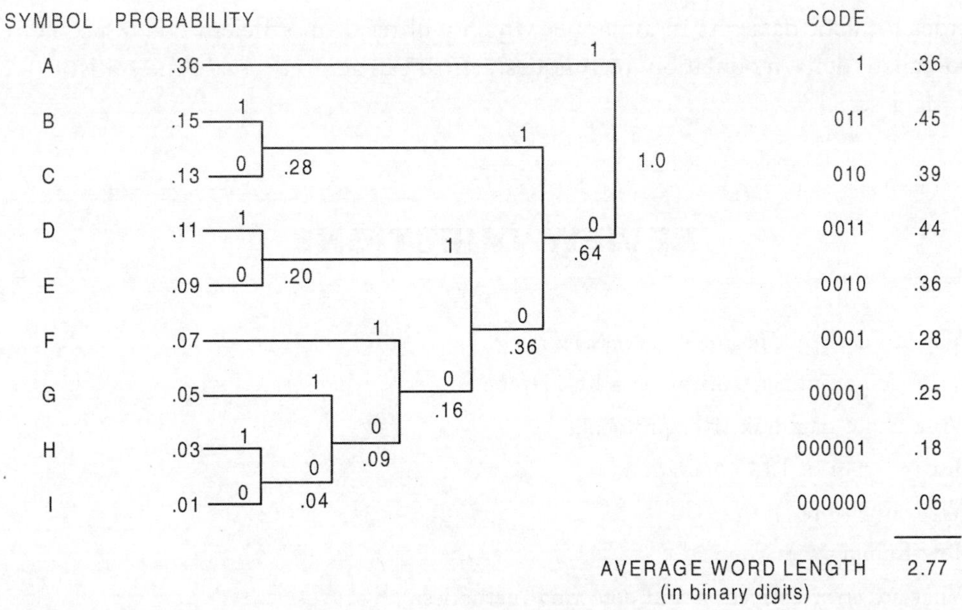

Figure 9.11 *Huffman Encoding.*

The encoding procedure consists of the following steps:

- List the symbols along with their probabilities in a vertical column in descending order, with the highest probability at the top and the lowest probability at the bottom.

- Connect each of the probabilities in a pair-wise fashion, always joining the lowest two unused probabilities until the probabilities merge to a single point (this process is called "binary fusion").
- Assign 1's and 0's to each of the pairs throughout the horizontal tree. What are errors?
- Assigning 0's and 1's can be done as shown, or with the 0's and 1's reversed, yielding a complementary code.
- To obtain the code for each source symbol, trace the path from the symbol on the left to the final single point on the right, then read the sequence of 0's and 1's backwards through the tree from right to left.

The average word length shown on the right is calculated by multiplying the length of the code for a given symbol by the probability for that symbol and then summing these together for all codes. This length, when divided into the length of a hypothetical block code length which might be used if compression were not applied (such as the 8 bits in a single byte), represents the degree of compression which can be obtained. Obviously, the accuracy of this estimate is highly dependent on the degree to which a given data set matches the statistics used. For example, if this procedure were applied to the 26 characters of the alphabet and then used to transmit a sequence consisting of nothing but the letter 'z,' the resulting compression would be worse than if the original block code had been used. Similarly, using codes intended for compression of written information to compress other types of data will often yield very marginal results.

In order to tailor data sets in a manner which will result in efficient codes, use is frequently made of so-called "delta-modulation" techniques, which can act to decrease the statistical "entropy" of a given data set.

REVIEW QUESTIONS

1. Why are data link protocols necessary ?
2. What do you understand by data link layer ?
3. Write about data link layer protocol.
4. Discuss types of LLC operation.
5. What are errors ?
6. How framing are done ?
7. What are error correcting and detecting methodes ?
8. Mention concept of parity.
9. What are CRC ?
10. What are Hamming codes ?
11. What are Huffman codes ?
12. Which error-detection method is used most frequently with asynchronous data streams ?

13. How many errors can parity reliably detect in a single character ?

14. What is one drawback when using parity for error detection ?

15. How many Hamming bits are used for the message in question 7 ?

16. How can the parity bit detect a damaged data unit ?

17. What is the difference between even parity and cannot detect ?

18. What are three types of redundancy checks used in data communications ?

19. How is the simple parity check related to the two-dimensional parity check ?

20. What does the CRC generator append to the data unit ?

21. What is the purpose of the Hamming code ?

22. How can we use the Hamming code to correct a burst error ?

23. Discuss the advantages and disadvantages of various framing techniques.

(IV–BCA(4.1)–DCCN)

24. Explain the CRC technique of error detection with a suitable example. *(IV–BCA(4.1)–DCCN)*

❑❑❑

10

ERROR CONTROL

Error control refers to mechanism to detect and correct errors that occur in the transmission of frames. There are some mechanism for error control. Collectively these mechanisms are all referred to as Automatic Repeat Request (ARQ). Three version of ARQ have been standardized :

1. Go-back-N ARQ
2. Stop-and-wait ARQ
3. Selective-repeat ARQ.

GO-BACK-N PROTOCOL

If there is one frame *k* missing, the receiver simply discard all subsequent frames *k+1, k+2, ...*, sending no acknowledgments. So the sender will retransmit frames from *k* onwards. This effectively sets the receiver window size to be 1.

This can be a waste of bandwidth with an understanding of sequence numbers and sliding window it is possible to quickly understand the go-back-N protocol. The sender uses a window size of K.

The receiver sends an ACK for each frame as it is received. If a corrupted frame, F(n), is received or F(n) is missing (didn't arrive) then the receiver sends a special nack(N) to request that the sender start retransmitting from frame F(n).

Go-back-N Error Recovery

Go-back-N error recovery is a procedure which is implemented in some communication protocol to provide reliability. Go-back-N ARQ is one of a number of error recovery procedures to detect and retransmit I-frames which have been corrupted due to errors in the physical link (c.f. saw, polling, selective repeat).

Features Required for Go-Back-N ARQ

To support go-back-N ARQ, a protocol must number each PDU which is sent. (PDUs are normally numbered using modulo arithmetic, which allows the same number to be re-used after a suitably long period of time. The time period is selected to ensure the same PDU number is never used again for a different PDU, until the first PDU has "left the network" (*e.g.*, it may have been acknowledged)). The local node must also keep a buffer of all PDUs which have been sent, but have not yet been acknowledged. The receiver at the remote node keeps a record of the highest numbered PDU which has been correctly received. This number corresponds to the last acknowledgement PDU which it may have sent.

Recovery of Lost PDUs Using Go-Back-N

The recovery of a corrupted PDU proceeds in three stages:

(*i*) First, the corrupted PDU is discarded at the remote node's receiver.

(*ii*) Second, the remote node requests retransmission of the missing PDU using a control PDU (sometimes called a nack or reject). The receiver discards all PDUs which do not have the number of the requested PDU.

(*iii*) The final stage consists of retransmission of the lost PDUs as shown in figure 10.1.

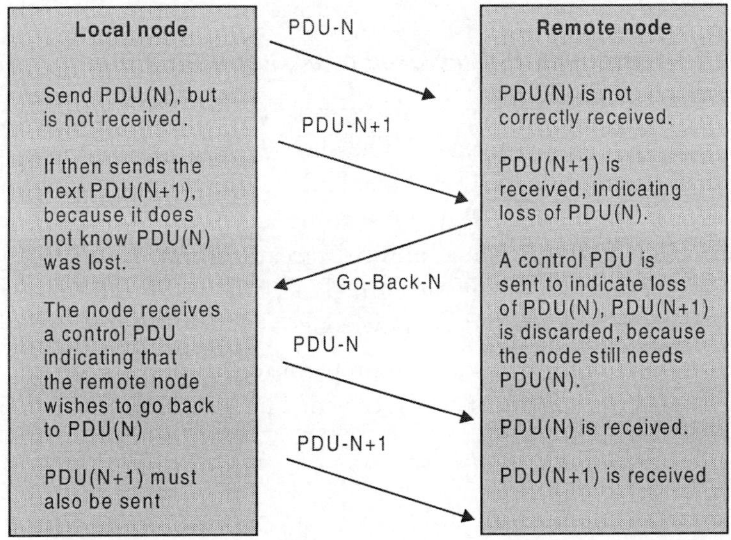

Figure 10.1 *Retransmission using Go-Back-N.*

A remote node may request retransmission of corrupted PDUs by initiating go-back-N error recovery by sending a control PDU indicating the last successfully received PDU. This allows the remote node to instruct the sending node where to begin retransmission of PDUs. The remote node does not store any out-of-sequence PDUs and therefore must discard all received PDUs until one is received with the expected sequence number.

Upon receipt of a go-back-N control PDU (by the local node), the transmitter winds-back the sequence of PDUs pending transmission to the indicated PDU in its buffer of unacknowledged PDUs. The transmitter then retransmits (goes back-to-N) the requested PDU followed by all successive PDUs. This is sometimes known as "wind back" of the transmitter.

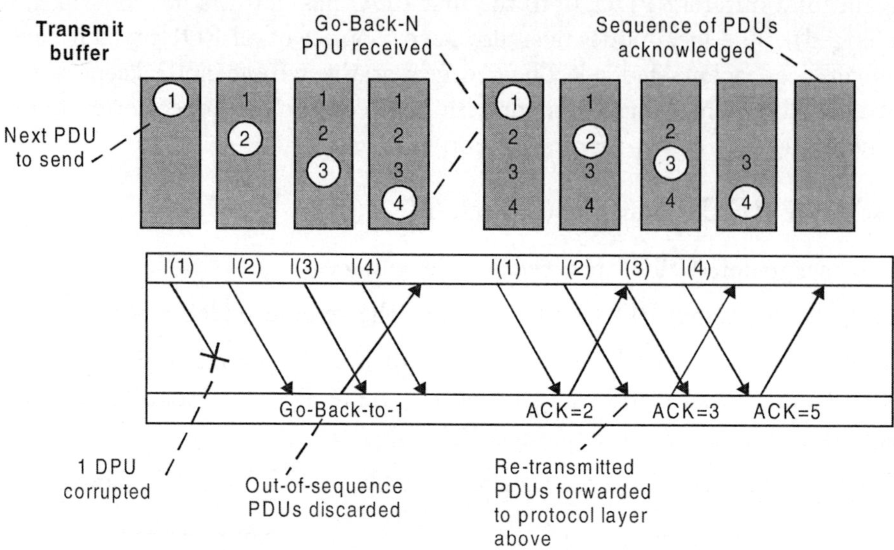

Figure 10.2 *PDU Followed by all Successive PDUs.*

Example of go-back-N. The sender in this example transmits four PDUs (1-4) and the first one (1) of these is not successfully received. The receiver notes that it was expecting a PDU numbered 1 and actually receives a PDU numbered 2. It therefore deduces that (1) was lost. It requests retransmission of the missing PDU by sending a go-back-N request (in this case N=1), and discards all received PDUs with a number greater than 1. The sender receives the go-back-N request and retransmits the missing PDU (1), followed by all subsequently sent PDUs which the receiver correctly receives and acknowledges.

If the retransmission is not successful, the protocol relies upon a protocol timer in the local node to detect that no acknowledgement was received. The lost PDUs may then be recovered by polling.

Polling

Polling is a technique whereby a master station identifies the status of the slave stations by asking each in turn for a status report. In many cases, communications links consist of just two nodes—so there is first one master station and one slave station.

During normal operation a steady flow of PDUs are transmitted by the sending node to the corresponding receiver. This receiver returns information to the transmitter to synchronise the operation of the protocols.

If a receiver fails to receive an acknowledgement for the PDUs it has transmitted, or when it has sent a PDU which requires the remote node to perform a specific action and this action has not been performed, it may commence a process known as "polling".

Polling may be used to provide a communications protocol which supports reliability.

Reliability

Reliable delivery has been succinctly defined as "data is accepted at one end of a link in the same order as was transmitted at the other end, without loss and without duplicates." This implies four constraints:

(*i*) No loss (at least one copy of each frame is sent)

(*ii*) No duplication (no more than one copy is sent)

(*iii*) FIFO delivery (the frames are forwarded in the original order)

(*iv*) A frame must be delivered within a reasonable period.

For a communication protocol to support reliability, requires that the protocol identifies each individual PDUs that is transmitted. The protocol implements an error recovery procedure *e.g.*, polling (check pointing in HDLC), or go-back-N (REJ in HDLC), and provides error-free procedures for link management.

There is very little data which is so important that it must be sent no matter how late. If the links in the network are therefore liable may lead to loss of packets, a reliable protocol should be used. When the underlying network is very reliable (as in an Ethernet LAN), best effort protocols may be sufficient.

Layered protocols usually also employ timers at each level, governing this interval. The service provided by a protocol layer may be unreliable for various reasons including:

(*i*) Corruption of bits within the physical medium or the interface to the physical media.

(*ii*) Faulty bit-timing resulting in erroneous decoding of the value of a received bit.

(*iii*) A software error within the software used to implement the communications protocol.

(*iv*) Insufficient buffer space within the communications equipment.

(*v*) Reliability may be provided at various levels of the OSI reference model. Examples of reliable communications protocols are:

- Data link layer—HDLC(ABM)
- Transport layer—TCP
- Four types of ARQ are common:
  - Stop and wait (the simplest)
  - Polling (sometimes known as "check pointing")
  - Go-back-N (sometimes known as "reject")
  - Selective repeat (sometimes known as "selective reject).

STOP AND WAIT ARQ

Stop and wait transmission is the simplest reliability technique and is adequate for a very simple communications protocol. A stop and wait protocol transmits a Protocol Data Unit (PDU) of information and then waits for a response. The receiver receives each PDU and sends an Acknowledgement (ACK) PDU if a data PDU is received correctly, and a Negative Acknowledgement (NACK) PDU if the data was not received. In practice, the receiver may not be able to reliably identify whether a PDU has been received, and the transmitter will usually also need to implement a timer to recover from the condition where the receiver does not respond.

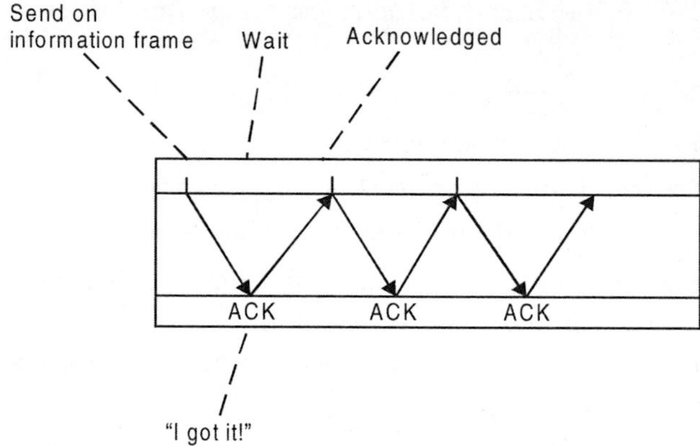

Figure 10.3 *Stop and Wait ARQ—Waiting for Acknowledgement (ACK) from the Remote Node.*

Under normal transmission the sender will receive an ACK for the data and then commence transmission of the next data block. For a long delay link, the sender may have to wait an appreciable time for this response. While it is waiting the sender is said to be in the "idle" state and is unable to send further data.

The blue arrows show the sequence of data PDUs being sent across the link from the sender (top to the receiver (bottom)). A stop and wait protocol relies on two way transmission (full duplex or half duplex) to allow the receiver at the remote node to return PDUs acknowledging the successful transmission. The acknowledgements are shown in green in the diagram, and flow back to the original sender. A small processing delay may be introduced between reception of the last byte of a data PDU and generation of the corresponding ACK.

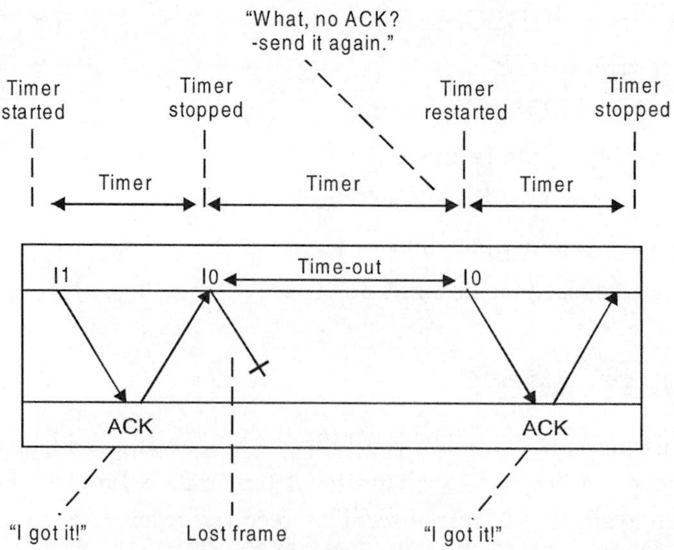

Figure 10.4 *Stop and Wait ARQ—Retransmission due to Timer Expiry.*

When PDUs are lost, the receiver will not normally be able to identify the loss (most receivers will not receive anything, not even an indication that something has been corrupted). The transmitter must then rely upon a timer to detect the lack of a response.

In the diagram, the second PDU of Data is corrupted during transmission. The receiver discards the corrupted data (by noting that it is followed by an invalid data checksum). The sender is unaware of this loss, but starts a timer after sending each PDU. Normally an ACK PDU is received before this the timer expires. In this case no ACK is received, and the timer counts down to zero and triggers retransmission of the same PDU by the sender. The sender always starts a timer following transmission, but in the second transmission receives an ACK PDU before the timer expires, finally indicating that the data has now been received by the remote node.

The state diagram (also showing the operation of nack) is shown below:

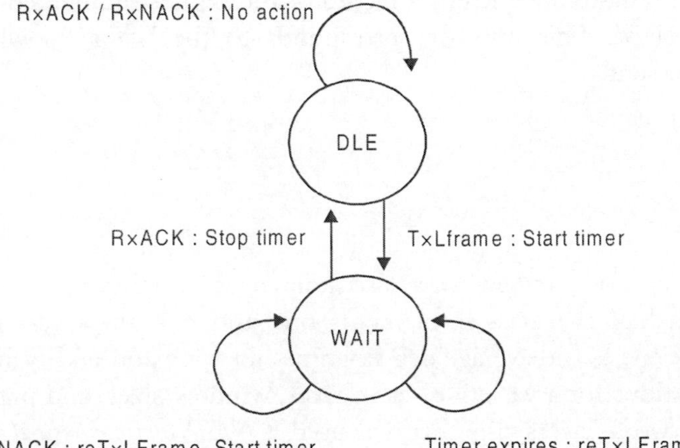

Figure 10.5 *State Diagram for a Simple Stop and Wait Protocol.*

SELECTIVE REPEAT (ARQ)

With Selective-repeat ARQ, the only frames retransmitted are those that time out. When a frame is received out of order, the receiver sends a SREJ Signal, indicating that frame has not been received. However, the receiver continues to accept incoming frames and buffers them until a valid frame is received. At that point, the receiver can place the frames in the proper order for delivery to higher-layer software.

Selective repeat would appear to be more efficient than go-back-N, because it minimizes the amount of retransmission. On the other hand, the receiver must maintain a buffer large enough to save POST-SREJ frames until the frame in error is retransmitted and must contain logic for reinserting that frame in the proper sequence. The transmitter, too, requires more complex logic to be able to send a frame out of sequence. Because of such complications, select-repeat ARQ is much less widely used than go-back-N ARQ. Selective repeat is a useful choise for a satellite link because of the long propagation delay involved.

Selective Repeat Error Recovery

Selective repeat error recovery is a procedure which is implemented in some communications protocols to provide reliability. It is the most complex of a set of procedures which may provide error recovery, it is however the most efficient scheme. Selective repeat is employed by the TCP transport protocol.

Features Required for Selective Repeat ARQ

Following are the features required for selective repeat ARQ as:

- To support go–back–N ARQ, a protocol must number each PDU which is sent.
- The local node must also keep a buffer of all PDUs which have been sent, but have not yet been acknowledged.
- The receiver at the remote node keeps a record of the highest numbered PDU which has been correctly received. This number corresponds to the last acknowledgement PDU which it may have sent.

FLOW CONTROL

Sliding Windows

Implement the *go-back-n* and/or *selective reject* also known as *selective repeat* protocols. If you implement both or if, say, half the class implements one and half the class the other, collect statistics comparing the efficiencies and average delivery times for your stop-and-wait, go-back-n, and selective reject implementations for a variety of error rates, window sizes, and propagation delays. Putting data link and network layers together we used *CNET write physical reliable* to avoid having to concentrate on data link layer concerns when we were really interested in the network layer. But there comes a time when you have to put the pieces together. For this project, take a working implementation of a reliable data link protocol (for example, the stop-and-wait protocol from section 5) and a working implementation of a routing protocol (hot potato or otherwise) and put them together in a single program.

It's not really enough here to get the two pieces of code to work together. You should also take care to separate the data link code from the routing code (ideally, you would have a separate header and source file for each layer), and to provide clear functional interfaces through which all inter-layer communication will pass.

Sliding Windows are a method of increasing the rate of data transfer. Type 2 connection-oriented operation calls for every protocol data unit (LLC frame) sent to be acknowledged. If we waited for every PDU to be acknowledged before we sent the next PDU, we would have a very slow data transfer rate.

For example, if we were contacting microsoft in Sunnyvale California, it might take 2 seconds for our LLC PDU to reach microsoft, and another 2 seconds for the acknowledgement to return. This would mean that we are only sending 1 PDU every 4 seconds. If our PDU was IEEE 802.3 MAC's limit of 1500 octets (8 × 1500 = 12 Kbits), we would actually be transferring at 3 Kbps (12 kbits/4 seconds). This would occur regardless of our actual transfer rate. Waiting for an acknowledgement is controlling the data transfer rate!

To overcome this problem, a sliding window system of data transmission is used. Each PDU is sequentially numbered (0–127). Rather than wait for an acknowledgement, the next PDU is numbered and then sent out. The receive station LLC layer acknowledges (using the received PDU's numbers) back to the transmit station. The LLC will allow up to 128 PDUs to be sent, and not acknowledged, before it sounds an error alarm.

The received station LLC layer keeps track of the PDUs it is receiving: if one should be lost during transit, it requests the source to restart transmitting at that PDU number. All PDUs after the lost PDU are discarded.

It is called a sliding window: the number of unacknowledged PDUs is determined by the time it takes to get to the destination, and for the destination to acknowledge the receipt of the PDU. This time is dependent on both the transfer rate and the physical distance the PDU must travel. It is set automatically: we do not have to worry about it.

SLIDING WINDOW PROTOCOLS

A Stop-and-Wait Data Link Protocol

The files stop-and-wait, stop-and-wait.h, and stop-and-wait.c contain an implementation of a stop-and-wait data link protocol. By using CNET write physical, we give permission to CNET to introduce errors into our transmissions. To deal with these errors, the stop-and-wait protocol: includes a checksum in each frame, sends an acknowledgement from receiver to sender after each successfully received frame, and sets a timer after each transmission to ensure that the sender will resend the frame if the acknowledgement never arrives.

As you read the stop-and-wait code, the checksum is computed using one of the checksum functions provided by CNET. If you want to try your own checksum algorithm, write your own function.

The checksum is stored in the header, so it's important to set the checksum field to a fixed value (this implementation uses 0) before computing the checksum for the frame. It is also important for the receiver to set the checksum aside and reset the checksum field to 0 before re-computing the checksum to determine whether the frame has arrived uncorrupted. The acknowledgement timer is set to 3*linkinfo propagation delay. This works fine if the receiver's frame-processing time is less than a one-way trip between nodes. If the frame-processing time is a lot less than a one-way trip, however, this leads to a much slower protocol than is necessary.

Stop and Wait for a 4-Node Fully Connected Network

The data link protocols as described previously assumed a two-node network. Each node was attached to its partner's link 1. In a more general situation, however, a node may have many neighbours, and will need to maintain data links with each of them.

For this project, extend the stop-and-wait protocol to work for a 4-node network in which each node is linked to every other node. One of the hard parts of this project is determining which link to send a packet out on.

Stop-and-Wait with Piggybacked Acknowledgements

Every frame sent across a link takes up bandwidth on the link, and interrupts the operating system on the receiving machine. As a result, it is good to reduce the total number of frames sent.

When the stop-and-wait protocol is running in duplex mode (that is, both nodes are acting as sender and receiver), data and acknowledgement frames are traveling in both directions across the link. To reduce the number of frames sent, we could package each acknowledgement with a data frame, thus serving two purposes with a single frame. This *piggybacking* of acknowledgements makes a data link protocol a bit more complicated, but it pays back with improved efficiency.

Piggybacking

Instead of sending ACK frame on its own, if there is an outgoing data frame in the next short interval, attach the ACK to it (using "ACK" field in header). Better use of bandwidth. ACK is only a few bits (here 1 bits). Costly to have to construct an entire frame for it. If no data frame going out after timeout, just send ACK frame on its own.

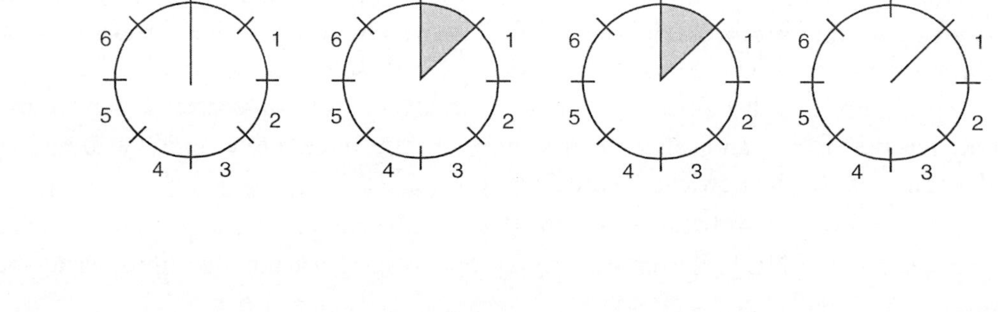

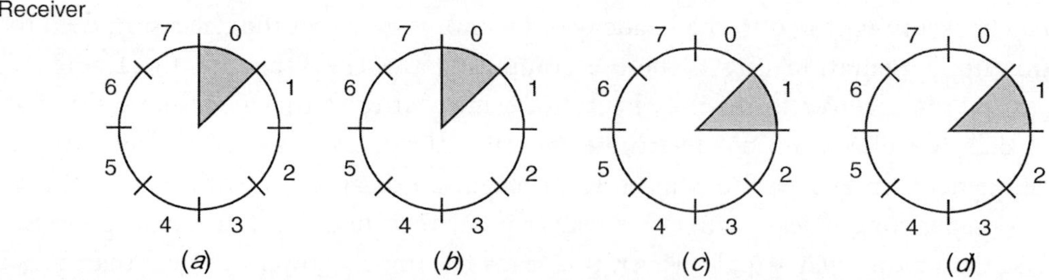

Figure 10.6. *Sliding window size 1. Sequence nos. 0 and 7 (a) At start receiver waits for 0 (b) Sender sends 0. (c) receiver receives 0 waits for 1. (d) Sender got ACK or 0. Hasn't got 1 from its network layer yet.*

Stop-and-Wait Protocol

Consider sending frames from a fast machine to a slow machine. What happens if the slow machine is reading the data at half of the rate that the fast machine is sending it? Eventually the sent data will be lost, never to be received. For this reason it is important to provide some kind of flow control.

The stop-and-wait protocol requires the receiver to send an acknowledgement PDU in return for every frame received. Such a PDU is often called an ACK. The sender will wait for the ACK before sending the next frame.

ONE BIT SLIDING WINDOW PROTOCOL

One bit sliding window protocol is also called stop-and-wait protocol. In this protocol, the sender sends out one frame, waits for acknowledgement before sending next frame, thus the name stop-and-wait.

Problem with stop-and-wait protocol is that it is very inefficient. At any one moment, only in frame is in transition. The sender will have to wait at least one round trip time before sending next. The waiting can be long for a slow network such as satellite link.

We can use large frames; or we can use pipelining: allow multiple frames to be in transition simultaneously.

Parameters for a sliding window: Each sliding window uses three parameters, they are as:

- The size of the window K
- The lower window edge LWE and
- The upper window edge UWE.

Normally, K remains as a constant while LWE and UWE vary as frames are transmitted and acknowledged.

Both the sender and receiver have their own set of parameters and their own interpretation.

HDLC—HIGH LEVEL DATA LINK CONTROL

There are some variations of HDLC. HDLC is adopted as part of X.25, HDLC uses bit-stuffing. Control field is used for sequence numbers, acknowledgements, and other purposes. There are three types of frames in HDLC, *information, supervisory* and *unnumbered.* The contents for these three types of control fields are as follows paragraph.

- Information: 0, 3-bit sequence, 1-bit P/F, 3-bit next
- Supervisory: 1, 0, 2-bit type, 1-bit P/F, 3-bit next
- Unnumbered: 1, 1, 2-bit type, 1-bit P/F, 3-bit modifier

These bits are explained in the following paragraph:

If first bit is zero, it is an information frame; if the first bit is 1 and second bit is 0, it is a supervisory frame; if the first bit is 1 and second bit is 1, it is a unnumbered frame.

In *information* frame, the next three bits are sequence number used in sliding window protocol. In supervisory frames, the next two bits specify four types: type 0 is ACK, the *next* field is used to indicate the frame expected; type 1 is nack, the *next* field is used to indicate the first frame not received correctly; type 2 is receive not ready, which acknowledges that all frames are received correctly upto but not including *next*; type 3 is selective reject which calls for retransmission of only the frame specified in the *next* field.

Unnumbered frames are sometimes used for control purpose as well. Different implementations of the HDLC vary considerably in using unnumbered frames. Five bits (type and modifiers) can be used which can specify a total of 32 different control commands.

The *P/F* bit stands for *poll/final*. This bit is used when a computer (or a concentrator) is polling a group of terminals. When used as *P*, the computer is inviting the terminal to send data. All the frames sent by the terminal, except the final one have the *P/F* set to *P*. The final one is set to *F*.

HDLC is a bit-oriented protocol that supports both half-duplex and full-duplex communications. By bit oriented we mean that the protocol treats frames as bit streams. In other words, it does not recognize or interpret byte values as some protocols.

Three types of stations run the HDLC protocol:

- Primary station (sometimes called the host station or control station). It manages data flow by issuing commands to other stations and acting on their responses.
- Secondary station (sometimes called the target station or guest station). It responds to commands issued by a primary station. Furthermore, it can respond to just one primary station at a time. It does not issue commands to other stations.
- Combined station as the name implies, it can act as both primary and secondary station. It can issue commands to and respond to commands from another combined station.

Station running HDLC can communicate in one of three operation modes:

1. Normal Response Mode (NRM). In NRM, the primary station controls the communication. That is the secondary station can send only when the primary station instructs or allows it to do so. This operation mode is common in two configuration. In a point-to-point link, the primary station communicates with a single secondary station. In a multipoint link (sometimes called a multi-drop link), the primary station can communicate with several secondary stations.
2. Asynchronous Response Mode (ARM). Like NRM, ARM involves communication between a primary station and one or more secondary stations. Here, however, the secondary station is more independent. Specifically, it can send data or control information to the primary station without explicit instructions or permission to do so. This mode is most common in the point-to-point links.
3. Asynchronous Balance Mode (ABM). ABM is used in configurations connecting combined stations. Either station can send data, control information, or commands this is typical in connections between two computers and in the x.25 interface standard.

Bit Oriented Protocols

Synchronous Data-Link control (SDLC) and the enhanced version High-Level Data-Link Control (HLDC) are bit–oriented data-link protocols that provide a means to break messages up into smaller sections, called frames. This ability lets a primary station interleave messages to several secondaries by sending each a frame of its message in turn, rather than sending entire messages at one time. As the communications continues through a network, each secondary is linked to the primary in a continual sequence until all the frames are sent . The secondaries then reassemble their messages from the frames they have received from the primary. To do this, there is a requirement to maintain the sequence of the message frames so that a secondary can correctly reassemble them.

Character Oriented Protocols

Even though character-oriented data-link protocols are in use today, it is not the intention of this text to dwell on them, but to illustrate enough about them to understand their use in applications. The main trust on details concerning data-link protocols is placed on the bit-oriented SDLC/HDLC protocols that are more widely used. The asynchronous and bi-sync protocols are used to illustrate the formats and requirements for character-oriented protocols.

Asynchronous Protocol

The asynchronous protocol has no requirement to establish bit and character synchronization between the sender and receiver. This task is performed through the nature of asynchronous data that start and stop bits are used to frame asynchronous data characters. The line is held at a logic one (mark) condition, often referred to as idle line 1s, as long as the link is established and data is not being sent. The first character transmitted is detected by receiver as a change from the idle line 1 to a 0 or space (start bit) condition this establishes both bit and character synchronization.

Bit synchronization is established beginning with the detection of the start bit and lasting for a time period dependent on the data rate. Character synchronization is establishes because the least significant bit of the character follows the start bit. Since there is no form of "preamble" message required to establish synchronization, actual messages are sent starting with the first character transmitted.

High Level Data Link Control (HDLC) Protocol

The HDLC protocol is a general purpose protocol which operates at the data link layer of the OSI reference model. The protocol uses the services of a physical layer, and provides either a best effort or reliable communications path between the transmitter and receiver (*i.e.,* with acknowledged data transfer). The type of service provided depends upon the HDLC mode which is used.

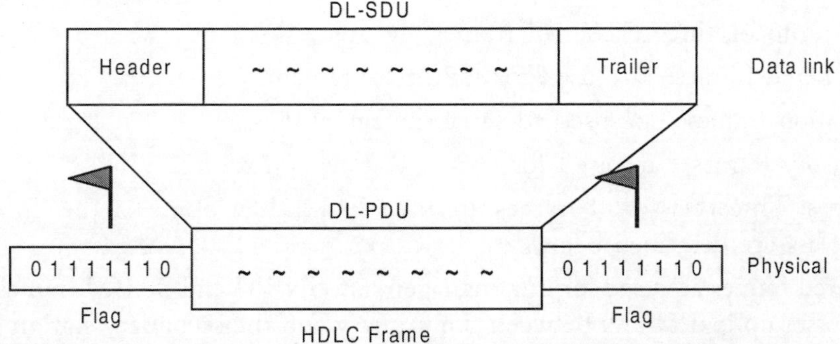

Figure 10.7 *HDLC Frame Structure Showing Flags, Header (Address and Control), Data and Trailer (CRC-16).*

Each piece of data is encapsulated in an HDLC frame by adding a trailer and a header. The header contains an HDLC address and an HDLC control field. The trailer is found at the end of the frame, and contains a Cyclic Redundancy Check (CRC) which detects any errors which may occur during transmission. The frames are separated by HDLC flag sequences which are transmitted between each frame and whenever there is no data to be transmitted.

Frame Formats

The standard frame of the HDLC protocol handles both data and control messages. It has the following format:

The length of the address field is commonly 0, 8 or 16 bits, depending on the data link layer protocol.

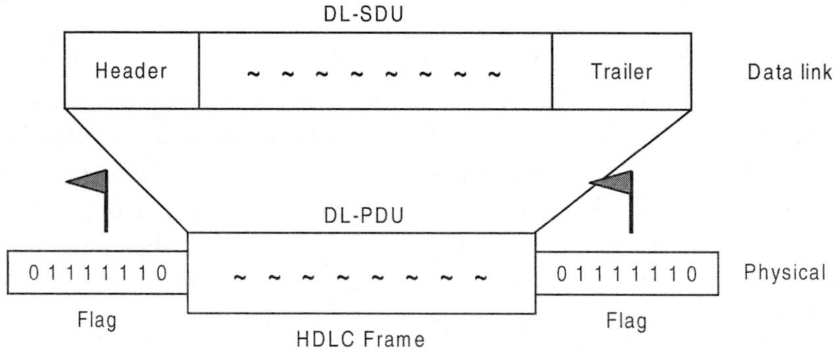

Figure 10.8 *HDLC Frame Format.*

For instance the SDLC use only 8 bit address, while SS#7 has no address field at all because it is always used in point to point links.

The 8 or 16 bit control field provides a flow control number and defines the frame type (control or data). The exact use and structure of this field depends upon the protocol using the frame. Data is transmitted in the data field, which can vary in length depending upon the protocol using the frame. Layer 3 frames are carried in the data field. Error control is implemented by appending a Cyclic Redundancy Check (CRC) to the frame, which is 16 bits long in most protocols.

Frame Classes

In the HDLC protocol, three classes of frames are used:

1. Unnumbered frames—are used for link management.
2. Information frames—are used to carry the actual data.
3. Supervisory frames—are used for error and flow control.

Frame types: Three classes of frames are used in HDLC. Some of the different types of frame in each class are described below.

Unnumbered frames are used for link management. SNRM and SABM frames, for example, are used both to set up logical link between the primary and the secondary station and to inform the secondary station of the mode of operation to be used. A logical link is subsequently cleared by the primary station sending a DISC frame. The UA frame is used as an acknowledgement to the other frames in this class.

There are four types of supervisory frames but only RR and RNR are used in both NRM and ABM. These frames are used both to indicate the willingness or otherwise of a secondary station to receive an information frame from the primary station, and for acknowledgement purposes. REJ and SREJ frames are used only in ABM which permits simultaneous two-way communication across a point to point link. The two frames are used to indicate to the other station that a sequence error has occurred, that is an information frame containing an out of sequence N(s) has been received. The SREJ frame is used with a selective repeat transmission procedure, whereas the REJ frame is used with a go back N procedure.

Layer 2 of the OSI model is the data link layer. One of the most common layer 2 protocols is the HDLC protocol. In fact, many other common layer 2 protocols are heavily based on HDLC, particularly its framing structure: namely, SDLC, SS#7, LAPB ,LAPD and ADCCP. The basic framing structure of the HDLC protocol is shown.

HDLC uses zero insertion/deletion process (commonly known as bit stuffing) to ensure that the bit pattern of the delimiter flag does not occur in the fields between flags. The HDLC frame is synchronous and therefore relies on the physical layer to provide method of clocking and synchronizing the transmission and reception of frames.

The HDLC protocol is defined by ISO for use on both point-to-point and multipoint (multidrop) data links. It supports full duplex transparent-mode operation and is now extensively used in both multipoint and computer networks.

Data Link Layer in ATM

ATM is a set of protocols by itself, it is different from TCP/IP. ATM can be implemented over different physical medium, such as T1, T3, SONET, FDDI. ATM reference model is presented in figure 10.9.

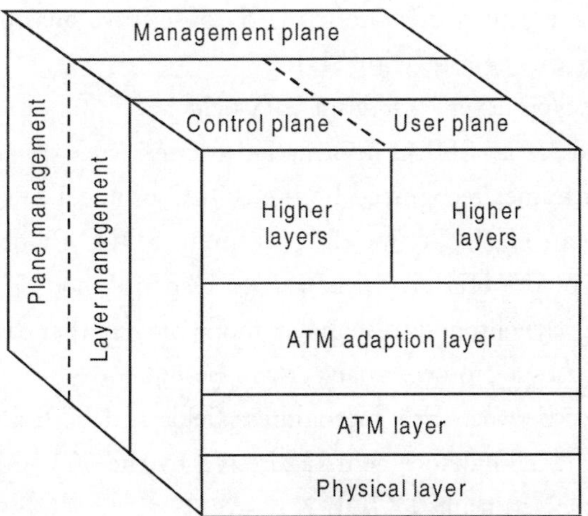

Figure 10.9 *ATM Reference Model.*

ATM reference model has four layers: physical layer, ATM layer, ATM adaptation layer, and higher layer (upper layer).

The physical layer deals with physical medium voltages, bit timing, and various other issues. ATM has been designed to be independent of the transmission medium. ATM cells (frames to other protocols) may be sent on a wire or fiber by themselves, or packaged inside the payload of other carrier systems.

The ATM layer deals with cells and cell transport. It defines the layout of a cell and tells what the header fields mean. It also deals with establishment and release of virtual circuits, and congestion control. The ATM adaptation layer is designed to bridge the gap between user application and the ATM layer. The reference model makes reference to three different *planes*. User plane provides for user information transfer, along with associated controls (*e.g.*, flow control, error control).

Control plane: performs call control and connection control functions. Management plane: includes plane management, which performs management functions related to a system as a whole and provides coordination between all the planes; and layer management, which performs management functions relating to resources and parameters residing in its protocol entities.

REVIEW QUESTIONS

1. Define protocol.
2. Why are data-link protocols necessary ?
3. What is the difference between a poll and a selection ?
4. How is bit and character synchronization achieved using the asynchronous protocol ?
5. In SDLC, what is indicated by a sequence of ten consecutive ones followed by a zero ?
6. In SDLC, what is the meaning of more than 15 consecutive ones on the line ?
7. What types of frames can be sent with SDLC ?
8. Which SDLC frame type never includes a data field ?
9. What are the six fields of an SDLC information frame ?
10. How are information frames recognized by the SDLC protocol ?
11. How do the fields in an HDLC frame differ from an SDLC frame ?
12. What is the purpose of the HDLC asynchronous response mode ?
13. What can the HDLC asynchronous disconnect mode provide that SDLC protocol does not have ?
14. Explain some of the uses a protocol analyzer can be put to.
15. What is the difference between Ethernet address fields and HDLC address fields ?
16. What are two fundamental enhancements addressed by the 802.3i specification ?
17. How is contention resolved using DQDB ?
18. How are dual buses employed by DQFB ?
19. How many total channels are available to be selected from using the X.25 LCI field ?
20. What are the differences between X.25 and HDLC information frames ?
21. What are the differences between X.25 flow control and HDLC supervisor frames ?

❑❑❑

11 DATA LINK LAYER PROTOCOLS

Data link layer is responsible for providing reliable data transfer across one physical link within the network. Some of its primary functions include defining frames, performing flow control.

Many point-to-point protocols exist at the data link layer including High-level Data Link Control (HDLC), Synchronous Data Link Control (SDLC), Link Access Procedure Balanced (LAPB), and Advanced Data Communications Control Procedure (ADCCP).

All of these protocols are very similar in nature and are found in older networks.

As we discussed in chapter 9, the data link layer is the layer above the MAC and it provides services to the network layer above it, some services are as:

- The network layer is interested in getting messages to the corresponding network layer module on an adjacent machine.
- The remote network layer peer should receive the identical message generated by the sender (*e.g.,* if the data link layer adds control information, the header information must be removed before the message is passed to the network layer).
- The network layer wants to be sure that all messages it sends, will be delivered correctly (*e.g.,* none lost, no corruption). Note that arbitrary errors may result in the loss of both data and control frames.
- The network layer wants messages to be delivered to the remote peer in the exact same order as they are sent.

Data Link Layer Protocols

For flow control and error control techniques for data link layer, there are different protocols as Stop-and-wait, sliding window, go-back-n, selective-reject (repeat).

Stop-and-Wait Data Link Protocols

Flow control deals with problem that sender transmits frames faster than receiver can accept, and solution is to limit sender into sending no faster than receiver can handle.

- *Consider the simplex case:* data is transmitted in one direction. (Note although data frames are transmitted in one direction, frames are going in both directions, *i.e.,* link is duplex).

- *Stop and wait:* sender sends one data frame, waits for acknowledgement (ACK) from receiver before proceeding to transmit next frame.

– This simple flow control will breakdown if ACK gets lost or errors occur, sender may wait for ACK that never arrives.

- Such elementary protocols are also called PAR (Positive Acknowledgement with Retransmission) or ARQ (Automatic Repeat Request).
- Data frames are transmitted in one direction (simplex protocols) where each frame is individually acknowledge by the receiver by a separate acknowledgement frame.
- The sender transmits one frame, starts a timer and waits for an acknowledgement frame from the receiver before sending further frames.
- A time-out period is used where frames not acknowledged by the receiver are retransmitted automatically by the sender.
- Frames received damaged by the receiver are not acknowledged and are retransmitted by the sender when the expected acknowledgement is not received and timed out.
- A one bit sequence number (0 or 1) is used to distinguish between original data frames and duplicate retransmitted frames to be discarded.
- Such protocols result in a substantial percentage of wasted bandwidth and may fail under early time-out situations.

SIMPLEX STOP-AND WAIT-PROTOCOL

Drop assumption that receiver can process incoming data infinitely fast stop-and-wait—protocols where the sender sends one frame and then waits for acknowledgement. In this protocol, the contents of the acknowledgement frame are unimportant.

Data transmission is one directional, but must have bidirectional line. Could have a half-duplex (one direction at a time) physical channel.

SIMPLEX PROTOCOL FOR A NOISY CHANNEL

What if the channel is noisy and we can lose frames (checksum incorrect). Simple approach, add a time out to the sender so it retransmits after a certain period and retransmit the frame.

Scenario of what could happen:

- A transmits frame one
- B receives A1
- B generates ACK
- ACK is lost
- A times out, retransmits
- B gets duplicate copy (sending on to network layer)

Use a *sequence number* 1-bit is sufficient because only concerned about two successive frames.

Positive Acknowledgement with Retransmission (PAR)—sender waits for positive acknowledgement before advancing to the next data item.

A problem because the ACK does not contain the sequence number of the frame which is being ACK'ed.

Scenario:

- A sends frame zero
- timeout of A
- resend frame A0
- B receives A0, ACKS
- B receives A0 again, ACKS again (does not accept)
- A gets A0 ACK, sends frame A1
- A1 gets lost
- A gets second A0 ACK, sends A2
- B gets A2 (rejects, not correct sequence number)
- will lose two packets before getting back on track (with A3,1)

Sliding Window Protocols

For large link parameter a, stop and wait protocol is inefficient. A universally accepted flow control procedure is the sliding window protocol, in which frames and acknowledgements are numbered using sequence numbers. Sender maintains a list of sequence numbers (frames) it is allowed to transmit, called sending window and receiver maintains a list of sequence numbers it is prepared to receive, called receiving window. A sending window of size N means that sender can send up to N frames without the need for an ACK.

- A window size of N implies buffer space for N frames
- For n-bit sequence number, we have 2n numbers: 0, 1, . . . ,2n
- 1, but the maximum window size N = 2n
- 1 (not 2n)
- ACK3 means that receiver has received frame 0 to frame 2 correctly, ready to receive frame 3 (and rest of N frames within window)

These protocols allow both link nodes (A, B) to send and receive data and acknowledgments simultaneously. Acknowledgments are piggybacked into an acknowledgment field in the data frame header not as separate frames. If no new data frames are ready for transmission in a specified time, a separate acknowledgement frame is generated to avoid time-out. Each outbound frame contains a sequence number ranging from 0 to 2^{n-1} (n-bit field). N = 1 for stop-and-wait sliding window protocols. In sending window, a set of sequence numbers maintained by the sender and correspond to frame sequence numbers of frames sent out but not acknowledged. The maximum allowed size of the sending window correspond to the maximum number of frames the sender can transmit before receiving any acknowledgement without blocking (pipelining). All frames in the sending window may be lost or damaged and thus must be kept in memory or buffers until they are acknowledged.

In receiving window, a set of sequence numbers maintained by the receiver and indicate the frames sequence numbers it is allowed to receive and acknowledge. The size of the receiving window is fixed at a specified initial size. Any frame received with a sequence number outside the receiving window is discarded. The sending window and receiving window may not have the same upper or lower limits or have the same size. When pipelining is used, an error in a frame is dealt with in one of two ways:

- Go-back-n:
  - The receiver discards all subsequent frames and sends no acknowledgements.
  - The sender times out and resends all the discarded frames starting with faulty frame.
- Selective repeat:
  - The receiving data link stores all good frames received after a bad frame.
  - Only the bad frame is retransmitted upon time-out by the sender.

One Bit Sliding Window Protocol

Two-way communication. One-way is not realistic. Have two kinds of frames (*kind* field):

1. Data
2. ACK (sequence number of last correctly received frame)

piggybacking—add acknowledgement to data frames going in reverse direction.

For better use of bandwidth. How long to wait for outgoing data frame before sending the ACK on its own.

Example of a *sliding window* protocol. Contains a sequence number whose maximum value *MaxSeq* is 2^{n-1}.

For stop-and-wait sliding window protocol n=1.

- Essentially protocol 3, except ACKs are numbered, which solves early time out problem.
- Protocol works, all frames delivered in correct order.
- Requires little buffer space.
- Poor line utilization (next page).

Problem with stop and wait protocols is that sender can only have one un ACKed frame outstanding.

Example:

- 1000 bit frames
- 1 Mbps channel (satellite)
- 270 ms propagation delay

Frame takes 1ms to send. With propagation delay the ACK is not seen at the sender again until time 541ms. Very poor channel utilization. Solution:

1. We can use larger frames, but the maximum size is limited by the bit error rate of the channel. The larger the frame, the higher the probability that it will become damaged during transmission.

2. Use *pipelining*: allow multiple frames to be in transmission simultaneously.

Pipelining

Sender does not wait for each frame to be ACK'ed. Rather it sends many frames with the assumption that they will arrive. Must still get back ACKs for each frame.

Example 1: Use a 3-bit sequence number (0-7). Now we can transmit 7 frames (seq. nr. 0-6) before receiving an ACK.

Example 2: What if we allow the sender to send 8 (0-7) instead of 7 (0-6) frames ?

Potential problem of window sizes (receiver window size of one):

MaxSeq is 7 (0 through 7) is valid. How big can sender window be ?

1. Send 0-7.
2. Receive 0-7 (one at a time) and send ACKs
3. All ACKs are lost
4. Message 0 times out and is retransmitted
5. Receiver accepts frame 0 (why ?—because that is next frame) and passes it to NL.

Window Size Rule: The sender window size (number of buffers) plus the receiver window size (number of buffers) must be $<=2^n$ where n is the number of bits in the sequence number.

Example 3: Provides more efficient use of space and works well if we follow the window size rule and do not get errors. What if an error occurs ?

What if 7 frames transmitted (seq nr 0-6), and sequence number 1 has an error. Frames 2-6 will be ignored at receiver side ? Sender will have to retransmit.

Two strategies for window size:

1. Go-back-n—receiver's window size of one (protocol 5).
2. selective repeat—receiver's window size larger than one, generally the sender and receiver have the same window size. (protocol 6).

Tradeoff between bandwidth and data link layer buffer space.

In either case will need buffer space on the sender side. Cannot release until an ACK is received.

Use a timer for each un ACK'ed frame that has been sent.

Can enable/disable network layer because no longer assume that network layer is ready (*NetworkLayerReady* event).

Example 4: Look at same example using protocol 6 with sender and receiver window size each equal to 4.

Now if 4 frames transmitted (seq nr 0-3), and sequence number 1 has an error. Frames 2-3 will *not* be ignored at receiver side, but they can be buffered.

What happens when frame 1 times out and is retransmitted ? Upon reception, the receiver can pass frames 1, 2 and 3 up to the network layer and update its receiver window.

Protocol Performance

The channel efficiency of a stop-and-wait protocol are calculated as:

- F = frame size = $D + H$ = data + header bits
- C = channel capacity (bps)
- I = propagation delay and IMP service time (seconds)
- A = ACK size (bits)

Time between frames: $F/C + 2I + A/C$

Time spent sending data: D/C .

REVIEW QUESTIONS

1. What is simplex stop-and-wait protocol ?
2. What is a noisy channel protocol ?
3. What is bit sliding window protocol ?
4. Give examples of the data link layer.

❑❑❑

12 CHANNEL

Recall that the physical layer is responsible for transmitting a bit stream on the transmission medium. The physical layer may share several bit streams over the one transmission medium using either TDM or FDM. In this way the transmission medium has been divided into a number of *channels*. For a particular (shared) transmission medium, each MAC sub-layer has access to the same set of channels. The problem for the MAC sub-layer is to decide how a particular channel will be shared.

1. In telecommunications in general, a channel is a separate path through which signals can flow.
2. In the Public Switched Telephone Network (PSTN), a channel is one of multiple transmission paths within a single link between network points. For example, the commonly used T-carrier system line service provides 24.64 Kbps channels for digital data transmission.
3. In radio and television, a channel is a separate incoming signal or program source that a user can select.
4. In optical fiber transmission using Dense Wavelength-Division Multiplexing (DWDM), a channel is a separate wavelength of light within a combined, multiplexed light stream.
5. On the world wide web, a channel is a preselected web site that can automatically send updated information for immediate display or viewing on request.
6. In computer and Internet marketing, a channel is a "middleman" between a product creator and the marketplace. Value-Added Resellers (VAR) and retail store chains are examples of channels in this context.
7. Using Internet relay chat, a channel is a specific chat group.
8. In IBM mainframe systems, a channel is a high bandwidth connection between a processor and other processors, workstations, printers, and storage devices within a relatively close proximity. It's also called a local connection as opposed to a remote (or telecommunication) connection.
9. In a Field-Effect Transistor (FET), a channel is the semiconductor path on which current flows.

Example: A transmission medium such as coaxial cable may provide a single half-duplex channel. It can be modeled as shown in figure 12.1.

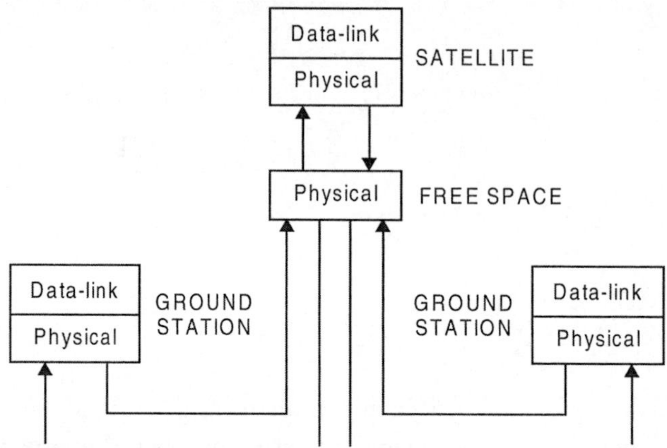

Figure 12.1 *Coaxial Cable as a Single Half-duplex Channel.*

Example: Consider the case when the transmission medium is wireless and is shared between 4 devices. In this case it may be that each physical layer allows the MAC sub-layer to transmit a bit stream over any of 3 frequency bands. Each frequency band is called a channel. Furthermore, if the same frequency is used to receive the bit stream then each channel is half-duplex.

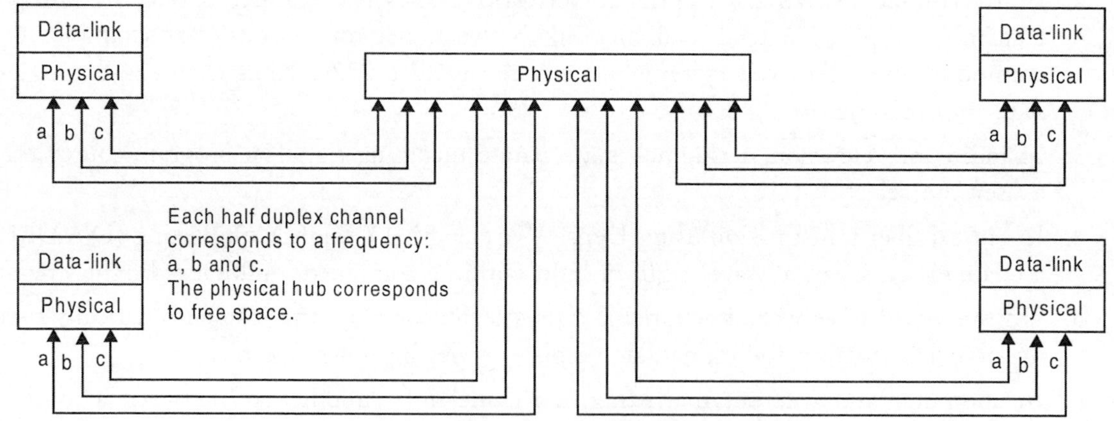

Figure 12.2 *Four Half-duplex Channel.*

By using hubs, and the appropriate network connections, many different shared medium communication systems can be modeled.

For example consider modeling a half-duplex one channel (*i.e.,* one frequency) satellite communication with two independent ground stations. A satellite with both a receiving and a transmitting channel as shown in figure 12.3, or any number of channels, becomes a natural extension.

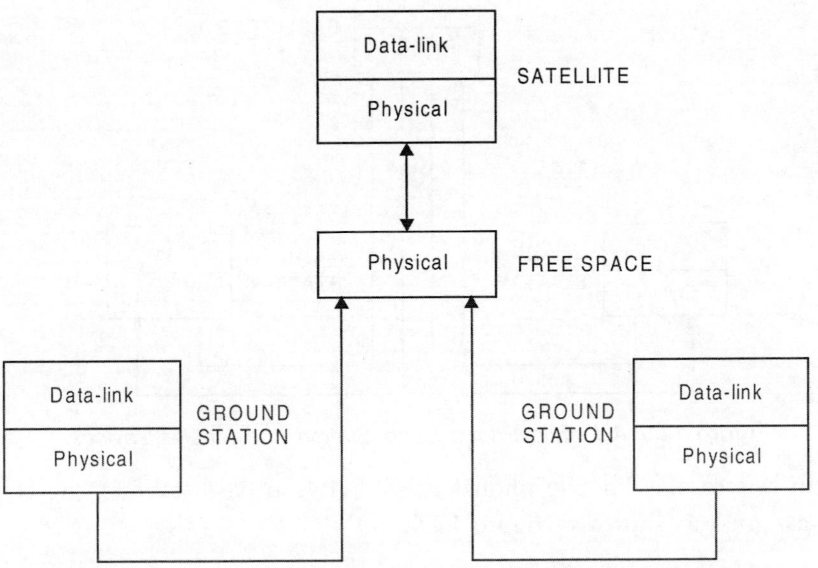

Figure 12.3 *Satellite Communication with Two Independent Ground Stations.*

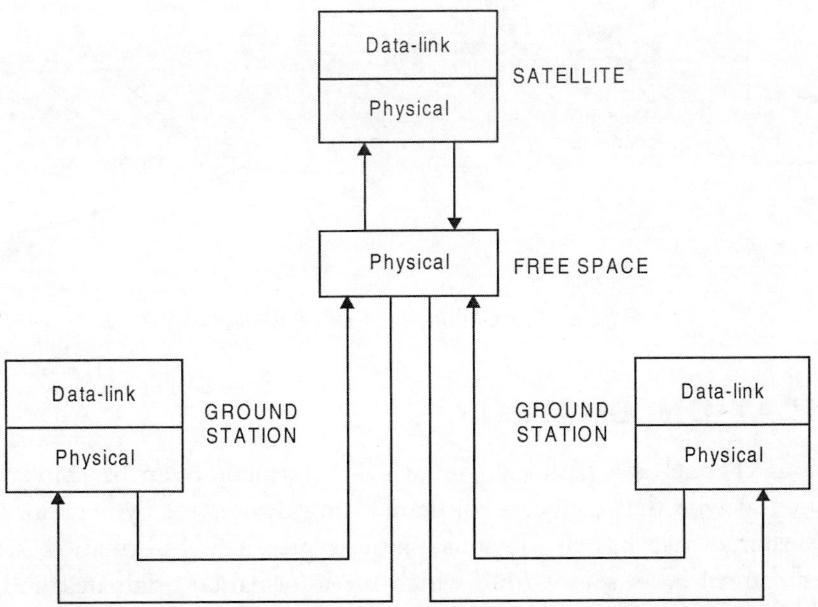

Figure 12.4 *Satellite Communication with any Number of Channels.*

A mobile phone base station and mobile devices is also easy to model. In this case each device has its own receive and transmit channel, so there is no sharing of channels.

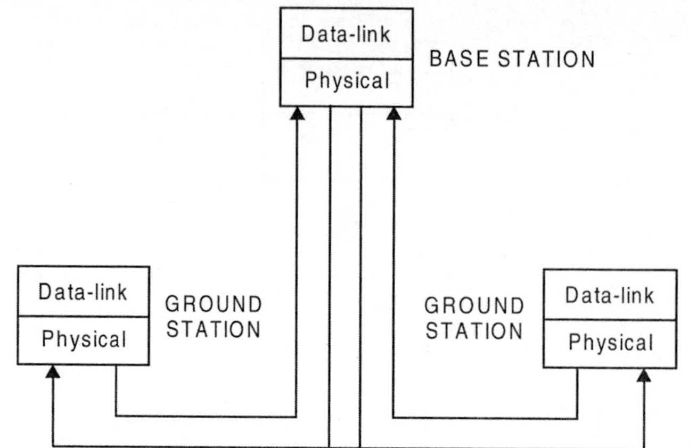

Figure 12.5 *A Mobile Phone Base Station and Mobile Devices.*

However in this case, as mobile phones move between base stations, the channel must be dynamically re-assigned as shown in figure 12.6.

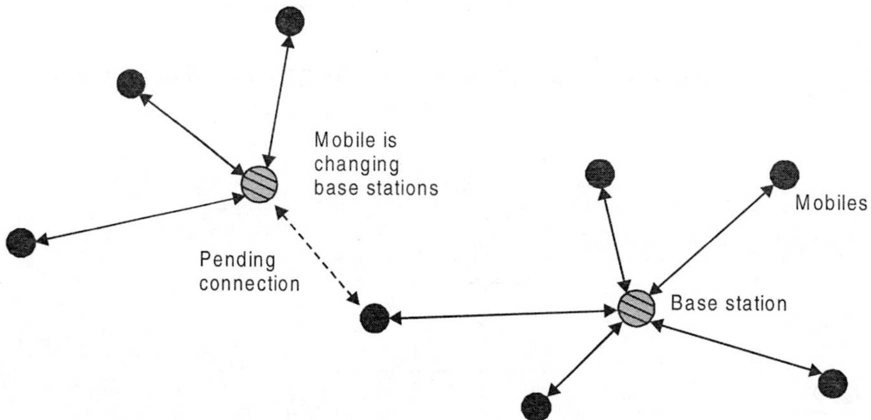

Figure 12.6 *Changing of Base Stations.*

COMMUNICATION CHANNEL

A communications channel is a pathway over which information can be conveyed. It may be defined by a physical wire that connects communicating devices, or by a radio, laser, or other radiated energy source that has no obvious physical presence. Information sent through a communications channel has a source from which the information originates, and a destination to which the information is delivered. Although information originates from a single source, there may be more than one destination, depending upon how many receive stations are linked to the channel and how much energy the transmitted signal possesses.

In a digital communications channel, the information is represented by individual data bits, which may be encapsulated into multi-bit message units. A byte, which consists of eight bits, is an example of a message unit that may be conveyed through a digital communications channel. A collection of bytes may itself be grouped into a frame or other higher-level message unit. Such multiple levels of encapsulation facilitate the handling of messages in a complex data communications network.

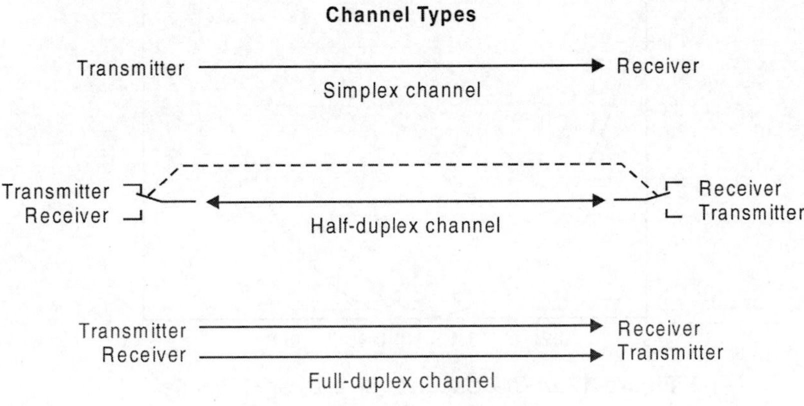

Figure 12.7 *Channel Types.*

The message source is the transmitter, and the destination is the receiver. A channel whose direction of transmission is unchanging is referred to as a simplex channel. For example, a radio station is a simplex channel because it always transmits the signal to its listeners and never allows them to transmit back.

A half-duplex channel is a single physical channel in which the direction may be reversed. Messages may flow in two directions, but never at the same time, in a half-duplex system. In a telephone call, one party speaks while the other listens. After a pause, the other party speaks and the first party listens. Speaking simultaneously results in garbled sound that cannot be understood.

A full-duplex channel allows simultaneous message exchange in both directions. It really consists of two simplex channels, a forward channel and a reverse channel, linking the same points. The transmission rate of the reverse channel may be slower if it is used only for flow control of the forward channel.

CHANNEL CAPACITY

One of the most famous of all results of information theory is Shannon's channel coding theorem. For a given channel there exists a code that will permit the error-free transmission across the channel at a rate R, provided R=<C, the channel capacity. Equality is achieved only when the SNR is infinite.

As we have already noted, the astonishing part of this theory is the existence of a channel capacity. Shannon's theorem is both internalizing and frustrating. It offers error-free transmission, but it makes no statement as to what code is required. In fact, all we may deduce from the proof of the theorem is that it must be a long one. No one has yet found a code that permits the use of a channel at its capacity. However, Shannon has thrown down the gauntlet, in as much as he has proved that the code exists.

We shall not give a description of how the capacity is calculated. However, an example is instructive. The Binary Channel (BC) is a channel with a binary input and output. Associated with each output is a probability p that the output is correct, and a probability it is not. For such a channel, the channel capacity turns out to be:

$$C=1 + p \log2 (p) + (1-p) \log2 (1-p)$$

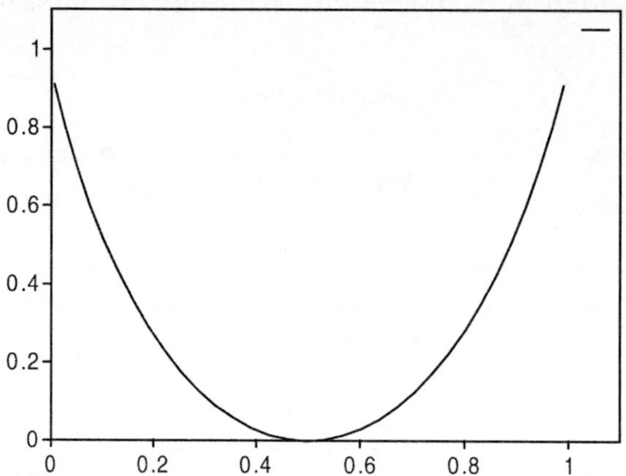

Figure 12.8 *The Capacity of a Linary Channel.*

Here, p is the bit error probability. If $p = 0$ then $C = 1$. If $p = 0.5$ then $C = 0$. Thus, if there is equal probability of receiving a 1 or 0, irrespective of the signal sent, the channel is completely unreliable and no message can be sent across it.

So defined, the channel capacity is a non-dimensional number. We normally quote the capacity as a rate, in bits/second. To do this we relate each output to a change in the signal. For a channel of bandwidth B, we can transmit at most 2B changes per second. Thus, the capacity in bits/second is 2BC. For the binary channel, we have:

$$C=2B\ (1 + p\ \log2(p) + (1 - p)\ \log2(1 - p))$$

For the binary channel the maximum bit rate W is 2B. We note that $C < W$, *i.e.*, the capacity is always less than the bit rate. The data rate D, or information rate describes the rate of transfer of data bits across the channel. In theory, we have:

$$W>=C>=D$$

As a matter of practical fact:

$$W>C>D$$

Shannon's channel coding theorem applies to the channel, not to the source. If the source is optimally coded, we can rephrase the channel coding theorem: A source of information with entropy H(X) can be transmitted error free over a channel provided $H(X)=<C$.

All the modulations described earlier are binary channels. For equal BER, all these schemes have the same capacity. We have noted, however, that QPSK only uses half the bandwidth of PSK for the same bit rate. We might suppose that for the same bandwidth, QPSK would have twice the capacity. This is not so. We have noted that PSK modulation is far from optimum in terms of bandwidth use. QPSK makes better use of the bandwidth. The increase in bit rate provided by QPSK does not reflect an increase in capacity; merely a better use of bandwidth.

The capacity of the binary channel is much less than that calculated from the Hartley-Shannon Law. The answer is that equation applies to systems whose outputs may take any values. We use systems obeying equation because they are technically convenient, not because they are desirable.

CHANNEL CODING: HAMMING DISTANCE

The task of source coding is to represent the source information with the minimum of symbols. When a code is transmitted over a channel in the presence of noise, errors will occur. The task of channel coding is to represent the source information in a manner that minimizes the error probability in decoding.

It is apparent that channel coding requires the use of redundancy. If all possible outputs of the channel correspond uniquely to a source input, there is no possibility of detecting errors in the transmission. To detect, and possibly correct errors, the channel code sequence must be longer than the source sequence. The rate R of a channel code is the average ratio of the source sequence length to the channel code length. Thus, $R < 1$.

A good channel code is designed so that, if a few errors occur in transmission, the output can still be identified with the correct input. This is possible because although incorrect, the output is sufficiently similar to the input to be recognizable. The idea of similarity is made more firm by the definition of a Hamming distance. Let x and y be two binary sequences of the same length. The Hamming distance between these two codes is the number of symbols that disagree. Suppose the code x is transmitted over the channel. Due to errors, y is received. The decoder will assign to y the code x that minimizes the Hamming distance between x and y. For example, consider the codewords:

(*i*) 10000

(*ii*) 01100

(*iii*) 10011

If the transmitter sends 10000 but there is a single bit error and the receiver gets 10001, it can be seen that the "nearest" codeword is in fact 10000 and so the correct codeword is found.

It can be shown that to detect n bit errors, a coding scheme requires the use of codewords with a Hamming distance of at least $n + 1$. It can also be shown that to correct n bit errors requires a coding scheme with at least a Hamming distance of $2n + 1$ between the codewords.

By designing a good code, we try to ensure that the Hamming distance between possible codewords x is larger than the Hamming distance arising from errors.

NOISY CHANNEL MODEL

The noisy channel model is used in spell checkers, question answering, speech recognition, and machine translation. It is intended to solve problems where one assumes all attempted words have been accidentally scrambled. Inputs noisy channel, outputs best guess for the true underlying attempt. For example, in spelling correction, watch the noisy channel and automatically train on the user's behaviour. Create Pr(scramble/word) where the scramble is accidentally inserting, deleting, substituting, or transposing that character based on the word (target character).

- Language is generated and passed through a noisy channel.
- Resulting noisy data are received.

- Goal is to recover the original data from the noisy data.
- Same model can be used in diverse areas of language processing *e.g.*, spelling correction, morphological analysis, pronunciation modeling, machine translation.

A Simplex Protocol for a Noisy Channel Voice Channel Communications

The voice channel (or dial-up line) is the line from our telephone/modem to the outside world.

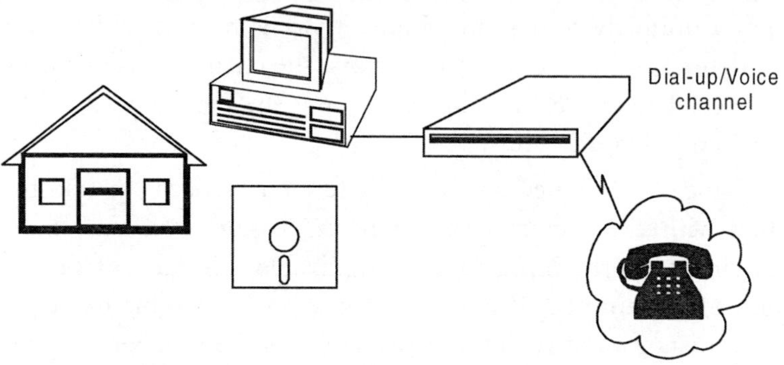

Figure 12.9 *Voice Channel Communications.*

As the name implies, "voice" channel is designed to carry human speech over the telephone wires.

Voice Channel Specification

Human speech covers the frequency range of 100 to 7000 Hz (hertz). However, research has shown that the intelligence part of human speech is carried in the 300–3400 Hz range. This range is called the voice band.

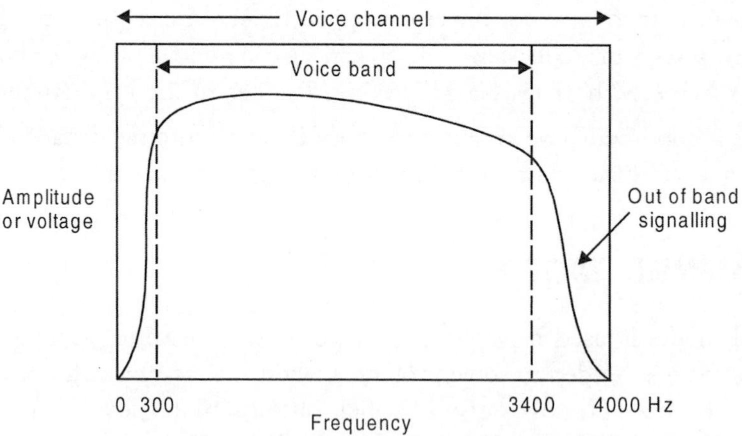

Figure 12.10 *Voice Channel Specification.*

The voice channel has a range of 0 to 4 kHz (4000 Hz). The area from 3400 to 4000 Hz is used for system control, and is called out of band signaling.

Voice Channel Constraints

Due to the limited Bandwidth (BW) of the voice channel (0–4 kHz), we are limited to the amount of data that we can pass through the voice channel. The Nyquist theorem addresses this limitation.

NYQUIST THEOREM

In a digital public phone system, the signal leaving our telephone (at our house) is an analog signal. It goes to the central office through the local loop. The local loop is the name for the

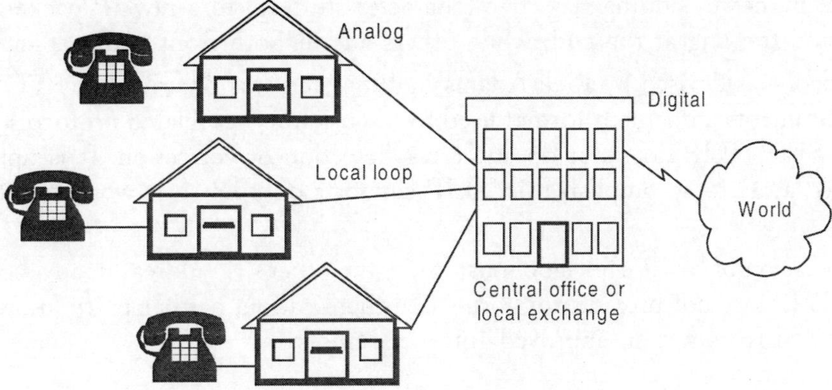

Figure 12.11 *Local Exchange.*

wires that run from our house to the central office. The central office (also called a local exchange) is the building that connects all of the neighbourhood phones. A local is the 1st 3 digits of your 7 digit phone number, or LDN (Listed Directory Number).

At the central office, the analog signal is converted into a digital signal that consists of 1s and 0s.

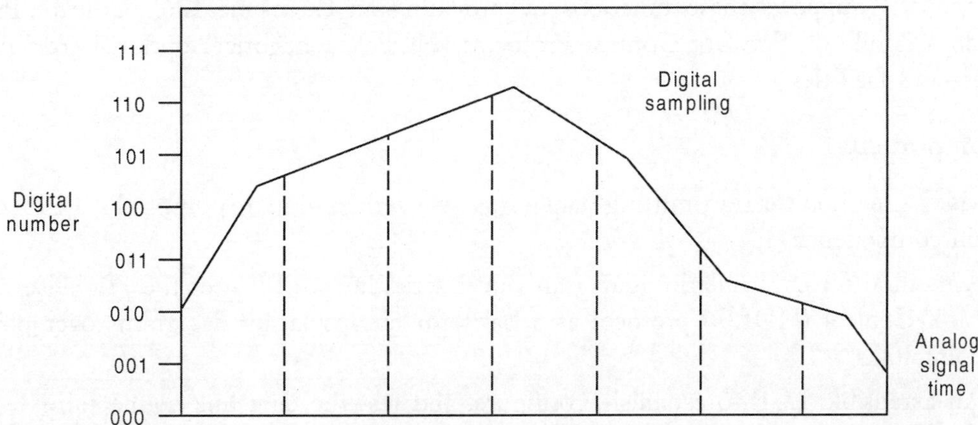

Figure 12.12 *Sampling.*

The Nyquist theorem states that to accurately reproduce an analog signal with a digital signal, the analog signal must be sampled a minimum of 2x the highest frequency of the analog signal.

This means that for the voice channel (0 to 4 kHz) to be digitized, we must sample the voice channel at 2x the highest frequency (4 kHz), which would be 8 kHz). This means that as soon as you digitize an analog signal, you must immediately double the bandwidth.

DATA LINK LAYER IN THE INTERNET

SLIP—Serial Line IP

SLIP stands for Serial Line IP. While we will discuss IP in detail in the network layer (because IP involves in routing), SLIP is used at data link layer for serial line connection to the Internet. SLIP assembles frames by adding flag byte (character stuffing) to a raw IP packet. Some SLIP Protocols just add the flag at the end; while others add at both front and rear.

The protocol was devised by Rick Adams in 1984, and was described in RFC 1055. RFC : Request For Comments a docment format used to discuss Internet related protocols, issues. Some problems with SLIP, SLIP does not do any error detection or correction. It is upto the higher layers (transport layer) to accomplish this. SLIP supports only IP, so it won't talk to novell and other protocols.

In earlier version of SLIP, each side must know the other's IP address in advance. This limits the use of it. SLIP does not provide any form of authentication, neither party knows whom it is really talking to. SLIP is not an approved Internet standard.

PPP—Point-to-Point Protocol

The *Point-to-Point Protocol (PPP)* originally emerged as an encapsulation protocol for transporting IP traffic over point-to-point links. PPP also established a standard for the assignment and management of IP addresses, asynchronous (start/stop) and bit-oriented synchronous encapsulation, network protocol multiplexing, link configuration, link quality testing, error detection, and option negotiation for such capabilities as network layer address negotiation and data-compression negotiation. PPP supports these functions by providing an extensible Link Control Protocol (LCP) and a family of Network Control Protocols (NCPs) to negotiate optional configuration parameters and facilities.

PPP Components

PPP provides a method for transmitting datagrams over serial point-to-point links. PPP contains three main components:

- A method for encapsulating datagrams over serial links. PPP uses the High-Level Data Link Control (HDLC) protocol as a basis for encapsulating datagrams over point-to-point links.
- An extensible LCP to establish, configure, and test the data link connection.
- A family of NCPs for establishing and configuring different network layer protocols. PPP is designed to allow the simultaneous use of multiple network layer protocols.

General Operation

To establish communications over a point-to-point link, the originating PPP first sends LCP frames to configure and (optionally) test the data link. After the link has been established and optional facilities have been negotiated as needed by the LCP, the originating PPP sends NCP frames to choose and configure one or more network layer protocols. When each of the chosen network layer protocols has been configured, packets from each network layer protocol can be sent over the link. The link will remain configured for communications until explicit LCP or NCP frames close the link, or until some external event occurs (for example, an inactivity timer expires or a user intervenes).

Microwave

Electromagnetic waves with wavelengths ranging from as long as one meter to as short as one millimeter or equivalently, with frequencies between 300 MHz (0.3 GHz) and 300 GHz. This broad definition includes both UHF and EHF (millimeter waves), and various sources use different boundaries. In all cases, microwave includes the entire SHF band (3 to 30 GHz, or 10 to 1 cm) at minimum, with RF engineering often putting the lower boundary at 1 GHz (30 cm), and the upper around 100 GHz (3mm).

Apparatus and techniques may be described qualitatively as "microwave" when the wavelengths of signals are roughly the same as the dimensions of the equipment, so that lumped-element circuit theory is inaccurate. As a consequence, practical microwave technique tends to move away from the discrete resistors, capacitors, and inductors used with lower frequency radio waves. Instead, distributed circuit elements and transmission-line theory are more useful methods for design and analysis. Open-wire and coaxial transmission lines give way to waveguides and stripline, and lumped-element tuned circuits are replaced by cavity resonators or resonant lines. Effects of reflection, polarization, scattering, diffraction and atmospheric absorption usually associated with visible light are of practical significance in the study of microwave propagation. The same equations of electromagnetic theory apply at all frequencies.

While the name may suggest a micrometer wavelength, it is better understood as indicating wavelengths very much smaller than those used in radio broadcasting. The boundaries between far infrared light, terahertz radiation, microwaves, and ultra-high-frequency radio waves are fairly arbitrary and are used variously between different fields of study.

Electromagnetic waves longer (lower frequency) than microwaves are called "radio waves". Electromagnetic radiation with shorter wavelengths may be called "millimeter waves", terahertz radiation or even *T-rays*. Definitions differ for millimeter wave band, which the IEEE defines as 110 GHz to 300 GHz.

Above 300 GHz, the absorption of electromagnetic radiation by Earth's atmosphere is so great that it is effectively opaque, until the atmosphere becomes transparent again in the so-called infrared and optical window frequency ranges.

To overcome the problems in SLIP, the Internet Engineering Task Force (IETF) set up a group to develop PPP, which is defined in RFC 1661 and further elaborated in a few other RFCs.

As its name implies, the Point-to-Point Protocol (PPP) is a data link layer protocol that operates over a point-to-point link—a link connecting two communicating link-level peers, one on each end of the link. The point-to-point link over which PPP operates might be a serial dialup telephone line (*e.g.*, a 56K modem connection), a SONET/SDH link, an X.25 connection, or over an ISDN circuit. As noted above, PPP has become the protocol of choice for connecting home users to their ISP's over a dialup connection.

Before dividing into the details of PPP, it is instructive to examine the original requirements that the IETF placed on the design of PPP.

Packet Framing: The PPP protocol data link layer sender must be able to take a network-level packet and frame (a.k.a encapsulate) it within the PPP data link layer frame such that the receiver will be able to identify the start and end of both the data link frame, and the network layer packet within the frame.

Transparency: The PPP protocol must not place any constraints on data appearing on the network layer packet (headers or data). Thus, for example, the PPP protocol can not forbid the use of certain bit patterns in the network layer packet. We'll return this issue shortly in our discussion of byte stuffing below.

Multiple Network Layer Protocols: The PPP protocol must be able to support multiple network layer protocols (*e.g.*, IP and DECnet) running over the *same* physical link at the *same* time. Just as the IP protocol is required to multiplex different transport level protocols (*e.g.*, TCP and UDP) over a single end-to-end connection, so too must PPP be able to multiplex different network layer protocols over a single point-to-point connection. This requirement means that at a minimum, PPP will likely require a "protocol type" field or some similar mechanism so the receiving side PPP can de-multiplex a received frame up to the appropriate network layer protocol.

Multiple Types of Links: In addition to being able to carry multiple higher level protocols, PPP must also be able to operate over a wide variety of link types, including links that are either serial (transmitting a bit at a time in a given direction) or parallel (transmitting bits in parallel), synchronous (transmitting a clock signal along with the data bits) or asynchronous, low speed or high speed, electrical or optical.

Error Detection: A PPP receiver must be able to detect bit errors in the received frame.

Connection Liveness:
PPP must be able to detect a failure at the link level (*e.g.*, the inability to transfer data from the sending side of the link to the receiving side of this link) and signal this error condition to the network layer.

Network Layer Address Negotiation: PPP must provide a mechanism for the communicating network layers (*e.g.*, IP) to learn or configure each other's network layer address.

Simplicity: PPP was required to meet a number of additional requirements beyond the seven listed above. On top of all of these requirements, first and foremost among all of the PPP requirements is that of "simplicity." RFC 1547 states "the watchword for a point-to-point protocol should be simplicity." A tall order indeed given all of the other requirements placed on the design of PPP! More than 50 RFC's now define the various aspects of this "simple" protocol.

While it may appear that many requirements were placed on the design of PPP, the situation could actually have been much more difficult. The design specifications for PPP also explicitly note protocol functionality that was PPP was *not* required to implement.

Error Correction: PPP is required to detect bit errors but is *not* required to correct them.

Flow Control: A PPP receiver is expected to be able to receive frames at the full rate of the underlying physical layer. If a higher layer can not receive packets at this full rate, it is then up to the higher layer to drop packets or throttle the sender at the higher layer. That is, rather than having the PPP sender throttle its own transmission rate, it is the responsibility of a higher level protocol to throttle the rate at which packets are delivered to PPP for sending.

Sequencing: PPP is *not* required to deliver frames to the link receiver in the same order in which they were sent by the link sender. It is interesting to note that while this flexibility is compatible with the IP service model (which allows IP packets to be delivered end-to-end in any order), other network layer protocols which operate over PPP do require sequenced end-to-end packet delivery.

Multipoint Links: PPP need only operate over links that have a single sender and a single receiver. Other link layer protocols (*e.g.*, HDLC) can accommodate multiple receivers (*e.g.*, an Ethernet-like scenario) on a link.

PPP DATA FRAMING

The PPP frame contains the following fields:

Flag Field: Every PPP frame begins and ends with a 1 byte flag field with a value of 01111110.

Address Field : The only possible value for this field is 11111111.

Control Field: The only possible value of this field is 00000011. Because both the address and control fields can currently take only a fixed value, one wonders why the fields are even defined in the first place. The PPP specification [RFC 1622] states that other values "may be defined at a later time," although none have been defined to date. Because these fields take fixed values, PPP allows the sender to simply not send the address and control bytes, thus saving two bytes of overhead in the PPP frame.

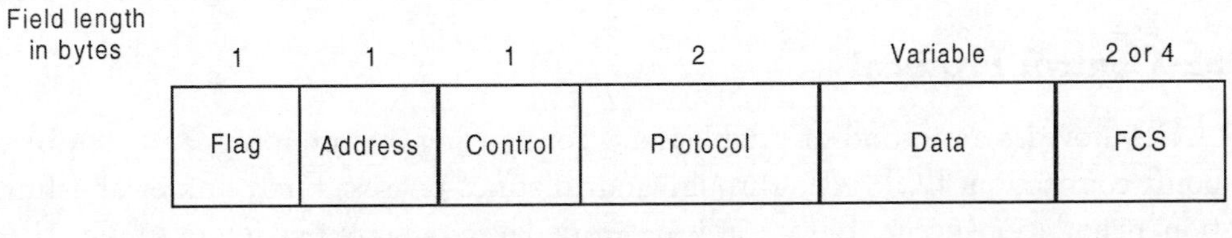

Figure 12.13 *PPP Data Frame Format.*

Protocol: The protocol field tells the PPP receiver the upper layer protocol to which the received encapsulated data (*i.e.*, the contents of the PPP frame's info field) belongs. On receipt of a PPP frame, the PPP receiver will check the frame for correctness and then pass the encapsulated data on to the appropriate protocol. [RFC 1700] defines the 16-bit protocol codes used by PPP.

Of interest to us are the IP protocol (*i.e.,* the data encapsulated in the PPP frame is an IP datagram) which has a value of 21 hexadecimal, other network layer protocols such as Appletalk (29) and DECnet (27), the PPP link control protocol (c021 hexadecimal) that we discuss in detail in the following section, and the IP control protocol (8021) which is called by PPP when a link is first activated in order to configure the IP-level connection between the two routers on each end of the link.

Information: This field contains the encapsulate packet (data) that is being sent by an upper layer protocol (*e.g.,* IP) over the PPP link. The default maximum length of the information field is 1500 bytes, although this can be changed when the link is first configured, as discussed below.

Checksum: The checksum field is used to detect bit errors in a transmitted frame. It uses either a two or four byte HDLC—standard cyclic redundancy code.

Byte Stuffing

Before closing our discussion of PPP framing, let us consider a problem that arises when any protocol uses a specific bit pattern (flag field) to delineate the beginning or end of the frame. For example, what happens if the flag field value of 01111110 appears in the information field ? Will the receiver incorrectly detect the end of the PPP frame ?

One way to solve this problem would be for PPP to forbid the upper layer protocol from sending data containing the flag field bit pattern. The PPP requirement of transparency discussed above obviates this possibility. An alternate solution, and the one taken in PPP and many other protocols, is to use a technique known as byte stuffing.

PPP defines a special control escape byte, 01111101. If the flag sequence, 01111110 appears anywhere in the frame, except in the flag field, PPP precedes that instance of the flag pattern with the control escape byte. That is, it "stuffs" (adds) a control escape byte into the transmitted data stream, before the 01111110, to indicate that the following 011111110 is *not* a flag value but is, in fact, actual data. A receiver that sees a 01111110 preceded by a 01111101 will, of course, remove the stuffed control escape to reconstruct the original data. Similarly, if the control escape byte bit pattern itself appears as actual data, it too must be preceded by a stuffed control escape byte. Thus, when the receiver see a single control escape byte by itself in the data stream, it knows that the byte was stuffed into the data stream. A pair of control escape bytes occurring back-to-back means that one instance of the control escape byte appears in the original data being sent.

PPP Link-Control Protocol

The PPP LCP provides a method of establishing, configuring, maintaining, and terminating the point-to-point connection. LCP goes through four distinct phases. First, link establishment and configuration negotiation occur. Before any network layer datagrams (for example, IP) can be exchanged, LCP first must open the connection and negotiate configuration parameters. This phase is complete when a configuration-acknowledgement frame has been both sent and received.

This is followed by link quality determination. LCP allows an optional link quality determination phase following the link-establishment and configuration-negotiation phase. In this phase, the link is tested to determine whether the link quality is sufficient to bring up network layer protocols. This phase is optional. LCP can delay transmission of network layer protocol information until this phase is complete.

At this point, network layer protocol configuration negotiation occurs. After LCP has finished the link quality determination phase, network layer protocols can be configured separately by the appropriate NCP and can be brought up and taken down at any time. If LCP closes the link, it informs the network layer protocols so that they can take appropriate action.

Finally, link termination occurs. LCP can terminate the link at any time. This usually is done at the request of a user but can happen because of a physical event, such as the loss of carrier or the expiration of an idle-period timer. Three classes of LCP frames exist. Link-establishment frames are used to establish and configure a link. Link-termination frames are used to terminate a link, and link-maintenance frames are used to manage and debug a link. These frames are used to accomplish the work of each of the LCP phases.

PROTOCOL OPERATION

The two basic functions in the protocol are link management and data transfer, which includes error and flow control.

Link Management

Prior to any kind of transmission (either between two stations connected by a point to point link or between a primary and secondary station a multi-drop link) a logical connection between the two communication parties must be established.

Data Transfer

In NRM all data (information frames) if transferred under the control of the primary station. The unnumbered poll frame with the P bit set to 1 is normally used by the primary to poll a secondary. If the secondary has no data to transmit, it returns an RNR frame with the F bit set. If data is waiting, it transmits the data, typically as a sequence of information frames.

The two most important aspects associated with the data transfer phase are error control and flow control. Essentially, error control uses a continues RQ procedure with either a selective repeat or a go-back-N transmission strategy, while flow controls based on a window mechanism.

PROTOCOL EFFICIENCY

The concept of link utilization does not consider that the amount of data actually sent is less than the length of the frame.

The *protocol efficiency* refers to the fraction of total data transmitted that represents the DU's themselves. This value is always less than 1 because each frame contains additional protocol information such as CRC and sequence number. Example data link protocols data link layer used in X.25 and other protocols, in Internet (SLIP and PPP), and in ATM.

REVIEW QUESTIONS

1. What is communication channel ?
2. Explain channel capacity.
3. Explain noisy channel model.
4. What is Nyquist theorem, explain ?
5. Explain data link layer in Internet.
6. Write short notes on SLIP and PPP protocol.
7. Explain protocol operations and efficiency.
8. What are the main components of PPP ?
9. What is the only absolute physical layer requirement imposed by PPP ?
10. How many fields make up the PPP frame, and what are they ?
11. How many phases does the PPP LCP go through, and what are they ?

❑❑❑

PART 4

THE MEDIA ACCESS CONTROL SUBLAYER (MAC)

13 Medium Access Control (MAC)

The Medium Access Control (MAC) protocol is used to provide the data link layer of the Ethernet LAN system. The MAC protocol encapsulate a SDU (payload data) by adding a 14 byte header (Protocol Control Information (PCI)) before the data and appending a 4-byte (32-bit) Cyclic Redundancy Check (CRC) after the data. The entire frame is preceded by a small idle period (the minimum inter-frame gap, 9.6 microsecond (μS)) and a 8 byte preamble.

The MAC is a sub-layer of the data link layer and provides an interface to the physical medium below it, the part that transmits and receives signals that contain data. The MAC sub-layer also communicates with the sub-layer above it allowing it to access and speak to the upper layer network protocols .

MEDIUM ACCESS CONTROL

The protocols given in the previous section assumed that the sender had a direct link to the receiver, and also that the link provided duplex communication, *i.e.,* so that frames could be being sent at the same time that's were being received.

Recall that the repeater is a simple layer 1 device and that, any number of repeaters may exist between two data link layer peers, transparently to the communication. Also recall that the hub is a general repeater. Frames from any of the data link layers will be transmitted to every other data link layer.

The use of a hub introduces new problems for the protocols because a transmitted frame will potentially be received by a number of different data link layers.

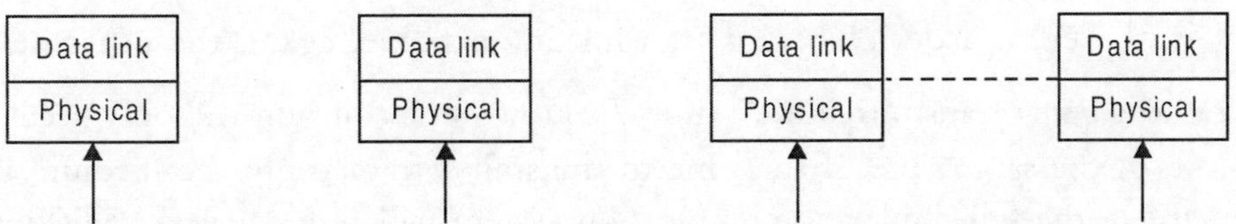

Figure 13.1 *Addressing of each Device in Shared Medium.*

So each device needs an *address*. The address is called the *Medium Access Control* (MAC) address—it is a unique identifier for every device connected to the *shared* medium.

Example: The most widely known type of MAC address is the Ethernet address. Every manufacturer of an Ethernet device has agreed to use a unique number for each and every device. The MAC address of my desktop computer is 00: 30: 65: *eb*: 6*c*: 4*c* which is 48 bits long. On UNIX systems you can usually discover the Ethernet address by using the ifconfig command.

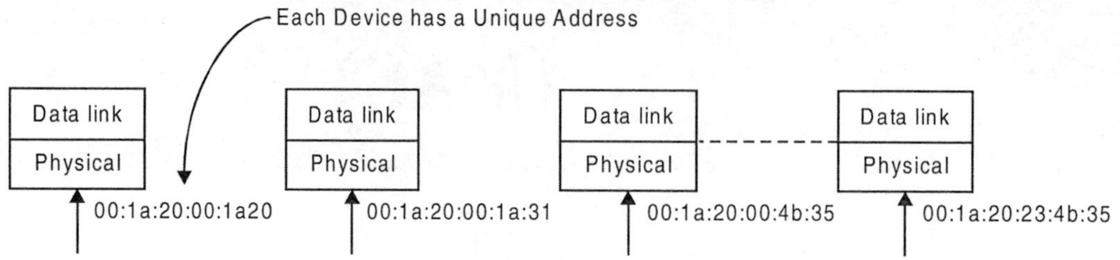

Figure 13.2 *MAC Addressing.*

Also, frames can collide if two layer 2 devices decide to transmit at or near the same time. The ways in which collisions occur is dependent on the physical layer.

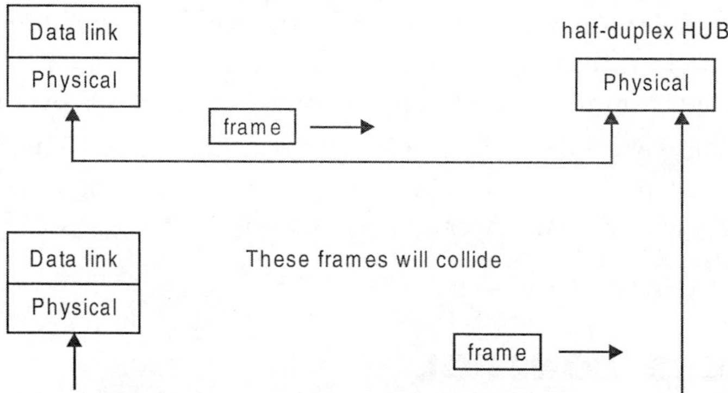

Figure 13.3 *Frame Collision with Physical Layer.*

Considering the half-duplex case, if the propagation delay between all devices and the hub is $\frac{T_p}{2}$ then, in the event that a device begins transmitting a frame, the other devices wont detect that the frame is being transmitted until time T_p (they don't receive the frame until time $T_p + T_f$). If they don't detect that the frame is being transmitted, then they might try to transmit their own frame which leads to a collision.

Considering the full-duplex case, if the propagation delay between all devices and the hub is $\frac{T_p}{2}$ then, in the event a device begins transmitting a frame, again, the other devices wont detect that frame is being transmitted until time T_p. However a collision will only occur if another device transmits at the same time. If the time to transmit a frame onto the medium is $T_f << T_p$ then, *ceteris paribus*, the full-duplex communication system will result in less collisions than the half-duplex system. As T_f gets closer to T_p the number of collisions in the full-duplex system approaches that of half-duplex because the potential collision time interval approaches equality.

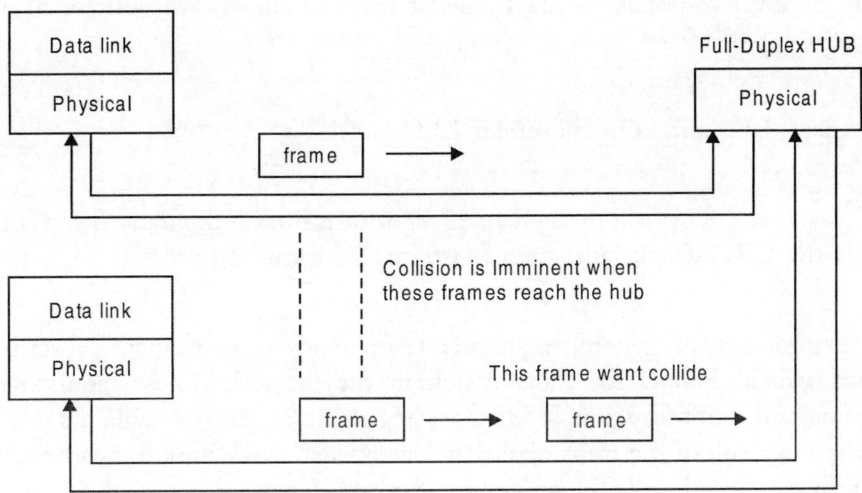

Figure 13.4 *Frame Collision.*

In terms of non-switched Ethernet, Medium Access Control (MAC) is an effective methodology that allows devices on a LAN to share their interconnecting media.

Due to the shared nature of the media, it is obvious that more than one device might send data at the same time, therefore Ethernet MAC has to be able to:

- Decide when to send data.
- What to do if its data collides with another device's data.
- How long to wait after a collision before retransmitting.

MAC FRAME FORMAT

Since there are various types of network interfaces (Ethernet, Token ring, FDDI, serial etc.) the MAC frame format differs by protocol according to it's design. However, most will have at a minimum the following fields:

MAC CONTROL	DESTINATION MAC ADDR	SOURCE MAC ADDR	LLC PDU	CRC

MAC Control

Contains all information designated by the protocol's specifications used for flow control, connection establishment and teardown (where appropriate) as well as error control (if appropriate).

Destination/Source MAC

Addresses of the destination and source machines. The source machine is the transmitting device, and the destination device is the receiver. The destination MAC is closer to the 'front' (left side in the diagram) of the frame for easier scanning, mostly because it is the destination device that is important as that is the device we are trying to reach.

When the receiver responds to the frame, it will use the source address to generate the destination portion of the frame.

LLC PDU

Logical link packet data unit from the upper LLC sub-layer.

CRC

Cyclic redundancy check. This is a mathematical algorithm run on the data to verify the integrity of the frame. If the CRC check fails, then the frame is discarded.

MAC Layer

The MAC layer provides the general requirements for many cable modem subscribers to share a single upstream data channel for transmission to the network. These requirements include collision detection and retransmission. The large geographic reach of a cable data network poses special problems as a result of the transmission delay between users close to head-end versus users at a distance from cable head-end. To compensate for cable losses and delay as a result of distance, the MAC layer performs ranging, by which each cable modem can assess time delay in transmitting to the head-end. The MAC layer supports timing and synchronization, bandwidth allocation to cable modems at the control of CMTS, error detection, handling and error recovery, and procedures for registering new cable modems.

Privacy of user data is achieved by encrypting link-layer data between cable modems and CMTS. Cable modems and CMTS head-end controller encrypt the payload data of link-layer frames transmitted on the cable network. A set of security parameters including keying data is assigned to a cable modem by the Security Association (SA). All of the upstream transmissions from a cable modem travel across a single upstream data channel and are received by the CMTS. In the downstream data channel a CMTS must select appropriate SA based on the destination address of the target cable modem. Baseline privacy employs the Data Encryption Standard (DES) block cipher for encryption of user data. The encryption can be integrated directly within the MAC hardware and software interface.

Network Layer

Cable data networks use IP for communication from the cable modem to the network. The Internet Engineering Task Force (IETF) DHCP forms the basis for all IP address assignment and administration in the cable network. A Network Address Translation (NAT) system may be used to map multiple computers that use a single high-speed access via cable modem.

Transport Layer

Cable data networks support both Transmission Control Protocol (TCP) and User Datagram Protocol (UDP) at the transport layer.

Application Layer

All of the Internet-related applications are supported here. These applications include e-mail, ftp, tftp, http, news, chat, and Signaling Network Management Protocol (SNMP). The use of SNMP provides for management of the CMTS and cable data networks.

Operations System

The Operations Support System Interface (OSSI) requirements of DOCSIS specify how a cable data network is managed. To date, the requirements specify an RF MIB. This enables system vendors to develop an EMS to support spectrum management, subscriber management, billing, and other operations.

Cable modem technology offers high-speed access to the Internet and world wide web services. Cable data networks integrate the elements necessary to advance beyond modem technology and provide such measures as privacy, security, data networking, Internet access, and quality-of-service features. The end-to-end network architecture enables a user cable modem to connect to a CMTS which, in turn, connects to a regional data center for access to Internet services. Thus, through a system of network connections, a cable data network is capable of connecting users to other users anywhere in the global network.

A name or token that identifies a network component. In Local Area Network (LAN), for example, every node has a unique address. On the Internet, every file has a unique address called a URL.

The Media Access Control (MAC) Sub-layer Functions

The 100VG-AnyLAN media access control functions include demand priority protocol control, link training, and MAC frame preparation.

Demand Priority is a network access method in which nodes issue a request (or demand) to the hub to send a packet on the network. Each request is labeled with either a normal-priority level for normal data packets, or a high-priority level for packets supporting time-critical multimedia applications. High-priority requests are granted access to the network before normal-priority requests, providing a method to guarantee appropriate service for time-sensitive applications. Normal-priority and high-priority labeling is completed by upper-level application software, and is passed (as part of the packet information) to the MAC sub-layer.

As illustrated in figure 13.5, the level 1 or root hub continuously scans node requests, using a round-robin arbitration procedure. The round-robin scanning allows the hub to determine which nodes, if any, are requesting to send a packet, and whether the request is for normal-priority or high-priority packets.

Each round-robin scanning cycle allows each node to request to send one packet on the network. Hubs connected as nodes also complete a round-robin scanning cycle, and issue a request to the root hub. Single-port nodes may only send one packet (if other nodes have pending requests). A lower-level hub with "n" nodes connected will be able to send "n" packets when it is selected during the round-robin process (if no other high-priority requests are pending).

Each hub maintains a separate list for normal-priority and high-priority requests. Normal-priority requests are serviced in port order until a high-priority request is received. After completing the packet transmission currently in progress, the hub will service the high-priority request. All high-priority packets will be serviced before the hub returns to service the normal-priority list. To guarantee access for normal-priority requests during an excess of high-priority traffic, the hub continually monitors node request-to-send response times. If the delay exceeds an established maximum time, the hub will automatically raise the normal-priority level to a high-priority level.

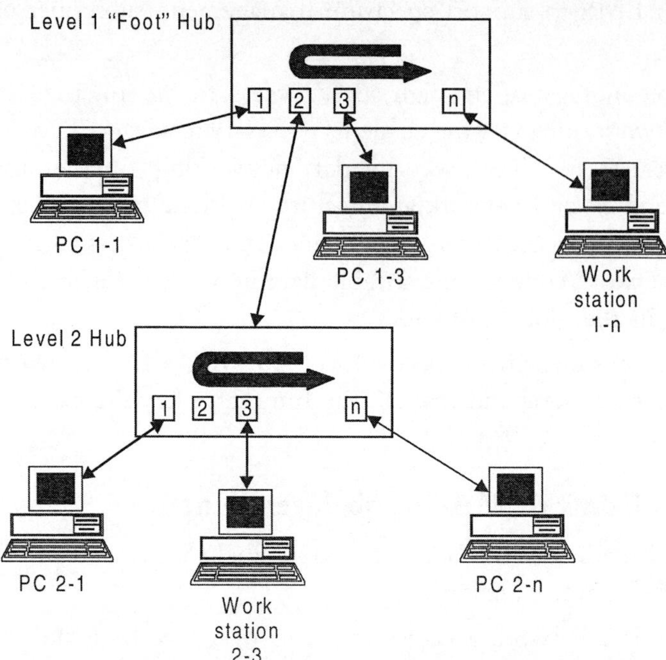

Figure 13.5 *Round-Robin Scanning.*

Figure 13.5, will be used to show an example of the hub round-robin scanning cycle. First, consider that all ports have normal-priority requests pending, and that the round-robin sequence is at the root or level 1 hub, port 1, at time t=0. The packet service order would be 1-1 (level 1 hub-port 1), 2-1 (level 2 hub-port 1), 2-3, 2-n, 1-3, and 1-n. If node 1-1, 2-3, and 1-3 issued a high-priority request at time t=0, the packet service order would be 1-1, 2-3, 1-3, 2-1, 2-n, and 1-n.

Link training is a link initialization procedure that optimizes or "trains" the internal hub and node circuitry for data reception and transmission, and verifies the operation of the link connecting the hub and the node.

During link training, the hub and the node exchange a series of special test packets. This procedure provides a functional test of the cable to verify that the cable is correctly wired and that data may be successfully transferred to and from the hub and the node.

Link training also allows the hub to automatically learn information about the node device connected to each port. Packets received by the hub from the training node contain information such as the device type (hub, bridge, router, network test/monitor equipment, etc.), operational mode (normal or monitor), and the station address of the device attached to that port.

Link training is initiated by the node when the hub and node are first powered on, or when the node is first connected to the hub. The node or hub may also request link-training when certain error conditions are detected.

MAC frame preparation is completed after receiving the packet from the logical link Control sub-layer. The MAC sub-layer adds the node source address, and any required bits to complete (or pad) the data field. A Frame Check Sequence (FCS) is then calculated and appended to the end of the packet. The FCS will be used by the receiving hub and node to determine if the packet has been received without errors.

CLASSIFICATION OF MAC PROTOCOLS

There are two kinds of MAC protocols:

1. **Contention protocols:** These protocols allow the possibility of frames colliding.
2. **Contention-less protocols:** These protocols don't allow the possibility of frames colliding.

The choice of a contention or contention-less protocol is mainly made on the basis of the transmission medium. In other words different MAC sub-layer protocols have been developed according to the type of physical layer.

CSMA

To overcome the low efficiency of the logical token bus protocol the Carrier Sense Multiple Access (CSMA) protocol can be used. In this case devices are allowed to transmit a frame at any time (multiple access). However each device will not transmit a frame if they are receiving a frame (carrier sense).

For the case of persistent CSMA, if a device detects that a frame is being received it will send its own frame immediately after the frame has been received. For the case of non-persistent CSMA the device will wait for some random period before transmitting.

Collisions can occur so this protocol is a contention protocol. If Collision Detection (CD) is used then colliding frames can be aborted.

Preamble

The purpose of the idle time before transmission starts is to allow a small time interval for the receiver electronics in each of the nodes to settle after completion of the previous frame. A node starts transmission by sending an 8 byte (64 bit) preamble sequence. This consists of 62 alternating 1's and 0's followed by the pattern 11. Strictly speaking the last byte which finished with the '11' is known as the "start of frame delimiter". When encoded using Manchester encoding, at 10 Mbps, the 62 alternating bits produce a 5 MHz square wave.

The purpose of the preamble is to allow time for the receiver in each node to achieve lock of the receiver digital phase lock which is used to synchronize the receive data clock to the transmit data clock. At the point when the first bit of the preamble is received, each receiver may be in an arbitrary state (*i.e.,* have an arbitrary phase for its local clock). During the course of the preamble it learns the correct phase, but in so doing it may miss (or gain) a number of bits. A special pattern, is therefore used to mark the last two bits of the preamble. When this is received, the Ethernet receive interface starts collecting the bits into bytes for processing by the MAC layer.

Header

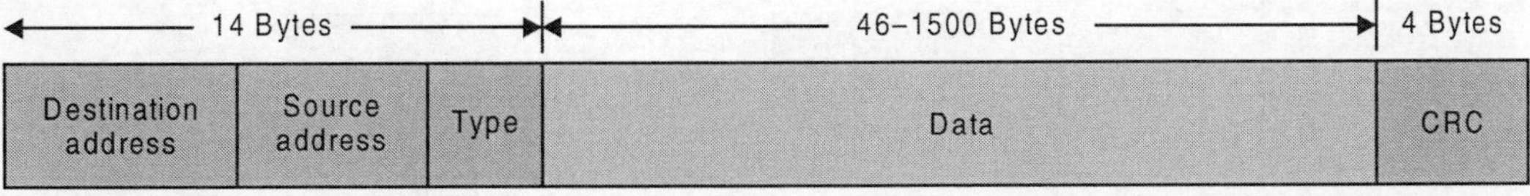

Figure 13.6 *MAC Encapsulation of a Packet of Data.*

The header consists of three parts:

1. A 6-byte destination address, which specifies either a single recipient node unicast mode, a group of recipient nodes (multicast mode),or the set of all recipient nodes (broadcast mode).
2. A 6-byte source address, which is set to the sender's globally unique node address. This may be used by the network layer protocol to identify the sender, but usually other mechanisms are used (*e.g.*, arp). Its main function is to allow address learning which may be used to configure the filter tables in a bridge.
3. A 2-byte type field, which provides a Service Access Point (SAP) to identify the type of protocol being carried (*e.g.*, the values 0 × 0800 is used to identify the IP network protocol, other values are used to indicate other network layer protocols). In the case of IEEE 802.3 LLC, this may also be used to indicate the length of the data part.

ALOHA

In the 1970's Norman Abramson and his colleagues at the university of Hawaii devised a new and elegant method to solve the channel allocation problem. This work is called the ALOHA system, used ground-based radio broadcasting, the basic idea is applicable to any system in which uncoordinated users are competing for the use of a single shared channel.

ALOHA is a contention protocol and is used when carrier sense is not available. Mainly this for satellite communication. The protocol allows devices to transmit at any time. Read your textbook to see the analysis of ALOHA for the case when slotted and unslotted ALOHA is used.

There are two versions of ALOHA: pure and slotted they differ with respect to whether time is divided into discrete slots into which all frames must fit pure ALOHA does not require global time synchronization; slotted ALOHA does.

1. A protocol for satellite and terrestrial radio transmissions. In pure aloha, a user can transmit at any time but risks collisions with other users' messages. "Slotted ALOHA" reduces the chance of collisions by dividing the channel into time slots and requiring that the user send only at the beginning of a time slot. ALOHA was the basis for Ethernet, a local area network protocol.

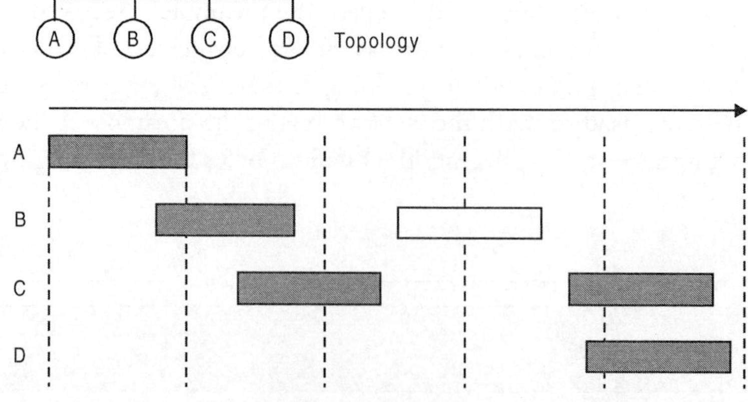

Figure 13.7 *ALOHA.1.*

2. ALOHA networks, Inc.—A San Francisco-based company specializing in providing satellite-based Internet access to large Internet service providers. Founded by the inventor of the ALOHA system, Norman Abramson.
3. ALOHA home—Software from media synergy that allows a user to add graphics, animation, and sound to e-mail messages.

Pure ALOHA

The basic idea of an ALOHA system is simple: let users transmit whenever they have data to be sent. There will be collisions, of course, and the colliding frames will be damaged. However, due to the feedback property of broadcasting, a sender can always find out whether its frame was destroyed by listening to the channel, the same way other users do. With a LAN, the feedback is immediate; with a satellite, there is a delay of 270 MSEC before the sender knows if the transmission was successful. If listening while transmitting is not possible for some reason, acknowledgments are needed. If the frame was destroyed, the sender just waits a random amount of time and sends it again. The waiting time must be random or the same frames will collide over and over, in lockstep. Systems in which multiple users share a common channel in a way that can lead to conflicts are widely known as contention systems.

A sketch of frame generation in an ALOHA system is given in figure 13.8.

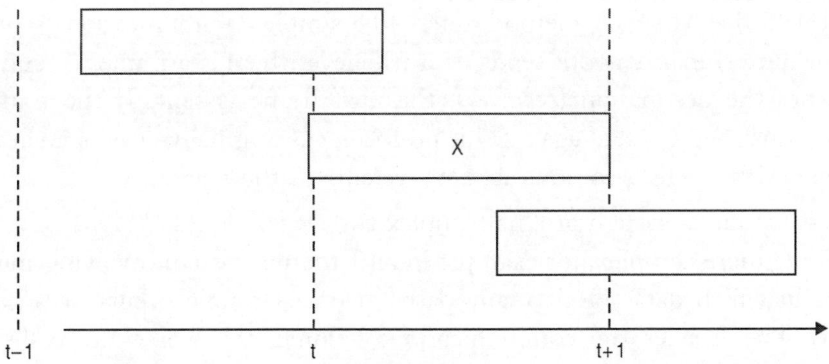

Figure 13.8 *ALOHA.2.*

Slotted ALOHA

In 1972, Roberts published a method for doubling the capacity of an ALOHA system. His proposal was to divide time into discrete intervals, each interval corresponding to one frame. This approach requires the users to agree on slot boundaries. One way to achieve synchronization would be to have one special station emit a pip at the start of each interval, like a clock.

In Roberts' method, which has come to be known as slotted ALOHA, in contrast to Abramson's pure ALOHA, a computer is not permitted to send whenever a carriage return is typed. Instead, it is required to wait for the beginning of the next slot. Thus, the continuous pure

ALOHA is turned into a discrete one. since the vulnerable period is now halved, the probability of no other traffic during the same slot as our test frame is e-g which leads to

$$S = ge\text{-}g$$

as shown in figure 13.9.

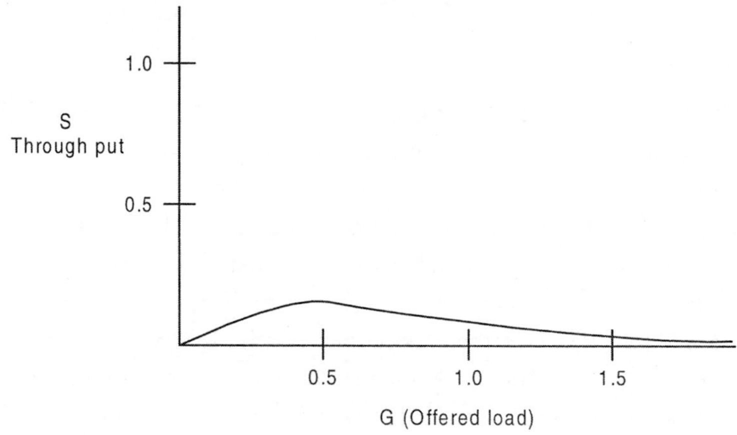

Figure 13.9 *ALOHA.3.*

ALOHA Protocol

ALOHA, also called the ALOHA method, refers to a simple communications scheme in which each source (transmitter) in a network sends data whenever there is a frame to send. If the frame successfully reaches the destination (receiver), the next frame is sent. If the frame fails to be received at the destination, it is sent again. This protocol was originally developed at the university of Hawaii for use with satellite communication systems in the pacific.

In a wireless broadcast system or a half-duplex two-way link, ALOHA works perfectly. But as networks become more complex, for example in an Ethernet system involving multiple sources and destinations in which data travels many paths at once, trouble occurs because data frames collide (conflict). The heavier the communications volume, the worse the collision problems become. The result is degradation of system efficiency, because when two frames collide, the data contained in both frames is lost.

To minimize the number of collisions, thereby optimizing network efficiency and increasing the number of subscribers that can use a given network, a scheme called slotted ALOHA was developed. This system employs signals called beacons that are sent at precise intervals and tell each source when the channel is clear to send a frame. Further improvement can be realized by a more sophisticated protocol called Carrier Sense Multiple Access with collision detection (CSMA).

In 1970s, Norman Abramson and his colleagues at the university of Hawaii devised a new and elegant method to solve the channel allocation problem. Many researchers have extended their work since then. Although Abramson's work, called the ALOHA system, used ground-based radio broadcasting, the basic idea is applicable to any system in which uncoordinated users are completing for the use of a single shared channel.

The two several of ALOHA are:

- PURE ALOHA
- SLOTTED ALOHA

The ALOHA protocol

- Simple: if you have packet to send, "just do it"
- If packet suffers collision, will try resending later

Analyzing the ALOHA Protocol:

Goal:

- Fixed length packets
- Packet transmission time is unit of time
- Throughput: S: number packets successfully (without collision) transmitted per unit time
  – in previous example, S = 0.2 packet/unit time
- Offered load: G: number packet transmissions attempted per unit time
  – note: S<G, but S depends on G
  – Poisson model: probability of k packet transmission attempts in t time units:
  Prob[k trans in t] = ((Gt)**k)(e**(–Gt))/(k!)
- Capacity of multiple access protocol: maximum value of S over all values of G

Analyzing ALOHA (cont)

focus on a given attempted packet transmission

S = rate attempted packet trans * prob[trans successful]

= G*prob[no other packet's overlap with attempted trans]

= G*prob[0 other attempted trans in 2 time units]

= Ge*(-2G)

ALOHA Throughput:

Maximum throughput is 18% of physical channel capacity.

RANDOM ACCESS PROTOCOLS

When node has packet to send:

transmit at full channel data rate R.

no a priori coordination among nodes

two or more transmitting nodes -> "collision",

random access MAC protocol specifies:

how to detect collisions

how to recover from collisions (*e.g.*, via delayed retransmissions)

Examples of random access MAC protocols:

1. Slotted ALOHA
2. ALOHA

3. CSMA and CSMA/CD
4. SLOTTED ALOHA

time is divided into equal size slots (= packet transmission time)

node with new packet: transmit at beginning of next slot

if collision: retransmit pkt in future slots with probability p, until successful.

Success (S), Collision (C), Empty (E) slots

SLOTTED ALOHA EFFICIENCY

Suppose N stations have packets to send each transmits in slot with probability p, probability of successful transmission S is:

by any specific single node: S= p (1–p)(N–1)

by any of N nodes

S = Prob (only one transmits)

= N p (1–p)(N–1)

for optimum p as N -> infinity ...

= 1/e = .37

PURE (UNSLOTTED) ALOHA

Unslotted ALOHA: simpler, no synchronization pkt needs transmission:

Send without awaiting for beginning of slot collision probability increases:

pkt sent at t0 collide with other pkts sent in [t0–1, t0+1]

PURE ALOHA

P(success by given node) = P(node transmits) .

P(no other node transmits in [t0–1,t0] .

P(no other node transmits in [t0,t0 +1]

= p.(1–p)(N–1) (1–p)(N–1)

P(success by any of N nodes) = N p.(1–p)(N–1) (1–p)(N–1)

... choosing optimum p as n -> infinity ...

= 1/(2e) = .18

S = throughput = "goodput"

CSMA: (Carrier Sense Multiple Access)

CSMA: listen before transmit:

- If channel sensed idle: transmit entire packet
- If channel sensed busy, defer transmission

Persistent CSMA: retry immediately with probability p when channel becomes idle (may cause instability) Non-persistent CSMA: retry after random interval CSMA collisions can occur.

Propagation delay means two nodes may not yet hear each other's transmission.

COLLISION:

- Entire packet transmission
- Time wasted
- Spatial layout of nodes along Ethernet

NETWORK ACCESS METHODS

There are various methods of managing access to a network. If all network stations tried to talk at once, the messages would become unintelligible, and no communication could occur. Therefore a method of being sure that stations coordinate the sending of messages must be achieved. There are several methods listed below which have various advantages and disadvantages.

- Contention
- Carrier-sense multiple access with collision detection
- (CSMA/CD)—Used by Ethernet

CSMA/CD (COLLISION DETECTION)

The protocol Carrier Sense Multiple Access (CSMA) with Collision Detection (CD) is used to control access to the shared Ethernet medium. Receiver processing algorithm is shown in figure 13.10.

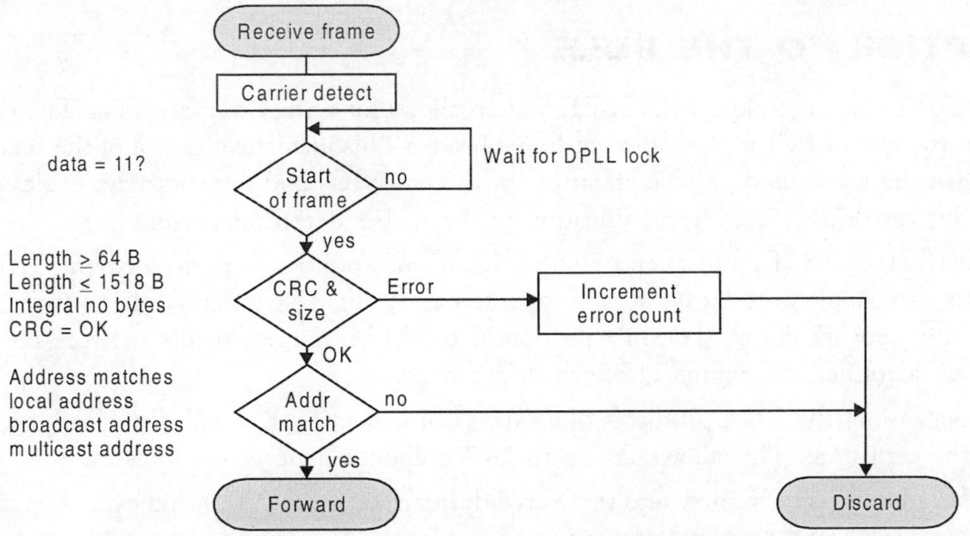

Figure 13.10 *Receiver Processing Algorithm.*

There are different types of frames, which are used in receiving processing. They are used as :

A Runt Frame

Any frame which is received and which is less than 64 bytes is illegal, and is called a "runt". In most cases, such frames arise from a collision, and while they indicate an illegal reception, they may be observed on correctly functioning networks. A receiver must discard all runt frames.

A Giant Frame

Any frame which is received and which is greater than the maximum frame size, and is called a "giant". In theory, the Jabber control circuit in the transceiver should prevent any node from generating such a frame, but certain failures in the physical layer may also give rise to over-sized Ethernet frames. Like runts, giants are discarded by the Ethernet receiver.

A Misaligned Frame

Any frame which does not contain an integral number of received octets (bytes) is also illegal. A receiver has no way of knowing which bits are legal, and how to compute the CRC-32 of the frame. Such frames are therefore also discarded by the Ethernet receiver.

OTHER ISSUES ABOUT FRAME

The Ethernet standard dictates a minimum size of frame, which requires at least 46 bytes of data to be present in every MAC frame. If the network layer wishes to send less than 46 bytes of data the MAC protocol adds sufficient number of zero bytes (0 × 00, is also known as null padding characters) to satisfy this requirement. The maximum size of data which may be carried in a MAC frame using Ethernet is 1500 bytes (this is known as the MTU in IP).

A protocol known as the "Address Resolution Protocol(ARP)" is used to identify the MAC source address of remote computers when IP is used over an Ethernet LAN.

EXCEPTION TO THE RULE

An extension to Ethernet, known as IEEE 802.1p allows for frames to carry a tag. The tag value adds an extra level of PCI to the Ethernet frame header. This increases the size of the total MAC frame when the tag is used. A side effect of this is that NICs and network devices designed to support this extension require a modification to the Jabber detection circuit.

The IEEE 802.3 (Ethernet) and 802.5 (Token ring) protocols specify that the MAC sub-layer must also supply a 48 bit address represented as 12 digit hexadecimal digits that uniquely identifies the network device. The first portion of the MAC address of the network device, the last portion identifies the unique id of the device itself.

In the case of the 802.x protocols, the first 24 bits identify the vendor, and the last 24 bits identify the card itself. This allows for up to 16.7 million unique card addresses.

MAC addresses are 'burned' into the Network Interface Card (NIC), and cannot be changed.

Carrier Sensed Multiple Access with Collision Detection (CSMA/CD) is the MAC used by non-switched Ethernet. It is easier to explain the CSMA/CD concept by looking at each phrase:

- **Carrier sensed:** Each device that wants to send data along the shared media "listens" to the media to detect if it is in use by other users.
- **Multiple access:** Any device can transmit if it detects that the media is clear.

- **Collision detection:** Each device monitors its data in case it collides with other data. Collisions can occur if two devices simultaneously listen to the media, decide it is clear and then transmit at the same time.

WORKING

When a device transmits data, it encapsulates the data into a frame with the destination address at the head of the frame. The frame is then broadcast onto the media. All other connected devices detect the broadcast. Each device reads the address at the head of the frame, but will only read the whole frame if it recognizes its own address in the header. Once the frame has been read, the device responds to the source (the source address is also in the frame header). The response could tell the source that the data was received successfully, or that it was corrupt and re-transmission is necessary.

Once a device has transmitted data, it monitors its progress across the media. If the device detects that the transmitted data is different from the monitored data, a collision is assumed to have occurred. To ensure that other devices involved in the collision are aware that a collision has taken place, the detecting device transmits a random bit pattern. This random pattern is known as a jam bit or jam sequence and it effectively "kills" the corrupted frames. The devices involved in the collision then enter a randomly determined wait-state, sometimes referred to as a binary exponential back-off, prior to attempting the retransmission of the affected frames. The back off is simply a randomly calculated period of time that can increase if successive collisions occur.

CSMA/CD is an excellent solution to the problems of shared media access, but its use is problematic when a network is heavily loaded. When the media is heavily congested, a higher proportion of frames can be corrupted. This is particularly noticeable in networks operating at a high bit rate (100BaseT). Switched Ethernet technology has been developed to overcome the limitations of CSMA/CD.

Frames

A frame can be defined as the unit of data transferred across the network, defined at the data link (network access) layer of the protocol stack.

Packets

A packet can be defined as the unit of data at any layer of the protocol stack, prior to, or after transmission.

It's not really quite that simple because some people prefer to further define data in terms of each layer of the TCP/IP protocol suite. There are some points related to the layers, they are as:

1. Data at the application layer is called a message.
2. Transport layer data is sometimes referred to as TCP or UDP segments.
3. At the Internet layer, data is sometimes talked of in terms of IP, ARP and RARP datagrams.

4. The datalink layer data is referred to as frames.
5. At the physical layer, data is sometimes referred to as bits—the lowest common denominator.

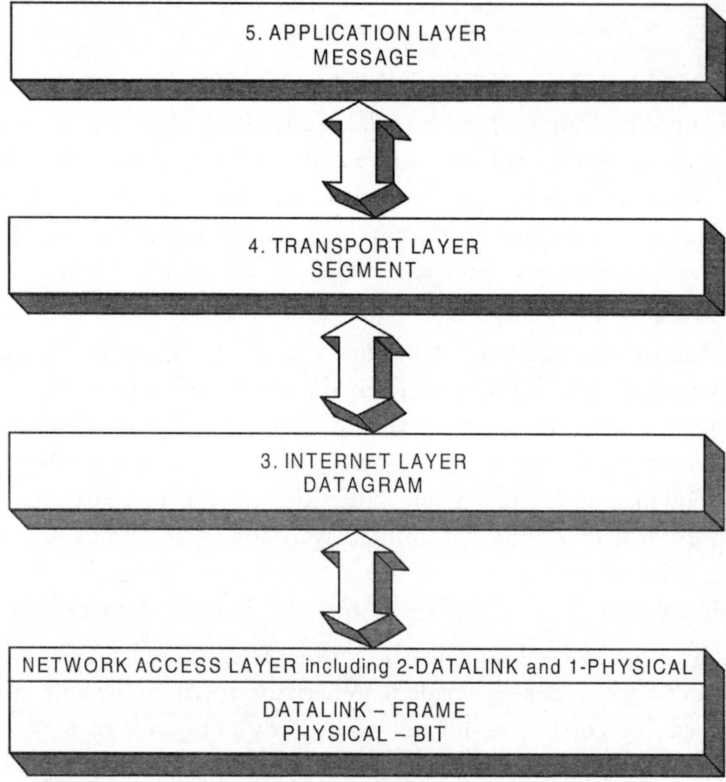

Figure 13.11 *Analysis of Packet at Different Layers.*

As data descends the source protocol stack, successive levels encapsulate the data with additional information. After a frame has been received at its destination, successive layers then de-encapsulate the data as it travels up the destination protocol stack.

Therefore, a packet can be discussed in terms of its subsets—messages, segments and datagrams. Frames are not discussed in any other terms, they simply encapsulate the data with a header and addressing information.

FORMAT OF A FRAME

Figure 13.12 illustrates the IEEE 802.3 frame format.

An octet is defined as eight bits of data. The Ethernet version 2.0 frame is similar to the IEEE 802.3 frame. For a device to be 802.3 compliant, it must be able to communicate with legacy version 2.0 devices.

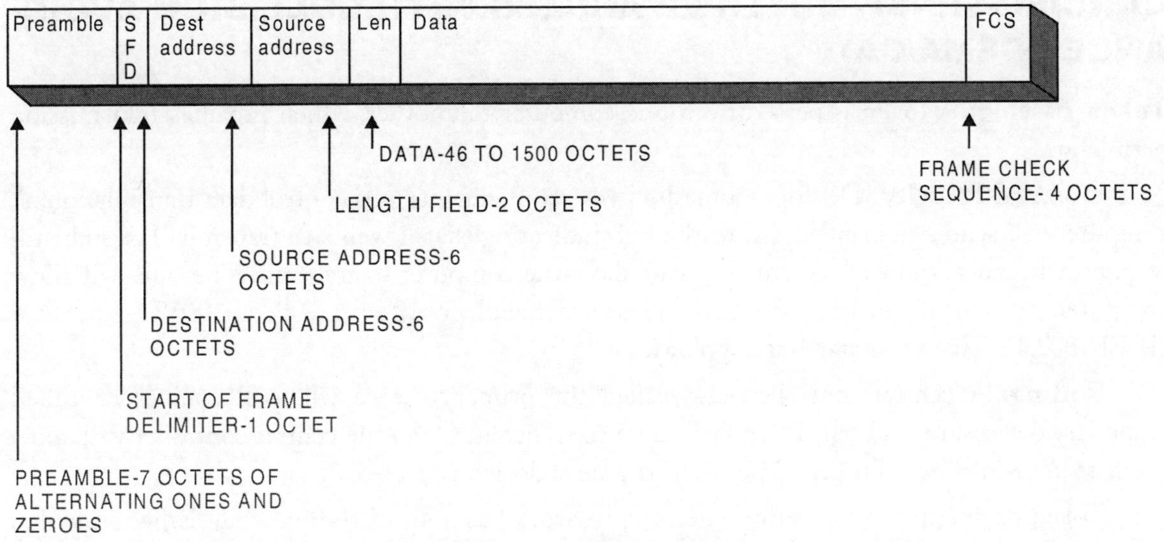

Figure 13.12 *Format of a Frame.*

WORKING OF EACH FIELD

Preamble—alerts and synchronizes the Network Interface Card (NIC) to the incoming data.

Start of frame delimiter—indicates the start of the frame.

Destination address—the MAC (Medium Access Control) address of the destination NIC. Three types of address exist:

Unicast—addresses a single device.

Multicast—addresses a group of devices.

Broadcast—addresses all devices.

Source address—the MAC address of the source NIC.

Length—indicates the length of the data field.

Data—carries the data being transferred. It has a maximum limit to stop devices sending too much data at any time. This gives fair access to the media to all devices.

Frame check sequence—provides a Cyclic Redundancy Check (CRC) on all data held in the frame. CRC is an error detection mechanism generated by the NICs. The source NIC generates a 32 bit CRC from the address, type and data fields. The destination NIC does the same calculations. If the destination NIC calculates the same for the CRC as the source, the frame was received error-free.

CARRIER-SENSE MULTIPLE ACCESS WITH COLLISION AVOIDANCE (CSMA/CA)

Token Passing: A token is passed from one computer to another, which provides transmission permission.

Demand Priority: Describes a method where intelligent hubs control data transmission. A computer will send a demand signal to the hub indicating that it wants to transmit. The hub still respond with an acknowledgement that will allow the computer to transmit. The hub will allow computers to transmit in turn. An example of a demand priority network is 100VG-AnyLAN (IEEE 802.12). It uses a star-bus topology.

Polling: A central controller, also called the primary device will poll computers, called secondary devices, to find out if they have data to transmit. Of so the central controller will allow them to transmit for a limited time, then the next device is polled.

Token passing performs better when the network has a lot of traffic, while Ethernet which uses CSMA/CD is generally faster but loses performance when the network has a lot of traffic. CSMA/CD is basically a method that allows network stations to transmit any time they want. They, however, sense the network line and detect if another station has transmitted at the same time they did. This is called a collision. If a collision happened, the stations involved will retransmit at a later, randomly set time in hopes of avoiding another collision.

NETWORK INTERFACE CARD

A network interface card is used to connect a computer to an Ethernet network. The card (shown in the Figure 13.13) provides an interface to the media. This may be either using an external

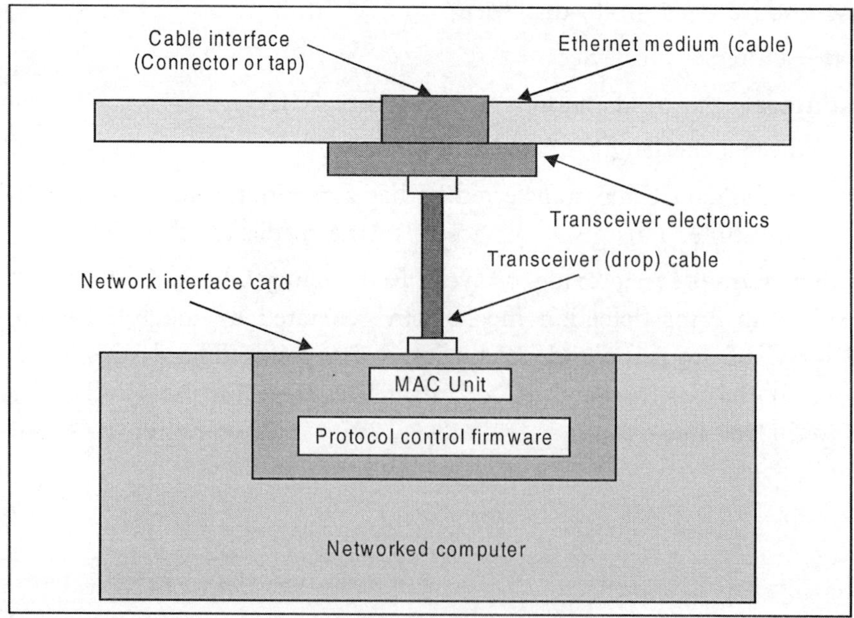

Figure 13.13 *Network Interface Card for Connection of a Computer to an Ethernet Network.*

transceiver (as shown) or through an internal integrated transceiver mounted on the network interface card PCB. The card usually also contains the protocol control firmware and Ethernet controller needed to support the Medium Access Control (MAC) data link protocol used by Ethernet.

REVIEW QUESTIONS

1. What aspects of networking is addressed by the MAC specification ?
2. What aspects of networking is addressed by the LLC specification ?
3. How does CSMA/CA resolve the problem of line contention ?
4. Which data link protocol is used as the basis for IEE 802.9 MAC frame ?
5. What is the purpose of the MAC frame's SID field ?
6. Which field indicates the type of MAC frame in use ?
7. Which MAC frame holds the higher level payload ?
8. Which type of user needs PPP ?
9. Describe each of the states of a PPP connection.
10. Name three protocols of the protocol field in the PPP frame.
11. What is the purpose of the LCP ?
12. What is the advantage of controlled access over random access ?
13. When do we increment the back off in a network that uses ALOHA ?
14. What is the purpose of the jam signal in CSMA/CD ?
15. How does CSMA/CD differ from CSMA/CA ?
16. Name three popular controlled access methods.
17. Discuss the difference between polling and selecting.
18. Why is token passing a controlled-access procedure ?
19. Name three channelization protocols.
20. What is a collision ?
21. What is the purpose of an NIC ?
22. What is the purpose of a transceiver ?
23. What is the difference between a multicast address and a broadcast address ?
24. Explain the CSMA/CD protocol.
25. How is pure ALOHA concept is used for channel utilisation? Why slotted ALOHA method is better than pure ALOHA ?

PART 5

LOCAL AREA NETWORK (LAN)

14

ETHERNET

ETHERNET TECHNOLOGIES

The term Ethernet refers to the family of Local Area Network (LAN) products covered by the IEEE 802.3 standard that defines what is commonly known as the CSMA/CD protocol. Three data rates are currently defined for operation over optical fiber and twisted-pair cables:

- 10 Mbps—10BaseT Ethernet
- 100 Mbps—Fast Ethernet
- 1000 Mbps—Gigabit Ethernet
- 10 Gigabit Ethernet is under development and will likely be published as the IEEE 802.3ae supplement to the IEEE 802.3 base standard in late 2001 or early 2002.

Other technologies and protocols have been touted as likely replacements, but the market has spoken. Ethernet has survived as the major LAN technology (it is currently used for approximately 85 percent of the world's LAN-connected PCs and workstations) because its protocol has the following characteristics:

1. Is easy to understand, implement, manage, and maintain
2. Allows low-cost network implementations
3. Provides extensive topological flexibility for network installation
4. Guarantees successful interconnection and operation of standards-compliant products, regardless of manufacturer.

Ethernet—History

The original Ethernet was developed as an experimental coaxial cable network in the 1970s by Xerox Corporation to operate with a data rate of 3 Mbps using a Carrier Sense Multiple Access Collision Detect (CSMA/CD) protocol for LANs with sporadic but occasionally heavy traffic requirements. Success with that project attracted early attention and led to the 1980 joint development of the 10-Mbps Ethernet version 1.0 specification by the three-company consortium: Digital Equipment Corporation, Intel Corporation, and Xerox Corporation.

The original IEEE 802.3 standard was based on, and was very similar to, the Ethernet version 1.0 specification. The draft standard was approved by the 802.3 working group in 1983 and was subsequently published as an official standard in 1985 (ANSI/IEEE Std. 802.3-1985). Since then, a number of supplements to the standard have been defined to take advantage of improvements in the technologies and to support additional network media and higher data rate capabilities, plus several new optional network access control features.

Throughout the rest of this chapter, the terms Ethernet and *802.3* will refer exclusively to network implementations compatible with the IEEE 802.3 standard.

Ethernet

In 1985, the Institute of Electrical and Electronic Engineers (IEEE) in the United States of America, produced a series of standards for Local Area Networks (LAN) called the IEEE 802 standards. These have found widespread acceptability and now form the core of most LANs. One of the IEEE 802 standards, IEEE 802.3, is a standard known as "Ethernet". This is the most widely used LAN technology in the world today. Ethernet was developed by the Xerox Corporation's Palo Alto Research Centre (known colloquially as Xerox PARC) in 1972 and was probably the first true LAN to be introduced. Although IEEE 802.3 differs somewhat from the original standard it is very similar, and both sets of standards may be used with the same LAN.

The IEEE standards have been adopted by the International Standards Organization (ISO), and is standardized in a series of standards known as ISO 8802-3. ISO was created in 1947 to construct world-wide standards for a wide variety of Engineering tasks. Adoption of ISO standards allows manufacturers to produce equipment which is guaranteed to operate anywhere it is finally used. ISO standards tend to be based on other standards (such as those produced by the IEEE), the only problem is that the ISO standards tend to be issued later, and are therefore less up to date.

The simplest form of Ethernet uses a passive bus operated at 10 Mbps. The bus is formed from a 50 Ohm coaxial cable which connects all the computers in the LAN. A single LAN may have up to 1024 attached systems, although in practice most LANs have far fewer. One or more pieces of coaxial cable are joined end to end to create the bus, known as an "Ethernet cable segment". Each segment is terminated at both ends by 50 Ohm resistors (to prevent reflections from the discontinuity at the end of the cable) and is also normally earthed at one end (for electrical safety). Computers may attach to the cable using transceivers and network interface cards.

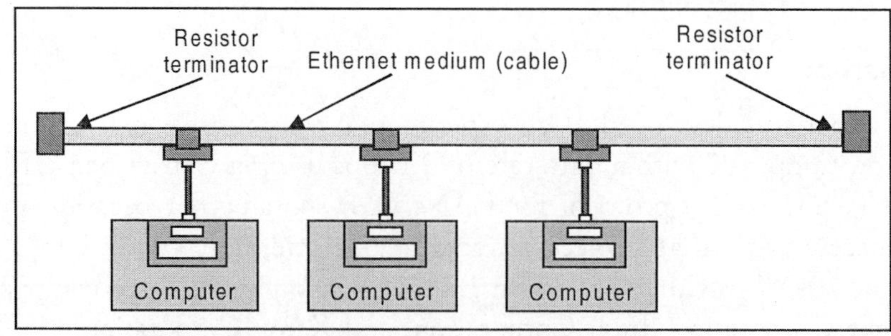

An Ethernet LAN Consisting of Three Computers Joined by a Shared Coaxial Cable.

Frames of data are formed using a protocol called Medium Access Control (MAC), and encoded using Manchester line encoding. Ethernet uses a simple Carrier-Sense Multiple Access protocol with Collision Detection (CSMA/CD) to prevent two computers trying to transmit at the same time (or more correctly to ensure both computers retransmit any frames which are corrupted by simultaneous transmission).

Ethernet LANs may be implemented using a variety of media (not just the coaxial cable described above). The types of media segments supported by Ethernet are:

- 10B5 Low loss coaxial cable (also known as "thick" Ethernet)
- 10B2 Low cost coaxial cable (also known as "thin" Ethernet)
- 10BT Low cost twisted pair copper cable (also known as Unshielded Twisted Pair (UTP))
- 10BF Fiber optic cable

The network design rules for using these types of media are summarised below:

Segment Type	Maximum Number of Systems Per Cable Segment	Maximum Distance of a Cable Segment
10B5 (Thick Coax)	100	500 m
10B2 (Thin Coax)	30	185 m
10BT (Twisted Pair)	2	100 m
10BFL (fiber optic)	2	2000 m

Network Design Rules for Different types of Cable

There is also a version of Ethernet which operates using twisted pair cabling or fiber optic links at 100 Mbps and at 1 Gbps. 100 Mbps networks may operate full duplex (using a fast Ethernet switch) or half duplex (using a fast Ethernet hub). 1 Gbps networks usually operate between a pair of Ethernet switches. Many LANs combine the various speeds of operation using dual-speed switches which allow the same switch to connect some ports to one speed of network, and other ports at another speed. The higher speed ports are usually used to connect switches to one another.

It is not possible to have a dual-speed hub, since a hub does not store and forward frames, however a number of manufacturers sell products they call "dual-speed hubs". In fact, such devices contain both a 10 Mbps and a 100 Mbps hubs, interconnected by a store-and-forward bridge.

Ethernet is the most popular physical layer LAN technology in use today. Other LAN types include Token ring, fast Ethernet, Fiber Distributed Data Interface (FDDI), Asynchronous Transfer Mode (ATM) and LocalTalk. Ethernet is popular because it strikes a good balance between speed, cost and ease of installation. These benefits, combined with wide acceptance in the computer marketplace and the ability to support virtually all popular network protocols, make Ethernet an ideal networking technology for most computer users today. The Institute for Electrical and Electronic Engineers (IEEE) defines the Ethernet standard as IEEE standard 802.3. This standard defines rules for configuring an Ethernet network as well as specifying how elements in an Ethernet network interact with one another. By adhering to the IEEE standard, network equipment and network protocols can communicate efficiently.

Fast Ethernet

For Ethernet networks that need higher transmission speeds, the fast Ethernet standard (IEEE 802.3u) has been established. This standard raises the Ethernet speed limit from 10 Megabits per second (Mbps) to 100 Mbps with only minimal changes to the existing cable structure. There are three types of fast Ethernet: 100BASE TX for use with level 5 UTP cable, 100BASE FX for use with fiber optic cable, and 100BASE T4 which utilizes an extra two wires for use with level 3 UTP cable. The 100BASE TX standard has become the most popular due to its close compatibility with the 10BASE T Ethernet standard. For the network manager, the incorporation of Fast Ethernet into an existing configuration presents a host of decisions. Managers must determine the number of users in each site on the network that need the higher throughput, decide which segments of the backbone need to be reconfigured specifically for 100BASE T and then choose the necessary hardware to connect the 100BASE T segments with existing 10BASE T segments. Gigabit Ethernet is a future technology that promises a migration path beyond fast Ethernet so the next generation of networks will support even higher data transfer speeds.

10 Gigabit Ethernet

A Local Area Network (LAN) architecture, Ethernet was invented by Dr. Robert M. Metcalfe at the Xerox Palo Alto Research Center in cooperation with DEC and Intel in 1976. The IEEE standard was first published in 1985, and formally titled as "IEEE 802.3 Carrier Sense Multiple Access with Collision Detection (CSMA/CD) access method and physical layer specifications." The IEEE standard has since been adopted by the International Organization for Standardization (ISO), making it the most prevalent networking standard. Today, 10/100 Mbps Ethernet is arguably the most popular LAN technology used to network enterprises, SOHOs and even homes. This gain in the Ethernet usage has been primarily because of its reputation for low cost, security, reliability, and transmission speed. Ethernet uses a bus or star topology and supports data transfer rates of 10 and 100 Mbps. The Ethernet specification specifies the physical and MAC (Media Access Control) layers. Ethernet uses the CSMA/CD access method to handle simultaneous demands.

A Chronology of Ethernet

A chronology of elements is listed as below:

1972— Ethernet used at Xerox PARC

1980— Consortium of DEC, Intel and Xerox announced the Blue Book

1982— Version 2 of the Blue Book issued.

1982— ISOC RFC 826 definition of the address resolution protocol for Ethernet

1984— ISOC RFC 894 definition of IP network using Ethernet links

1985— IEEE 802.3 (slightly incompatible with V2)

1988— IEEE published a collection of supplements

1988— ISOC RFC 1042 definition of IP network using IEEE 802.3/LLC links

1989— ISO 802.3a Ethernet for thin coaxial cable (10B2)

1990— IEEE 802.3i Ethernet over CAT-5 unshielded twisted (10Base T)

1990— IEEE 802.1d Ethernet bridging

1993— 10BT Hubs and bridges have become a common component in LANs, and start replacing 10B2/10B5.

1993— IEEE 802.3j defines Ethernet over fiber (10BF)

1993— IEEE 802.1d MAC layer bridges (ISO 10038)

1995— IEEE 802.3u defines fast Ethernet (100BTX, 100BT4, 100BFX)

1996— Fast Ethernet and fiber links have become common

1998— 100BT has become a common component in LANs

1998— IEEE 802.3z defines Gigabit Ethernet over fiber (later in 802.3 ab over UTP)

2001— IEEE 802.11 (wireless) and Gigabit Ethernet have become common LAN components

The IEEE 802.3 standard defines Ethernet at the physical and data link layers of the OSI network model. Most Ethernet systems use the following:

1. Carrier Sense Multiple Access with Collision Detection (CSMA/CD) for controlling access to the network media.
2. Use base-band broadcasts
3. A method for packing data into data packets called frames
4. Transmit at 10Mbps, 100Mbps, and 1Gbps.
5. Ethernet/IEEE 802.3
6. CSMA/CD

Ethernet was developed by Xerox Corporation's *Palo Alto Research Center* (PARC) in the 1970s. Ethernet was the technological basis for the IEEE 802.3 specification, which was initially released in 1980. Shortly thereafter, Digital Equipment Corporation, Intel Corporation, and Xerox Corporation jointly developed and released an Ethernet specification (version 2.0) that is substantially compatible with IEEE 802.3. Together, Ethernet and IEEE 802.3 currently maintain the greatest market share of any Local Area Network (LAN) protocol. Today, the term *Ethernet* is often used to refer to all *carrier sense multiple access/collision detection* (CSMA/CD) LANs that generally conform to Ethernet specifications, including IEEE 802.3.

When it was developed, Ethernet was designed to fill the middle ground between long-distance, low-speed networks and specialized, computer-room networks carrying data at high speeds for very limited distances. Ethernet is well suited to applications where a local communication medium must carry sporadic, occasionally heavy traffic at high peak data rates.

ETHERNET/IEEE 802.3 COMPARISON

Ethernet and IEEE 802.3 specify similar technologies. Both are CSMA/CD LANs. Stations on a CSMA/CD LAN can access the network at any time. Before sending data, CSMA/CD stations "listen" to the network to see if it is already in use. If it is, the station wishing to transmit waits. If the network is not in use, the station transmits. A collision occurs when two stations listen for network traffic, "hear" none, and transmit simultaneously. In this case, both transmissions are damaged, and the stations must retransmit at some later time. *Back-off* algorithms determine when the colliding stations retransmit. CSMA/CD stations can detect collisions, so they know when they must retransmit.

Both Ethernet and IEEE 802.3 LANs are broadcast networks. In other words, all stations see all frames, regardless of whether they represent an intended destination. Each station must examine received frames to determine if the station is a destination. If so, the frame is passed to a higher protocol layer for appropriate processing.

Differences between Ethernet and IEEE 802.3 LANs are subtle. Ethernet provides services corresponding to layers 1 and 2 of the OSI reference model, while IEEE 802.3 specifies the physical layer (layer 1) and the channel-access portion of the link layer (layer 2), but does not define a logical link control protocol. Both Ethernet and IEEE 802.3 are implemented in hardware. Typically, the physical manifestation of these protocols is either an interface card in a host computer or circuitry on a primary circuit board within a host computer.

Physical Connections

IEEE 802.3 specifies several different physical layers, whereas Ethernet defines only one. Each IEEE 802.3 physical layer protocol has a name that summarizes its characteristics. The coded components of an IEEE 802.3 physical-layer name are shown in figure 14.1.

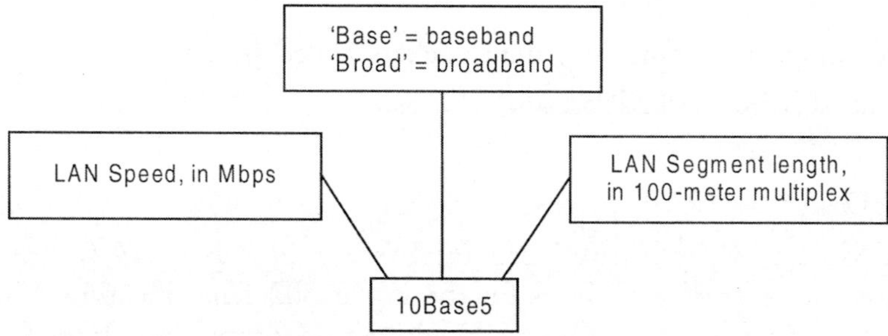

Figure 14.1 *IEEE 802.3 Physical-Layer Name Components.*

Table 14.1 Ethernet Version 2 and IEEE 802.3 Physical Characteristics

Characteristics	*Ethernet Value*	*IEEE 802.3 Values*				
		10Base5	*10Base2*	*1Base5*	*10BaseT*	*10Broad36*
Data rate (Mbps)	10	10	10	1	10	10
Signalling method	Baseband	Baseband	Baseband	Baseband	Baseband 100	Broadband
Maximum segment length (m)	500	500	185	250	Unshielded twisted-pairwire	1800
Media	50-ohm coax (thick)	50-ohm coax (thick)	50-ohm coax (thick)	Unshielded twisted-pairwire	Unshielded twisted-pairwire	75-ohm coax
Topology	Bus	Bus	Bus	Star	Star	Bus

Ethernet is most similar to IEEE 802.3 10Base5. Both of these protocols specify a bus topology network with a connecting cable between the end stations and the actual network medium. In the case of Ethernet, that cable is called a transceiver cable. The transceiver cable connects to a transceiver device attached to the physical network medium. The IEEE 802.3 configuration is much the same, except that the connecting cable is referred to as an Attachment Unit Interface (AUI), and the transceiver is called a Medium Attachment Unit (MAU). In both cases, the connecting cable attaches to an interface board (or interface circuitry) within the end station.

Ethernet, one of the pivotal technologies that made local area networks possible, was developed in the 1970s by Digital, Intel and Xerox. This original design is often referred to by the initials of its creators-DIX.

Ethernet works by connecting an almost unlimited number of devices to the same cable. Usually, a host can just transmit whenever the cable is not in use. In the relatively uncommon case where two devices start transmitting at the same time, a *collision* occurs. Both senders then wait a random amount of time before transmitting again. In any case, every device on the cable can receive every packet, but discards all those not addressed to it. This scheme, one of many that can regulate access to a hardware medium, is referred to CSMA/CD, an acronym for Carrier Sense Multiple Access/Collision Detect.

There has been much debate over Ethernet performance. The performance of any CSMA/CD network will depend on several considerations, including the method of determining silent times after a collision, the length of the cabling, the size of packets, and the amount of traffic. The Ethernet standard defines how silent times are determined, and the network engineer can seldom influence this feature anyhow. The remaining factors are summarized in table 14.2, though be aware that the standard places constraints on several of these.

Table 14.2 Ethernet Performance

Performance Factor	*Desirable Feature*	
Cable length	Short	Short cables reduce the chance of collisions, since electrical signals take less time to propagate between hosts.
Packet size	Large	Large packets reduce the chances of a collision, since collisions can only occur during a fixed time window at the beginning of a packet.
Amount of traffic	Light (< 20% capacity)	More traffic means more collisions; for standard 10 Mbit/s Ethernet, try not to exceed 2 Mbit/s on any single segment.

In the early 1980s, IEEE began developing standards for LAN technologies, including Ethernet. Unfortunately, the new standard, IEEE 802.3, is not compatible with the older DIX specification. Due to Ethernet's already large installed base, both the newer IEEE standard and the persistent DIX pseudo-standard are in use.

Ethernet operates at 10 Mbps and its packets are between 64 and roughly 1500 bytes in length. A 6-byte address is used, which is divided into a 3-byte vendor ID and a 3-byte vendor-defined field. Ethernet manufacturers are assigned a unique vendor ID, and are then responsible for insuring that all of their devices have unique addresses in the last 3 bytes. An all-ones address is interpreted to mean *broadcast*, and all hosts attached to the cable process such a packet. A group of addresses are assigned for multicast use, and most newer Ethernet cards permit software to select a subset of the multicast addresses for reception.

The IEEE Ethernet standard is not available online, because the sale of standards documents are a major income source for IEEE and other standards organizations.

Ethernet encapsulation standards describe how IP packets should be converted into Ethernet packets. ARP (Address Resolution Protocol) describes how IP addresses are translated to Ethernet addresses.

ETHERNET CABLING

Several types of cabling are used for Ethernet:

- **10 Base 5,** or *Thicknet*, uses a single 75-ohm coaxial cable in a bus topography, connecting each device with a "vampire tap" clamped over a hole drilled in the cable. Segments may be up to 500 meters in length. Not recommended for new installations.
- **10 Base 2,** or *Thinnet*, uses a string of RJ-58 coaxial cables in a bus topography, with BNC T connectors attached to each device, and 52-ohm terminators at each end. Maximum segment length is 200 meters.
- **Base T** uses twisted pair wiring (preferably shielded) in a star topography, with each segment connecting a single device to a repeater, usually referred to as a hub. Unlike other Ethernet cabling schemes, which specify physical cable types, 10-Base T specifies requirements for various electrical properties of the wiring. The only reliable way to meet these requirements is by checking wiring with a cable tester, an essential tool for large 10-Base T installations.
- **10 Broad 36,** the only broadband Ethernet design, permits operation over closed-circuit cable television systems, requiring three adjacent TV channels to be allocated for a single Ethernet segment.
- **Fiber optic** Ethernet segments have been developed by several companies, though there is no fiber standard to my knowledge.

Ethernet Standard Encapsulation

In order to transport IP packets across an Ethernet, two issues must be addressed. First, how should an IP packet be converted to an Ethernet packet ? Second, how should an IP address be converted to an Ethernet address ?

How to convert an IP packet to an Ethernet packet depends in large part on what type of Ethernet is used. Two methods are most common:

DIX Version 2 Ethernet—has a type field which indicates what type of data is contained in the packet. A standard type field (0800 hex) indicates that an IP packet begins at the end of the Ethernet header. Documented in RFC 894, this was (and may still be) the most common encapsulation mechanism for IP.

IEEE 802 Ethernet—defines an Ethernet-specific header (802.3), and a media-independent header (802.2). An 802.2 extension called SNAP permits a DIX type code to be specified. Encapsulating IP with this scheme produces a packet starting with an 802.3 header, then an 802.2 header, then a SNAP header, then the IP packet.

IEEE 802.3 Ethernet—is sometimes used directly, without the 802.2 or SNAP headers. This makes packets smaller, but since the 802.3 header does not contain a type field, this method can't be used with multiple protocols on the same Ethernet, or confusion would result. Since IP requires ARP (a second protocol) to operate over Ethernet, this method is never used. However, it is common for NetWare.

Using repeaters, bridges, and routers, it's fairly simple to interoperate Ethernet implementations to the point of Sharing DIX and IEEE 802 frames on the same cable. However, bizarre interactions are possible, particularly with regard to the slight MTU size variances. If a TCP host transmitting a stream of maximally sized RFC 894 (DIX) packets, they will require IP fragmentation before transport using RFC 1042 (IEEE 802) encapsulation.

TYPES OF ETHERNET

Often referred to as thicknet, 10Base5 was the first incarnation of Ethernet technology. The industry used thicknet in the 1980s until 10Base2 thinnet appeared. Compared to thicknet, Thinnet offered the advantage of thinner (5 millimeters vs 10 millimeters) and more flexible cabling, making it easier to wire office buildings for Ethernet.

The most common form of traditional Ethernet, however, is 10Base T. 10Base T offers better electrical properties than thicknet or thinnet, because 10Base T cables utilize Unshielded Twisted Pair (UTP) wiring rather than coaxial. 10Base T also proved more cost effective than alternatives like fiber optic cabling.

The table below details these traditional Ethernet technologies. Besides the type of cable involved, another important aspect of Ethernet networking is the segment length. A segment is a network connection made by a single unbroken network cable. Ethernet cables and segments can only span a limited physical distance, after which transmissions will likely fail due to line noise, reduced signal strength and other degredation. Per the Ethernet specifications, manufacturers of Ethernet equipment must meet the below minimum specifications for segment length.

Table 14.3

Name	*Segment Length (Max.)*	*Cable*
10 Base5	500 m/1640 ft.	RG 8 or RG 11 coaxial
10 Base2	185 m/606 ft.	RG 58 A/U or RG 58 C/U coaxial
10 BaseT	100 m/328 ft.	Category 3 or better unshielded twisted pair

Numerous other lesser-known Ethernet standards exist, including 10Base FL, 10Base FB, and 10Base FP for fiber optic networks and 10Broad36 for broadband (cable television) cabling.

Fast Ethernet

In the mid-1990s, fast Ethernet technology matured and met its design goals of a) increasing the performance of traditional Ethernet while b) avoiding the need to completely re-cable existing Ethernet networks. Fast Ethernet comes in two major varieties:

100Base T (using unshielded twisted pair cable)

100Base FX (using fiber optic cable)

By far the most popular of these is 100Base T, a standard that includes 100Base TX (category 5 UTP), 100Base T2 (category 3 or better UTP), and 100Base T4 (100Base T2 cabling modified to include two additional wire pairs).

Gigabit Ethernet

Whereas fast Ethernet improved traditional Ethernet from 10 megabit to 100 megabit speed, gigabit Ethernet boasts the same order-of-magnitude improvement over fast Ethernet by offering speeds of 1000 megabits (1 gigabit). Gigabit Ethernet was first made to travel over optical and copper cabling, but the 1000Base T standard successfully supports it as well. 1000Base T uses category 5 cabling similar to 100 Mbps Ethernet, although achieving gigabit speed requires the use of additional wire pairs.

10Base5—Uses thicknet coaxial cable which requires a transceiver with a vampire tap to connect each computer. There is a drop cable from the transceiver to the Attachment Unit Interface (AIU). The AIU may be a DIX port on the network card. There is a transceiver for each network card on the network. This type of Ethernet is subject to the 5-4-3 rule meaning there can be 5 network segments with 4 repeaters, and three of the segments can be connected to computers. It uses bus topology. Maximum segment length is 500 Meters with the maximum overall length at 2500 meters. Minimum length between nodes is 2.5 meters. Maximum nodes per segment is 100.

1. **10Base2:** Uses thinnet coaxial cable. Uses a BNC connector and bus topology requiring a terminator at each end of the cable. The cable used is RG-58 A/U or RG-58 C/U with an impedance of 50 ohms. RG-58U is not acceptable. Uses the 5-4-3 rule meaning there can be 5 network segments with 4 repeaters, and three of the segments can be connected to computers. The maximum length of one segment is 185 meters. Barrel connectors can be used to link smaller pieces of cable on each segment, but each barrel connector reduces signal quality. Minimum length between nodes is 0.5 meters.
2. **10BaseT:** Uses Unshielded Twisted Pair (UTP) cable. Uses star topology. Shielded Twisted Pair (STP) is not part of the 10Base T specification. Not subject to the 5-4-3 rule. They can use category 3, 4, or 5 cable, but perform best with category 5 cable. Category 3 is the minimum. Require only 2 pairs of wire. Cables in ceilings and walls must be plenum rated. Maximum segment length is 100 meters. Minimum length between nodes is 2.5 meters. Maximum number of connected segments is 1024. Maximum number of nodes per segment is 1 (star topology). Uses RJ-45 connectors.

3. **10BaseF:** Uses fiber optic cable. Can have up to 1024 network nodes. Maximum segment length is 2000 meters. Uses specialized connectors for fiber optic. Includes different categories:
4. **10BaseFL:** Used to link computers in a LAN environment, which is not commonly done due to high cost.
5. **10BaseFP:** Used to link computers with passive hubs to get cable distances up to 500 meters.
6. **10BaseFB:** Used as a backbone between hubs.
7. **100Base T:** Also known as fast Ethernet. Uses RJ-45 connectors. Topology is star. Uses CSMA/CD media access. Minimum length between nodes is 2.5 meters. Maximum number of connected segments is 1024. Maximum number of nodes per segment is 1 (star topology). IEEE 802.3 specification.
8. **100Base TX:** Requires category 5 two pair cable. Maximum distance is 100 meters.
9. **100Base T4:** Requires category 3 cable with 4 pair. Maximum distance is 100 meters.
10. **100Base FX:** Can use fiber optic to transmit up to 2000 meters. Requires two strands of fiber optic cable.
11. **100VG-AnyLAN:** Requires category 3 cable with 4 pair. Maximum distance is 100 meters with cat 3 or 4 cable. Can reach 150 meters with cat 5 cable. Can use fiber optic to transmit up to 2000 meters. This Ethernet type supports transmission of Token ring network packets in addition to Ethernet packets. IEEE 802.12 specification. Uses demand-priority media access control. The topology is star. It uses a series of interlinked cascading hubs. Uses RJ-45 connectors.

The IEEE naming convention is as follows:

- The transmission speed in Mbps
- Baseband (base) or broadband data transmission
- The maximum distance a network segment could cover in hundreds of meters.
- Comparisons of some Ethernet types. (Distances are in meters)

Ethernet Type	*Cable*	*Minimum Length between Nodes*	*Maximum Segment Length*	*Maximum Overall Length*
10Base2	Thinnet	0.5	185	925
10Base5	Thicknet	2.5	500	2500
10BaseF	Fiber		2000	
10Base T	UTP	2.5	100	

Types of Ethernet Frames

There are different types of Ethernet Frames. They are as follows :

1. **Ethernet 802.2:** These frames contain fields similar to the Ethernet 802.3 frames with the addition of three Logical Link Control (LLC) fields. Novell NetWare 4.x networks use it.

2. **Ethernet 802.3:** It is mainly used in Novell NetWare 2.x and 3.x networks. The frame type was developed prior to completion of the IEEE 802.3 specification and may not work in all Ethernet environments.
3. **Ethernet II:** This frame type combines the 802.3 preamble and SFD fields and include a protocol type field where the 802.3 frame contained a length field. TCP/IP networks and networks that use multiple protocols normally use this type of frames.
4. **Ethernet SNAP:** This frame type builds on the 802.2 frame type by adding a type field indicating what network protocol is being used to send data. This frame type is mainly used in AppleTalk networks.

The packet size of all the above frame types is between 64 and 1,518 bytes.

Ethernet Message Formats

The Ethernet data format is defined by RFC 894 and 1042. The addresses specified in the Ethernet protocol are 48 bit addresses.

Ethernet Data

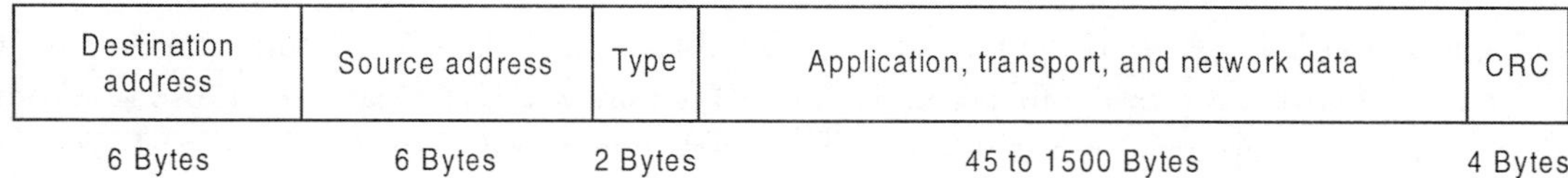

Figure 14.2 *Ethernet Data Format.*

The types of data passed in the type field are as follows:

- 0800 IP Datagram
- 0806 ARP request/reply
- 8035 RARP request/reply

There is a maximum size of each data packet for the Ethernet protocol. This size is called the Maximum Transmission Unit (MTU). What this means is that sometimes packets may be broken up as they are passed through networks with MTUs of various sizes. SLIP and PPP protocols will normally have a smaller MTU value than Ethernet. This document does not describe Serial Line Interface Protocol (SLIP) or Point to Point Protocol (PPP) encapsulation.

THE BASIC ETHERNET FRAME FORMAT

The IEEE 802.3 standard defines a basic data frame format that is required for all MAC implementations, plus several additional optional formats that are used to extend the protocol's basic capability. The basic data frame format contains the seven fields shown in figure 14.3.

- **Preamble (PRE):** Consists of 7 bytes. The PRE is an alternating pattern of ones and zeros that tells receiving stations that a frame is coming, and that provides a means to synchronize the frame-reception portions of receiving physical layers with the incoming bit stream.

- **Start-of-frame delimiter (SOF):** Consists of 1 byte. The SOF is an alternating pattern of ones and zeros, ending with two consecutive 1-bits indicating that the next bit is the leftmost bit in the left-most byte of the destination address.
- **Destination address (DA):** Consists of 6 bytes. The DA field identifies which station(s) should receive the frame. The left-most bit in the DA field indicates whether the address is an individual address (indicated by a 0) or a group address (indicated by a 1). The second bit from the left indicates whether the DA is globally administered (indicated by a 0) or locally administered (indicated by a 1). The remaining 46 bits are a uniquely assigned value that identifies a single station, a defined group of stations, or all stations on the network.
- **Source addresses (SA):** Consists of 6 bytes. The SA field identifies the sending station. The SA is always an individual address and the left-most bit in the SA field is always 0.
- **Length/Type:** Consists of 4 bytes. This field indicates either the number of MAC-client data bytes that are contained in the data field of the frame, or the frame type ID if the frame is assembled using an optional format. If the length/type field value is less than or equal to 1500, the number of LLC bytes in the data field is equal to the length/type field value. If the length/type field value is greater than 1536, the frame is an optional type frame, and the length/type field value identifies the particular type of frame being sent or received.
- **Data:** Is a sequence of *n* bytes of any value, where *n* is less than or equal to 1500. If the length of the data field is less than 46, the data field must be extended by adding a filler (a pad) sufficient to bring the data field length to 46 bytes.
- **Frame check sequence (FCS)**—Consists of 4 bytes. This sequence contains a 32-bit Cyclic Redundancy Check (CRC) value, which is created by the sending MAC and is recalculated by the receiving MAC to check for damaged frames. The FCS is generated over the DA, SA, length/type, and data fields.

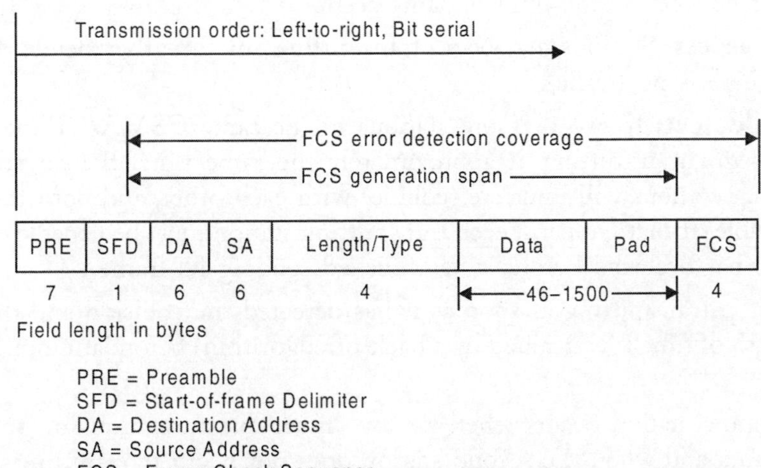

Figure 14.3 *The Basic IEEE 802.3 MAC Data Frame Format.*

FRAME TRANSMISSION

Whenever an end station MAC receives a transmit-frame request with the accompanying address and data information from the LLC sub-layer, the MAC begins the transmission sequence by transferring the LLC information into the MAC frame buffer.

1. The preamble and start-of-frame delimiter are inserted in the PRE and SOF fields.
2. The destination and source addresses are inserted into the address fields.
3. The LLC data bytes are counted, and the number of bytes is inserted into the length/type field.
4. The LLC data bytes are inserted into the data field. If the number of LLC data bytes is less than 46, a pad is added to bring the data field length up to 46.
5. An FCS value is generated over the DA, SA, length/type, and data fields and is appended to the end of the data field.
6. After the frame is assembled, actual frame transmission will depend on whether the MAC is operating in half-duplex or full-duplex mode.
7. The IEEE 802.3 standard currently requires that all Ethernet MACs support half-duplex operation, in which the MAC can be either transmitting or receiving a frame, but it cannot be doing both simultaneously. Full-duplex operation is an optional MAC capability that allows the MAC to transmit and receive frames simultaneously.
8. Half-duplex transmission—The CSMA/CD access method

The CSMA/CD protocol was originally developed as a means by which two or more stations could share a common media in a switch-less environment when the protocol does not require central arbitration, access tokens, or assigned time slots to indicate when a station will be allowed to transmit. Each Ethernet MAC determines for itself when it will be allowed to send a frame.

The CSMA/CD access rules are summarized by the protocol's acronym:

- **Carrier sense:** Each station continuously listens for traffic on the medium to determine when gaps between frame transmissions occur.
- **Multiple access:** Stations may begin transmitting any time they detect that the network is quiet (there is no traffic).
- **Collision detect:** If two or more stations in the same CSMA/CD network (collision domain) begin transmitting at approximately the same time, the bit streams from the transmitting stations will interfere (collide) with each other, and both transmissions will be unreadable. If that happens, each transmitting station must be capable of detecting that a collision has occurred before it has finished sending its frame.

Each must stop transmitting as soon as it has detected the collision and then must wait a quasi random length of time (determined by a back-off algorithm) before attempting to retransmit the frame.

The worst-case situation occurs when the two most-distant stations on the network both need to send a frame and when the second station does not begin transmitting until just before the frame from the first station arrives. The collision will be detected almost immediately by the second station, but it will not be detected by the first station until the corrupted signal has propagated all the way back to that station. The maximum time that is required to detect a collision (the collision window, or "slot time") is approximately equal to twice the signal propagation time between the two most-distant stations on the network.

This means that both the minimum frame length and the maximum collision diameter are directly related to the slot time. Longer minimum frame lengths translate to longer slot times and larger collision diameters; shorter minimum frame lengths correspond to shorter slot times and smaller collision diameters.

The trade-off was between the need to reduce the impact of collision recovery and the need for network diameters to be large enough to accommodate reasonable network sizes. The compromise was to choose a maximum network diameter (about 2500 meters) and then to set the minimum frame length long enough to ensure detection of all worst-case collisions.

The compromise worked well for 10 Mbps, but it was a problem for higher data-rate Ethernet developers. Fast Ethernet was required to provide backward compatibility with earlier Ethernet networks, including the existing IEEE 802.3 frame format and error-detection procedures, plus all applications and networking software running on the 10-Mbps networks.

Although signal propagation velocity is essentially constant for all transmission rates, the time required to transmit a frame is inversely related to the transmission rate. At 100 Mbps, a minimum-length frame can be transmitted in approximately one-tenth of the defined slot time, and any collision that occurred during the transmission would not likely be detected by the transmitting stations. This, in turn, meant that the maximum network diameters specified for 10 Mbps networks could not be used for 100-Mbps networks. The solution for fast Ethernet was to reduce the maximum network diameter by approximately a factor of 10 (to a little more than 200 meters).

The same problem also arose during specification development for gigabit Ethernet, but decreasing network diameters by another factor of 10 (to approximately 20 meters) for 1000 Mbps operation was simply not practical. This time, the developers elected to maintain approximately the same maximum collision domain diameters as 100 Mbps networks and to increase the apparent minimum frame size by adding a variable-length non data extension field to frames that are shorter than the minimum length (the extension field is removed during frame reception).

Figure 14.4 shows the MAC frame format with the gigabit extension field, and table 14.4 shows the effect of the trade-off between the transmission data rate and the minimum frame size for 10 Mbps, 100 Mbps, and 1000 Mbps Ethernet.

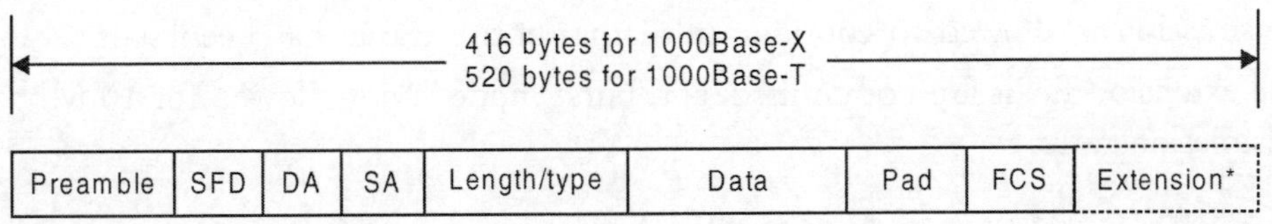

Figure 14.4 *MAC Frame with Gigabit Carrier Extension.*

Table 14.4 Limits for Half-Duplex

Operation parameter	10 Mbps	100 Mbps	1000 Mbps
Minimum frame size	64 bytes	64 bytes	520 bytes (with extension field added)
Maximum collision diameter, DTE to DTE	100 meters UTP	100 meters UPT 412 meters fiber	100 meters UTP 316 meters fiber
Maximum collision diameter with repeaters	2500 meters	205 meters	200 meters
Maximum number of repeaters in network path	5	2	1

520 bytes applies to 1000Base T implementations. The minimum frame size with extension field for 1000Base X is reduced to 416 bytes because 1000Base X encodes and transmits 10 bits for each byte.

Another change to the Ethernet CSMA/CD transmit specification was the addition of frame bursting for gigabit operation. Burst mode is a feature that allows a MAC to send a short sequence (a burst) of frames equal to approximately 5.4 maximum-length frames without having to relinquish control of the medium. The transmitting MAC fills each inter-frame interval with extension bits, as shown in figure 14.5, so that other stations on the network will see that the network is busy and will not attempt transmission until after the burst is complete.

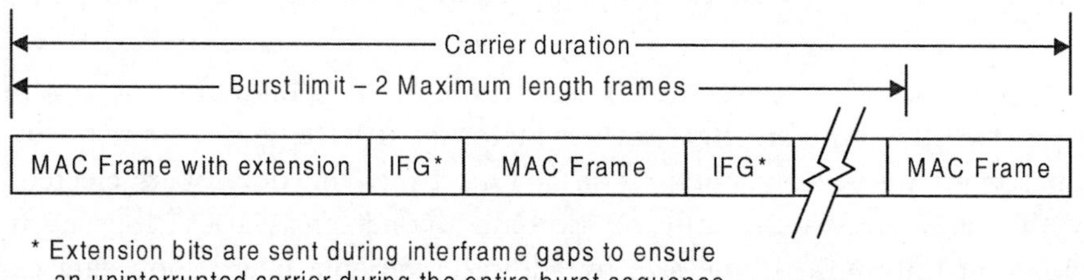

Figure 14.5 *A Gigabit Frame-Burst Sequence.*

If the length of the first frame is less than the minimum frame length, an extension field is added to extend the frame length to the value indicated in table 14.3. Subsequent frames in a frame-burst sequence do not need extension fields, and a frame burst may continue as long as the burst limit has not been reached. If the burst limit is reached after a frame transmission has begun, transmission is allowed to continue until that entire frame has been sent.

Frame extension fields are not defined, and burst mode is not allowed for 10 Mbps and 100 Mbps transmission rates.

Full-Duplex Transmission—An Optional Approach to Higher Network Efficiency

Full-duplex operation is an optional MAC capability that allows simultaneous two-way transmission over point-to-point links. Full-duplex transmission is functionally much simpler than half-duplex transmission because it involves no media contention, no collisions, no need to schedule retransmissions, and no need for extension bits on the end of short frames. The result is not only more time available for transmission, but also an effective doubling of the link bandwidth because each link can now support full-rate, simultaneous, two-way transmission.

Transmission can usually begin as soon as frames are ready to send. The only restriction is that there must be a minimum-length inter frame gap between successive frames, as shown in figure 14.6 and each frame must conform to Ethernet frame format standards.

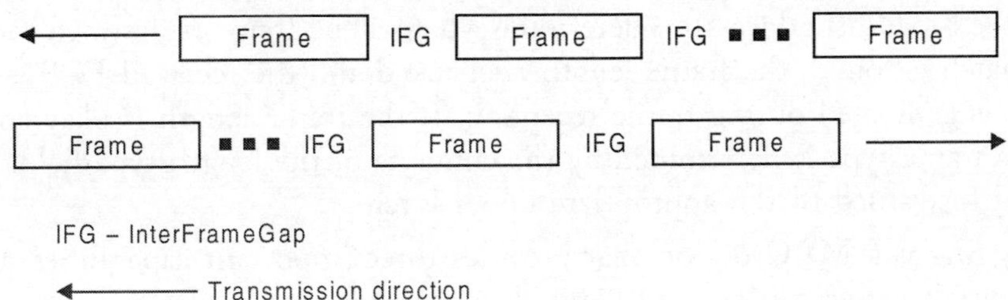

Figure 14.6 *Full Duplex Operation Allows Simultaneous Two-Way Transmission on the Same Link.*

FLOW CONTROL

Full-duplex operation requires concurrent implementation of the optional flow-control capability that allows a receiving node (such as a network switch port) that is becoming congested to request the sending node (such as a file server) to stop sending frames for a selected short period of time. Control is MAC-to-MAC through the use of a pause frame that is automatically generated by the receiving MAC. If the congestion is relieved before the requested wait has expired, a second pause frame with a zero time-to-wait value can be sent to request resumption of transmission. An overview of the flow control operation is shown in figure 14.7.

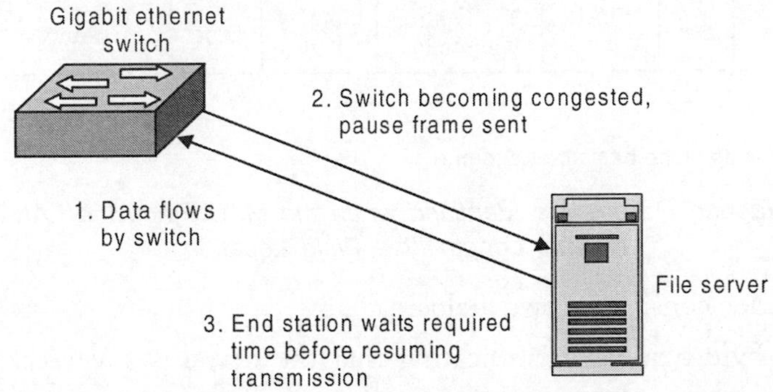

Figure 14.7 *An Overview of the IEEE 802.3 Flow Control Sequence.*

The full-duplex operation and its companion flow control capability are both options for all Ethernet MACs and all transmission rates. Both options are enabled on a link-by-link basis, assuming that the associated physical layers are also capable of supporting full-duplex operation.

Pause frames are identified as MAC control frames by an exclusive assigned (reserved) length/type value. They are also assigned a reserved destination address value to ensure that an incoming pause frame is never forwarded to upper protocol layers or to other ports in a switch.

FRAME RECEPTION

Frame reception is essentially the same for both half-duplex and full-duplex operations, except that full-duplex MACs must have separate frame buffers and data paths to allow for simultaneous frame transmission and reception.

Frame reception is the reverse of frame transmission. The destination address of the received frame is checked and matched against the station's address list (its MAC address, its group addresses, and the broadcast address) to determine whether the frame is destined for that station. If an address match is found, the frame length is checked and the received FCS is compared to the FCS that was generated during frame reception. If the frame length is okay and there is an FCS match, the frame type is determined by the contents of the length/type field. The frame is then parsed and forwarded to the appropriate upper layer.

VLAN tagging is a MAC option that provides three important capabilities not previously available to Ethernet network users and network managers:

Provides a means to expedite time-critical network traffic by setting transmission priorities for outgoing frames.

Allows stations to be assigned to logical groups, to communicate across multiple LANs as though they were on a single LAN. Bridges and switches filter destination addresses and forward VLAN frames only to ports that serve the VLAN to which the traffic belongs.

Simplifies network management and makes adds, moves, and changes easier to administer.

A VLAN-tagged frame is simply a basic MAC data frame that has had a 4-byte VLAN header inserted between the SA and length/type fields, as shown in figure 14.8.

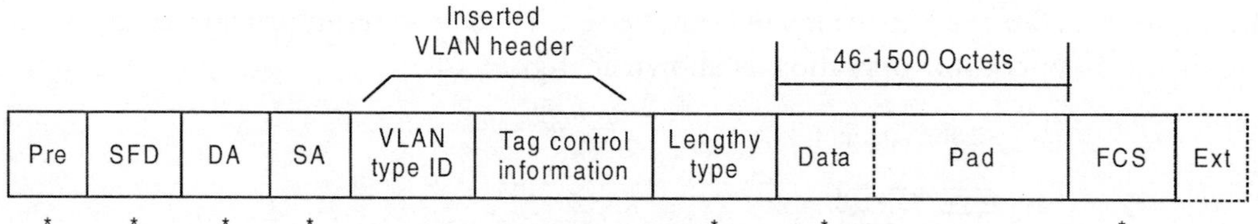

Figure 14.8 *VLAN-Tagged Frames are Identified when the MAC Finds the LAN Type Value in the Normal Length/Type Field Location.*

The VLAN header consists of two fields:

- A reserved 2-byte type value, indicating that the frame is a VLAN frame.
- A two-byte tag-control field that contains both the transmission priority (0 to 7, where 7 is the highest) and a VLAN ID that identifies the particular VLAN over which the frame is to be sent.
- The receiving MAC reads the reserved type value, which is located in the normal length/type field position, and interprets the received frame as a VLAN frame. Then the following occurs:

- If the MAC is installed in a switch port, the frame is forwarded according to its priority level to all ports that are associated with the indicated VLAN identifier.
- If the MAC is installed in an end station, it removes the 4-byte VLAN header and processes the frame in the same manner as a basic data frame.
- VLAN tagging requires that all network nodes involved with a VLAN group be equipped with the VLAN option.

ETHERNET TOPOLOGIES AND PROTOCOLS

Traditional Ethernet employs a bus topology, meaning that all devices or hosts on the network use the same shared communication line. Each device possesses an Ethernet address, also known as MAC address. Sending devices use Ethernet addresses to specify the intended recipient of messages.

Data sent over the Ethernet exists in the forms of frames. An Ethernet frame contains a header, a data section, and a footer having a combined length of no more than 1518 bytes. The Ethernet header contains the addresses of both the intended recipient and the sender.

Data sent over the Ethernet is automatically broadcast to all devices on the network. By comparing their Ethernet address against the address in the frame header, each Ethernet device tests each frame to determine if it was intended for them and reads or discards the frame as appropriate. Network adapter incorporate this function into their hardware.

Devices wanting to transmit on the Ethernet first perform a preliminary check to determine whether the medium is available or whether a transmission is currently in progress. If the Ethernet is available, the sending device transmits onto the wire. It's possible, however, that two devices will perform this test at approximately the same time and both transmit simultaneously.

By design, as a performance tradeoff, the Ethernet standard does not prevent multiple simultaneously transmission. These so-called collisions, when they occur, cause both transmissions to fail and require both sending devices to retransmit. Ethernet uses an algorithm based on random delay times to determine the proper waiting period between retransmissions. The network adapter also implements this algorithm.

In traditional Ethernet, this protocol for broadcasting, listening, and detecting collisions is known as CSMA/CD (Carrier Sense Multiple Access/Collision Detection). Some newer forms of Ethernet do not use CSMA/CD. Instead, they use the so-called full duplex Ethernet protocol, which supports point-to-point simultaneously sends and receives with no listening required.

Ethernet Devices

As mentioned earlier, Ethernet cables are limited in their reach, and these distances (as short as 100 meters) are insufficient to cover medium-sized and large network installations. A repeater in Ethernet networking is a device that allows multiple cables to be joined and greater distances to be spanned. A bridge device can join an Ethernet to another network of a different type, such as a wireless network.

One popular type of repeater device is an Ethernet hub. Other devices sometimes confused with hubs are switch and routers.

Ethernet network adapters also exist in multiple forms. Newer personal computers often include a built-in Ethernet adapter. Otherwise, one can purchase and install an add-in card. PCI cards are most popular for desktop computers and PCMCIA ("credit card") adapters most popular for notebooks. USB Ethernet adapters also exist for both desktops and laptops. Wireless Ethernet adapters can also be configured to work with newer computers.

ETHERNET NETWORK ELEMENTS

Ethernet LANs consist of network nodes and interconnecting media. The network nodes fall into two major classes:

Data Terminal Equipment (DTE): Devices that are either the source or the destination of data frames. DTEs are typically devices such as PCs, workstations, file servers, or print servers that, as a group, are all often referred to as end stations.

Data Communication Equipment (DCE): Intermediate network devices that receive and forward frames across the network. DCEs may be either standalone devices such as repeaters, network switches, and routers, or communications interface units such as interface cards and modems.

Throughout this chapter, standalone intermediate network devices will be referred to as either *intermediate nodes* or DCEs. Network interface cards will be referred to as NICs.

The current Ethernet media options include two general types of copper cable: Unshielded Twisted-Pair (UTP) and Shielded Twisted-Pair (STP), plus several types of optical fiber cable.

ETHERNET NETWORK TOPOLOGIES AND STRUCTURES

LANs take on many topological configurations, but regardless of their size or complexity, all will be a combination of only three basic interconnection structures or network building blocks.

The simplest structure is the point-to-point interconnection, shown in figure 14.9. Only two network units are involved, and the connection may be DTE-to-DTE, DTE-to-DCE, or DCE-to-DCE. The cable in point-to-point interconnections is known as a network link. The maximum allowable length of the link depends on the type of cable and the transmission method that is used.

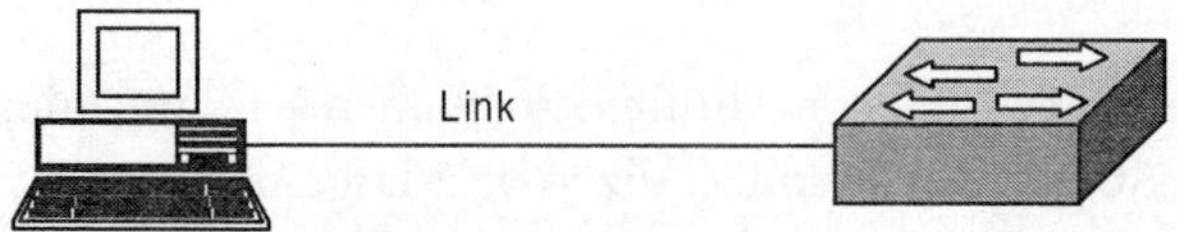

Figure 14.9 *Example Point-to-Point Interconnection.*

The original Ethernet networks were implemented with a coaxial bus structure, as shown in figure 14.10. Segment lengths were limited to 500 meters, and up to 100 stations could be connected to a single segment. Individual segments could be interconnected with repeaters, as long as multiple paths did not exist between any two stations on the network and the number

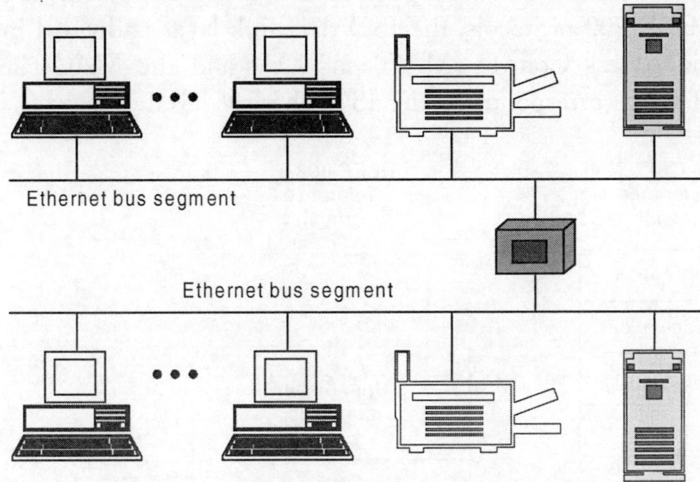

Figure 14.10 *Example Coaxial Bus Topology.*

of DTEs did not exceed 1024. The total path distance between the most-distant pair of stations was also not allowed to exceed a maximum prescribed value.

Although new networks are no longer connected in a bus configuration, some older bus-connected networks do still exist and are still useful.

Since the early 1990s, the network configuration of choice has been the star-connected topology, shown in figure 14.11. The central network unit is either a multi-port repeater (also known as a hub) or a network switch. All connections in a star network are point-to-point links implemented with either twisted-pair or optical fiber cable.

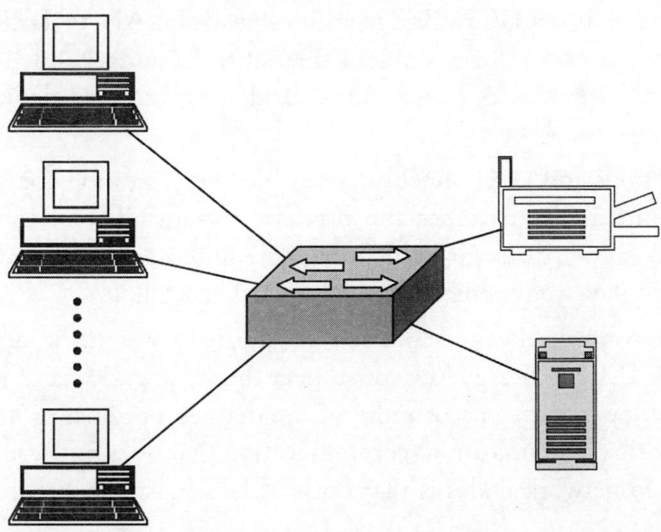

Figure 14.11 *Example Star-Connected Topology.*

The IEEE 802.3 Logical Relationship to the ISO Reference Model

Figure 14.12 shows the IEEE 802.3 logical layers and their relationship to the OSI reference model. As with all IEEE 802 protocols, the ISO data link layer is divided into two IEEE 802 sub-layers, the Media Access Control (MAC) sub-layer and the MAC-client sub-layer. The IEEE 802.3 physical layer corresponds to the ISO physical layer.

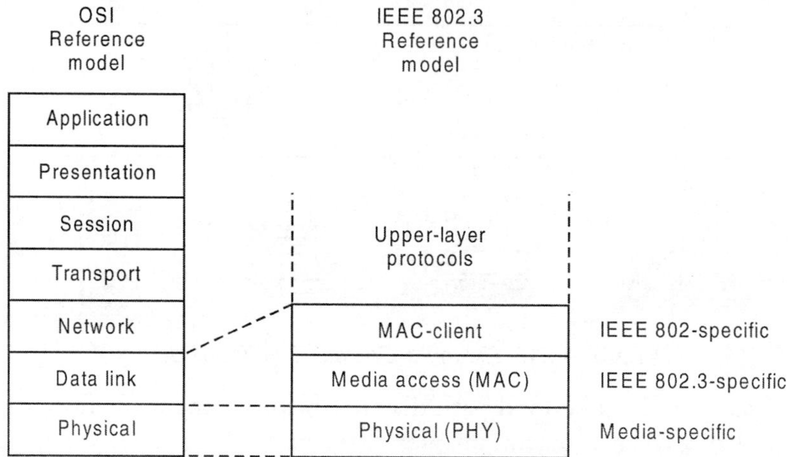

Figure 14.12 *Ethernet's Logical Relationship to the ISO Reference Model.*

The MAC-client sub-layer may be one of the following:

Logical Link Control (LLC), if the unit is a DTE. This sub-layer provides the interface between the Ethernet MAC and the upper layers in the protocol stack of the end station. The LLC sub-layer is defined by IEEE 802.2 standards.

Bridge entity, if the unit is a DCE. Bridge entities provide LAN-to-LAN interfaces between LANs that use the same protocol (for example, Ethernet to Ethernet) and also between different protocols (for example, Ethernet to Token ring). Bridge entities are defined by IEEE 802.1 standards.

Because specifications for LLC and bridge entities are common for all IEEE 802 LAN protocols, network compatibility becomes the primary responsibility of the particular network protocol. Figure 14.13 shows different compatibility requirements imposed by the MAC and physical levels for basic data communication over an Ethernet link.

The MAC layer controls the node's access to the network media and is specific to the individual protocol. All IEEE 802.3 MACs must meet the same basic set of logical requirements, regardless of whether they include one or more of the defined optional protocol extensions. The only requirement for basic communication (communication that does not require optional protocol extensions) between two network nodes is that both MACs must support the same transmission rate.

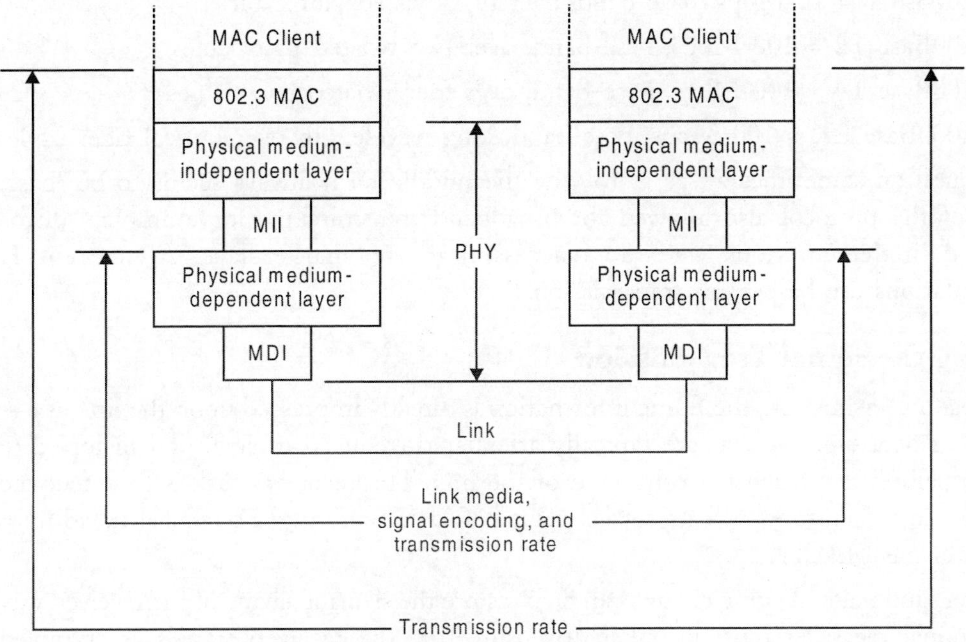

Figure 14.13 *MAC and Physical Layer Compatibility Requirements for Basic Data Communication.*

The 802.3 physical layer is specific to the transmission data rate, the signal encoding, and the type of media interconnecting the two nodes. Gigabit Ethernet, for example, is defined to operate over either twisted-pair or optical fiber cable, but each specific type of cable or signal-encoding procedure requires a different physical layer implementation.

THE ETHERNET MAC SUBLAYER

The MAC sublayer has two primary responsibilities:

1. Data encapsulation, including frame assembly before transmission, and frame parsing/error detection during and after reception.
2. Media access control, including initiation of frame transmission and recovery from transmission failure.

The Ethernet Physical Layers

Because Ethernet devices implement only the bottom two layers of the OSI protocol stack, they are typically implemented as Network Interface Cards (NICs) that plug into the host device's motherboard. The different NICs are identified by a three-part product name that is based on the physical layer attributes.

The naming convention is a concatenation of three terms indicating the transmission rate, the transmission method, and the media type/signal encoding. For example, consider this:

- 10Base T = 10 Mbps, base-band, over two twisted-pair cables
- 100Base T2 = 100 Mbps, base-band, over two twisted-pair cables
- 100Base T4 = 100 Mbps, base-band, over four-twisted pair cables
- 1000Base LX = 100 Mbps, base-band, long wavelength over optical fiber cable

A question sometimes arises as to why the middle term always seems to be "base." Early versions of the protocol also allowed for broadband transmission (for example, 10Broad), but broadband implementations were not successful in the marketplace. All current Ethernet implementations use base-band transmission.

Encoding for Signal Transmission

In base-band transmission, the frame information is directly impressed upon the link as a sequence of pulses or data symbols that are typically attenuated (reduced in size) and distorted (changed in shape) before they reach the other end of the link. The receiver's task is to detect each pulse as it arrives and then to extract its correct value before transferring the reconstructed information to the receiving MAC.

Filters and pulse-shaping circuits can help restore the size and shape of the received waveforms, but additional measures must be taken to ensure that the received signals are sampled at the correct time in the pulse period and at same rate as the transmit clock:

The receive clock must be recovered from the incoming data stream to allow the receiving physical layer to synchronize with the incoming pulses. Compensating measures must be taken for a transmission effect known as baseline wander.

Clock recovery requires level transitions in the incoming signal to identify and synchronize on pulse boundaries. The alternating 1s and 0s of the frame preamble were designed both to indicate that a frame was arriving and to aid in clock recovery. However, recovered clocks can drift and possibly lose synchronization if pulse levels remain constant and there are no transitions to detect (for example, during long strings of 0s).

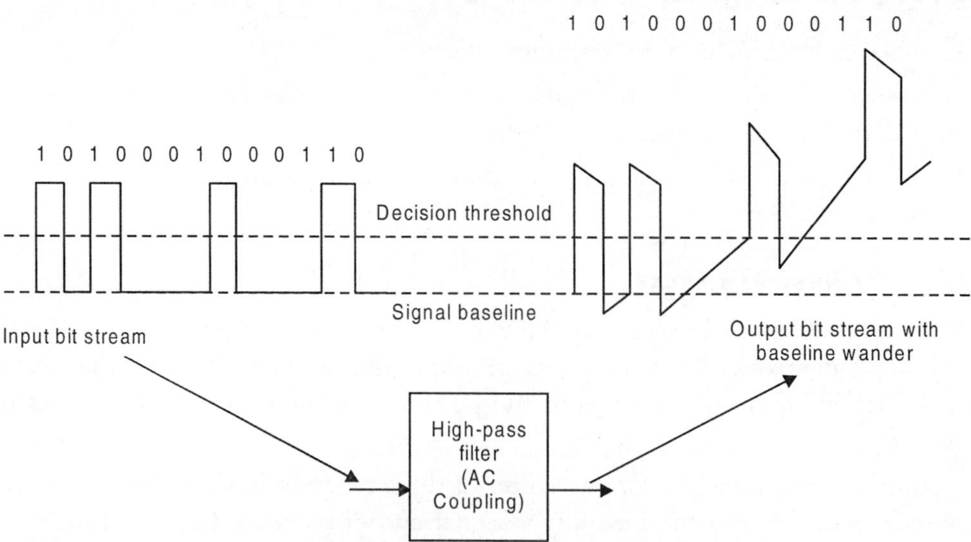

Figure 14.14 *A Concept Example of Baseline Wander.*

Baseline wander results because Ethernet links are AC-coupled to the transceivers and because AC coupling is incapable of maintaining voltage levels for more than a short time. As a result, transmitted pulses are distorted by a droop effect similar to the exaggerated example shown in figure 14.14. In long strings of either 1s or 0s, the droop can become so severe that the voltage level passes through the decision threshold, resulting in erroneous sampled values for the affected pulses.

Fortunately, encoding the outgoing signal before transmission can significantly reduce the effect of both these problems, as well as reduce the possibility of transmission errors. Early Ethernet implementations, up to and including 10Base T, all used the Manchester encoding method, shown in figure 14.15. Each pulse is clearly identified by the direction of the midpulse transition rather than by its sampled level value.

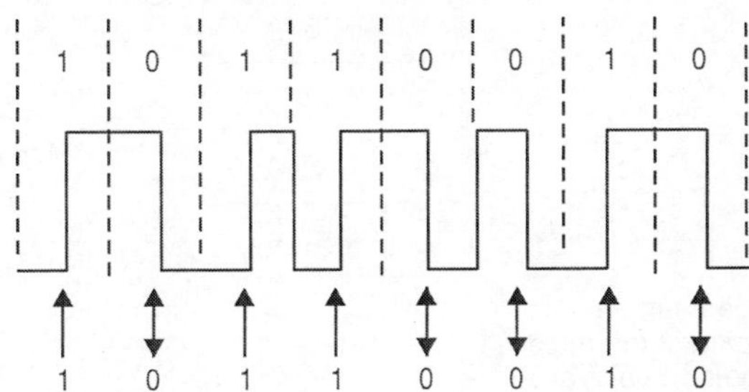

Figure 14.15 *Transition-Based Manchester Binary Encoding.*

Unfortunately, Manchester encoding introduces some difficult frequency-related problems that make it unsuitable for use at higher data rates. Ethernet versions subsequent to 10Base T all use different encoding procedures that include some or all of the following techniques:

Using data scrambling: A procedure that scrambles the bits in each byte in an orderly (and recoverable) manner. Some 0s are changed to 1s, some 1s are changed to 0s, and some bits are left the same. The result is reduced run-length of same-value bits, increased transition density, and easier clock recovery.

Expanding the code space: A technique that allows assignment of separate codes for data and control symbols (such as start-of-stream and end-of-stream delimiters, extension bits, and so on) and that assists in transmission error detection.

Using forward error-correcting codes: An encoding in which redundant information is added to the transmitted data stream so that some types of transmission errors can be corrected during frame reception.

The 802.3 Physical Layer Relationship to the ISO Reference Model

Although the specific logical model of the physical layer may vary from version to version, all Ethernet NICs generally conform to the generic model shown in figure 14.16.

The physical layer for each transmission rate is divided into sub-layers that are independent of the particular media type and sub-layers that are specific to the media type or signal encoding.

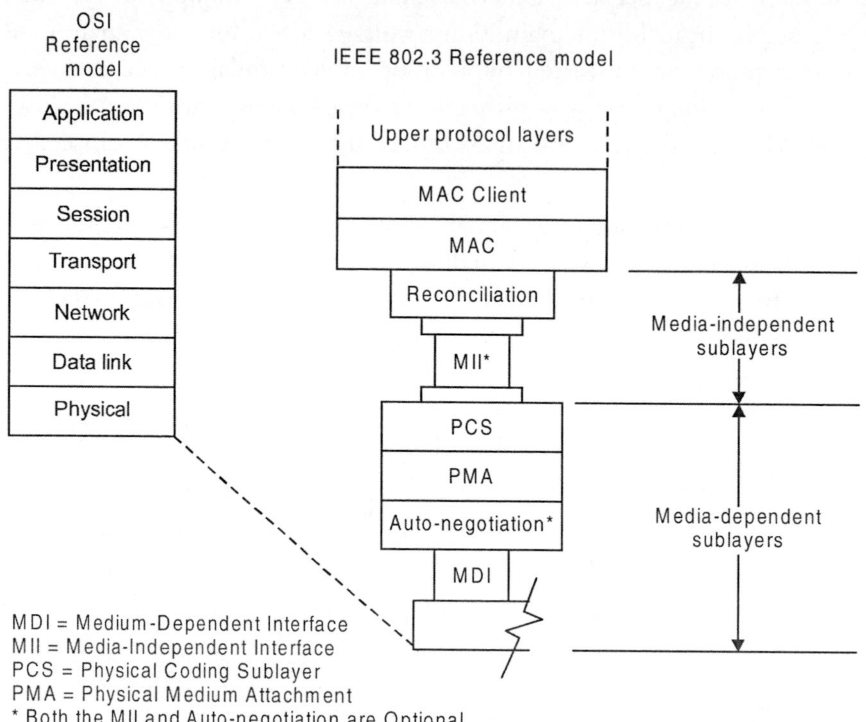

Figure 14.16. *The Generic Ethernet Physical Layer Reference Model.*

The reconciliation sub-layer and the optional Media-Independent Interface (MII in 10 Mbps and 100 Mbps Ethernet, GMII in gigabit Ethernet) provide the logical connection between the MAC and the different sets of media-dependent layers. The MII and GMII are defined with separate transmit and receive data paths that are bit-serial for 10 Mbps implementations, nibble-serial (4 bits wide) for 100 Mbps implementations, and byte-serial (8 bits wide) for 1000 Mbps implementations. The media-independent interfaces and the reconciliation sub-layer are common for their respective transmission rates and are configured for full-duplex operation in 10Base T and all subsequent Ethernet versions.

The media-dependent Physical Coding Sub-layer (PCS) provides the logic for encoding, multiplexing, and synchronization of the outgoing symbol streams as well symbol code alignment, demultiplexing, and decoding of the incoming data.

The Physical Medium Attachment (PMA) sub-layer contains the signal transmitters and receivers (transceivers), as well as the clock recovery logic for the received data streams. The Medium-Dependent Interface (MDI) is the cable connector between the signal transceivers and the link.

The Auto-negotiation sub-layer allows the NICs at each end of the link to exchange information about their individual capabilities, and then to negotiate and select the most favorable operational mode that they both are capable of supporting. Auto-negotiation is optional in early Ethernet implementations and is mandatory in later versions.

Depending on which type of signal encoding is used and how the links are configured, the PCS and PMA may or may not be capable of supporting full-duplex operation.

10 Mbps Ethernet—10Base T

10Base T provides Manchester-encoded 10 Mbps bit-serial communication over two unshielded twisted-pair cables. Although the standard was designed to support transmission over common telephone cable, the more typical link configuration is to use two pair of a four-pair category 3 or 5 cable, terminated at each NIC with an 8-pin RJ-45 connector (the MDI), as shown in figure 14.17. Because each active pair is configured as a simplex link where transmission is in one direction only, the 10Base T physical layers can support either half-duplex or full-duplex operation.

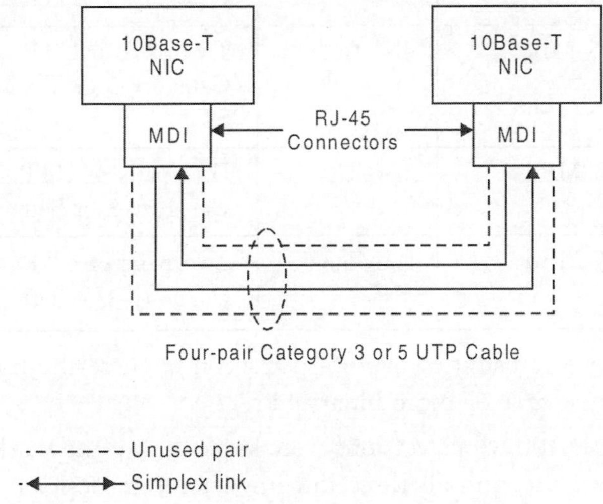

Figure 14.17 *The Typical 10Base T Link is a Four-Pair UTP Cable in Which Two Pairs are not Used.*

Although 10Base T may be considered essentially obsolete in some circles, it is included here because there are still many 10Base T Ethernet networks, and because full-duplex operation has given 10Base T an extended life.

10Base T was also the first Ethernet version to include a link integrity test to determine the health of the link. Immediately after power-up, the PMA transmits a normal link pulse (NLP) to tell the NIC at the other end of the link that this NIC wants to establish an active link connection:

- If the NIC at the other end of the link is also powered up, it responds with its own NLP.
- If the NIC at the other end of the link is not powered up, this NIC continues sending an NLP about once every 16 ms until it receives a response. The link is activated only after both NICs are capable of exchanging valid NLPs.

100 Mbps—Fast Ethernet

Increasing the Ethernet transmission rate by a factor of ten over 10Base T was not a simple task, and the effort resulted in the development of three separate physical layer standards for 100 Mbps over UTP cable: 100Base TX and 100Base T4 in 1995, and 100Base T2 in 1997. Each was defined with different encoding requirements and a different set of media-dependent sub-layers, even though there is some overlap in the link cabling. Table 14.5 compares the physical layer characteristics of 10Base T to the various 100Base versions.

Table 14.5 Summary of 100Base T Physical Layer Characteristics

Ethernet Version	*Transmit Symbol Rate*[1]	*Encoding*	*Cabling*	*Full-Duplex Operation*
10Base T	10 MBd	Manchester	Two pairs of UTP Category-3 or better	Supported
100Base TX	125 MBd	4B/5B	Two pairs of UTP Category-5 or Type 1 STP	Supported
100Base T4	33 MBd	8B/6T	Four pairs of UTP Category-3 or better	Not supported
100Base T2	25 MBd	PAM5 × 5	Two pairs of UTP Category-3 or better	Supported

One baud is equal one transmitted symbol per second, where the transmitted symbol may contain the equivalent value of 1 or more binary bits.

Although not all three 100 Mbps versions were successful in the marketplace, all three have been discussed in the literature, and all three did impact future designs. As such, all three are important to consider here.

100Base X

100Base X was designed to support transmission over either two pairs of category 5 UTP copper wire or two strands of optical fiber. Although the encoding, decoding, and clock recovery procedures are the same for both media, the signal transmission is different—electrical pulses in copper and light pulses in optical fiber. The signal transceivers that were included as part of the PMA function in the generic logical model of figure 14.18 were redefined as the separate Physical Media-Dependent (PMD) sub-layers shown in figure 14.18.

The 100Base X encoding procedure is based on the earlier FDDI optical fiber physical media-dependent and FDDI/CDDI copper twisted-pair physical media-dependent signaling standards developed by ISO and ANSI. The 100Base TX physical media-dependent sub-layer (TP-PMD) was implemented with CDDI semiconductor transceivers and RJ-45 connectors; the fiber PMD was implemented with FDDI optical transceivers and the low cost fiber Interface connector (commonly called the duplex SC connector).

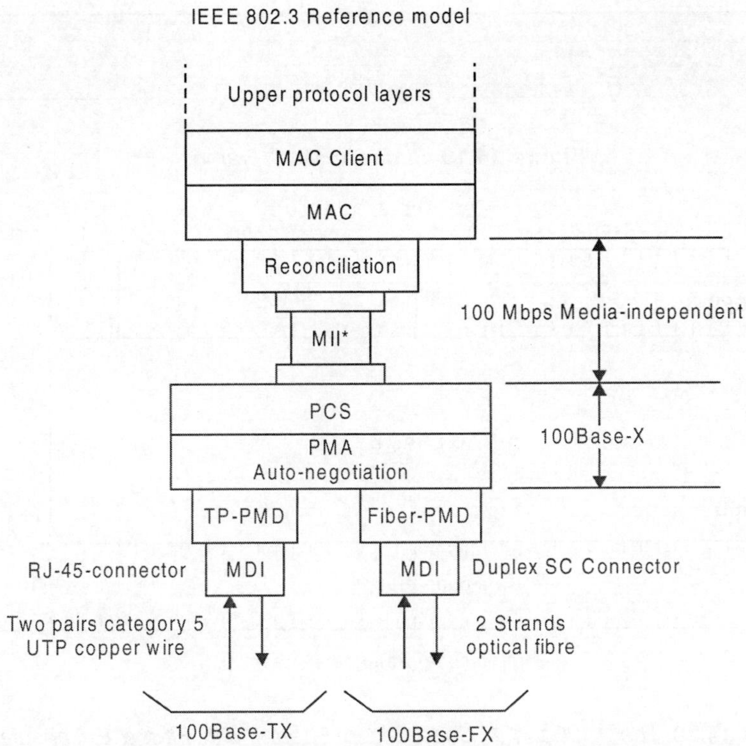

Figure 14.18 *The 100Base X Logical Model.*

The 4B/5B encoding procedure is the same as the encoding procedure used by FDDI, with only minor adaptations to accommodate Ethernet frame control. Each 4-bit data nibble (representing half of a data byte) is mapped into a 5-bit binary code-group that is transmitted bit-serial over the link. The expanded code space provided by the 32 5-bit code-groups allow separate assignment for the following:

- The 16 possible values in a 4-bit data nibble (16 code-groups).
- Four control code-groups that are transmitted as code-group pairs to indicate the start-of-stream delimiter (SSD) and the end-of-stream delimiter (ESD). Each MAC frame is "encapsulated" to mark both the beginning and end of the frame. The first byte of preamble is replaced with SSD code-group pair that precisely identifies the frame's code-group boundaries. The ESD code-group pair is appended after the frame's FCS field.
- A special IDLE code-group that is continuously sent during interframe gaps to maintain continuous synchronization between the NICs at each end of the link. The receipt of IDLE is interpreted to mean that the link is quiet.

Eleven invalid code-groups that are not intentionally transmitted by a NIC (although one is used by a repeater to propagate receive errors). Receipt of any invalid code-group will cause the incoming frame to be treated as an invalid frame.

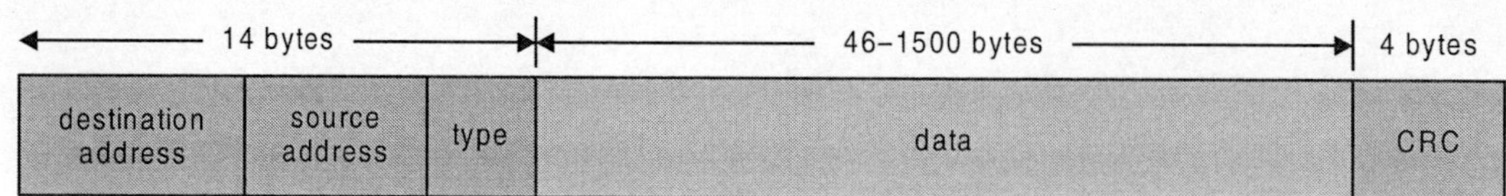

Figure 14.19 *Shows a MAC Frame.*

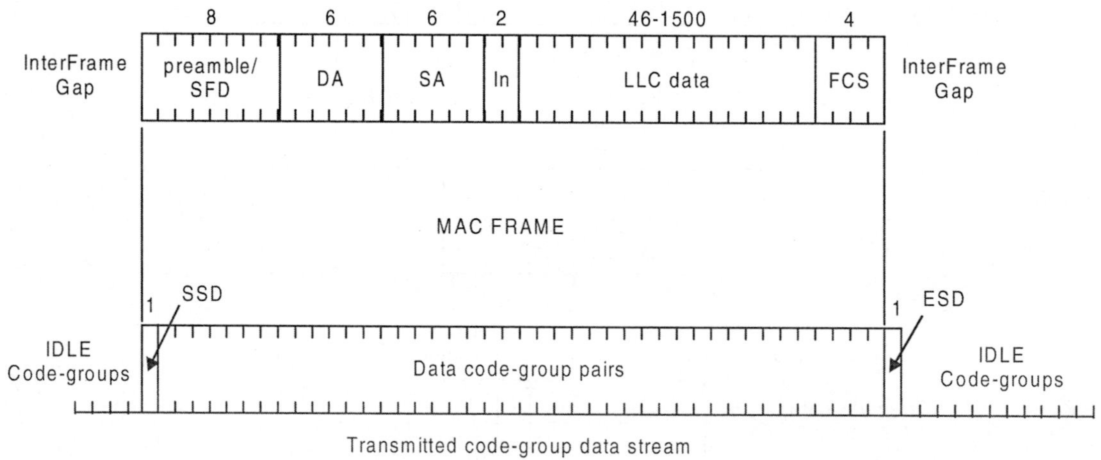

Figure 14.20 *The 100Base X Code-Group Stream with Frame Encapsulation.*

100Base TX transmits and receives on the same link pairs and uses the same pin assignments on the MDI as 10Base T. 100Base TX and 100Base FX both support half-duplex and full-duplex transmission.

100Base T4

100Base T4 was developed to allow 10Base T networks to be upgraded to 100 Mbps operation without requiring existing four-pair category 3 UTP cables to be replaced with the newer category 5 cables. Two of the four pairs are configured for half-duplex operation and can support transmission in either direction, but only in one direction at a time. The other two pairs are configured as simplex pairs dedicated to transmission in one direction only. Frame transmission uses both half-duplex pairs, plus the simplex pair that is appropriate for the transmission direction, as shown in figure 14.21. The simplex pair for the opposite direction provides carrier sense and collision detection. Full-duplex operation cannot be supported on 100Base T4.

100Base T4 uses an 8B6T encoding scheme in which each 8-bit binary byte is mapped into a pattern of six ternary (three-level: +1, 0, –1) symbols known as 6T code-groups. Separate 6T code-groups are used for IDLE and for the control code-groups that are necessary for frame transmission. IDLE received on the dedicated receive pair indicates that the link is quiet.

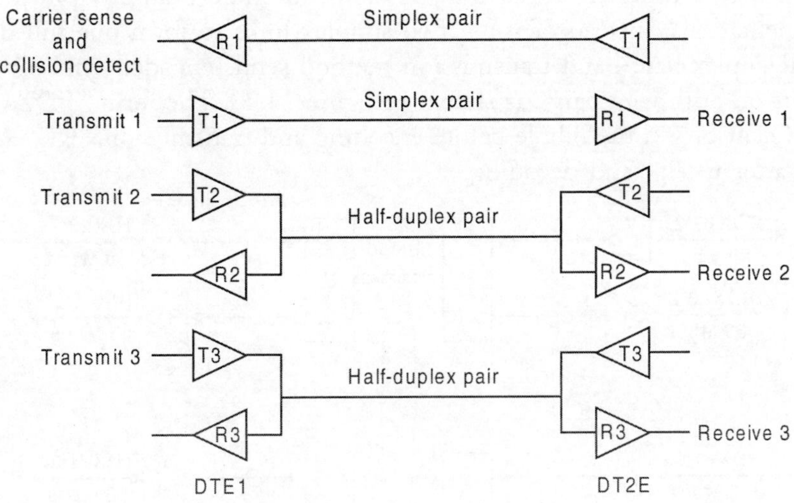

Figure 14.21 *The 100Base T4 Wire-Pair Usage During Frame Transmission.*

During frame transmission, 6T data code-groups are transmitted in a delayed round-robin sequence over the three transmit wire-pairs, as shown in figure 14.22 . Each frame is encapsulated with start-of-stream and end-of-packet 6T code-groups that mark both the beginning and end of the frame, and the beginning and end of the 6T code-group stream on each wire pair. Receipt of a non-IDLE code-group over the dedicated receive-pair any time before the collision window expires indicates that a collision has occurred.

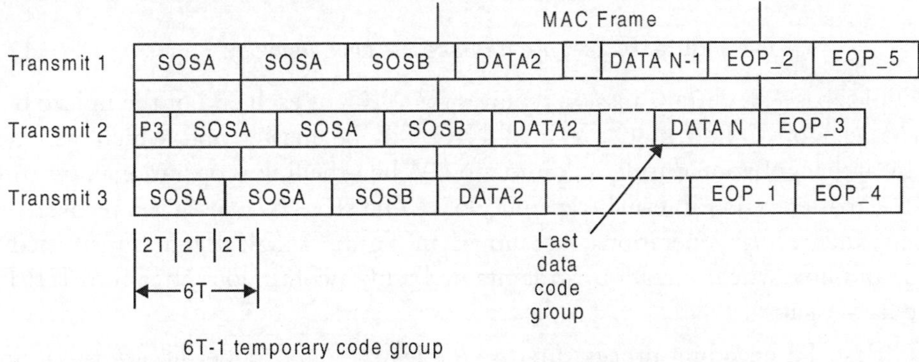

Figure 14.22 *The 100Base T4 Frame Transmission Sequence.*

100Base T2

The 100Base T2 specification was developed as a better alternative for upgrading networks with installed category 3 cabling than was being provided by 100Base T4. Two important new goals were defined:

- To provide communication over two pairs of category 3 or better cable
- To support both half-duplex and full-duplex operation.

100Base T2 uses a different signal transmission procedure than any previous twisted-pair Ethernet implementations. Instead of using two simplex links to form one full-duplex link, the 100Base T2 dual-duplex base-band transmission method sends encoded symbols simultaneously in both directions on both wire pairs, as shown in figure 14.23. The term "TDX<3:2>" indicates the 2 most significant bits in the nibble before encoding and transmission. "RDX<3:2>" indicates the same 2 bits after receipt and decoding.

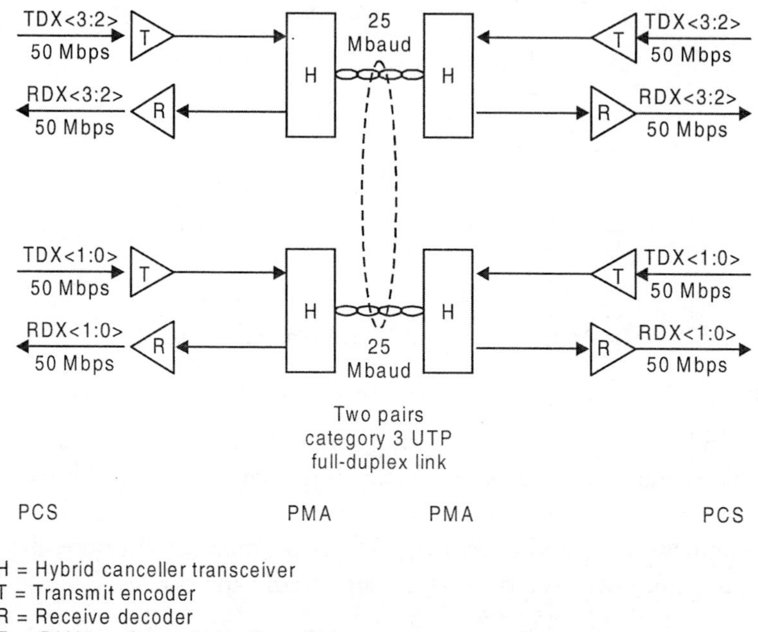

Figure 14.23 *The 100Base T2 Link Topology.*

Dual-duplex base-band transmission requires the NICs at each end of the link to be operated in a master/slave loop-timing mode. Which NIC will be master and which will be slave is determined by autonegotiation during link initiation. When the link is operational, synchronization is based on the master NIC's internal transmit clock. The slave NIC uses the recovered clock for both transmit and receive operations, as shown in figure 14.24. Each transmitted frame is encapsulated, and link synchronization is maintained with a continuous stream of IDLE symbols during inter-frame gaps.

The 100Base T2 encoding process first scrambles the data frame nibbles to randomize the bit sequence. It then maps the two upper bits and the two lower bits of each nibble into two five-level (+2, +1, 0, –1, –2) Pulse Amplitude-Modulated (PAM5) symbols that are simultaneously transmitted over the two wire pairs (PAM5 × 5). Different scrambling procedures for master and slave transmissions ensure that the data streams traveling in opposite directions on the same wire pair are uncoordinated.

Signal reception is essentially the reverse of signal transmission. Because the signal on each wire pair at the MDI is the sum of the transmitted signal and the received signal, each receiver subtracts the transmitted symbols from the signal received at the MDI to recover the symbols in the incoming data stream. The incoming symbol pair is then decoded, unscrambled, and reconstituted as a data nibble for transfer to the MAC.

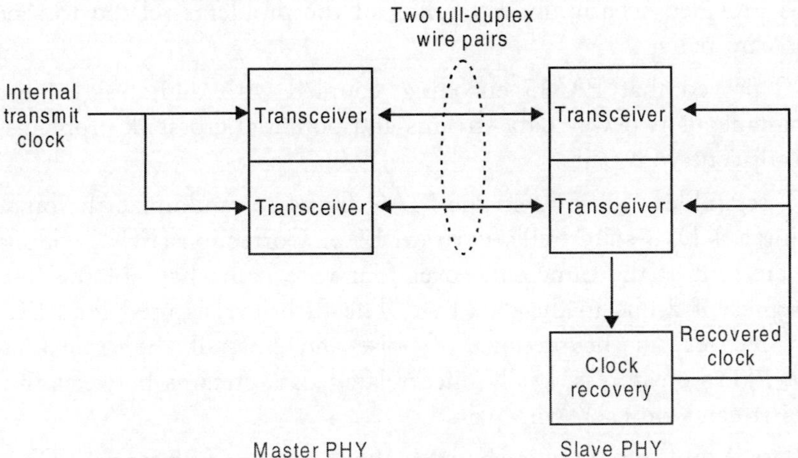

Figure 14.24 *The 100Base T2 Loop Timing Configuration.*

1000 MBPS—GIGABIT ETHERNET

The gigabit Ethernet standards development resulted in two primary specifications: 1000Base T for UTP copper cable and 1000Base X STP copper cable, as well as single and multimode optical fiber.

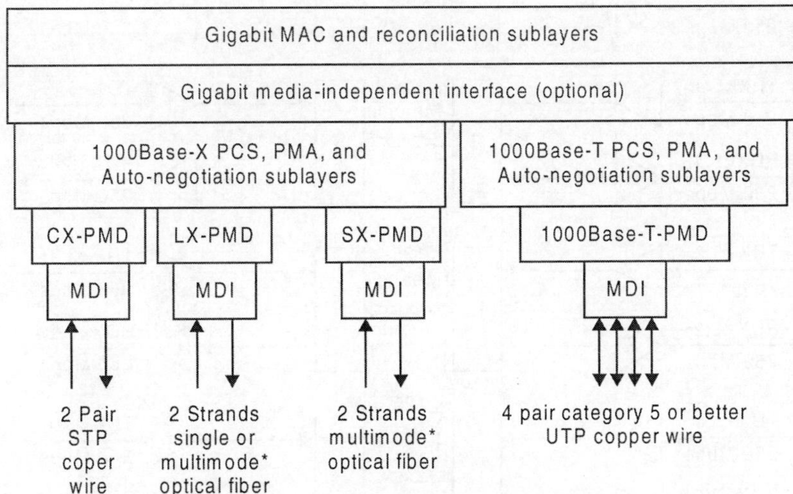

Figure 14.25 *Gigabit Ethernet Variations.*

1000Base T

1000Base T Ethernet provides full-duplex transmission over four-pair category 5 or better UTP cable. 1000Base T is based largely on the findings and design approaches that led to the development of the fast Ethernet physical layer implementations:

100Base TX proved that binary symbol streams could be successfully transmitted over category 5 UTP cable at 125 MB.

100Base T4 provided a basic understanding of the problems related to sending multilevel signals over four wire pairs.

100Base T2 proved that PAM5 encoding, coupled with digital signal processing, could handle both simultaneous two-way data streams and potential crosstalk problems resulting from alien signals on adjacent wire pairs.

1000Base T scrambles each byte in the MAC frame to randomize the bit sequence before it is encoded using a 4-D, 8-state trellis Forward Error Correction (FEC) coding in which four PAM5 symbols are sent at the same time over four wire pairs. Four of the five levels in each PAM5 symbol represent 2 bits in the data byte. The fifth level is used for FEC coding, which enhances symbol recovery in the presence of noise and crosstalk. Separate scramblers for the master and slave PHYs create essentially uncorrelated data streams between the two opposite-travelling symbol streams on each wire pair.

The 1000Base T link topology is shown in figure 14.26. The term "TDX<7:6>" indicates the 2 most significant bits in the data byte before encoding and transmission. "RDX<7:6>" indicates the same 2 bits after receipt and decoding.

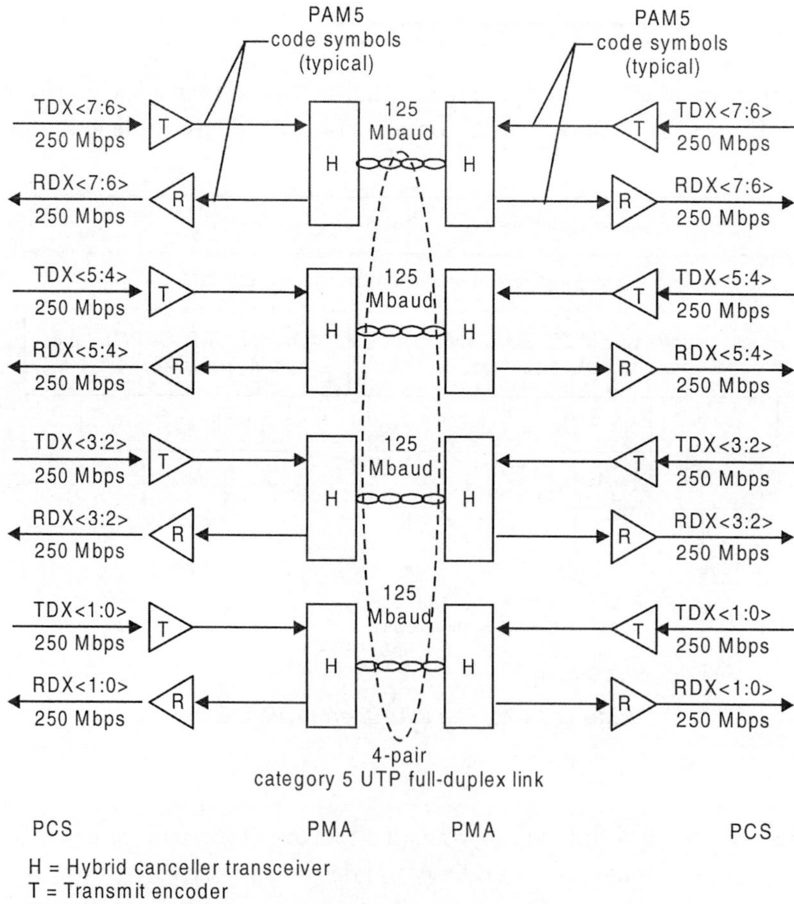

Figure 14.26 *The 1000Base T Link Topology.*

The clock recovery and master/slave loop timing procedures are essentially the same as those used in 100Base T2. Which NIC will be master (typically the NIC in a multi-port intermediate network node) and which will be slave is determined during auto-negotiation.

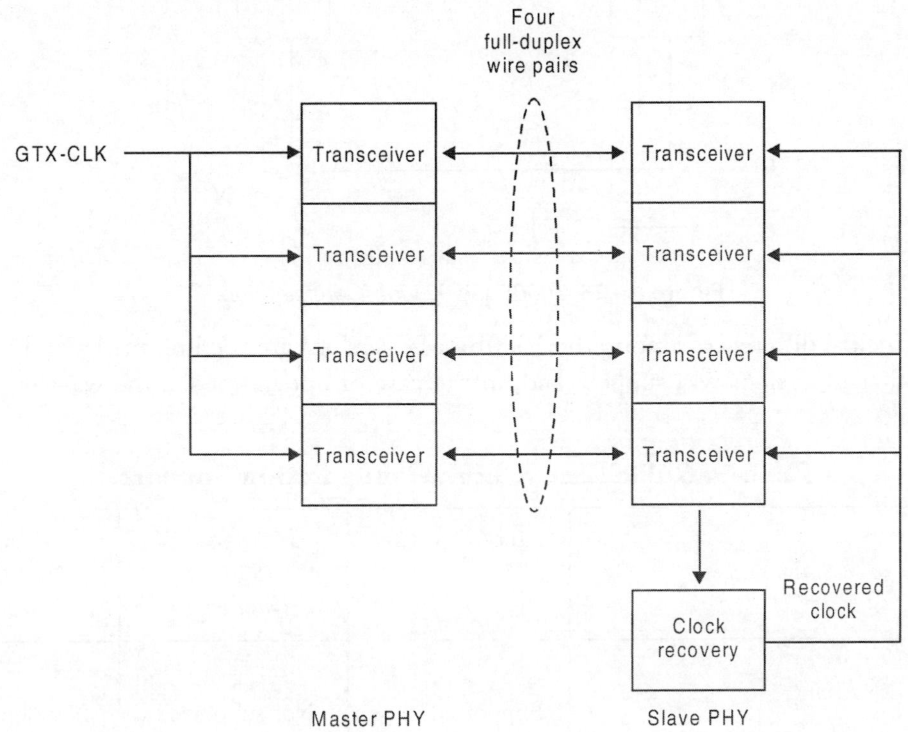

Figure 14.27 *1000Base T Master/Slave Loop Timing Configuration.*

Each transmitted frame is encapsulated with start-of-stream and end-of-stream delimiters, and loop timing is maintained by continuous streams of IDLE symbols sent on each wire pair during inter-frame gaps. 1000Base T supports both half-duplex and full-duplex operation.

1000Base X

All three 1000Base X versions support full-duplex binary transmission at 1250 Mbps over two strands of optical fiber or two STP copper wire-pairs, as shown in figure 14.28. Transmission coding is based on the ANSI fiber channel 8B/10B encoding scheme. Each 8-bit data byte is mapped into a 10-bit code-group for bit-serial transmission. Like earlier Ethernet versions, each data frame is encapsulated at the physical layer before transmission, and link synchronization is maintained by sending a continuous stream of IDLE code-groups during inter-frame gaps. All 1000Base X physical layers support both half-duplex and full-duplex operation.

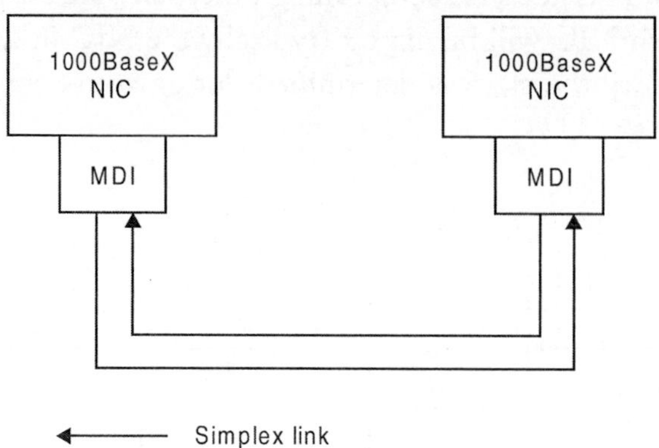

Figure 14.28 *1000Base X Link Configuration.*

The principal differences among the 1000Base X versions are the link media and connectors that the particular versions will support and, in the case of optical media, the wavelength of the optical signal.

Table 14.6 1000Base X Link Configuration Support

Link Configuration	*1000Base CX*	*1000Base SX (850 nm Wavelength)*	*1000Base LX (1300 nm Wavelength)*
150 STP copper	Supported	Not supported	Not supported
125/62.5 μm multimode optical fiber[1]	Not supported	Supported	Supported
125/50 μm multimode optical fiber	Not supported	Supported	Supported
125/10 μm single mode optical fiber	Not supported	Not supported	Supported
Allowed connectors	IEC style 1 or Fiber Channel style 2	SFF MT-RJ or Duplex SC	SFF MT-RJ or Duplex SC

[1]The 125/62.5 μm specification refers to the cladding and core diameters of the optical fiber.

IEEE-802.3 PROTOCOL

The IEEE-802.3 protocol is based on the Xerox Network Standard (XNS) called Ethernet. The IEEE-802.3 protocol is commonly called Ethernet but it is just one version. These are the four versions of the Ethernet frame:

Ethernet_802.2 Frame type used on Netware 3.12 & 4.01

Ethernet_802.3 Frame type used on Netware 3.x & 2.x (raw)

Ethernet_II Frame type used on DEC, TCP/IP

Ethernet_SNAP Frame type used on Appletalk (Sub-Net Access Protocol)

CSMA/CD (Carrier Sense Multiple Access/Collision Detect)

Bus arbitration is performed on all versions of Ethernet using the CSMA/CD (Carrier Sense Multiple Access/Collision Detect) protocol. Bus arbitration is another way of discussing how to control who is allowed to talk on the medium (and when). Put simply, it is used to determine who's turn it is to talk.

In CSMA/CD, all stations, on the same segment of cable, listen for the carrier signal. If they hear the carrier, then they know that someone else it talking on the wire. If they don't hear carrier then they know that they can talk. This is called the carrier sense portion of CSMA/CD.

All stations share the same segment of cable, and can talk on it similar to a party line. This is the multiple access portion of CSMA/CD.

If 2 stations should attempt to talk at the same time, a collision is detected, and both stations back off—for a random amount of time—before they try again. This is the collision detect portion of CSMA/CD.

IEEE 802.3 Ethernet Media Types

IEEE 802.3 defines five media types of IEEE 802.3 Ethernet types shown below:

IEEE 802.3—10Base5 Thick Coax 10Mbps Base-band 500m

IEEE 802.3a—10Base2 Thin Coax 10Mbps Base-band 185m

IEEE 803b—10Broad36 Broadband 10Mbps Broad-band 3600m

IEEE 802.3—1Base5 StarLAN1Mbps Base-band 500m

IEEE 802.3i—10Base T Twisted-Pair 10Mps Base-band 100m

IEEE 802.3—10Base5 (Thick Coax) is used only as backbones to networks. Backbones are lines that connect buildings and network equipment together (such as bridges, routers, brouter, hubs, concentrators, gateways, etc.). 10Base5 is now being replaced by either thin coax or fiber optics.

IEEE 802.3a—10Base2 is commonly used in new installations as a backbone to connect buildings and network equipment together. 10Base2 (thin coax) is also used to connect work stations together, but the preferred choice is to use 10Base T.

IEEE 802.3b—10Broad36 is rarely used; it combines analog and digital signals together. Broadband means that a mixture of signals can be sent on the same medium.

IEEE 802.3e —StarLAN is a slow 1 Mbps standard that has been replaced by thin coax or twisted pair.

IEEE 802.3i—10Base T is commonly used to connect workstations to network hubs. The network hubs can use 10Base T (twisted pair) to connect to other hubs.

ETHERNET/IEEE 802.3

Ethernet was developed by Xerox Corporation's Palo Alto Research Center (PARC) in the 1970s. Ethernet was the technological basis for the IEEE 802.3 specification, which was initially released in 1980. Shortly thereafter, Digital Equipment Corporation, Intel Corporation, and Xerox Corporation jointly developed and released an Ethernet specification (version 2.0) that is substantially compatible with IEEE 802.3. Together, Ethernet and IEEE 802.3 currently maintain the greatest market share of any Local-Area Network (LAN) protocol. Today, the term Ethernet is often used to refer to all Carrier Sense Multiple Access/Collision Detection (CSMA/CD) LANs that generally conform to Ethernet specifications, including IEEE 802.3.

When it was developed, Ethernet was designed to fill the middle ground between long-distance, low-speed networks and specialized, computer-room networks carrying data at high speeds for very limited distances. Ethernet is well suited to applications where a local communication medium must carry sporadic, occasionally heavy traffic at high peak data rates.

Ethernet/IEEE 802.3 Comparison

Ethernet and IEEE 802.3 specify similar technologies. Both are CSMA/CD LANs. Stations on a CSMA/CD LAN can access the network at any time. Before sending data, CSMA/CD stations "listen" to the network to see if it is already in use. If it is, the station wishing to transmit waits. If the network is not in use, the station transmits. A collision occurs when two stations listen for network traffic, "hear" none, and transmit simultaneously. In this case, both transmissions are damaged, and the stations must retransmit at some later time. Back-off algorithms determine when the colliding stations retransmit. CSMA/CD stations can detect collisions, so they know when they must retransmit.

Both Ethernet and IEEE 802.3 LANs are broadcast networks. In other words, all stations see all frames, regardless of whether they represent an intended destination. Each station must examine received frames to determine if the station is a destination. If so, the frame is passed to a higher protocol layer for appropriate processing.

Differences between Ethernet and IEEE 802.3 LANs are subtle. Ethernet provides services corresponding to layers 1 and 2 of the OSI reference model, while IEEE 802.3 specifies the physical layer (layer 1) and the channel-access portion of the link layer (Layer 2), but does not define a logical link control protocol. Both Ethernet and IEEE 802.3 are implemented in hardware. Typically, the physical manifestation of these protocols is either an interface card in a host computer or circuitry on a primary circuit board within a host computer.

Physical Connections

IEEE 802.3 specifies several different physical layers, whereas Ethernet defines only one. Each IEEE 802.3 physical layer protocol has a name that summarizes its characteristics. The coded components of an IEEE 802.3 physical-layer name are shown in figure 14.29.

Ethernet is most similar to IEEE 802.3 10Base5. Both of these protocols specify a bus topology network with a connecting cable between the end stations and the actual network

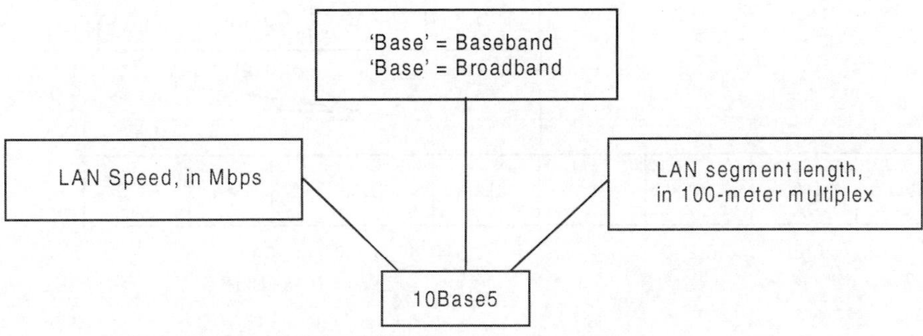

Figure 14.29 *IEEE 802.3 Physical-Layer Name Components.*

medium. In the case of Ethernet, that cable is called a transceiver cable. The transceiver cable connects to a transceiver device attached to the physical network medium. The IEEE 802.3 configuration is much the same, except that the connecting cable is referred to as an Attachment Unit Interface (AUI), and the transceiver is called a Medium Attachment Unit (MAU). In both cases, the connecting cable attaches to an interface board (or interface circuitry) within the end station.

Frame Formats

Ethernet and IEEE 802.3 frame formats are shown in figure 14.30. Both Ethernet and IEEE 802.3 frames begin with an alternating pattern of (7 octets of 1010....) ones and zeros called a preamble. The preamble tells receiving stations that a frame is coming.

The byte before the destination address in both an Ethernet and a IEEE 802.3 frame is a Start-of-Frame (SOF) delimiter (1 octet 10101011). This byte ends with two consecutive one bits, which serve to synchronize the frame reception portions of all stations on the LAN. Both preamble and Start-of-Frame (SOF) delimiter fields are handled in the physical layer.

Immediately following the Start-of-Frame (SOF) delimiter in both Ethernet and IEEE 802.3 LANs are the destination and source address fields. Both Ethernet and IEEE 802.3 addresses are 6 bytes long. Addresses are contained in hardware on the Ethernet and IEEE 802.3 interface cards. The first 3 bytes of the addresses are specified by the IEEE on a vendor-dependent basis, while the last 3 bytes are specified by the Ethernet or IEEE 802.3 vendor. The source address is always a uni-cast (single node) address, while the destination address may be uni-cast, multicast (group), or broadcast (all nodes).

In Ethernet frames, the 2-byte field following the source address is a type field. This field specifies the upper-layer protocol to receive the data after Ethernet processing is complete.

In IEEE 802.3 frames, the 2-byte field following the source address is a length field, which indicates the number of bytes of data that follow this field and precede the Frame Check Sequence (FCS) field.

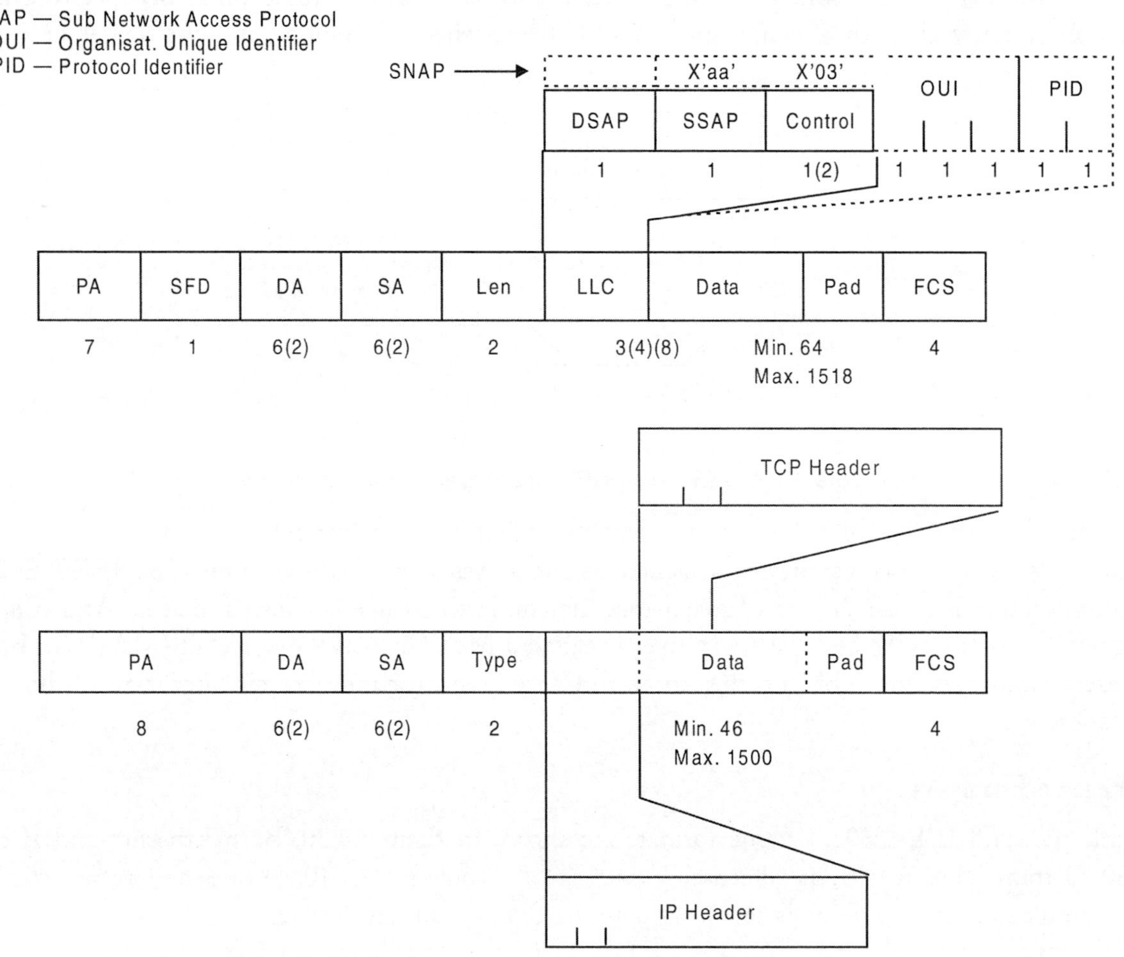

Figure 14.30 *Ethernet and IEEE 802.3 Frame Formats.*

Following the type/length field is the actual data contained in the frame. After physical-layer and link-layer processing is complete, this data will eventually be sent to an upper-layer protocol. In the case of Ethernet, the upper-layer protocol is identified in the type field. In the case of IEEE 802.3, the upper-layer protocol must be defined within the data portion of the frame, if at all. If data in the frame is insufficient to fill the frame to its minimum 64-byte size, padding bytes are inserted to ensure at least a 64-byte frame.

After the data field is a 4-byte FCS field containing a Cyclic Redundancy Check (CRC) value. The CRC is created by the sending device and recalculated by the receiving device to check for damage that might have occurred to the frame in transit.

REVIEW QUESTIONS

1. List five Ethernet/802.3 specifications that apply to the OSI model physical layer.
2. What are the Ethernet distance limitations for tappable and untappable segments ?
3. What are the minimum and maximum distances between nodes on an Ethernet network ?
4. Which network topology is used with Ethernet network ?
5. Which data link protocol is the basis for the Ethernet data link process ?
6. What are the purposes for the preamble preceding Ethernet packets ?
7. What is the data rate for the original 802.3 specification ?
8. What is used in token formats to assure that a delimiter form does not appear elsewhere in a message ?
9. What type of token is used to allow a station to access a token bus network ?
10. How does an originating station on a Token ring know if its message has been received and copied by a destination station ?
11. What does the originating station do when it detects its message has been sent and copied ?
12. Give an advantage of a Token ring network compared to an Ethernet bus network.
13. Give a disadvantage of a Token ring network compared to an Ethernet bus network.
14. List five Ethernet/802.3 specifications that apply to the OSI model physical layer.
15. Why is there no need for CSMA/CD on a full-duplex Ethernet LAN ?
16. Compare the data rates for traditional Ethernet, fast Ethernet, and gigabit Ethernet.
17. What internet model layers are of concern to LANs ?

15 TOKEN RING

TOKEN RING/IEEE 802.5

The Token ring network was originally developed by IBM in the 1970s. It is still IBM's primary Local Area Network (LAN) technology, and is second only to Ethernet/IEEE 802.3 in general LAN popularity. The IEEE 802.5 specification is almost identical to, and completely compatible with, IBM's Token ring network. In fact, the IEEE 802.5 specification was modeled after IBM Token ring, and continues to shadow IBM's Token ring development. The term Token ring is generally used to refer to both IBM's Token ring network and IEEE 802.5 networks.

TOKEN RING/IEEE 802.5 COMPARISON

Token ring and IEEE 802.5 networks are basically quite compatible, although the specifications differ in relatively minor ways. IBM's Token ring network specifies a star, with all end stations attached to a device called a Multi Station Access Unit (MSAU), whereas IEEE 802.5 does not specify a topology (although virtually all IEEE 802.5 implementations also are based on a star). Other differences exist, including media type (IEEE 802.5 does not specify a media type, while IBM Token ring networks use twisted-pair wire) and routing information field size. Figure 15.1 summarizes IBM Token ring network and IEEE 802.5 specifications.

TOKEN RING

Developed by IBM, Token ring, is standardized to IEEE 802.5. Token ring uses a star topology, but it is wired so the signal will travel from hub to hub in a logical ring. These networks use a data token passed from computer to computer around the ring to allow each computer to have network access. The token comes from the Nearest Active Upstream Neighbor (NAUN). When a computer receives a token, if it has no attached data and the computer has data for transmission, it attaches its data to the token then sends it to its Nearest Active Downstream Neighbour (NADN). Each computer downstream will pass the data on since the token is being used until the data reaches its recipient. The recipient will set two bits to indicate it received the data and transmit the token and data. When the computer that sent the data receives the package, it can verify that the data was received correctly. It will remove the data from the token and pass the token to its NADN.

	IBM Token Ring Network	IEEE 802.5
Data rates	4.16 Mbps	4.16 Mbps
Station/segment	260 (S.T.P.) 72 (U.T.P.)	250
Topology	Star	Not specified
Media	Twisted pair	Not specified
Signaling	Baseband	Baseband
Access method	Token passing	Token passing
Encoding	Differential Manchester	Differential Manchester

Figure 15.1 *IBM Token Ring Network/IEEE 802.5 Comparison.*

CHARACTERISTICS

Maximum cable length is 45 meters when UTP cable is used and 101 meters when STP is used. Topology is star-wired ring. It uses type 1 STP and type 3 UTP. Connectors are RJ-45 or IBM type A. Minimum length between nodes is 2.5 meters. Maximum number of hubs or segments is 33. Maximum nodes per network is 72 nodes with UTP and 260 nodes with STP. Speed is 4 or 16 Mbps. Data frames may be 4,000 to 17,800 bytes long.

TOKEN RING HUBS

A Token ring network uses a Multi-Station Access Unit (MAU) as a hub. It may also be known as a Smart Multi-Station Access Unit (SMAU). A MAU normally has ten ports. Two ports are Ring In (RI) and Ring Out (RO) which allow multiple MAUs to be linked to each other. The other 8 ports are used to connect to computers.

Token ring and IEEE 802.5 networks are basically compatible, although the specifications differ in minor ways. IBM's Token ring network specifies a star, with all end stations attached to a device called a Multi-Station Access Unit (MSAU). In contrast, IEEE 802.5 does not specify a topology, although virtually all IEEE 802.5 implementations are based on a star. Other differences exist, including media type (IEEE 802.5 does not specify a media type, although IBM Token ring networks use twisted-pair wire) and routing information field size.

PHYSICAL CONNECTIONS

IBM Token ring network stations are directly connected to MSAUs, which can be wired together to form one large ring. Patch cables connect MSAUs to adjacent MSAUs, while lobe cables connect MSAUs to stations. MSAUs include bypass relays for removing stations from the ring.

TOKEN RING OPERATION

Token ring and IEEE 802.5 are two principal examples of token-passing networks (FDDI is the other). *Token-passing networks* move a small frame, called a token, around the network. Possession of the token grants the right to transmit. If a node receiving the token has no information to send, it passes the token to the next end station. Each station can hold the token for a maximum period of time.

If a station possessing the token does have information to transmit, it seizes the token, alters 1 bit of the token (which turns the token into a start-of-frame sequence), appends the information that it wants to transmit, and sends this information to the next station on the ring. While the information frame is circling the ring, no token is on the network (unless the ring supports early token release), which means that other stations wanting to transmit must wait. Therefore, collisions cannot occur in Token ring networks. If early token release is supported, a new token can be released when frame transmission is complete.

The information frame circulates the ring until it reaches the intended destination station, which copies the information for further processing. The information frame continues to circle the ring and is finally removed when it reaches the sending station. The sending station can check the returning frame to see whether the frame was seen and subsequently copied by the destination.

Unlike CSMA/CD networks (such as Ethernet), token-passing networks are *deterministic*, which means that it is possible to calculate the maximum time that will pass before any end station will be capable of transmitting. This feature and several reliability features, which are discussed in the section "fault-management mechanisms," later in this chapter, make Token ring networks ideal for applications in which delay must be predictable and robust network operation is important. Factory automation environments are examples of such applications.

Token ring networks use a sophisticated priority system that permits certain user-designated, high-priority stations to use the network more frequently. Token ring frames have two fields that control priority: the priority field and the reservation field.

Only stations with a priority equal to or higher than the priority value contained in a token can seize that token. After the token is seized and changed to an information frame, only stations with a priority value higher than that of the transmitting station can reserve the token for the next pass around the network. When the next token is generated, it includes the higher priority of the reserving station. Stations that raise a token's priority level must reinstate the previous priority after their transmission is complete.

Fault-Management Mechanisms

Token ring networks employ several mechanisms for detecting and compensating for network faults. For example, one station in the Token ring network is selected to be the *active monitor*. This station, which potentially can be any station on the network, acts as a centralized source of timing information for other ring stations and performs a variety of ring-maintenance functions. One of these functions is the removal of continuously circulating frames from the ring. When a sending device fails, its frame may continue to circle the ring. This can prevent other stations from transmitting their own frames and essentially can lock up the network. The active monitor can detect such frames, remove them from the ring, and generate a new token.

The IBM Token ring network's star topology also contributes to overall network reliability. Because all information in a Token ring network is seen by active MSAUs, these devices can be programmed to check for problems and selectively remove stations from the ring, if necessary.

A Token ring algorithm called *beaconing* detects and tries to repair certain network faults. Whenever a station detects a serious problem with the network (such as a cable break), it sends a beacon frame, which defines a failure domain. This domain includes the station reporting the failure, its Nearest Active Upstream Neighbor (NAUN), and everything in between. Beaconing initiates a process called *auto reconfiguration*, in which nodes within the failure domain automatically perform diagnostics in an attempt to reconfigure the network around the failed areas. Physically, the MSAU can accomplish this through electrical reconfiguration.

Frame Format

Token ring and IEEE 802.5 support two basic frame types: tokens and data/command frames. Tokens are 3 bytes in length and consist of a start delimiter, an access control byte, and an end delimiter. Data/command frames vary in size, depending on the size of the information field. Data frames carry information for upper-layer protocols, while command frames contain control information and have no data for upper-layer protocols.

Token Frame Fields

The three token frame fields are summarized in the descriptions that follow:

Start Delimiter: Alerts each station of the arrival of a token (or data/command frame). This field includes signals that distinguish the byte from the rest of the frame by violating the encoding scheme used elsewhere in the frame.

Access-Control Byte: Contains the priority field (the most significant 3 bits) and the reservation field (the least significant 3 bits), as well as a token bit (used to differentiate a token from a data/command frame) and a monitor bit (used by the active monitor to determine whether a frame is circling the ring endlessly).

End Delimiter: Signals the end of the token or data/command frame. This field also contains bits to indicate a damaged frame and identify the frame that is the last in a logical sequence.

Data/Command Frame Fields

Data/command frames have the same three fields as token frames, plus several others. The Data/command frame fields are described in the following summaries:

Start Delimiter: Alerts each station of the arrival of a token (or data/command frame). This field includes signals that distinguish the byte from the rest of the frame by violating the encoding scheme used elsewhere in the frame.

Access-Control Byte: Contains the priority field (the most significant 3 bits) and the reservation field (the least significant 3 bits), as well as a token bit (used to differentiate a token from a data/command frame) and a monitor bit (used by the active monitor to determine whether a frame is circling the ring endlessly).

Frame-Control Bytes: Indicates whether the frame contains data or control information. In control frames, this byte specifies the type of control information.

Destination and Source Addresses: Consists of two 6-byte address fields that identify the destination and source station addresses.

Data: Indicates that the length of field is limited by the ring token holding time, which defines the maximum time a station can hold the token.

Frame Check Sequence (FCS): Is filed by the source station with a calculated value dependent on the frame contents. The destination station recalculates the value to determine whether the frame was damaged in transit. If so, the frame is discarded.

End Delimiter: Signals the end of the token or data/command frame. The end delimiter also contains bits to indicate a damaged frame and identify the frame that is the last in a logical sequence.

Frame Status: Is a 1-byte field terminating a command/data frame. The frame status field includes the address-recognized indicator and frame-copied indicator.

TOKEN PASSING

Token ring and IEEE 802.5 are the primary examples of token-passing networks. Token-passing networks move a small frame, called a token, around the network. Possession of the token grants the right to transmit. If a node receiving the token has no information to send, it simply passes the token to the next end station. Each station can hold the token for a maximum period of time.

If a station possessing the token does have information to transmit, it seizes the token, alters one bit of the token (which turns the token into a start-of-frame sequence), appends the information it wishes to transmit, and finally sends this information to the next station on the ring. While the information frame is circling the ring, there is no token on the network (unless the ring supports early token release), so other stations wishing to transmit must wait. Therefore, collisions cannot occur in Token ring networks. If early token release is supported, a new token can be released when frame transmission is completed.

The information frame circulates the ring until it reaches the intended destination station, which copies the information for further processing. The information frame continues to circle the ring and is finally removed when it reaches the sending station. The sending station can check the returning frame to see whether the frame was seen and subsequently copied by the destination.

Unlike CSMA/CD networks (such as Ethernet), token-passing networks are deterministic. In other words, it is possible to calculate the maximum time that will pass before any end station will be able to transmit. This feature and several reliability features, which are discussed in the section "fault management mechanisms" later in this chapter, make Token ring networks ideal for applications where delay must be predictable and robust network operation is important. Factory automation environments are examples of such applications.

Token Ring Network

A Token ring network is a Local Area Network (LAN) in which all computers are connected in a ring or star topology and a bit or token-passing scheme is used in order to prevent the collision of data between two computers that want to send messages at the same time. The Token ring protocol is the second most widely-used protocol on local area networks after Ethernet. The IBM Token ring protocol led to a standard version, specified as IEEE 802.5. Both protocols are used and are very similar. The IEEE 802.5 Token ring technology provides for data transfer rates of either 4 or 16 megabits per second. Very briefly, here is how it works:

1. Empty information frames are continuously circulated on the ring.
2. When a computer has a message to send, it inserts a token in an empty frame (this may consist of simply changing a 0 to a 1 in the token bit part of the frame) and inserts a message and a destination identifier in the frame.
3. The frame is then examined by each successive workstation. If the workstation sees that it is the destination for the message, it copies the message from the frame and changes the token back to 0.
4. When the frame gets back to the originator, it sees that the token has been changed to 0 and that the message has been copied and received. It removes the message from the frame.
5. The frame continues to circulate as an "empty" frame, ready to be taken by a workstation when it has a message to send.

The token scheme can also be used with bus topology LANs. The standard for the Token ring protocol is IEEE 802.5. The Fiber Distributed-Data Interface (FDDI) also uses a Token ring protocol.

IBM Token ring network stations are directly connected to MSAUs, which can be wired together to form one large ring as shown in figure 15.2. Patch cables connect MSAUs to adjacent MSAUs. Lobe cables connect MSAUs to stations. MSAUs include bypass relays for removing stations from the ring.

Token ring networks use a sophisticated priority system that permits certain user-designated, high-priority stations to use the network more frequently. Token ring frames have two fields that control priority: the priority field and the reservation field. Only stations with a priority equal to or higher than the priority value contained in a token can seize that token. Once the token is seized and changed to an information frame, only stations with a priority value higher than that of the transmitting station can reserve the token for the next pass around the network.

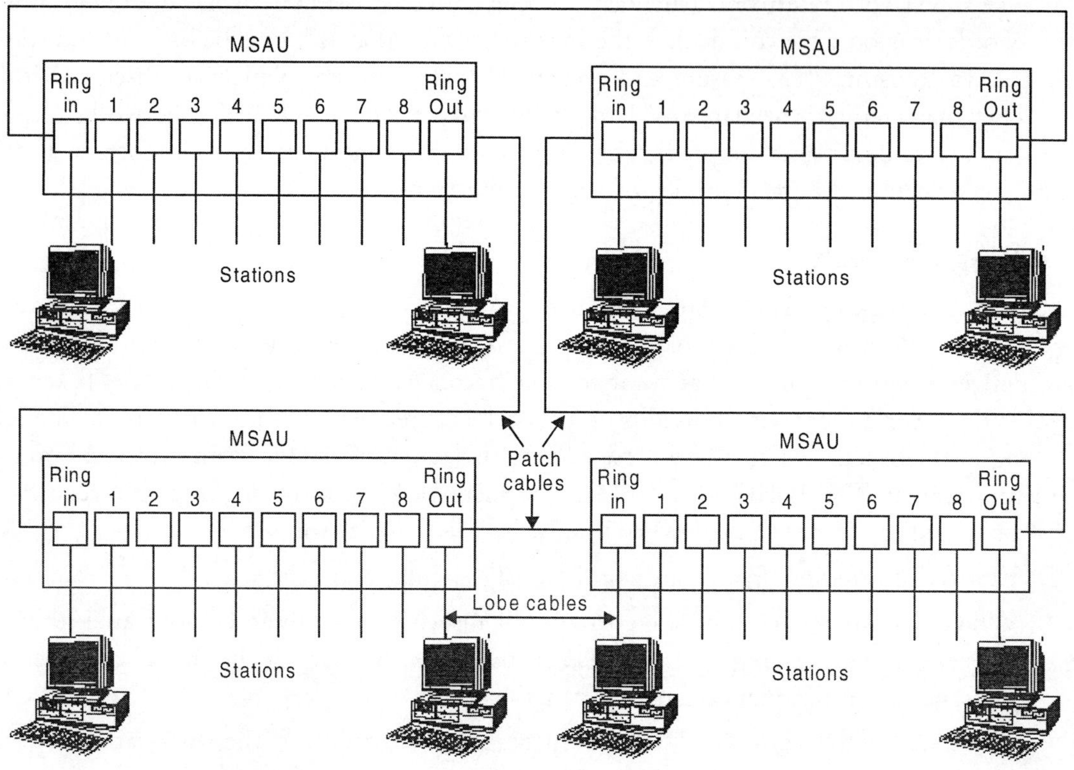

Figure 15.2 *IBM Token Ring Network Physical Connections.*

When the next token is generated, it includes the higher priority of the reserving station. Stations that raise a token's priority level must reinstate the previous priority after their transmission is complete.

Fault Management Mechanisms

Token ring networks employ several mechanisms for detecting and compensating for network faults. For example, one station in the Token ring network is selected to be the active monitor. This station, which can potentially be any station on the network, acts as a centralized source of timing information for other ring stations and performs a variety of ring maintenance functions. One of these functions is the removal of continuously circulating frames from the ring. When a sending device fails, its frame may continue to circle the ring. This can prevent other stations from transmitting their own frames and essentially lock up the network. The active monitor can detect such frames, remove them from the ring, and generate a new token.

The IBM Token ring network's star topology also contributes to overall network reliability. Since all information in a Token ring network is seen by active MSAUs, these devices can be programmed to check for problems and selectively remove stations from the ring if necessary.

A Token ring algorithm called beaconing detects and tries to repair certain network faults. Whenever a station detects a serious problem with the network (such as a cable break), it sends a beacon frame. The beacon frame defines a failure domain, which includes the station reporting the failure, its Nearest Active Upstream Neighbor (NAUN), and everything in between. Beaconing initiates a process called autoreconfiguration, where nodes within the failure domain automatically perform diagnostics in an attempt to reconfigure the network around the failed areas. Physically, the MSAU can accomplish this through electrical reconfiguration.

Frame Format

Token ring networks define two frame types: tokens and data/command frames. Both formats are shown in figure 15.3.

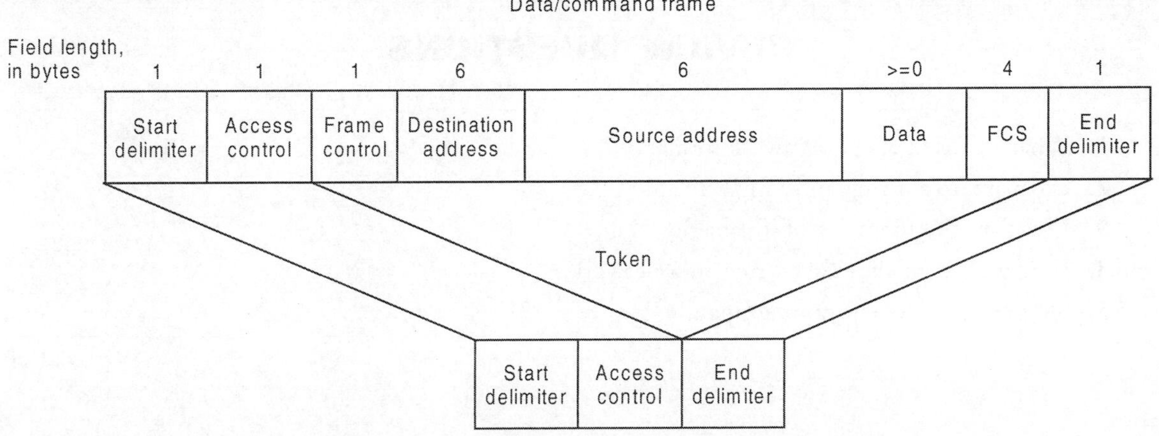

Figure 15.3 *IEEE 802.5/Token Ring Frame Formats.*

Tokens

Tokens are 3 bytes in length and consist of a start delimiter, an access control byte, and an end delimiter. The start delimiter serves to alert each station to the arrival of a token (or data/command frame). This field includes signals that distinguish the byte from the rest of the frame by violating the encoding scheme used elsewhere in the frame.

The access control byte contains the priority and reservation fields, as well as a token bit (used to differentiate a token from a data/command frame) and a monitor bit (used by the active monitor to determine whether a frame is circling the ring endlessly).

Finally, the end delimiter signals the end of the token or data/command frame. It also contains bits to indicate a damaged frame and a frame that is the last in a logical sequence.

Data/Command Frames

Data/command frames vary in size, depending on the size of the information field. Data frames carry information for upper-layer protocols; command frames contain control information and have no data for upper-layer protocols.

In data/command frames, a frame control byte follows the access control byte. The frame control byte indicates whether the frame contains data or control information. In control frames, this byte specifies the type of control information.

Following the frame control byte are the two address fields, which identify the destination and source stations. As with IEEE 802.3, addresses are 6 bytes in length. The data field follows the address fields. The length of this field is limited by the ring token holding time, which defines the maximum time a station may hold the token.

Following the data field is the Frame Check Sequence (FCS) field. This field is filled by the source station with a calculated value dependent on the frame contents. The destination station recalculates the value to determine whether the frame may have been damaged in transit. If so, the frame is discarded. As with the token, the end delimiter completes the data/command frame.

REVIEW QUESTIONS

1. What is Token ring ? Draw its format.
2. Compare Token ring and IEEE 802.5.
3. What are the functions of Token ring hub ?
4. How we are passing Token ring in a network ?
5. Give detail of token frame format.

❑❑❑

16

BLUETOOTH

A short-range radio technology aimed at simplifying communications among Internet devices and between devices and the Internet. It also aims to simplify data synchronization between Internet devices and other computers.

Products with Bluetooth technology must be qualified and pass interoperability testing by the Bluetooth special interest group prior to release. Bluetooth's founding members include Ericsson, IBM, Intel, Nokia and Toshiba.

Bluetooth is a telecommunications industry specification that describes how mobile phones, computers, and personal digital assistants (PDAs) can be easily interconnected using a short-range wireless connection. Using this technology, users of cellular phones, pagers, and personal digital assistants can buy a three-in-one phone that can double as a portable phone at home or in the office, get quickly synchronized with information in a desktop or notebook computer, initiate the sending or receiving of a fax, initiate a print-out, and in general, have all mobile and fixed computer devices be totally coordinated.

Bluetooth requires that a low-cost transceiver chip be included in each device. The transceiver transmits and receives in a previously unused frequency band of 2.45 GHz that is available globally (with some variation of bandwidth in different countries). In addition to data, up to three voice channels are available. Each device has a unique 48-bit address from the IEEE 802 standard. Connections can be point-to-point or multipoint. The maximum range is 10 meters. Data can be exchanged at a rate of 1 megabit per second (up to 2 Mbps in the second generation of the technology). A frequency hop scheme allows devices to communicate even in areas with a great deal of electromagnetic interference. Built-in encryption and verification is provided.

Bluetooth protocols, called *Profiles*, have in fact been ported to Ultrawide Band (UWB), and Bluetooth protocols could eventually be seen across IP-based networks running on all manner of both wired and wireless physical layers. As you can see, there's a lot more to Bluetooth than headsets. The Bluetooth has been held back in terms of broader use by the very limited nature of the radio, not by its real capabilities. Still, because of the large installed base of Bluetooth devices today, most notably all of those headsets, the current Bluetooth radio is likely to be around for some time.

WIRELESS TECHNOLOGY

Bluetooth wireless technology is a short-range radio technology. Bluetooth wireless technology makes it possible to transmit signals over short distances between telephones, computers and other devices and thereby simplify communication and synchronization between devices. It is a global standard that:

- eliminates wires and cables between both stationary and mobile devices
- facilitates both data and voice communication
- offers the possibility of ad hoc networks and delivers the ultimate synchronicity between all your personal devices

The Bluetooth wireless technology comprises hardware, software and interoperability requirements. Beyond unleashing devices by replacing cables, Bluetooth wireless technology provides a universal bridge to existing data networks, a peripheral interface, and a mechanism to form small private ad hoc groupings of connected devices away from fixed network infrastructures.

Bluetooth radio uses a fast acknowledgement and frequency-hopping scheme to make the link robust, even in noisy radio environments. To find those companies that have incorporated the Ericsson Bluetooth solution, please look under "related links".

Wirelessly, powerfully, efficiently, Bluetooth wireless technology works however you work. It works whenever you work, seamlessly connecting all of your mobile devices.

Bluetooth wireless technology revolutionizes the personal connectivity market by providing freedom from wired connections—enabling links between mobile computers, mobile phones, portable handheld devices, and connectivity to the Internet. Interface, synchronize, exchange ? All of the above, and more. Bluetooth technology redefines the very way we experience connectivity.

Working

Every where hardware that complies with the Bluetooth wireless specification ensures communication compatibility worldwide. As a low cost, low power solution with industry wide support, Bluetooth wireless technology allows you to bring connectivity with you. You define the boundaries of your productivity—in Europe, in Asia, in America, in whatever place your business may take you.

Establishing a standard means integrating well tested technology with the power efficiency and low-cost of a compliant radio system. Establishing a standard also means a group of industry leading promoter companies who drive the specification forward.

Bluetooth technology works because it has been developed as a cross industry solution that marries a vision of engineering innovation with an understanding of business and consumer expectations.

Bluetooth wireless technology is supported by product and application development in a wide range of market segments, including software developers, silicon vendors, peripheral and camera manufacturers, mobile PC manufacturers and handheld device developers, consumer electronics manufacturers, car manufacturers, and test and measurement equipment manufacturers.

Wireless data networks exist in such number and variety as to be difficult to categorize and compare.

Some wireless data networks run over wireless voice networks, such as mobile telephone networks. CPDP, HSCSD, PDC-P, and GPRS are examples. Other wireless networks run on their own physical layer networks, utilizing anything from antennas built into handheld devices to large antennas mounted on towers. 802.11, LMDS, and MMDS are examples. A few wireless networks are intended only to connect small devices over short distances. Bluetooth is an example.

Wireless networks which run over other wireless networks often utilize the lower layer networks to provide security and encryption. Stand-alone wireless networks either provide their own security and encryption features or rely upon VPN's (Virtual Private Networks) to provide those features. In many cases, multiple layers of security and encryption may be desirable.

Some wireless networks are fixed, meaning that antennas do not move frequently. Other wireless networks are mobile, meaning that the antenna can move constantly. This is sometimes a feature of the specific implementation and antenna design, instead of an inherent limitation of the wireless network specification.

Wireless networks may operate on licensed or unlicensed portions of the frequency spectrum.

Major types of wireless networks include:

Table 16.1 Major Wireless

CDPD	Cellular Digital Packet Data
HSCSD	High Speed Circuit Switched Data
PDC-P	Packet Data Cellular
GPRS	General Packet Radio Service
1XRTT	1x Radio Transmission Technology
Bluetooth	
IrDA	
LMDS	Local Multipoint Distribution Service
MMDS	Multichannel Multipoint Distribution Service
802.11	Wi-Fi

BLUETOOTH POWER CLASSES

Bluetooth provides three types of power classes, although class 3 devices are not in general availability (Table 16.3).

Bluetooth security is based upon device authentication, not user authentication. Each device is either trusted or un-trusted. Bluetooth devices are identified by unique 48-bit identifiers, much like Ethernet MAC addresses.

Table 16.2 Characteristics

Fixed/Mobile	Mobile
Circuit/Packet	Both
Max Bandwidth	1Mb
Range	10 meters
Frequency	2.40 GHz–2.483.5 GHz (U.S. and Europe) or 2.472 GHz–2.497 GHz (Japan)
Host Network	None
Definer	Bluetooth SIG

Bluetooth is a specification for short distance wireless communication between two devices.

Table 16.3 Power Classes of Bluetooth

Type	*Power Level*	*Operating Range*
Class 3 Devices	100 mW	Up to 100 meters
Class 2 Devices	10 mW	Up to 10 meters
Class 1 Devices	1 mW	0.1–10 meters

Making the Best of Bluetooth Security

Bluetooth specifications include basic link security measures. By default, most Bluetooth devices operate in unprotected "non-secure" mode. Two additional modes are defined: mode 3 secures the entire wireless link, while mode 2 leaves security up to each authorized application. For best results, use mode 3 to enforce link authentication and encryption for all Bluetooth traffic, and discourage or ban business use of devices that support only mode 1.

Further steps to make best use of these built-in Bluetooth measures include:

- Turn off Bluetooth interfaces when not in use, and disable Bluetooth's discovery feature, whereby each device announces itself to all nearby devices. These common-sense practices reduce the window of opportunity for Bluetooth attacks.
- Configure Bluetooth devices to use the lowest power that meets business needs. Class 3 devices transmit at 1 mW and cannot communicate beyond 10 meters, while class 1 devices transmit at 100 mW to reach up to 100 meters. Adjusting power does not eliminate outsider attack, but it can reduce that possibility.
- Because link keys are stored on paired Bluetooth devices, password protect both devices to prevent use of lost/stolen units. If possible, do not permanently store the pairing PIN code on Bluetooth devices.

To defend against such attacks, combine the good configuration choices and practices described above with Bluetooth product assessment, patching and security auditing.

Bluetooth Radio and Baseband

The Bluetooth radio is the hardware transceiver unit that implements the Bluetooth radio specification. The purpose of the specification is to provide compatibility between Bluetooth devices that operate in the 2.4 GHz ISM band, and to define the quality of the system. Further information on the Bluetooth radio specifications may be found in the Bluetooth core specification document.

The Bluetooth baseband consists mainly of a Link Controller (LC) that carries out baseband protocols and low-layer link routines. Protocols defined within the scope of the baseband specification include (among others) physical channels and links, data packet definitions, error correction and detection, logical channels, channel control, and hop selection. For more information about the Bluetooth baseband specification, see the Bluetooth core specification document.

BLUETOOTH SECURITY MODES

Bluetooth features three security modes.

Table 16.4 Security Modes of Bluetooth

Mode	*Name*	*Description*
1	Non-secure	No security is implemented
2	Service-level security	Access is granted to individual services
3	Link-level security	Security is enforced at a common level for all applications at the beginning of the connection

BLUETOOTH SECURITY LEVELS

Bluetooth features three possible security levels.

Table 16.5 Security Levels of Bluetooth

Mode	*Description*
3	No authentication or authorization is required
2	Authentication is required; authorization is not required
1	Authorization and authentication are required

BLUETOOTH SECURITY WEAKNESSES

Bluetooth weakness include:

The Bluetooth challenge-response key generation is weak. This scheme may use a static number or a number for a period of time, which can reduce the effectiveness of the authentication.

Bluetooth's challenge response is simplistic. A one way challenge for authentication is susceptible to man-in-the-middle attacks. Mutual authentication via user verification should be used.

The keys used by Bluetooth are weak. The initialization key needs to be more robust and the unit key is a public-generated key that can be reused. A set of keys should be used instead. The master key is shared between Bluetooth connections. This key is a broadcast and should have a better scheme than what is used.

The encryption algorithm scheme utilized in Bluetooth uses a single algorithm and allows repeat authentication. A more robust method that limits authentication and increases the encryption should be used.

Bluetooth implementations normally limit the PIN number range. A PIN number is usually only four digits and the scalability for large environments is difficult.

REVIEW QUESTIONS

1. Name two applications for a Bluetooth network.
2. Match the layers in Bluetooth and the internet model.
3. What are the two types of links between a Bluetooth master and a Bluetooth slave ?
4. What are Bluetooth security modes ?
5. What are Bluetooth security levels ?
6. What are Bluetooth security weaknesses ?

❑❑❑

17

Virtual LAN (VLAN)

Today's cost-effective, high-performance LAN switches offer users superior segmentation, low-latency packet forwarding, and increased bandwidth across the corporate backbone. LAN switches also can segment networks into logically defined virtual workgroups. This logical segmentation, commonly referred to as Virtual LAN (VLAN) communication, offers a fundamental change in how LANs are designed, administered, and managed. While logical segmentation provides substantial benefits in LAN administration, security, and management of network broadcast activity across the enterprise, there are many components of VLAN solutions that must be considered prior to large-scale VLAN deployment.

These additional VLAN components include:

- High-performance switches that logically segment connected end stations.
- Transport protocols that carry VLAN traffic across shared LAN, and ATM backbones.
- Layer 3 routing solutions that extend VLAN communications between workgroups.
- System compatibility and interoperability with previously installed LAN systems.
- Network management solutions that offer centralized control, configuration, and traffic management functions.

VLAN Benefits

Solves problems associated with moves, adds, and changes. They reduce a large part of the administration costs when users change locations within a building or campus.

- Tighter network security with establishment of secure user groups.
- Better management and control of broadcast activity.
- Micro-segmentation of the network without sacrificing scalability, load distribution of traffic across traffic-intensive switches ("hot spots" within the network), and the relocation of workgroup servers into secured, centralized locations, security, and management of network broadcast activity across the enterprise, there are many components of VLAN solutions that must be considered prior to large-scale VLAN deployment.

These additional VLAN components include:

- High-performance switches that logically segment connected end stations.
- Transport protocols that carry VLAN traffic across shared LAN, and ATM backbones.
- Layer 3 routing solutions that extend VLAN communications between workgroups.
- System compatibility and interoperability with previously installed LAN systems.
- Network management solutions that offer centralized control, configuration, and traffic management functions.

Virtual Circuits

All communications across a data network are carries out over previously established virtual circuits. These can be set up either on demand by user or permanently by network management. With on-demand connections, the user device sends a request for a Switched Virtual Connection (SVC) to be set up to a central control unit known as the Signaling Control Point (SCP).

The SCP then determines the availability of both the required destination and the transmission bandwidth appropriate to call across the network. With Permanent Virtual Circuits (PVC), the route is already determined when demand is made. The PVC is a logical predefined path or link through a carrier network.

Value Added Network

A Value Added Network (VAN) is a private network provider (sometimes called a turnkey communication line) that is hired by a company to facilitate electronic data interchange. The VAN services are such as legal research or access to a specialized database, for a fee.

TELEPHONE TRAFFIC DEFINITIONS

The estimating of the switching quantities for an automatic telephone exchange is based primarily on the amount of traffic which it will be required to handle. Calculations of the probable average, and maximum amount of traffic are necessary to determine the optimum number of switches required in the various switching ranks.

The more important quantities used in traffic calculations are:

Traffic Unit (T.U.): The traffic unit is used to measure the traffic flow. The number of traffic units carried by a group of switches is numerically equal to the product of the number of calls per hour and the average duration of the calls in hours. The traffic flow in traffic units is equal to the average number of simultaneous calls.

Busy Hour: This is defined as the hour of the day in each exchange when the originating traffic carried is the greatest.

Busy Hour Calling Rate: This is the average number of calls initiated per subscriber during the busy hour.

Grade of Service: The flow of traffic initiated by subscribers varies widely throughout the day, and from one day to the next. If during any traffic peak the number of outlets from a switching stage are all occupied, additional calls at that instant cannot be extended and completed and will thus be lost. The proportion of calls that are lost to the total number of calls in the busy hour determines the quantity known as the grade of service for that particular switching stage.

Availability: The number of trunks to which a switch has access is known as the availability. If a subscriber's uni-selector has, say 25 outlets, each of which is coupled to the first selector, then the availability of the uni-selector is 25.

Full-Availability Models

A full-availability system is one in which there are *S* sources of traffic and *N* outlets and any free source can seize any free outlet, regardless of the state of the system. The simplest example is a matrix with S × N cross-points as shown in figure 17.1.

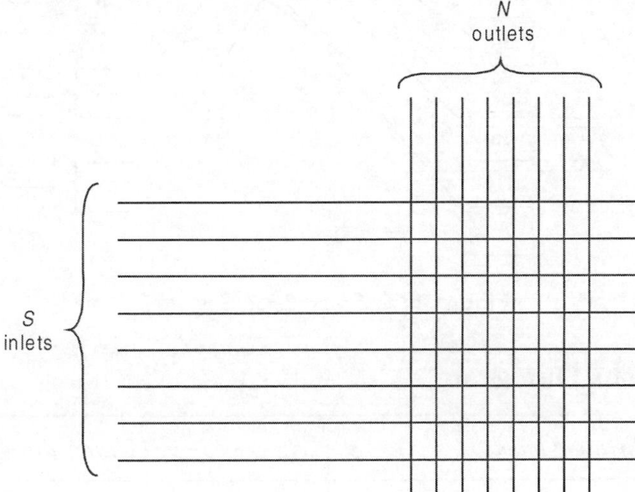

Figure 17.1 *SXN Matrix.*

Probability of Blocking

In order to find out if the system will perform as it should, some measure of performance is required. The most often used measure is the probability of blocking, which is the proportion of calls, in the long term that are rejected. If we consider the general case of a two stage link system in which the corresponding outlets on the second-stage switches form a route as indicated in figure 17.2.

1. There are two ways in which a call may be blocked.
2. There may be on free route circuit.
3. There may be no path available between the inlet carrying the incoming call and the free route circuits.

The diagram shows both of these conditions; route 3 has no free circuits available, whereas if inlet A on first-stage switch 1 is wanting to be connected to route 2, on which there are free route circuits, it cannot be, because there is no available link.

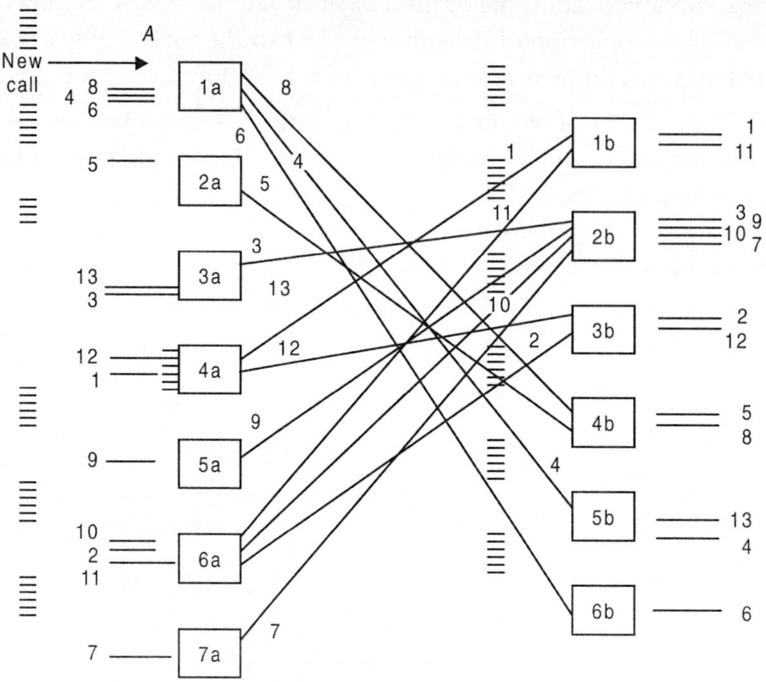

Figure 17.2 *Stage Link System.*

Virtual Circuit Versus Datagram

Virtual Circuit Model	*Datagram Model*
• Typically wait full RTT for connection setup before sending first data packet.	• There is no round trip time delay waiting for connection setup; a host can send data as soon as it is ready.
• While the connection request contains the full address for destination, each data packet contains only a small identifier, making the per-packet header overhead small.	• Source host has no way of knowing if the network is capable of delivering a packet or if the destination host is even up.
• If a switch or a link in a connection fails, the connection is broken and a new one needs to be established.	• Since packets are treated independently, it is possible to route around link and node failures.
• Connection setup provides an opportunity to reserve resources.	• Since every packet must carry the full address of the destination, the overhead per packet is higher than for the connection-oriented model.

SWITCHING TECHNOLOGY

In the next three subsections, we present the three switching techniques used in networks: circuit switching, datagram packet switching and virtual circuit packet switching.

Circuit Switching

The two different bit-streams flow on two separate circuits.

Circuit switching is the transmission technology that has been used since the first communication networks in the nineteenth century. In circuit switching, a caller must first establish a connection to a callee before any communication is possible. During the connection establishment, resources are allocated between the caller and the callee. Generally, resources are frequency intervals in a Frequency Division Multiplexing (FDM) scheme or more recently time slots in a Time Division Multiplexing (TDM) scheme. The set of resources allocated for a connection is called a circuit, as depicted in figure 17.3. A path is a sequence of links located between nodes called *switches*. The path taken by data between its source and destination is determined by the circuit on which it is flowing, and does not change during the lifetime of the connection. The circuit is *terminated* when the connection is closed.

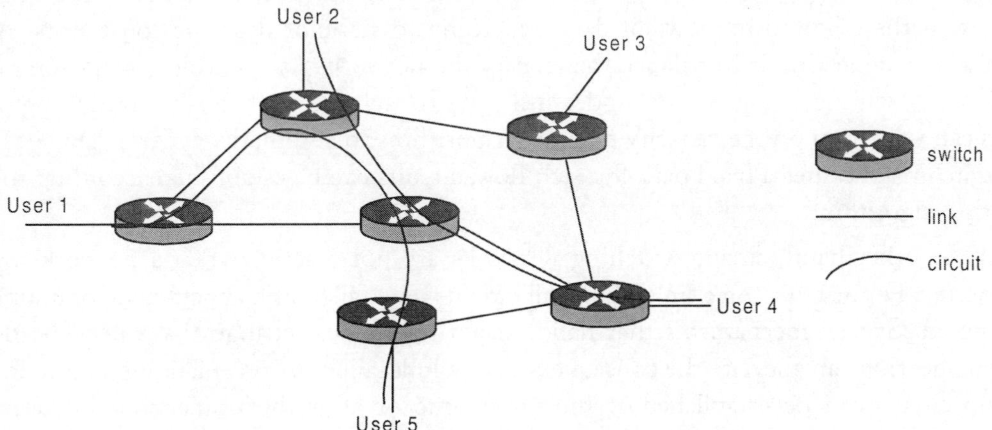

Figure 17.3 *Circuit Switching.*

In circuit switching, resources remain allocated during the full length of a communication, after a circuit is established and until the circuit is terminated and the allocated resources are freed. Resources remain allocated even if no data is flowing on a circuit, hereby wasting link capacity when a circuit does not carry as much traffic as the allocation permits. This is a major issue since frequencies (in FDM) or time slots (in TDM) are available in finite quantity on each link, and establishing a circuit consumes one of these frequencies or slots on each link of the circuit. As a result, establishing circuits for communications that carry less traffic than allocation permits can lead to resource exhaustion and network saturation, preventing further connections from being established. If no circuit can be established between a sender and a receiver because of a lack of resources, the connection is *blocked.*

A second characteristic of circuit switching is the time cost involved when establishing a connection. In a communication network, circuit-switched or not, nodes need to lookup in a *forwarding table* to determine on which link to send incoming data, and to actually send data from the input link to the output link. Performing a lookup in a forwarding table and sending the data on an incoming link is called *forwarding*. Building the forwarding tables is called *routing*. In circuit switching, routing must be performed for each communication, at circuit establishment time. During circuit establishment, the set of switches and links on the path between the sender and the receiver is determined and messages are exchanged on all the links between the two end hosts of the communication in order to make the resource allocation and build the routing tables. In circuit switching, forwarding tables are hardwired or implemented using fast hardware, making data forwarding at each switch almost instantaneous. Therefore, circuit switching is well suited for long-lasting connections where the initial circuit establishment time cost is balanced by the low forwarding time cost.

The circuit identifier (a range of frequencies in FDM or a time slot position in a TDM frame) is changed by each switch at forwarding time so that switches do not need to have a complete knowledge of all circuits established in the network but rather only local knowledge of available identifiers at a link. Using local identifiers instead of global identifiers for circuits also enables networks to handle a larger number of circuits.

Traffic engineering (TE) consists in optimizing resource utilization in a network by choosing appropriate paths followed by flows of data, according to static or dynamic constraints. A main goal of traffic engineering is to balance the load in the network, *i.e.,* to avoid congestion on links on a network while other links are under-utilized. To achieve such goals, traffic engineering methods can vary from offline capacity planning algorithms to automatic, dynamic changes. Since circuit switching allocates a fixed path for each flow, circuits can be established according to traffic engineering algorithms.

On the other hand, circuit switching networks are not reactive when a network topology change occurs. For instance, on a link failure, all circuits on a failed link are cut and communication is interrupted. Special mechanisms that handle such topological changes have been be devised. Traffic engineering can alleviate the consequences of a link failure by pre-planning failure recovery. A backup circuit can be established at the same time or after the primary circuit used for a communication is set up, and traffic can be rerouted from the failed circuit to the backup circuit if a link of the primary circuit fails. Circuit switching networks are intrinsically sensitive to link failures and rerouting must be performed by additional traffic engineering mechanisms.

Datagram Packet Switching

Conceived in the 1960's, *packet switching* is a more recent technology than circuit switching which addresses a disadvantage of circuit switching: the need to allocate resources for a circuit, thus incurring link capacity wastes when no data flows on a circuit. Packet switching introduces the idea of cutting data on a flow into packets which are transmitted over a network without any resource being allocated. If no data is available at the sender at some point during a communication, then no packet is transmitted over the network and no resources are wasted. Packet switching is the generic name for a set of two different techniques: datagram packet switching and virtual circuit packet switching. Here, we give an overview of datagram packet switching.

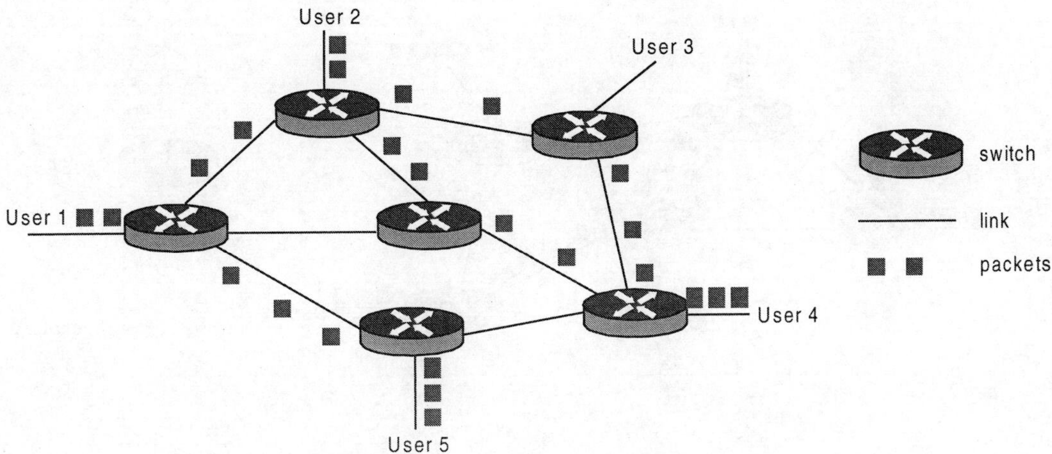

Figure 17.4 *Datagram Packet Switching.*

Packets from a given flow are independent and a router can forward two packets from the same flow on two different links.

Different from circuit switching, datagram packet switching does not require to establish circuits prior to transmission of data and terminate circuits after the transmission of data. The switches, called routers, have to make a lookup in the forwarding table, called *routing table*, for each incoming packet. A routing table contains a mapping between the possible final destinations of packets and the outgoing link on their path to the destination. Routing tables can be very large because they are indexed by possible destinations, making lookups and routing decisions computationally expensive, and the full forwarding process relatively slow compared to circuit switching. In datagram packet switching networks, each packet must carry the address of the destination host and use the destination address to make a forwarding decision. Consequently, routers do not need to modify the destination addresses of packets when forwarding packets.

Since each packet is processed individually by a router, all packets sent by a host to another host are not guaranteed to use the same physical links. If the routing algorithm decides to change the routing tables of the network between the instants two packets are sent, then these packets will take different paths and can even arrive out of order. For instance, packets use two different paths to go from one user to another user. Second, on a network topology change such as a link failure, the routing protocol will automatically re-compute routing tables so as to take the new topology into account and avoid the failed link. As opposed to circuit switching, no additional traffic engineering algorithm is required to reroute traffic.

Since routers make routing decisions locally for each packet, independently of the flow to which a packet belongs. Therefore, traffic engineering techniques, which heavily rely on controlling the route of traffic, are more difficult to implement with datagram packet switching than with circuit switching.

Virtual Circuit Packet Switching

Virtual circuit packet switching (VC-switching) is a packet switching technique which merges datagram packet switching and circuit switching to extract both of their advantages. VC-switching

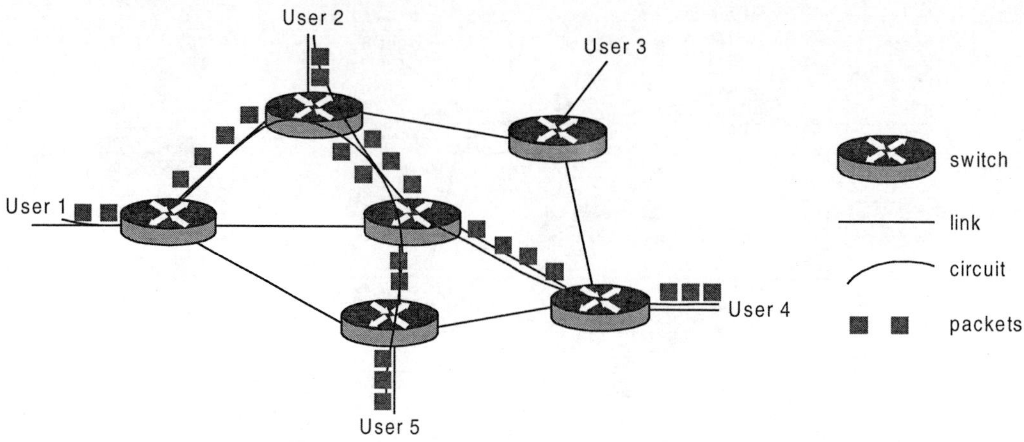

Figure 17.5 *Virtual Circuit Packet Switching.*

is a variation of datagram packet switching where packets flow on so-called logical circuits for which no physical resources like frequencies or time slots are allocated (see figure 17.5). Each packet carries a circuit identifier which is local to a link and updated by each switch on the path of the packet from its source to its destination. A virtual circuit is defined by the sequence of the mappings between a link taken by packets and the circuit identifier packets carry on this link. This sequence is set up at connection establishment time and identifiers are reclaimed during the circuit termination.

There is a trade-off between connection establishment and forwarding time costs that exists in circuit switching and datagram packet switching. In VC-switching, routing is performed at circuit establishment time to keep packet forwarding fast. Other advantages of VC-switching include the traffic engineering capability of circuit switching, and the resources usage efficiency of datagram packet switching. Nevertheless, a main issue of VC-Switched networks is the behavior on a topology change. As opposed to datagram packet switched networks which automatically re-compute routing tables on a topology change like a link failure, in VC-switching all virtual circuits that pass through a failed link are interrupted. Hence, rerouting in VC-switching relies on traffic engineering techniques.

REVIEW QUESTIONS

1. What is VPN ?
2. What is a VPN used for ?
3. Do I have to use a VPN ?
4. What alternative do I have to VPN ?
5. Where can I get a VPN ?

❑❑❑

18 Wireless Transmission

Wireless Operations: Permits services, such as long range communications, that are impossible or impractical to implement with the use of wires. The term is commonly used in the telecommunications industry to refer to telecommunications systems (*e.g.*, radio transmitters and receivers, remote controls, computer networks, network terminals, etc.) which use some form of energy (*e.g.*, Radio Frequency (RF), infrared light, laser light, visible light, acoustic energy, etc.) to transfer information without the use of wires. Information is transferred in this manner over both short and long distances.

WIRELESS COMMUNICATION

The term "wireless" has become a generic and all-encompassing word used to describe communications in which electromagnetic waves or RF (rather than some form of wire) carry a signal over part or the entire communication path. Common examples of wireless equipment in use today include:

- Professional LMR (Land Mobile Radio) and SMR (Specialized Mobile Radio) typically used by business, industrial and public safety entities.
- Consumer two way radio including FRS (Family Radio Service), GMRS (General Mobile Radio Service) and Citizens Band (CB) radios.
- The amateur radio service (Ham Radio).
- Consumer and professional Marine VHF radios.
- Cellular telephones and pagers: Provide connectivity for portable and mobile applications, both personal and business.
- Global Positioning System (GPS): Allows drivers of cars and trucks, captains of boats and ships, and pilots of aircraft to ascertain their location anywhere on earth.
- Cordless computer peripherals: The cordless mouse is a common example; keyboards and printers can also be linked to a computer via wireless.
- Cordless telephone sets: These are limited-range devices, not to be confused with cell phones.

- Satellite television: Allows viewers in almost any location to select from hundreds of channels.
- Wireless gaming: New gaming consoles allow players to interact and play in the same game regardless of whether they are playing on different consoles. Players can chat, send text messages as well as record sound and send it to their friends. Controllers also use wireless technology. They do not have any cords but they can send the information from what is being pressed on the controller to the main console which then processes this information and makes it happen in the game. All of these steps are completed in milliseconds.

Wireless networking (*i.e.*, the various types of unlicensed 2.4 GHz WiFi devices) is used to meet many needs. Perhaps the most common use is to connect laptop users who travel from location to location. Another common use is for mobile networks that connect via satellite. A wireless transmission method is a logical choice to network a LAN segment.

The above discussed technologies require physical connections in order to transmit signals. Wireless transmission means sending and receiving signals without wires. Examples include radio, microwave, and satellite. Today we use all of these forms to transmit data. For example, we (UTPA) have a mobile network truck (net-mobile) that can travel to remote site and hook up with Internet using satellite network.

TRANSMISSION MEDIA—UNGUIDED

Unguided transmission media is data signals that flow through the air. They are not guided or bound to a channel to follow. They are classified by the type of wave propagation.

RF Propagation

There are three types of RF (Radio Frequency) propagation:

1. Ground wave
2. Ionospheric
3. Line of Sight (LOS)

Ground wave propagation follows the curvature of the Earth. Ground waves have carrier frequencies up to 2 MHz. AM radio is an example of ground wave propagation.

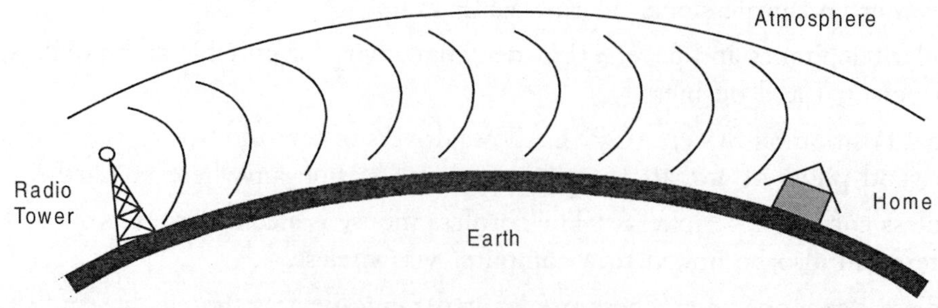

Figure 18.1 *Line of Sight.*

Ionospheric propagation bounces off of the earth's ionospheric layer in the upper atmosphere. It is sometimes called double hop propagation. It operates in the frequency range of 30–85 MHz. Because it depends on the earth's ionosphere, it changes with the weather and time of day. The signal bounces off of the ionosphere and back to earth. Ham radios operate in this range.

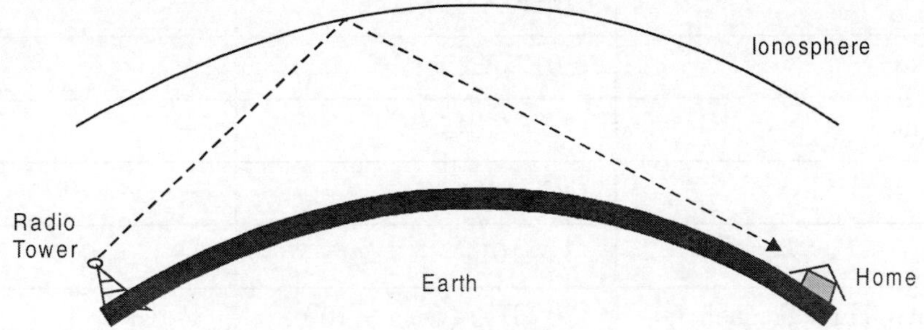

Figure 18.2 *Line of Sight Propogation.*

Line of sight propagation transmits exactly in the line of sight. The receive station must be in the view of the transmit station. It is sometimes called space waves or tropospheric propagation. It is limited by the curvature of the earth for ground-based stations (100 km, from horizon to horizon). Reflected waves can cause problems. Examples of line of sight propagation are: FM radio, microwave and satellite.

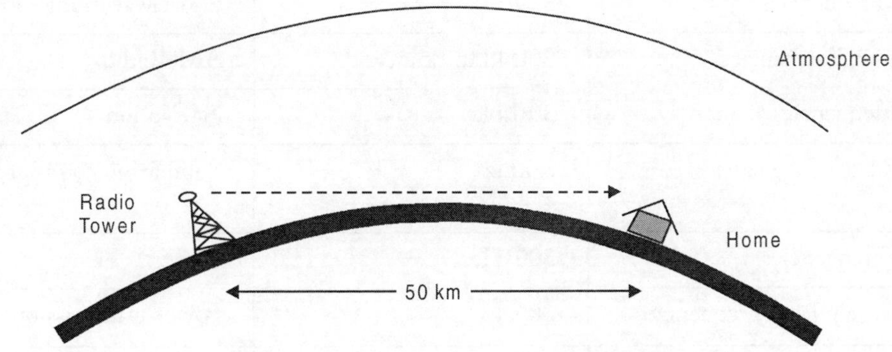

Figure 18.3 *Tropospheric Propagation.*

Radio Frequencies (Table 18.1)

Radio frequencies are in the range of 300 kHz to 10 GHz. We are seeing an emerging technology called wireless LANs. Some use radio frequencies to connect the workstations together, some use infrared technology.

Microwave

Microwave transmission is line of sight transmission. The transmit station must be in visible contact with the receive station. This sets a limit on the distance between stations depending on the local geography. Typically the line of sight due to the earth's curvature is only 50 km to the horizon! Repeater stations must be placed so the data signal can hop, skip and jump across the country.

Table 18.1 The Frequency Spectrum Operates from 0 Hz (DC) to Gamma Rays (1019 Hz)

Name	*Frequency (Hertz)*	*Examples*
Gamma rays	1019+	—
X-Rays	1017	—
Ultra-violet light	7.5 × 1015	—
Visible light	4.3 × 1014	—
Infrared light	3 × 1011	—
EHF—Extremely High Frequencies	30 GHz (Giga = 10^9)	Radar
SHF—Super High Frequencies	3 GHz	Satellite and microwaves
UHF—Ultra High Frequencies	300 MHz (Mega = 10^6)	UHF TV (Ch. 14–83)
VHF—Very High Frequencies	30 MHz	FM & TV (Ch2–13)
HF—High Frequencies	3 MHz	Short wave radio
MF—Medium Frequencies	300 kHz (kilo = 10^3)	AM Radio
LF—Low Frequencies	30 kHz	Navigation
VLF—Very Low Frequencies	3 kHz	Submarine communications
VF—Voice Frequencies	300 Hz	Audio
ELF—Extremely Low Frequencies	30 Hz	Power transmission

Microwaves Sources

Vacuum tube devices operate on the ballistic motion of electrons in a vacuum under the influence of controlling electric or magnetic fields, and include the magnetron, klystron, Traveling-Wave Tube (TWT), and gyrotron. These devices work in the density modulated mode, rather than the current modulated mode. This means that they work on the basis of clumps of electrons flying ballistically through them, rather than using a continuous stream.

USES

Communication

Before the advent of fiber-optic transmission, most long distance telephone calls were carried via microwave point-to-point links through sites like the AT&T long lines. Starting in the early 1950s, frequency division multiplex was used to send up to 5,400 telephone channels on each microwave radio channel, with as many as ten radio channels combined into one antenna for the *hop* to the next site, up to 70 km away.

Remote Sensing

Radar uses microwave radiation to detect the range, speed, and other characteristics of remote objects. Development of radar was accelerated during World War II due to its great military utility. Now radar is widely used for applications such as air traffic control, weather forecasting, navigation of ships, and speed limit enforcement.

A Gunn diode oscillator and waveguide are used as a motion detector for automatic door openers (although these are being replaced by ultrasonic devices).

Navigation

Global Navigation Satellite Systems (GNSS) including the Chinese Beidou, the American Global Positioning System (GPS) and the Russian GLONASS broadcast navigational signals in various bands between about 1.2 GHz and 1.6 GHz.

Power

A microwave oven passes (non-ionizing) microwave radiation (at a frequency near 2.45 GHz) through food, causing dielectric heating by absorption of energy in the water, fats and sugar contained in the food. Microwave ovens became common kitchen appliances in western countries in the late 1970s, following development of inexpensive cavity magnetrons. Water in the liquid state possesses many molecular intentions which broaden the absorption peak. In the vapour phase, isolated water molecules absorb at round 22 GHz, almost ten times the frequency of the microwave oven.

Microwave heating is used in industrial processes for drying and curing products. Many semiconductor processing techniques use microwaves to generate plasma for such purposes as reactive ion etching and Plasma-Enhanced Chemical Vapour Deposition (PECVD).

Spectroscopy

Microwave radiation is used in Electron Paramagnetic Resonance (EPR or ESR) spectroscopy, typically in the X-band region (~9 GHz) in conjunction typically with magnetic fields of 0.3 T. This technique provides information on unpaired electrons in chemical systems, such as free radicals or transition metal ions such as Cu(II).

Microwave Frequency Bands

The microwave spectrum is usually defined as electromagnetic energy ranging from approximately 1 GHz to 100 GHz in frequency, but older usage includes lower frequencies. Most common applications are within the 1 to 40 GHz range. Microwave frequency bands, as defined by the Radio Society of Great Britain (RSGB), are shown in the Table 18.2 below:

Table 18.2. Microwave Frequency Bands

Letter Designation	*Frequency Range*
L band	1 to 2 GHz
S band	2 to 4 GHz
C band	4 to 8 GHz
X band	8 to 12 GHz
K_u band	12 to 18 GHz
K band	18 to 26.5 GHz
K_a band	26.5 to 40 GHz
Q band	30 to 50 GHz
U band	40 to 60 GHz
V band	50 to 75 GHz
E band	60 to 90 GHz
W band	75 to 110 GHz
F band	90 to 140 GHz
D band	110 to 170 GHz

Microwave Frequency Measurement

Microwave frequency can be measured by either electronic or mechanical techniques. Frequency counters or high frequency heterodyne systems can be used. Here the unknown frequency is compared with harmonics of a known lower frequency by use of a low frequency generator, a harmonic generator and a mixer. Accuracy of the measurement is limited by the accuracy and stability of the reference source. Mechanical methods require a tunable resonator such as an absorption wavemeter, which has a known relation between a physical dimension and frequency.

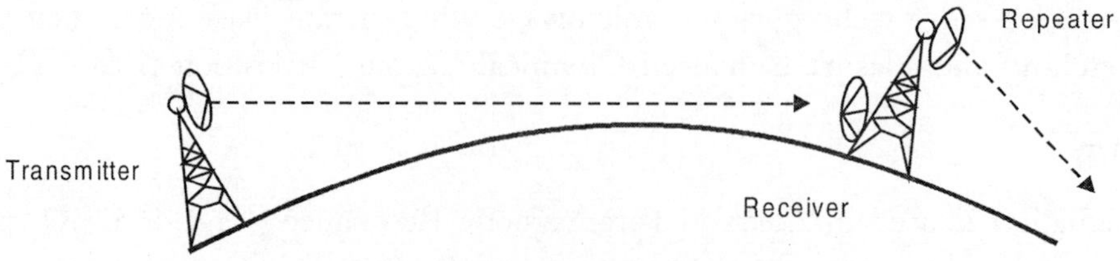

Figure 18.4 *Microwave.*

Advantages

There are some advantages as:

- They require no right of way acquisition between towers.
- They can carry high quantities of information due to their high operating frequencies.
- Low cost land purchase: each tower occupies only a small area.
- High frequency/short wavelength signals require small antenna.

Disadvantages

There are some disadvantages as:

- Attenuation by solid objects: birds, rain, snow and fog.
- Reflected from flat surfaces like water and metal.
- Diffracted (split) around solid objects.
- Refracted by atmosphere, thus causing beam to be projected away from receiver.

SATELLITE

Communications Satellite

Earth-orbiting system capable of receiving a signal (*e.g.*, data, voice, TV) and relaying it back to the ground. Communications satellites have been a significant part of domestic and global communications since the 1970s. Typically they move in geosynchronous orbits about 22,300 mi (35,900 km) above the earth and operate at frequencies near 4 gigahertz (GHz) for downlinking and 6 GHz for uplinking.

In the context of spaceflight, a **satellite** is an object which has been placed into orbit by human endeavour. Such objects are sometimes called **artificial satellites** to distinguish them from natural satellites such as the Moon.

The first artificial satellite, Sputnik 1, was launched by the Soviet Union in 1957. By 2010 thousands of satellites had been launched into orbit around the Earth. These originate from more than 50 countries and have used the satellite launching capabilities of ten nations. A few hundred satellites are currently operational, whereas thousands of unused satellites and satellite fragments orbit the Earth as space debris. A few space probes have been placed into orbit around other bodies and become artificial satellites to the Moon, Venus, Mars, Jupiter and Saturn.

Satellites are used for a large number of purposes. Common types include military (spy) and civilian Earth observation satellites, communication satellites, navigation satellites, weather satellites, and research satellites. Space stations and human spacecraft in orbit are also satellites. Satellite orbits vary greatly, depending on the purpose of the satellite, and are classified in a number of ways. Well-known (overlapping) classes include low Earth orbit, polar orbit, and geostationary orbit.

Satellites are usually semi-independent computer controlled systems. Satellite subsystems attend many tasks, such as power generation, thermal control, telemetry, attitude control and orbit control.

Satellites are transponders (units that receive on one frequency and retransmit on another) that are set in geostationary orbits directly over the equator. These geostationary orbits are 36,000 km from the earth's surface. At this point, the gravitational pull of the earth and the centrifugal force of earth's rotation are balanced and cancel each other out. Centrifugal force is the rotational force placed on the satellite that wants to fling it out into space.

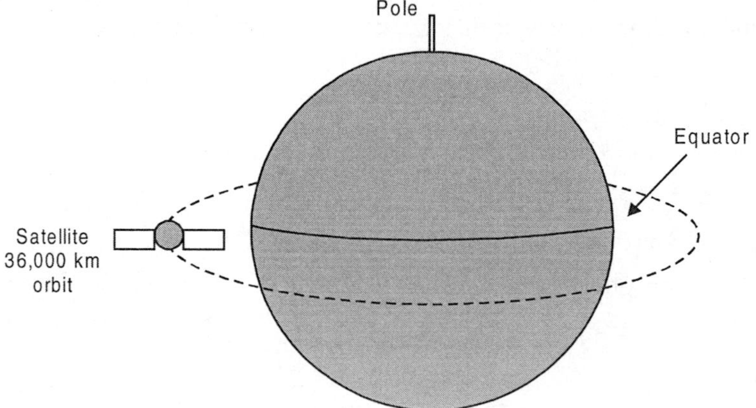

Figure 18.5 *Satellite 1.*

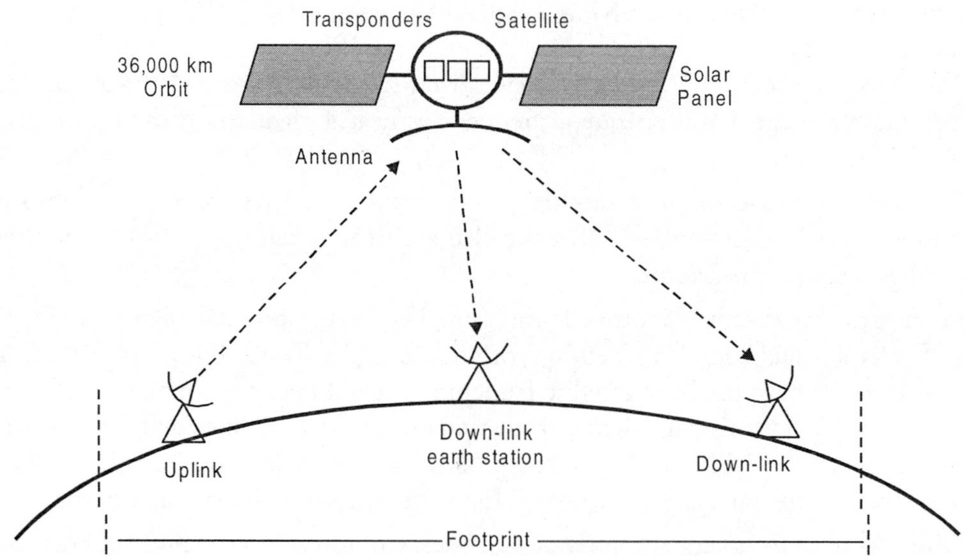

Figure 18.6 *Satellite 2.*

The uplink is the transmitter of data to the satellite. The downlink is the receiver of data. Uplinks and downlinks are also called earth stations because they are located on the Earth. The footprint is the "shadow" that the satellite can transmit to, the shadow being the area that can receive the satellite's transmitted signal.

The problem of live-of-sight and repeaters are overcome by using satellites which are the most widely used data transmission media in modern days. A communication satellite is a microwave relay station placed in outer space. INSAT-1B is such a satellite that can be accessible from anywhere in India. In satellite communication, microwave signal is transmitted from a transmitter on earth to the satellite at space. The satellite amplifies the weak signal and transmits it back to the receiver. The main advantage of satellite communication is that it is a single microwave relay station visible from any point of a very large area. In microwave the data transmission rate is 16 gigabits per second. They are mostly used to link big metropolitan cities.

Space Surveillance Network

The United States Space Surveillance Network (SSN) has been tracking space objects since 1957, when the Soviets opened the space age with the launch of Sputnik I. Since then, the SSN has tracked more than 26,000 space objects orbiting Earth. The SSN currently tracks more than 8,000 man-made orbiting objects. The rest have re-entered Earth's atmosphere and disintegrated, or survived re-entry and impacted the earth. The space objects now orbiting earth range from satellites weighing several tons to pieces of spent rocket bodies weighing only 10 pounds. About seven percent of the space objects are operational satellites (*i.e.*, ~560 satellites), the rest are space debris.

USSTRATCOM is primarily interested in the active satellites, but also tracks space debris which upon re-entry might otherwise be mistaken for incoming missiles. The SSN tracks space objects that are 10 centimeters in diameter (baseball size) or larger.

Non-Military Satellite Services

There are three basic categories of non-military satellite services:

Fixed Satellite Service

Fixed satellite services handle hundreds of billions of voice, data, and video transmission tasks across all countries and continents between certain points on the Earth's surface.

Mobile Satellite Systems

Mobile satellite systems help connect remote regions, vehicles, ships, people and aircraft to other parts of the world and/or other mobile or stationary communications units, in addition to serving as navigation systems.

Scientific Research Satellite (commercial and noncommercial)

Scientific research satellites provide us with meteorological information, land survey data (*e.g.*, remote sensing), Amateur (HAM) radio, and other different scientific research applications such as earth science, marine science, and atmospheric research.

IRIDIUM TELECOM SYSTEM

The Iridium telecom system is a new satellite system that will be the largest private aerospace project. It is a mobile telecom system intended to compete with cellular phones. It relies on satellites in Lower Earth Orbit (LEO). The satellites will orbit at an altitude of 900–10,000 km in a polar, non-stationary orbit. Sixty-six satellites are planned. The user's handset will require less power and will be cheaper than cellular phones. There will be 100% coverage of the Earth.

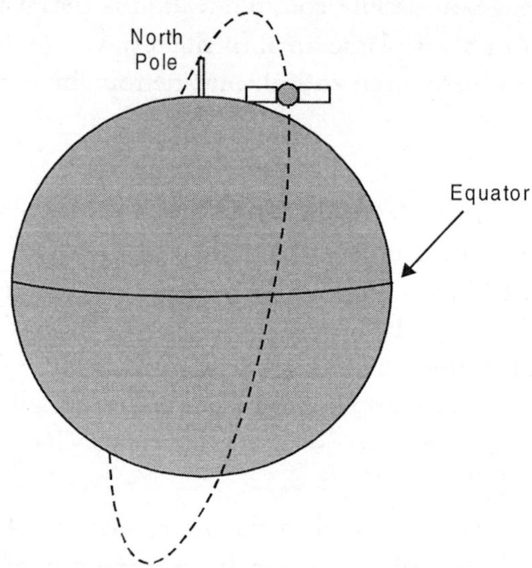

Figure 18.7 *Iridium Telecom System.*

Unfortunately, although the Iridium project was planned for 1996–1998, with 1.5 million subscribers by end of the decade, at the time of this writing, it looked very financially unstable.

The Iridium system is a satellite-based, wireless personal communications network designed to permit any type of telephone transmission—voice, paging, facsimile or data—to reach its destination anywhere on Earth.

It revolutionized communications for business professionals, travelers, residents of rural or undeveloped areas, disaster relief teams, and others who need the features and convenience of a wireless hand-held telephone with a single worldwide number.

Unlike conventional telecommunications networks, the satellite-based system tracks the location of the telephone, providing global transmission even if the subscriber's location is unknown. In areas where compatible cellular service is available, the dual-mode telephone provides the option of transmitting a call via the local cellular system.

Iridium telephones provides high-quality voice connections and interface with laptop computers, personal digital assistants, palmtop organizers, and other communications equipment.

The relatively short distance reduces the delay and enhances the quality of the telephone conversation. Each satellite covers an area 4,000 Km wide. The phone call is transferred from cell to cell and from satellite to satellite as the spacecraft rise and set during their orbital motion. The gateways are continuously linked to at least two satellites of the constellation.

Iridium Satellites

66 operational plus 6 in-orbit backup satellites are located in 6 orbital planes with the inclination of 86.4 degrees. Orbital period 100 minutes, 28 seconds.

General Characteristics:
Satellite weight—700 kg (1500 lb),
Spot beams—48 per satellite,
link margin—16 decibels (average),
lifetime—5–8 years.

Table 18.3 Allocated Frequencies

Direction	*Frequency*
Iridium Phone-Satellite	1616–1626.5 MHz
Satellite-Iridium Phone/Pager	1616–1626.5 MHz
Satellite-Satellite	23.18–23.38 GHz
Satellite-Gateway	19.4–19.6 GHz
Gateway-Satellite	29.1–29.3 GHz

Iridium Phones and Pagers

With the Iridium system all communications services - voice and paging - are delivered regardless of the user location or the availability of traditional telecommunications networks.

A variety of subscriber equipment is available to communicate with the Iridium network, including dual-mode handsets, specialized aeronautical and marine units, numeric and alphanumeric pagers.

An Iridium portable telephone is quite similar to a conventional handheld cellular terminal. Dimension, weight, battery lifetime were like terrestrial cellular phones. Still, it can operate in dual-mode, that is cellular mode or Iridium mode: the Iridium terminal is also a cellular terminal and could be used where cellular networks are available.

An Iridium pager offeres the first true "global roaming" capability in a small, belt-worn, personal message receiver.

MOBILE TELEPHONE SYSTEM

Mobile Phones—Technology

The mobile phone, also known as cellular phone, has become one of the most successful inventions in the 20th century. In the late 90s, mobile phones became one of the major communication devices. The first commercial mobile phone system started in 1979 in Japan. According to cellular online, the global mobile phone subscribers in 2003 are around 1.52 billion, which is about 20 percent of the current world population. This figure 18.7 showed the success of the mobile phone industries. In about 20 years' time, this technology conquered the global and became a demand for the majority of people in the world. It provided communication for people no matter anywhere and anytime.

Mobile phones were meant to be a device which enables users to have the ease on telecommunication freely wherever they want. But in the late 90's, SMS (Short Message Service), a new technology was brought out. SMS is a transmission of short text message from mobile phones to mobile phones. This became a revolution making mobile phones to develop into a device that not only allows simple voice to voice telecommunication. Mobile phone now not only became an entertainment device (featuring functions such as camera, FM and MP3 players etc) but also allowing users to access through internet, Personal Digital Assistant (PDA) functions and also having video conference using the latest 3G network. Someday, mobile phones might be able to replace computers.

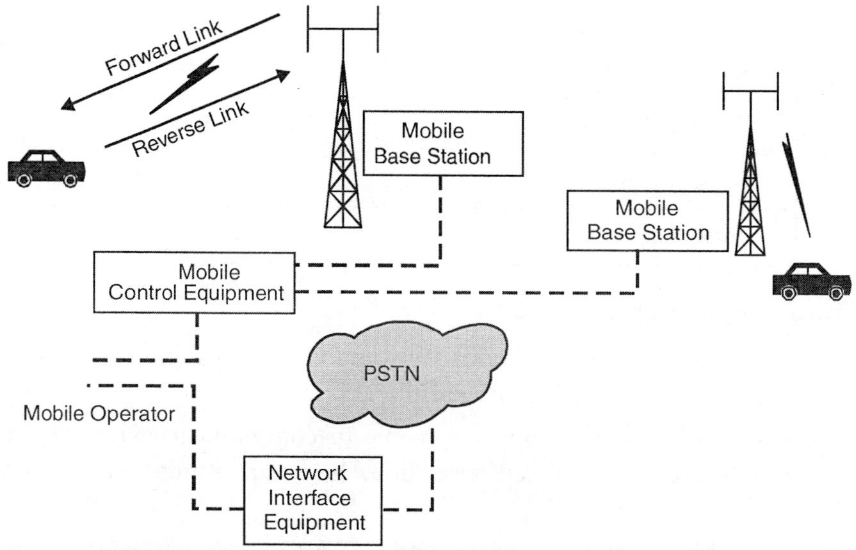

Figure 18.8 *Mobile Telephone Service Network.*

From the early stages of analog cellular to now the latest 3G mobile phone system, the mobile phone developed rapidly in the past 20 years. Each stage of development provided a big improve to the industries. From early stages of voice to voice simple communication, to the WAP and GPRS internet connection and now the high speed Internet connection through the internet, it showed that mobile phones is one of the leading technology in the high technology industry. The convenience brought by this technology indeed changed the life of many people and society. Many things such as banking, gathering information such as reports or latest news, control the share market via GPRS etc are what the technology helped to improve and ease the life of people. Japan is the country which the mobile phone technology develops the fastest in the world. Before the 3G technology was launched in other countries, the Japanese had already mastered the technology. A discussion about the fast development of mobile phone industry Japan will be included in the essay.

Studies believed that a new mobile phone network system, 4G will be in the market in the nearby future. 4G, or known as the fourth generation mobile is a whole new radio access network. Stronger and clearer signals and higher speed (broadband speed, 100 times faster than the 3G connection) connection through the Internet are the highlights of the 4G technology. Although the 3G technology had only been promoted no long ago, this new technology is now under development stage and believed to be put out in the market in year 2010. It is believed that the 4G will be a big leap and a whole new revolution for the mobile phone industry and the users.

Along with the development of mobile phones, many subsidiary technology developed by the mobile phone companies were also developed and influencing other products such as Bluetooth, symbian (an operating system (OS) specially designed for mobile phones) and some software companies that designs software for the Symbian OS. These technologies improved the interactive among mobile phones and the users. It provided a much convenience and wider usage for the mobile phone users. More and more companies now are trying to gain a share in the mobile phone market. Many big companies which are developing PDA OS such as Window CE (pocket PC), PALM and Linux are also engaging their OS with mobile phones functions. This proved that the mobile phone industry is indeed a good market to invest in. The competition in the market is also another reason causing the mobile phone industry to develop in such a short time.

Since mobile phone was developed and used by a large population of people, it changed the lifestyle of many people. On positive views, mobile phone provided a fast and immediate communication for people, which built up a much closer relationship within each another. Though, the negative views of mobile phone became a popular discussion now. Symptoms such as radiation which causes cancer from the mobile phones and mobile phone addiction are now argued to be the disadvantage of the technology. The danger brought by using mobile phones such as the unsafe of using mobile phone during driving or radiation of mobile phone causing danger to certain places such as the gas station are also problems for mobile phone users.

REVIEW QUESTIONS

1. Name the three ways for wireless data to be propagation.
2. What are the three types of frames used by wireless LANs ?
3. What is the access method used by wireless LANs ?
4. Explain in detail, all the wireless transmission medias.
5. How satellite communication take place ?
6. What is Iridium telecom system ?
7. What is mobile telephone system technology ?

❑❑❑

19

FRAME RELAY

INTRODUCTION

Frame Relay is a high-performance WAN protocol that operates at the physical and data link layers of the OSI reference model. Frame relay originally was designed for use across Integrated Services Digital Network (ISDN) interfaces. Today, it is used over a variety of other network interfaces as well. This chapter focuses on frame relay's specifications and applications in the context of WAN services.

Frame relay is an example of a packet-switched technology. Packet-switched networks enable end stations to dynamically share the network medium and the available bandwidth. The following two techniques are used in packet-switching technology:

- Variable-length packets
- Statistical multiplexing

Variable-length packets are used for more efficient and flexible data transfers. These packets are switched between the various segments in the network until the destination is reached.

Statistical multiplexing techniques control network access in a packet-switched network. The advantage of this technique is that it accommodates more flexibility and more efficient use of bandwidth. Most of today's popular LANs, such as Ethernet and Token ring, are packet-switched networks.

Frame relay often is described as a streamlined version of X.25, offering fewer of the robust capabilities, such as windowing and retransmission of last data that are offered in X.25. This is because frame relay typically operates over WAN facilities that offer more reliable connection services and a higher degree of reliability than the facilities available during the late 1970s and early 1980s that served as the common platforms for X.25 WANs. As mentioned earlier, frame relay is strictly a layer 2 protocol suite, whereas X.25 provides services at layer 3 (the network layer) as well. This enables frame relay to offer higher performance and greater transmission efficiency than X.25, and makes frame relay suitable for current WAN applications, such as LAN interconnection.

BACKGROUND OF FRAME RELAY

Frame relay was originally conceived of as a protocol for use over ISDN interfaces, and initial proposals to this effect were submitted (in 1984) to the Consultative Committee for International Telegraph and Telephone (CCITT). Work on frame relay was also undertaken in the American National Standards Institute (ANSI)—accredited T1S1 standards committee in the U.S.

PRINCIPLES OF FRAME RELAY

The rapid increase in high bandwidth communication is the main reason for improving and using frame relay technology. There are two main factors which influence the rapid demand for high speed networking:

- The rapid increase in use of LANs
- The use of fiber optic links

These factors led to new technologies and two principles: Frame relay and cell relay. Frame relay technology was intended to be an intermediate solution for the demand for high bandwidth networking. It is a packet switching technology which relies on low error rate digital transmission links and high performance processors. Frame relay technology was designed to cover the following:

- Low latency and higher throughput
- Bandwidth on demand
- Dynamic sharing of bandwidth
- Backbone network

Frame relay is a standard communication protocol that is specified in CCITT recommendations I.122 and Q.922 which add relay and routing functions to the data link layer (layer 2 of the OSI reference model).

Some of the functions associated with packet transport, such as error correction, flow control, etc., are still formed, but on an end-to-end basis by the end-user devices, instead of by the network. Frames are constructed by encapsulating layer 2 messages (excluding the CRC and flags), with a two byte header, a CRC, and a flag delimiter. The *frame relay* header consists of a data link connection identifier (DLCI) that allows the network to route each frame on a hop-by-hop basis along a virtual path defined either at call setup or subscription time. The start and end flags, and the CRC are identical to those used by HDLC or SDLC, based interfaced packages.

As described in the protocol architecture diagram, a initiates the communication process by sending a request for session establishment to the transport layer via the presentation and session layers. The transport layer forwards call control information through the ISDN via the D channel using Q.931 procedures. The signaling message is routed through the network and is used to define the virtual path and calls parameters that will be used during the data transfer stage.

Once the connection is established, data is transferred through the network between applications A and B on a hop-by-hop basis by using the DLCI in the frame header and routing information at each node as determined during call setup. One of the characteristic of frame relay is that it minimizes the amount of processing performed on each frame by the network and allows for very fast transfer of information.

Frame Relay Standardization

Initial proposals for the standardization of frame relay were presented to the Consultative Committee on International Telephone and Telegraph (CCITT) in 1984. Because of lack of interoperability and lack of complete standardization, however, frame relay did not experience significant deployment during the late 1980s.

A major development in frame relay's history occurred in 1990 when Cisco, Digital Equipment Corporation (DEC), Northern Telecom, and StrataCom formed a consortium to focus on frame relay technology development. This consortium developed a specification that conformed to the basic frame relay protocol that was being discussed in CCITT, but it extended the protocol with features that provide additional capabilities for complex internetworking environments. These frame relay extensions are referred to collectively as the Local Management Interface (LMI).

Since the consortium's specification was developed and published, many vendors have announced their support of this extended frame relay definition. ANSI and CCITT have subsequently standardized their own variations of the original LMI specification, and these standardized specifications now are more commonly used than the original version.

Internationally, frame relay was standardized by the International Telecommunication Union—Telecommunications Standards Section (ITU-T). In the United States, frame relay is an American National Standards Institute (ANSI) standard.

Frame Relay Devices

Devices attached to a frame relay WAN fall into the following two general categories:

- Data terminal equipment (DTE)
- Data circuit-terminating equipment (DCE)

DTEs generally are considered to be terminating equipment for a specific network and typically are located on the premises of a customer. In fact, they may be owned by the customer. Examples of DTE devices are terminals, personal computers, routers, and bridges.

DCEs are carrier-owned internetworking devices. The purpose of DCE equipment is to provide clocking and switching services in a network, which are the devices that actually transmit data through the WAN. In most cases, these are packet switches. Figure 19.1 shows the relationship between the two categories of devices.

The connection between a DTE device and a DCE device consists of both a physical layer component and a link layer component. The physical component defines the mechanical, electrical, functional, and procedural specifications for the connection between the devices. One of the most commonly used physical layer interface specifications is the Recommended Standard (RS)-232 specification. The link layer component defines the protocol that establishes the connection between the DTE device, such as a router, and the DCE device, such as a switch. This chapter examines a commonly utilized protocol specification used in WAN networking: the frame relay protocol.

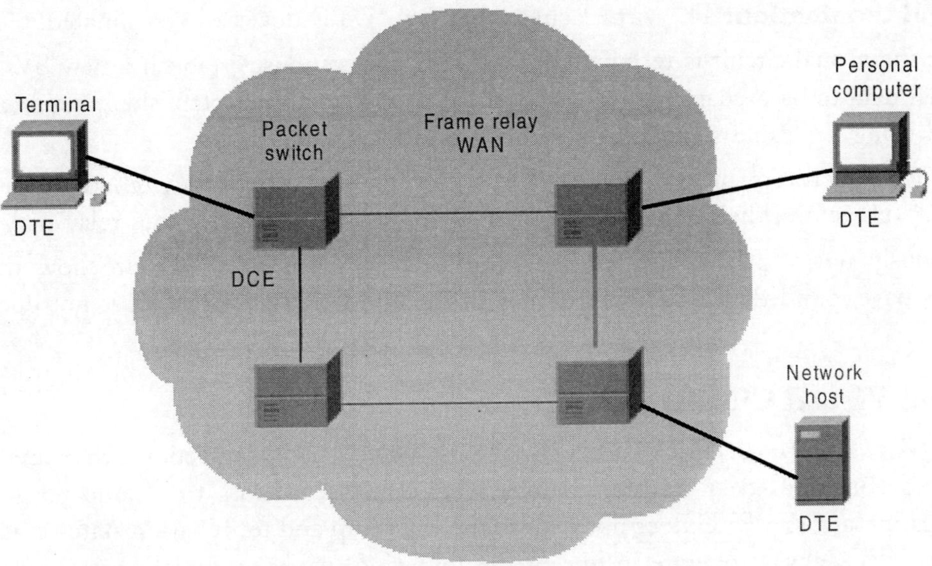

Figure 19.1 *DCEs Generally Reside within Carrier-Operated WANs.*

Frame Relay Virtual Circuits

Frame relay provides connection-oriented data link layer communication. This means that a defined communication exists between each pair of devices and that these connections are associated with a connection identifier. This service is implemented by using a frame relay virtual circuit, which is a logical connection created between two Data Terminal Equipment (DTE) devices across a frame relay Packet-Switched Network (PSN).

Virtual circuits provide a bidirectional communication path from one DTE device to another and are uniquely identified by a Data-Link Connection Identifier (DLCI). A number of virtual circuits can be multiplexed into a single physical circuit for transmission across the network. This capability often can reduce the equipment and network complexity required to connect multiple DTE devices.

A virtual circuit can pass through any number of intermediate DCE devices (switches) located within the frame relay PSN. Frame relay virtual circuits fall into two categories: Switched Virtual Circuits (SVCs) and Permanent Virtual Circuits (PVCs).

Switched Virtual Circuits

Switched Virtual Circuits (SVCs) are temporary connections used in situations requiring only sporadic data transfer between DTE devices across the frame relay network. A communication session across an SVC consists of the following four operational states:

- **Call setup:** The virtual circuit between two frame relay DTE devices is established.
- **Data transfer:** Data is transmitted between the DTE devices over the virtual circuit.

- **Idle:** The connection between DTE devices is still active, but no data is transferred. If an SVC remains in an idle state for a defined period of time, the call can be terminated.
- **Call termination:** The virtual circuit between DTE devices is terminated.

After the virtual circuit is terminated, the DTE devices must establish a new SVC if there is additional data to be exchanged. It is expected that SVCs will be established, maintained, and terminated using the same signaling protocols used in ISDN.

Few manufacturers of frame relay DCE equipment support switched virtual circuit connections. Therefore, their actual deployment is minimal in today's frame relay networks.

Previously not widely supported by frame relay equipment, SVCs are now the norm. Companies have found that SVCs save money in the end because the circuit is not open all the time.

Permanent Virtual Circuits

Permanent Virtual Circuits (PVCs) are permanently established connections that are used for frequent and consistent data transfers between DTE devices across the frame relay network. Communication across a PVC does not require the call setup and termination states that are used with SVCs. PVCs always operate in one of the following two operational states:

- **Data transfer:** Data is transmitted between the DTE devices over the virtual circuit.
- **Idle:** The connection between DTE devices is active, but no data is transferred. Unlike SVCs, PVCs will not be terminated under any circumstances when in an idle state.

DTE devices can begin transferring data whenever they are ready because the circuit is permanently established.

Data-Link Connection Identifier

Frame relay virtual circuits are identified by *Data Link Connection Identifiers (DLCIs)*. DLCI values typically are assigned by the frame relay service provider (for example, the telephone company). Figure 19.2 Illustrates how two different DTE devices can be assigned the same DLCI value within one frame relay WAN.

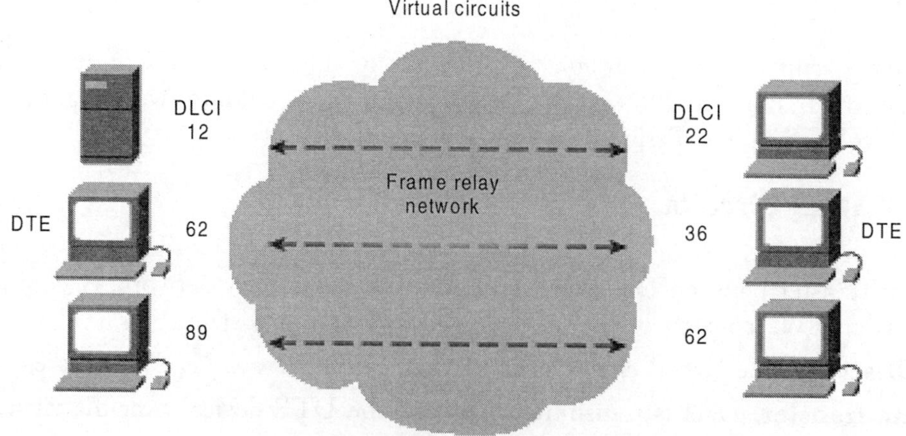

Figure 19.2

Frame Relay DLCIs have local significance, which means that their values are unique in the LAN, but not necessarily in the frame relay WAN.

Congestion-Control Mechanisms

Frame relay reduces network overhead by implementing simple congestion-notification mechanisms rather than explicit, per-virtual-circuit flow control. Frame relay typically is implemented on reliable network media, so data integrity is not sacrificed because flow control can be left to higher-layer protocols. Frame relay implements two congestion-notification mechanisms:

- Forward-Explicit Congestion Notification (FECN)
- Backward-Explicit Congestion Notification (BECN)

FECN and BECN each is controlled by a single bit contained in the frame relay frame header. The frame relay frame header also contains a Discard Eligibility (DE) bit, which is used to identify less important traffic that can be dropped during periods of congestion.

The FECN bit is part of the address field in the frame relay frame header. The FECN mechanism is initiated when a DTE device sends frame relay frames into the network. If the network is congested, DCE devices (switches) set the value of the frames' FECN bit to 1. When the frames reach the destination DTE device, the address field (with the FECN bit set) indicates that the frame experienced congestion in the path from source to destination. The DTE device can relay this information to a higher-layer protocol for processing. Depending on the implementation, flow control may be initiated, or the indication may be ignored.

The BECN bit is part of the address field in the frame relay frame header. DCE devices set the value of the BECN bit to 1 in frames traveling in the opposite direction of frames with their FECN bit set. This informs the receiving DTE device that a particular path through the network is congested. The DTE device then can relay this information to a higher-layer protocol for processing. Depending on the implementation, flow-control may be initiated, or the indication may be ignored.

Frame Relay Discard Eligibility

The *Discard Eligibility (DE) bit* is used to indicate that a frame has lower importance than other frames. The DE bit is part of the address field in the frame relay frame header.

DTE devices can set the value of the DE bit of a frame to 1 to indicate that the frame has lower importance than other frames. When the network becomes congested, DCE devices will discard frames with the DE bit set before discarding those that do not. This reduces the likelihood of critical data being dropped by frame relay DCE devices during periods of congestion.

Frame Relay Error Checking

Frame relay uses a common error-checking mechanism known as the *Cyclic Redundancy Check (CRC)*. The CRC compares two calculated values to determine whether errors occurred during the transmission from source to destination. Frame relay reduces network overhead by implementing error checking rather than error correction. Frame relay typically is implemented on reliable network media, so data integrity is not sacrificed because error correction can be left to higher-layer protocols running on top of frame relay.

Frame Relay Local Management Interface

The Local Management Interface (LMI) is a set of enhancements to the basic frame relay specification. The LMI was developed in 1990 by Cisco Systems, StrataCom, Northern Telecom, and Digital Equipment Corporation. It offers a number of features (called extensions) for managing complex internet-works. Key frame relay LMI extensions include global addressing, virtual circuit status messages, and multicasting.

The LMI global addressing extension gives frame relay Data Link Connection Identifier (DLCI) values global rather than local significance. DLCI values become DTE addresses that are unique in the frame relay WAN. The global addressing extension adds functionality and manageability to frame relay internet-works. Individual network interfaces and the end nodes attached to them, for example, can be identified by using standard address-resolution and discovery techniques. In addition, the entire frame relay network appears to be a typical LAN to routers on its periphery.

LMI virtual circuit status messages provide communication and synchronization between frame relay DTE and DCE devices. These messages are used to periodically report on the status of PVCs, which prevents data from being sent into black holes (that is, over PVCs that no longer exist).

The LMI multicasting extension allows multicast groups to be assigned. Multicasting saves bandwidth by allowing routing updates and address-resolution messages to be sent only to specific groups of routers. The extension also transmits reports on the status of multicast groups in update messages.

Frame Relay Network Implementation

A common private frame relay network implementation is to equip a T1 multiplexer with both frame relay and non-frame relay interfaces. Frame relay traffic is forwarded out the frame relay interface and onto the data network. Non-frame relay traffic is forwarded to the appropriate application or service, such as a Private Branch Exchange (PBX) for telephone service or to a video-teleconferencing application.

A typical frame relay network consists of a number of DTE devices, such as routers, connected to remote ports on multiplexer equipment via traditional point-to-point services such as T1, fractional T1, or 56-Kb circuits. An example of a simple frame relay network is shown in figure 19.3.

The majority of frame relay networks deployed today are provisioned by service providers that intend to offer transmission services to customers. This is often referred to as a public frame relay service. Frame relay is implemented in both public carrier-provided networks and in private enterprise networks. The following section examines the two methodologies for deploying frame relay.

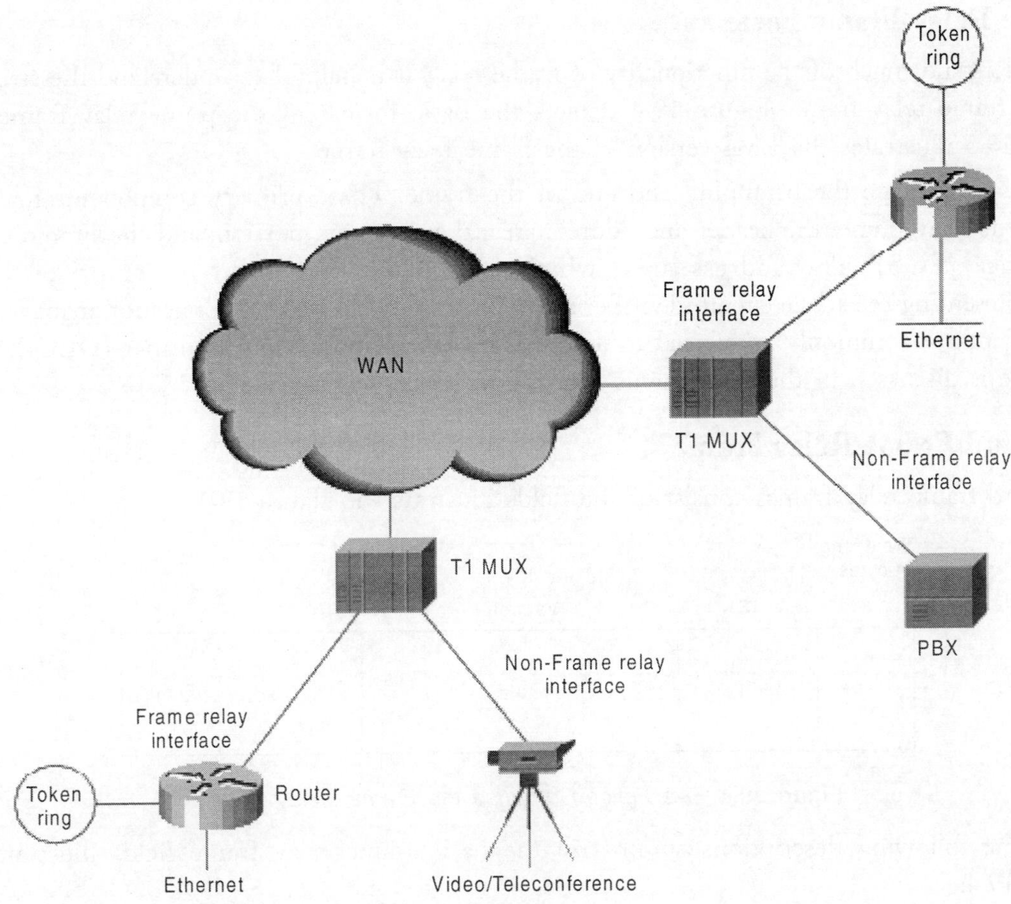

Figure 19.3 *A Simple Frame Relay Network Connects Various Devices to Different Services Over a WAN.*

Public Carrier-Provided Networks

In public carrier-provided frame relay networks, the frame relay switching equipment is located in the central offices of a telecommunications carrier. Subscribers are charged based on their network use but are relieved from administering and maintaining the frame relay network equipment and service.

Generally, the DCE equipment also is owned by the telecommunications provider. DTE equipment either will be customer-owned or perhaps will be owned by the telecommunications provider as a service to the customer. The majority of today's frame relay networks are public carrier-provided networks.

Private Enterprise Networks

More frequently, organizations worldwide are deploying private frame relay networks. In private frame relay networks, the administration and maintenance of the network are the responsibilities of the enterprise (a private company). All the equipment, including the switching equipment, is owned by the customer.

Frame Relay Frame Formats

To understand much of the functionality of frame relay, it is helpful to understand the structure of the frame relay frame. Figure 19.4 depicts the basic format of the frame relay frame, and figure 19.5 illustrates the LMI version of the frame relay frame.

Flags indicate the beginning and end of the frame. Three primary components make up the frame relay frame: the header and address area, the user-data portion, and the Frame Check Sequence (FCS). The address area, which is 2 bytes in length, is comprised of 10 bits representing the actual circuit identifier and 6 bits of fields related to congestion management. This identifier commonly is referred to as the Data Link Connection Identifier (DLCI). Each of these is discussed in the descriptions that follow.

Standard Frame Relay Frame

Standard frame relay frames consist of the fields illustrated in figure 19.4.

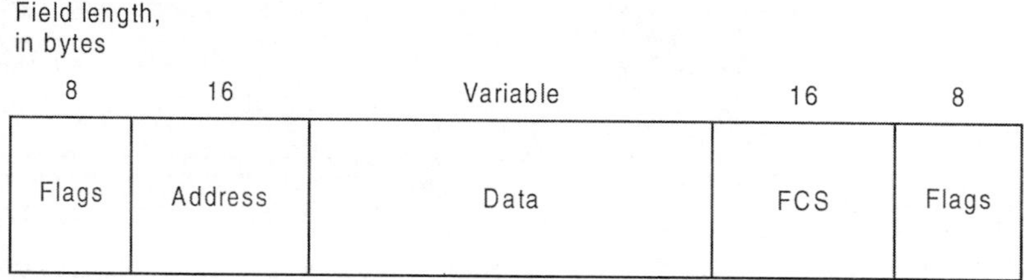

Figure 19.4 *Five Fields Comprise the Frame Relay Frame.*

The following descriptions summarize the basic frame relay frame fields illustrated in figure 19.4.

- **Flags:** Delimits the beginning and end of the frame. The value of this field is always the same and is represented either as the hexadecimal number 7E or as the binary number 01111110.
- **Address:** Contains the following information:
  - *DLCI:* The 10-bit DLCI is the essence of the frame relay header. This value represents the virtual connection between the DTE device and the switch. Each virtual connection that is multiplexed onto the physical channel will be represented by a unique DLCI. The DLCI values have local significance only, which means that they are unique only to the physical channel on which they reside. Therefore, devices at opposite ends of a connection can use different DLCI values to refer to the same virtual connection.
  - *Extended Address (EA):* The EA is used to indicate whether the byte in which the EA value is 1 is the last addressing field. If the value is 1, then the current byte is determined to be the last DLCI octet. Although current frame relay implementations all use a two-octet DLCI, this capability does allow longer DLCIs to be used in the future. The eighth bit of each byte of the address field is used to indicate the EA.
  - *C/R:* The C/R is the bit that follows the most significant DLCI byte in the address field. The C/R bit is not currently defined.

– *Congestion Control:* This consists of the 3 bits that control the frame relay congestion-notification mechanisms. These are the FECN, BECN, and DE bits, which are the last 3 bits in the address field.

Forward-Explicit Congestion Notification (FECN) is a single-bit field that can be set to a value of 1 by a switch to indicate to an end DTE device, such as a router, that congestion was experienced in the direction of the frame transmission from source to destination. The primary benefit of the use of the FECN and BECN fields is the capability of higher-layer protocols to react intelligently to these congestion indicators. Today, DECnet and OSI are the only higher-layer protocols that implement these capabilities.

Backward-Explicit Congestion Notification (BECN) is a single-bit field that, when set to a value of 1 by a switch, indicates that congestion was experienced in the network in the direction opposite of the frame transmission from source to destination.

Discard Eligibility (DE) is set by the DTE device, such as a router, to indicate that the marked frame is of lesser importance relative to other frames being transmitted. Frames that are marked as "discard eligible" should be discarded before other frames in a congested network. This allows for a basic prioritization mechanism in frame relay networks.

- **Data:** Contains encapsulated upper-layer data. Each frame in this variable-length field includes a user data or payload field that will vary in length up to 16,000 octets. This field serves to transport the higher-layer protocol packet (PDU) through a frame relay network.
- **Frame check sequence:** Ensures the integrity of transmitted data. This value is computed by the source device and verified by the receiver to ensure integrity of transmission.

LMI Frame Format

Frame relay frames that conform to the LMI specifications consist of the fields illustrated in figure 19.5.

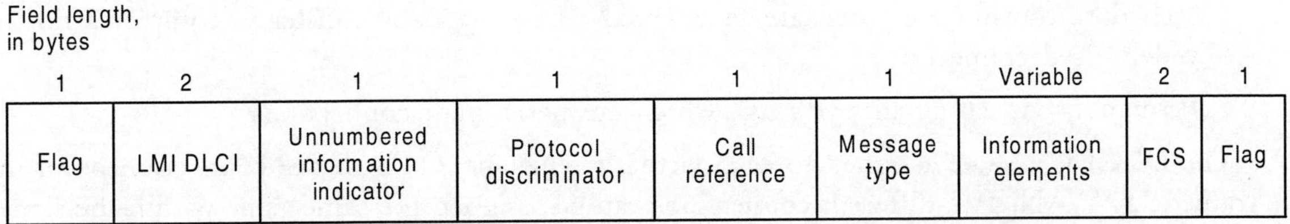

Figure 19.5 *Nine Fields Comprise the Frame Relay that Conforms to the LMI Format.*

The following descriptions summarize the fields illustrated in figure 19.5.

- **Flag:** Delimits the beginning and end of the frame.
- **LMI DLCI:** Identifies the frame as an LMI frame instead of a basic frame relay frame. The LMI-specific DLCI value defined in the LMI consortium specification is DLCI = 1023.
- **Unnumbered information indicator:** Sets the poll/final bit to zero.

- **Protocol discriminator:** Always contains a value indicating that the frame is an LMI frame.
- **Call reference:** Always contains zeros. This field currently is not used for any purpose.
- **Message type:** Labels the frame as one of the following message types:
  - *Status-inquiry message:* Allows a user device to inquire about the status of the network.
  - *Status message:* Responds to status-inquiry messages. Status messages include keep alives and PVC status messages.
- **Information elements:** Contains a variable number of individual information elements (IEs). IEs consist of the following fields:
  - *IE identifier:* Uniquely identifies the IE.
  - *IE length:* Indicates the length of the IE.
  - *Data:* Consists of 1 or more bytes containing encapsulated upper-layer data.
- **Frame check sequence (FCS):** Ensures the integrity of transmitted data.

Frame relay is a networking protocol that works at the bottom two levels of the OSI reference model: the physical and data link layers. It is an example of packet-switching technology, which enables end stations to dynamically share network resources.

Frame relay devices fall into the following two general categories:

- Data Terminal Equipments (DTEs), which include terminals, personal computers, routers, and bridges
- Data Circuit-Terminating Equipments (DCEs), which transmit the data through the network and are often carrier-owned devices (although, increasingly, enterprises are buying their own DCEs and implementing them in their networks)

Frame relay networks transfer data using one of the following two connection types:

- Switched virtual circuits (SVCs), which are temporary connections that are created for each data transfer and then are terminated when the data transfer is complete (not a widely used connection)
- Permanent virtual circuits (PVCs), which are permanent connections

The DLCI is a value assigned to each virtual circuit and DTE device connection point in the frame relay WAN. Two different connections can be assigned the same value within the same frame relay WAN—one on each side of the virtual connection.

In 1990, Cisco Systems, StrataCom, Northern Telecom, and Digital Equipment Corporation developed a set of frame relay enhancements called the Local Management Interface (LMI). The LMI enhancements offer a number of features (referred to as extensions) for managing complex internet-works, including the following:

- Global addressing
- Virtual circuit status messages
- Multicasting

FRAME RELAY PROTOCOL DATA UNIT

Frame relay frame structure is essentially identical to that defined for lap-D. The frame relay format can be distinguished from lap-D by its absence of a control. Each frame relay PDU consists of the following fields:

- **Flag field:** The flag is used to pre-form high level data link synchronization which indicates the beginning and end of the frame with the unique pattern 01111110. To ensure that the 01111110 pattern does not appear somewhere inside the frame, bit stuffing and de-stuffing procedures are used.
- **Address field:** Each address field may occupy either octet 2 to 3, octet 2 to 4, or octet 2 to 5, depending on the range of the address in use. A two-octet address field comprising the EA=Address Field extension bits and the C/R=Command/Response bit.
- **DLCI-data link connection identifier bits:** The DLCI is used to identify the virtual connection so that the receiving end knows which information connection this frame belongs to. It should be pointed out that this DLCI has only local significance. Several virtual connections can be multiplexed over the same physical channel.
- **FECN, BECN, DE BITS:** These are congestion reporting capability bits:
  - FECN=Forward Explicit Congestion Notification bit
  - BECN=Backward Explicit Congestion Notification bit
  - DE=Discard Eligibility bit
- **Information field:** The maximum number of data bytes that may be put in a frame is a system parameter. The actual maximum frame length may be negotiated at call set-up time. The standard specifies that the maximum information field size (to be supported by any network) is at least 262 octets. Since end-to-end protocols typically operate on the basis of larger information units, it is recommended that the network support the maximum value of at least 1600 octets, to avoid the need for segmentation and reassembling by end users.
- **Frame check sequence (FCS) field:** Since the bit error rate of the medium is not completely negligible, it is necessary to implement error detection at each switching node to avoid wasting bandwidth due to the transmission of erred frames. The error detection mechanism used in frame relay is based on the Cyclic Redundancy Check (CRC).

CONGESTION CONTROL IN FRAME RELAY NETWORK

The frame relay network uses a simplified protocol at each switching node. The simplicity is achieved when link-by-link flow control is missing. As a result, the performance of frame relay networks has largely been determined by the offered load. When the offered load is high, due to the bursts in some services, temporary overload at some frame relay nodes causes a collapse in network throughput. Therefore, some effective mechanisms are required to control the congestion.

The congestion control in frame relay networks includes the following elements:

- **Admission control:** This is the principle mechanism used in frame relay to ensure that resource requirement, once accepted, can be guaranteed. It is also generally used to achieve high network performance. The network decides whether to accept a new connection request based on the relation of the requested traffic descriptor and the network's residual capacity. The traffic descriptor is defined as a set of parameters communicated to the switching nodes at call set-up time or service subscription time, which characterizes the connection's statistical properties. The traffic descriptor consists of three elements:
- **Committed information rate (CIR):** The average rate (in bit/s) at which the network guarantees to transfer information units over a measurement interval T. This T interval is defined as: T = BC/CIR.
- **Committed burst size (BC):** The maximum number of information units that can be transmitted during the interval T.
- **Excess burst size (BE):** The maximum number of uncommitted information units (in bits) that the network will attempt to carry during the interval T.

TRAFFIC ENFORCEMENT

Once a connection has been established in the network, the edge node of the frame relay network must monitor the connection's traffic flow to ensure that the actual usage of network resources does not exceed this specification. Frame relay defines some restrictions on the user's information rate. It allows the network to enforce the end user's information rate and discard information when the subscribed access rate is exceeded.

CONGESTION NOTIFICATION

Explicit congestion notification is proposed as the congestion avoidance policy. It tries to keep the network operating at its desired equilibrium point so that a certain QOS for the network can be met. To do so, special congestion control bits have been incorporated into the address field of the frame relay: FECN and BECN. The basic idea is to avoid data accumulation inside the network.

FRAME RELAY VS. X.25

X.25 was designed to provide error-free delivery using high error-rate links. Frame relay takes advantage of the new, lower error rate links, enabling it to eliminate many of the services provided by X.25. The elimination of functions and fields, combined with digital links, enables frame relay to operate at speeds 20 times greater than X.25.

X.25 is defined for layers 1, 2 and 3 of the ISO model, while frame relay is defined for layers 1 and 2 only. This means that frame relay has significantly less processing to do at each node, which improves throughput by order of magnitude.

X.25 prepares and sends packets, while frame relay prepares and sends frames. X.25 packets contain several fields used for error and flow control, none of which is needed by frame relay. The frames in frame relay contain an expanded address field that enables frame relay nodes to direct frames to their destinations with minimal processing .

X.25 has a fixed bandwidth available. It uses or wastes portions of its bandwidth as the load dictates. Frame relay can dynamically allocate bandwidth during call setup negotiation at both the physical and logical channel level.

REVIEW QUESTIONS

1. What is frame relay ? Explain.
2. What is the principle of frame relay ?
3. What are frame relay devices ?
4. Draw frame relay virtual circuits.
5. What are different frame relay virtual circuits ?
6. What are different frame relay congestion control mechanisms ?
7. Give details of frame relay frame format.
8. What are differences between frame relay and X.25 ?

❑❑❑

20 ATM (ASYNCHRONOUS TRANSFER MODE)

Asynchronous Transfer Mode (ATM) technology is based on the efforts of the International Telecommunication Union Telecommunication Standardization Sector (ITU-T) study group XVIII to develop Broadband Integrated Services Digital Network (BISDN) for the high-speed transfer of voice, video, and data through public networks.

Through the efforts of the ATM forum (jointly founded in 1991 by Cisco systems, NET/ADAPTIVE, Northern Telecom, and Sprint), ATM is capable of transferring voice, video, and data through private networks and across public networks. ATM continues to evolve today as the various standards groups finalize specifications that allow interoperability among the equipment produced by vendors in the public and private networking industries.

ATM uses Very Large-Scale Integration (VLSI) technology to segment data (for example, frames from the data link layer of the OSI reference model) at high speeds into units called *cells*. Each cell consists of 5 octets of header information and 48 octets of payload data, as shown in figure 20.1.

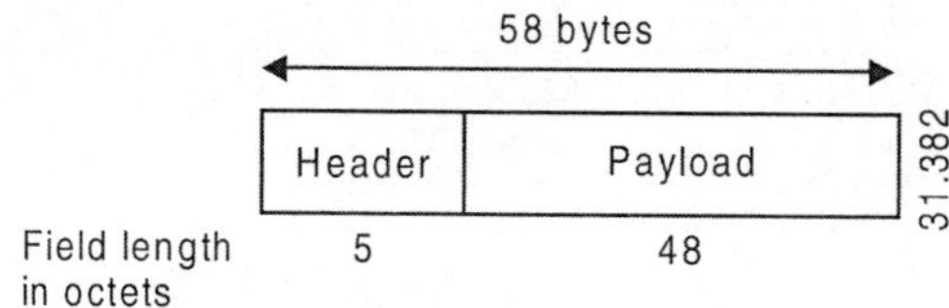

Figure 20.1 *ATM Cell Format.*

Cells transit ATM networks by passing through devices known as ATM *switches*, which analyze information in the header to switch the cell to the output interface that connects the switch to the next appropriate switch as the cell works its way to its destination.

ATM is a cell-switching and multiplexing technology that combines the benefits of circuit switching (constant transmission delay and guaranteed capacity) with those of packet switching (flexibility and efficiency for intermittent traffic). Like X.25 and frame relay, ATM defines the interface between the user equipment (such was workstations and routers) and the network (referred to as the User-Network Interface, or UNI). This definition supports the use of ATM switches (and ATM switching techniques) within both public and private networks.

Because it is an asynchronous mechanism, ATM differs from *synchronous transfer mode* methods, where Time Division Multiplexing (TDM) techniques are employed to preassign users to time slots. ATM time slots are made available on demand, with information identifying the source of the transmission contained in the header of each ATM cell. TDM is inefficient relative to ATM because if a station has nothing to transmit when its time slot comes up, that time slot is wasted. The converse situation, where one station has lots of information to transmit, is also less efficient. In this case, that station can only transmit when its turn comes up, even though all the other time slots are empty. With ATM, a station can send cells whenever necessary. Figure 20.2 contrasts TDM and ATM multiplexing techniques.

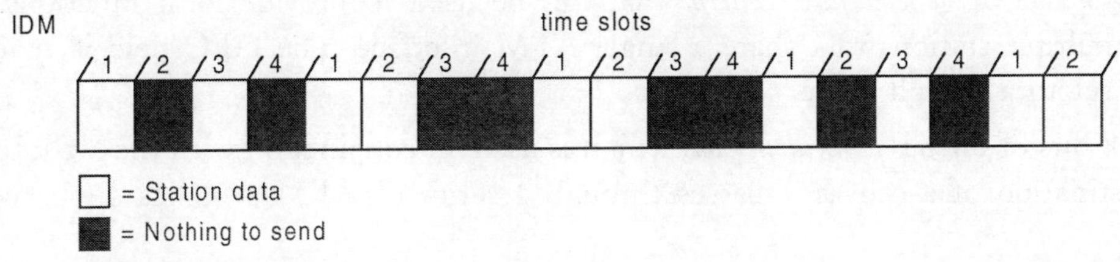

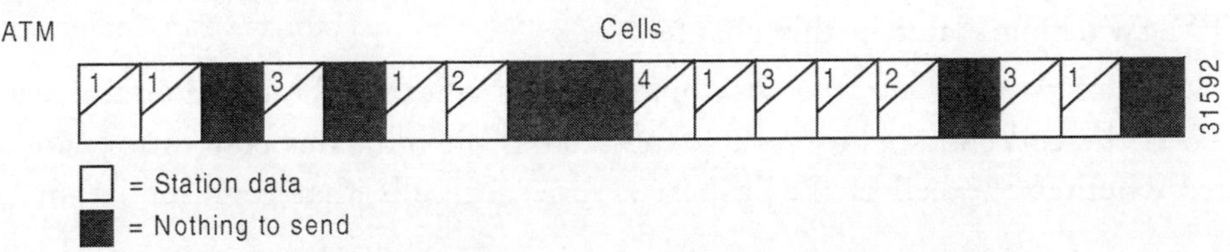

Figure 20.2 *TDM and ATM Multiplexing Techniques.*

Another critical ATM design characteristic is its star topology. The ATM switch acts as a hub in the ATM network, with all devices attached directly. This provides all the traditional benefits of star-topology networks, including easier troubleshooting and support for network configuration changes and additions.

Furthermore, ATM's switching fabric provides additive bandwidth. As long as the switch can handle the aggregate cell transfer rate, additional connections to the switch can be made. The total bandwidth of the system increases accordingly. If a switch can pass cells among all its interfaces at the full rate of all interfaces, it is described as *non-blocking*. For example, an ATM switch with 16 ports each at 155 megabits per second (Mbps) would require about 2.5 gigabits per second (Gbps) aggregate throughput to be non-blocking.

ATM Cell Header Formats

The ATM standards groups have defined two header formats. The UNI header format is defined by the UNI specification, and the Network Node Interface (NNI) header format is defined by the NNI specification.

The UNI specification defines communications between ATM end-stations (such as workstations and routers) and ATM switches in private ATM networks. The format of the UNI cell header is shown in figure 20.3.

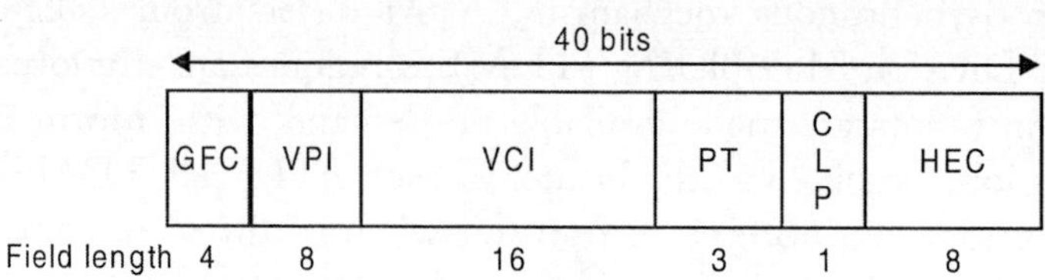

Figure 20.3 *UNI Header Format.*

The UNI header consists of the following fields:

GFC—4 bits of *generic flow control* that can be used to provide local functions, such as identifying multiple stations that share a single ATM interface. The GFC field is typically not used and is set to a default value.

VPI—8 bits of *virtual path identifier*, which is used, in conjunction with the VCI, to identify the next destination of a cell as it passes through a series of ATM switches on its way to its destination.

VCI—16 bits of *virtual channel identifier*, which is used, in conjunction with the VPI, to identify the next destination of a cell as it passes through a series of ATM switches on its way to its destination. For more information about how the VPI and VCI fields are used, see the section "ATM switching," later in this chapter.

PT—3 bits of *payload type*, the first bit indicates whether the cell contains user data or control data. If the cell contains user data, the second bit indicates congestion, and the third bit indicates whether the cell is the last in a series of cells that represent a single AAL5 frame.

CLP—1 bit of *congestion loss priority*, which indicates whether the cell should be discarded if it encounters extreme congestion as it moves through the network. For more information about how ATM uses this bit, see the section "quality of service," later in this chapter.

HEC—8 bits of *header error control*, which is a checksum calculated only on the header itself.

The NNI specification defines communications between ATM switches. The format of the NNI header is shown in figure 20.4.

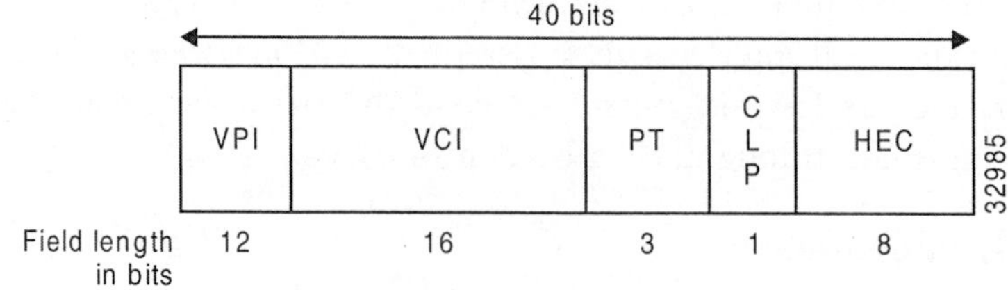

Figure 20.4 *NNI Header Format*

The GFC field is not present in the format of the NNI header. Instead, the VPI field occupies the first 12 bits, which allows ATM switches to assign larger VPI values. With that exception, the format of the NNI header is identical to the format of the UNI header.

A HISTORY OF ATM

ATM is the culmination of all the developments in switching and transmission in the last twenty years. This includes the advent of packet-switching and the change from coaxial to optical.

SWITCHING

Circuit Switching

This was the first type of data transfer mechanism used. A dedicated line on the network path is allocated to the parties involved in the transfer over the network. Channel capacity has to be available and reserved between each pair of nodes on the path, and each node has to have a switching capability. For different applications, utilization of the line can vary enormously. However there is little delay and effective transparency for the user. It is very efficient for Constant Bit Rate (CBR).

Packet Switching

Data to be sent is broken down into chunks or packets. Each packet contains data and header information for control *e.g.*, routing. At each node the packet is received, stored briefly and passed on. At each node the packets may be put on a queue for further movement into the network. There are two approaches to transport :

1. Datagram, where each packet can take any path through the network as long as they all reach the destination.
2. Virtual circuit, where all the packets are routed through the same path without having the path dedicated.

Datagram allows for dynamic handling of congestion and no call setup is necessary. Virtual channels allow for sequencing, error and flow control.

Multi-Rate Circuit Switching

This is an enhancement of the synchronous Time-Division Multiplexing (TDM) approach used initially in circuit switching. In circuit switching a station must operate at a fixed data rate which must be used regardless of application. In multi-rate switching, multiplexing is introduced. A station attaches to the network by means of a single physical link which carries multiple fixed data-rate channels (B-channel @ 64 kbps). Traffic on each channel can be switched independently through the network to various destinations. This is used for simple ISDN. So the user has a number of data rate choices but they are fixed so Variable Bit Rate (VBR) is difficult to accommodate efficiently.

FRAME RELAY

Frame relay is essentially identical to packet switching. Frame relay saw its development as a result of high data rates and low error rates in modern high speed communications systems. In old packet switching, there was considerable overhead involved in error recovery, redundancy enhancement and routing information. With frame relay the packets are now of variable length and not fixed length, meaning that they were designed to operate at up to 2 Mbps. This was very good for VBR.

Cell Relay

This is an evolution from frame relay and multi-rate circuit switching. Cell relay uses fixed sized packets called cells.

Multirate circuit switching also had fixed channels. Cell relay allows for the definition of virtual channels with data rates dynamically defined. Using a small cell size allows almost constant data rate even though it uses packets.

From frame relay, cell relay takes improved error control into account, and allows more errors to be handled at a higher logical level. The fixed-size cells reduce overhead even more and thus allows rates of tens to hundreds of Mbps.

So we have seen progression from two areas—circuit switching for CBR, and packet switching for VBR. Cell relay is equally as good with either CBR or VBR as is shown in figure 20.5.

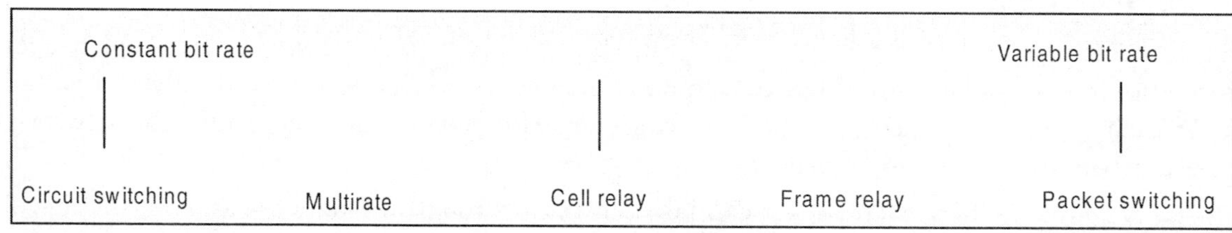

Figure 20.5 *Cell Relay.*

TRANSMISSION

In the late 1800s signals were analog and telephones were allocated a single channel per line for transmission. Development of the vacuum tube led to analog system employing FDM (Frequency Division Multiplexing), in 1925 and coax was installed in 1936. This developed to the microwave level of 4, 6 and 11 GHz frequency regions, and in 1969 digital wireless system was initiated. Aided by the invention of transistors and the concept of PCM (Pulse Code Modulation), by 1972, a digital channel bank featuring toll quality was developed. Soon after, a high bit rate digital system employing TDM (Time-Division Multiplexing), was realized but was relatively expensive.

It was not until the advent of optical transmission systems that any real use of TDM could be made. Optical transmission is accomplished by modulating transmitted information by a laser diode or LED, passing the information signal over optical fiber and reconstructing the information by the 'pin' diode or the Avalanche Photo Diode (APD). Now PCM and TDM saw use in 45 Mbps optical communications systems, which have developed to 1.2, 1.7, and 2.4 Gbps. These systems eventually converge into SDH/SONET.

But before that, in the mid-80's the most common digital hierarchy in use was PDH (Plescio-synchronous Digital Hierarchy), which is still used in the form of DS-1/2/3/4 signals. It is called 'plescio' (almost) because the transmission is neither wholly synchronous nor asynchronous. Thus, PDH, was superceded by SDH, which took the PDH signals and multiplexed them into an STM (Synchronous Time-division Multiplexing) of n = STM-n signal. So development went from asynchronous multiplexing used in PDH for conversion to a higher bit rate to synchronous multiplexing in SDH. That means that given any of the current signals, a generic STM-n signal can be constructed through the synchronous multiplexing procedure used in SDH.

So, we have a switching technology—cell relay, and a transmission technology—SDH over optical fiber. Cell relay supports VBR, CBR and varied applications. SDH allows large amounts of data top be transmitted efficiently over a network. The combination of these two ideas together give the basis for ATM—asynchronous transfer mode.

ATM is a high-speed network technology that is designed for LANs, WANs, carrier and service provider networks, and Internet core networks. It is a connection-oriented switching technology, as opposed to a connectionless technology such as IP. ATM creates a virtual circuit (dedicated path) between source and destination across its switching fabric. These circuits can guarantee bandwidth and quality-of-service.

ATM's fixed cell size provides performance and predictable traffic flows. Picture a busy intersection. A semi tractor-trailer is attempting to negotiate a tight turn. All the rest of the traffic in the intersection is held up while this happens. Now picture the same intersection where all the vehicles are sports cars. In the latter case, traffic flows smoothly, and even predictably, because there are no traffic jams.

ATM cells negotiate ATM switches with the same efficiency, providing several benefits :

- Cell switching is efficient and fast for the reasons just described.
- Traffic flow is predictable due to the fixed cell size.
- Delivery of time-sensitive traffic (live voice and video) can be guaranteed.
- ATM includes QOS (Quality of Service) features that can be used to guarantee bandwidth for certain types of traffic.

There has been great debate over whether ATM is better than IP and vice versa. Many people find this debate odd, since the technologies are quite different and not even in the same protocol layer. The battle is really about whether networks should be connection oriented (ATM) or best effort (IP). ATM's fixed cell size and virtual circuit capability makes it the best choice for real time multimedia. Carriers and service providers use ATM in their core networks because it lets them provide service guarantees to their customers. However, IP's simple packet forwarding model has proved its usefulness in the Internet, where traffic is bursty and unpredictable. This model allows millions of people to share the bandwidth of the Internet without setting up virtual circuits in advance. However, the IP model starts to break down under traffic loads and congestion. In addition, the unpredictable delays of IP networks are a problem for real-time traffic.

ATM was originally defined by the telephone companies and has been heavily promoted by them as an end-to-end networking technology, as well as a voice technology. In this respect, ATM is both a LAN and WAN technology that can potentially allow customers to replace their separate voice and data networks with a single network to handle both voice and data, as well as other multimedia content such as video.

In the early 1990s, ATM was widely considered the next-generation networking technology that would extend all the way to the desktop. But broadcast LANs were already entrenched in most organizations and Internet technologies exploded on the scene. And while ATM was hyped for its speed, gigabit Ethernet (1,000 Mbits/sec) and now 10 gigabit Ethernet offer cheaper and more easily managed services.

Still, ATM is a viable technology for backbones, even in gigabit Ethernet environments. ATM is easily scalable and integrates with most existing technologies.

More recently, new technologies such as DWDM (Dense Wave-Division Multiplexing) and optical networking may undo ATM and even SONET. DWDM puts hundreds and potentially thousands of lambda circuits on a single fiber. That means core networks will support very high capacity switched optical circuits, reducing the need for packet switched core networks. Imagine having an entire beam (wavelength) of light allocated for your personal use, switched into place when you need it and taken down when you have finished. That is what the new optical networks could provide. See "optical networks" for more information. With those trends in mind, the following sections provide an overview of ATM technology.

ATM REFERENCE MODEL

Figure 20.6 is a reference model that illustrates the organization of ATM functionality and the inter-relationships between the layers of functionality.

In the ATM reference model, the ATM layer and the ATM adaptation layers are roughly analogous parts of the data link layer of the Open System Interconnection (OSI) reference

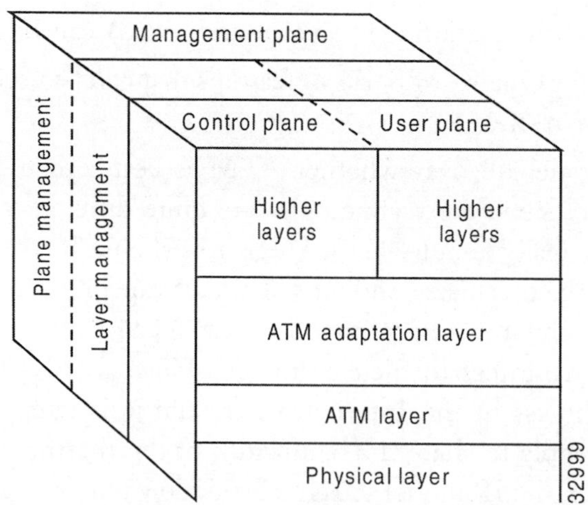

Figure 20.6 *ATM Reference Model.*

model, and the ATM physical layer is analogous to the physical layer of the OSI reference model. The control plane is responsible for generating and managing signaling requests. The user plane is responsible for managing the transfer of data. Above the ATM adaptation layer are higher-layer protocols representing traditional transports and applications.

Physical Layer

The ATM physical layer controls transmission and receipt of bits on the physical medium. It also keeps track of ATM cell boundaries and packages cells into the appropriate type of frame for the physical medium being used.

The ATM physical layer is divided into two parts : the physical medium sub-layer and the transmission convergence sub-layer. The physical medium sub-layer is responsible for sending and receiving a continuous flow of bits with associated timing information to synchronize transmission and reception. Because it includes only physical-medium-dependent functions, its specification depends on the physical medium used.

ATM can use any physical medium capable of carrying ATM cells. Some existing standards that can carry ATM cells are SONET (Synchronous Optical Network)/SDH, DS-3/E3, 100-Mbps local fiber (Fiber Distributed Data Interface [FDDI] physical layer), and 155-Mbps local fiber (fiber channel physical layer). Various proposals for use over twisted-pair wire are also under consideration.

The transmission convergence sub-layer is responsible for the following :

- Cell delineation—Maintains ATM cell boundaries.
- Header error control sequence generation and verification—Generates and checks the header error control code to ensure valid data.
- Cell rate decoupling—Inserts or suppresses idle (unassigned) ATM cells to adapt the rate of valid ATM cells to the payload capacity of the transmission system.
- Transmission frame adaptation—Packages ATM cells into frames acceptable to the particular physical-layer implementation.
- Transmission frame generation and recovery—Generates and maintains the appropriate physical layer frame structure.

ATM LAYER

The ATM layer is responsible for establishing connections and passing cells through the ATM network. To do this, it uses the information contained in the header of each ATM cell. For more information about how information in the header is used to pass cells through an ATM network.

ATM Adaptation Layer

The ATM Adaptation Layer (AAL) translates between the larger Service Data Units (SDUs) (for example, video streams, and data packets) of upper-layer processes and ATM cells. Specifically, the ATM Adaptation Layer (AAL) receives packets from upper-level protocols (such as AppleTalk, Internet Protocols [IP], and NetWare) and breaks them into the 48-byte segments that form the payload field of an ATM cell. Several ATM adaptation layers are currently specified. Table 20.1 summarizes the characteristics of each AAL.

Table 20.1 ATM Adaptation Layers

Characteristics	*AAL1*	*AAL3/4*	*AAL4*	*AAL5*
Requires timing between source and destination	Yes	No	No	No
Data rate	Constant	Variable	Variable	Variable
Connection mode	Connection-oriented	Connection-oriented	Connectionless	Connection-oriented
Traffic types	Voice and circuit emulation	Data	Data	Data

Figure 20.7 shows how AAL1 prepares a cell for transmission.

The payload data consists of a synchronous sample—for example, 1 byte of data generated at a sampling rate of 125 microseconds.

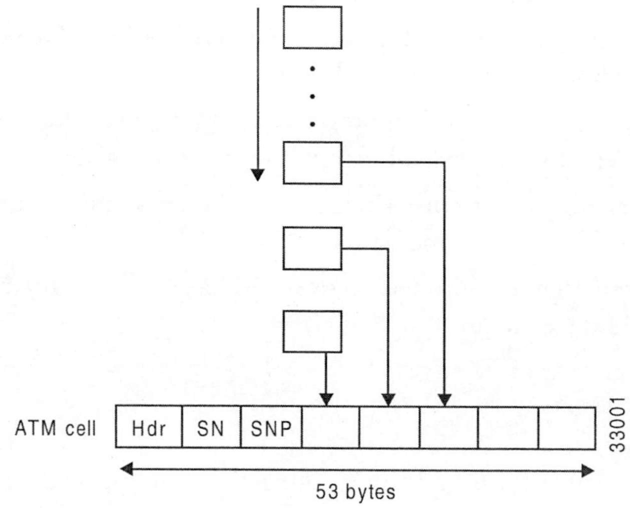

Figure 20.7 *AAL1 Cell Preparation.*

AAL1

The Sequence Number (SN) field and Sequence Number Protection (SNP) fields provide the information that the receiving AAL1 needs to verify that it has received the cells in the correct order. The remainder of the payload field is filled with enough single bytes to equal 48 bytes.

AAL1 is appropriate for transporting telephone traffic and uncompressed video traffic. It requires timing synchronization between the source and destination and, for that reason, depends on a media that supports clocking, such as SONET. The standards for supporting clock recovery are currently being defined.

AAL3/4

AAL3/4 was designed for network service providers and is closely aligned with Switched Multi-megabit Data Service (SMDS). AAL3/4 will be used to transmit SMDS packets over an ATM network.

As shown in figure 20.8, the Convergence Sub-layer (CS) creates a Protocol Data Unit (PDU) by pre-pending a beginning/end tag header to the frame and appending a length field as a trailer.

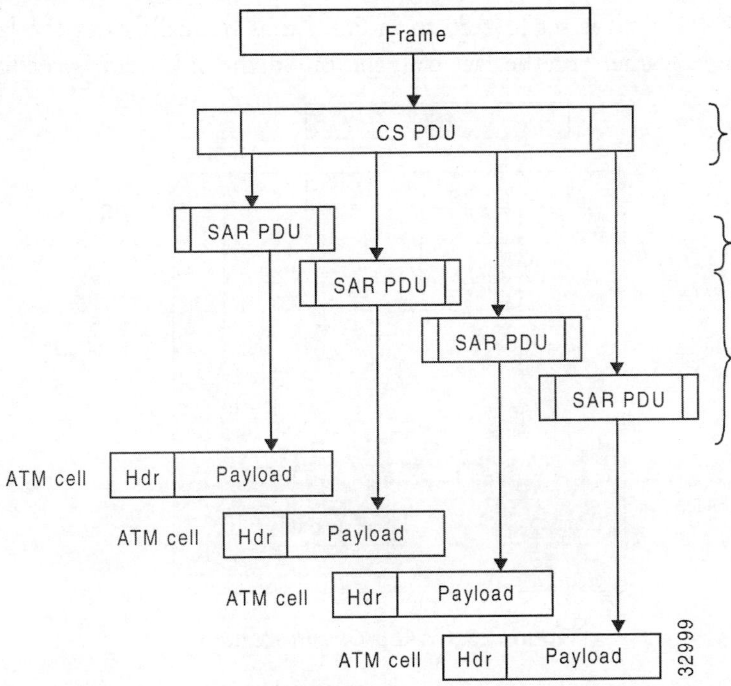

Figure 20.8 *AAL3/4 Cell Preparation.*

The Segmentation and Reassembly (SAR) sub-layer fragments the PDU and pre-pends to each PDU fragment a header consisting of the following fields :

- *Type*—Identifies whether the cell is the beginning of a message, continuation of a message, or end of a message.
- *Sequence number*—Identifies the order in which cells should be reassembled.
- *Multiplexing identifier*—Identifies cells from different traffic sources interleaved on the same Virtual Circuit Connection (VCC) so that the correct cells are reassembled at the destination.

The SAR sub-layer also appends a CRC-10 trailer to each PDU fragment. The completed SAR PDU becomes the payload field of an ATM cell to which the ATM layer pre-pends the standard ATM header.

AAL5

Figure 20.9 shows how AAL5 prepares a cell for transmission. First, the convergence sub-layer of AAL5 appends a variable-length pad and a 8-byte trailer to a frame. The pad is long enough to ensure that the resulting PDU falls on the 48-byte boundary of the ATM cell. The trailer includes the length of the frame and a 32-bit CRC computed across the entire PDU, which allows AAL5 at the destination to detect bit errors and lost or cells that are out of sequence.

Next, the segmentation and reassembly segments the CS PDU into 48-byte blocks. Then the ATM layer places each block into the payload field of an ATM cell. For all cells except the last cell, a bit in the PT field is set to zero to indicate that the cell is not the last cell in a series that represent a single frame. For the last cell, the bit in the PT field is set to one.

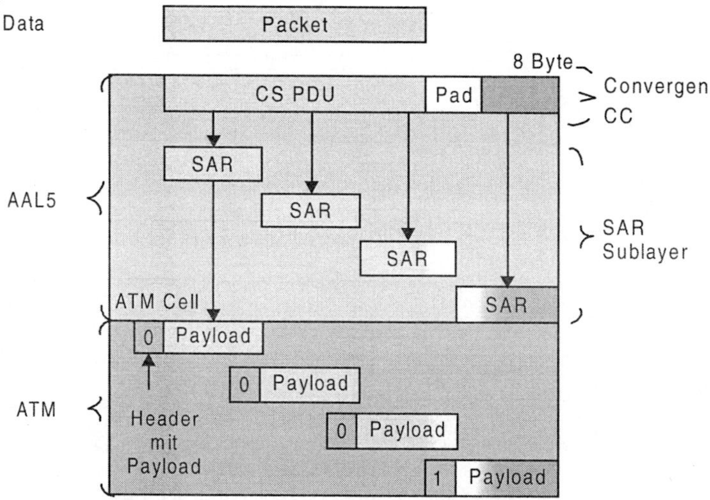

Figure 20.9 *AAL5 Cell Preparation.*

When the cell arrives at its destination, the ATM layer extracts the payload field from the cell; the SAR sub-layer reassembles the CS PDU; and the CS uses the CRC and the length field to verify that the frame has been transmitted and reassembled correctly.

AAL5 is the adaptation layer used to transfer most non-SMDS data, such as classical IP over ATM and Local Area Network (LAN) emulation.

ADDRESSING

The ATM forum has adopted the sub-network model of addressing, in which the ATM layer is responsible for mapping network layer addresses to ATM addresses. Several ATM address formats have been developed—one for public networks and three for private networks. Typically, public ATM networks will use E.164 numbers, which are also used by Narrowband Integrated Services Digital Network (NISDN) networks.

Figure 20.10 shows the format of private network ATM addresses. The three formats are Data Country Code (DCC), International Code Designator (ICD), and Network Service Access Point (NSAP) encapsulated E.164 addresses.

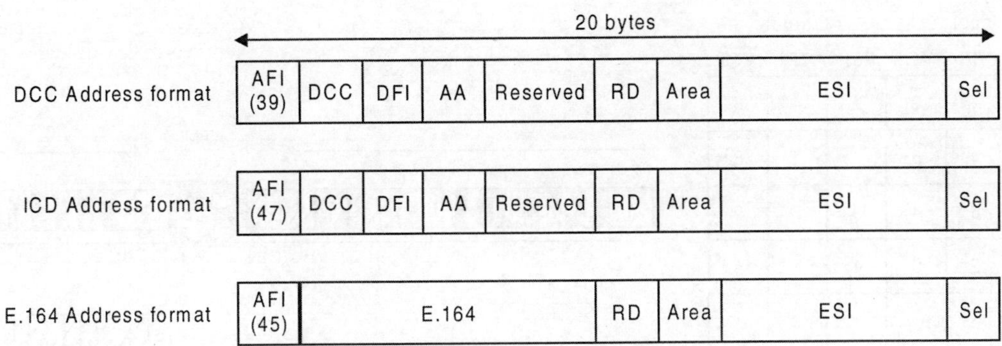

Figure 20.10 *ATM Address Formats*

The fields of an ATM address are as follows :

AFI—1 byte of authority and format identifier. The AFI field identifies the type of address. The defined values are 45, 47, and 39 for E.164, ICD, and DCC addresses, respectively.

DCC—2 bytes of data country code.

DFI—1 byte of Domain Specific Part (DSP) format identifier.

AA—3 bytes of administrative authority.

RD—2 bytes of routing domain.

Area—2 bytes of area identifier.

ESI—6 bytes of end system identifier, which is an IEEE 802 Media Access Control (MAC) address.

Sel—1 byte of NSAP selector.

ICD—2 bytes of international code designator.

E.164—8 bytes of Integrated Services Digital Network (ISDN) telephone number.

The ATM address formats are modeled on ISO NSAP addresses, but they identify Sub-Network Point of Attachment (SNPA) addresses. Incorporating the MAC address into the ATM address makes it easy to map ATM addresses into existing LANs.

ATM SWITCHING

ATM switches use the VPI and VCI fields of the cell header to identify the next network segment that a cell needs to transit on its way to its final destination. A virtual channel is equivalent to a virtual circuit—that is, both terms describe a logical connection between the two ends of a communications connection. A virtual path is a logical grouping of virtual circuits that allows an ATM switch to perform operations on groups of virtual circuits.

The main function of an ATM switch is to receive cells on a port and switch those cells to the proper output port based on the VPI and VCI values of the cell. This switching is dictated by a switching table that maps input ports to output ports based on the values of the VPI and VCI fields, as shown in figure 20.11.

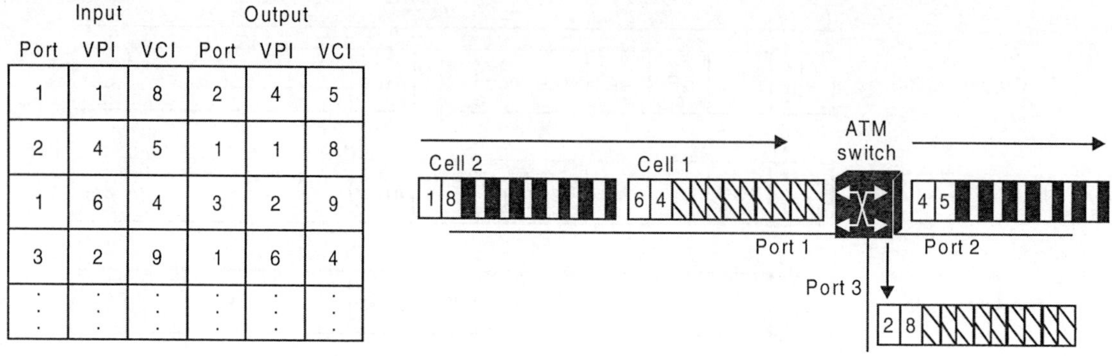

Input Port	Input VPI	Input VCI	Output Port	Output VPI	Output VCI
1	1	8	2	4	5
2	4	5	1	1	8
1	6	4	3	2	9
3	2	9	1	6	4
⋮	⋮	⋮	⋮	⋮	⋮

Figure 20.11 *Maintenance of Virtual Connections through an ATM Switch.*

Say, for example, that two cells arrive on port 1 of the ATM switch in figure 20.12. First, the switch examines the VPI and VCI fields of cell 1 and finds that the fields have a value of 6 and 4, respectively. The switch examines the switch table to determine on which port it should send the cell. It finds that when it receives a VPI of 6 and a VCI of 4 on port 1, it should send the cell on port 3 with a VPI of 2 and a VCI of 9. So, for cell 1, the switch changes the VPI to 2 and the VCI to 9 and sends the cell out on port 3.

Next, the switch examines cell 2, which has a VPI of 1 and a VCI of 8. The table directs the switch to send out on port 2 cells received on port 1 that have a VPI of 1 and a VCI of 8, respectively, and to change the VPI and VCI to 4 and 5, respectively.

Conversely, when a cell with a VPI and VCI of 2 and 9, respectively, comes in on port 3, the table directs the switch to send the cell out on port 1 with a VPI and VCI of 6 and 4, respectively. When a cell with a VPI and VCI of 4 and 5, respectively, comes in on port 2, the table directs the switch to send the cell out on port 1 with a VPI and VCI of 1 and 8, respectively. Note that VPI and VCI values are significant only to the local interface.

Figure 20.12 shows how the VPI field is used to group virtual channels (identified by their VCI values) into logical groups. By reducing the number of fields that have to be changed as each cell passes through the switch, the performance of the switch increases.

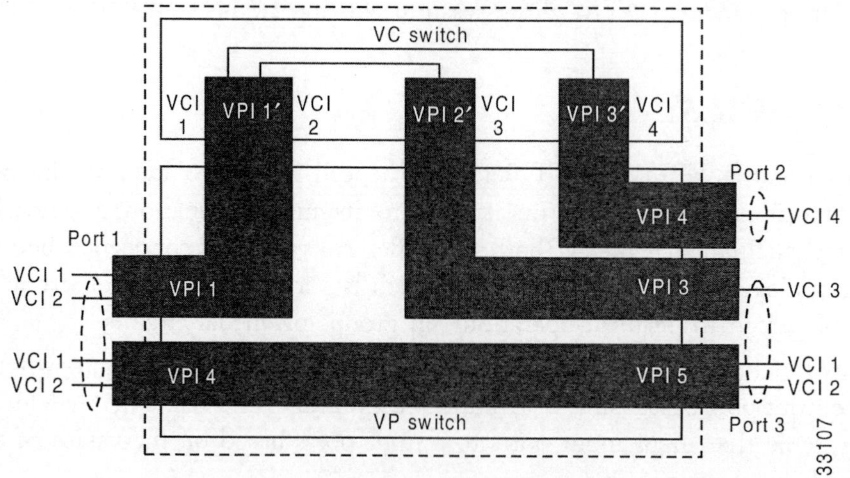

Figure 20.12 *Virtual Paths Form Logical Groups of Virtual Channels.*

VIRTUAL CHANNELS

In figure, cells that enter the ATM switch on port 1 and have a VPI value of 4 are processed through the "VP switch," which changes the VPI value of each cell to 5, but leaves the VCI value intact, and sends the cell out on port 3. Cells that have a VPI value of 1 are processed through the "VC switch." For cells that have a VCI value of 1, the VC switch changes the VPI to 4 and the VCI to 4 and sends the cell out on port 2. For cells that have a VCI value of 2, the VC switch changes the VPI to 3 and the VCI to 3 and sends the cell out on port 3.

Connection Types

ATM supports two connection types, as shown in figure 20.13.

- *Point-to-point:* Connections of this type can be unidirectional or bidirectional.
- *Point-to-multipoint:* Connections of this type are unidirectional only.

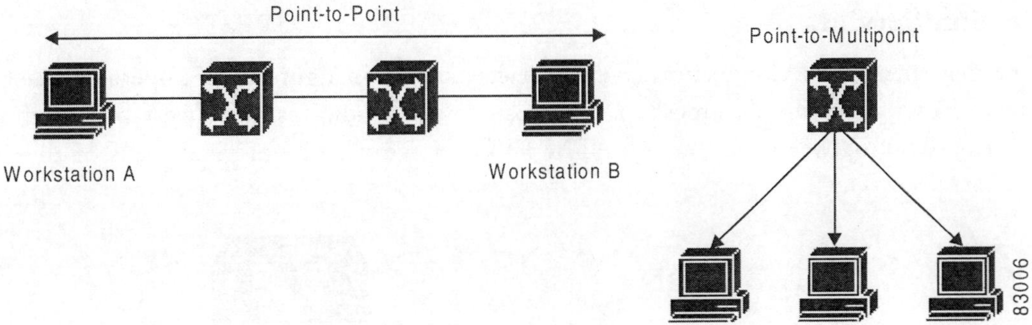

Figure 20.13 *ATM Connection Types.*

It would be desirable for ATM to support multipoint-to-multipoint links, which would be equivalent to a broadcast VCC. Unfortunately, the AAL5 standard does not provide a way for the receiver to identify individual cells from specific sources when cells are interleaved from multiple sources. This would not allow proper reassembly of cells into frames, unless all of the cells of a specific frame are sent in proper order, without any interleaving.

A multicast server is one solution to this problem. A multicast server can exist in an ATM network, and all members of a multicast group can establish point-to-point VCCs to it. The multicast server would then create a point-to-multipoint VCC to all members on the group, with itself at the root, as shown in figure 20.14.

Any data sent to the multicast server is serialized, sent out by the point-to-multipoint tree, and received by the members of the group. The value of this approach is that cells from different sources are serialized and sent in order rather than interleaved. The multicast server can also support dynamic groups because members can be added and deleted as leaves on the tree.

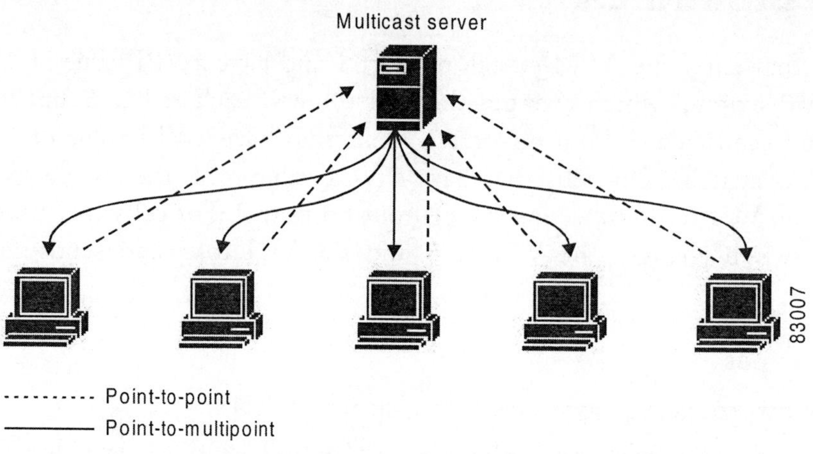

Figure 20.14 *ATM Multicast Server.*

Connection Services

ATM Permanent Virtual Connection (PVC) service, shown in figure 20.15, operates much like frame relay—a virtual connection mesh, partial mesh, or star is administratively established through the ATM network between the routers. ATM PVC service was the original focus of the ATM forum.

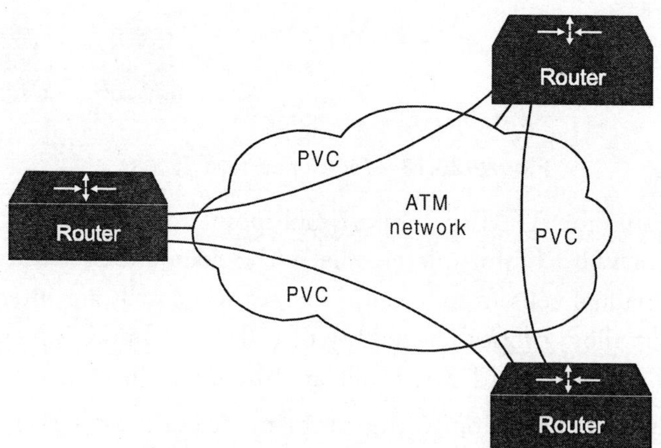

Figure 20.15 *ATM PVC Service.*

Advantages of ATM PVC service include a direct ATM connection between routers and the simplicity of the specification and subsequent implementation. Disadvantages include static connectivity and the administrative overhead of provisioning virtual connections manually.

Quality of Service

When an ATM end station connects to the ATM network, it is essentially making a contract with the network based on Quality of Service (QOS) parameters. This contract specifies an envelope that describes the intended traffic flow. This envelope specifies values for peak bandwidth, average sustained bandwidth, and burst size.

It is the responsibility of the ATM device to adhere to the contract by means of traffic shaping. Traffic shaping is the use of queues to constrain data bursts, limit peak data rate, and smooth jitter so that the traffic will fit within the promised envelope.

ATM switches have the option of using traffic policing to enforce the contract. The switch can measure the actual traffic flow and compare it against the agreed upon traffic envelope. If it finds that traffic is outside of the agreed upon parameters, the switch can set the CLP bit of the offending cells. Setting the CLP bit makes the cell discard eligible, which means that the switch, or any other switch handling the cell, is allowed to drop the cell during periods of congestion, as shown in figure 20.16.

Traffic Policing

Congestion control is a primary concern of ATM designers. For example, dropping just one cell that is part of a FDDI frame can result in the retransmission of 93 cells. Retransmission can lead to an exponential increase in congestion as ATM switches drop individual cells from different packets, resulting in retransmission of more packets, which causes even more cells to be dropped.

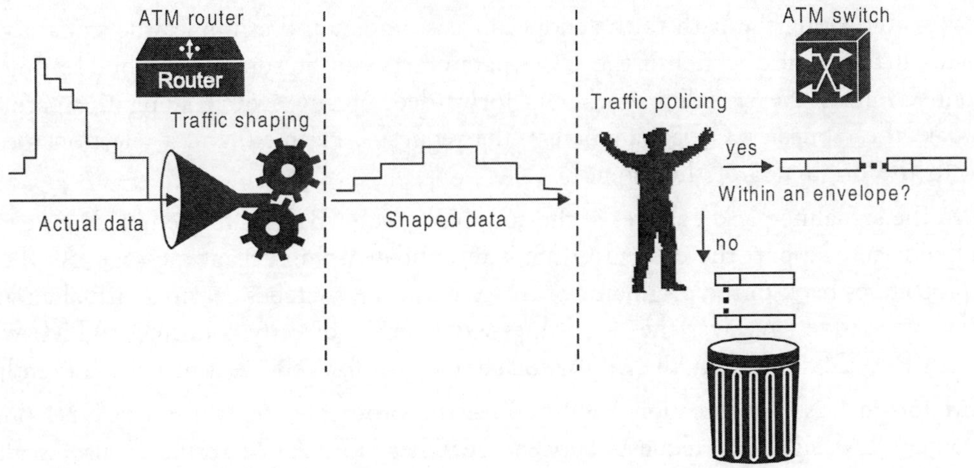

Figure 20.16 *Traffic Shaping and Traffic Policing.*

The ATM forum is currently working to define a congestion-control scheme, but that effort is not likely to be completed before mid-1995.

Signaling

When an ATM device, such as router A in figure 20.17, wants to establish a connection with another ATM device such as router B, router A sends a signaling request packet to its directly connected ATM switch. This request contains the ATM address of the desired ATM endpoint (router B, in this case), as well as any QOS parameters required for the connection.

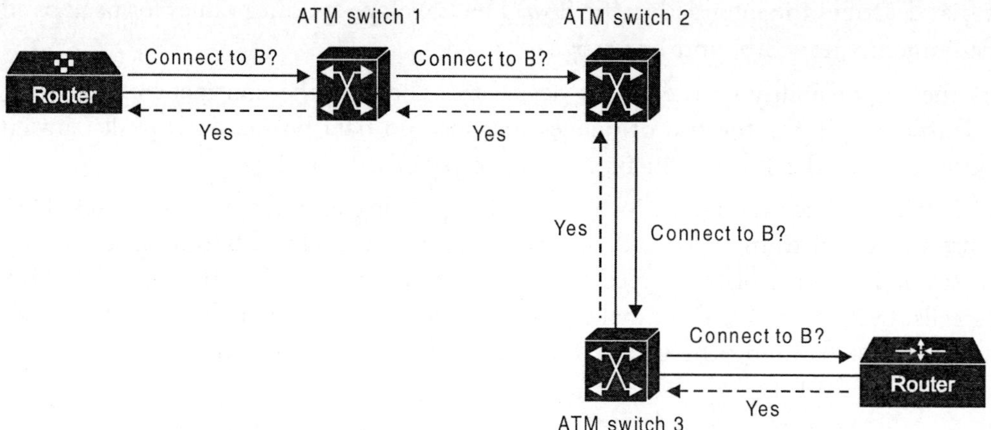

Figure 20.17 *Signaling Requests Transit the Network.*

The signaling packet is reassembled by the switch and examined. If the switch has a switch table entry for router B's ATM address, and it can accommodate the QOS requested for the connection, it sets up the virtual connection on the input link and forwards the request out the interface specified in the switching table for the ATM NSAP of router B.

Every switch along the path to the endpoint reassembles and examines the signaling packet and forwards it to the next switch if the QOS parameters can be supported while setting up the virtual connection as the signaling packet is forwarded. If any switch along the path cannot accommodate the requested QOS parameters, the request is rejected, and a rejection message is sent back to the originator of the request.

When the signaling packet arrives at the endpoint (router B), it is reassembled and evaluated. If the endpoint can support the desired QOS, it responds with an accept message. As the accept message propagates back to the originator of the request, the switches set up a virtual circuit. The originator of the request receives the accept message from its directly connected ATM switch, as well as the VPI/VCI value that the originator should use for cells destined for the endpoint.

ATM forum UNI specification V3.0 defines the protocols, known as the NNI protocols, used to route ATM signaling requests between switches. The ATM forum is also working on Private NNI (P-NNI) protocols for use in multi-switch private ATM networks. The ATM forum has also defined a P-NNI phase 0 protocol, based on UNI 3.0 signaling and static routes; it is continuing work on a P-NNI phase 1 protocol that supports dynamic routing.

REVIEW QUESTIONS

1. Why is ADSL asymmetric ?
2. What is the size of an ATM cell ?
3. What fields make up an ATM cell ? How many bytes are in each field ?
4. What does a virtual channel identifier identify ?

5. What is the purpose of the ATM Adaptation Layer (AAL) convergence sub-layer ?
6. Which AAL layer applies to traffic already in ATM cell format ?
7. How does frame relay differ from ATM ?
8. Which data link protocol is used as the basis for a frame relay format ?
9. Which frame relay format field resembles ATM's cell loss priority field ?
10. How is an ATM virtual-connection identified ?
11. Name the ATM layers and their functions.
12. In regard to quality of service, how do user-related attributes differ from network-related attributes in ATM ?
13. What is ATM ? Explain its protocol architecture and applications.

21 FIBER DISTRIBUTED DATA INTERFACE

FIBER DISTRIBUTED DATA INTERFACE (FDDI)

FDDI is an American National Standards Institute (ANSI) topology standard that uses fiber-optic cable and token-passing media access. FDDI is implemented using both multimode and single mode fiber cable and can reach transmissions speeds of up to 100Mbps at distances of more than 2 kilometers. FDDI combines the strengths of Token Ring, the speed of Fast Ethernet, and the security of fiber-optic cable. Such advantages make FDDI a strong candidate for creating network backbones and connecting private LANs to create MANs and WANs.

Unlike the regular 802.5 network standard, FDDI uses a dual-ring configuration. The first, or primary, ring is used to transfer the data around the network, and the secondary ring is used for redundancy and fault tolerance; the secondary ring waits to take over if the primary ring fails. If the primary ring fails, the secondary ring kicks in automatically, with no disruption to network users.

FDDI has a few significant advantages some of which stem directly from the fact that is uses fiber-optic cable as its transmission media. These include a resistance to EMI, the security offered by fiber, and the longer distances available with fiber cable. In addition to the advantages provided by the fiber-optic cable, FDDI itself has a few strong points, including

- Fault-tolerant design By using a dual-ring configuration, FDDI provides some fault tolerance. If one cable fails, the other can be used to transmit the data throughout the network.
- Speed because of the use of multiple tokens Unlike the IEEE 802.5 standard, FDDI uses multiple tokens, which increase the overall network speed.
- Beaconing FDDI uses beaconing as a built-in error-detection method, making finding faults, such as cable breaks, a lot easier.

Like every technology, there are always a few caveats:

- High cost the costs associated with FDDI and the devices and cable needed to implement and FDDI solution are very costly; too costly for many small organizations.

- Implementation difficulty FDDI setup and management can be very complex, requiring trained professionals with significant experience to manage and maintain the cable and infrastructure.

The Fiber Distributed Data Interface (FDDI) standard was produced by the ANSI X3T9.5 standards committee in the mid-1980s. During this period, high-speed engineering workstations were beginning to tax the capabilities of existing Local-Area Networks (LANs) (primarily Ethernet and token ring). A new LAN was needed that could easily support these workstations and their new distributed applications. At the same time, network reliability was becoming an increasingly important issue as system managers began to migrate mission-critical applications from large computers to networks. FDDI was developed to fill these needs.

After completing the FDDI specification, ANSI submitted FDDI to the International Organization for Standardization (ISO). ISO has created an international version of FDDI that is completely compatible with the ANSI standard version.

Today, although FDDI implementations are not as common as Ethernet or token ring, FDDI has gained a substantial following that continues to increase as the cost of FDDI interfaces diminishes. FDDI is frequently used as a backbone technology as well as a means to connect high-speed computers in a local area.

Technology Basics

FDDI specifies a 100-Mbps, token-passing, dual-ring LAN using a fiber-optic transmission medium. It defines the physical layer and media-access portion of the link layer, and so is roughly analogous to IEEE 802.3 and IEEE 802.5 in its relationship to the Open System Interconnection (OSI) reference model.

Although it operates at faster speeds, FDDI is similar in many ways to token ring. The two networks share many features, including topology (ring), media-access technique (token passing), reliability features (redundant rings, for example), and others. One of the most important characteristics of FDDI is its use of optical fiber as a transmission medium. Optical fiber offers several advantages over traditional copper wiring, including security (fiber does not emit electrical signals that can be tapped), reliability (fiber is immune to electrical interference), and speed (optical fiber has much higher throughput potential than copper cable).

FDDI defines use of two types of fiber: *single mode* (sometimes called *mono-mode*) and *multimode*. Modes can be thought of as bundles of light rays entering the fiber at a particular angle. Single-mode fiber allows only one mode of light to propagate through the fiber, while multimode fiber allows multiple modes of light to propagate through the fiber. Because multiple modes of light propagating through the fiber may travel different distances (depending on the entry angles), causing them to arrive at the destination at different times (a phenomenon called *modal dispersion*), single-mode fiber is capable of higher bandwidth and greater cable run distances than multimode fiber. Due to these characteristics, single-mode fiber is often used for inter-building connectivity, while multimode fiber is often used for intra-building connectivity. Multimode fiber uses Light-Emitting Diodes (LEDs) as the light-generating devices, while single-mode fiber generally uses lasers.

FDDI Specifications

FDDI is defined by four separate specifications:

Media Access Control (MAC)—Defines how the medium is accessed, including frame format, token handling, addressing, algorithm for calculating a cyclic redundancy check value, and error recovery mechanisms.

Physical Layer Protocol (PHY)—Defines data encoding/decoding procedures, clocking requirements, framing, and other functions.

Physical Layer Medium (PMD)—Defines the characteristics of the transmission medium, including the fiber-optic link, power levels, bit error rates, optical components, and connectors.

Station Management (SMT)—Defines the FDDI station configuration, ring configuration, and ring control features, including station insertion and removal, initialization, fault isolation and recovery, scheduling, and collection of statistics.

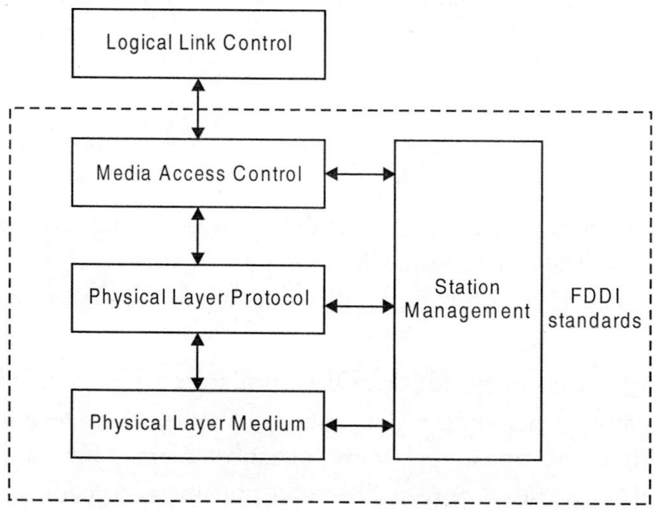

Figure 21.1 *FDDI Standards.*

Physical Connections

FDDI specifies the use of dual rings. Traffic on these rings travels in opposite directions. Physically, the rings consist of two or more point-to-point connections between adjacent stations. One of the two FDDI rings is called the *primary* ring; the other is called the *secondary* ring. The primary ring is used for data transmission, while the secondary ring is generally used as a backup.

Class B or Single-Attachment Stations (SAS) attach to one ring; Class A or Dual-Attachment Stations (DAS) attach to both rings. SASs are attached to the primary ring through a *concentrator*, which provides connections for multiple SASs. The concentrator ensures that failure or power down of any given SAS does not interrupt the ring. This is particularly useful when PCs, or similar devices that frequently power on and off, connect to the ring.

A typical FDDI configuration with both DASs and SASs is shown in figure 21.2.

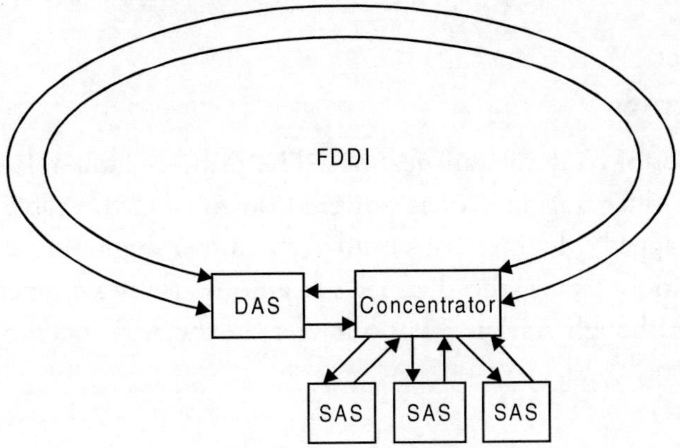

Figure 21.2 *FDDI Nodes: DAS, SAS, and Concentrator.*

Each FDDI DAS has two ports, designated A and B. These ports connect the station to the dual FDDI ring. Therefore, each port provides a connection for both the primary and the secondary ring, as shown in figure 21.3.

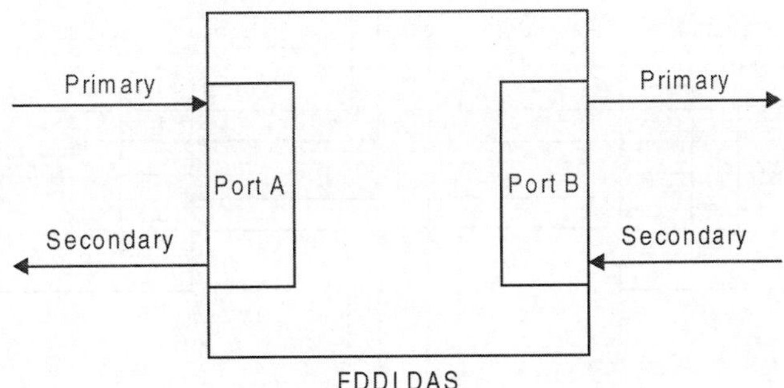

Figure 21.3 *FDDI DAS Ports.*

Traffic Types

FDDI supports real-time allocation of network bandwidth, making it ideal for a variety of different application types. FDDI provides this support by defining two types of traffic: *synchronous* and *asynchronous*. Synchronous traffic can consume a portion of the 100 Mbps total bandwidth of an FDDI network, while asynchronous traffic can consume the rest. Synchronous bandwidth is allocated to those stations requiring continuous transmission capability. Such capability is useful for transmitting voice and video information, for example. Other stations use the remaining bandwidth asynchronously. The FDDI SMT specification defines a distributed bidding scheme to allocate FDDI bandwidth.

Asynchronous bandwidth is allocated using an eight-level priority scheme. Each station is assigned an asynchronous priority level. FDDI also permits extended dialogues, where stations may temporarily use all asynchronous bandwidth. The FDDI priority mechanism can essentially lock out stations that cannot use synchronous bandwidth and have too low an asynchronous priority.

Fault-Tolerant Features

FDDI provides a number of fault-tolerant features. The primary fault-tolerant feature is the dual ring. If a station on the dual ring fails or is powered down or if the cable is damaged, the dual ring is automatically "wrapped" (doubled back onto itself) into a single ring, as shown in figure 21.4. In this figure, when station 3 fails, the dual ring is automatically wrapped in stations 2 and 4, forming a single ring. Although station 3 is no longer on the ring, network operation continues for the remaining stations.

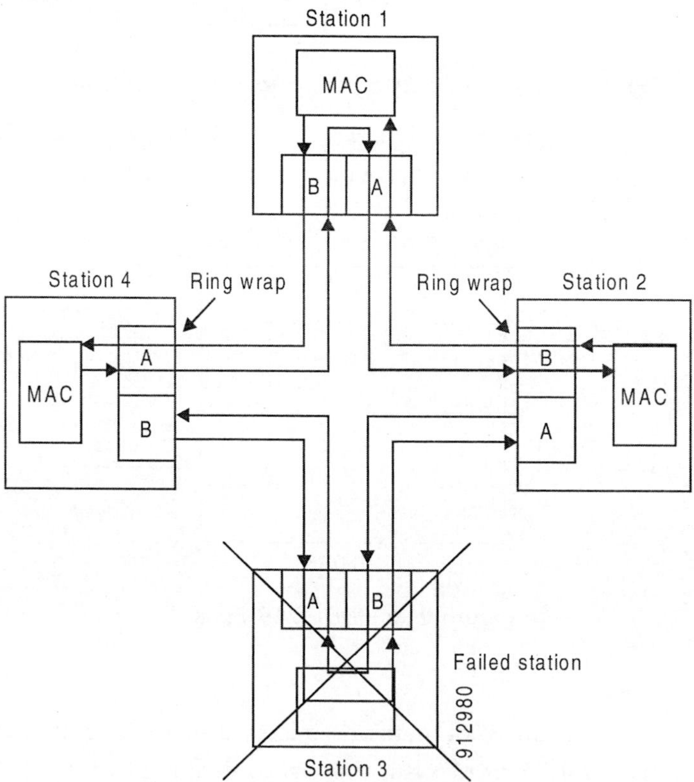

Figure 21.4 *Station Failure, Ring Recovery Configuration.*

Figure 21.5 shows how FDDI compensates for a wiring failure. Stations 3 and 4 wrap the ring within themselves when wiring between them fails.

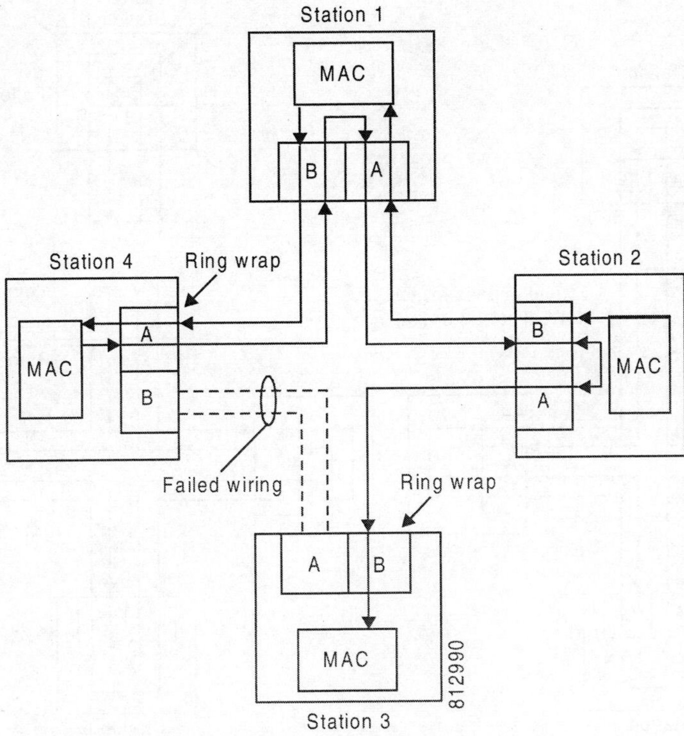

Figure 21.5 *Failed Wiring, Ring Recovery Configuration.*

As FDDI networks grow, the possibility of multiple ring failures grows. When two ring failures occur, the ring will be wrapped in both cases, effectively segmenting the ring into two separate rings that cannot communicate with each other. Subsequent failures cause additional ring segmentation.

Optical bypass switches can be used to prevent ring segmentation by eliminating failed stations from the ring. This is shown in figure 21.6.

Critical devices such as routers or mainframe hosts can use another fault-tolerant technique called *dual homing* to provide additional redundancy and help guarantee operation. In dual-homing situations, the critical device is attached to two concentrators. One pair of concentrator links is declared the active link; the other pair is declared passive. The passive link stays in backup mode until the primary link (or the concentrator to which it is attached) is determined to have failed. When this occurs, the passive link is automatically activated.

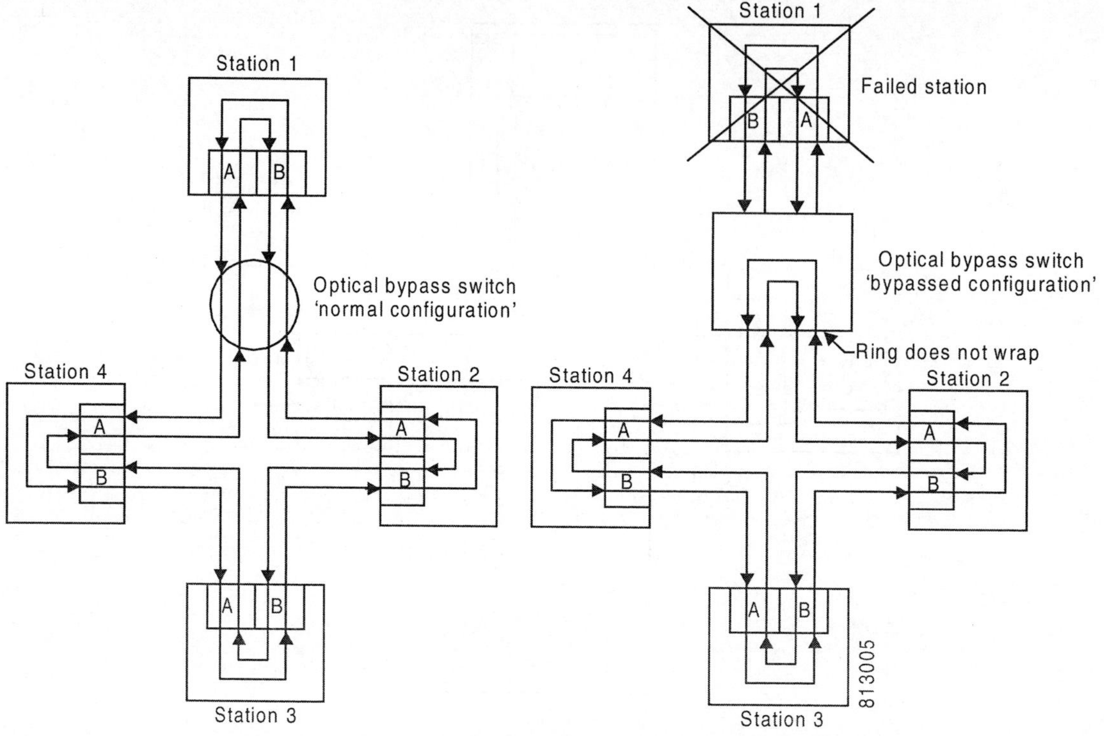

Figure 21.6 *Use of Optical Bypass Switch.*

Frame Format

FDDI frame formats (shown in figure 21.7) are similar to those of token ring.

The fields of an FDDI frame are as follows:

Preamble—Prepares each station for the upcoming frame.

Start delimiter—Indicates the beginning of the frame. It consists of signaling patterns that differentiate it from the rest of the frame.

Frame control—Indicates the size of the address fields, whether the frame contains asynchronous or synchronous data, and other control information.

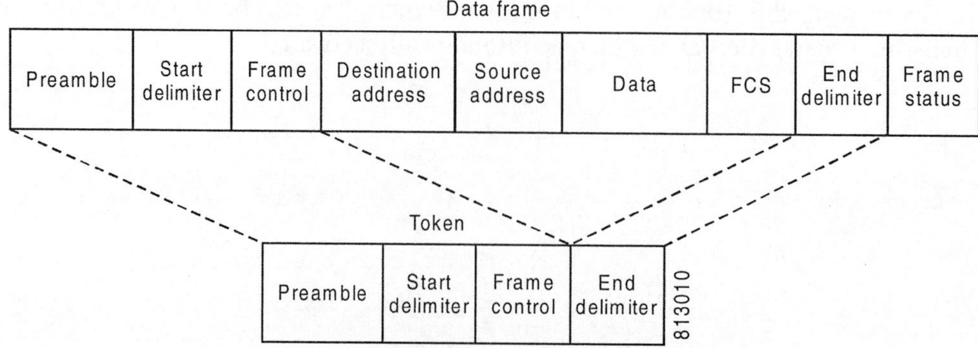

Figure 21.7 *FDDI Frame Format.*

Destination address—Contains a uni-cast (singular), multicast (group), or broadcast (every station) address. As with Ethernet and token ring, FDDI destination addresses are 6 bytes.

Source address—Identifies the single station that sent the frame. As with Ethernet and token ring, FDDI source addresses are 6 bytes.

Data—Contains either information destined for an upper-layer protocol or control information.

Frame Check Sequence (FCS)—Filled by the source station with a calculated Cyclic Redundancy Check (CRC) value dependent on the frame contents (as with token ring and Ethernet). The destination station recalculates the value to determine whether the frame may have been damaged in transit. If so, the frame is discarded.

End delimiter—Contains non-data symbols that indicate the end of the frame.

Frame status—Allows the source station to determine if an error occurred and if the frame was recognized and copied by a receiving station.

FDDI STATION TYPES

There are two main types of stations, class A which attach directly to dual rings; or class B which attach to a station acting as a concentrator.

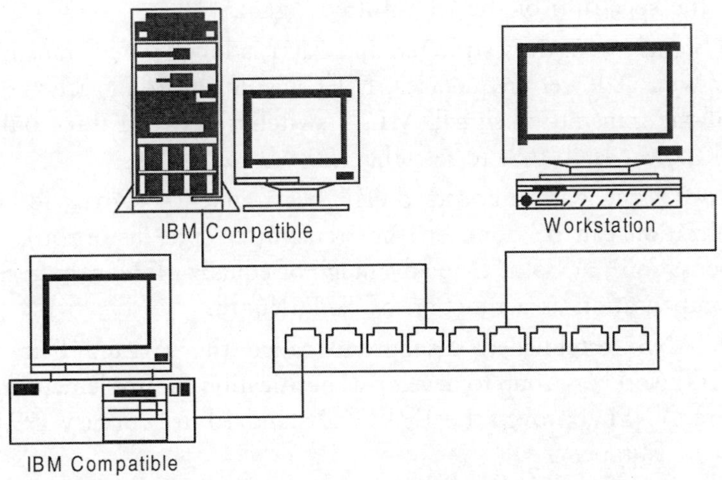

Figure 21.8 *Logical Networks Versus Physical Networks.*

A concentrator is a specialized workstation that attaches to the ring and has multiple ports that allow attachment of other devices in a physical star configuration. These may be cascaded.

A logical network describes how the network operates. A physical network describes how the network has been cabled. It is thus possible to have a physical star, logical bus network. In other words, the network operates as a bus network, but the cabling has been implemented using star topology.

CDDI

The high cost of fiber-optic cable has been a major impediment to the widespread deployment of FDDI to desktop computers. At the same time, Shielded Twisted-Pair (STP) and Unshielded Twisted-Pair (UTP) copper wire is relatively inexpensive and has been widely deployed. The implementation of FDDI over copper wire is known as Copper Distributed Data Interface (CDDI).

Before FDDI could be implemented over copper wire, a problem had to be solved. When signals strong enough to be reliably interpreted as data are transmitted over twisted-pair wire, the wire radiates Electromagnetic Interference (EMI). Any attempt to implement FDDI over twisted-pair wire had to ensure that the resulting energy radiation did not exceed the specifications set in the United States by the Federal Communications Commission (FCC) and in Europe by the European Economic Council (EEC). Three technologies reduce energy radiation:

- **Scrambling:** When no data is being sent, FDDI transmits an idle pattern that consists of a string of binary ones. When this signal is sent over twisted-pair wire, the EMI is concentrated at the fundamental frequency spectrum of the idle pattern, resulting in a peak in the frequency spectrum of the radiated interference. By scrambling FDDI data with a pseudo-random sequence prior to transmission, repetitive patterns are eliminated. The elimination of repetitive patterns results in a spectral peak that is distributed more evenly over the spectrum of the transmitted signal.
- **Encoding:** Signal strength is stronger, and EMI is lower when transmission occurs over twisted-pair wire at lower frequencies. MLT3 is an encoding scheme that reduces the frequency of the transmitted signal. MLT3 switches between three output voltage levels so that peak power is shifted to less than 20 MHz.
- **Equalization:** Equalization boosts the higher frequency signals for transmission over UTP. Equalization can be done on the transmitter (pre-distortion), or at the receiver (post-compensation), or both. One advantage of equalization at the receiver is the ability to adjust compensation as a function of cable length.

In June 1990, ANSI established a subgroup called the Twisted Pair-Physical Medium Dependent (TP-PMD) working group to develop a specification for implementing FDDI protocols over twisted-pair wire. ANSI approved the TP-PMD standard in February 1994. Approval of the standard is pending in Europe.

Devices called concentrators provide functions similar to hubs. Most concentrators use dual attachment station network cards but single attachment concentrators may be used to attach more workstations to the network.

FDDI token passing allows multiple frames to circulate around the ring at the same time. Priority levels of a data frame and token can be set to allow servers to send more data frames. Time sensitive data may also be given higher priority. The second ring in a FDDI network is a method of adjusting when there are breaks in the cable. The primary ring is normally used, but if the nearest downstream neighbor stops responding the data is sent on the secondary ring in attempt to reach the computer. Therefore a break in the cable will result in the secondary ring being used. There are two network cards which are:

Dual Attachment Stations (DAS) used for servers and concentrators are attached to both rings.

Single Attachment Stations (SAS) attached to one ring and used to attach workstations to concentrators.

A router or switch can link an FDDI network to a Local Area Network (LAN). Normally FDDI is used to link LANs together since it covers long distances.

Today, although FDDI implementations are not as common as Ethernet or token ring, FDDI has gained a substantial following that continues to increase as the cost of FDDI interfaces diminishes. FDDI is frequently used as a backbone technology as well as a means to connect high-speed computers in a local area.

DQDB: DISTRIBUTED QUEUE DUAL BUS DEFINED IN IEEE 802.6

Distributed Queue Dual Bus (DQDB) is a data link layer communication protocol for Metropolitan Area Networks (MANs), specified in the IEEE 802.6 standard, designed for use in MANs. DQDB is designed for data as well as voice and video transmission based on cell switching technology (similar to ATM). DQDB, which permits multiple systems to interconnect using two unidirectional logical buses, is an open standard that is designed for compatibility with carrier transmission standards such as SMDS, which is based on the DQDB standards.

For a MAN to be effective it requires a system that can function across long, city-wide distances of several miles, have a low susceptibility to error, adapt to the number of nodes attached and have variable bandwidth distribution. Using DQDB, networks can be thirty miles long and function in the range of 34 Mbps to 155 Mbps. The data rate fluctuates due to many hosts sharing a dual bus as well as the location of a single host in relation to the frame generator, but there are schemes to compensate for this problem making DQDB function reliably and fairly for all hosts.

DQDB Concept

- A dual bus, with stations attached to both buses
- A frame generator at the end of each bus, creating frames of empty slots
- Stations can read from a bus, and can OR in data to a bus
- Station failure must leave the bus operating (isolation)

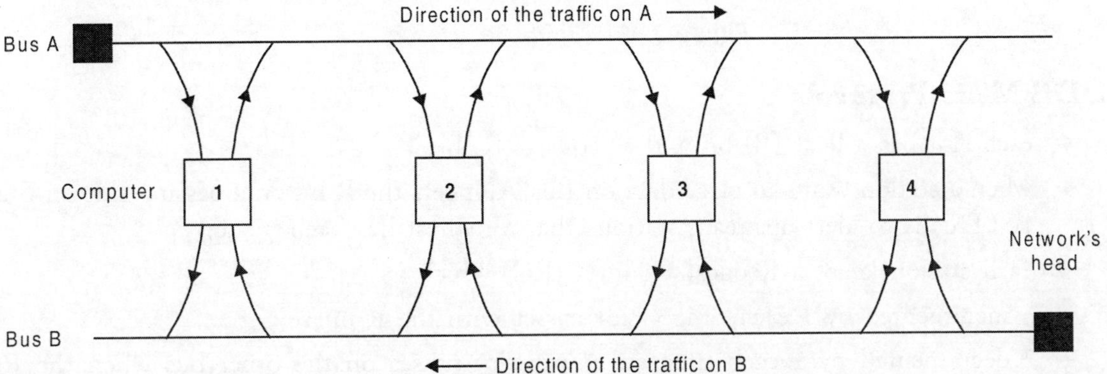

Figure 21.9 *DQDB Architecture.*

DQDB Frame Structure

- A basic 125 microsec. frame is used, containing multiple slots.
- Each slot has:

  4 octet preamble

  53 octet payload (ATM compatible)

  numbers of slots vary according to bus speed, *e.g.*, 8/frame for 34 Mbps

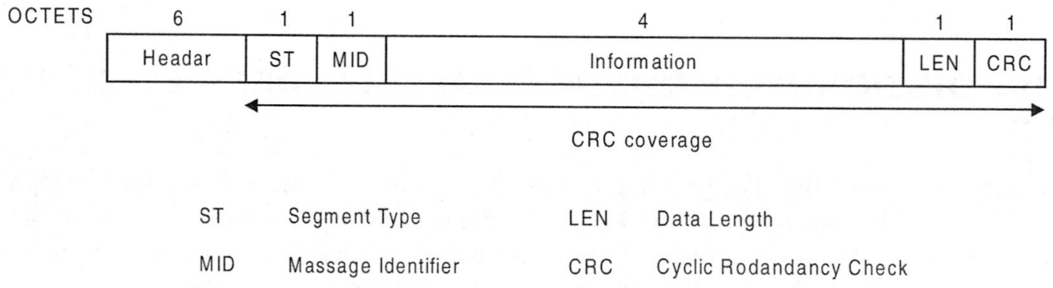

Figure 21.10 *DQDB Cell Format.*

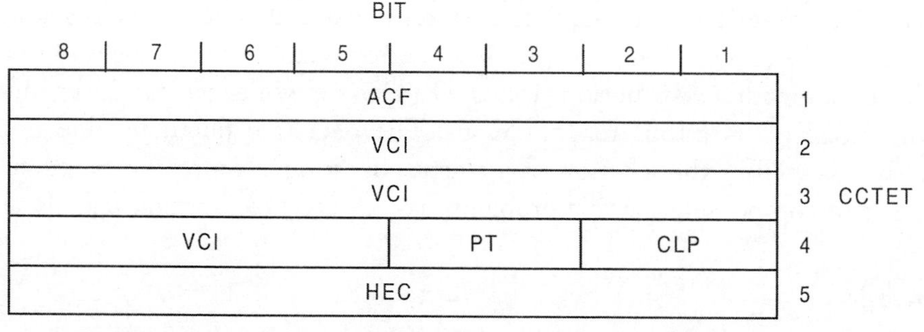

Figure 21.11 *DQDB Cell Header.*

DQDB MAC Protocol

- each slot has a busy (B) bit and a request (R) bit
- when a station wants to place data on Bus-A, it sets the R bit on a passing slot on Bus-B. (This is to alert upstream stations that a request has been made.)
- each station keeps a Request Counter (RC) which is:
  - incremented by 1 each time a slot passes with the R bit set
  - decremented by 1 each time an empty slot passes on the other bus when the RC reaches 0, the station can use the next empty (B not set) slot on the other bus.

REVIEW QUESTIONS

1. What are the tasks of the FDDI Media Access Control (MAC) protocol ?
2. What is the primary responsibility of the Station Management Protocol(SMT) ?
3. What are the uses of the Physical (PHY) and Physical Dependent (PMD) FDDI protocol ?
4. What is the difference between dual and single attached station used in the FDDI topology ?
5. What is the purpose of a wiring concentrator ?
6. What methods are used to interconnect smaller FDDI networks into one large network ?
7. How are dual-ring systems used to maintain a link when a station fails ?

❑❑❑

22 INTEGRATED SERVICES DIGITAL NETWORK (ISDN)

ISDN (Integrated Services Digital Network) An international telecommunications standard for providing a digital service from the customer's premises to the dial-up telephone network. ISDN turns one existing wire pair into two channels and four wire pairs into 23 channels for the delivery of voice, data or video. Unlike an analog modem, which converts digital signals into an equivalency in audio frequencies, ISDN deals only with digital transmission. Analog telephones and fax machines are used over ISDN lines, but their signals are converted into digital by the ISDN modem.

ISDN uses 64 Kbps circuit-switched channels, called "B channels" (bearer channels), to carry voice and data. It uses a separate D channel (delta channel) for control signals. The D channel signals the carrier's voice switch to make calls, put them on hold and activate features such as conference calling and call forwarding. It also receives information about incoming calls, such as the identity of the caller. Since the D channel connects directly to the telephone system's SS7 signaling network, ISDN calls are dialed much faster than regular telephone calls.

ISDN's basic service is BRI (Basic Rate Interface), which is made up of two 64 Kbps B channels and one 16 Kbps D channel (2B+D). If both channels are combined into one, called "bonding," the total data rate becomes 128 Kbps and is four and a half times the bandwidth of a V.34 modem (28.8 Kbps).

ISDN's high-speed service is PRI (Primary Rate Interface). It provides 23 B channels and one 64 Kbps D channel (23B+D), which is equivalent to the 24 channels of a T1 line. When several channels are bonded together, high data rates can be achieved. For example, it is common to bond six channels for quality videoconferencing at 384 Kbps. In Europe, PRI includes 30 B channels and one D channel, equivalent to an E1 line. Connecting an ISDN device connecting ISDN to a computer requires a Network Terminator (NT1) and ISDN Terminal Adapter (TA). The NT1 plugs into the two-wire line from the telephone company with an RJ-11 connector and provides four-wire output to the TA. Within the U.S., the NT1 is typically built into the TA; but in Europe and Japan, they are separate devices.

Often called an "ISDN modem" because the device may support an analog telephone or fax machine, the TA itself is technically not a modem, because it provides a digital to digital connection.

External TAs plug into the serial port while internal TAs plug into an expansion slot. Some TAs hook into the parallel port for higher speed. The TA may also include an analog modem and automatically switch between analog and digital depending on the type of call.

TAs support bonding for Internet operation, which links the channels together for higher speed, but the ISP must provide the Multilink PPP protocol (MPPP) to support this operation.

Although announced in the mid-1980s, it took more than a decade before ISDN usage became widespread. When people asked when would it arrive, the answer was ISDN : "I still don't know."

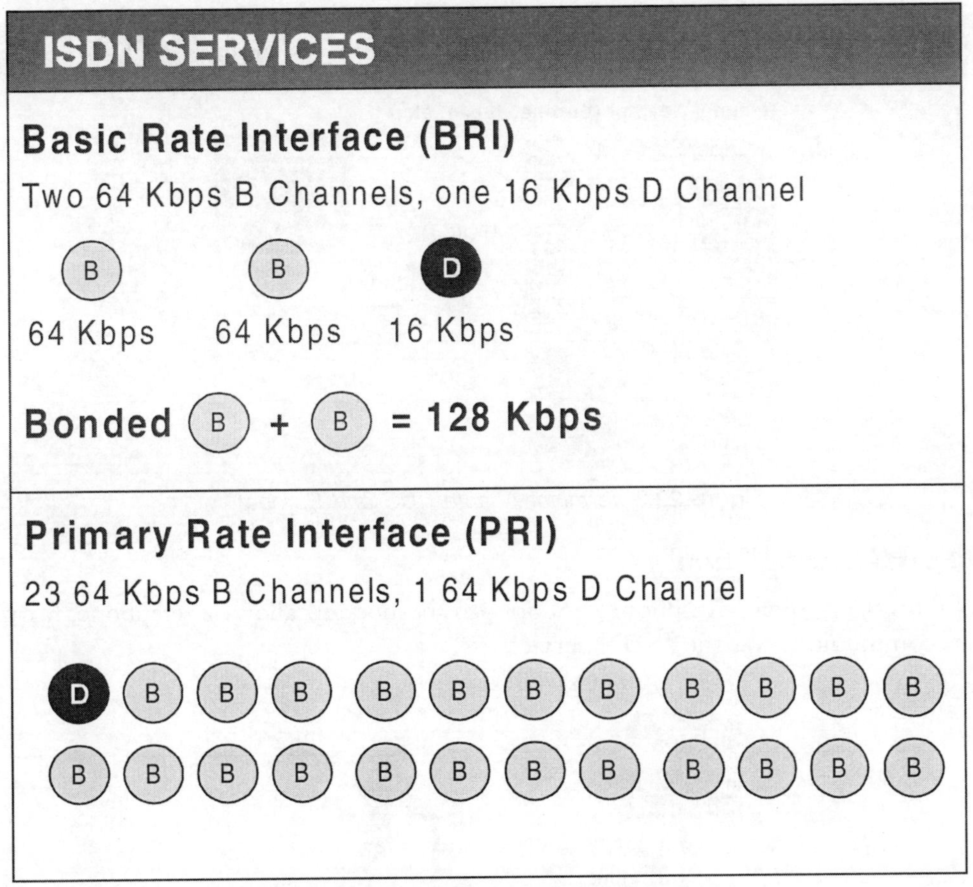

Figure 22.1 *ISDN Services.*

Terminal Adapter

TAs in the U.S. generally have a built-in NT1 and attach via a two-wire "U" interface. In Europe and Japan, the NT1 is installed by the telephone company and attaches to the TA via a four-wire "T" interface. The NT2 component, which is built into most devices, is a logical interface for multiple access and attaches via the "S" interface.

Terminal Adapter (U.S.)

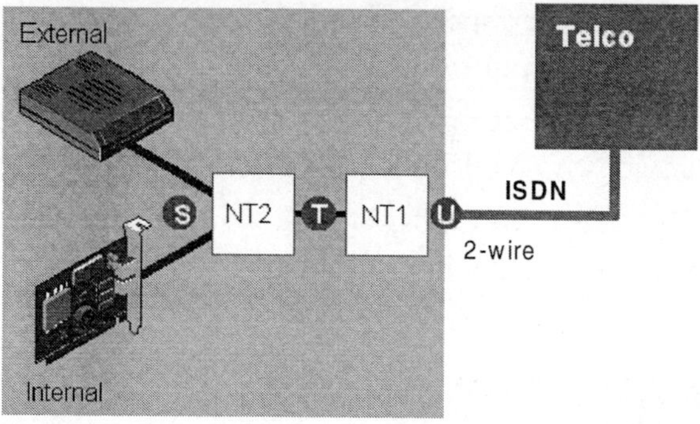

Terminal Adapter (Europe, Japan, etc.)

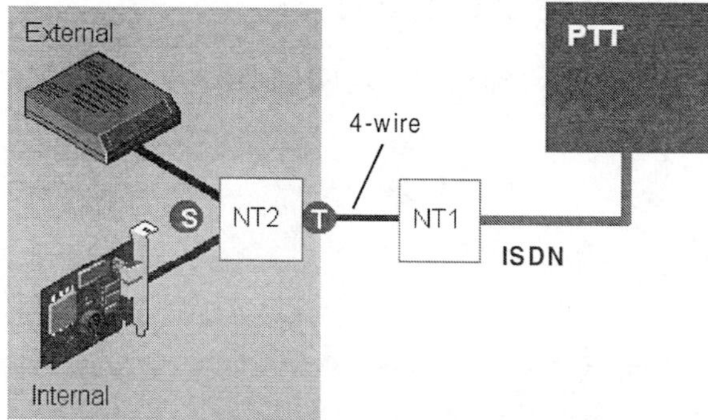

Figure 22.2 *Terminal Adapter (US and Europe).*

Typical SOHO Installation

An ISDN terminal adapter with phone support (ISDN modem) allows a telephone, fax machine and PC to communicate via the ISDN service.

Typical ISDN SOHO Hookup

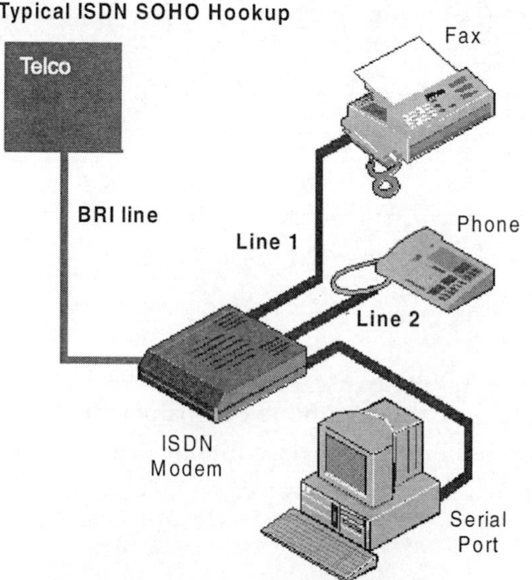

Figure 22.3 *Soho Installation.*

Typical LAN Installation

LANs typically connect to ISDN via a router, which enables multiple users to share the available channels. For Internet access, the router supplies temporary IP addresses to each of the nodes. Routers may also provide analog phone support.

Integrated Services Digital Network (ISDN) refers to a set of digital services that are becoming available to end users. ISDN involves the digitization of the telephone network so that voice, data, text, graphics, music, video, and other source material can be provided to end users from a single end-user terminal over existing telephone wiring. Proponents of ISDN imagine a worldwide network much like the present telephone network, except that digital transmission is used and a variety of new services are available.

ISDN is an effort to standardize subscriber services, user/network interfaces, and network and internet-work capabilities. Standardizing subscriber services attempts to ensure a level of international compatibility. Standardizing the user/network interface stimulates development and marketing of these interfaces by third-party manufacturers. Standardizing network and Internet-work capabilities helps achieve the goal of worldwide connectivity by ensuring that ISDN networks easily communicate with one another.

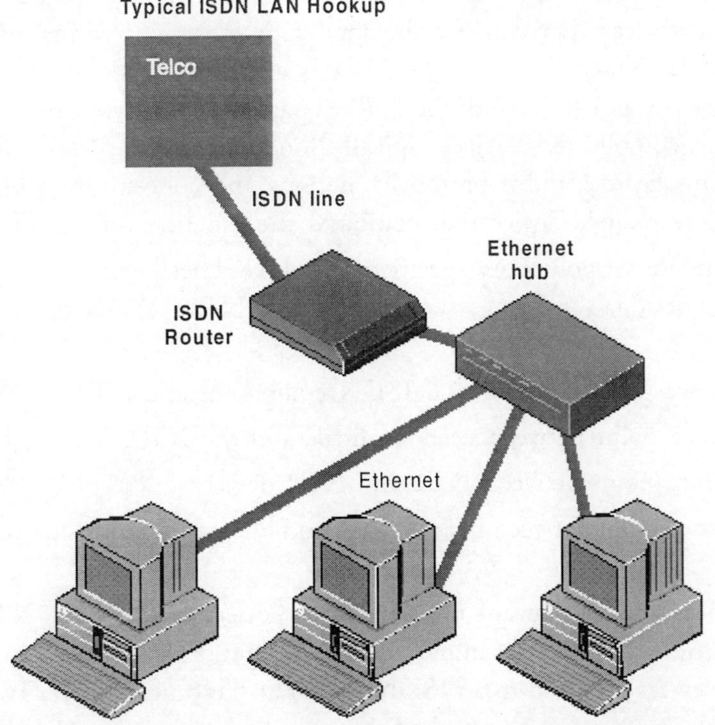

Figure 22.4 *LAN Installation.*

ISDN applications include high-speed image applications (such as group IV facsimile), additional telephone lines in homes to serve the telecommuting industry, high-speed file transfer, and video conferencing. Voice, of course, will also be a popular application for ISDN.

Many carriers are beginning to offer ISDN under tariff. In North America, large Local-Exchange Carriers (LECs) are beginning to provide ISDN service as an alternative to the T1 connections (digital carrier facilities provided by telephone companies) that currently carry bulk Wide-Area Telephone Service (WATS) services.

Components

ISDN components include terminals, Terminal Adapters (TAs), network-termination devices, line-termination equipment, and exchange-termination equipment. ISDN terminals come in two types. Specialized ISDN terminals are referred to as Terminal Equipment type 1 (TE1). Non-ISDN terminals such as DTE that predate the ISDN standards are referred to as Terminal Equipment type 2 (TE2). TE1s connect to the ISDN network through a four-wire, twisted-pair digital link. TE2s connect to the ISDN network through a terminal adapter. The ISDN TA can either be a stand-alone device or a board inside the TE2. If the TE2 is implemented as a standalone device, it connects to the TA via a standard physical-layer interface. Examples include EIA/TIA-232-C (formerly RS-232-C), V.24, and V.35.

Beyond the TE1 and TE2 devices, the next connection point in the ISDN network is the Network Termination type 1 (NT1) or Network Termination type 2 (NT2) device. These are network-termination devices that connect the four-wire subscriber wiring to the conventional two-wire local loop. In North America, the NT1 is a Customer Premises Equipment (CPE) device. In most other parts of the world, the NT1 is part of the network provided by the carrier. The NT2 is a more complicated device, typically found in digital Private Branch Exchanges (PBXs), that performs layer 2 and 3 protocol functions and concentration services. An NT1/2 device also exists; it is a single device that combines the functions of an NT1 and an NT2.

A number of reference points are specified in ISDN. These reference points define logical interfaces between functional groupings such as TAs and NT1s. ISDN reference points include the following :

R—The reference point between non-ISDN equipment and a TA.

S—The reference point between user terminals and the NT2.

T—The reference point between NT1 and NT2 devices.

U—The reference point between NT1 devices and line-termination equipment in the carrier network.

The U reference point is relevant only in North America, where the NT1 function is not provided by the carrier network. A sample ISDN configuration is shown in figure 22.5. This figure shows three devices attached to an ISDN switch at the central office. Two of these devices are ISDN-compatible, so they can be attached through an S reference point to NT2 devices. The third device (a standard, non-ISDN telephone) attaches through the R reference point to a TA. Any of these devices could also attach to a NT1/2 device, which would replace both the NT1 and the NT2. And, although they are not shown, similar user stations are attached to the far right ISDN switch.

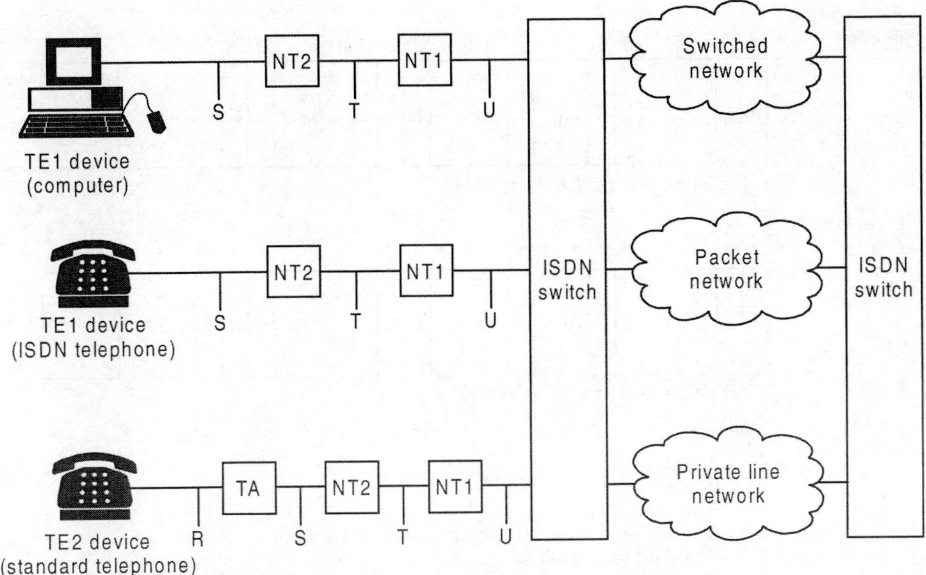

Figure 22.5 *Sample ISDN Configuration.*

ISDN SERVICES

The ISDN Basic Rate Interface (BRI) service offers two B channels and one D channel (2B+D). BRI B-channel service operates at 64 kbps and is meant to carry user data; BRI D-channel service operates at 16 kbps and is meant to carry control and signaling information, although it can support user data transmission under certain circumstances. The D channel signaling protocol comprises layers 1 through 3 of the OSI reference model. BRI also provides for framing control and other overhead, bringing its total bit rate to 192 kbps. The BRI physical layer specification is International Telecommunication Union Telecommunication Standardization Sector (ITU-T).

ISDN Primary Rate Interface (PRI) service offers 23 B channels and one D channel in North America and Japan, yielding a total bit rate of 1.544 Mbps (the PRI D channel runs at 64 kbps). ISDN PRI in Europe, Australia, and other parts of the world provides 30 B plus one 64-kbps D channel and a total interface rate of 2.048 Mbps. The PRI physical-layer specification is ITU-T I.431.

Layer 1

ISDN physical-layer (Layer 1) frame formats differ depending on whether the frame is outbound (from terminal to network) or inbound (from network to terminal). Both physical-layer interfaces are shown in figure 22.6.

The frames are 48 bits long, of which 36 bits represent data. The bits of an ISDN physical-layer frame are used as follows :

F—Provides synchronization.

L—Adjusts the average bit value.

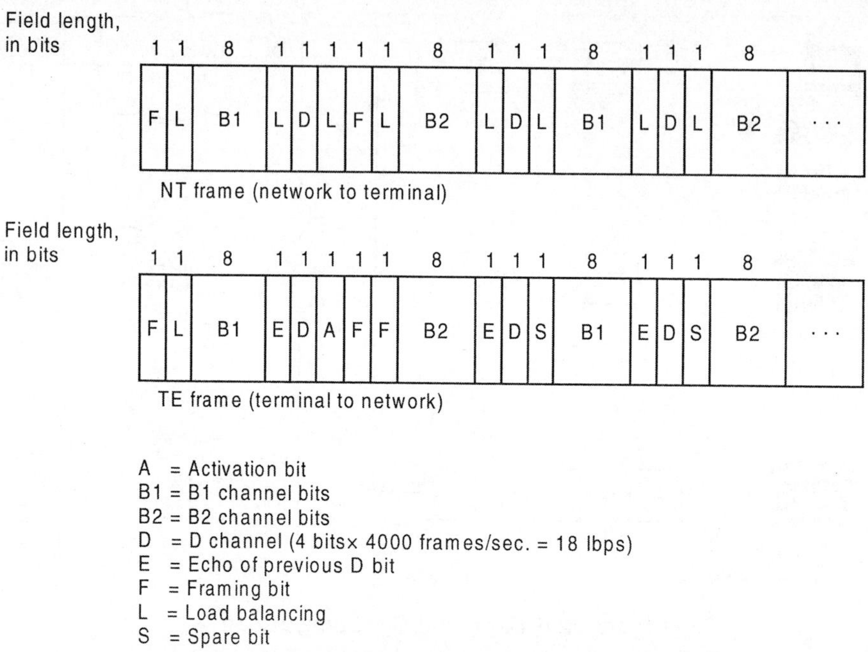

Figure 22.6 *ISDN Physical-Layer Frame Formats.*

E—Used for contention resolution when several terminals on a passive bus contend for a channel.

A—Activates devices.

S—Unassigned.

B1, B2, and D—Used for user data.

Multiple ISDN user devices can be physically attached to one circuit. In this configuration, collisions can result if two terminals transmit simultaneously. ISDN therefore provides features to determine link contention. When an NT receives a D bit from the TE, it echoes back the bit in the next E-bit position. The TE expects the next E bit to be the same as its last transmitted D bit.

Terminals cannot transmit into the D channel unless they first detect a specific number of ones (indicating "no signal") corresponding to a pre-established priority. If the TE detects a bit in the echo (E) channel that is different from its D bits, it must stop transmitting immediately. This simple technique ensures that only one terminal can transmit its D message at one time. After successful D message transmission, the terminal has its priority reduced by requiring it to detect more continuous ones before transmitting. Terminals cannot raise their priority until all other devices on the same line have had an opportunity to send a D message. Telephone connections have higher priority than all other services, and signaling information has a higher priority than non-signaling information.

Layer 2

Layer 2 of the ISDN signaling protocol is Link Access Procedure, D channel, also known as LAPD. LAPD is similar to High-Level Data Link Control (HDLC) and Link Access Procedure,

Balanced (LAPB) As the expansion of the LAPD acronym indicates, it is used across the D channel to ensure that control and signaling information flows and is received properly. The LAPD frame format figure 22.7 is very similar to that of HDLC and, like HDLC, LAPD uses *supervisory*, *information*, and *unnumbered* frames. The LAPD protocol is formally specified in ITU-T Q.920 and ITU-T Q.921.

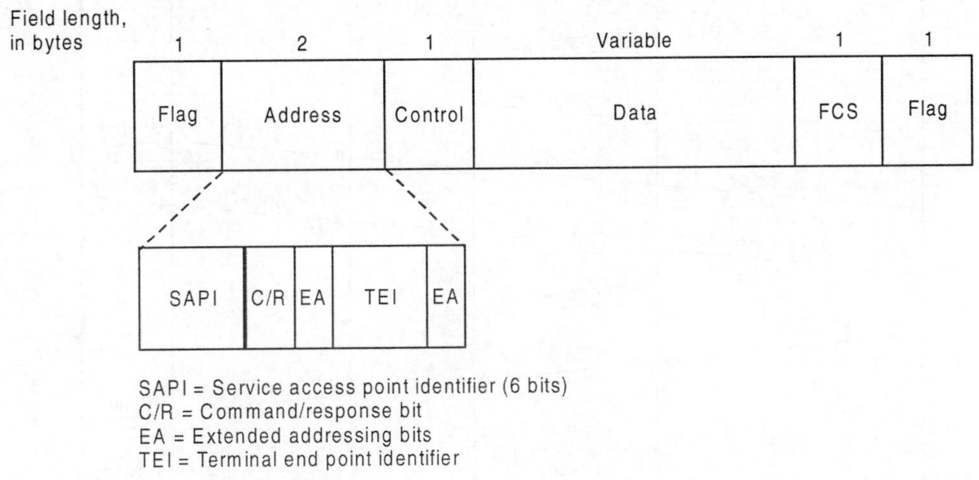

Figure 22.7 *LAPD Frame Format.*

The LAPD *flag and control* fields are identical to those of HDLC. The LAPD *address* field can be either one or two bytes long. If the extended address bit of the first byte is set, the address is 1 byte; if it is not set, the address is 2 bytes. The first address field byte contains the Service Access Point Identifier (SAPI), which identifies the portal at which LAPD services are provided to layer 3. The C/R bit indicates whether the frame contains a command or a response. The Terminal End-point Identifier (TEI) field identifies either a single terminal or multiple terminals. A TEI of all ones indicates a broadcast.

Layer 3

Two layer 3 specifications are used for ISDN signaling : ITU-T (formerly CCITT) I.450 (also known as ITU-T Q.930) and ITU-T I.451 (also known as ITU-T Q.931). Together, these protocols support user-to-user, circuit-switched, and packet-switched connections. A variety of call establishment, call termination, information, and miscellaneous messages are specified, including SETUP, CONNECT, RELEASE, USER INFORMATION, CANCEL, STATUS, and DISCONNECT. These messages are functionally similar to those provided by the X.25 protocol figure 22.8, from ITU-T I.451, shows the typical stages of an ISDN circuit-switched call.

Integrated Services Digital Network (ISDN) refers to a set of digital services that are becoming available to end users. ISDN involves the digitization of the telephone network so that voice, data, text, graphics, music, video, and other source material can be provided to end users from a single end-user terminal over existing telephone wiring. Proponents of ISDN imagine a worldwide network much like the present telephone network, except that digital transmission is used and a variety of new services are available.

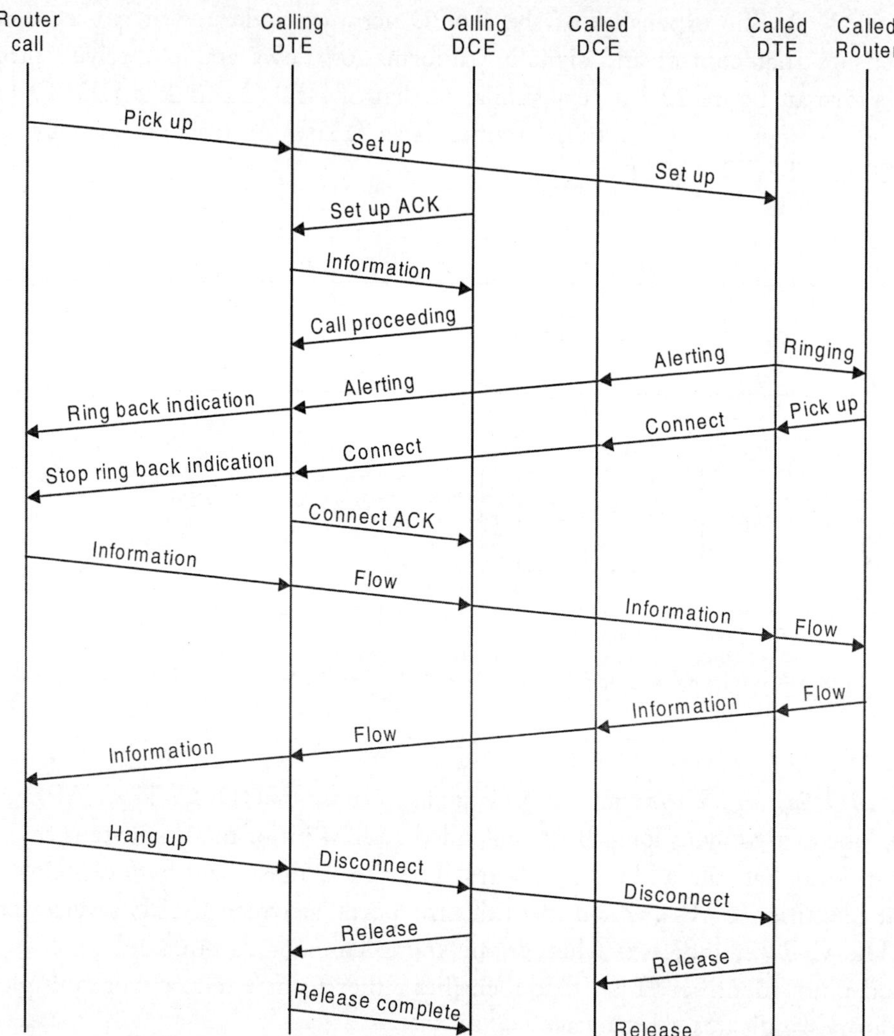

Figure 22.8 *ISDN Circuit-Switched Call Stages.*

ISDN is an effort to standardize subscriber services, user/network interfaces, and network and internet-work capabilities. Standardizing subscriber services attempts to ensure a level of international compatibility. Standardizing the user/network interface stimulates development and marketing of these interfaces by third-party manufacturers. Standardizing network and internet-work capabilities helps achieve the goal of worldwide connectivity by ensuring that ISDN networks easily communicate with one another.

ISDN applications include high-speed image applications (such as group IV facsimile), additional telephone lines in homes to serve the telecommuting industry, high-speed file transfer, and video conferencing. Voice, of course, will also be a popular application for ISDN.

Many carriers are beginning to offer ISDN under tariff. In North America, large Local-Exchange Carriers (LECs) are beginning to provide ISDN service as an alternative to the T1 connections (digital carrier facilities provided by telephone companies) that currently carry bulk Wide-Area Telephone Service (WATS) services.

The Integrated Services Digital Network (ISDN) is a method used to bridge "the last mile" between the central office and the premise connection (home). ISDN uses the existing wiring, so no new cabling is required.

There are two basic services offered:

Basic Rate Interface (BRI) consists of 2B + D channels. Which stands for 2 bearer channels of 64 kbps each for data and one D channel of 16 kbps for handshaking and control. Having a separate channel for handshaking and control is called "out of band" signalling. The 2B channels can be bonded together for a single data channel with a 128 kbps transfer rate.

Primary Rate Interface (PRI) consists of 23B + D channels. Which stands for 23 bearer channels of 64 kbps each for data and one D channel of 64 kbps for handshaking and control. The bearer channels can be bonded in any combination as required.

ISDN lines can be dedicated lines that are always up and connected, or they can be Dial on Demand (DOD) lines. When the line is required, the connection is dialed up and made. The connection time for an ISDN line is very quick, in the order of 0.5 second or so. This can result in a substantial cost saving if used over long distance (or paying by the minute). The line charges are only for when data is being transferred, and not when it is sitting idle.

ISDN—OSI LAYERS

The D channel uses up to the OSI network layer, while the B channel uses both the data link and physical layers.

OSI Model	*ISDN*	
Network	D Channel	
Data Link	D Channel	B Channel
Physical	D Channel	B Channel

Figure 22.9 *ISDN—OSI Layers.*

ISDN—OSI MODEL

The line encoding used by ISDN is standard telecommunication 2BIQ (which stands for 2 binary elements encoded in 1 quaternary). A dibit (digital bit) is represents two binary elements for each voltage change. The following table 22.1 illustrated the 2BIQ encoding used by ISDN.

Table 22.1. Illustrates the 2BIQ Encoding used by ISDN

Dibit	*Voltage*
10	+3
11	+1
01	–1
00	–3

ISDN PREMISE CONNECTION

The following diagram illustrates a basic ISDN connection from the central office to the premise:

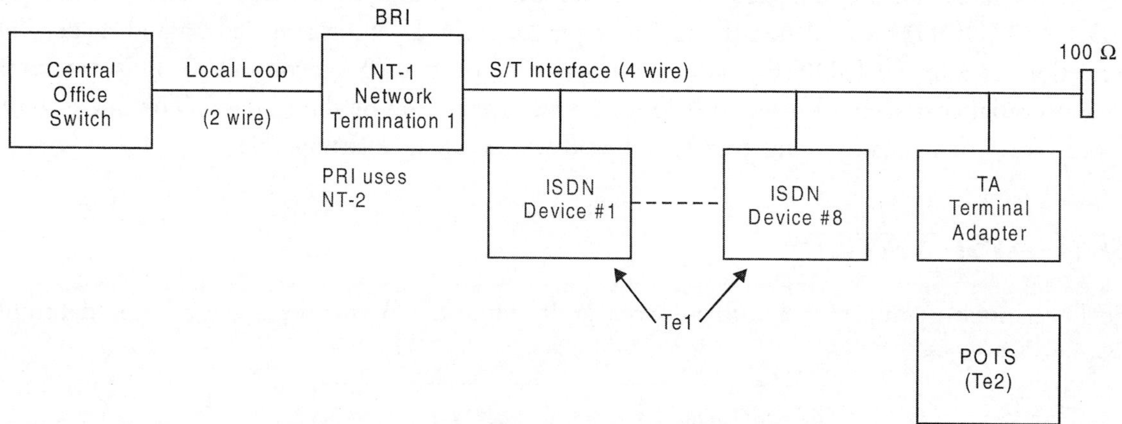

Figure 22.10 *ISDN Premise Connnection.*

ISDN Premise Connection

The central office must have ISDN capabilities in the switch to connect to an ISDN premise. The connection from the CO the premise uses the existing analog phone lines. At the BRL premise, a Network Termination 1 (NT-1) device converts the 2 wire analog line to a 4 wire system called the S/T interface. A PRI rate interface is the S/T interface (a bus topology) that terminates in a 100 W termination.

A total of 8 ISDN terminal equipment 1 (TE) devices are allowed to connect to the S/T Interface. If access is required to traditional analog devices—such as a plain Old Telephone Set (POTS), called Terminal Equipment 2 (TE 2) devices—a Terminal Adapter (TA) can be used to provide access.

ISDN Advantages

ISDN is a mature technology, it has been around since the late 1980s. It has been tired, tested and works.

- It is governed by a world-wide set of standards.
- It provides symmetrical transfer rates: the transmit rate is the same as the receive rate.

- It has consistent transfer rates. If you have a 64 kbps bearer channel then that's the speed that you transfer at.
- It is competitive priced compared to other technologies.

ISDN Disadvantages

An external power supply is required. The telco's son't supply power for isdn lines. If the power fails, the phones won't work.

Special digital phones are required or a terminal adapter to talk to the existing POTS devices.

- It is very expensive to upgrade a central office switch ($500,000+) to ISDN.
- If the ISDN fails—the phone fails.

X.25

In the 1970s, a set of protocols was needed to provide users with Wide-Area Network (WAN) connectivity across Public Data Networks (PDNs). PDNs such as TELENET and TYMNET had achieved remarkable success, but it was felt that protocol standardization would increase subscription to PDNs by providing improved equipment compatibility and lower cost. The result of the ensuing development effort was a group of protocols, the most popular of which is X.25.

X.25 was developed by the common carriers (telephone companies, essentially) rather than any single commercial enterprise. The specification is therefore designed to work well regardless of a user's system type or manufacturer. Users contract with the common carriers to use their Packet-Switched Networks (PSNs) and are charged based on PSN use. Services offered (and charges levied) are regulated by the Federal Communications Commission (FCC).

One of X.25's unique attributes is its international nature. X.25 and related protocols are administered by an agency of the United Nations called the International Telecommunications Union (ITU). The International Telecommunication Union Telecommunication Standardization Sector (ITU-T) (formerly CCITT) is the ITU committee responsible for voice and data communications. ITU-T members include the FCC, the European postal telephone and telegraph organizations, the common carriers, and many computer and data communications companies. As a result, X.25 is truly a global standard.

TECHNOLOGY BASICS OF X.25

X.25 defines a telephone network for data communications. To begin communication, one computer calls another to request a communication session. The called computer can accept or refuse the connection. If the call is accepted, the two systems can begin full-duplex information transfer. Either side can terminate the connection at any time.

The X.25 specification defines a point-to-point interaction between Data Terminal Equipment (DTE) and Data Circuit-Terminating Equipment (DCE). DTEs (terminals and hosts in the user's facilities) connect to DCEs (modems, packet switches, and other ports into the PDN, generally located in the carrier's facilities), which connect to Packet Switching Exchanges (PSEs, or simply *switches*) and other DCEs inside a PSN and, ultimately, to another DTE. The relationship between the entities in an X.25 network is shown in figure 22.11.

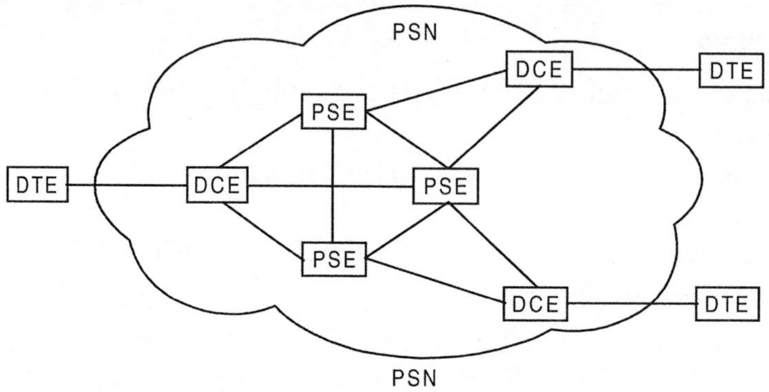

Figure 22.11 *X.25 Model.*

A DTE can be a terminal that does not implement the complete X.25 functionality. A DTE is connected to a DCE through a translation device called a Packet Assembler/Disassembler (PAD). The operation of the terminal-to-PAD interface, the services offered by the PAD, and the interaction between the PAD and the host are defined by ITU-T *Recommendations* X.28, X.3, and X.29, respectively.

The X.25 specification maps to layers 1 through 3 of the OSI reference model. Layer 3 X.25 describes packet formats and packet exchange procedures between peer layer 3 entities. Layer 2 X.25 is implemented by Link Access Procedure, Balanced (LAPB). LAPB defines packet framing for the DTE/DCE link. Layer 1 X.25 defines the electrical and mechanical procedures for activating and deactivating the physical medium connecting the DTE and the DCE. This relationship is shown in figure 22.12. Note that layers 2 and 3 are also referred to as the ISO standards ISO 7776 (LAPB) and ISO 8208 (X.25 packet layer).

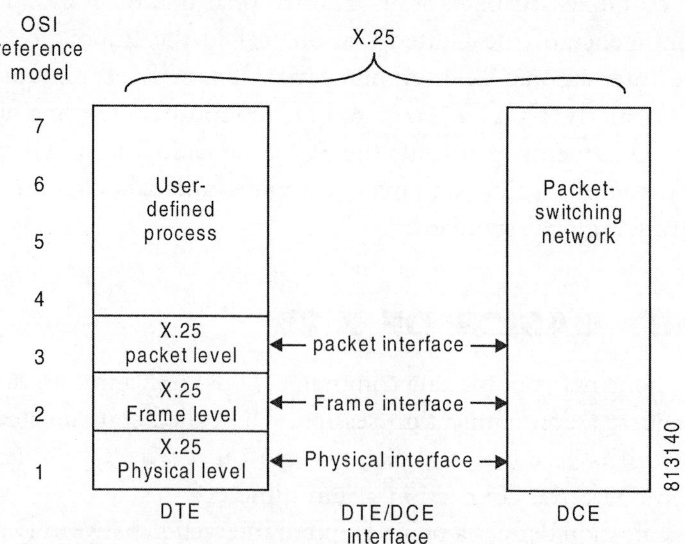

Figure 22.12 *X.25 and the OSI Reference Model.*

End-to-end communication between DTEs is accomplished through a bidirectional association called a *virtual circuit.* Virtual circuits permit communication between distinct network elements through any number of intermediate nodes without the dedication of portions of the physical medium that characterizes physical circuits. Virtual circuits can either be permanent or switched (temporary). *Permanent virtual circuits* are commonly called PVCs; *switched virtual circuits* are commonly called SVCs. PVCs are typically used for the most-often-used data transfers, while SVCs are used for sporadic data transfers. Layer 3 X.25 is concerned with end-to-end communication involving both PVCs and SVCs.

Once a virtual circuit is established, the DTE sends a packet to the other end of the connection by sending it to the DCE using the proper virtual circuit. The DCE looks at the virtual circuit number to determine how to route the packet through the X.25 network. The layer 3 X.25 protocol multiplexes between all the DTEs served by the DCE on the destination side of the network and the packet is delivered to the destination DTE.

Frame Format

An X.25 frame is composed of a series of fields, as shown in figure 22.13. Layer 3 X.25 fields make up an X.25 packet and include a header and user data. Layer 2 X.25 (LAPB) fields include frame-level control and addressing fields, the embedded layer 3 packet, and a Frame Check Sequence (FCS).

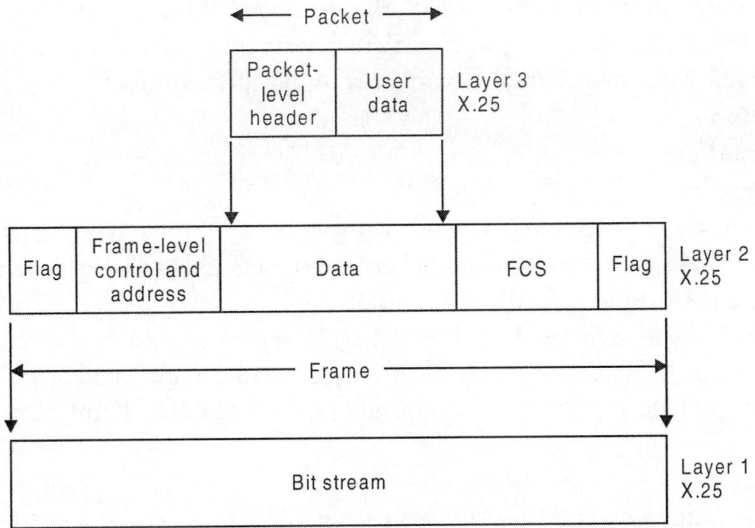

Figure 22.13 *X.25 Frame.*

Layer 3

The layer 3 X.25 header is made up of a General Format Identifier (GFI), a Logical Channel Identifier (LCI), and a Packet Type Identifier (PTI). The GFI is a 4-bit field that indicates the general format of the packet header. The LCI is a 12-bit field that identifies the virtual circuit. The LCI is locally significant at the DTE/DCE interface. In other words, the PDN connects two logical channels, each with an independent LCI, on two DTE/DCE interfaces to establish a virtual circuit. The PTI field identifies one of X.25's 17 packet types.

Addressing fields in call setup packets provide source and destination DTE addresses. These are used to establish the virtual circuits that constitute X.25 communication. ITU-T *Recommendation* X.121 specifies the source and destination address formats. X.121 addresses (also referred to as *International Data Numbers*, or IDNs) vary in length and can be up to 14 decimal digits long. Byte four in the call setup packet specifies the source DTE and destination DTE address lengths. The first four digits of an IDN are called the Data Network Identification Code (DNIC). The DNIC is divided into two parts, the first (three digits) specifying the country and the last specifying the PSN itself. The remaining digits are called the National Terminal Number (NTN), and are used to identify the specific DTE on the PSN. The X.121 address format is shown in figure 22.14.

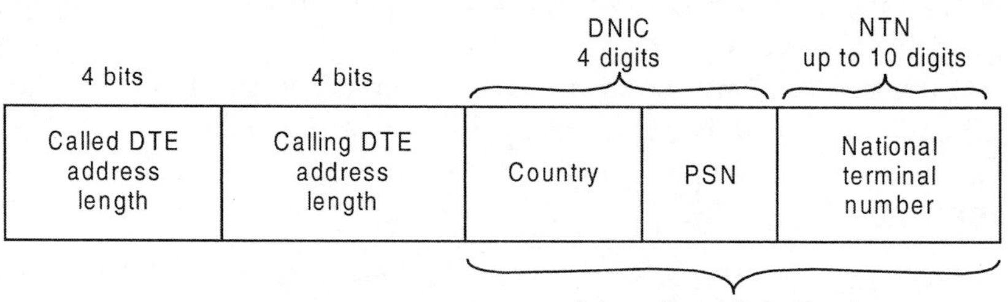

Figure 22.14 *X.121 Address Format.*

The addressing fields that make up the X.121 address are only necessary when an SVC is used, and then only during call setup. Once the call is established, the PSN uses the LCI field of the data packet header to specify the particular virtual circuit to the remote DTE.

Layer 3 X.25 uses three virtual circuit operational procedures :

- Call setup
- Data transfer
- Call clearing

Execution of these procedures depends on the virtual circuit type being used. For a PVC, layer 3 X.25 is always in data transfer mode because the circuit has been permanently established. If an SVC is used, all three procedures are used.

Packets are used to transfer data. Layer 3 X.25 segments and reassembles user messages if they are too long for the maximum packet size of the circuit. Each data packet is given a sequence number, so error and flow control can occur across the DTE/DCE interface.

Layer 2

Layer 2 X.25 is implemented by LAPB. LAPB allows both sides (the DTE and the DCE) to initiate communication with the other. During information transfer, LAPB checks that the frames arrive at the receiver in the correct sequence and error-free.

As with similar link-layer protocols, LAPB uses three frame format types :

Information (I) frame—These frames carry upper-layer information and some control information (necessary for full-duplex operation). Send and receive sequence numbers and the poll final (P/F) bit perform flow control and error recovery. The *send sequence number* refers to the number of the current frame. The *receive sequence number* records the number of the frame to be received next. In full-duplex conversation, both the sender and the receiver keep send and receive sequence numbers. The poll bit is used to force a final bit message in response; this is used for error detection and recovery.

Supervisory (S) *frames*—These frames provide control information. They request and suspend transmission, report on status, and acknowledge the receipt of I frames. They do not have an information field.

Unnumbered (U) *frames*—These frames, as the name suggests, are not sequenced. They are used for control purposes. For example, they can initiate a connection using standard or extended windowing (modulo 8 versus 128), disconnect the link, report a protocol error, or similar functions.

The LAPB frame is shown in figure 22.15.

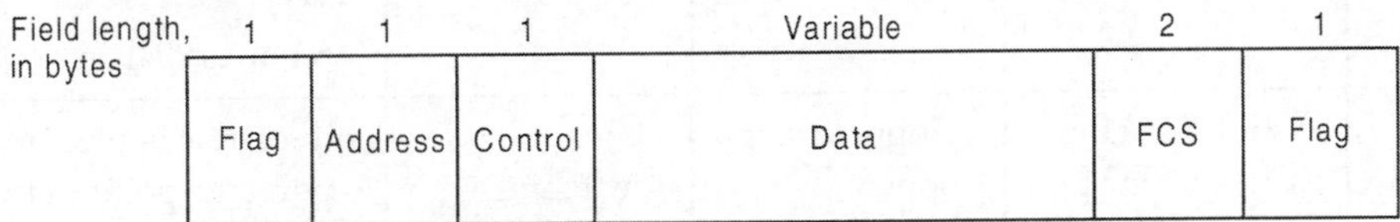

Figure 22.15 *LAPB Frame.*

The fields of a LAPB frame are as follows :

Flag—Delimits the LAPB frame. Bit stuffing is used to ensure that the flag pattern does not occur within the body of the frame.

Address—Indicates whether the frame carries a command or a response.

Control—Provides further qualifications of command and response frames, and also indicates the frame format (U, I, or S), frame function (for example, *receiver ready* or *disconnect*), and the send/receive sequence number.

Data—Carries upper-layer data. Its size and format vary depending on the layer 3 packet type. The maximum length of this field is set by agreement between a PSN administrator and the subscriber at subscription time.

Frame check sequence (FCS)—Ensures the integrity of the transmitted data.

Layer 1

Layer 1 X.25 uses the X.21 bits physical-layer protocol, which is roughly equivalent to EIA/TIA232C (formerly RS-232-C). X.21 bits was derived from ITU-T recommendations V.24 and V.28, which identify the interchange circuits and electrical characteristics (respectively) of a DTE to DCE interface. X.21 bis supports point-to-point connections, speeds of up to 19.2 kbps, and synchronous, full-duplex transmission over four-wire media. The maximum distance between DTE and DCE is 15 meters.

Comparing WAN Technologies

Here a comparative table is summarized for different WAN Technologies.

Table 22.2 Comparing WAN Technologies

WAN Technology	*Speed*	*Supported Media*	*Switching Method Used*	*Key Characteristics*
ISDN	BRI: 64Kbps to 128Kbps PRI: 64Kbps to 1.5Mbps	Copper/fiber-optic	Can be used for circuit-switching or packet-switching connections	ISDN can be used to transmit all types of traffic, including voice, video, and data, BRI uses 2B+D channels, PRI uses 23B+D channels. B channels are 64Kbps. ISDN uses the public network and requires dial-in access.
T-carrier (T1, T3)	T1: 1.544Mbps T3: 44.736Mbps	Copper/fiber-optic	Circuit switching	T-carrier is used to create point-to-point network connections for private networks.
FDDI	100Mbps	Fibre-optic	N/A	Uses a dual-ring configuration for fault tolerance. Uses a token-passing media-access method. Uses beaconing for error detection.
X.25	56Kbps/64Kbps	Copper/fiber-optic	Packet switching	X.25 is limited to 56Kbps. X.25 provides a packet-switching network over standard phone lines.
SONET/ Ocx	51.8Mbps	Fiber-optic to 2.4Gbps	N/A	SONET defines synchronous data transfer over optical cable.

REVIEW QUESTIONS

1. What does the acronym ISDN mean ?
2. What does the acronym BISDN stand for ?
3. How does the ISDN system differ from the regular telephone system ?
4. What is meant by integrated services ?
5. What type of information is conveyed on the B channel ?
6. What is the D channel used for ?

7. What is the composition of the basic rate interface (BRI) ?
8. What is the data rate for a BRI service ?
9. What function does the Terminal Adapter (TA) provide ?
10. What is the difference between Terminal Equipment 1(TE1) and TE2 ?
11. Which ISDN function unit applies to the physical layer of the OSI model ?
12. List some of the devices interfaces to the ISDN system by the network termination unit.
13. Which data link protocol does the ISDN protocol closely follow ?
14. Which IEEE 802 specification addresses integrated services ?
15. What type of line is a DSL ?

❑❑❑

23 Switched Multimegabit Data Service

INTRODUCTION

Switched Multimegabit Data Service (SMDS) is a high-speed, packet-switched, datagram-based WAN networking technology used for communication over Public Data Networks (PDNs). SMDS can use fibre- or copper-based media; it supports speeds of 1.544 Mbps over Digital Signal level 1 (DS-1) transmission facilities, or 44.736 Mbps over Digital Signal level 3 (DS-3) transmission facilities. In addition, SMDS data units are large enough to encapsulate entire IEEE 802.3, IEEE 802.5, and Fibre Distributed Data Interface (FDDI) frames. This chapter summarizes the operational elements of the SMDS environment and outlines the underlying protocol. The chapter closes with discussions of SMDS access classes and cell formats.

SMDS NETWORK COMPONENTS

SMDS networks consist of several underlying devices to provide high-speed data service. These include Customer Premises Equipment (CPE), carrier equipment, and the Subscriber Network Interface (SNI). CPE is terminal equipment typically owned and maintained by the customer. CPE includes end devices, such as terminals and personal computers, and intermediate nodes, such as routers, modems, and multiplexers. Intermediate nodes, however, sometimes are provided by the SMDS carrier. Carrier equipment generally consists of high-speed WAN switches that must conform to certain network equipment specifications, such as those outlined by Bell Communications Research (Bellcore). These specifications define network operations, the interface between a local carrier network and a long-distance carrier network, and the interface between two switches inside a single carrier network.

The SNI is the interface between CPE and carrier equipment. This interface is the point at which the customer network ends and the carrier network begins. The function of the SNI is to render the technology and operation of the carrier SMDS network transparent to the customer. Figure 23.1 illustrates the relationships among these three components of an SMDS network.

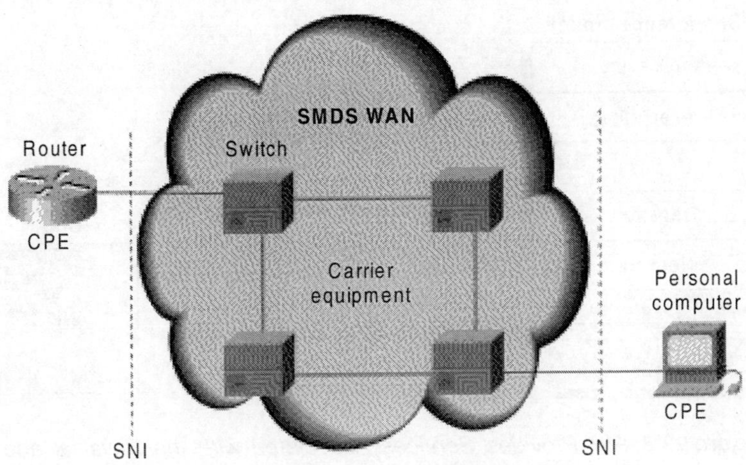

Figure 23.1 *The SNI Provides an Interface between the CPE and the Carrier Equipment in SMDS.*

SMDS Interface Protocol

The SMDS Interface Protocol (SIP) is used for communications between CPE and SMDS carrier equipment. SIP provides connectionless service across the Subscriber Network Interface (SNI), allowing the CPE to access the SMDS network. SIP is based on the IEEE 802.6 Distributed Queue Dual Bus (DQDB) standard for cell relay across Metropolitan-Area Networks (MANs). The DQDB was chosen as the basis for SIP because it is an open standard that supports all the SMDS service features. In addition, DQDB was designed for compatibility with current carrier transmission standards, and it is aligned with emerging standards for Broadband ISDN (BISDN), which will allow it to interoperate with broadband video and voice services. Figure 23.2 illustrates where SIP is used in an SMDS network.

SIP Levels

SIP consists of three levels. SIP level 3 operates at the Media Access Control (MAC) sub-layer of the data link layer of the OSI reference model. SIP level 2 operates at the MAC sub-layer of the data link layer. SIP Level 1 operates at the physical layer of the OSI reference model. Figure 23.2 illustrates how SIP maps to the OSI reference model, including the IEEE data link sub-layers.

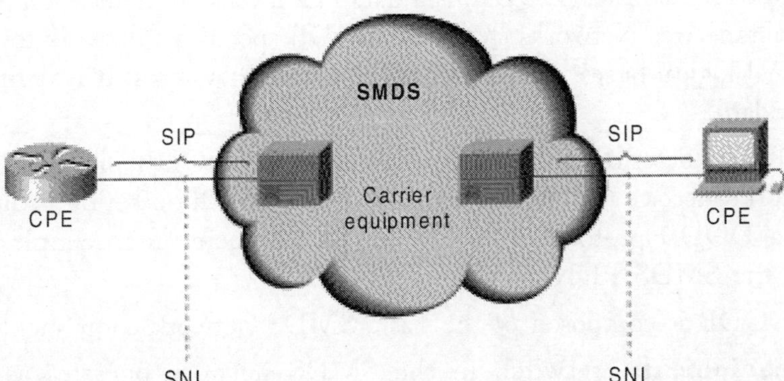

Figure 23.2 *SIP Provides Connectionless Service between the CPE and Carrier Equipment.*

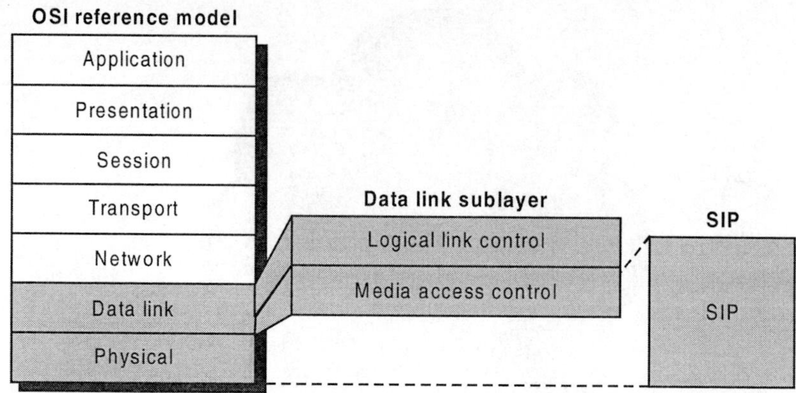

Figure 23.3 *SIP Provides Services Associated with the Physical and Data Link Layers of the OSI Model.*

SIP level 3 begins operation when user information is passed to it in the form of SMDS Service Data Units (SDUs). SMDS SDUs then are encapsulated in a SIP level 3 header and trailer. The resulting frame is called a level 3 Protocol Data Unit (PDU). SIP level 3 PDUs then are passed to SIP Level 2.

SIP level 2, which operates at the Media Access Control (MAC) sub-layer of the data link layer, begins operating when it receives SIP level 3 PDUs. The PDUs then are segmented into uniformly sized (53-octet) level 2 PDUs, called cells. The cells are passed to SIP level 1 for placement on the physical medium.

SIP Level 1 operates at the physical layer and provides the physical-link protocol that operates at DS-1 or DS-3 rates between CPE devices and the network. SIP Level 1 consists of the transmission system and Physical Layer Convergency Protocol (PLCP) sub-layers. The transmission system sub-layer defines the characteristics and method of attachment to a DS-1 or DS-3 transmission link. The PLCP specifies how SIP level 2 cells are to be arranged relative to the DS-1 or DS-3 frame. PLCP also defines other management information.

DISTRIBUTED QUEUE DUAL BUS

The Distributed Queue Dual Bus (DQDB) is a data link layer communication protocol designed for use in Metropolitan-Area Networks (MANs). DQDB specifies a network topology composed of two unidirectional logical buses that interconnect multiple systems. It is defined in the IEEE 802.6 DQDB standard.

An access DQDB describes just the operation of the DQDB protocol (in SMDS, SIP) across a user-network interface (in SMDS, across the SNI). Such operation is distinguished from the operation of a DQDB protocol in any other environment (for example, between carrier equipment within the SMDS PDN).

The access DQDB is composed of the basic SMDS network components:

- **Carrier equipment:** A switch in the SMDS network operates as one station on the bus.

- **CPE:** One or more CPE devices operate as stations on the bus.
- **SNI:** The SNI acts as the interface between the CPE and the carrier equipment.

Figure 23.4 depicts a basic access DQDB, with two CPE devices and one switch (carrier equipment) attached to the dual bus.

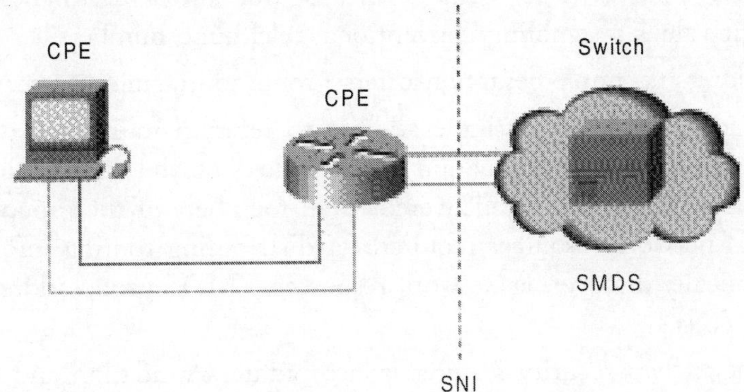

Figure 23.4 *A Basic Access DQDB May Consist of an End Node, a Router, and a Switch.*

An SMDS access DQDB typically is arranged in a single-CPE configuration or a multi-CPE configuration.

A single-CPE access DQDB configuration consists of one switch in the carrier SMDS network and one CPE station at the subscriber site. Single-CPE DQDB configurations create a two-node DQDB sub-network. Communication occurs only between the switch and the one CPE device across the SNI. No contention is on the bus because no other CPE devices attempt to access it.

A multi-CPE configuration consists of one switch in the carrier SMDS network and a number of interconnected CPE devices at the subscriber site (all belonging to the same subscriber). In multi-CPE configurations, local communication between CPE devices is possible. Some local communication will be visible to the switch serving the SNI, and some will not.

Contention for the bus by multiple devices requires the use of the DQDB distributed queuing algorithm, which makes implementing a multi-CPE configuration more complicated than implementing a single-CPE configuration.

SMDS Access Classes

SMDS *access classes* enable SMDS networks to accommodate a broad range of traffic requirements and equipment capabilities. Access classes constrain CPE devices to a sustained or average rate of data transfer by establishing a maximum sustained information transfer rate and a maximum allowed degree of traffic burstiness. (Burstiness, in this context, is the propensity of a network to experience sudden increases in bandwidth demand.) SMDS access classes sometimes are implemented using a credit-management scheme. In this case, a credit-management algorithm creates and tracks a credit balance for each customer interface. As packets are sent into the network, the credit balance is decremented. New credits are allocated periodically, up to an established maximum. Credit management is used only on DS-3-rate SMDS interfaces, not on DS-1-rate interfaces.

Five access classes are supported for DS-3-rate access (corresponding to sustained information rates). Data rates supported are 4, 10, 16, 25, and 34 Mbps.

SMDS Addressing Overview

SMDS Protocol Data Units (PDUs) carry both a source and a destination address. SMDS addresses are 10-digit values resembling conventional telephone numbers.

The SMDS addressing implementation offers group addressing and security features.

SMDS group addresses allow a single address to refer to multiple CPE stations, which specify the group address in the destination address field of the PDU. The network makes multiple copies of the PDU, which are delivered to all members of the group. Group addresses reduce the amount of network resources required for distributing routing information, resolving addresses, and dynamically discovering network resources. SMDS group addressing is analogous to multicasting on LANs.

SMDS implements two security features: source address validation and address screening. *Source address validation* ensures that the PDU source address is legitimately assigned to the SNI from which it originated. Source address validation prevents address spoofing, in which illegal traffic assumes the source address of a legitimate device. *Address screening* allows a subscriber to establish a private virtual network that excludes unwanted traffic. If an address is disallowed, the data unit is not delivered.

SMDS Reference : SIP Level 3 PDU Format

Figure 23.5 illustrates the format of the SMDS Interface Protocol (SIP) level 3 Protocol Data Unit (PDU).

The following descriptions briefly summarize the function of the SIP level 3 PDU fields illustrated in figure 23.5.

Field length, in bytes

1	1	2	6	6	1	4 bits	4 bits	2	12	9188	04	1	1	2
RSVD	BEtag	BAsize	DA	SA	M+ HLPI	X+	HEL	X+	HE	Info+ Pad	CRC	RSVD	BEtag	Length

RSVD = Reserved
Betag = Beginning-end tag
Basize = Buffer allocation size
DA = Destination address
SA = Source address
HLPI = Higher0layer protocol identifier
X+ = Carried across network unchanged
HEL = Header extension length
HE = Header extension
Info+Pad = Information + padding (to ensure that this field ends on a 32-bit boundary)
CRC = Cycle redundancy check

Figure 23.5 *A SIP Level 3 Protocol Data Unit Consists of 15 Fields.*

- **X+:** Ensures that the SIP PDU format aligns with the DQDB protocol format. SMDS does not process or change the values in these fields, which may be used by systems connected to the SMDS network.
- **RSVD:** Consists of zeros.
- **BEtag:** Forms an association between the first and last segments of a segmented SIP level 3 PDU. Both fields contain identical values and are used to detect a condition in which the last segment of one PDU and the first segment of the next PDU are both lost, which results in the receipt of an invalid level 3 PDU.
- **BAsize:** Contains the buffer allocation size.
- **Destination address (DA):** Consists of two parts:
  - *Address type:* Occupies the 4 most significant bits of the field. The Address Type can be either 1100 or 1110. The former indicates a 60-bit individual address, while the latter indicates a 60-bit group address.
  - *Address:* Gives the individual or group SMDS address for the destination. SMDS address formats are consistent with the North American Numbering Plan (NANP).

  The 4 most significant bits of the Destination Address subfield contain the value 0001 (the internationally defined country code for North America). The next 40 bits contain the binary-encoded value of the 10-digit SMDS address. The final 16 (least significant) bits are populated with ones for padding.
- **Source address (SA):** Consists of two parts:
  - *Address type:* Occupies the 4 most significant bits of the field. The Source Address Type field can indicate only an individual address.
  - *Address:* Occupies the individual SMDS address of the source. This field follows the same format as the Address subfield of the Destination Address field.
- **Higher layer protocol identifier (HLPI):** Indicates the type of protocol encapsulated in the information field. The value is not important to SMDS, but it can be used by certain systems connected to the network.
- **Header extension length (HEL):** Indicates the number of 32-bit words in the Header Extension (HE) field. Currently, the field size for SMDS is fixed at 12 bytes. (Thus, the HEL value is always 0011.)
- **Header extension (HE):** Contains the SMDS version number. This field also conveys the carrier-selection value, which is used to select the particular inter-exchange carrier to carry SMDS traffic from one local carrier network to another.
- **Information and padding (Info + Pad):** Contains an encapsulated SMDS Service Data Unit (SDU) and padding that ensures that the field ends on a 32-bit boundary.
- **Cyclic redundancy check (CRC):** Contains a value used for error checking.
- **Length:** Indicates the length of the PDU.

SMDS Reference: SIP Level 2 Cell Format

Figure 23.6 illustrates the format of the SMDS Interface Protocol (SIP) level 2 cell format.

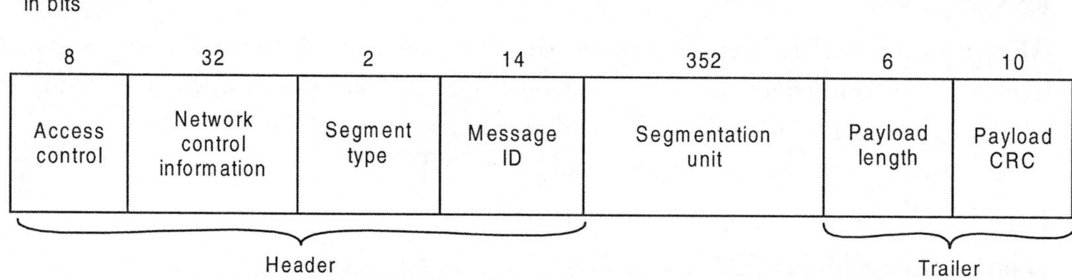

Figure 23.6 *Seven Fields Comprise the SMDS SIP Level 2 Cell.*

The following descriptions briefly summarize the functions of the SIP level 2 PDU fields illustrated in figure 23.6:

- **Access control:** Contains different values, depending on the direction of information flow. If the cell was sent from a switch to a CPE device, only the indication of whether the level 3 Protocol Data Unit (PDU) contains information is important. If the cell was sent from a CPE device to a switch, and if the CPE configuration is multi-CPE, this field can carry request bits that indicate bids for cells on the bus going from the switch to the CPE device.
- **Network control information:** Contains a value indicating whether the PDU contains information.
- **Segment type:** Indicates whether the cell is the first, the last, or a middle cell from a segmented level 3 PDU. Four possible segment type values exist:
  - *00:* Continuation of message
  - *01:* End of message
  - *10:* Beginning of message
  - *11:* Single-segment message
- **Message ID:** Associates level 2 cells with a level 3 PDU. The message ID is the same for all the segments of a given level 3 PDU. In a multi-CPE configuration, level 3 PDUs originating from different CPE devices must have a different message ID. This allows the SMDS network receiving interleaved cells from different level 3 PDUs to associate each level 2 cell with the correct level 3 PDU.
- **Segmentation unit:** Contains the data portion of the cell. If the level 2 cell is empty, this field is populated with zeros.
- **Payload length:** Indicates how many bytes of a level 3 PDU actually are contained in the segmentation unit field. If the level 2 cell is empty, this field is populated with zeros.
- **Payload cyclic redundancy check (CRC):** Contains a CRC value used to detect errors in the following fields:

- Segment Type
- Message ID
- Segmentation Unit
- Payload Length
- Payload CRC

The payload CRC value does not cover the access control or the network control information fields.

SWITCHED MULTI-MEGABIT DATA SERVICE (SMDS) OVERVIEW

Switched Multi-megabit Data Service (SMDS) is a telecommunications service that provides connectionless, high-performance, packet-switched data transport. It is neither a PROTOCOL nor a TECHNOLOGY. Rather, it supports standard protocols and communications interfaces using current (and future) technology.

SMDS allows users to transparently extend their data communications capabilities over a wider geographical area. Since it is a SERVICE offered by the telephone companies, SMDS permits this expansion using existing Customer Premises Equipment (CPE) and protocols, with minimal investment in dedicated leased lines as the number of line terminations increases.

SMDS has been defined by the IEEE 802.6 Metropolitan Area Network (MAN) standard, as implemented by Bellcore. It can use a variety of technologies, including Broadband ISDN (B-ISDN) and Distributed Queue Dual Bus (DQDB). Current North American implementations utilize DQDB with DS1 (1.5 Mbps) or DS3 (45 Mbps) lines. Other implementations utilize E1 lines at speeds in excess of 1.9 Mbps or E3 lines. Future SMDS networks will couple B-ISDN with SONET OC3 at 155 Mbps.

The development of this service has paralleled the emerging Asynchronous Transfer Mode (ATM) standards. Like ATM, SMDS uses CELL RELAY TRANSPORT. Both services use 53-octet cells for transport and can accommodate packet lengths of 9188 octets (however, the maximum length for SMDS is 9188 octets and the maximum length for ATM is 65535 octets). Because of this, SMDS is considered to be an intermediate between the packet-switched services offered today and the ATM service of the future.

The SMDS Service Path

The SMDS service allows you to create a connectionless network between CPE [single unit, chained units, and/or Local Area Networks (LANs)] at various sites nationwide. The physical SMDS service path consists of three parts:

- Customer premises
- Dedicated access line
- Public SMDS network

The customer premises includes the CPE and CPE LANs, an attached router, and the SMDS Data Service Unit/Channel Service Unit (DSU/CSU) which terminates the access line.

The dedicated access line is either a DS1 line operating at 1.5 Mbps, DS3 line operating at 45 Mbps, or appropriate E1 or E3 line. The public SMDS network consists of the local and inter-exchange carriers, their switching stations, and network connections.

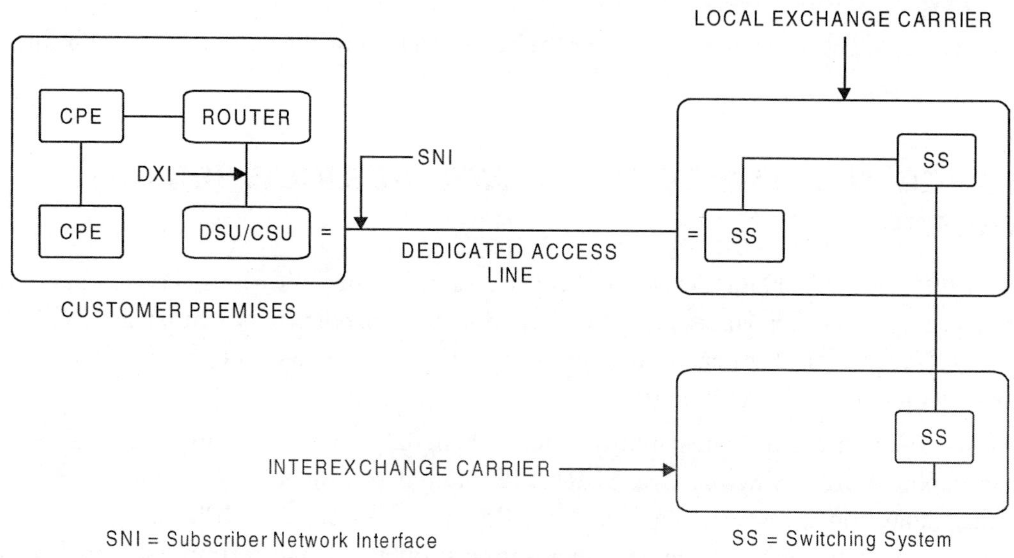

Figure 23.7

Three protocols tie these three physical elements together:

- IEEE 806.2 DQDB MAN Access protocol
- SMDS Interface Protocol (SIP)
- Data Exchange Interface (DXI) protocol

The MAN access protocol defines the basics of connecting LANs within a metropolitan area. The DQDB access protocol is also contained within the IEEE 806.2 standard. This protocol defines how a customer accesses the network from the SNI to the SS.

The SIP protocol is also defined in IEEE 806.2. This protocol is a specific implementation of the MAN access protocol designed for SMDS. It functions at the physical and data link layers.

The DXI protocol is a Bit-Oriented Protocol (BOP) implementation designed by the SMDS Interest Group (SIG) as a standard communications protocol at the physical and link layers between the router and DSU/CSU. It is supported by all major SMDS equipment vendors.

Relationship between SMDS and the OSI Architecture

The MAN access protocol and SIP have a layered architecture, that while not exactly like the 7-layer architecture described by the open systems interconnect model, does parallel the layers.

These protocols operate in the chained layers of the OSI model, layers 1, 2, and 3: the physical layer, data link layer, and packet layer, respectively. Most of the SMDS functionality is at the link level, layer 2 of the OSI model. This layer can be broken functionally into two sub-layers:

- LLC—Logical Link Control
- MAC—Medium Access Control

The diagram on the next page compares the OSI model with the various protocols operating within an SMDS network. (IP is any layer 3 protocol on the CPE, *i.e.,* Internetworking protocol.)

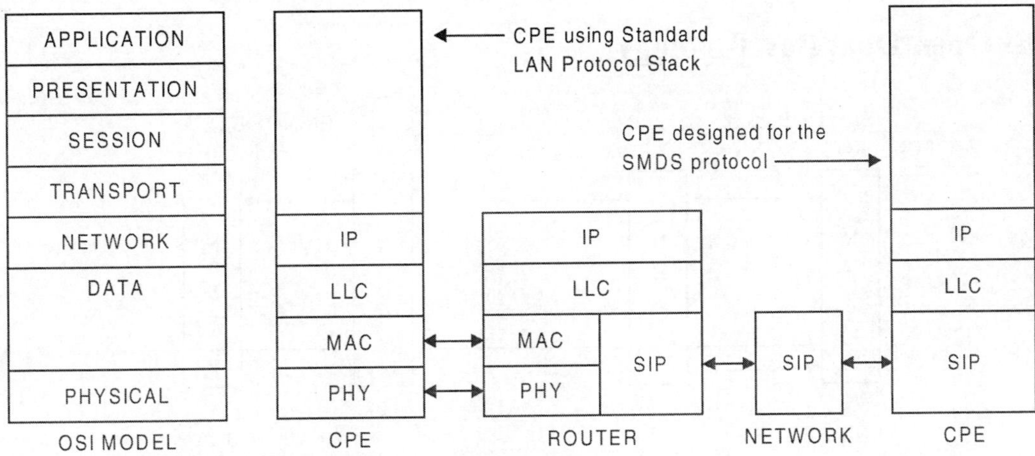

Figure 23.8

Distributed Queue Dual Bus Features

The current SMDS implementation makes use of DQDB features to transport the 53-octet cells throughout the network. DQDB provides the SMDS network with many advantages:

- Dual-bus architecture, where each bus' operation is independent of the others
- Cell relay transmission, using a reservation MAC process
- Compatibility with LANs and FDDI
- Ability to use many types of media, including:
  - Coaxial cable
  - Microwave system
  - Fibre optics
- Fault tolerance (looped dual bus)
- Rates from 1.544 to 155 Mbps
- Operation independent of the number/address of stations
- Simultaneous support of circuit- and packet-switched data

DQDB provides the interface between the MAC and the actual transmission facilities. Only the physical layer is aware of the transmission system in use. A different Physical Layer Convergence Protocol (PLCP) is implemented for each type of transmission system to ensure a consistent set of services between the DQDB layer and the physical layer.

The two most-common implementations of DQDB are open dual bus and looped dual bus. Open dual bus is a less-expensive topology than looped dual bus. However, the looped dual bus topology provides fault tolerance: a cable break in this topology results in an open dual bus topology, providing a seamless fault recovery with uninterrupted service for the customer.

The two DQDB buses are not interconnected in either topology. Each node on the each bus knows its position in the queue for that particular bus, with the first node acting as head of bus. The head of bus node can only write to that bus; the end of bus node can only read from that bus. All other nodes may both read from and write to either bus.

DQDB Open Dual Bus Topology

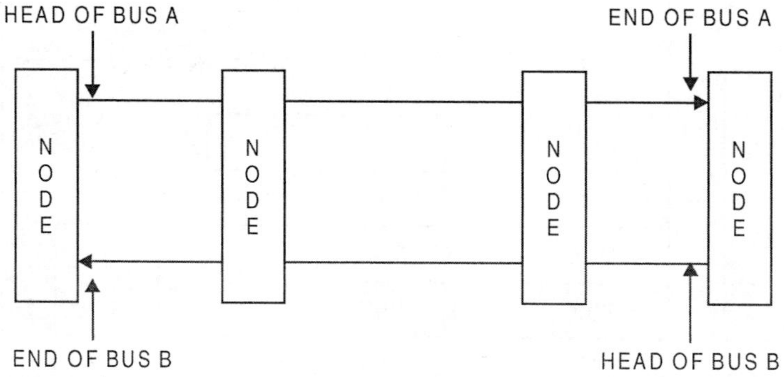

Figure 23.9

DQDB Looped Bus Topology

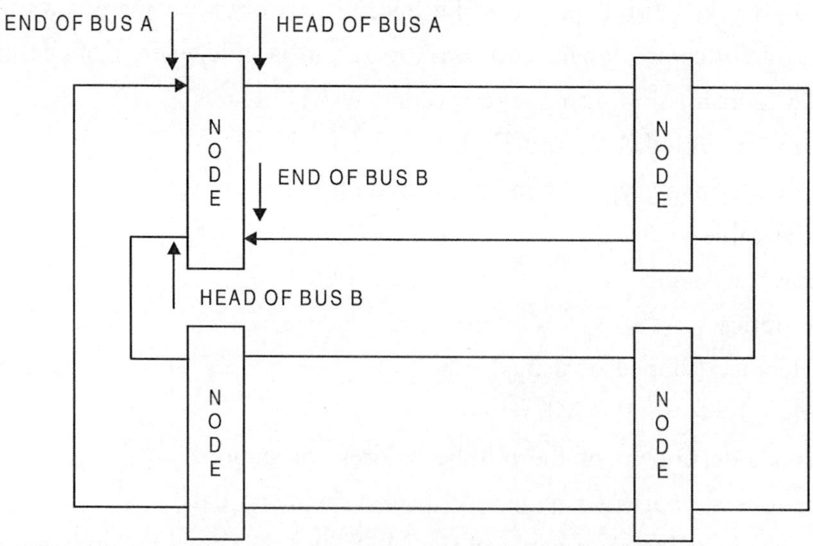

Figure 23.10

Fault Tolerance on a Looped Dual Bus Topology

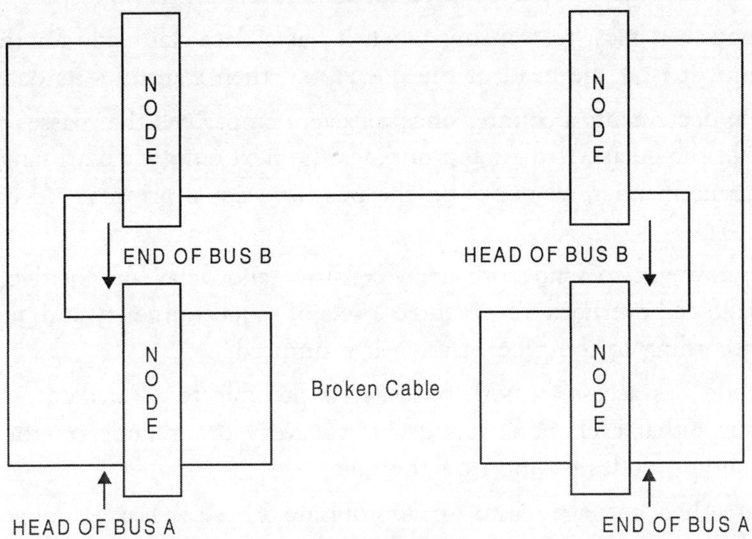

Figure 23.11

Using the dual buses, a switching station creates transmission slots (each 53 octets) and maintains a count of available slots. Each SMDS cell created contains 44 octets of data and 9 octets of DQDB and SIP management overhead. This overhead includes:

- Header:
  - Busy or empty
  - Slot type (when applicable)
  - Request type
  - Virtual Channel Identifier
  - Payload type
  - Priority
  - Head Check Sequence
  - Segment type and sequence number
  - Message Identifier (MID)
- Trailer:
  - Payload length and Cyclical Redundancy Check

The nodes on the SMDS network access this overhead material for each data cell that received on either bus. If the cell is empty (and the node is not first in the queue to transmit), the cell is either passed through the node unchanged or used to send a waiting cell to a node beyond it on the bus.

If the cell is busy, the node checks further to ascertain whether the contents of that cell are addressed to it. Cells not addressed to the node are passed through untouched. If the cell is addressed to the node, the cell contents are dumped to the node and the cell overhead information is changed to indicate that the cell is empty.

All incoming cells are empty when the node is the head of bus. Cells received by the end of bus, if not intended for that node, are discarded whether full or not.

Each node sends a request to transmit when it has a data cell ready for transmission. The node then waits until it is at the head of the queue and then transmits its data.

The node then decrements a counter once for every empty cell that passes on the bus, until it has become first in the queue. It then appropriates the next empty cell arriving on the bus and dumps its data. In this manner, all nodes on the bus have equal priority and equal access time to the bus.

It is possible, however, to send both delay-sensitive and delay- insensitive material on the same bus. The SMDS cell overhead allows three levels of request urgency and queue assignments may be allocated according to the type of request submitted.

Since each node has access to both buses, it is possible to send data to nodes in either direction. This assures that each node has access to every other node on the SMDS system regardless of the sending nodes position on the bus.

These cells are then packaged into an appropriate Physical Layer Convergence Protocol (PLCP) frame and sent out over the line.

The DQDB slot is created by the network switch and passed to the node functioning as head of bus. This slot consists of 1 octet of network overhead (access control) and a 52 octet payload segment. This is diagrammed as follows:

The Standard DQDB Slot

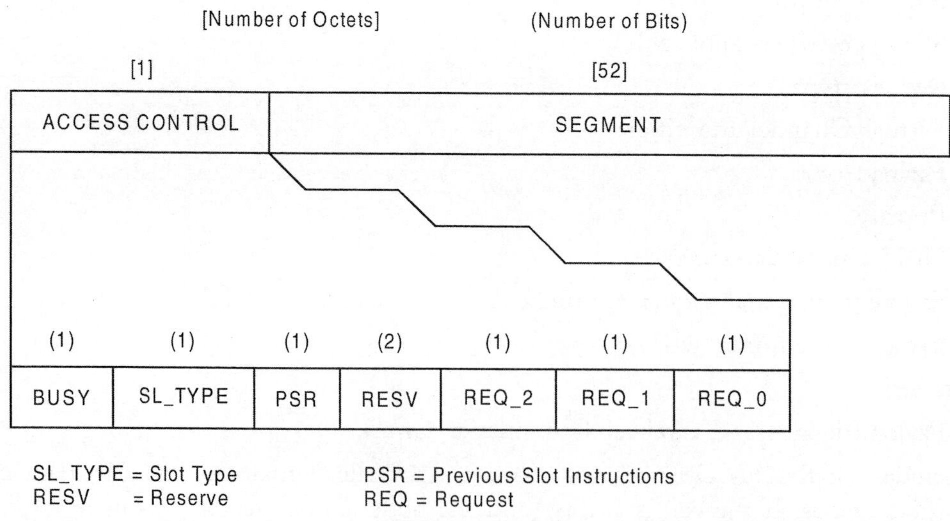

Figure 23.12

The SEGMENT of this slot, when full, contains a DQDB MAC SERVICE PROTOCOL DATA UNIT consisting of a 2 octet DMPDU header, a 44 octet segmentation unit, and a 2 octet DMPDU trailer.

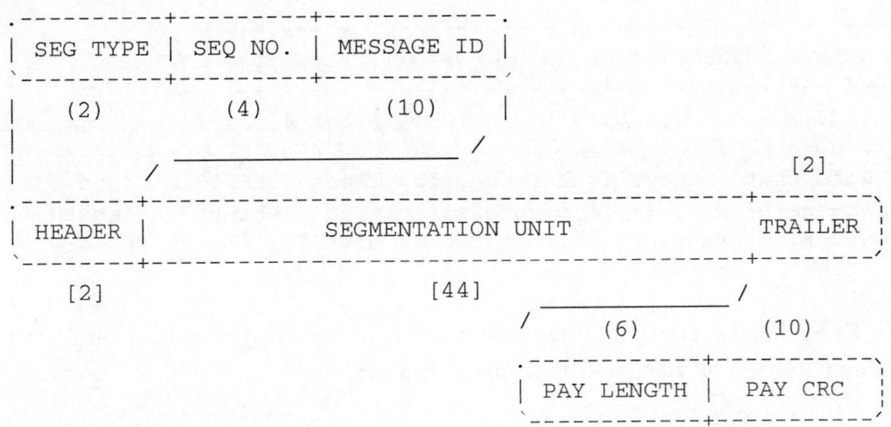

The SEGMENTATION UNIT is a 44-octet piece of the initial MAC PDU. This IMPDU is generated by the router, which adds management overhead to the MAC service data unit generated by the CPE. An IMPDU may range in size from 28 octets to a maximum of 9248 octets. The DSU/CSU is responsible for splitting the IMPDU into 44 octet segments.

```
.--------+----------+-----------------+-----+--------+---------.
| HEADER | HDR EXT  |     MAC SDU     | PAD | CRC 32 | TRAILER |
`--------+----------+-----------------+-----+--------+---------'
```

SMDS Interface Protocol

The SMDS Interface Protocol (SIP) is an implementation of DQDB that is based on connectionless service to the MAC and the queued arbitrated portion of DQDB. It utilizes four optional features of DQDB in addition:

- 60-Bit addressing (DQDB will support other addressing schemes; SMDS does not)
- Non-zero Header Extensions
- Head of Bus (HOB) functions at customer's end-station equipment
- Open bus topology, where the HOB for the A bus is the SS and the HOB for the B bus is the CPE

The protocol data units for SIP, although designated with a different nomenclature, contain similar elements that perform similar functions:

- The Service Data Unit for SIP is the same MAC Service Data Unit generated by the CPE.
- The SMDS Frame generated by the ROUTER [called the Layer 3 Protocol Data Unit (L3_PDU) in SIP] is comparable to the IMPDU for DQDB.
- The SIP 53 octet cell, created by the DSU/CSU on the customer's premises, is known as the Layer 2 Protocol Data Unit (L2_PDU). These cells are comparable to the DMPDU for DQDB.

The SIP Layer 3 Protocol Data Unit

The SIP L3_PDU is generated by the router by incorporating management control information before and after the SDU generated by the CPE.

```
.--------+-------------------+-----+--------+---------.
| HEADER | INFORMATION (SDU) | PAD | CRC 32*| TRAILER |
`--------+-------------------+-----+--------+---------'
   [36]         [0-9188]      [0-3] [0 or 4]    [4]
```

```
* Note that the cyclical Redundancy Check (CRC 32) is optional
with the L3_PDU. If it is present, it is 4 octets in length.
However, present or not, the CRC 32 bits for the L3_PDU are
ignored by the SMDS network.
```

The L3_PDU header contains information used in verifying the PDU integrity as well as addressing information. The header format is as follows:

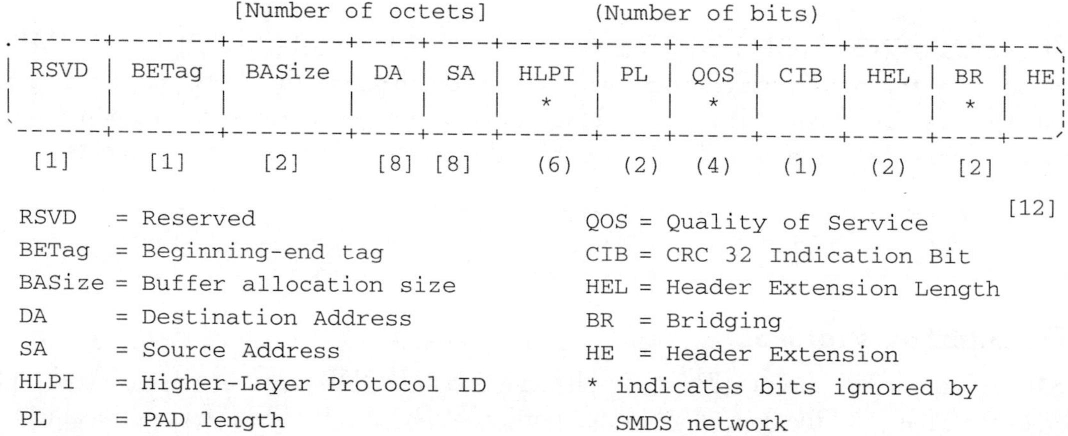

The BASize octets indicate the length of the L3_PDU. The CIB indicates the presence or absence of the 32 bit CRC in the PDU.

The header extension is also present in the SIP L3_PDU and is always 12 octets in length. This extension is a mechanism to include optional SMDS-specific information in the data unit. It must contain the SIP version in use and may contain 0-3 inter-exchange carriers of choice.

The destination and source addresses are each 8 octets in length. For each address, the 64 bits include a 4 bit address type and a 60 bit address based on the E.163 or E.164 address plan. In current implementations, you may include by INDIVIDUAL and GROUP addresses of up to 15 digits.

The INTERVIEW SMDS application programs currently support only the North American addressing, a "1" followed by 10 digits and the sequence: "F", "F", "F", "F".

The 4 octet L3_PDU trailer has the following format:

```
.------+-------+--------.
| RSVD | BETag | LENGTH |
`------+-------+--------'
```

```
RSVD  = Reserved
BETag = Beginning-end tag
```

The BETag in the header is used to indicate the beginning of the L3_PDU; in the trailer, the BETag indicates the end of the specific L3_PDU.

The LENGTH is compared with the BASize octets in the header when the L3_PDU transmission is complete. This functions as the node's first quality check, quickly determining if the entire L3_PDU has been received, *i.e.*, whether to assemble the L3_PDU or to discard the cells' contents.

The SIP Layer 2 Protocol Data Unit

The SIP L2_PDU has the same basic format as the DMPDU of DQDB:

- 7 Octet HEADER
- 44 Octet SEGMENTATION UNIT
- 2 Octet TRAILER

The header contains the access control information (1 octet), the network control information (4 octets), the segment type, the sequence number, and the message identifier.

The trailer contains the payload length (6 bits) and the payload cyclical redundancy check (10 bits).

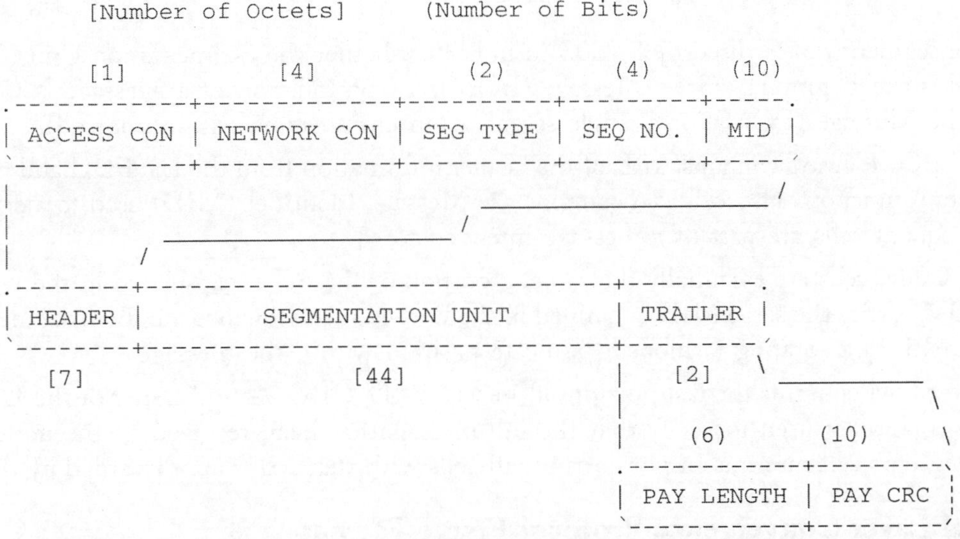

The ACCESS CONTROL and NETWORK CONTROL INFORMATION portions of the Header contain information analogous to the access control portion of the DQDB slot and the DQDB payload header, respectively. This includes:

- Access Control
  - Busy or empty
  - Request priority
- Network Control Information
  - Virtual Circuit Identifier (VCI)
  - Payload type
  - Segment priority (PRI)
  - Header Check Sequence (HCS)

For SMDS the network control information must be the hexadecimal sequence FF, FF, F0, 22.

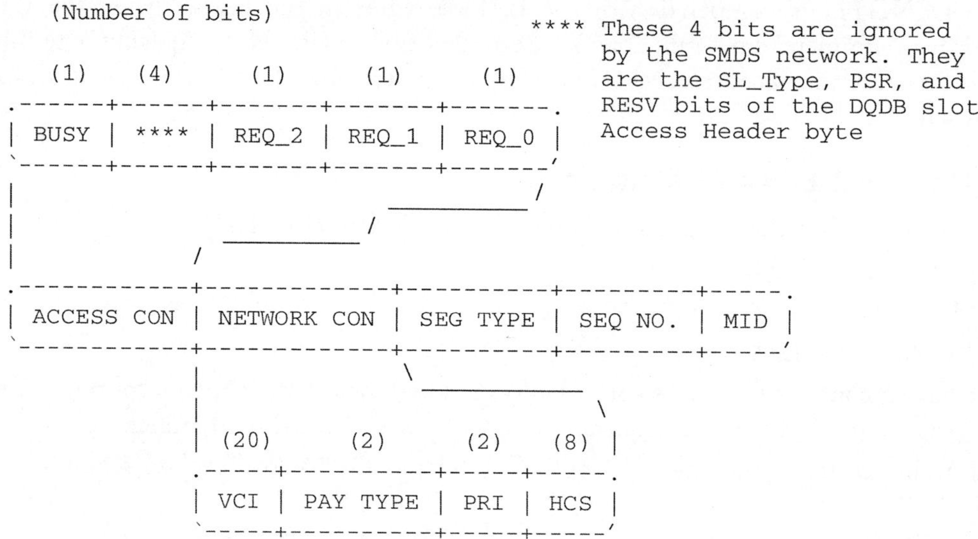

The segment type is used by SMDS to indicate whether the Segmentation Unit (SU) in a given cell is the Beginning of the Message (BOM), a Continuation of a Message (COM), the End of the Message (EOM), or a single segment (an entire frame within one cell).

The BOM always contains ALL of the header information from the L3_PDU and performs a "call setup" function. This cell also contains the Message Identifier (MID) used to alert a node that subsequent cells are part of a message intended for it.

All COM cells are essentially the same: a portion of the SU encapsulated in the L2_PDU. Each COM carries the same MID contained in the BOM and a sequence number that increments from 0 to 15, in a rotating fashion, to indicate position within the message.

The EOM contains the last portion of the SU, PAD, CRC 32, and trailer of the L3_PDU. This information is used to verify that the full message has been received by the node. If any of the message's cells are missing or corrupt, all cells with that MID are discarded by the node.

Physical Layer Convergence Protocol Frame Format

The L2_PDUs are formatted into a PLCP frame for transmission over the DS1 or E1 lines. (The INTERVIEW currently does not support SMDS on DS3 or E3 lines.)

The PLCP frame format consists of 10 "rows" each 57 octets in length. For DS1, the last row also contains a 6 octet trailer.

For the PLCP frame, the MOST-SIGNIFICANT BIT is transmitted over the line first. This is contrary to most other protocols monitored by the interview (including the raw data display during bit-image data playback via synchronous with display idle: ON) and is not the way data is normally stored in the unit. The received process reverses the bit order of the data as it is received, so that the first bit of each octet is stored as the most-significant bit in memory.

The DS1 frame has a duration of 3 milliseconds. It is transmitted at a rate of 1.536 Mbps. The E1 frame is similar in size.

The format of the PLCP frame for DS1 is shown on the next two pages. The first 2 octets of each row function as synchronous bytes.

```
  [1]  [1]  [1]  [1]               [53 octets]
.----+----+----+----+-----------------------------------.
| A1 | A2 | P9 | Z4 |          L2_PDU                   |
+----+----+----+----+-----------------------------------+
| A1 | A2 | P8 | Z3 |          L2_PDU                   |
+----+----+----+----+-----------------------------------+
| A1 | A2 | P7 | Z2 |          L2_PDU                   |
+----+----+----+----+-----------------------------------+
| A1 | A2 | P6 | Z1 |          L2_PDU                   |
+----+----+----+----+-----------------------------------+
| A1 | A2 | P5 | F1 |          L2_PDU                   |
+----+----+----+----+-----------------------------------+
| A1 | A2 | P4 | B1 |          L2_PDU                   |
+----+----+----+----+-----------------------------------+
| A1 | A2 | P3 | G1 |          L2_PDU                   |
+----+----+----+----+-----------------------------------+
| A1 | A2 | P2 | M2 |          L2_PDU                   |
+----+----+----+----+-----------------------------------+
| A1 | A2 | P1 | M1 |          L2_PDU                   |
+----+----+----+----+-----------------------------------+---------.
| A1 | A2 | P0 | C1 |          L2_PDU                   | TRAILER |
`----+----+----+----+-----------------------------------+---------'

Key:
  A1 = 11110110 (fixed)               A2 = 00101000 (fixed)
  Px = Path Overhead Identifier       Zx = Growth octets
  F1 = PLCP Path User Channel         B1 = Bit-Interleaved Parity 8
  G1 = PLCP Path Status                       (BIP-8)
  C1 = Cycle/Stuff Counter            Mx = SIP Layer 1 Control Info
```

SIP Addressing Scheme

The SIP destination and source addresses for the United States are 10-digit numbers preceded by a "1" and followed by four Binary-Coded Decimal (BCD) "F"s. International addresses include the appropriate country code, telephone number, and node designation, not exceeding 15 BCD digits (not supported by the INTERVIEW SMDS application programs at this time). Two types of addresses are used:

- Individual addresses
- Group addresses

Each individual address uniquely identifies a single Subscriber Network Interface (SNI). However, up to 16 individual addresses may be assigned to a single SNI, each equally valid.

Each group address is used to identify a group of up to 128 individual addresses. The switching system is able to support up to 1024 group addresses.

A given individual address is able to participate in a maximum of 32 group addresses. Each SNI is able to be a part of up to 48 group addresses.

In addition to indicating the source node and the destination node, the SIP address functions as part of the security system of the SMDS network. As the BOM of each SMDS packet is received, the source address is verified to ensure that the sender is not inserting another subscriber's address. The SS will verify that the source address is:

- An individual address, not a group address
- Legitimately assigned to the SNI from which the packet originates

Both source and destination addresses are also used in the ADDRESS SCREENS that may be maintained by the SS. Address screens may be used to create Closed User Groups (CUGs) within the SMDS network. This allows for the creation of virtual private networks within the context of the public-access SMDS network. Up to 128 address screens may be maintained by the SS for any SNI on the network.

An INDIVIDUAL ADDRESS SCREEN consists of a set of "allowed" or "disallowed" addresses used to screen the destination packets sent by a specific node and the source addresses of received packets for that node. This type of screen may be used to prevent unauthorized traffic from reaching a "sensitive" node and also to prevent unauthorized use of CPE.

A GROUP ADDRESS SCREEN is used to screen the destination addresses of packets sent by the CPE at a node. This type of screen is usually used for a CUG. SMDS NETWORK MANAGEMENT.

The current implementation of SMDS in North America has Customer Network Management (CNM) capabilities. This implementation allows the CUSTOMER to maintain control over the network functions, including:

- Performance management
- Fault management
- Accounting management
- Configuration management
- Security management

The CNM implementation currently in place for SMDS is the Simple Network Management Protocol (SNMP). This is a LAN network management supported by many vendors and used on many non-TCP/IP networks.

REVIEW QUESTIONS

1. What is SMDS ?
2. What are the different components of SMDS ?
3. What are SMDS access classes ?
4. What are SMDS interface protocol ?

❑❑❑

PART 6

NETWORK LAYER

24

NETWORK LAYER OVERVIEW

NETWORK LAYER

The network layer determines that how data transmits between the network devices. It also translates the logical address into the physical address *e.g.*, computer name into MAC address. It is also responsible for defining the route, managing the network problems and addressing. Router works on the network layer and if a sending device does not break the data into the similar packets as the receiving device then network layer split the data into the smaller units and at the receiving end the network layer reassemble the data.

Network layer routes the packets according to the unique network addresses. Router works as the postoffice and network layer stamps the letters (data) for the specific destinations.

Protocols: These protocols work on the network layer IP, ICMP, ARP, RIP, OSI, IPX and OSPF.

Network Devices: Network devices including Router, Brouter, Frame Relay device and ATM switch devices work on the network layer.

The network layer provides services to the transport layer through virtual circuits or datagrams. In both cases, its main job is routing packets from the source to the destination. In virtual circuit subnets, a routing decision is made when the virtual circuit is set up. In datagram subnets, it is made on every packet.

Many routing algorithms are used in computer networks. Static algorithms include shortest path routing, flooding, and flow-based routing. Dynamic algorithms include distance vector routing and link state routing. Most actual networks use one of these. Other important routing techniques are hierarchical routing, routing for mobile hosts, broadcast routing, and multicast routing.

Subnets can become congested, increasing the delay and lowering the throughput for packets. Techniques include traffic shaping, flow specifications, and bandwidth reservation. If congestion does occur, it must be dealt with. Choke packets can be sent back, load can be shed, and other methods applied.

Networks differ in various ways, so when multiple networks are connected together problems can occur. Sometimes problems can be finessed by tunneling a packet through a hostile network, but if the source and the destination networks are different, this approach fails. Fragmentation may be called for if different networks are having different maximum sizes.

The Internet has a rich variety of protocols related to the network layer. These include the data protocol, IP, but also the control protocols ICMP, ARP, and RARP, and the routing protocols OSPF and BGP. The Internet is rapidly running out of IP addresses, so a new version of IP, IPv6 has been developed.

Unlike the datagram-based Internet, ATM networks use virtual circuits inside. There must be a set up before data can be transferred and torn down after transmission is completed. Quality of service and congestion control are major issues with ATM networks.

Data Link Layer deals with machine-to-machine communication while network layer, lowest layer that deals with host-to-host communication, call this end-to-end communication.

Network layer associate with four issues:

- Interface between the host and the network (the network layer is typically the boundary between the host and subnet).
- Routing.
- Congestion and deadlock.
- Internetworking (A path may traverse different network technologies(*e.g.*, Ethernet, point-to-point links, etc.).

NETWORK LAYER INTERFACE

The network layer should shield the transport layer from having to know details of the underlying subnet should not do anything different if sending across Ethernet or across the country on the Internet.

- Datagram model: the host is responsible (Data-grams are not guaranteed reliably delivered)
- Virtual Circuit model: subnet is responsible.

DARPA Internet community viewpoint: The subnet is inherently unreliable no matter how it is designed. Thus, host are forced to do error control anyway. Given that they perform error control, why have the network layer duplicate the same function ?

The DARPA TCP/IP Internet is connectionless. Common carrier viewpoint: The connection oriented approach is the right way. Users don't want complex error control protocols in host computers. User's want reliable, trouble-free service. (X.25)

Network Interface Layer

The *network interface layer* (also called the network access layer) is responsible for placing TCP/IP packets on the network medium and receiving TCP/IP packets off the network medium. TCP/IP was designed to be independent of the network access method, frame format, and medium. In this way, TCP/IP can be used to connect different network types. These include LAN technologies such as Ethernet and token ring and WAN technologies such as X.25 and frame relay. Independence from any specific network technology gives TCP/IP the ability to be adapted to new technologies such as Asynchronous Transfer Mode (ATM).

The network interface layer encompasses the data link and physical layers of the OSI model. Note that the Internet layer does not take advantage of sequencing and acknowledgement services that might be present in the data-link layer. An unreliable network interface layer is assumed, and reliable communications through session establishment and the sequencing and acknowledgement of packets is the responsibility of the transport layer.

Internet Layer

The *Internet layer* is responsible for addressing, packaging, and routing functions. The core protocols of the Internet layer are IP, ARP, ICMP, and IGMP.

- The *Internet Protocol* (IP) is a routable protocol responsible for IP addressing, routing, and the fragmentation and reassembly of packets.
- The *Address Resolution Protocol* (ARP) is responsible for the resolution of the Internet layer address to the network interface layer address such as a hardware address.
- The *Internet Control Message Protocol* (ICMP) is responsible for providing diagnostic functions and reporting errors due to the unsuccessful delivery of IP packets.
- The *Internet Group Management Protocol* (IGMP) is responsible for the management of IP multicast groups.

The Internet layer is analogous to the network layer of the OSI model.

OVERVIEW OF OTHER NETWORK LAYER ISSUES

The network layer is responsible for routing packets from the source to destination. The routing algorithm is the piece of software that decides where a packet goes next (*e.g.*, which output line, or which node on a broadcast channel).

For connectionless networks, the routing decision is made for each datagram. For connection-oriented networks, the decision is made once, at circuit setup time.

NETWORK PROTOCOLS

Routed protocols are transported by routing protocols across an Internet-work. In general, routed protocols in this context also are referred to as network protocols. These network protocols perform a variety of functions required for communication between user applications in source and destination devices, and these functions can differ widely among protocol suites. Network protocols occur at the upper four layers of the OSI reference model: the transport layer, the session layer, the presentation layer, and the application layer.

Routing in the Internet

Routing is the technique by which data finds its way from one host computer to another. In the Internet context there are three major aspects of routing:

- Physical Address Determination
- Selection of inter-network gateways
- Symbolic and Numeric Addresses

The first of these is necessary when an IP datagram is to be transmitted from a computer. It is necessary to encapsulate the IP datagram within whatever frame format is in use on the local network or networks to which the computer is attached. This encapsulation clearly requires the inclusion of a local network address or physical address within the frame.

The second of these is necessary because the Internet consists of a number of local networks interconnected by one or more gateways. Such gateways, generally known as routers, sometimes have physical connections or ports onto many networks. The determination of the appropriate gateway and port for a particular IP datagram is called routing and also involves gateways interchanging information in standard ways.

The third aspect which involves address translation from a reasonably human friendly form to numeric IP addresses is performed by a system known as the Domain Name System or DNS for short.

NETWORK LAYER OVERVIEW

When constructing an Internet-work, attention must be given to several critical issues such as addressing, flow control, error control, routing, access control, and the size message that is permitted on the network. When dealing with identical or similar networks, the first two layers of the OSI model are in control, and these issues are addressed by lower two layers. However, when an internet-work comprises dissimilar networks, then the third layer of the OSI model, namely, the network layer, must enter the picture. The network layer performs several functions, including providing services to the transport (layer 4), performing congestion control, and formatting data messages so they are recognized by the destination network. The network layer is also responsible for the end-to-end routing or switching of data from source network to destination network.

For illustrating, how the network layer works, we will use the TCP/IP model instead of OSI model. TCP/IP layer that function similar to OSI's network layer is the Internet layer, which also is called the network layer. The heart and soul of this layer is Internet Protocol (IP) – the IP of TCP/IP. IP is a connectionless datagram service and is responsible for routing packets between nodes.

In short, IP receives data bits from the upper layer, assembles the bits into packets (*i.e.*, IP Data grams) and then selects the best route based on some criterion, called a metric (*e.g.*, distance, number of router "hops," bandwidth), which the packets should take to reach their destination. Since IP is connectionless, every packet must contain the address of the destination node. This address, called an Internet or IP address, is assigned to an Internet node by a network administrator or by an automated protocol (*e.g.*, DHCP) as part of the node's initial network configuration. An IP address uniquely identifies a host similar to the way a street address uniquely identifies a residence or the way a social security number, driver's license number, or student ID number uniquely identifies a person. It is used by the network layer as a road map to locate a host within the Internet.

NETWORK LAYER PROTOCOLS

Virtual Circuit

A virtual circuit is a circuit or path between points in a network that appears to be a discrete, physical path but is actually a managed pool of circuit resources from which specific circuits are allocated as needed to meet traffic requirements.

All communications across a data network are carries out over previously established virtual circuits. These can be set up either on demand by user or permanently by network management. With on-demand connections, the user device sends a request for a Switched Virtual Connection (SVC) to be set up to a central control unit known as the Signaling Control Point (SCP).

The SCP then determines the availability of both the required destination and the transmission bandwidth appropriate to call across the network.

With Permanent Virtual Circuits (PVC), the route is already determined when demand is made. The PVC is a logical predefined path or link through a carrier network.

A permanent virtual circuit (PVC) is a virtual circuit that is permanently available to the user just as though it were a dedicated or leased line continuously reserved for that user. A switched virtual circuit (SVC) is a virtual circuit in which a connection session is set up for a user only for the duration of a connection. PVCs are an important feature of frame relay networks and SVCs are proposed for later inclusion.

Datagram Networks

Two basic approaches to packet switching are common: The most common is datagram switching (also known as a "best-effort network" or a network supporting the connection-less network service).This is what is used in the network layer of the Internet.

Datagram Packet Networks

Datagram transmission uses a different scheme to determine the route through the network of links. Using datagram transmission, each packet is treated as a separate entity and contains a header with the full information about the intended recipient. The intermediate nodes examine the header of a packet and select an appropriate link to an intermediate node which is nearer the destination. In this system, the packets do not follow a pre-established route, and the intermediate nodes (usually known as "routers") do not require prior knowledge of the routes that will be used.

A datagram network is analogous to sending a message as a series of postcards through the postal system. Each card is independently sent to the final destination (using the postal system). To receive the whole message, the receiver must collect all the postcards and sort them into the original order. Not all postcards need be delivered by the postal system, and not all take the same length of time to arrive.

In a datagram network delivery is not guaranteed (although they are usually reliably sent). Enhancements, if required, to the basic service (*e.g.*, reliable delivery) must be provided by the end systems (*i.e.*, user's computers) using additional software. The most common datagram network is the Internet which uses the IP network protocol. Applications which do not require more than a best effort service can be supported by direct use of packets in a datagram network (using the User Datagram Protocol (UDP) transport protocol). Such applications include Internet Video,

Voice Communication, messages notifying a user that she/he has received new email, etc. Most Internet applications need additional functions to provide reliable communication (such as end-to-end error and sequence control). Examples include sending email, browsing a web site, or sending a file using the File Transfer Protocol (FTP). This reliability ensures all the data is received in the correct order with no duplication or omissions. It is provided by additional layers of software algorithms implemented in the end systems (A,D). Two examples of this are the Transmission Control Protocol (TCP), and the Trivial File Transfer Protocol (TFTP) which uses UDP.

One merit of the datagram approach is that not all packets need to follow the same path (route) through the network (although frequently packets do follow the same route). This removes the need to set-up and tear-down the path, reducing the processing overhead, and a need for intermediate systems to execute an additional protocol.

Packets may also be routed around busy parts of the network when alternate paths exist. This is useful when a particular intermediate system becomes busy or overloaded with excessive volumes of packets to send. It can also provide a high degree of fault tolerance, when an individual intermediate system or communication circuit fails. As long as a route exists through the network between two end systems, they are able to communicate. Only if there is no possible way to send the packets, will the packets be discarded and not delivered. The fate (success/failure) of an application therefore depends only on existence of an actual path between the two End Systems (ESs). This is known as "fate sharing"—since the application shares the "fate" of the network.

There is another type of network known as a virtual circuit network. This has some advantages in particular scenarios. Although it is not covered as a part of the course, there is a web page comparing the two approaches.

Switching

Switching algorithms are relatively simple and are basically the same for most routing protocols. In most cases, a host determines that it must send a packet to another host. Having acquired a router's address by some means, the source host sends a packet addressed specifically to a router's physical (Media Access Control [MAC]-layer) address, but with the protocol (network-layer) address of the destination host.

On examining the packet's destination protocol address, the router determines that it either knows or does not know how to forward the packet to the next hop. If the router does not know how to forward the packet, it typically drops the packet. If the router knows how to forward the packet, it changes the destination physical address to that of the next hop and transmits the packet.

The next hop may or may not be the ultimate destination host. If not, the next hop is usually another router, which executes the same switching decision process. As the packet moves through the Internet work, its physical address changes but its protocol address remains constant.

The preceding discussion describes switching between a source and a destination end system. The International Organization for Standardization (ISO) has developed a hierarchical terminology that is useful in describing this process. Using this terminology, network devices without the ability to forward packets between sub-networks are called End Systems (ESs), while network devices with these capabilities are referred to as Intermediate Systems (ISs). ISs are further divided into those that can communicate within routing domains (intra-domain ISs) and those that communicate both within and between routing domains (inter-domain ISs). A routing domain is generally considered to be a portion of an Internet work under common administrative authority, regulated by a particular set of administrative guidelines. Routing domains are also called autonomous systems with certain protocols, routing domains can also be divided into routing areas, but intra-domain routing protocols are still used for switching both within and between areas.

PHYSICAL ADDRESS DETERMINATION

If a computer wishes to transmit an IP datagram it needs to encapsulate in a frame appropriate to the physical medium of the network it is attached to. For the successful transmission of such a frame it is necessary to determine the physical address of the destination computer. This can be achieved fairly simply using a Table 24.1 that will map IP addresses to physical addresses, such a table may include addresses for IP nets and a default address as well as the physical addresses corresponding to the IP addresses of locally connected computers.

Such a table could be configured into a file and read into memory at boot up time. However it is normal practice for a computer to use a protocol known as ARP (Address Resolution Protocol) and defined by RFC 826. This operates *dynamically* to maintain the translation table known as the ARP cache.

On most unix systems the contents of the ARP cache can be displayed using the command arp -a. Here is typical output from the arp -a command.

A computer determines its own physical address at boot up by examining the hardware and its own IP address by reading a configuration file at boot up time but it is necessary to fill the ARP cache. This is done by the computer making ARP request broadcasts whenever it encounters an IP address that cannot be mapped to a physical address by consulting the cache.

By making such requests a host can fill up the ARP cache. ARP cache entries will eventually time-out and a new query will have to be made. This allows a computer to respond to changing topology. Typical time-outs are about 20 minutes. An ARP request to a non-existent computer may be repeated after a few seconds up to a modest maximum number of times.

If a computer is connected to more than one network via separate ports then a separate ARP cache will be maintained for each interface. Alternatively there will be a further entry in the ARP cache associating an entry with a particular interface.

It may be thought that ARP requests will be made for every Internet computer a computer wishes to contact. This is not true, a reference to an IP address not on a local or directly connected network will be re-directed to an IP router computer with an IP address that is on a local directly connected network.

Table 24.1 The Format of an ARP Request on an Ethernet

General	*Use*	*Size in Bytes*	*Typical Values*
Ethernet Header	Ethernet Destination Address	6	A broadcast address
	Ethernet Source Address	6	Identifies computer making request
	Frame Type	2	Set to 0 × 0806 for ARP request and 0 × 8035 for an ARP reply
ARP request/reply	Hardware Type	2	Set to 1 for an Ethernet
	Protocol Type Hardware Address Size in bytes	2 1	Set to 0 × 0800 for IP addresses Set to 6 for Ethernet
	Protocol Address Size in bytes	1	Set to 4 for IP
	Operation	2	1 for request, 2 for reply
	Sender Ethernet Address	6	-
	Sender IP Address	4	-
	Destination Ethernet Address	6	Not filled in on ARP request
	Destination IP Address	4	-

Since ARP requests are broadcast, any computer maintaining an ARP cache can monitor all such broadcasts and extract the sending computer's physical and IP address and update its own ARP cache as necessary. When a computer boots up it can send an ARP request as a means of announcing its presence on the local network. It is possible to associate more than one IP address with a single physical address.

Note that the ARP request format is designed to be capable of supporting protocols other than IP and Ethernet as long as it is possible to broadcast on the local network.

REVERSE ADDRESS RESOLUTION PROTOCOL(RARP)

Short for reverse address resolution protocol, a TCP/IP protocol that permits a physical address, such as an Ethernet address, to be translated into an IP address. Hosts such as diskless workstations often only know their hardware interface addresses, or MAC addresses, when booted but not their IP addresses. They must discover their IP addresses from an external source, usually a RARP server. RARP is defined in RFC 903.

Protocol an agreed-upon format for transmitting data between two devices. The protocol determines the following:

- The type of error checking to be used.
- Data compression method, if any.

- How the sending device will indicate that it has finished sending a message.
- How the receiving device will indicate that it has received a message.

There are a variety of standard protocols from which programmers can choose. Each has particular advantages and disadvantages; for example, some are simpler than others, some are more reliable, and some are faster.

From a user's point of view, the only interesting aspect about protocols is that your computer or device must support the right ones if you want to communicate with other computers. The protocol can be implemented either in hardware or in software.

Discless workstations were once widely used. These had a local processor and RAM but all disc space was supplied from a server using NFS or some similar system. In the absence of local configuration files, boot-up involved the use of a very simple file transfer protocol known as TFTP, however before this could be used the workstation needed to know its IP address. In order to determine this Reverse Address Resolution Protocol (RARP) described in RFC 903 was used. This used the same message format as ARP but used operation types 3 and 4 for requests and responses. Only suitably configured RARP servers would reply to such requests.

RARP may still be encountered in conjunction with devices such as laser printers.

INTERNET ROUTING—INTERNAL ROUTING TABLES

Within any host there will be a routing table that the host uses to determine which physical interface address to use for outgoing IP data-grams. Once this table has been consulted the ARP cache(s) will be consulted to determine the physical address.

If a computer receives an IP datagram on any interface there are two possibilities, one is that the datagram is intended for that computer in which case it will be passed to the relevant application. The other is that the datagram is addressed to some other computer in which case the computer will attempt to re-transmit on one or other of the available interfaces.

There are four basic items of information in such a table:

- A destination IP address.
- A gateway IP address. This will be the same as the destination IP address for directly connected destinations.
- Various flags usually displayed as U, G, H and sometimes D and M. U means the route is up. G means the route is via a gateway. H means the destination address is a host address as distinct from a network address.
- The physical interface identification.
- The destination address may appear as "default".
- The host operation is to first look for the destination address as a host address in the routing table, if it is not found then look for the destination net address in the routing table and if that is not found then use one of the default addresses (there may be several).

- A host dedicated to providing a gateway service between several networks is known as a router and may have a very large routing table (64 MB is not unknown) and will run special protocols to interchange routing information with other hosts and routers.
- A general purpose host may have connections to at most two or three networks and a correspondingly simple table.

THE RIP (RFC 1058) PROTOCOL

Using RIP hosts will periodically broadcast (or send to all neighbor routers if there is no broadcast facility) its entire routing table or those parts that have changed recently. RIP information is transmitted using UDP/IP using messages of the form as given in Table 24.2.

Table 24.2 RIP Information

Field	*Bytes*	*Typical Values*
command	1	Request Reply Obsolete Obsolete Poll Poll Entry
Version	1	1 or 2
Reserved	2	Must be zero
Address Family	2	2 for IP addresses
Reserved	2	Must be zero
IP Address	4	Address of host
Reserved	8	Must be Zero
Metric	4	a number in the range 1 to 16

The metric is the hop-count to the host whose IP address is quoted. A value of 16 implies the host is unreachable. The 20 bytes specifying address family, IP address and metric may be repeated up to 25 times. An IP address of 0.0.0.0 is regarded as a default address.

Routers will receive RIP information and will use it to determine their shortest route to a particular host. RIP information is sent to neighbors or broadcast every 30 seconds. RIP information is processed by daemon processes (either **routed** or **gated** on unix hosts) listening on the well known port number 520.

RIP suffers from very slow convergence in the face of topology changes because routers are not under any obligation to identify failed links and, more importantly, their consequences and propagate the facts to other routers. RIP is an example of a distance vector protocol.

THE OSPF (RFC 1247) PROTOCOL

The O means open, *i.e.*, non-proprietary protocol. OSPF is a Link State Protocol (LSP). This means that each router maintains link status information and this is exchanged between routers wishing to build routing Tables 24.3. Unlike RIP OSPF uses IP directly, OSPF packets being identified by a special value in the IP datagram protocol field. All OSPF messages have a common initial 8 bytes as shown in Table 24.3.

Table 24.3 OSPF Message

Field	*Bytes*	*Typical Values*
Version	1	2
Packet Type	1	Hello Database Description Link state request Link state update link state acknowledgement
Packet Length	2	Packet length in bytes
Router ID	4	IP address of sending host
Area ID	4	ID of area to which packet belongs
Checksum	2	As for IP datagram
Authentication type	2	No authentication Simple password
Authentication data	8	For type 1 only

Hello Packets

These are used between routers to identify each other and establish common operating procedures.

Database Description Packets

These are used to enable routers to transmit a complete database of link states. Link states are expressed in terms of source and destination addresses and the type of service bits used in IP datagrams. These specify a low delay link state, a high throughput link state and a high reliability link state. There are proposals to include a low monetary cost link state. The individual link status information records are known as link state advertisements.

LSP Requests

These enable a router to request specific link information from a neighbor

LSP Update

At any time a router may transmit new link state advertisements.

REVIEW QUESTIONS

1. Why does the Internet use a connectionless network service?
2. Why is the largest octet in an Internet address 255?
3. What is the network address?
4. What is the purpose of subnetting?
5. What is a default mask?
6. How does next-hop routing decrease the number of table entries in a router?
7. How does network-specific routing decrease the number of table entries in a router?
8. How does host-specific routing decrease the number of table entries in a router?
9. What is geographic routing?
10. Name the five protocols in the network layer.
11. What is the purpose of ARP?
12. Why is an ARP request broadcast ? Why is an ARP reply unicast?
13. What do we mean when we say IP is a best-effort delivery service?
14. What is the name of a packet in the IP layer?
15. What is the purpose of protocol field in the IP header?
16. Why does the IP checksum cover just the header?
17. Why the RARP and IGMP missing from ipv6?
18. Why would an Internet need an autonomous system?
19. What is the difference between an interior protocol and exterior routing protocol ? Name an example of each.
20. What kind of information is in a routing table?
21. Name the four types of OSPF connections.
22. What is path vector routing?
23. What is the role of the Dijkstra algorithm in unicast routing?
24. Name the three main categories of IGMP messages and briefly discuss their functions.

25

INTERNETWORKING

INTERNETWORKING BASICS

In this chapter, some fundamental concepts and terms used in the evolving language of internetworking are addressed. In the same way that this book provides a foundation for understanding modern networking, this chapter summarizes some common themes presented throughout the remainder of this book. Topics include flow control, error checking, and multiplexing, but this chapter focuses mainly on mapping the Open System Interconnection (OSI) model to networking/internetworking functions, and also summarizing the general nature of addressing schemes within the context of the OSI model. The OSI model represents the building blocks for internet-works. Understanding the conceptual model helps you understand the complex pieces that make up an internetwork.

What is an Internetwork ?

An *internet-work* is a collection of individual networks, connected by intermediate networking devices, that functions as a single large network. Internetworking refers to the industry, products, and procedures that meet the challenge of creating and administering internetworks (Figure 25.1.)

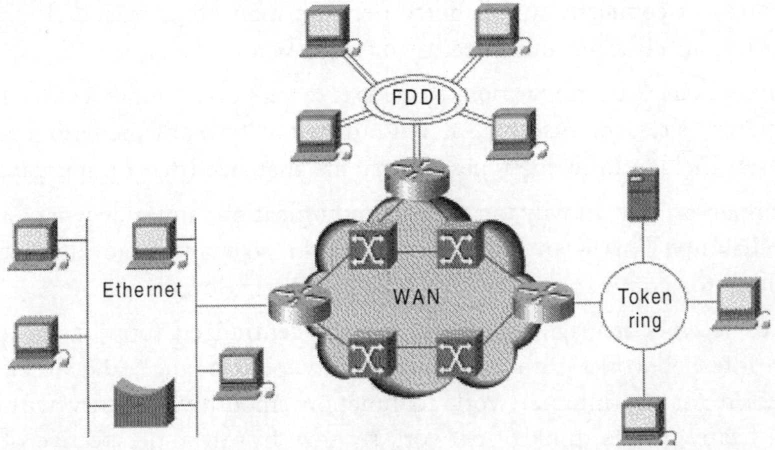

Figure 25.1 *Different Network Technologies can be Connected to Create an Internetwork.*

illustrates some different kinds of network technologies that can be interconnected by routers and other networking devices to create an internet-work.

HISTORY OF INTERNETWORKING

The first networks were time-sharing networks that used mainframes and attached terminals. Such environments were implemented by both IBM's Systems Network Architecture (SNA) and digital's network architecture.

Local-Area Networks (LANs) evolved around the PC revolution. LANs enabled multiple users in a relatively small geographical area to exchange files and messages, as well as access shared resources such as file servers and printers.

Wide-Area Networks (WANs) interconnect LANs with geographically dispersed users to create connectivity. Some of the technologies used for connecting LANs include T1, T3, ATM, ISDN, ADSL, frame relay, radio links, and others. New methods of connecting dispersed LANs are appearing everyday.

Today, high-speed LANs and switched internet-works are becoming widely used, largely because they operate at very high speeds and support such high-bandwidth applications as multimedia and videoconferencing.

Internetworking evolved as a solution to three key problems: isolated LANs, duplication of resources, and a lack of network management. Isolated LANs made electronic communication between different offices or departments impossible. Duplication of resources meant that the same hardware and software had to be supplied to each office or department, as did separate support staff. This lack of network management meant that no centralized method of managing and troubleshooting networks existed.

INTERNETWORKING CHALLENGES

Implementing a functional internet-work is no simple task. Many challenges must be faced, especially in the areas of connectivity, reliability, network management, and flexibility. Each area is key in establishing an efficient and effective internet-work.

The challenge when connecting various systems is to support communication among disparate technologies. Different sites, for example, may use different types of media operating at varying speeds, or may even include different types of systems that need to communicate.

Because companies rely heavily on data communication, internet-works must provide a certain level of reliability. This is an unpredictable world, so many large internet-works include redundancy to allow for communication even when problems occur.

Furthermore, network management must provide centralized support and troubleshooting capabilities in an internet-work. Configuration, security, performance, and other issues must be adequately addressed for the internet-work to function smoothly. Security within an internet-work is essential. Many people think of network security from the perspective of protecting the private network from outside attacks. However, it is just as important to protect the network from internal attacks, especially because most security breaches come from inside. Networks must also be secured so that the internal network cannot be used as a tool to attack other external sites.

Early in the year 2000, many major web sites were the victims of Distributed Denial of Service (DDOS) attacks. These attacks were possible because a great number of private networks currently connected with the Internet were not properly secured. These private networks were used as tools for the attackers. Because nothing in this world is stagnant, internet-works must be flexible enough to change with new demands.

INTERNETWORKING DEVICE COMPARISON

Internetworking devices offer communication between Local Area Network (LAN) segments. There are four primary types of internetworking devices: repeaters, bridges, routers, and gateways. These devices can be differentiated very generally by the Open System Interconnection (OSI) layer at which they establish the LAN-to-LAN connection. Repeaters connect LANs at OSI layer 1; bridges connect LANs at layer 2; routers connect LANs at layer 3; and gateways connect LANs at layers 4 through 7. Each device offers the functionality found at its layer(s) of connection and uses the functionality of all lower layers. This idea is portrayed graphically in figure 25.2.

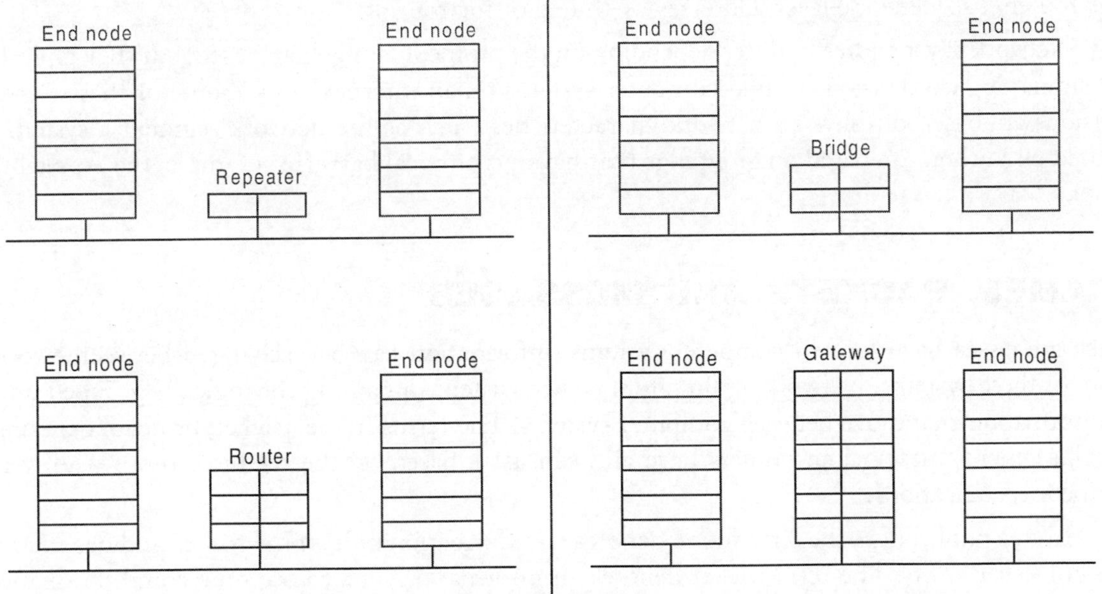

Figure 25.2 *Internetworking Product Functionality.*

ADDRESSING

Locating computer systems on an internet-work is an essential component of any network system. There are various addressing schemes used for this purpose, depending on the protocol family being used. In other words, AppleTalk addressing is different from TCP/IP addressing, which in turn is different from OSI addressing, and so on.

Two important types of addresses are link-layer addresses and network-layer addresses. Link-layer addresses (also called physical or hardware addresses) are typically unique for each network connection. In fact, for most Local-Area Networks (LANs), link-layer addresses are resident in the interface circuitry and are assigned by the organization that defined the protocol standard represented by the interface. Because most computer systems have one physical network connection, they have only a single link-layer address. Routers and other systems connected to multiple physical networks can have multiple link-layer addresses. As their name implies, link-layer addresses exist at layer 2 of the OSI reference model.

Network-layer addresses (also called virtual or logical addresses) exist at layer 3 of the OSI reference model. Unlike link-layer addresses, which usually exist within a flat address space, network-layer addresses are usually hierarchical. In other words, they are like mail addresses, which describe a person's location by providing a country, a state, a zip code, a city, a street, an address on the street, and finally, a name. One good example of a flat address space is the U.S. social security numbering system, where each person has a single, unique social security number.

Hierarchical addresses make address sorting and recall easier by eliminating large blocks of logically similar addresses through a series of comparison operations. For example, we can eliminate all other countries if an address specifies the country Ireland. Easy sorting and recall is one reason that routers use network-layer addresses as the basis for routing.

Network-layer addresses differ depending on the protocol family being used, but they typically use similar logical divisions to find computer systems on an internet-work. Some of these logical divisions are based on physical network characteristics (such as the network segment a system is located on); others are based on groupings that have no physical basis (for example, the AppleTalk zone).

FRAMES, PACKETS AND MESSAGES

Once addresses have located computer systems, information can be exchanged between two or more of these systems. Networking literature is inconsistent in naming the logically grouped units of information that move between computer systems. The terms frame, packet, protocol data unit, PDU, segment, message, and others have all been used, based on the whim of those who write protocol specifications.

In this publication, the term frame denotes an information unit whose source and destination is a link-layer entity. The term packet denotes an information unit whose source and destination is a network-layer entity. Finally, the term message denotes an information unit whose source and destination entity exists above the network layer. Message is also used to refer to particular lower-layer information units with a specific, well-defined purpose.

KEY ORGANIZATIONS

Without the services of several key standards organizations, the world of networking would be substantially more chaotic than it is currently. Standards organizations provide forums for discussion, help turn discussion into formal specifications, and proliferate the specifications once they complete the standardization process.

Most standards organizations have specific processes for turning ideas into formal standards. Although these processes differ slightly between standards organizations, they are similar in that they all iterate through several rounds of organizing ideas, discussing the ideas, developing draft standards, voting on all or certain aspects of the standards, and finally formally releasing the completed standard to the public.

Standards Organizations

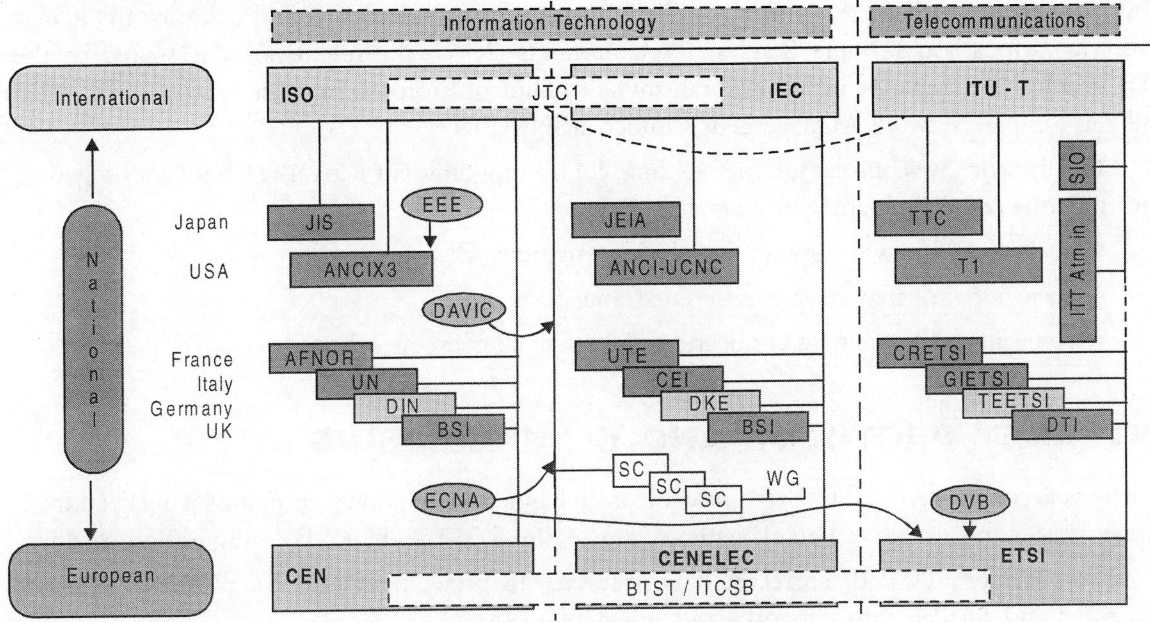

Figure 25.3 *Key Organizations.*

Some of the better-known standards organizations follow:

- **International Organization for Standardization (ISO)**

An international standards organization responsible for a wide range of standards, including those relevant to networking. This organization is responsible for the OSI reference model and the OSI protocol suite.

- **American National Standards Institute (ANSI)**

The coordinating body for voluntary standards groups within the United States ANSI is a member of ISO. ANSI's best-known communications standard is FDDI.

- **Deutsches Institute for Normung (DIN)**

The coordinating body for voluntary standards groups within Germany. DIN is a member of ISO.

- **Electronic Industries Association (EIA)**

A group that specifies electrical transmission standards. EIA's best-known standard is EIA/TIA-232 (formerly RS-232).

- **Institute of Electrical and Electronic Engineers (IEEE)**

A professional organization that defines network standards. IEEE LAN standards (including IEEE 802.3 and IEEE 802.5) are the best-known IEEE communications standards and are the predominant LAN standards in the world today.

• International Telecommunication Union Telecommunication Standardization Sector (ITU-T) (formerly the Committee for International Telegraph and Telephone [CCITT])

An international organization that develops communication standards. The best-known ITU-T standard is X.25.

• Internet Activities Board (IAB)

A group of internetwork researchers who meet regularly to discuss issues pertinent to the Internet. This board sets much of the policy for the Internet through decisions and assignment of task forces to various issues. Some Request for Comments (RFC) documents are designated by the IAB as Internet standards, including Transmission Control Protocol/Internet Protocol (TCP/IP) and the Simple Network Management Protocol (SNMP).

Finally, when we consider internetworking, connecting different network technologies together, one finds the same problems, only worse:

- packets may travel through many different networks
- each network may have a different frame format
- some networks may be connectionless, other connection oriented

INTERNET PROTOCOL AND IP ADDRESSING

When you configure the TCP/IP protocol on a Microsoft windows computer, an IP address, subnet mask, and usually a default gateway are required in the TCP/IP configuration settings.

To configure TCP/IP correctly, it is necessary to understand how TCP/IP networks are addressed and divided into networks and sub-networks.

The success of TCP/IP as the network protocol of the Internet is largely because of its ability to connect together networks of different sizes and systems of different types. These networks are arbitrarily defined into three main classes (along with a few others) that have predefined sizes, each of which can be divided into smaller sub-networks by system administrators. A subnet mask is used to divide an IP address into two parts. One part identifies the host (computer), the other part identifies the network to which it belongs. To better understand how IP addresses and subnet masks work, look at an IP (Internet Protocol) address and see how it is organized.

IP ADDRESSES: NETWORKS AND HOSTS

An IP address is a 32-bit number that uniquely identifies a host (computer or other device, such as a printer or router) on a TCP/IP network.

IP addresses are normally expressed in dotted-decimal format, with four numbers separated by periods, such as 192.168.123.132. To understand how subnet masks are used to distinguish between hosts, networks, and sub-networks, examine an IP address in binary notation. For example, the dotted-decimal IP address 192.168.123.132 is (in binary notation) the 32 bit number 11000000101000111101110000100. This number may be hard to make sense of, so divide it into four parts of eight binary digits.

These eight bit sections are known as octets. The example IP address, then, becomes 11000000.10101000.01111011.10000100. This number only makes a little more sense, so for most uses, convert the binary address into dotted-decimal format (192.168.123.132). The decimal numbers separated by periods are the octets converted from binary to decimal notation.

For a TCP/IP Wide Area Network (WAN) to work efficiently as a collection of networks, the routers that pass packets of data between networks do not know the exact location of a host for which a packet of information is destined. Routers only know what network the host is a member of and use information stored in their route table to determine how to get the packet to the destination host's network. After the packet is delivered to the destination's network, the packet is delivered to the appropriate host.

For this process to work, an IP address has two parts. The first part of an IP address is used as a network address, the last part as a host address. If you take the example 192.168.123.132 and divide it into these two parts you get the following:

```
192.168.123. Network .132 Host
-or-
192.168.123.0 - network address. 0.0.0.132 - host address.
```

SUBNET MASK

The second item, which is required for TCP/IP to work, is the subnet mask. The subnet mask is used by the TCP/IP protocol to determine whether a host is on the local subnet or on a remote network.

In TCP/IP, the parts of the IP address that are used as the network and host addresses are not fixed, so the network and host addresses above cannot be determined unless you have more information. This information is supplied in another 32-bit number called a subnet mask. In this example, the subnet mask is 255. 255. 255. 0. It is not obvious what this number means unless you know that 255 in binary notation equals 11111111; so, the subnet mask is:

```
11111111.11111111.11111111.0000000
```

Lining up the IP address and the subnet mask together, the network and host portions of the address can be separated:

```
11000000.10101000.01111011.10000100 - IP address (192.168.123.132)
11111111.11111111.11111111.00000000 - Subnet mask (255.255.255.0)
```

The first 24 bits (the number of ones in the subnet mask) are identified as the network address, with the last 8 bits (the number of remaining zeros in the subnet mask) identified as the host address. This gives you the following:

```
11000000.10101000.01111011.00000000 - Network address (192.168.123.0)
00000000.00000000.00000000.10000100 - Host address (000.000.000.132)
```

So now you know, for this example using a 255. 255. 255. 0 subnet mask, that the network ID is 192.168.123.0, and the host address is 0.0.0.132. When a packet arrives on the 192.168.123.0 subnet (from the local subnet or a remote network), and it has a destination address of 192.168.123.132, your computer will receive it from the network and process it.

Almost all decimal subnet masks convert to binary numbers that are all ones on the left and all zeros on the right. Some other common subnet masks are:

```
Decimal  Binary  255.255.255.192
1111111.11111111.1111111.11000000  255.255.255.224
1111111.11111111.1111111.11100000
```

Internet RFC 1878 describes the valid subnets and subnet masks that can be used on TCP/IP networks.

NETWORK CLASSES

Internet addresses are allocated by the Inter-NIC the organization that administers the Internet. These IP addresses are divided into classes. The most common of these are classes A, B, and C. Classes D and E exist, but are not generally used by end users. Each of the address classes has a different default subnet mask. You can identify the class of an IP address by looking at its first octet. Following are the ranges of class A, B, and C Internet addresses, each with an example address:

Class A networks use a default subnet mask of 255. 0. 0. 0 and have 0–127 as their first octet. The address 10.52.36.11 is a class A address. Its first octet is 10, which is between 1 and 126, inclusive.

Class B networks use a default subnet mask of 255. 255. 0. 0 and have 128–191 as their first octet. The address 172.16.52.63 is a class B address. Its first octet is 172, which is between 128 and 191, inclusive.

Class C networks use a default subnet mask of 255. 255. 255. 0 and have 192–223 as their first octet. The address 192.168.123.132 is a class C address. Its first octet is 192, which is between 192 and 223, inclusive.

In some scenarios, the default subnet mask values do not fit the needs of the organization, because of the physical topology of the network, or because the numbers of networks (or hosts) do not fit within the default subnet mask restrictions. The next section explains how networks can be divided using subnet masks.

SUB-NETTING

A class A, B, or C TCP/IP network can be further divided, or sub-netted, by a system administrator. This becomes necessary as you reconcile the logical address scheme of the Internet (the abstract world of IP addresses and subnets) with the physical networks in use by the real world.

A system administrator who is allocated a block of IP addresses may be administering networks that are not organized in a way that easily fits these addresses. For example, you have a wide area network with 150 hosts on three networks (in different cities) that are connected by a TCP/IP router. Each of these three networks has 50 hosts. You are allocated the class C network 192.168.123.0. (For illustration, this address is actually from a range that is not allocated on the Internet.) This means that you can use the addresses 192.168.123.1 to 192.168.123.254 for your 150 hosts.

Two addresses that cannot be used in your example are 192.168.123.0 and 192.168.123. 255 because binary addresses with a host portion of all ones and all zeros are invalid. The zero address is invalid because it is used to specify a network without specifying a host. The 255 address (in binary notation, a host address of all ones) is used to broadcast a message to every host on a network. Just remember that the first and last address in any network or subnet cannot be assigned to any individual host.

You should now be able to give IP addresses to 254 hosts. This works fine if all 150 computers are on a single network. However, your 150 computers are on three separate physical networks. Instead of requesting more address blocks for each network, you divide your network into subnets that enable you to use one block of addresses on multiple physical networks.

In this case, you divide your network into four subnets by using a subnet mask that makes the network address larger and the possible range of host addresses smaller. In other words, you are 'borrowing' some of the bits usually used for the host address, and using them for the network portion of the address. The subnet mask 255. 255. 255. 192 gives you four networks of 62 hosts each. This works because in binary notation, 255. 255. 255. 192 is the same as 1111111.11111111.1111111.11000000. The first two digits of the last octet become network addresses, so you get the additional networks 00000000 (0), 01000000 (64), 10000000 (128) and 11000000 (192). (Some administrators will only use two of the sub-networks using 255. 255. 255. 192 as a subnet mask. In these four networks, the last 6 binary digits can be used for host addresses.

Using a subnet mask of 255. 255. 255. 192, your 192.168.123.0 network then becomes the four networks 192.168.123.0, 192.168.123.64, 192.168.123.128 and 192.168.123.192. These four networks would have as valid host addresses:

```
192.168.123.1–62  192.168.123.65–126  192.168.123.129–190
192.168.123.193-254
```

Remember, again, that binary host addresses with all ones or all zeros are invalid, so you cannot use addresses with the last octet of 0, 63, 64, 127, 128, 191, 192, or 255.

You can see how this works by looking at two host addresses, 192.168.123.71 and 192.168.123.133. If you used the default class C subnet mask of 255. 255. 255. 0, both addresses are on the 192.168.123.0 network. However, if you use the subnet mask of 255. 255. 255. 192, they are on different networks; 192.168.123.71 is on the 192.168.123.64 network, 192.168.123.133 is on the 192. 168. 123. 128 network.

DEFAULT GATEWAYS

If a TCP/IP computer needs to communicate with a host on another network, it will usually communicate through a device called a router. In TCP/IP terms, a router that is specified on a host, which links the host's subnet to other networks, is called a default gateway. This section explains how TCP/IP determines whether or not to send packets to its default gateway to reach another computer or device on the network.

When a host attempts to communicate with another device using TCP/IP, it performs a comparison process using the defined subnet mask and the destination IP address versus the subnet mask and its own IP address. The result of this comparison tells the computer whether the destination is a local host or a remote host.

If the result of this process determines the destination to be a local host, then the computer will simply send the packet on the local subnet. If the result of the comparison determines the destination to be a remote host, then the computer will forward the packet to the default gateway defined in its TCP/IP properties. It is then the responsibility of the router to forward the packet to the correct subnet.

TCP/IP network problems are often caused by incorrect configuration of the three main entries in a computer's TCP/IP properties. By understanding how errors in TCP/IP configuration affect network operations, you can solve many common TCP/IP problems.

- **Incorrect Subnet Mask:** If a network uses a subnet mask other than the default mask for its address class, and a client is still configured with the default subnet mask for the address class, communication will fail to some nearby networks but not to distant ones. As an example, if you create four subnets (such as in the sub-netting example) but use the incorrect subnet mask of 255. 255. 255. 0 in your TCP/IP configuration, hosts will not be able to determine that some computers are on different subnets than their own. When this happens, packets destined for hosts on different physical networks that are part of the same class C address will not be sent to a default gateway for delivery. A common symptom of this is when a computer can communicate with hosts that are on its local network and can talk to all remote networks except those that are nearby and have the same class A, B, or C address. To fix this problem, just enter the correct subnet mask in the TCP/IP configuration for that host.

- **Incorrect IP Address:** If you put computers with IP addresses that should be on separate subnets on a local network with each other, they will not be able to communicate. They will try to send packets to each other through a router that will not be able to forward them correctly. A symptom of this problem is a computer that can talk to hosts on remote networks, but cannot communicate with some or all computers on their local network. To correct this problem, make sure all computers on the same physical network have IP addresses on the same IP subnet. If you run out of IP addresses on a single network segment, there are solutions that go beyond the scope of this article.

- **Incorrect Default Gateway:** A computer configured with an incorrect default gateway will be able to communicate with hosts on its own network segment, but will fail to communicate with hosts on some or all remote networks. If a single physical network has more than one router, and the wrong router is configured as a default gateway, a host will be able to communicate with some remote networks, but not others. This problem is common if an organization has a router to an internal TCP/IP network and another router connected to the Internet.

THE INTERNET-WORK PROTOCOL (IP)

The IP (Internet Protocol) is a protocol which uses datagram to communicate over a packet switched network. The IP protocol operates at the network layer protocol of the OSI reference model and is a part of a suite of protocols originally developed by the US Department of Defense (DoD).

The Internet-work Protocol (IP) provides a best effort network layer service for connecting computers to form a computer network. Each computer is identified by one or more globally unique IP addresses. The network layer PDUs are known as either "packets" or "data-grams". Each packet carries the IP address of the sending computer and also the address of the intended recipient or recipients of the packet. Other management information is also carried.

The IP network service transmits data-grams between intermediate nodes using IP routers. The routers themselves are simple, since no information is stored concerning the data-grams which are forwarded on a link. The most complex part of an IP router is concerned with determining the optimum link to use to reach each destination in a network. This process is known as "routing". Although this process is computationally intensive, it is only performed at periodic intervals.

An IP network normally uses a dynamic routing protocol to find alternate routes whenever a link becomes unavailable. This provides considerable robustness from the failure of either links or routers, but does not guarantee reliable delivery. Some applications are happy with this basic service and use a simple transport protocol known as the User Datagram Protocol (UDP) to access this best effort service.

Most Internet users need additional functions such as end-to-end error and sequence control to give a reliable service (equivalent to that provided by virtual circuits). This reliability is provided by the Transmission Control Protocol (TCP) which is used end-to-end across the Internet.

In a LAN environment, the protocol is normally carried by Ethernet, but for long distance links, a data link protocol such as HDLC is usually used. Other protocols associated with the IP network layer are the Internet Control Message Protocol (ICMP) and the Address Resolution Protocol (ARP).

ALLOCATION OF IP ADDRESSES

IP addresses are allocated via the network information center. When the Internet was young a message to the network information center was all that was necessary to obtain a block of IP addresses. Today it is more usual to obtain a block of addresses from your Internet service provider or direct from one of several regional registries. All the regional registries maintain databases that can be queried using the who is command, however it is sometimes necessary to try several registries.

Here's an example of a registry being queried to determine the ownership of an IP network. RIPE is the European Internet registry.

The full list of who is servers are:

- whois.arin.net
- whois.apnic.net
- whois.nic.mil
- rs.internic.net
- whois.ripe.net

AUTONOMOUS SYSTEMS

The key to high level Internet routing is the grouping of Internet hosts into autonomous systems which usually correspond to commercial or administrative entities. All autonomous systems have a distinctive and unique number. Details of autonomous systems are available from the *who is* servers in the same way as details of IP networks. Unfortunately the syntax of such queries differs between the various servers, the *ripe* server requires *ASnnnn* whereas the *arin* server requires just the number. Here is a brief list of some autonomous system numbers.

Table 25.1 Autonomous System Numbers

Number	*Network*
786	JANET
1849	UUnet UK (was Pipex)
2529	Demon
3300	ATT Uni-source (Netherlands)
5413	Xara
6453	Tele-globe Montreal
6683	DANTE
8297	Tele-globe Virginia

INTERNET PROTOCOL

In the TCP/IP protocol suite, all packets are delivered by the IP datagram delivery service. Packet delivery is not guaranteed by this service. A packet can be misdirected, duplicated, or lost on the way to its destination. The service is connectionless because all packets are transmitted independently of any other packets. This is in contrast to a telephone network, for instance, where a connection is established and maintained.

To keep track of the delivery status, TCP/IP applications using the IP datagram delivery service expect to receive replies from the destination node.

IP defines the form that packets must take and the ways that packets are handled when they are transmitted or received. The form the packet takes is called an IP datagram. It is the basic unit of information that is passed across a TCP/IP network. The IP datagram consists of a header and a data section. The header section contains the sender's (source) IP address and the receiver's (destination) IP address and other information. Figure 25.4 shows the general form of an IP datagram.

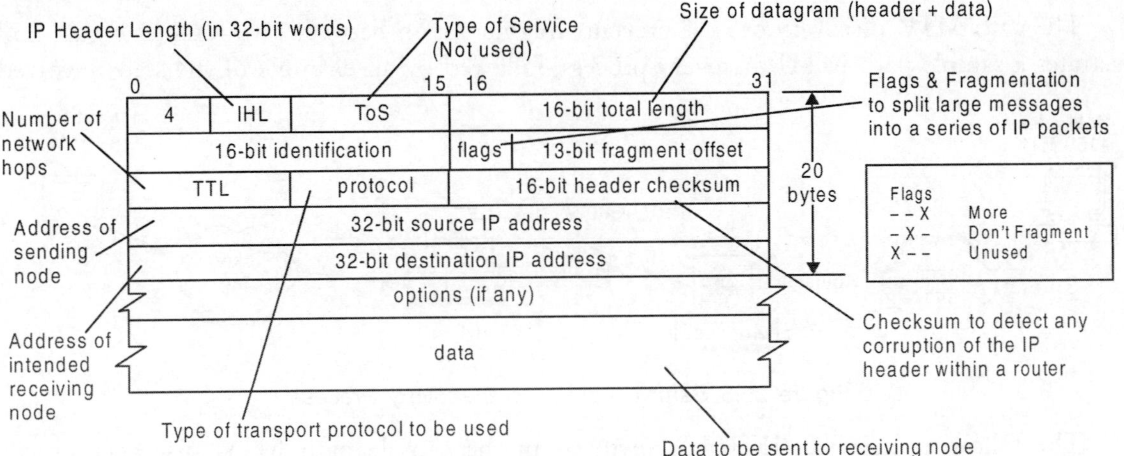

Figure 25.4 *IP Data Gram.*

Basic Frame of an IP Datagram

The IP address for a node is a logical address and is independent of any particular hardware or network topology. It has the same form, regardless of the media type. The IP address (version 4) is a 4-byte (32-bit) numeric value that identifies both a network and a local host or node (computer or other device) on that network. The 4-byte IP address is usually represented in dotted decimal notation. Each byte is represented by a decimal number, and periods separate the bytes, for example, 129. 47. 6. 17.

The data-link layer transmits IP packets in the data section of its physical frame. Because IP supports a 64-KB packet length, an IP datagram might not fit in a data-link frame. Also, in traveling to its destination, a datagram can traverse many different media with different physical frame lengths. An IP router might have to forward a packet across media in which the inbound and outbound frame lengths differ.

To handle these potential problems with packet transmission, IP specifies a method for breaking data-grams into fragments. The fragments are reassembled when they arrive at the final destination. Reassembling fragments reconstructs the entire IP datagram.

Path Maximum Transfer Unit

The Maximum Transfer Unit (MTU) is the maximum size of data packets that can be transferred across a given physical network. For local area networks, such as Ethernet, the MTU is determined by the network hardware. For wide area networks that use serial lines to interconnect packet switches, the MTU is determined by software.

The path MTU is the smallest of all MTUs, for the hops along a path from the source host to the destination host. The path MTU governs the size of the largest IP packet that can be sent across the path without fragmentation. This feature conforms to RFC 1191.This feature is automatically enabled when you enable TCP/IP.

Path MTU Discovery Process

There are two advantages to this feature. The path MTU avoids fragmentation anywhere along the path and it reduces the protocol overhead.

The path MTU discovery process prevents fragmentation between two routers. Figure 25.5 illustrates a sample path MTU discovery process, followed by an example of the steps involved.

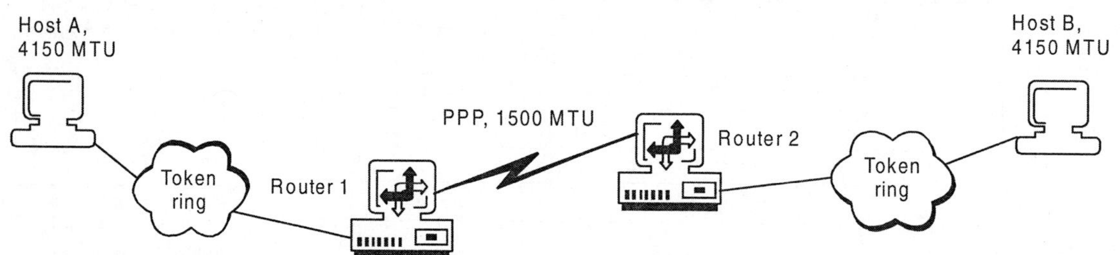

Figure 25.5 *Sample Path MTU Discovery Process*

The following describes the steps involved in the sample path MTU discovery process illustrated above:

1. Host A opens a File Transfer Protocol (FTP) connection to Host B.
2. Host A and Host B negotiate the maximum segment size (MSS) during their connection. This is the largest TCP segment that a host can send across a network. The MSS is 4,110 bytes, which is 4,150 bytes minus 40 bytes for the IP and TCP headers.
3. Host A sends a 4,150-byte packet to 4,110 bytes of data and 40 bytes of header information to Host B. The Don't Fragment (DF) flag in the IP header is set to yes in Host A.
4. Router 1 receives the packet from Host A. Then Router 1 determines that the packet is larger than 1,500 bytes, which is the maximum packet size that can be sent over a PPP network.
5. Router 1 sends Host A an ICMP destination unreachable error message. This message indicates that Router 1 must fragment packets larger than 1,500 bytes.
6. Host A receives the error message from Router 1. In response, it adjusts the maximum segment size to 1,460 bytes.
7. Host A resends the data from Step 3. Each packet consists of 1,460 bytes of data and 40 bytes of header information.
8. Router 1 accepts the packets and forwards them to Router 2, which then sends them to Host B.

Assigning IP Network Addresses

IP network addresses should be assigned by one person at your company. We recommend that a network administrator assign IP network addresses. Therefore, to obtain a new address, see your network administrator. If you are a network administrator this section will help you assign IP network addresses.

For a node using the TCP/IP protocol suite to communicate with other nodes, including nodes on other private networks and on the Internet, an IP network address is required. Your IP network address could be determined in one of the following ways:

- If you are accessing the Internet through an Internet Service Provider (ISP), you can be assigned an IP address by your ISP.
- If you are connected directly to the Internet community or if you cannot connect to the Internet using the registered IP address range you were assigned by your ISP.
- If your network is not attached to the public Internet community, you can select an arbitrary IP network number. However, if you plan to attach your network to the Internet later, you should use the guidelines in RFC 1918.

The addresses for all the nodes on the network must meet the following criteria:

- All addresses within a network must use the same prefix. For example, any node on network 129.47 must have an address in the form 129.47. x. x.
- Each node must have a unique IP address.

IP ADDRESSES

IP addresses consist of a 32 bit number and is represented by the dot-decimal format. for example: 142.110.237.1 is an IP address. There are 4 decimal digits separated by three dots. Each digit is allowed the range of 0 to 255 which corresponds to 8 bits (one byte) of information.

A portion of an IP address represents the network address and the remaining portion the host address. For example: 142.110.237.1 is the IP address of a firewall. The network that the firewall resided on is 142.110.237.0 (Note: IP addresses that end in a 0 represent network addresses). The host address of the firewall is 0.0.0.1 (Note: the network portion of the IP address is represented by 0s). Each host on the network and Internet must have a unique IP address. There are ways around having each host a unique IP address and they are discussed under firewalls.

The Network Information Center (NIC) assigns network addresses to the Internet. You must apply to receive a IP network address. Depending on the class (more on this later) of the IP address, you can then assign as many host IP addresses as allowed.

An alternative is to "rent" IP addresses from your local Internet Service Provider (ISP). They usually own the rights to a block of IP addresses and will rent them out for a fee.

IP Address Classifications

There is a formal structure to the assignment of IP addresses. IP addresses are assigned by the Network Information Center (NIC) who is a central authority with the responsibility of assigning network addresses. There are several classifications of IP addresses. They include network addresses and special purpose addresses.

Class A Addresses

IP address range	1. 0. 0. 0 to 127. 0. 0. 0
Number of networks available:	125 (see special addresses below)
Number of hosts per network:	16, 777, 214
Net Mask:	255. 0. 0. 0 (first 8 bits are ones)
Special Addresses:	10. 0. 0. 0 is used for networks not connected to the Internet 127. 0. 0. 0 is the loopback address for testing (see ping)

```
                    1 1 1 1 1 1 1 1 1 1 2 2 2 2 2 2 2 2 2 2 3 3
0 1 2 3 4 5 6 7 8 9 0 1 2 3 4 5 6 7 8 9 0 1 2 3 4 5 6 7 8 9 0 1
```

0	Network ID	Host ID

Class A addresses always have bit 0 set to 0, bits 1-7 are used as the network ID. Bits 8-31 are used as the host ID. Class A networks are used by very large companies such as IBM, US Dept. of Defense and AT&T.

Class B Addresses

IP address range	128. 0. 0. 0 to 191. 0. 0. 0
Number of networks available:	16, 382 (see special addresses below)
Number of hosts per network:	65, 534
Net Mask:	255. 255. 0. 0 (first 16 bits are ones)
Special Addresses:	172. 16. 0. 0 to 172. 31. 0. 0 are used for networks not connected to the Internet

```
                    1 1 1 1 1 1 1 1 1 1 2 2 2 2 2 2 2 2 2 2 3 3
0 1 2 3 4 5 6 7 8 9 0 1 2 3 4 5 6 7 8 9 0 1 2 3 4 5 6 7 8 9 0 1
```

1 0	Network ID	Host ID

Class B addresses always have bit 0 and 1 set to 10, bits 2-15 are used as the network ID. Bits 16-31 are used as the host ID. Class B networks are assigned to large companies and universities.

Class C Addresses

IP address range	192. 0. 0. 0 to 223. 0. 0. 0
Number of networks available:	2, 097, 150 (see special addresses below)
Number of hosts per network:	254
Net Mask:	255. 255. 255. 0 (first 16 bits are ones)
Special Addresses:	192. 168. 1. 0 to 192. 168. 255. 0 are used for networks not connected to the Internet

```
                    1 1 1 1 1 1 1 1 1 1 2 2 2 2 2 2 2 2 2 2 3 3
0 1 2 3 4 5 6 7 8 9 0 1 2 3 4 5 6 7 8 9 0 1 2 3 4 5 6 7 8 9 0 1
```

1 1 0	Network ID	Host ID

Class C addresses always have bits 0-2 set to 110, bits 3-24 are used as the network ID. Bits 25-31 are used as the host ID. Class C network addresses are assigned to small companies and local Internet providers.

Class D Addresses

IP address range	224. 0. 0. 0 to 239. 0. 0. 0
Use:	Multicasting addresses

0	1	2	3	4	5	6	7	8	9	10	11	12	13	14	15	16	17	18	19	20	21	22	23	24	25	26	27	28	29	30	31
1	1	1	0	Multicast Address																											

Class D addresses always have bits 0-3 set to 1110, bits 4-31 are used as the Multicast address. Class D network addresses are used by multicasting. Multicasting is a method of reducing network traffic. Rather than send a separate datagram to each host if multiple host require the same information. A special multicast address can be used where one datagram is read by many hosts.

Class E Addresses

IP address range	240. 0. 0. 0 to 255. 0. 0. 0
Use:	Reserved by the Internet for its own use.

If you try to ping a Class E address, you should get the error message that says that it is an invalid IP address.

Uniform Resource Locators (URLs)

URLs, or Uniform Resource Locators, are the method by which documents or data are addressed in the World Wide Web. The URL contains the following information:

- the internet name of the site containing the resource (document or data).
- the *type* of service the resource is served by (*e.g.*, HTTP, Gopher, WAIS).
- the Internet *port number* of the service. If this is omitted the browser assumes a commonly accepted default value.
- the location of the resource in the directory structure of the server.

Structure of an URL

The following is an outline of the most common form of a URL:

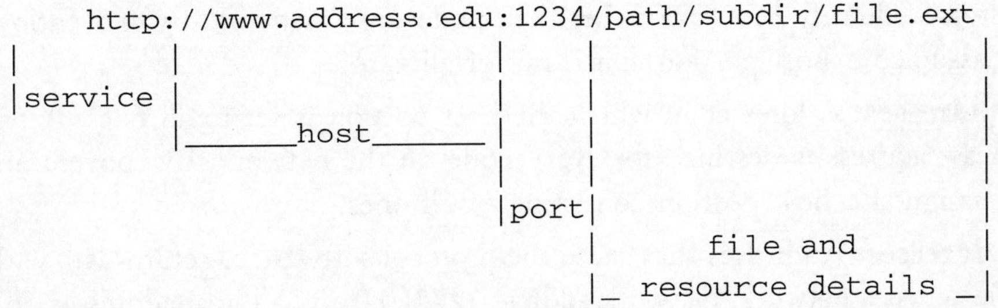

Service

The above figure gives a general outline of URL structure. This outline if followed by most, but not all, URLs. Specific cases are discussed in subsequent sections.

The first part is the service specifier, (here HTTP service) which specifies the access method. Specifically this is the part *before* the colon. Some examples of services are: `http:`,`gopher:`,`wais:` and `ftp:`.

Address and Port number

The second part is usually the internet address of the server, indicated by the double forward slash (//). This address can also contain the (optional) port number the service listens at. The full name is then specified by a string like `//www.address.edu:1234/`, where:`1234` means Port number 1234. If you want to use the default port number you can leave out both the colon and the number, *i.e.*, `//www.address.edu/`.

Resource Location

The forward slash after the host and port specifications indicates the end of the address and the beginning of the specification for the file/resource to be accessed. This field varies depending on the service being accessed. A few simple examples follow: more detailed ones are given in the documents listed below.

Special Cases

In some cases the internet address and resource location are omitted. The common examples of this are `news:` (for accessing Usenet news group information) and `mailto:` (for sending e-mail).

Query Strings

The URL scheme also allows you to include a *query string* that is to be passed to the designated URL. This is indicated by placing a question mark at the end of the URL, followed by the desired query string. For example:

```
http://www.where.edu/cgi-bin/program?query_string_data
```

Reserved IP Addresses

The IP addressing rules reserve the following types of IP addresses for special purposes:

- **Network addresses:** IP addresses in which the host portion is set to all zeros. For example,129.47.0.0 is the network address (or network number) for a class B network. Network addresses identify networks rather than nodes on a network. By convention, no node is ever assigned a host portion consisting of all zeros.
- **Broadcast addresses:** Addresses in which the host portion is set to all ones. A packet with a broadcast address is destined for every node on the network. By convention, no node is ever assigned a host portion consisting of all ones.
- **Loopback addresses:** Addresses that cause the protocol software to return data without sending traffic across a network. Network address 127.0.0.0 and all host addresses on that network (for example, 127.0.0.1) are reserved.

- **Multicast addresses:** Addresses that are used to send packets to a group of hosts or routers. They range from 224.0.0.1 to 239. 255. 255. 255.
- **Reserved addresses:** Addresses in which the network portion consists of all zeros or all ones.

REVIEW QUESTIONS

1. What is internetworking?
2. What are basics of Internet work?
3. What are the internetworking challenges?
4. Give addressing format of a frame and packet.
5. What are the different key organizations?
6. What are Internet protocol and ip addressing?
7. What is sub-netting?
8. How autonomous system works?
9. What is basic frame of an IP data-gram?

❑❑❑

26

ROUTING BASICS

BASIC ROUTING PROTOCOLS

Routers operate on layer 3 of the Open System Interconnection Reference Model, usually referred to as the OSI Model. Protocols are the language that routers use when speaking to each other. All routers operate on layer 3 of the OSI model and are capable of using multiple protocols such as RIP, IGRP/EIGRP, OSPF and BGP. Each of these protocols have advantages and disadvantages. Each protocol also has an ideal use, whether it is a small or large network.

RIP

Routing Information Protocol was originally designed for XEROX PUP, PARC Universal Protocol. It became a part of networking when it was defined in RFC 1058 in 1988. RIP is a widely used open protocol that is easy to configure and good for use in small networks. If RIP is used on a large network with many paths, and more than 16 hops RIP will leave a lot to be desired. In small networks, RIP is the preferred protocol because of the ease of use.

EIGRP/IGRP

Interior Gateway Routing Protocol was developed by Cisco in the mid 1980s as a proprietary protocol to negate the problems seen with RIP. In the early 1990s Cisco developed EIGRP as a way to overcome the limitations seen in RIP and IGRP. According to Cisco, IGRP will be removed from their IOS, Internetwork Operating System, which Cisco uses to control for their routers. EIGRP is good for networks of all sizes and is very easy to configure.

OSPF

OSPF, Open Shortest Path First, was developed by the Interior Gateway Protocol (IGP) working group of the Internet Engineering Task Force (IETF). Since it was developed by IETF, it is an open protocol, not a proprietary one. OSPF is more complicated and not as easy to use as RIP since it uses link-state routing. Link-state routing is that every node constructs a map of the connectivity to the network in the form of a graph. This way the router knows which nodes are connected to which other nodes.

Link-state advertisements are sent to all devices, which causes an initial flood. After the initial flood from the setup phase OSPF is very efficient in operation. It uses three different databases for neighbours, link states and routes.

BGP

Border Gateway Protocol, BGP, is the standard protocol that the Internet operates on. This protocol is not usually used on small home networks or even larger business networks due to the complexity of setting it up. While it is an open protocol, everything is manual, including neighbours, which is automatic with all of the other protocols discussed here. This is only included for reference as it is very unlikely that the average home user will ever come in contact with this protocol.

ROUTING INFORMATION PROTOCOL

As large networks can, in general, be viewed as a collection of domain. Some prefer the term autonomous system to domain to reflect the fact that they can operate independently. In such networks we can define two main categories of routing strategies: interior and exterior protocols. Interior protocols control routing among routers within an autonomous system. Exterior protocols control routing among routers from different autonomous systems.

One example of an interior protocol long used in the internet is the routing information protocol RIP.

RIP is the protocol used by the routed program developed at the university of California at Berkeley to perform routing on their local networks. Routers that connect multiple networks use rip to let each other know the shortest route to a specified network. Typically they use a hop count, the number of intermediate routers, to measure distance. For example, Figure 26.1 Shows several networks are connected by routers. The hop count from network n1 to n2 is 1, and the hop count from n1 to n4 is 2, using the shortest route. None of the routers knows that yet, however. The algorithm starts when each router sends a message along each of its networks. This message indicates that all of the networks to which the router is connected can be reached in one hop. When routers on that network get the message, they know which networks they can reach using two hops.

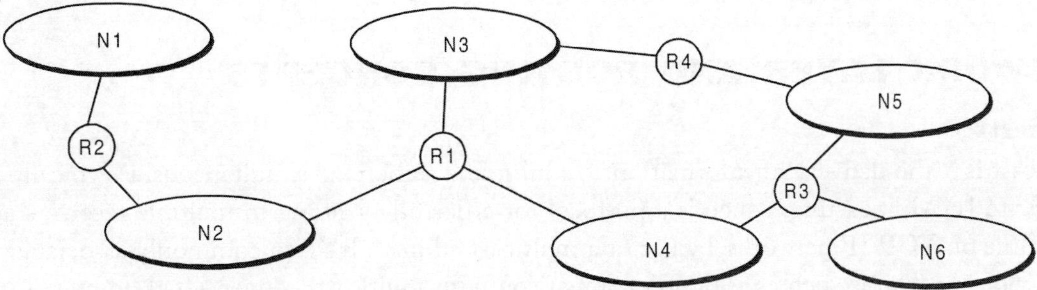

Figure 26.1 *Several Routers are Connected by Routers.*

They store this information in their routing tables and periodically broadcast it over the networks. By repeatedly receiving information, storing it, and broadcast it, each router eventually knows the smallest number of hops to a given network.

NETWORK ROUTING

Most people are familiar with the general concept of routing. Essentially it means that if we want to go from point a to point b we have to determine a way to get there. For example, if we live in Indore, and want to drive to Bhopal for our vacation, we will probably spend some time studying road maps to determine the best way to get there. Similarly, if we want to transfer information between computers in those two locations that are connected via a wan, network protocols must determine how to get it there.

When LANS are organized around a single bus or ring, routing is not a problem. If they are connected with more bridges, the bridges make the routing decisions. The topologies are not very complex, and the bridges do the routing rather easily.

Some stations often communicate directly with more stations than do others. Presumably they represent locations in heavily populated areas or locations with a high volume of information traffic. The stations with fewer connections might have fewer needs or correspond to more remote sites. For example, nodes a and b might represent sites in major metropolitan areas, and nodes x and y may correspond to locations in locations in remote parts of the country.

Suppose one station wants to communicate with another to which it is not connected directly. Network protocols must find a path that connect them. To make matters more complex, there may be many paths. For example, suppose x sends something to y. Two possible paths are x-a-b-c-d-y and x-a-z-d-y. Which is better ? The answer typically depends on a comparison of the costs and the time required to send the information over each path.

The comparison is not always straightforward. We might think that the paths through a, z, and d is better because it is shorter than the alternative. Shorter is not always better, however, as anyone traveling by car knows. Many people will choose to drive a longer distance if it means using a road that has more lanes, is in better condition, or has more rest stops than a shorter alternative. Even though they drive farther they may reach their destination more quickly and with less difficulty.

NETWORK LAYER AND ROUTING CONCEPTS

Multicast

Multicast is a the delivery of information to multiple destinations simultaneously. Typically used to refer to IP Multicasting, which is a protocol for efficiently sending to multiple receivers at the same time on TCP/IP networks, by use of a multicast address. It's also commonly associated with audio/video protocols such as RTP. By comparison with multicast, conventional point-to-single-point delivery is called uni-cast.

There are two basic kinds of multicast delivery:

- dense multicast
- sparse multicast

Modern multicast algorithms are often capable of combining and managing the two.

Multicast is not in general use in the commercial Internet, due to interoperability problems and the lack of a compelling business model for multicast.

However, some communities within the public Internet make regular use of multicast, and multicast is used for special applications within private IP networks.

List of IP multicast protocols:

- Protocol Independent Multicast (PIM)
- Distance Vector Multicast Routing Protocol (DVRMP)
- Multicast OSPF (MOSPF)
- Multicast BGP (MBGP)
- Internet Group Management Protocol (IGMP)

Routing Tables

Routing table do not normally specify the entire route. Instead they specify the next node in a route to a specified destination and the cost to get there. For example, consider the network in figure 26.2, where a cost is associated with the connection between two adjacent nodes. Suppose we want to find the cheapest route, the one that minimizes the sum of the costs of the connections between adjacent nodes in the route. For example, there are several routes from A to F, but the cheapest one goes from A to B (cost of 2), B to E (cost of 3), and E to F (cost of 2) for a total route cost of 7.

Figure shows partial routing tables of nodes A, B, and E. Node a table indicates that anything destined for node B, E, or F should be sent directly to B, where Node B routing table will indicate the next node in the cheapest route. Similarly, anything destined for character or D should be sent to node F. From there, character's routing table indicates the next step.

To illustrate, suppose an application at node a wants to send data to node F. Logic at a looks for an entry in its routing table with destination F. The entry states that node B is the successor on the route, and the network protocol sends the data to B. Logic at B examines its routing table looking for an entry corresponding to destination F. The table's third entry indicates the data should go to node E next. Finally, the routing table at node E indicates that F is the next node on the route.

DIJKSTRA'S ALGORITHM

Dijkstra's algorithm, sometimes called the shortest path algorithm or forward search algorithm, is a centralized, static algorithm, although it can be made adaptive by executing it periodically.

It also requires that a node executing it have information regarding link costs among the network nodes. Several networks such as ARPANET and TYMNER 11 use this algorithm.

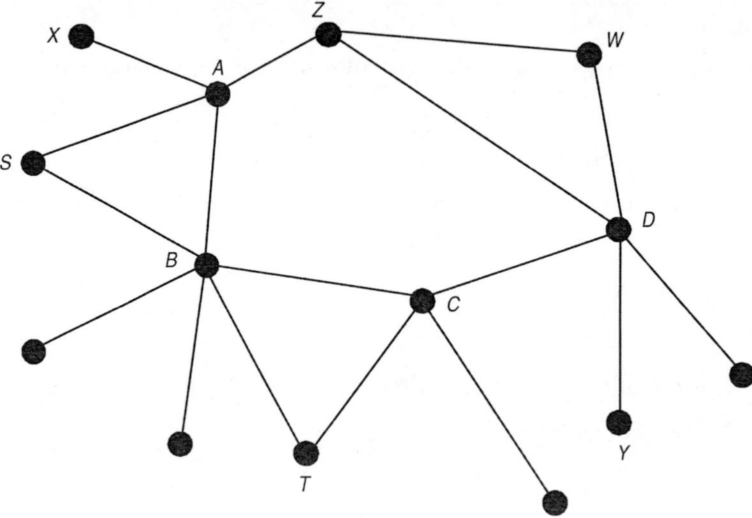

Network and Associated Connection Costs

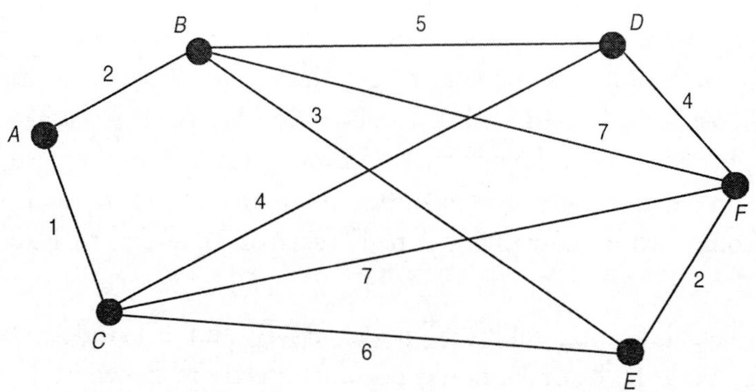

Figure 26.2 *Cost between Two ADJ Nodes.*

Each node execute Dijkstra's algorithm to determine the cheapest route to each network node as shown in figure 26.3. In cases where a route cost is simply the number of intermediate nodes, the cheapest route is also the shortest one. The algorithm is an iterative one, building A set of nodes, one by one, with each iteration. Each node in the set has the property that the cheapest route to it from the given node is known.

Given below algorithm shows an outline of the algorithm. Initially, it defines A set S consisting of just one node, A, the node executing the algorithm. It then defines A function where, for each node X, cost(X) = the cost of cheapest route from A to X for which intermediate nodes are in S. Initially, since S contains only node a, cost(X) is the cost of direct link from A to X. If there is no such link, cost(X) is assigned an arbitrarily large number. The function prior(X) in the algorithm contains the node preceding X in the cheapest route.

Values Defined by Dijkstra's Algorithm for the Network

			COST FUNCTION FOR					PRIOR FUNCTION FOR				
S	*W*	*X*	*B*	*C*	*D*	*E*	*F*	*R*	*C*	*D*	*E*	*F*
{*A*}	{*B*, *C*}	*C*	2	1	¥	¥	¥	*A*	*A*	—	—	—
{*A*, *C*}	{*B*, *D*, *E*, *F*}	*B*	2	1	4	7	8	*A*	*A*	*C*	*C*	*C*
{*A*, *B*, *C*}	{*D*, *E*, *F*}	*D*	2	1	4	6	8	*A*	*A*	*C*	*B*	*C*
{*A*, *B*, *C*, *D*}	{*E*, *F*}	*E*	2	1	4	6	6	*A*	*A*	*C*	*B*	*D*
{*A*, *B*, *C*, *D*, *E*}	{*F*}	*F*	2	1	4	6	6	*A*	*A*	*C*	*B*	*D*

Cost Comparisons for Dijkstra's Algorithm

V	Cost(*V*)	COST (*C*) + COST OF LINK CONNECTING *C* TO *V*
B	2	No link from *C* to *V*
D	¥	1 + 3 = 4
E	¥	1 + 6 = 7
F	¥	1 + 7 = 8

Figure 26.3 *Dijkstra's Algorithm to Determine Cheapest Route.*

The algorithm contains a loop. With each pass it determines a set W consisting of all nodes not in S but with a direct link to something in S as in figure. It choose of all nodes X in W for which cost(X) =< cost(Y) for any other node Y in W. It then adds X to set S and updates the cost function cost(V) for every V not yet in S. It compares the current cost(V) with cost(X) plus the cost of any direct link from X to V. If the latter value is smaller, the algorithm redefines cost(V) to be that value. The intent is to determine whether the addition of X to S allows a cheaper route from A to V through nodes in S.

The correctness of the algorithm is not obvious. If we apply this algorithm to the given network in the figure, so, in step 1, the set S contains only the source node A. The only nodes connected to A are B and character, and the costs of those edges are 2 and 1, respectively. Consequently, cost(B) = 2 and cost(character) = 1. Initial values for cost(D), cost(E), and cost(F) are arbitrarily large and are designated by infinity. Also, prior(B) = A and prior(character) = A. Since the algorithm has not yet found any routes to D, E, and F, the prior function is undefined at those nodes.

As we enter the loop, the set W contains nodes B and C, because they are the only ones connected to A.

Next, since cost (C) < cost (B), we choose X = C and add it to S. The last line in the loop now requires that we examine cost(V) for each V not yet in S. This consists of nodes B, D, E, and F. Since the cost function represents the cheapest path from a through nodes in S, we must ask whether the additional node in S provides a cheaper route. In other words, consider any node V not in S. If cost (C) plus the cost of the direct link from C to V represents a cheaper route. The table as shown in figure value defined by this algorithm.

Necessary comparisons for each node V not in S. For nodes D, E, and F, the latter values are smaller, and node character is established as their prior node. The second row of table reflects these changes. The second pass through the loop proceeds similarly. Node B is added to S because

Cost(B) is smaller among nodes outside of S. Furthermore, the inclusion of B in S provides A cheaper route to E (through nodes in S). Row 3 of table shows how the entries under E change. Node B is the new prior node for E and cost (E) is now 6. If we follow the algorithm and verify that rows 4 and 5 in table are correct. When the algorithm finishes, the table's last row shows that the cheapest routes to B, D, E, and F cost 2, 1, 4, 6,and 6, respectively and connection cost is as shown in figure.

The prior function can be used to recover the actual route. For example, if we want the actual route from A to F, prior (F) = D specifies that D precedes F on that route. Prior(D) = C specifies that precedes D, and prior (C) = A means a precedes C. Thus, the cheapest route from A to F is A-C-D-F.

FLOYD'S ALGORITHM

Floyd's algorithm uses the dynamic programming method to solve the all-pairs shortest-path problem on a dense graph. The method makes efficient use of an adjacency matrix to solve the problem. Consider an edge-weighted graph, where C(v,w) represents the weight on edge (v,w).

Let be the shortest path from vertex V to W that passes only through vertices in, if such a path exists. That is, the path has the form:

- Since, the paths are correspond to the edges of G.
- Therefore, the path lengths correspond to the weights on the edges of G.

Floyd's algorithm computes the sequence of matrices. The distances in represent paths with intermediate vertices in. Since, we can obtain the distances in from those in by considering only the paths that pass through vertex. Figure 26.4 illustrates how this is done.

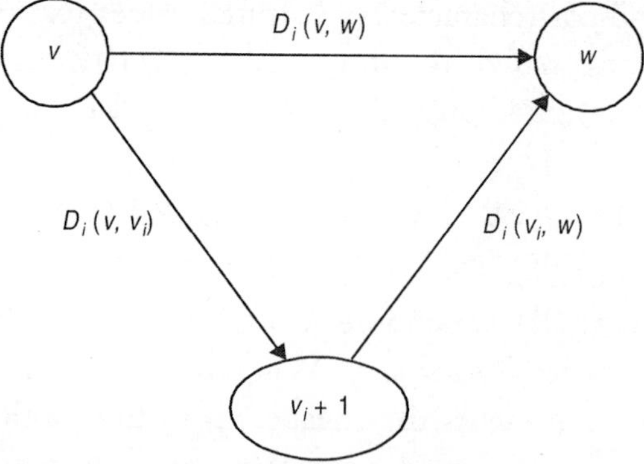

Figure 26.4 *Calculating in Floyd's Algorithm.*

For every pair of vertices (v,w), we compare the distance, (which represents the shortest path from V to W that does not pass through) with the sum (which represents the shortest path from V to W that does pass through). Thus, is computed as follows:

EXTERIOR ROUTING

Exterior routing occurs between autonomous systems, and is of concern to service providers and other large or complex networks. The basic routable element is the autonomous system, a collection of CIDR prefixes identified by an autonomous system number. While there may be many different interior routing scheme, a single exterior routing system manages the global Internet, based primarily on the BGP-4 exterior routing protocol.

OSPF-2 PROTOCOL OVERVIEW

Open Shortest Path First (OSPF) is a recent entry into the Internet interior routing scene. OSPF version 2 is documented in RFC 1583. Sanctioned by the IETF, it is intended to become Internet's preferred interior routing protocol. OSPF is a link-state routing protocol with a complex set of options and features. Not all of these features are available on all implementations, but some of its advantages are:

- **Scalability:** OSPF is specifically designed to operate with larger networks. It does not impose a hop-count restriction and permits its domain to be subdivided for easier management.
- **Full sub-netting support:** OSPF can fully support sub-netting, including VLSM and non-contiguous subnets.
- **Hello packets:** OSPF uses small "hello" packets to verify link operation without transferring large tables. In stable networks, large updates occur only once every 30 minutes.
- **TOS routing:** OSPF can route packets by different criterion based on their Type of Service (TOS) field. For example, file transfers could be routed over a satellite link while terminal I/O could avoid such high delays. This requires cooperative applications on the end systems.
- **Tagged routes:** Routes can be tagged with arbitrary values, easing interoperation with EGPs, which can tag OSPF routes with AS numbers.

OSPF has some disadvantages as well. Chief among them are its complexity and its demands on memory and computation. Although link-state protocols are not difficult to understand, OSPF muddles the picture with plenty of options and features.

OSPF divides its routing domain into areas. Area 0, the backbone, is required. This divides interior routing into two levels. If traffic must travel between two areas, the packets are first routed to the backbone. This may cause non-optimal routes, since inter area routing is not done until the packet reaches the backbone. Once there, it is routed to the destination area, which is then responsible for final delivery. This layering permits addresses to be consolidated by area, reducing the size of the link state databases. Small networks can operate with a single OSPF area, which must be area 0.

OSPF divides networks into several classes, including point-to-point, multi-access, and non-broadcast multi-access. A serial link connecting two routers together would be a point-to-point link, while an Ethernet or token ring segment would be a multi-access link. A frame relay or X.25 cloud would be classified as non-broadcast multi-access.

Multi-access networks (like Ethernet) use a Designated Router (DR) to avoid the problem of each router forming a link with every other router on a Ethernet, resulting in a N^2 explosion in the number of links. Instead, the DR manages all the link state advertisements for the Ethernet. Selecting the DR requires an election process, during which a Backup Designated Router (BDR) is also selected. OSPF provides a priority feature to help the network engineer influence the choice of DR and BDR, but in practice this is difficult. Link layer multicasting is also used, if available, to avoid broadcasts and better target routing updates.

Non-broadcast multi-access networks (like X.25) also use the designated router concept, but since broadcasts (and presumably multicasts) are not supported, the identity of neighboring routers must be specified manually. ADR on such a network without a complete list of neighbors will cause a loss of connectivity, even though the network is otherwise functional. If possible, it is recommend that configuring such networks as a collection of point-to-point links, simply to avoid the intricacies of DR election.

OSPF's primary means of verifying continuing operation of the network is via its hello protocol. Every OSPF speaker sends small hello packets out each of its interfaces every ten seconds. It is through receipt of these packets that OSPF neighbors initially learn of each other's existence. Hello packets are not forwarded or recorded in the OSPF database, but if none are received from a particular neighbor for forty seconds, that neighbor is marked down. LSAs are then generated marking links through a down router as down. The hello timer values can be configured, though they must be consistant across all routers on a network segment.

The originating router read vertises an LSA after it has remained unchanged for thirty minutes. If an LSA ages to more than an hour, it is flushed from the databases. These timer values are called architectural constants by the RFC.

OSPFs various timers interact as follows:

- If a link goes down for twenty seconds, then comes back up, OSPF doesn't notice.
- If a link flaps constantly, but at least one of every four hello packets make it across, OSPF doesn't notice.
- If a link goes down for anywhere from a minute to half an hour, OSPF floods an LSA when it goes down, and another LSA when it comes back up.
- If a link stays down for more than half an hour, LSAs originated by remote routers (that have become unreachable) begin to age out. When the link comes back up, all these LSAs will be reflooded.
- If a link is down for more than an hour, any LSAs originated by remote routers will have aged out and been flushed. When the link comes back up, it will be as if it were brand new.

RIP Protocol Overview

Of Internet interior routing protocols, RIP is probably the most widely used. It is a distance vector protocol based on a 1970s Xerox design. Ported to TCP/IP when LANs first appeared in the early 80s, RIP has changed little in the past decade and suffers from several limitations, some of which have been overcome with RIP-2, which is not discussed here. RFC 1058 documents RIP.

Parameter	RIP Default Value
Infinity 16 (fixed)	
Update time	30 sec
Invalid time	180 sec
Flush time	120 sec
Hold-down	Not used

- *Width restriction.* RIP uses a 4-bit metric to count router hops to a destination. A RIP network can be no wider than 15 hops (16 is infinity). If hop counts are elevated on slower or less reliable links, this can quickly becomes a problem.
- *No direct subnet support.* RIP was deployed prior to sub-netting and has no direct support for it. It can be used in sub-netted environments, subject to restrictions. VLSM can not be used in RIP networks.
- *Bandwidth consumptive.* Every 30 seconds or so, a RIP router will broadcast lists of networks and subnets it can reach. Depending on the lengths of these lists, which depend on the size of the network, bandwidth usage can become prohibitive on slow links.
- *Difficult diagnosis.* Like any distance-vector protocol, RIP can be difficult to debug, since the routing algorithm is distributed over many different routers. Most reported RIP problems could probably be traced to poor understanding, incorrect configuration and inadequate diagnosis.
- *Weak security.* RIP itself has no security features, but some developers have produced RIP implementations that will only accept updates from configured hosts, for example. Various security attacks can be imagined.

However, RIP has several benefits. It is in widespread use, the only interior gateway protocol that can be counted on to really run everywhere. Configuring a RIP system requires little effort, beyond setting path costs. Finally, RIP uses an algorithm that does not impose serious computation or storage requirements on hosts or routers.

SPF Algorithm

The Shortest Path First (SPF) routing algorithm is the basis for OSPF operations. When an SPF router is powered up, it initializes its routing-protocol data structures and then waits for indications from lower-layer protocols that its interfaces are functional.

After a router is assured that its interfaces are functioning, it uses the OSPF Hello protocol to acquire neighbours, which are routers with interfaces to a common network. The router sends hello packets to its neighbours and receives their hello packets. In addition to helping acquire neighbours, hello packets also act as keepalives to let routers know that other routers are still functional.

On multiaccess networks (networks supporting more than two routers), the Hello protocol elects a designated router and a backup designated router. Among other things, the designated router is responsible for generating LSAs for the entire multiaccess network. Designated routers allow a reduction in network traffic and in the size of the topological database.

When the link-state databases of two neighbouring routers are synchronized, the routers are said to be adjacent. On multiaccess networks, the designated router determines which routers should become adjacent. Topological databases are synchronized between pairs of adjacent routers. Adjacencies control the distribution of routing-protocol packets, which are sent and received only on adjacencies. Each router periodically sends an LSA to provide information on a router's adjacencies or to inform others when a router's state changes. By comparing established adjacencies to link states, failed routers can be detected quickly, and the network's topology can be altered appropriately. From the topological database generated from LSAs, each router calculates a shortest-path tree, with itself as root. The shortest-path tree, in turn, yields a routing table.

OSPF—Algorithm

The OSPF routing algorithm is based on Dijkstra shortest path algorithm. The term "shortest path" is inaccurate because what we really want to find is the "optimum path". To find the optimum path in a network means to find a path with a minimal cost, considering factors like time, money and quality of the received data. The route is not chosen only by the cost, because in every network three constraints must be considered:

1. Delay
2. Throughput
3. Connectivity

if delay is excessive or if throughput is too little, the network does not meet the needs of the users. The third constraint is quite obvious: The gateways and networks must be able to reach each other; otherwise, all other least-cost criteria are irrelevant.

The Basic Algorithm

- Least-cost criteria weights are assigned to the paths in the network.
- Each node is labeled (identified) with its least-cost criteria from the source along to a known path. Initially, no paths are known, so each node is labeled with infinity. However, updates to the values (once the weights are established) are the same as an initialization.
- Each node is examined in relation to all nodes adjacent to it. (The source node is the first node considered and becomes the working node). This step is actually a one time occurrence wherein the source node is initialized with all the costs of all its adjacent nodes.
- Least-cost criteria labels are assigned to each of the nodes adjacent to the working node. Labels change if a shorter path is found from this node to the source node. In OSPF, this would occur with the sending of link status messages on a broadcast basis to all other gateways.
- After the adjacent nodes are labeled (or relabeled), all other nodes in the network are examined. if one has a smaller value in its label, its label becomes permanent and it becomes the working node.

- If the sum of the node's label is less than the label on an adjacent node, the adjacent node's label is changed because a shorter path has been found to the source node.
- Another working node is selected and the process repeats itself until all possibilities has been searched. The final labels reveal the least-cost, end-to-end path between the source and the other nodes. These nodes are considered to be within a set N as it pertains to the source node.

The following general statements describe the preceding discussion:

1. Let D(v) = sum of link weights on a given path.
2. Let C(i,j) = the cost between node i and j.
3. Set N = {1}
4. For each node (v) not in N, set D(v) = C(1,v).
5. For each step, find a node w not in N for which D(w) is a minimum; add w to set N.
6. Update D(v) for all nodes still not in N by D(v) = min [D(v), D(w) + C(w,v)].
7. Repeat steps 4 through 6 until all nodes are in set N.

The process is performed on each node, and a routing table is created for the node's use. Each node's table is constructed in the same manner just discussed.

Example: Routing topology for node A

Step	N	A(B)	A(C)	A(D)	A(E)	A(F)	A(G)	A(H)	A(I)	A(J)
Initial	{A}	8	4	.	.	.	.	.	.	.
1	{A,B}	8	(4)	5	8	.	.	.	11	.
2	{A,C,D}	7	4	(5)	7	.	.	.	11	.
3	{A,C,D,B}	7	4	5	(7)	11	.	.	11	.
4	{A,C,D,B,E}	(7)	4	5	7	11	9	.	11	.
5	{A,C,D,B,E,F}	7	4	5	7	11	(9)	14	11	.
6	{A,C,D,B,E,F,G}	7	4	5	7	11	9	(10)	10	.
7	{A,C,D,B,E,F,G,H}	7	4	5	7	11	9	10	(10)	18
8	{A,C,D,B,E,F,G,H,I}	7	4	5	7	(11)	9	10	10	15
9	{A,C,D,B,E,F,G,H,I,J}	7	4	5	7	11	9	10	10	(15)

to go back to the index press here

OSPF—Routing Protocol

The OSPF routing protocol was designed by the OSPF working group of the Internet engineering task force. This protocol is an IGP: Gateways/routers are all within one autonomous system. Also, as we stated earlier, OSPF is a link state or shortest path first protocol, in contrast to most of the internet protocols, which are based on some type of Bellman-ford approach. The protocol, although it relies on techniques outside of the internet environment, is tailored specifically for an internet and includes such capabilities as subnet addressing and type of service (TOS) routing.

OSPF bases its routing decisions on two fields in the IP datagram: the destination IP address and the TOS. Once the decision is made on how to the IP datagram, the datagram is routed without additional headers; that is, no additional encapsulation occurs. This approach is different from many networks in which PDUs are encapsulated with some type of internal network header to control the routing protocol within the sub-network.

OSPF is classified as a dynamic, adaptive protocol in that it adjusts to problems in the network and provides short convergence periods to stabilize the routing table. It is also designed to prevent looping of traffic, which is quite important in mesh networks or in LANs where multiple bridges may be available to connect different LANs.

OSPF—Operations

Each router contains a routing directory (called a "routing database"). The database contains information about interfaces at the router that are operable as well as status information about each neighbor to a routers. the database is the same for all participating routers.

The information focuses on the topology of the networks with a directed graph. Routers and networks forms the vertices of the graph. Periodically this information is broadcast (flooded) to all the routers in the autonomous system. An OSPF router computes the shortest path to all the other routers in the autonomous system regarding itself as the working node (the root).

A very flexible and powerful approach to this protocol is that separate cost metrics can be computed for each TOS. If the calculations reveal that two paths are of equal value, OSPF will distribute the traffic equally on these paths.

OSPF can support one to many networks. The networks can be grouped into what is termed an "area", and the design of the protocol allows an area to be hidden from other areas. Indeed, an area can be hidden from the full autonomous system.

Due to increasing concerns about security, OSPF includes authentication procedures. Routers must go through some simple procedure to authenticate the traffic between them. We have more to say about the authentication aspects of this protocol shortly.

OSPF works with directed graphs which are quite similar to the Dijkstra algorithm explained before. The graph contains values between two points, either networks or gateway. The values represent the weighted shortest path value, with the router established as the root. Consequently, the shortest path tree from the router to any point in an Internet is determined by the router performing the calculation. The calculation only reveals the next hop to the destination in the hop-to-hop forwarding process. The topological database used in the calculation is derived from the information obtained by advertisements of the routers to their neighbors, with periodic flooding throughout the autonomous system.

Thus far we have discussed in general terms how OSPF performs routing within the autonomous system. The method to determine routing information outside the autonomous system is referred to as "external routing". Routing information pertaining to this capability is typically derived from OSPF as well as other protocols, such as the EGP. Alternately, routing information could be established through static routes between the autonomous systems.

Two types of external routing capabilities exist with OSPF. In type 1 external routing, the external metrics are the same as the internal OSPF link state metric. Type 2 external metrics only use the cost of the router to the external autonomous system. The type 2 method is simple and based on the assumption that routing between autonomous systems is the major cost of routing the packet (which in some actual operation is not true). This approach eliminates conversion between internal link state metrics of OSPF and external costs (in which the autonomous system may have little influence).

The OSPF working group also adapted a very sound concept of autonomous system "areas" in which contiguous networks and hosts may be grouped together. In this situation, each area runs its own SPF algorithm. It also has its own topological database that differs from other areas. The purpose of the area is to isolate and partition portions of the autonomous system and to reduce the amount of information a router must maintain about the full autonomous system. Also, having such an area means that the overhead information transmitted between the routers to maintain OSPF routing tables is substantially reduced.

OSPF uses the term "backbone" to define that part of an autonomous system conveys packets between areas. The full path of a packet proceeds as follow:

1. intra-area path to a router attached to the backbone;
2. the backbone path to the destination area router;
3. the destination intra-area path to the destination network.

The resources (links, routers) of a backbone should be contiguous. This configuration is permissible; the intervening networks simply become "virtual links" within the backbone for the purposes of constructing the topological database.

Additional OSPF Features

Additional OSPF features include equal-cost, multipath routing, and routing based on upper-layer type-of-service (TOS) requests. TOS-based routing supports those upper-layer protocols that can specify particular types of service. An application, for example, might specify that certain data is urgent. If OSPF has high-priority links at its disposal, these can be used to transport the urgent datagram.

OSPF supports one or more metrics. If only one metric is used, it is considered to be arbitrary, and TOS is not supported. If more than one metric is used, TOS is optionally supported through the use of a separate metric (and, therefore, a separate routing table) for each of the eight combinations created by the three IP TOS bits (the delay, throughput, and reliability bits). For example, if the IP TOS bits specify low delay, low throughput, and high reliability, OSPF calculates routes to all destinations based on this TOS designation.

Bellman-Ford Algorithm

Bellman-ford algorithm solves the single-source shortest-path problem in the general case in which edges of a given algorithm can have negative weight as long as G contains no negative cycles.

This algorithm, like Dijkstra's algorithm uses the notion of edge relaxation but does not use with greedy method. Again, it uses d[u] as an upper bound on the distance d[u, v] from U to V.

The algorithm progressively decreases an estimate d[v] on the weight of the shortest path from the source vertex S to each vertex V in V until it achieve the actual shortest-path. The algorithm returns Boolean TRUE if the given algorithm contains no negative cycles that are reachable from source vertex S otherwise it returns Boolean FALSE.

```
BELLMAN-FORD (G, w, s)
1. INITIALIZE-SINGLE-SOURCE (G, s)
2. for each vertex i = 1 to V[G] - 1 do
3.     for each edge (u, v) in E[G] do
4.     RELAX (u, v, w)
5. For each edge (u, v) in E[G] do
6.     if d[u] + w(u, v) < d[v] then
7.         return FALSE
8. return TRUE
```

Analysis

- The initialization in line 1 takes θ (v) time
- For loop of lines 2–4 takes O(E) time and For-loop of line 5–7 takes O(E) time.

Thus, the Bellman-ford algorithm runs in O(E) time.

RIP

RIP is a distance-vector protocol that allows routers to exchange information about destinations for computing routes throughout the network. Destinations may be networks or a special destination used to convey a default route. In RIP, Bellman-ford algorithms make each router periodically broadcast its routing tables to all its neighbors. Then a router knowing its neighbors' tables can decide to which destination neighbor to forward a packet.

Working of Bellman-Ford algorithm

Routers that use this algorithm have to maintain the distance tables (which is a one-dimension array—"a vector"), which tell the distances and shortest path to sending packets to each node in the network. The information in the distance table is always updated by exchanging information with the neighboring nodes. The number of data in the table equals to that of all nodes in networks (excluded itself). The columns of table represent the directly attached neighbors whereas the rows represent all destinations in the network. Each data contains the path for sending packets to each destination in the network and distance/or time to transmit on that path (we call this as "cost"). The measurements in this algorithm are the number of hops, latency, the number of outgoing packets, etc.

FORMAL ALGORITHM

The starting assumption for distance-vector routing is each node knows the cost of the link of each of its directly connected neighbors. Next, every node sends a configured message to its directly connected neighbors containing its own distance table. Now, every node can learn and update its distance table with cost and next hops for all nodes network. Repeat exchanging until no more information between the neighbors.

Consider a node X that is interested in routing to destination Y via a directly attached neighbor Z. Node X's distance table entry, Dx(Y,Z) is the sum of the cost of the direct-one hop link between X and Z, c(X,Z), plus neighboring Z's currently known minimum-cost path (shortest path) from itself (Z) to Y. That is Dx(Y,Z) = c(X,Z) + minw{Dz(Y,w)}. The minw is taken over all the Z's.

This equation suggests that the form of neighbor-to-neighbor communication that will take place in the DV algorithm—each node must know the cost of each of its neighbors' minimum-cost path to each destination. Hence, whenever a node computes a new minimum cost to some destination, it must inform its neighbors of this new minimum cost.

Simpler Algorithm

- Send my routing table to all my neighbors whenever my link table changes
- When I get a routing table from a neighbor on port P with link metric M:
  - add L to each of the neighbor's metrics
  - for each entry (D, P', M') in the updated neighbor's table:
  - if I do not have an entry for D, add (D, P, M') to my routing table
  - if I have an entry for D with metric M, "add (D, P, M') to my routing table if M' < M" if my routing table has changed, I send all the new entries to all my neighbors.

Flooding Algorithm

A flooding algorithm is an algorithm for distributing material to every part of a connected network. The name derives from the concept of inundation by a flood.

Flooding algorithms are used in systems such as usenet and peer-to-peer file sharing systems and as part of some routing protocols, including OSPF, DVMRP, and those used in ad-hoc wireless networks. There are several variants of flooding algorithm most work roughly as follows.

1. Each node acts as both a transmitter and a receiver.
2. Each node tries to forward every message to every one of its neighbors.

This results in every message eventually being delivered to all reachable parts of the network.

Real-world flooding algorithms have to be more complex than this, since precautions have to be taken to avoid wasted duplicate deliveries and infinite loops, and to allow messages to eventually expire from the system.

Flooding algorithms are also useful for solving many mathematical problems, including maze problems and many problems in graph theory.

INTERNET GROUP MANAGEMENT PROTOCOL

Internet Group Management Protocol (IGMP) is the protocol used to support multicasting. To use multicasting, a process on a host must be able to join and leave a group. A process is a user program that is using the network. Group access is identified by the group address and the interface (NIC). A host must keep track of the groups that at least one process belongs to and the number of processes that belong to the group. IGMP is defined in RFC 1112.

IGMP messages are used by multicast routers to track group memberships on each of its networks. It uses these rules:

The first time a process on a host joins a multicast group, the host will send an IGMP report. This means that every time the host needs to receive messages from a new group to support its processes, it will send a report.

Multicast routers will send IGMP queries regularly to determine whether any hosts are running processes that belong to any groups. The group address of the query is set to 0, the TTL field is set to 1, and the destination IP address is 224.0.0.1 which is the all hosts group address which address all the multicast capable routers and hosts on a network.

A host sends one IGMP response for each group that contains one or more processes. The router expects one response from each host for each group that one or more of its processes require access to.

A host does not send a report when its last process leaves a group (when the group access is no longer required by a process). The multicast router relies on query responses to update this information.

IGMP is defined in RFC 1112. Hosts and routers use IGMP to support multicasting. Multicast routers must know which hosts belong to what group at any given point of time. The IGMP message is 8 bytes. consisting of:

- Bits 0 to 3—IGMP version number
- Bits 4 to 7—IGMP type 1=query sent by a multicast router. 2 is a response sent by a host.
- Bits 8 to 15—unused
- Bits 16 to 31—Checksum
- The last 4 bytes—32 bit group address which is the same as the class D IP address.

IGMP message formats are encapsulated in an IP datagram which contain a time to live (TTL) field. The default is to set the TTL field to 1 which means the datagram will not leave its sub-network. An application can increase its TTL field in a message to locate a server distance in terms of hops.

Addresses from 224.0.0.0 to 224.0.0.255 are not forwarded by multicast routers since these addresses are intended for applications that do not need to communicate with other networks. Therefore these addresses can be used for group multicasting on private networks with no concern for addresses being used for multicasting on other networks.

INTERNET ROUTING ARCHITECTURE

In the original Internet structure, there was a hierarchy of gateways. This hierarchy reflected the fact that the Internet was built upon the existing ARPANET. When the Internet was created, the ARPANET was the backbone of the network: a central delivery medium to carry long-distance traffic. This central system was called the *core*, and the centrally managed gateways that interconnected it were called the *core gateways*.

In that hierarchical structure, routing information about all of the networks in the Internet was passed into the core gateways. The core gateways processed the information, and then exchanged it among themselves using the Gateway to Gateway Protocol (GGP). The processed routing information was then passed back out to the external gateways. The core gateways maintained accurate routing information for the entire Internet.

Using the hierarchical core router model to distribute routing information has a major weakness: every route must be processed by the core. This places a tremendous processing burden on the core, and as the Internet grew larger the burden increased. In network-speak, we say that this routing model does not "scale well." For this reason, a new model emerged.

Even in the days of a single Internet, core groups of independent networks called *Autonomous Systems* (AS) existed outside of the core. The term "autonomous system" has a formal meaning in TCP/IP routing. An autonomous system is not merely an independent network. It is a collection of networks and gateways with its own internal mechanism for collecting routing information and passing it to other independent network systems. The routing information passed to the other network systems is called *reach-ability information*. Reach-ability information simply says which networks can be reached through that autonomous system. The Exterior Gateway Protocol (EGP) was the protocol used to pass reach-ability information between autonomous systems and into the core.

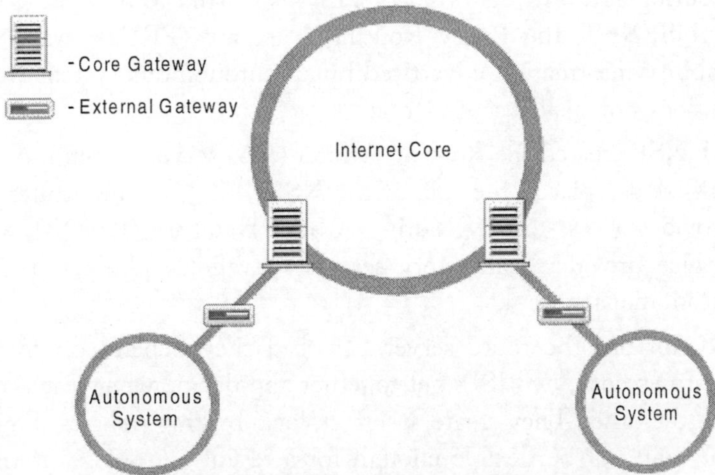

Figure 26.5 *Gateway Hierarchy.*

The new routing model is based on co-equal collections of autonomous systems, called *routing domains*. Routing domains exchange routing information with other domains using Border Gateway Protocol (BGP). Each routing domain processes the information it receives from other domains. Unlike the hierarchical model, this model does not depend on a single core system to choose the "best" routes. Each routing domain does this processing for itself; therefore, this model is more expandable. Figure 26.6 represents this model with three intersecting circles. Each circle is a routing domain. The overlapping areas are border areas, where routing information is shared. The domains share information, but do not rely on any one system to provide all routing information.

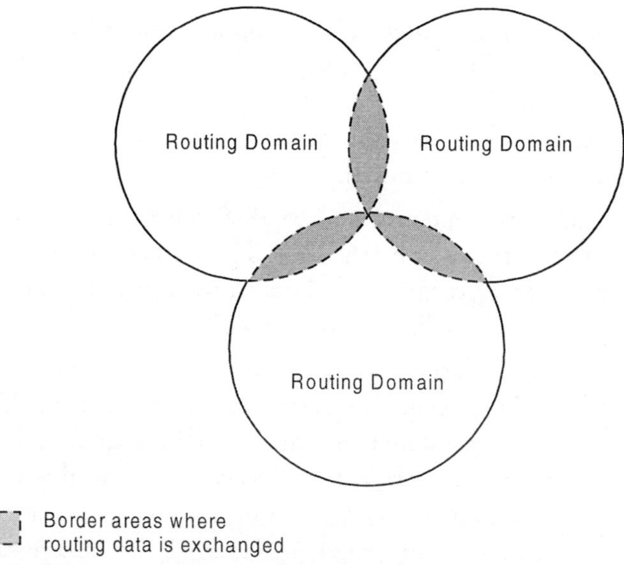

Figure 26.6 *Routing Domains.*

The problem with this model is how are "best" routes determined in a global network if there is no central routing authority, like the core, that is trusted to determine the "best" routes ? In the days of the NSFNET, the Policy Routing Database (PRDB) was used to determine whether the reach-ability information advertised by an autonomous system was valid. But now, even the NSFNET does not play a central role.

To fill this void, NSF created the Routing Arbiter (RA) servers when it created the Network Access Points (NAPs) that replaced the role of the NSFNET. A route arbiter is located at each NAP. The server provides access to the Routing Arbiter Database (RADB), which replaced the PRDB. Internet service providers can query servers to validate the reach-ability information advertised by an autonomous system.

Many ISPs do not use the route servers. Instead they depend on formal and informal bilateral agreements. In essence, two ISPs get together and decide what reach-ability information each will accept from the other. They create, in effect, local routing policies. This is a slow manual process that probably will not be flexible enough for a rapidly growing Internet.

The RADB is only part of the Internet Routing Registry (IRR). As befits a distributed routing architecture, there are multiple organizations that validate and register routing information. Europeans were the pioneers in this. The Reseaux IP Europeens (RIPE) Network Control Center (NCC) provides the routing registry for European IP networks. Big network carriers, like MCI and ANS, provide registries for their customers. All of the registries share a common format based on the RIPE-181 standard.

Creating an effective routing architecture continues to be a major challenge for the Internet that will certainly evolve over time. No matter how it is derived, eventually the routing information winds up in your local gateway, where it is used by IP to make routing decisions.

REVIEW QUESTIONS

1. What is Routing?
2. What are routing components?
3. What are different routing issues?
4. What do you understand by routing table?
5. Give all routing types.
6. What are routing protocols?
7. Give Dijkstra's algorithm.
8. Write Floyd's algorithm.
9. Write short nots on OSPF and BELLMAN-FORD algorithms.
10. What is a rip?
11. Give Internet routing architecture.
12. What is static and dynamic routing ? Discuss one routing algorithm with suitable example.

(IV-BCA (4.1)-DCCN)

PART 7

Flow and Congestion Control

27

Flow Control Basics

Flow control is a function that prevents network congestion by ensuring that transmitting devices do not overwhelm receiving devices with data. A high-speed computer, for example, may generate traffic faster than the network can transfer it or faster than the destination device can receive and process it. The three commonly used methods for handling network congestion are buffering, transmitting source-quench messages, and windowing.

Buffering is used by network devices to temporarily store bursts of excess data in memory until they can be processed. Occasional data bursts are easily handled by buffering. Excess data bursts can exhaust memory, however, forcing the device to discard any additional data-grams that arrive.

Source-quench messages are used by receiving devices to help prevent their buffers from overflowing. The receiving device sends source-quench messages to request that the source reduce its current rate of data transmission. First, the receiving device begins discarding received data due to overflowing buffers. Second, the receiving device begins sending source-quench messages to the transmitting device at the rate of one message for each packet dropped. The source device receives the source-quench messages and lowers the data rate until it stops receiving the messages. Finally, the source device then gradually increases the data rate as long as no further source-quench requests are received.

Windowing is a flow-control scheme in which the source device requires an acknowledgment from the destination after a certain number of packets have been transmitted. With a window size of 3, the source requires an acknowledgement after sending three packets, as follows. First, the source device sends three packets to the destination device. Then, after receiving the three packets, the destination device sends an acknowledgement to the source. The source receives the acknowledgement and sends three more packets. If the destination does not receive one or more of the packets for some reason, such as overflowing buffers, it does not receive enough packets to send an acknowledgement. The source then retransmits the packets at a reduced transmission rate.

ERROR-CHECKING BASICS

Error-checking schemes determine whether transmitted data has become corrupt or otherwise damaged while traveling from the source to the destination. Error checking is implemented at several of the OSI layers.

One common error-checking scheme is the Cyclic Redundancy Check (CRC), which detects and discards corrupted data. Error-correction functions (such as data retransmission) are left to higher-layer protocols. A CRC value is generated by a calculation that is performed at the source device. The destination device compares this value to its own calculation to determine whether errors occurred during transmission. First, the source device performs a predetermined set of calculations over the contents of the packet to be sent. Then, the source places the calculated value in the packet and sends the packet to the destination. The destination performs the same predetermined set of calculations over the contents of the packet and then compares its computed value with that contained in the packet. If the values are equal, the packet is considered valid. If the values are unequal, the packet contains errors and is discarded.

PRINCIPLES OF CONGESTION CONTROL

In the previous sections, we've examined both the general principles and specific TCP mechanisms used to provide for a reliable data transfer service in the face of packet loss. We mentioned earlier that, in practice, such loss typically results from the overflowing of router buffers as the network becomes congested. Packet retransmission thus treats a symptom of network congestion (the loss of a specific transport-layer packet) but does not treat the cause of network congestion—too many sources attempting to send data at too high a rate. To treat the *cause* of network congestion, mechanisms are needed to throttle the sender in the face of network congestion.

In this section, we consider the problem of congestion control in a general context, seeking to understand *why* congestion is a "bad thing," *how* network congestion is manifested in the performance received by upper-layer applications, and various approaches that can be taken to avoid, or react to, network congestion. This more general study of congestion control is appropriate since, as with reliable data transfer, it is high on the "top-10" list of fundamentally important problems in networking.

The causes and the "costs" of congestion

Let's begin our general study of congestion control by examine three increasingly complex scenarios in which congestion occurs. In each case, we'll look at why congestion occurs in the first place, and the "cost" of congestion in terms of resources not fully utilized and poor performance received by the end systems.

Scenario 1: Two senders, a router with infinite buffers

We begin by considering perhaps the simplest congestion scenario possible: two hosts (A and B) each have a connection that share a single hop between source and destination, as shown in figure 27.1.

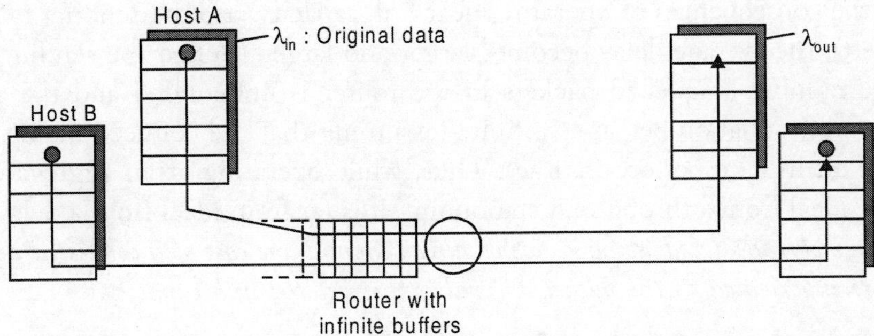

Figure 27.1 *Congestion Scenario 1: Two Connections Sharing a Single Hop with Infinite Buffers.*

Let's assume that the application in host A is sending data into the connection (*e.g.*, passing data to the transport-level protocol via a socket) at an average rate of in bytes/sec. These data are "original" in the sense that each unit of data is sent into the socket only once. The underlying transport-level protocol is a simple one: data is encapsulated and sent; no error recovery (*e.g.*, retransmission), flow control, or congestion control is performed. Host B operates in a similar manner and we assume for simplicity that it too is sending at a rate of in bytes/sec. Packets from hosts A and B pass through a router and over a shared outgoing link of capacity C. The router has buffers that allow it to store incoming packets when the packet arrival rate exceeds the outgoing link's capacity. In this first scenario, we'll assume that the router has an infinite amount of buffer space.

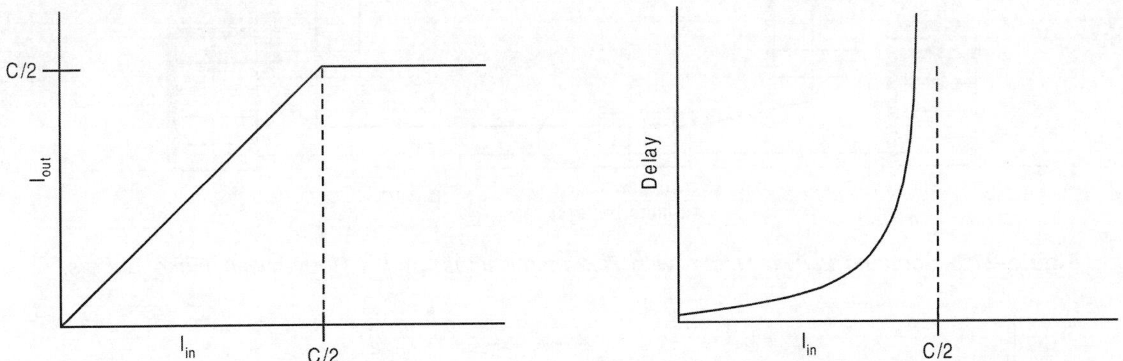

Figure 27.2 *Congestion Scenario 2: Throughput and Delay as a Function of Host Sending Rate.*

Figure plots the performance of host A's connection under this first scenario. The left graph plots the per-connection throughput (number of bytes per second at the receiver) as a function of the connection sending rate. For a sending rate between zero and C/2, the throughput at the receiver equals the sender's sending rate—everything sent by the sender is received at the receiver with a finite delay. When the sending rate is above C/2, however, the throughput is only C/2. This upper limit on throughput is a consequence of the sharing of link capacity between two connections—the link simply can not deliver packets to a receiver at a steady state rate that exceeds C/2. No matter how high hosts A and B set their sending rates, they will each never see a throughput higher than C/2.

Achieving a per-connection throughput of C/2 might actually appear to be a "good thing," as the link is fully utilized in delivering packets to their destinations. The right graph in figure, however, shows the consequences of operating near link capacity. As the sending rate approaches C/2 (from the left), the average delay becomes larger and larger. When the sending rate exceeds C/2, the average number of queued packets in the router is unbounded and the average delay between source and destination becomes infinite (assuming that the connections operate at these sending rates for an infinite period of time). Thus, while operating at an aggregate throughput of near C may be ideal from a throughput standpoint, it is far from ideal from a delay standpoint. *Even in this (extremely) idealized scenario, we've already found one cost of a congested network—large queuing delays are experienced as the packet arrival rate nears the link capacity.*

Scenario 2: Two senders, a router with finite buffers

Let us now slightly modify scenario 1 in the following two ways. First, the amount of router buffering is assumed to be finite. Second, we assume that each connection is reliable. If a packet containing a transport-level segment is dropped at the router, it will eventually be retransmitted by the sender. Because packets can be retransmitted, we must now be more careful with our use of the term "sending rate." Specifically, let us again denote the rate at which the application sends original data into the socket by in bytes/sec. The rate at which the transport layer sends segments (containing original data *or* retransmitted data) into the network will be denoted in' bytes/sec. in' is sometimes referred to as the offered load to the network.

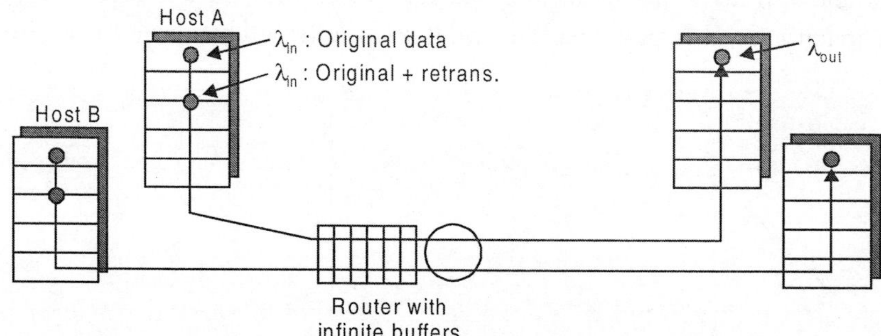

Figure 27.3 *Scenario 2: Two Hosts (with Retransmissions) and a Router with Finite Buffers.*

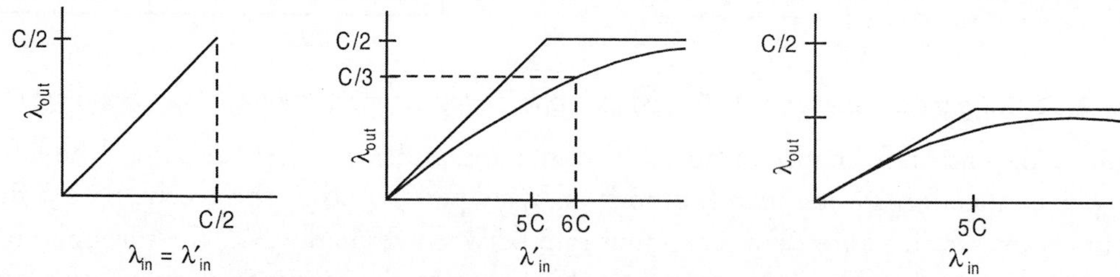

Figure 27.4 *Scenario 2 Performance: (a) No Retransmissions (b) Only Needed Retransmissions (c) Extraneous, Undeeded Retransmissions.*

The performance realized under scenario 2 will now depend strongly on how retransmission is performed. First, consider the unrealistic case that host A is able to somehow (magically!) determine whether or not a buffer is free in the router and thus sends a packet only when a buffer is free. In this case, no loss would occur, in would be equal to in and the throughput of the connection would be equal to in. This case is shown in figure (a). From a throughput standpoint, performance is ideal—everything that is sent is received. Note that the average host sending rate cannot exceed C/2 under this scenario, since packet loss is assumed never to occur.

Consider next the slightly more realistic case that the sender retransmits only when a packet is known for certain to be lost. (Again, this assumption is a bit of a stretch. However, it possible that the sending host might set its timeout large enough to be virtually assured that a packet that has not been ACKed has been lost.) In this case, the performance might look something like that shown in figure (b). To appreciate what is happening here, consider the case that the offered load, 'in' (the rate of original data transmission plus retransmissions), equals .6C. According to figure-(b), at this value of the offered load, the rate at which data are delivered to the receiver application is C/3. Thus, out of the .6C units of data transmitted, .3333 bytes/sec (on average) are original data and .26666 bytes per second (on average) are retransmitted data. *We see here another "cost" of a congested network—the sender must perform retransmissions in order to compensate for dropped (lost) packets due to buffer overflow.*

Finally, let us consider the more realistic case that the sender may timeout prematurely and retransmit a packet that has been delayed in the queue, but not yet lost. In this case, both the original data packet and the retransmission may both reach the receiver. Of course, the receiver needs but one copy of this packet and will discard the retransmission. In this case, the "work" done by the router in forwarding the retransmitted copy of the original packet was "wasted," as the receiver will have already received the original copy of this packet. The router would have better used the link transmission capacity transmitting a different packet instead. *Here then is yet another "cost" of a congested network—unneeded retransmissions by the sender in the face of large delays may cause a router to use its link bandwidth to forward unneeded copies of a packet.* Figure (c) shows the throughput versus offered load when each packet is assumed to be forwarded (on average) at least twice by the router. Since each packet is forwarded twice, the throughput achieved will be bounded above by the two-segment curve with the asymptotic value of C/4.

Scenario 3: Four senders, routers with finite buffers, and multi-hop paths

In our final congestion scenario, four hosts transmit packets, each over overlapping two-hop paths, as shown in figure 27.5. We again assume that each host uses a timeout/retransmission mechanism to implement a reliable data transfer service, that all hosts have the same value of in, and that all router links have capacity C bytes/sec.

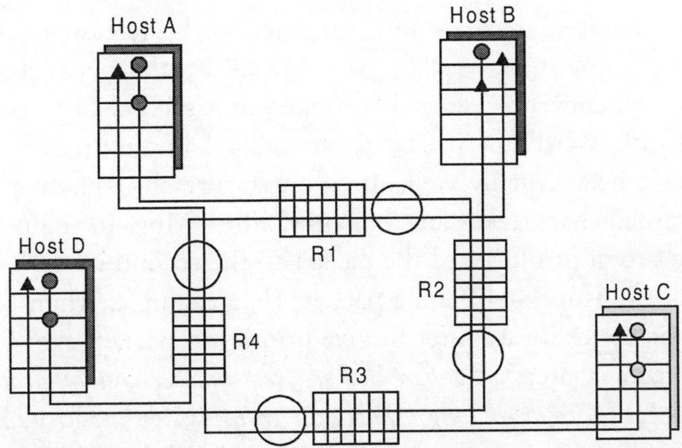

Figure 27.5 *Four Senders, Routers with Finite Buffers, and Multi-hop Paths.*

Let us consider the connection from host A to host C, passing through routers R1 and R2. The A-C connection shares router R1 with the D-B connection and shares router R2 with the B-D connection. For extremely small values of λ_{in}, buffer overflows are rare (as in congestion scenarios 1 and 2), and the throughput approximately equals the offered load. For slightly larger values of λ_{in}, the corresponding throughput is also larger, as more original data is being transmitted into the network and delivered to the destination, and overflows are still rate. Thus, for small values of in, an increase in results in an increase in out.

Having considered the case of extremely low traffic, let us next examine the case that λ_{in} (and hence λ_{in}') is extremely large. Consider router R2. The A-C traffic arriving to router R2 (which arrives at R2 after being forwarded from R1) can have an arrival rate at R2 that is at most C, the capacity of the link from R1 to R2, regardless of the value of λ_{in}. If λ_{in}' is extremely large for all connections (including the B-D connection), then the arrival rate of B-D traffic at R2 can be much larger than that of the A-C traffic. Because the A-C and B-D traffic must compete at router R2 for the limited amount of buffer space, the amount of A-C traffic that successfully gets through R2 (*i.e.*, is not lost due to buffer overflow) becomes smaller and smaller as the offered load from B-D gets larger and larger. In the limit, as the offered load approaches infinity, an empty buffer at R2 is immediately filled by a B-D packet and the throughput of the A-C connection at R2 goes to zero. This, in turn, *implies that the A-C end-end throughput goes to zero* in the limt of heavy traffic. These considerations give rise to the offered load versus throughput tradeoff shown in figure 27.6.

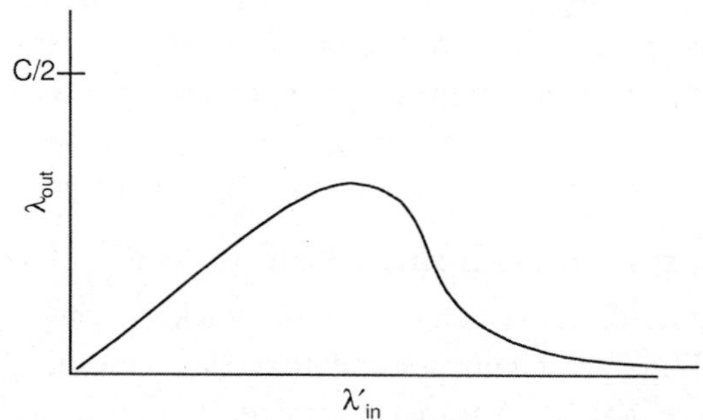

Figure 27.6 *Scenario 2 Performance with Finite bBuffers and Multi-hope Paths.*

The reason for the eventual decrease in throughput with increasing offered load is evident when one considers the amount of wasted "work" done by the network. In the high traffic scenario outlined above, whenever a packet is dropped at a second-hop router, the "work" done by the first-hop router in forwarding a packet to the second-hop router ends up being "wasted." The network would have been equally well off (more accurately, equally as bad off) if the first router had simply discarded that packet and remained idle. More to the point, the transmission capacity used at the first router to forward the packet to the second router could have been much more profitably used to transmit a different packet. (For example, when selecting a packet for transmission, it might be better for a router to give priority to packets that have already traversed some number of upstream routers). *So here we see yet another cost of dropping a packet due to congestion — when a packet is dropped along a path, the transmission capacity that was used at each of the upstream routers to forward that packet to the point at which it is dropped ends up having been wasted.*

APPROACHES TOWARD CONGESTION CONTROL

In section, we will examine TCP's specific approach towards congestion control in great detail. Here, we identify the two broad approaches that are taken in practice towards congestion control, and discuss specific network architectures and congestion control protocols embodying these approaches.

At the broadest level, we can distinguish among congestion control approaches based on the whether or not the network layer provides any explicit assistance to the transport layer for congestion control purposes.

End-end congestion control. In an end-end approach towards congestion control, the network layer provides *no explicit support* to the transport layer for congestion control purposes. Even the presence of congestion in the network must be inferred by the end systems based only on observed network behavior (*e.g.*, packet loss and delay). We will see that TCP must necessarily take this end-end approach towards congestion control, since the IP layer provides no feedback to the end systems regarding network congestion. TCP segment loss (as indicated by a timeout or a triple duplicate acknowledgement) is taken as an indication of network congestion and TCP decreases its window size accordingly. We also see that new proposals for TCP use increasing round-trip delay values as indicators of increased network congestion.

Network-Assisted Congestion Control

With network-assisted congestion control, network-layer components (*i.e.*, routers) provide explicit feedback to the sender regarding the congestion state in the network. This feedback may be as simple as a single bit indicating congestion at a link. This approach was taken in the early IBM SNA and DEC DECnet architectures, was recently proposed for TCP/IP networks, and is used in ATM ABR congestion control as well, as discussed below. More sophisticated network-feedback is also possible. For example, one form of ATM ABR congestion control that we will study shortly allows a router to explicitly inform the sender of the transmission rate it (the router) can support on an outgoing link.

For network-assisted congestion control, congestion information is typically fedback from the network to the sender in one of two ways, as shown in figure 27.7. Direct feedback may

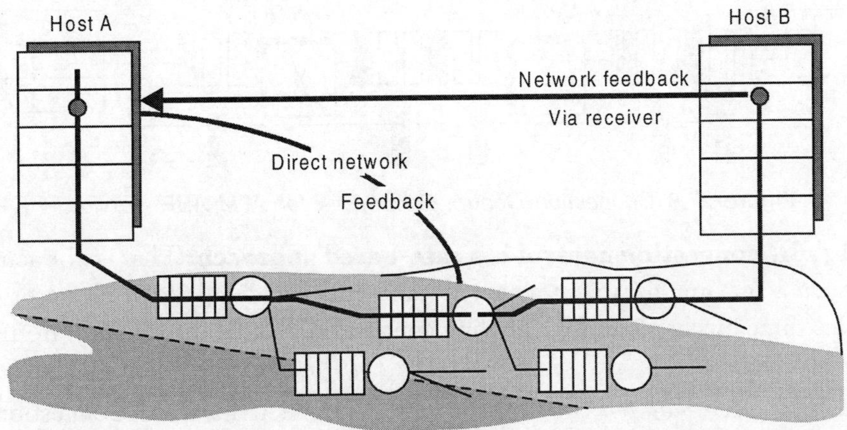

Figure 27.7 *Two Feedback Pathways for Network-indicated Congestion Information.*

be sent from a network router to the sender. This form of notification typically takes the form of a choke packet. The second form of notification occurs when a router marks/updates a field in a packet flowing from sender to receiver to indicate congestion. Upon receipt of a marked packet, the receiver then notifies the sender of the congestion indication. Note that this latter form of notification takes up to a full round-trip time.

ATM ABR CONGESTION CONTROL

We conclude this section with a brief case study of the network-assisted congestion control mechanisms used in ATM ABR (Available Bit Rate) service. ABR has been designed as an elastic data transfer service in a manner reminiscent of TCP. When the network is under loaded, ABR service should be able to take advantage of the spare available bandwidth; when the network is congested, ABR service should throttle its transmission rate to some predetermined minimum transmission rate.

Figure 27.8 shows the framework for ATM ABR congestion control. In our discussion below we adopt ATM terminology (*e.g.*, using the term "switch" rather than "router," and the term "call" rather than "packet"). With ATM ABR service, data cells are transmitted from a source to a destination through a series of intermediate switches. Interspersed with the data cells are so-called RM (Resource Management) cells; we will see shortly that these RM cells can be used to convey congestion-related information among the hosts and switches. When an RM cell is at a destination, it will be "turned around" and sent back to the sender (possibly after the destination has modified the contents of the RM cell). It is also possible for a switch to generate an RM cell itself and send this RM cell directly to a source. RM cells can thus be used to provide both direct network feedback and network-feedback-via-the-receiver, as shown in figure.

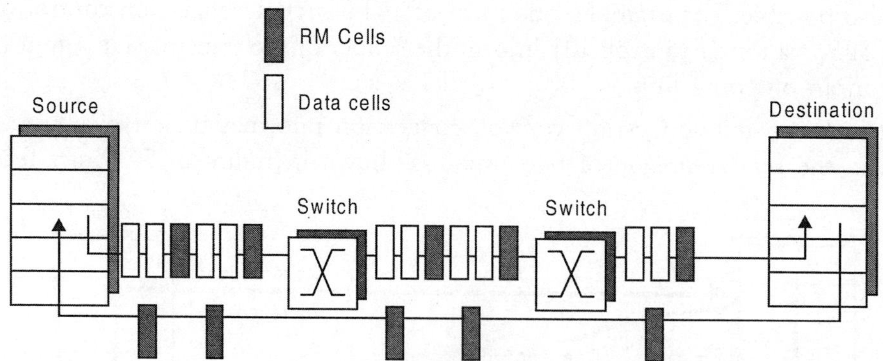

Figure 27.8 *Congestion Control Framework for ATM ABR Service.*

- **ATM ABR congestion control is a rate-based approach:** That is, the sender explicitly computes a maximum rate at which it can send and regulates itself accordingly. ABR provides three mechanisms for signaling congestion-related information from the siwtches to the receiver.
- **EFCI bit:** Each *data cell* contains an EFCI (Explicit Forward Congestion Indication) bit. A congested network switch can set the EFCI bit in a data cell to 1 to signal congestion to the destination host. The destination must check the EFCI bit in all

received data cells. When an RM cell arrives at the destination, if the most recently-received data cell had the EFCI bit set to 1, then the destination sets the CI (Congestion Indication) bit of the RM cell to 1 and sends the RM cell back to the sender. Using the EFCI in data cells and the CI bit in RM cells, a sender can thus be notified about congestion at a network switch.

- **CI and NI bits:** As noted above, sender-to-receiver RM cells are interspersed with data cells. The rate of RM cell interspersion is a tunable parameter, with one RM cell every 32 data cells being the default value. These RM cells have a CI bit and a NI (No Increase) bit that can be set by a congested network switch. Specifically, a switch can set the NI bit in a passing RM cell to1 under mild congestion and can set the CI bit to 1 under severe congestion conditions. When a destination host receives an RM cell, it will send the RM cell back to the sender with its CI and NI bits intact except that CI may be set to 1 by the destination as a result of the EFCI mechanism described above.
- **Explicit rate (ER) setting:** Each RM cell also contains a 2-byte ER (Explicit Rate) field. A congested switch may lower the value contained in the ER field in a passing RM cell. In this manner, the ER field will be set to the minimum supportable rate of all switches on the source-to-destination path.

CONGESTION AND DEADLOCK

As networks grow larger and accommodate more nodes, routing strategies must deal with an ever-increasing number of packets. The increased demand can put network operations in peril. What happens when one or more network links fail ? What happens if the number of packets that must be transmitted exceeds the network's ability to do so ? A potentially serious consequence is congestion, or the excessive buildup of packets at one or more network nodes.

Once again we can draw on the useful analogy of traffic control in an urban area. Highways and roads must be designed with the anticipated amount of traffic in mind. Anyone who has driven in an urban area knows the problem. During rush hour the amount of traffic is excessive and a highway's ability to handle it diminishes. An accident or road construction can put several lanes or an entire stretch of highway out of commission. In either case traffic slows (or stops completely), causing terrible congestion.

Similarly, congestion in a network reduces its usefulness. Packets experience longer delays and network users see the network as unresponsive and unable to meet their needs.

Congestion at a node hampers the node's ability to receive packets as quickly, and incoming packets begin to accumulate there as well. This can have a chain reaction effect in which all nodes begin to experience congestion, making the problem worse. There are several ways to handle congestion:

Packet elimination—if an excessive buildup of packets occurs at a node,

1. **Eliminate some of them:** This reduces the number of outstanding packets waiting for transmission and reduces the network load. The drawback, of course, is that the destroyed packets do not reach their destination destroying packets sounds drastic, but if the congestion is sporadic the network protocols can handle it well and the inconvenience to the unlucky user whose packets are destroyed is minimal.

2. **Flow control:** Flow control protocols are designed to control the number of packets sent. However they are not a true congestion control approach. The problem is that flow control limits the number of packets between two points, whereas congestion often involves packets coming into a node from many sources. Thus, even if nodes regulate the number of packets they send, congestion still can occur if too many nodes are sending them.
3. **Buffer allocation:** This approach can be used with virtual circuits. Virtual circuit is an established route between network nodes that is determined before any data packets are actually sent. Once a route is established, protocols at a node on that route can reverse buffers specifically for the virtual circuit.
4. **Choke packets:** This approach provides a more dynamic way to deal with congestion. Each node monitors the activity on its outgoing links, tracking the utilization of each. If the utilization of the lines is small the danger of congestion is low. If utilization of any line exceeds some specified criterion, the nodes protocols responds by putting itself into a special warning state. When in the warning state, the node will respond by sending a special choke packet in response to any incoming packets. When the source receives the choke packet it responds by reducing the number of packets it is sending for a specified period of time.

CONGESTION CONTROL

When one part of the subnet (*e.g.*, one or more routers in an area) becomes overloaded, congestion results. Because routers are receiving packets faster than they can forward them, one of two things must happen:

1. The subnet must prevent additional packets from entering the congested region until those already present can be processed.
2. The congested routers can discard queued packets to make room for those that are arriving.

We now consider the problem of congestion and some possible solutions.

The congestion control mechanisms limit the number of simultaneous TCP segments in the network. The algorithms used for congestion control are designed to be simple to implement and require only a few lines of code.

Since uIP only handles one in-flight TCP segment per connection, the amount of simultaneous segments cannot be further limited, thus the congestion control mechanisms are not needed. lwIP has the ability to have multiple in-flight segments and therefore implements all of TCP's congestion control mechanisms.

CONGESTION AVOIDANCE AND CONTROL

In November, 1988, Jacobson & Karels wrote congestion avoidance and control, where they described five of seven new algorithms included into BSD TCP 4.0.

The seven new algorithms included into BSD TCP 4.0. were:

- Round-trip time variance estimation.
- Exponential retransmit timer back-off.
- Slow-Start.
- More aggressive receiver ACK policy.
- Dynamic window sizing on congestion.
- Karn's clamped retransmit back-off.
- Fast retransmit
- The flow on a TCP connection should obey a *conservation of packets* principle; if this principle were obey, congestion collapse would become the exception rather than the rule. By *conservation of packets* we mean that for a connection *in equilibrium*, *i.e.*, running stably with a full window of data in transit, the packet flow is what physicist would call *conservative*, *i.e.*, a new packet isn't put into the network until an old packet leaves.

There are only three ways for packet conservation to fail:

- The connection doesn't get to equilibrium.
- A sender injects a new packet before an old one has exited.
- Equilibrium can't be reached because of lack of path resources.

Failure 1 has to be from a connection that is either starting or restarting after a packet loss. Another way to look at the conservation property is to say that the sender uses ACKS as a *clock* to strobe new packets into the network. Since the receiver can generate ACKS no faster than data packets can get through the network, the protocol is *self-clocking*. But the same thing that makes a self-clocked system stable when it's running, makes it hard to start; *i.e.*, to get data flowing there must be ACKS to clock out packets, but to get ACKS there must be data flowing. To start the clock the *slow-start* algorithm was developed to gradually increase the amount of data in transit:

- Add a congestion window, *cwnd*, to the per-connection state.
- When starting or restarting after a loss, set *cwnd* to one packet.
- On each ACK for new data, increase *cwnd* by one packet.
- When sending, send the minimum of the *receiver's advertised window* and *cwnd.*

The algorithm guarantee that a connection will send data at a rate at most twice the maximum possible on the path.

Failure 2 has to deal with *conservation at equilibrium*; it requires a good *round-trip timing*. A good round trip time estimator, the core of the retransmit timer, is the single most important estimating the variation, *s*, of the round trip time, RTT. From queueing theory we know that RTT and the variation of RTT increase quickly with load.

The TCP protocol specification suggests estimating *mean round trip time* via the *low-pass filter* :

$$SRTT = \alpha * SRTT + (1-\alpha) * RTT$$

Where SRTT is the average RTT estimate, RTT is a round trip time measurement from the most recently ACKED data packet, and α is a filter gain constant with a suggested value of 0.9. Once the SRTT estimate is updated, the retransmit timeout interval, RTO, for the next packet sent is set to β * SRTT. The parameter β account for RTT variation. The suggested β=2 can adapt to loads of at most 30%. Above this point, a connection will respond to load increases by retransmitting packets that have only be delayed in transit. This force the network to do useless work, wasting bandwidth on duplicates of packets that will eventually be delivered, at a time when it's known to be having trouble with useful work.

New Congestion Avoidance Algorithm

In April 1990, through an e-mail, Van Jacobson refined the congestion avoidance algorithm.

Congestion avoidance algorithm is intended to do two things:

- Prevent the pipe from going empty after a loss (if the pipe doesn't go empty, you won't have to waste round-trip times refilling it).
- Correctly account for the amount of data actually in the pipe (since that's what congestion avoidance is supposed to be estimating and adapting to).

For (1), remember that a packet loss is a signal that the pipe is congested and a packet loss can be detected of one of two different ways:

- via a retransmit timeout.
- When some small number (3-4) of consecutive duplicate ACKS has been received (also called duplicate ACK threshold).

In case a.-, the pipe is guarantee to be empty, so we want slow-start.

In case b.-, if the duplicate ACK threshold is small compared to the bandwidth-delay product (*bdp*), we have detected the loss with the pipe almost full, *i.e.*, given a dup-ack threshold of 3 packets (3 dup-ack inferring a packet loss) and a *bdp* of 16 packets (24KB assuming 1500 bytes MTU), the pipe is 75% full when loss is detected. As soon as the *bdp* is higher, the pipe will be almost full when loss is detected (maintaining the same dup-ACK threshold of 3 packets). Since the pipe is (almost) full, there's no need to slow-start after the fast-retransmit.

For (2), a duplicate ACK means that the receiver got an out-of-order packet, been the usual case of this a missing packet. *i.e.*, if there are *W* packets in transit (*W=window size*) and one is dropped, the receiver will get *W-1* out-of-order packets and will generate *W-1* duplicate ACK. If the dup-ACK threshold is set high enough (*i.e.* 3 packets), we can reasonably assume that reaching the dup-ACK threshold means a dropped packet.

But there's more information in the ACK: receiver can only generate an ACK in response to a packet arrival, *i.e.*, a duplicate ACK means that a packet has left the network; if the sender is limited by the congestion window, a packet can now be sent (*the congestion window is a count of how many packets will fit in the pipe; the acknowledgement says a packet has left the pipe so a new one can be added to take its place*). So, conceptually, the new algorithm will be:

When the dupack threshold is reached, set *ssthresh* to ½ the current congestion window *cwnd* and retransmit the missing packet.

Set now *cwnd* to *ssthresh* (original **Tahoe** specification used to set *cwnd* to one segment to force a *slow-start*).

Change now the sender's output routine to use an effective window of:

*min(snd_wnd, cwnd + dupacks * mss)*

END-END CONGESTION CONTROL: WINDOW-BASED CONGESTION CONTROL

Sending transport entity maintains congestion window over sequence number space

- can send a packet if packet seq. # in window
- distinct from flow control window

on timeout

- loss assumed
- decrease congestion window size
- increase timeout value (in case packet was delayed)

ACK received: increase window size

- Everything is OK, so allow even larger window.

END-END CONGESTION CONTROL: TCP

Uses window-based congestion control

two variables used

- *cwnd*: congestion window size
- *ssthresh*: threshold for slowing down rate of increase

TCP slow start + congestion avoidance

- assume 4K segment size
- TCP window size = min(flow control window size, congestion control window size).

```
initialize: cwnd=1
   ssthresh=16
loop: if (ACK received and cwnd <= ssthresh)
   cwnd = cwnd+1
else if (ACK received and cwnd > ssthresh)
   cwnd = cwnd + 1/ssthresh
else if packet timeout
   ssthresh = cwnd/2   /* new thresh half current win */
   cwnd = 1            /* new window size back to 1 */
forever
```

NETWORK-INDICATED CONGESTION CONTROL

Window-based control strictly end-end

- Network layer not involved, but congestion occurs in network layer!

One network-indicated approach: network "marks" packets passing through congested node

- Receiver sees congestion indication mark and tells sender to slow down
- Congestion-experienced flag in ISO CLNP, CWI (changes window indicator in IBM SNA virtual route pacings

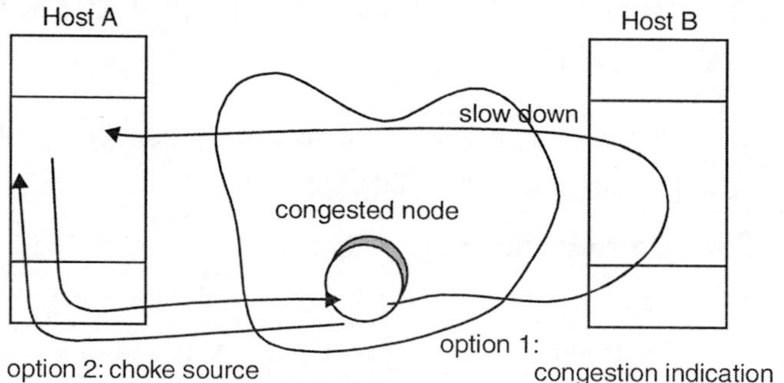

Figure 27.9 *Congestion control.*

Second network-indicated approach: upon detecting congestion, congested router sends explicit message back to traffic sources to slow them down

- Text: choke packets
- Source quench in ICMP (Internet control message protocol)
- VR-RWI bit in SNA VR pacing

Network Indicated Congestion Control: Difficulties

Receiver-initiated control may have long feedback time in high-speed networks

- Sender may have 1000's sent (but unACKed) packets before congestion indicator receiver
- Pipe filled already.

Both approaches require coupling of network and transport layer

- OK for homogeneous networks
- Difficult in internetworked environment, with different network layers.

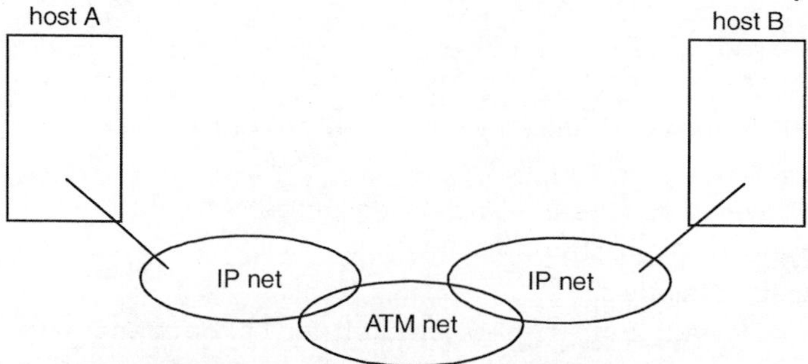

Figure 27.10 *Congestion control difficulties.*

RATE-BASED CONGESTION CONTROL

Congestion control particularly hard in high-speed networks, *e.g.,* 1 Gbit per second ling, 225byte packet takes 1 micro second to transmit. Thousands of packets "in the wire" propagating cross country, When congestion occurs, too late to react. Avoid congestion by regulating flow of packets into network.

Smoother flows will avoid bursts of packets from different senders arriving at same node and causing congestion. Smooth out packet bursts at network edge on per session basis before they enter network.

RATE BASED CONGESTION CONTROL: LEAKY BUCKET

Goal: regulate rate at which sender can inject packets into network A packet must match up with (and remove) a token before entering network.

Tokens added to bucket at rate r: controls *long term* rate of packet entry into network. At most b tokens accumulate in bucket. Bucket size b control *"burstiness"* of arrivals. Maximum number of packets entering network in t time units is b+rt XTP uses rate and burst parameters analogous to r,b.

CONGESTION CONTROL BY BUFFER PRE-ALLOCATION

Lack of buffering in network is fundamental cause of congestion. Avoid congestion by allocating buffers to an end-end connection.

If insufficient buffers for a new connection, block it (as in circuit switching). Buffers dedicated to connection, link still shared protects behaving connections from misbehaving one. Data link layer involved in transport layer congestion control.

CONGESTION AVOIDANCE MECHANISMS

It is important to understand that TCP's strategy is to control congestion once it happens, as opposed to trying to avoid congestion in the first place. In fact TCP repeatedly increases the load it imposes on the network in an effort to find the point at which congestion occurs, and then backs off from this point. Said another way, TCP *needs* to create losses to find the available bandwidth of the connection. An appealing alternative, but one that has not yet been widely adopted, is to predict when congestion is about to happen, and to reduce the rate at which hosts send data just before packets start being discarded. We call such a strategy congestion *avoidance*, to distinguish it from congestion *control.*

This section describes three different congestion avoidance mechanisms. The first two take a similar approach—they put a small amount of additional functionality into the router to assist the end node in the anticipation of congestion. The third mechanism is very different from the first two—it attempts to avoid congestion purely from the end nodes.

PRE-ALLOCATION OF RESOURCES

Pre-allocation schemes aim to prevent congestion from happening in the first place. For example, we can require that resources be pre-allocated before any packets can be sent, guaranteeing that resources will be available to process each packet.

In virtual circuit networks, for example, the sender opens a connection before sending data. The circuit setup operation selects a path through the subnet, and each router on the path dedicates buffer space and bandwidth to the new circuit. What happens when a user attempts to open a virtual circuit and the subnet is congested ? The subnet can refuse to open the connection, forcing the user to wait until sufficient resources become available.

Traffic Shaping

Control the rate at which packets are sent (not just how many). Widely used in ATM networks. At set up, the sender and carrier negotiate a traffic pattern (shape). Leaky Bucket algorithm used to control rate in a datagram network. A single-server queue with constant service time. If bucket (buffer) overflows then packets are discarded. Enforces a constant output rate regardless of burst ness of input. Does nothing when input is idle. In contrast the token Bucket algorithm causes a token to be generated periodically, which during idle periods can be saved up.

Related to traffic shaping is flow specification, where a particular quality of service is agreed upon between sender, receiver and carrier.

DISCARDING PACKETS (NO PRE-ALLOCATION)

At the other end of the spectrum, we could pre-allocate no resources in advance, and take our chances that resources will be available when we need them. When insufficient resources are present to process existing packets, discard queued packets to make room for newly arriving ones. Who retransmits the discarded packets ? Two cases: connection oriented and connectionless. In datagram (connectionless) networks, the sending host (transport layer) retransmits discarded packets (if appropriate). In virtual circuit networks, the previous-hop router retransmits the packet when it fails to receive an acknowledgement.

Failure to pre-allocate resources leads to two problems: potential deadlock and unfairness. First, let us consider deadlock. Suppose that all of a router's buffers hold packets. Because the router has no free buffers, it cannot accept additional frames. Unfortunately, it also ignores frames containing ACKs that would free up some of those buffers! Suppose further, that two adjacent routers, A and B, are sending packets to each other. Since both are waiting for the other to accept a packet, neither can proceed. This condition is known as a deadlock. Solution: Reserve at least one buffer for each input line and use it to hold incoming packets. Note that we can extract the ACK field and still discard the packet, if we don't have buffers to hold it. Advantage of discarding packets when congested is easy to implement.

Disadvantages:

1. Wastes resources. The network may have expended considerable resources processing a packet that is eventually discarded.

2. Non-deterministic. There are fewer guarantees than with virtual circuits that packets will ever reach their destination.
3. Requires that sending hosts pay attention to congestion. If the network can't prevent a host from sending data, a host can overload the network. In particular, a "broken" host may cause the network to become overly congested.
4. In the extreme case, congestion collapse occurs. The network becomes so overloaded, that few packets reach their destination. Meanwhile, the sending hosts continue to generate more data (both retransmissions and new packets). This condition occurred several times in 1987, and the Internet/Arpanet became unusable for a period of hours to days.

ISARITHMIC CONGESTION CONTROL

Another approach to congestion avoidance is to limit the total number flow of packets in the subnet at any one time. The idea is similar to the token ring:

1. When a router accepts a packet from a host, it must obtain a permit before sending the packet into the subnet.
2. Obtaining a permit is analogous to "seizing the token", but there can be many permits in the subnet. When a router obtains a permit, it destroys it.
3. The destination router regenerates the permit when it passes the packet to the destination host.

Issues:

1. Although we have limited the total number of packets in the subnet, we have no control over where in the subnet those packets will be. Thus, a router in one part of the subnet might be congested, while a router in another part remains idle, but unable to process packets for lack of permits.
2. Regenerating lost permits is difficult, because no single node knows how many permits are currently in the subnet.
3. Distribute among the routers or centralize for a known access point.

CONGESTION CONTROL IN MULTICASTING

So far, the algorithms for congestion control work for single source and single destination. With multicasting (single source, multiple destination), the issue is different. Often the transmission route has a form of a tree.

RSVP—RESOURCE RESERVATION PROTOCOL

The basic idea behind RSVP is the following.

- The sender and the receivers establish an initial path, along which multiple routers may be involved.

- Each receiver then sends a reservation request to the sender in reverse direction. The request is processed by each of the routers on the way.
- If sufficient bandwidth is available, the request is granted and forwarded to next router on its way to the sender; otherwise, the request is rejected.
- When the sender receives the reservation from a receiver, it knows that the reservation has been made properly.
- When a different receiver makes a request to the same sender asking for the same multicast information, the channel can be shared.
- When all parties involved have set up the paths, multicast can take place.

The Network Layer in ATM Networks:

- The network layer functionality is provided in ATM through the ATM Layer.
- ATM Layer is a connection oriented protocol based on virtual circuit (officially called a virtual channel).
- ATM Layer does not provide acknowledgement, requiring the physical media highly reliable.
- ATM Layer guarantees orderly delivery of cells (packets, frames in other protocol stack's term) on the same virtual channel.
- ATM layer defines two different interfaces:
  - The UNI (User-Network Interface) provides interface between application program (User) and the network.
  - The NNI (Network-Network Interface) provides interface between networks.

RSVP

As we learned in the previous section, in order for a network to provide QoS guarantees, there must be a signaling protocol that allows applications running in hosts to reserve resources in the Internet. RSVP, is such a signaling protocol for the Internet.

When people talk about *resources* in the Internet context, they usually mean link bandwidth and router buffers. To keep the discussion concrete and focused, however, we shall assume that the word *resource* is synonymous with *bandwidth*. For our pedagogic purposes, RSVP stands for bandwidth reservation protocol.

The Essence of RSVP

The RSVP protocol allows applications to reserve bandwidth for their data flows. It is used by a host, on the behalf of an application data flow, to request a specific amount of bandwidth from the network. RSVP is also used by the routers to forward bandwidth reservation requests. To implement RSVP, RSVP software must be present in the receivers, senders, and routers. The two principle characteristics of RSVP are:

• It provides reservations for bandwidth in multicast trees (uni-cast is handled as a special case).

• It is receiver-oriented, *i.e.*, the receiver of a data flow initiates and maintains the resource reservation used for that flow.

These two characteristics are illustrated in figure 27.11.

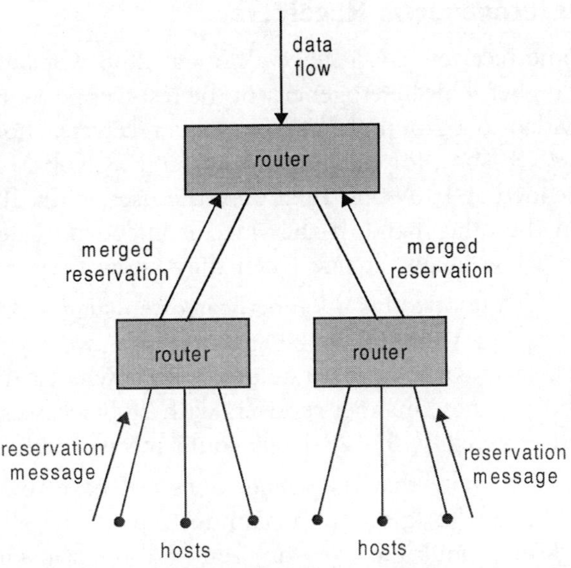

Figure 27.11 *RSVP Multicast- and Receiver-oriented.*

The above diagram shows a multicast tree with data flowing from the top of the tree to six hosts. Although data originates from the sender, the reservation messages originate from the receivers. When a router forwards a reservation message upstream towards the sender, the router may merge the reservation message with other reservation messages arriving from downstream.

Before discussing RSVP in greater detail, we need to recall the notion of a session. As with RTP, a session can consist of multiple multicast data flows. Each sender in a session is the source of one or more data flows; for example, a sender might be the source of a video data flow and an audio data flow. Each data flow in a session has the same multicast address. To keep the discussion concrete, we assume that routers and hosts identify the session to which a packet belongs by the packet's multicast address. This assumption is somewhat restrictive; the actual RSVP specification allows for more general methods to identify a session. Within a session, the data flow to which a packet belongs also needs to be identified. This could be done, for example, with the flow identifier field in IPv6.

We emphasize that the RSVP standard does not specify how the network provides the reserved bandwidth to the data flows. It is merely a protocol that allows the applications to reserve the necessary link bandwidth. Once the reservations are in place, it is up to the routers in the Internet to actually provide the reserved bandwidth to the data flows. This provisioning is done with the scheduling mechanisms (priority scheduling, weighted fair queuing, etc.).

It is also important to understand that RSVP is not a routing protocol—it does not determine the links in which the reservations are to be made. Instead it depends on an underlying routing protocol (uni-cast or multicast) to determine the routes for the flows. Once the routes are in place, RSVP can reserve bandwidth in the links along these routes. (We shall see shortly that when a route changes, RSVP re-reserves resources.) And once the reservations are in place, the routers' packet schedulers can actually provide the reserved bandwidth to the data flows. Thus, RSVP is only one piece—albeit an important piece—in the QoS guarantee puzzle.

RSVP is sometimes referred to as a *signaling protocol.* By this it is meant that RSVP is a protocol that allows hosts to establish and tear-down reservations for data flows. The term "signaling protocol" comes from the jargon of the circuit-switched telephony community.

Heterogeneous Receivers

Some receivers can receive a flow at 28.8 Kbps, others at 128 Kbps, and yet others at 10 Mbps or higher. This heterogeneity of the reserves poses an interesting question. If a sender is multicasting a video to a group of heterogeneous receivers, should the sender encode the video for low quality at 28.8 Kbps, for medium quality at 128 Kbps, or for high quality at 10 Mbps ? If the video is encoded at 10 Mbps, then only the users with 10 Mbps access will be able to watch the video. On the other hand, if the video is encoded at 28.8 kbps, then the 10 Mbps users will have to see a low-quality image when they know they can something much better.

To resolve this dilemma it is often suggested that video and audio be encoded in layers. For example, a video might be encoded into two layers: a base layer and an enhancement layer. The base layer could have a rate of 20 Kbps whereas the enhancement layer could have a rate of 100 Kbps; in these manner receivers with 28.8 accesses could receive the low-quality base-layer image, and receivers with 128 Kbps could receive both layers to construct a high-quality image.

We note that the sender does not have to know the receiving rates of all the receivers. It only needs to know the maximum rate of the all its receivers. The sender encodes the video or audio into multiple layers and sends all the layers up to the maximum rate into multicast tree. The receivers pick out the layers that are appropriate for their receiving rates. In order to not excessively waste bandwidth in the network's links, the heterogeneous receivers must communicate to the network the rates they can handle. We shall see that RSVP gives foremost attention to the issue of reserving resources for heterogeneous receivers.

A Few Simple Examples

Let us first describe RSVP in the context of a concrete one-to-many multicast example. Suppose there is a source that is transmitting into the Internet the video of a major sporting event. This session has been assigned a multicast address, and the source stamps all of its outgoing packets with this multicast address. Also suppose that an underlying multicast routing protocol has established a multicast tree from the sender to four receivers as shown below; the numbers next to the receivers are the rates at which the receivers want to receive data. Let us also assume that the video is layered encoded to accommodate this heterogeneity of receiver rates.

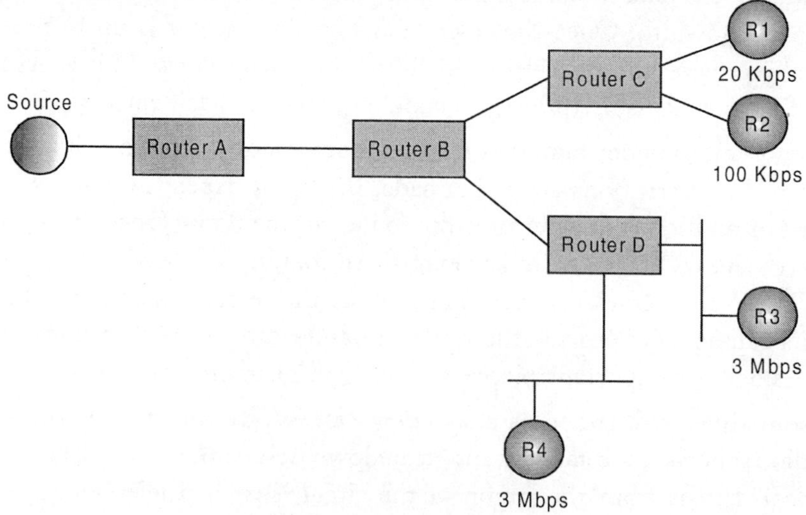

Figure 27.12 *An RSVP.*

Crudely speaking, RSVP operates as follows for this example. Each receiver sends a reservation message upstream into the multicast tree. This reservation message specifies the rate at which the receiver would like to receive the data from the source. When the reservation message reaches a router, the router adjusts its packet scheduler to accommodate the reservation. It then sends a reservation upstream. The amount of bandwidth reserved upstream from the router depends on the bandwidths reserved downstream. In the example in figure, receivers R1, R2, R3 and R4 reserve 20 kbps, 120 kbps, 3 Mbps and 3 Mbps, respectively. Thus router D's downstream receivers request a maximum of 3 Mbps. For this one-to-many transmission, router D sends a reservation message to router B requesting that router B reserve 3 Mbps on the link between the two routers. Note that only 3 Mbps is reserved and not 3+3=6 Mbps; this is because receivers R3 and R4 are watching the same sporting event, so there reservations may be merged. Similarly, router C requests that router B reserve 100 Kbps on the link between routers B and C; the layered encoding ensures that receiver R1's 20 Kbps stream is included in the 100 Mbps stream. Once router B receives the reservation message from its downstream routers and passes the reservations to its schedulers, it sends a new reservation message to its upstream router, router A. This message reserves 3 Mbps of bandwidth on the link from router A to router B, which is again the maximum of the downstream reservations.

We see from this first example that RSVP is receiver-oriented, *i.e.*, the receiver of a data flow initiates and maintains the resource reservation used for that flow. Note that each router receives a reservation message from each of its downstream links in the multicast tree and sends only one reservation message into its upstream link.

As another example, suppose that four persons are participating in a video conference, as shown in figure. Each person has three windows open on her computer to look at the other three persons. Suppose that the underlying routing protocol has established the multicast tree among the four hosts as shown in the diagram below. Finally, suppose each person wants to see each of the videos at 3 Mbps. Then on each of the links in this multicast tree, RSVP would reserve 9 Mbps in one direction and 3 Mbps in the other direction. Note that RSVP does not merge reservations in this example, as each person wants to receive three distinct streams.

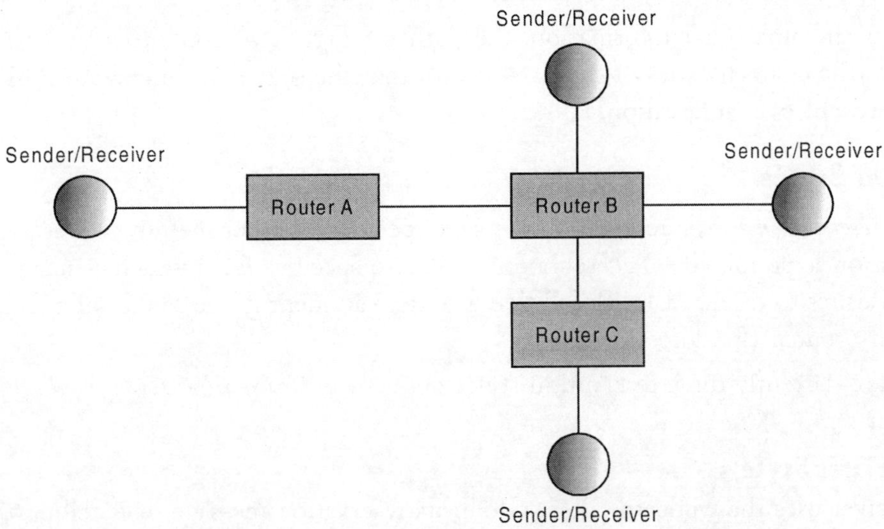

Figure 27.13 *An RSVP Video Conference Example.*

Now consider an audio conference among the same four persons over the same multicast tree. Suppose *b* bps is needed for an isolated audio stream. Because in an audio conference it is rare that more than two persons speak at the same time, it is not necessary to reserve *3*b* bps into each receiver; *2*b* should suffice. Thus, in this last application we can conserve bandwidth by merging reservations.

Call Admission

Just as the manager of a restaurant should not accept reservations for more tables than the restaurant has, the amount of bandwidth on a link that a router reserves should not exceed the link's capacity. Thus whenever a router receives a new reservation message, it must first determine if its downstream links on the multicast tree can accommodate the reservation. This *admission test* is performed whenever a router receives a reservation message. If the admission test fails, the router rejects the reservation and returns an error message to the appropriate receiver(s).

RSVP does not define the admission test; but it assumes that the routers perform such a test and that RSVP can interact with the test.

Path Messages

So far we have only discussed the RSVP reservation messages, which originate at the receivers and flow upstream towards the senders. *Path messages* are another important RSVP message type; they originate at the senders and flow downstream towards the receivers.

The principle purpose of the path messages is to let the routers know on which links they should forward the reservation messages. Specifically, a path message sent within the multicast tree from a router A to a router B contains router A's uni-cast IP address. Router B puts this address in a path-state table, and when it receives a reservation message from a downstream node it accesses the table and learns that it should send a reservation message up the multicast tree to router A. In the future some routing protocols may supply reverse path forwarding information directly, replacing the reverse-routing function of the path state.

Along with some other information, the path messages also contain a *sender Tspec*, which defines the traffic characteristics of the data stream that the sender will generate. This Tspec can be used to prevent over reservation.

Reservation Styles

Through its *reservation style*, a reservation message specifies whether merging of reservations from the same session is permissible. A reservation style also specifies from which senders in a session the receiver desires to receive data. Recall that a router can identify the sender of a datagram from the datagram's source IP address.

There are currently three reservation styles defined: *wildcard-filter style; fixed-filter style; and shared-explicit style.*

Wildcard-Filter Style

When a receiver uses the wildcard-filter style in its reservation message, it is telling the network that it wants to receive all flows from all upstream senders in the session and that its bandwidth reservation is to be shared among the senders.

Fixed-Filter Style

When a receiver uses the fixed-filter style in its reservation message, it specifies a list of senders from which it wants to receive a data flow along with a bandwidth reservation for each of these senders. These reservations are distinct, *i.e.,* they are not to be shared.

Shared-Explicit Style

When a receiver uses the shared-explicit style in its reservation message, it specifies a list of senders from which it wants to receive a data flow along with a single bandwidth reservation. This reservation is to be shared among all the senders in the list.

Shared reservations, created by the wildcard filter and the shared-explicit styles, are appropriate for a multicast session whose sources are unlikely to transmit simultaneously. Packetized audio is an example of an application suitable for shared reservations; because a limited number of people talk at once, each receiver might issue a wildcard-filter or a shared-explicit reservation request for twice the bandwidth required for one sender (to allow for over speaking). On the other hand, the fixed-filter reservation, which creates distinct reservations for the flows from different senders, is appropriate for video teleconferencing.

Examples of Reservation Styles

Following the Internet RFC, we now give examples for the three reservation styles. In figure 27.14, a router has two incoming interfaces, labeled A and B, and two utgoing interfaces, labeled C and D. The many-to-many multicast session has three senders—S1, S2 and S3—and three receivers—R1, R2 and R3. Figure 27.12 also shows that interface D is connected to a LAN.

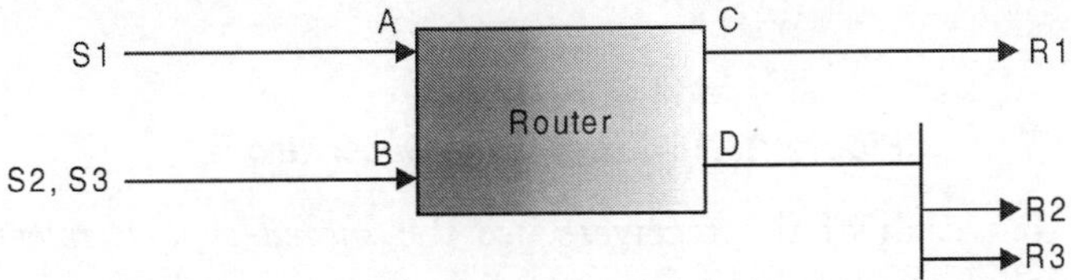

Figure 27.14 *Sample Scenario for RSVP Reservation Styles.*

Suppose first that all of the receivers use the *wildcard-filter reservation.* As shown in figure 27.15, receivers R1, R2, and R3 want to reserve 4b, 3b, and 2b, respectively, where b is a given bit rate. Then the router reserves 4b on interface C and 3b on interface D. Because of the wildcard-filter reservation, the two reservations from R2 and R3 are merged for interface D: the larger of the two reservations is used rather than the sum of reservations. The router then sends a reservation message upstream to interface A and another to interface B; each of these reservation messages requests is 4b, which is the larger of 3b and 4b.

Now suppose that all of the receivers use the *fixed-filter reservation.* As shown in figure 27.16, receiver R1 wants to reserve 4b for source S1 and 5b for source S2; also shown in the figure are the reservation requests from R2 and R3. Because of the fixed-filter style, the router reserves two disjoint chunks of bandwidth on interface C: one chunk of 4b for S1 and another chunk of 5b for S2. Similarly, the router reserves two disjoint chunks of bandwidth on interface D: one chunk of 3b for S1 (the maximum of b and 3b) and one chunk of b for S3. On interface A, the router

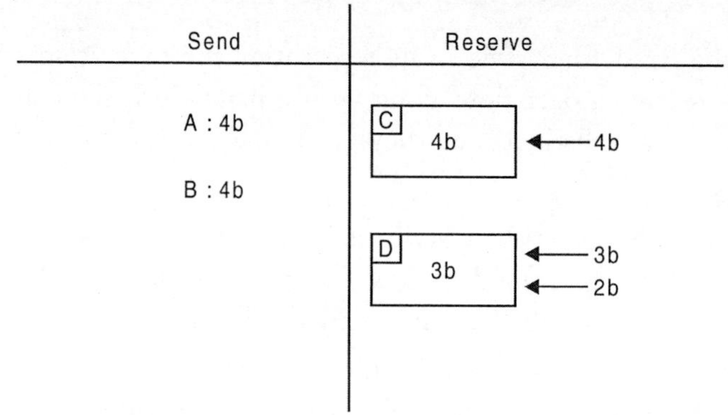

Figure 27.15 *Wildcard Filter Reservations.*

sends a message with a reservation for S1 of 4b (the maximum of 3b and 4b). On interface B, the router sends a message with a reservation of 5b for S2 and b for S3.

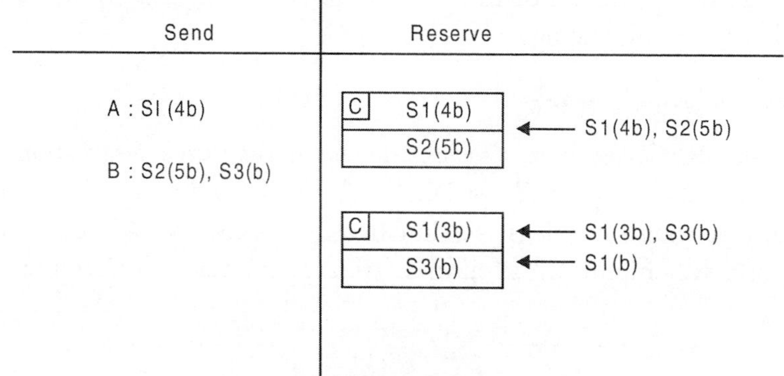

Figure 27.16 *Fixed Filter Reservations.*

Finally suppose that each of the receivers use the *shared-explicit reservation*. As shown in figure 27.17, receiver R1 desires a pipe of 1b which is to be shared between sources S1 and S2, receiver R2 desires a pipe of 3b to be shared between sources S1 and S3, and receiver R3 wants a pipe of 2b for source S2. Because of the shared-explicit style, the reservations from R2 and R3 are merged for interface D: only one pipe is reserved on interface D, although it is reserved at the maximum of the reservation rates. RSVP will reserve on interface B a pipe of 3b to be shared by S2 and S3; note that 3b is the maximum of the downstream reservations for S2 and S3.

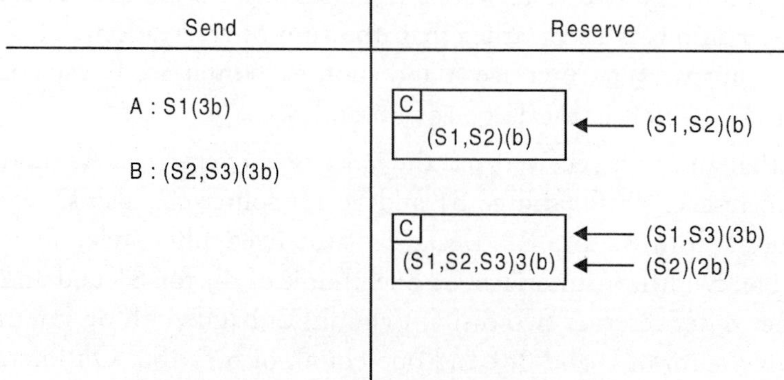

Figure 27.17 *Shared-explicit Reservations.*

In each of the above examples the three receivers used the same reservation style. Because receivers make independent decisions, the receivers participating in a session could use different styles. RSVP does not permit, however, reservations of different styles to be merged.

Soft State

The reservations in the routers and hosts are maintained with *soft states*. By this it is meant that each reservation for bandwidth stored in a router has an associated timer. If a reservation's timer expires, then the reservation is removed. If a receiver desires to maintain a reservation, it must periodically refresh the reservation by sending reservation messages. A receiver can also change its reservation (*e.g.*, the amount of bandwidth or the senders it wants to receive from) by adjusting its reservation in its stream of refresh messages.

The senders must also refresh the path state by periodically sending path messages. When a route changes, the next path message initializes the path state on the new route and future reservation messages will establish reservation state in the route. The state on the old segments of the route wills time out.

Soft state, whereby the state is maintained with refresh messages, is used by many other protocols in data networking. For example, as we learned in chapter 5, in the routing tables in transparent bridges, the entries are refreshed by data packets that arrive to the bridge; entries that are not refreshed are timed-out. A protocol that takes explicit actions to modify or release state is called a *hard-state* protocol. An example of a hard-state protocol is TCP, whereby the connection does not timeout if it stops being used; instead one side of the connection must explicitly destroy the connection.

Transport of Reservation Messages

RSVP messages are sent hop-by-hop directly over IP. Thus the RSVP message is placed in the information field of the IP datagram; the protocol number in the IP datagram is set to 46. Because IP is unreliable, RSVP messages are not acknowledged upon arrival. If an RSVP path or reservation message is lost, a replacement refresh message should arrive soon.

An RSVP reservation message that originates in a host will have the host's IP address in the source address field of the encapsulating IP datagram. It will have the IP address of the first router along the reserve-path in the multicast tree in destination address in the encapsulating IP datagram. When the IP datagram arrives at the first router, the router strips off the IP fields and passes the reservation message to the router's RSVP module. The RSVP module examines the messages multicast address (*i.e.*, session identifier) and style type, examines its current state, and then acts appropriately; for example, the RSVP module may merge the reservation with a reservation originating from another interface and then send a new reservation message to the next router upstream in the multicast tree.

Insufficient Resource

Because a reservation request that fails an admission test may embody a number of requests merged together, a reservation error must be reported to all the concerned receivers. These reservation errors are reported within ResvError messages. The receivers can then reduce the amount of resource that they request and try reserving again. The RSVP standard provides mechanisms to allow the back tracking of the reservations when insufficient resources are available; unfortunately, these mechanisms add significant complexity to the RSVP protocol. Furthermore, RSVP suffers from the so-called killer-reservation problem, whereby a receiver requests over and over again a large reservation, each time getting its reservation rejected due to lack of sufficient resources. Because this large reservation may have been merged with smaller reservations downstream, the large reservation may be excluding smaller reservations from being established. To solve this thorny problem, RSVP uses the ResvError messages to establish additional state in routers, called blockade state. Blockade state in a router modifies the merging procedure to omit the offending reservation from the merge, allowing a smaller request to be forwarded and established. The blockade state adds yet further complexity to the RSVP protocol and its implementation.

ROUTING AND SWITCHING

- The ATM standard doesn't specify any particular routing algorithm.
- Between switches, only the VPI is used; VCI is used only between a host and a switch (at the begin and end of the VP).
- Each of the interior switches (ones that don't connect to hosts) keeps a table (vpi_table) that specifies source, destination, incoming link, incoming VPI, outgoing link, outgoing VPI.

The switch is responsible for transferring incoming traffic to an appropriate outgoing link. The switch can be any type.

Traffic Shaping

- ATM uses a specific algorithm, the Generic Cell Rate Algorithm (GCRA) to form the shape of the traffic.
- GCRA has two parameters: the maximum allowed arrival rate (PCR), and the amount of variation that is tolerable (CDVT).
- A sender must not transmit cells faster than PCR (or inter-cell arrival time can't be greater than T = 1/PCR). A tolerance is set (CDVT). If the amount of time next early arrival cell is within CDVT, the cell is still considered conforming. If it exceeds this limit, it is not conforming. The switch can decide to drop it, or keep it only if no congestion occurred.

This algorithm in effect is the same as the leaky bucket algorithm.

Congestion Control

While traffic shaping is passive, ATM implements some other mechanism to control congestion. Different strategies are used.

Admission Control

In low speed network, it is often adequate to react to congestion, that is, when congestion occurred, tell the source to slow down (such as choke packet). In high speed network, this often doesn't work. By the time choke packet is received by the sender, thousands more packets have been sent.

The key here is to control the admission. When a new connection is requested, the source must specify the bandwidth requirement, service type (priority) and delay property. The ATM can decide whether or not to accept the connection request.

Resource Reservation

Closely related to the admission control is resource reservation. Use setup message to reserve the bandwidth.

Rate-Based Congestion Control

Traffic in ATM is divided into a few classes based on the bandwidth it requires.

- ABR: available bit rate service. This type of traffic has to negotiate the bandwidth available with the network, such as background file transfer.
- CBR: constant bit rate service. This type of service requires a constant bit rate. It cannot be changed, such as T1.
- RT-VBR: variable bit rate: real time. The bit rate varies, such as real time video conference.
- NRT-VBR: variable bit rate: non-real time, such as multimedia email.

There are two major solutions:

- *Credit-based control:* Essentially a dynamic sliding window protocol. Senders can transmit cells only if credits are available (credits are set by the recipient).
- *Rate-based control:* After every k data cells, each sender transmits a RM (Resource Management) cell. This cell travels along the same path as the data cells (because of VP and VC, this is feasible). The destination host, upon receiving, updating it, sends this RM cell back to the sender. The sender receives this cell, assesses the congestion situation and adjusts the rate.

Two other mechanisms can be used with Rate-Based control: Overloaded switches can spontaneously generate RM cells and send them back to the sender; the overloaded switches can set the middle PTI bit on data cells indicating the congestion.

Routers

A router is an Intermediate System (IS) which operates at the network layer of the OSI reference model. Routers may be used to connect two or more IP networks, or an IP network to an internet connection.

A router consists of a computer with at least two network interface cards supporting the IP protocol. The router receives packets from each interface via a network interface and forwards the received packets to an appropriate output network interface. Received packets have all link layer protocol headers removed, and transmitted packets have a new link protocol header added prior to transmission.

The router uses the information held in the network layer header (*i.e.,* IP header) to decide whether to forward each received packet, and which network interface to use to send the packet.

Most packets are forwarded based on the packet's IP destination address, along with routing information held within the router in a routing table. Before a packet is forwarded, the processor checks the Maximum Transfer Unit (MTU) of the specified interface. Packets larger than the interface's MTU must be fragmented by the router into two or more smaller packets. If a packet is received which has the Don't Fragment (DF) bit set in the packet header, the packet is not fragmented, but instead discarded. In this case, an ICMP error message is returned to the sender (*i.e.,* to the original packet's IP source address) informing it of the interface's MTU size. This forms the basis for path MTU discovery (PMTU).

The routing and filter tables resemble similar tables in link layer bridges and switches. Except, that instead of specifying link hardware addresses (MAC addresses), the router table specify network (IP addresses). The routing table lists known IP destination addresses with the appropriate network interface to be used to reach that destination. A default entry may be specified to be used for all addresses not explicitly defined in the table. A filter table may also be used to ensure that unwanted packets are discarded. The filter may be used to deny access to particular protocols or to prevent unauthorized access from remote computers by discarding packets to specified destination addresses.

A router forwards packets from one IP network to another IP network. Like other systems, it determines the IP network from the logical AND of an IP address with the associated sub-network address mask. One exception to this rule is when a router receives an IP packet to a network broadcast address. In this case, the router discards the packet. Forwarding broadcast packet can lead to severe storms of packets, and if uncontrolled could lead to network overload.

A router introduces delay (latency) as it processes the packets it receives. The total delay observed is the sum of many components including:

- Time taken to process the frame by the data link protocol
- Time taken to select the correct output link (i.e., filtering and routing)
- Queuing delay at the output link (when the link is busy)
- Other activities which consume processor resources (computing routing tables, network management, generation of logging information)

The router queue of packets waiting to be sent also introduces a potential cause of packet loss. Since the router has a finite amount of buffer memory to hold the queue, a router which receives packets at too high a rate may experience a full queue. In this case, the router has no other option than to simply discard excess packets. If required, these may later be retransmitted by a transport protocol.

Routers are often used to connect together networks which use different types of links (for instance an HDLC link connecting a WAN to a local Ethernet LAN). The optimum (and maximum) packet lengths (*i.e.,* the maximum transmission unit (MTU)) are different for different types of network. A router may therefore use IP to provide segmentation of packets into a suitable size for transmission on a network.

Associated protocols perform network error reporting (ICMP), communication between routers (to determine appropriate routes to each destination) and remote monitoring of the router operation (network management).

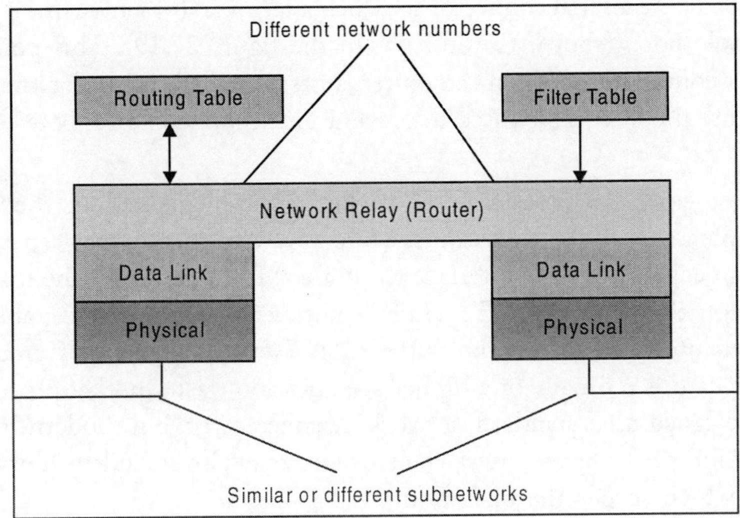

Figure 27.18 *Architecture of a Router.*

OPERATION OF A ROUTER

A modern router is a complex piece of equipment. The outside of the equipment is usually very simple, consisting of a number of network interface ports (shown on the left in the figure 27.19 to which cables may be connected and a few indicator lights to indicate that the router is functional.

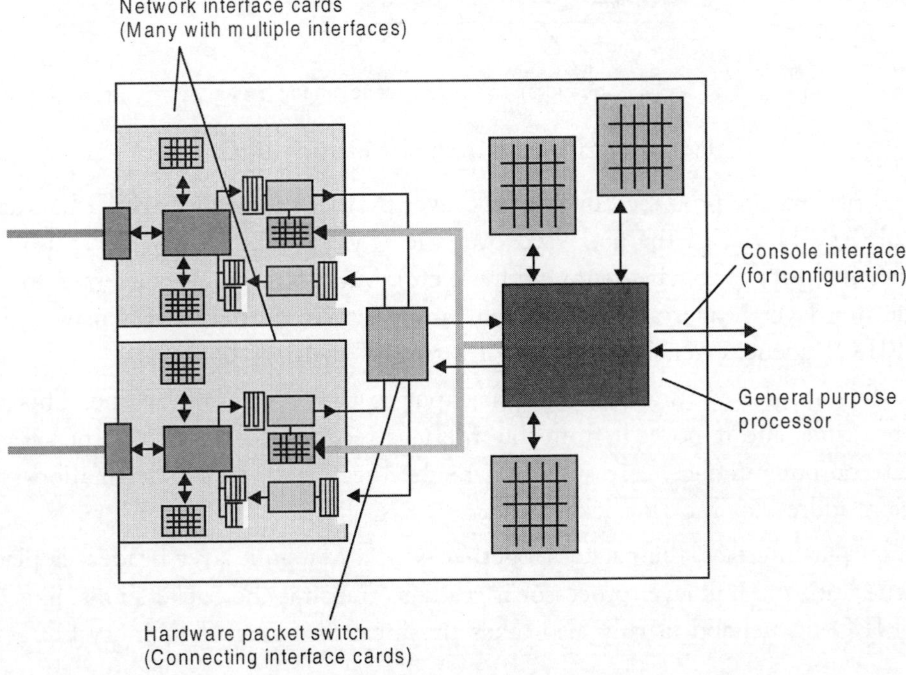

Figure 27.19 *Operation of a Router.*

Most routers also have a serial connector to which a terminal (or a modem) may be connected, known as the "console port" (shown to the right in the figure 27.19). This port is usually used to control the router configuration when the router is first installed. It may be the only port which is allowed to configure the filter table (used to prevent unauthorized access between the connected networks).

In the simplest case, the processing of packets is implemented in the general purpose processor which implements all the algorithms. More advanced routers may separate "forwarding" (the tasks of moving packets from one interface to another) from "routing" (the task of determining the best path through the network) and include a number of processors capable of performing these tasks. A router interface card resembles the LAN Network Interface Cards (NICs) used in PCs except that the card is normally of a higher specification (faster packet processing). The very first routers were designed used standard network interface cards, but modern high performance routers use special high performance interface cards and may also include a "Forwarding Engine" on-board the card which speeds the operation.

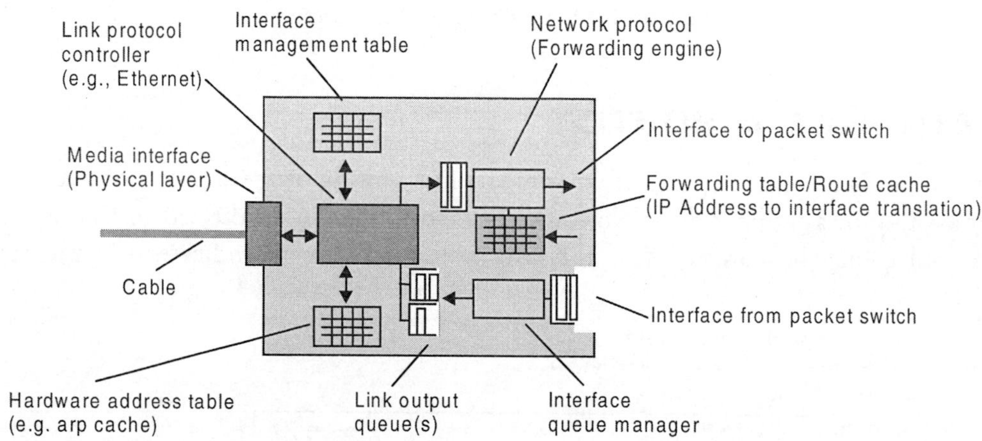

Figure 27.20 *Router Network Interface Card.*

Received packets are processed by the link layer protocol controller, which handles the link layer protocol (*e.g.*, HDLC, Ethernet) used over the physical link (cable). This also checks the received frame integrity (size, checksum, address, etc). Valid frames are converted to packets by removing the link layer header and are queued in the receive queue. This is usually a First-In-First-Out (FIFO) queue, often in the form of a ring of memory buffers.

The buffers are passed (drained) into the input to the forwarding engine. This takes each buffer, one at a time, and removes it from the interface receiver. The packet is then forwarded to an appropriate output interface, corresponding to the "best" path to the destination specified in the destination address of the IP packet header.

At the output interface, the packet (together with a new link layer header) is placed into a transmit queue until the link layer processor is ready to transmit the packet. This, like the receive queue, is a FIFO queue, and usually also takes the form of a ring of memory buffers.

Each out-going packet requires a new link layer protocol header to be added (encapsulation) with the destination address set to the next system to the receive the packet. The link protocol controller also maintains the hardware address table associated with the interface. This usually involves using the Address Resolution Protocol (ARP) to find out the hardware (Medium Access Control) addresses of other computers or routers directly connected to the same cable (or LAN). The packet is finally sent using the media interface with the hardware address set to the next hop system. When complete, the buffer (memory) allocated to the frame, is "freed", that is, it is returned as an empty buffer to the receive queue, where it may be used to store a new received packet.

You may think from this that the job of forwarding is not too difficult, and involves a lot of copying of the packet data from one place to another. You would be wrong on both counts! Forwarding actually involves lots of decisions. Modern routers avoid copying the data in a packet if at all possible—this is a significant processing cost, and may easily slow down a router to a very low throughput. Instead, where ever possible, the router will leave the packet data in the same place and instead pass information about where a packet is stored in memory.

INTRODUCTION TO FORWARDING

Here a simple description of the forwarding process is given. After determining the link layer frame is valid, the forwarding engine then starts processing the network layer information. It reads the network layer (IP) packet headers and checks various parts of the header, to ensure the packet is not damaged or illegal. It then uses a local forwarding table (known as the "Forwarding Information Base (FIB)") to identify where in the network the packet should be routed to (*i.e.*, which output interface should be used).

Once the appropriate output interface has been identified, the forwarding engine then requests the packet switch to form a connection to the appropriate output interface. The packet is then moved through the router to the output network interface controller. Although large routers actually implement a switch as a hardware component, smaller routers do not actually contain a "real" switch. In other routers, the switch takes the form of a shared memory data structure in which all received packets are stored. The switching operation therefore consists of removing a pointer from the receive queue, and copying the value of the pointer to the appropriate transmit queue. In some cases, the entire packet data is copied from one bank of receive memory to another transmit memory using a computer bus.

The operation of the router is controlled by one or more general purpose processor which is usually similar to a standard high-end PC CPU. The processor's performs various tasks, which may be divided into three groups:

- Process Switching
- Fast Switching
- Routing

The first two tasks are considered first, and concern packet forwarding. The final task may in some routers be performed by a separate processor.

ROUTING BASICS

Routing is moving information across an internet work from source to destination. Along the way, at least one intermediate node is typically encountered. Routing is often contrasted with bridging which seems to accomplish precisely the same thing. The primary difference between the two is that bridging occurs at layer 2 (the link layer) of the OSI reference model, while routing occurs at layer 3 (the network layer). This distinction provides routing and bridging with different information to use in the process of moving information from source to destination. As a result, routing and bridging accomplish their tasks in different ways and, in fact, there are several different kinds of routing and bridging.

ROUTING COMPONENTS

Routing involves two basic activities: determination of optimal routing paths and the transport of information groups (typically called packets) through an internet work. In this publication, the latter of these is referred to as switching. Switching is relatively straightforward. Path determination, on the other hand, can be very complex.

Path Determination

A metric is a standard of measurement—for example, path length—that is used by routing algorithms to determine the optimal path to a destination. To aid the process of path determination, routing algorithms initialize and maintain routing tables, which contain route information. Route information varies depending on the routing algorithm used.

Routing algorithms fill routing tables with a variety of information. Destination/next hop associations tell a router that a particular destination can be gained optimally by sending the packet to a particular router representing the "next hop" on the way to the final destination. When a router receives an incoming packet, it checks the destination address and attempts to associate this address with a next hop. Figure 27.21 shows an example of a destination/next hop routing table.

To reach network:	Send to:
27	Node A
57	Node B
17	Node C
24	Node A
52	Node A
16	Node B
26	Node A
⋮	⋮

Figure 27.21 *Destination/Next Hop Routing Table.*

Routing tables can also contain other information, such as information about the desirability of a path. Routers compare metrics to determine optimal routes. Metrics differ depending on the design of the routing algorithm being used. Routers communicate with one another (and maintain their routing tables) through the transmission of a variety of messages. The routing update message is one such message. Routing updates generally consist of all or a portion of a routing table. By analyzing routing updates from all routers, a router can build a detailed picture of network topology. A link-state advertisement is another example of a message sent between routers. Link-state advertisements inform other routers of the state of the sender's links. Link information can also be used to build a complete picture of network topology. Once the network topology is understood, routers can determine optimal routes to network destinations.

REPEATERS, HUBS, BRIDGES, SWITCHES, ROUTERS AND GATEWAYS

Switches

Many optical networks incorporate optical switches. Networks that require protection switching (switching between redundant paths), where key attributes must operate reliably after a long

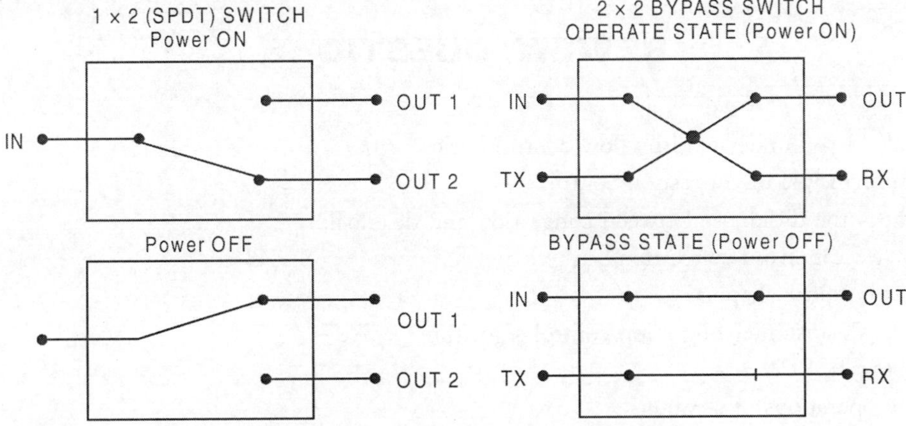

Figure 27.22 *Typical Switch Configuration.*

period in one position, system monitoring, and diagnosis commonly feature these devices. Speed is not a crucial parameter for these applications, as speed as high as tens of milliseconds are acceptable. However in the future, dynamic optical routing will require much faster switching speeds. Figure 27.22 illustrates common switch configurations.

Opto-Mechanical Switches

Opto-mechanical switches are the oldest type of optical switch and the most widely deployed at the time. These devices achieve switching by moving fiber or other bulk optic elements by means of stepper motors or relay arms. This causes them to be relatively slow with switching times in the 10–100 ms range. They can achieve excellent reliability, insertion loss, and crosstalk. Usually, opto-mechanical optical switches collimate the optical beam from each input and output fiber and move these collimated beams around inside the device. This allows for low optical loss, and allows distance between the input and output fiber without deleterious effects. These devices have more bulk compared to other alternatives, although new micro-mechanical devices overcome this.

Thermo-Optic Switches

Thermo-optic switches are normally based on waveguides made in polymers or silica. For operation, they rely on the change of refractive index with temperature created by a resistive heater placed above the waveguide. Their slowness does not limit them in current applications.

Electro-Optic Switches

These are typically semiconductor-based, and their operation depends on the change of refractive index with electric field. This characteristic makes them intrinsically high-speed devices with low power consumption. However, neither the electro-optic nor thermo-optic optical switches can yet match the insertion loss, back reflection, and long-term stability of opto-mechanical optical switches.

The latest technology incorporates all-optical switches that can cross-connect fibers without translating the signal into the electrical domain. This greatly increases switching speed, allowing today's and networks to increase data rates. However, this technology is only now in development, and deployed systems cost much more than systems that use traditional opto-mechanical switches.

REVIEW QUESTIONS

1. What do you understand by flow control basics?
2. Write principle of congestion control.
3. What is the difference between congestion and deadlock?
4. How we can avoid congestion?
5. What is traffic shaping?
6. What is isarithmic congestion control algorithm?
7. What is RSVP?
8. Write operations of a router.
9. What is switch? What are the different types of switches?
10. What do you understand by congestion? Discuss one method to control congestion.

❑❑❑

28

BRIDGE BASICS

BRIDGING BASICS

Bridges became commercially available in the early 1980s. At the time of their introduction, bridges connected and enabled packet forwarding between homogeneous networks. More recently, bridging between different networks has also been defined and standardized.

Several kinds of bridging have emerged as important. Transparent bridging is found primarily in Ethernet environments. Source-route bridging is found primarily in token ring environments. Translational bridging provides translation between the formats and transit principles of different media types (usually Ethernet and token ring). Source-route transparent bridging combines the algorithms of transparent bridging and source-route bridging to allow communication in mixed Ethernet/token ring environments.

The diminishing price and the recent inclusion of bridging capability in many routers have taken substantial market share away from pure bridges. Those bridges that have survived include features such as sophisticated filtering, pseudo-intelligent path selection, and high throughput rates. Although an intense debate about the benefits of bridging versus routing raged in the late 1980s, most people now agree that each has its place and that both are often necessary in any comprehensive internetworking scheme.

TECHNOLOGY BASICS

Bridging occurs at the link layer, which controls data flow, handles transmission errors, provides physical (as opposed to logical) addressing, and manages access to the physical medium. Bridges provide these functions by using various link-layer protocols that dictate specific flow control, error handling, addressing, and media-access algorithms. Examples of popular link-layer protocols include Ethernet, token ring, and FDDI.

Bridges are not complicated devices. They analyze incoming frames, make forwarding decisions based on information contained in the frames, and forward the frames toward the destination. In some cases (for example, source-route bridging), the entire path to the destination is contained in each frame. In other cases (for example, transparent bridging), frames are forwarded one hop at a time toward the destination. For more information on source-route bridging and transparent bridging.

Upper-layer protocol transparency is a primary advantage of bridging. Because bridges operate at the link layer, they are not required to examine upper-layer information. This means that they can rapidly forward traffic representing any network-layer protocol. It is not uncommon for a bridge to move AppleTalk, DECnet, TCP/IP, XNS, and other traffic between two or more networks.

Bridges are capable of filtering frames based on any Layer 2 fields. For example, a bridge can be programmed to reject (not forward) all frames sourced from a particular network. Since link-layer information often includes a reference to an upper-layer protocol, bridges can usually filter on this parameter. Further, filters can be helpful in dealing with unnecessary broadcast and multicast packets.

By dividing large networks into self-contained units, bridges provide several advantages. First, because only some percentage of traffic is forwarded, the bridge diminishes the traffic experienced by devices on all connected segments. Second, the bridge acts as a firewall for some potentially damaging network errors. Third, bridges allow for communication between a larger numbers of devices than would be supported on any single LAN connected to the bridge. Fourth, bridges extend the effective length of a LAN, permitting attachment of distant stations that were not previously connected.

The purposes of a Bridge are the following:

- Isolates networks by MAC addresses
- Manages network traffic by filtering packets
- Translates from one protocol to another
- Bridge segment to segment characteristics

Isolates Networks by MAC Addresses

For example, you have one segment called segment 100: it has 50 users in several departments using this network segment. The engineering Dept. is CAD (Computer Aided Design) -oriented, while the accounting Dept. is into heavy number crunching (year end reports, month end statements, etc.).

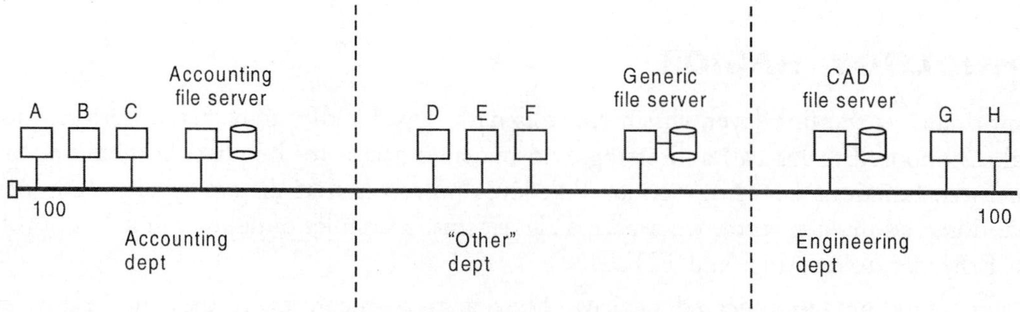

Figure 28.1 *Different Types of Servers.*

On this network, any traffic between clients A, B or C and the accounting file server (in the accounting Dept.) will be heard across the segment 100. Likewise, any traffic between the engineering Dept. clients G, H or I (to the CAD file server) will be heard throughout the network segment. The result is that "other" department accesses to the generic file server are incredibly slow: this is because of the unnecessary traffic that's being generated from other departments (engineering & accounting).

The solution is to use one bridge to isolate the accounting Dept., and another bridge to isolate the engineering department. The bridges will only allow packets to pass through that are not on the local segment. The bridge will first check its "routing" table to see if the packet is on the local segment. If it is, it will ignore the packet, and not forward it to the remote segment. If client A sent a packet to the accounting file server then bridge #1 will check its routing table (to see if the Accounting File Server is on the local port). If it is on the local port, then bridge #1 will not forward the packet to the other segments.

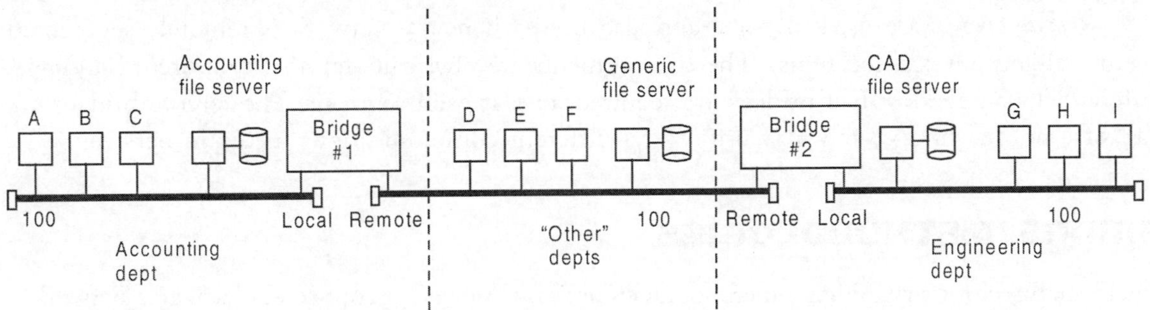

Figure 28.2 *Different Types of Servers with Bridges.*

If Client A sent a packet to the generic file server, bridge #1 will again check its routing table to see if the generic file server is on the local port. If it is not, then bridge #1 will forward the packet to the remote port.

In this manner, the network is segmented, and the local department traffic is isolated from the rest of the network. Overall network bandwidth increases because the accounting Dept. does not have to fight with the Engineering Dept. (for access to the segment). Each segment has reduced the amount of traffic on it and the result is faster access. Each department still has complete access to the other segments, but only when required.

Manages Network Traffic by Filtering Packets

Bridges listen to the network traffic, and build an image of the network on each side of the bridge. This image of the network indicates the location of each node (and the bridge's port that accesses it). With this information, a bridge can make a decision whether to forward the packet across the bridge—if the destination address is not on the same port or, it can decide to not forward the packet (if the destination is on the same port).

This process of deciding whether or not to forward a packet is termed "filtering packets." Network traffic is managed by deciding which packets can pass through the bridge; the bridge filters packets.

Translates from One Protocol to Another

The MAC layer also contains the bus arbitration method used by the network. This can be CSMA/CD, as used in Ethernet, or token passing, as used in token ring. Bridges are aware of the bus arbitration and special translation bridges can be used to translate between Ethernet and token ring.

Bridge Segment to Segment Characteristics

Bridges physically separate a network segment by managing the traffic (that's based on the MAC address). Bridges are store and forward devices. They receive a packet on the local segment, store it, and wait for the remote segments to be clear before forwarding the packet. The two physical types of bridges are local and remote bridges.

Local bridges are used (as in the previous examples) where the network is being locally (talking physical location now) segmented. The two segments are physically close together: same building, same floor, etc. Only one bridge is required.

Remote bridges are used in pairs, and also used where the network is remotely segmented (again, talking physical locations). The two segments are physically far apart: different buildings, different floors, etc. 2 × half bridges are required: one at each segment. The remote bridges are half of a normal bridge, and may use several different communications media in between.

BRIDGE METHODOLOGIES

There are three primary bridging methodologies used by bridges for connecting local area networks :

1. Transparent bridges
2. Spanning Tree Protocol
3. Source Routing.

Transparent bridges were originally developed to support the connection of Ethernet networks. The spanning tree protocol was developed to improve transparent bridging. Source routing bridges are used by token ring. Source routing bridges require a solid understanding of token ring concepts, and as such will be covered under the section discussing token ring.

1. Transparent Bridges

Transparent bridges examine the MAC address of the frames to determine whether the packet is on the local segment or on the distant segment. Early bridges required the system administrator to manually build the routing table to tell a bridge which addresses were on which side of the bridge. Manually building a routing table is called fixed or static routing. Modern bridges are self-learning: they listen to the network frame *source addresses* to determine which side of the bridge the node is on, and build a routing table that way. The following network will be used as an example of a self-learning transparent bridge's routing table construction.

As frames flow on bridge #1's local port, bridge #1 examines the source address of each frame. Eventually, after all nodes on the local port have become active, bridge #1 associates their address as being on the local port. Any frames with a destination address (other than the nodes on the local port) are forwarded to the remote port. As far as bridge #1 is concerned, nodes on bridge #2's local port appear as if they were on bridge #1's remote port.

Bridge #1	
Local	*Remote*
A,B,C FSI	D,E,F,G,H,I FS2,FS3

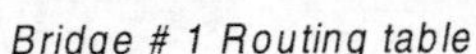

Bridge # 1 Routing table

Bridge #2	
Remote	*Local*
A,B,C,D,E,F FS1,FS2	G,H,I FS3

Bridge # 1 Routing table

Figure 28.3 *Bridge Tables.*

Bridge #2 builds its routing table in a similar manner to bridge #1. Note the differences.

Advantages of Transparent Bridges

1. Self learning
2. Requires no manual configuration
3. Considered plug and work
4. Independent of higher level protocols (TCP/IP, IPX/SPX, Netbeui, etc.).

Disadvantages of Transparent Bridges

Can only work with one path between segments loops are not allowed. A loop would confuse the bridge as to which side of the bridge a node was really on (*i.e.*, local or remote ?).

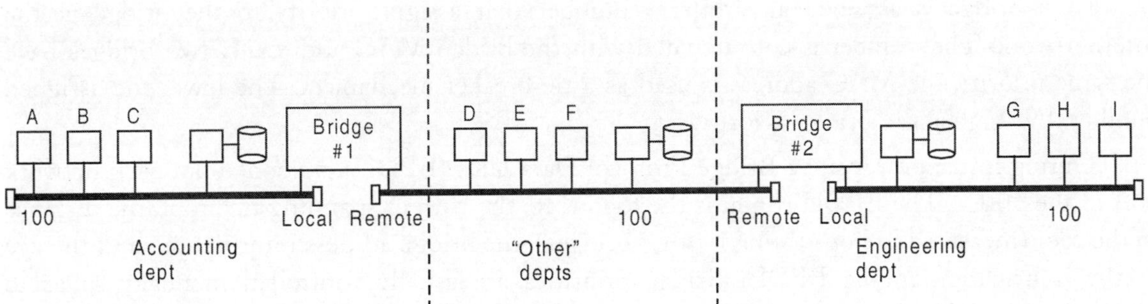

Figure 28.4 *Transparent Bridges.*

Transparent bridges are not acceptable for use on MANs or WANs, because many paths can be taken to reach a destination. In the above example, it is simple to determine that a loop occurs, but in a large corporate network with several hundred bridges, it may be next to impossible to determine. As such, bridges are most commonly used in LAN to LAN connectivity and not in MANs or WANs.

2. Spanning Tree Protocol—IEEE 802.1D

The spanning tree protocol was developed to address the problems of loops in transparent bridging. The IEEE 802.1D (Institute of Electrical and Electronic Engineers) committee formed the spanning tree protocol.

The Spanning Tree Protocol (STP) converts a loop into a tree topology by disabling a bridge link. This action ensures that there is a unique path from any node to every other node (in a

MAN or WAN). Disabled bridges are kept in a stand-by mode of operation until a network failure occurs. At that time, the spanning tree protocol will attempt to construct a new tree, using any of the previously disabled links.

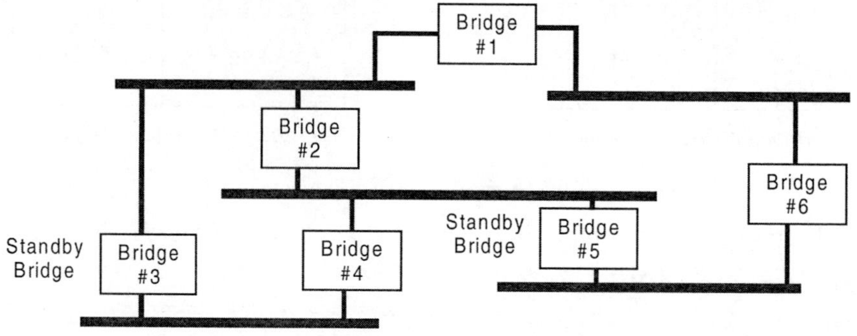

Figure 28.5 *Spanning Tree.*

The spanning tree protocol is a bridge-to-bridge communication where all bridges cooperate to form the overall bridge topology. The spanning tree algorithm is dynamic, and periodically checks every one to four seconds to see if the bridge topology has changed.

Bridge #3 and #5 are stand-by bridges, and have their links disabled. This results in only a single path to each network segment.

Each bridge is assigned an arbitrary number that assigns priority to the bridge in the Internet-work. The number is concatenated with the bridge MAC address. If two bridges have the same priority, the MAC address is used as a tie breaker mechanism. The lower the assigned number, the higher the bridge priority.

During initial power-up, a Bridge Protocol Data Unit (BPDU) is flooded out each network port of the bridge. The BPDU contains the following: the current spanning tree root, the distance to the root (measured in hops through other bridges), the bridge address information, and the age of the information in the BPDU. Bridge priorities are usually controlled manually so as to configure the traffic flow over the Internet-work on a preferred path.

Problems can arise where, for example, the spanning tree algorithm may select a path from Los Angeles to New York City—and back to San Francisco—rather than the preferred route of Los Angeles to San Francisco.

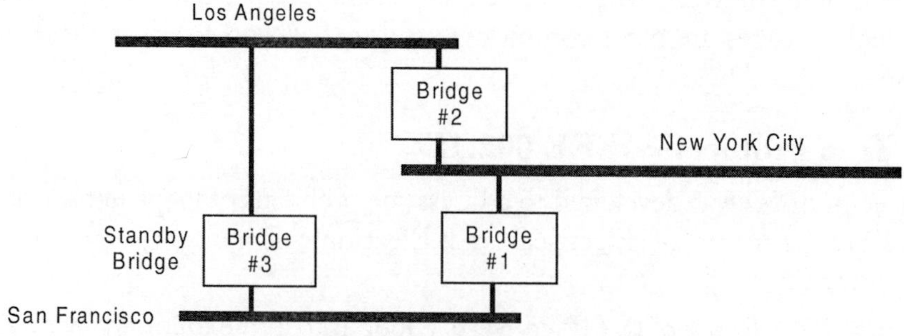

Figure 28.6 *Application of Bridge.*

REASONS TO USE A BRIDGE

There are four basic reasons to use a bridge:

- *Security:* Stops networks from forwarding sensitive data.
- *Bandwidth:* Reduce traffic by segmentation.
- *Reliability:* If 1 segment goes down, it does not take down the complete LAN.
- *Translation:* Translate different data link protocols such as token ring to Ethernet.

BRIDGE ADDRESSING

Bridges work at the data link layer and they recognize the MAC addresses. Spanning tree protocol adds a bridge Protocol Data Unit (BPDU) for bridge to bridge communications. Source route bridges and token ring provide special data link layer communication.

COLLAPSED BACKBONES

Collapsed backbones take the network backbone and electronically collapse it into a high speed electronic card cage. Usually, collapsed backbones operate at 100 Mbps. The card cage holds plug-in cards for repeaters, hubs, bridges, routers, routers and gateways.

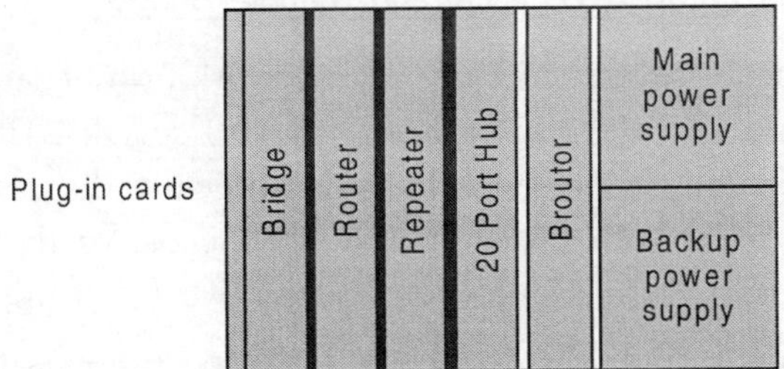

Figure 28.7 *Plug-in Cards.*

Software is provided to remotely configure all plug-in cards using SNMP. SNMP is a network management protocol that stands for simple network management Protocol. It is a standard for intelligent network devices to communicate their configuration to administrators who are operating from remote workstations and the workstations can be located thousands of miles away!

TYPES OF BRIDGES

Bridges can be grouped into categories based on various product characteristics. Using one popular classification scheme, bridges are either local or remote.

- Local bridges provide a direct connection between multiple LAN segments in the same area.
- Remote bridges connect multiple LAN segments in different areas, usually over telecommunications lines.

These two configurations are shown in figure 28.8.

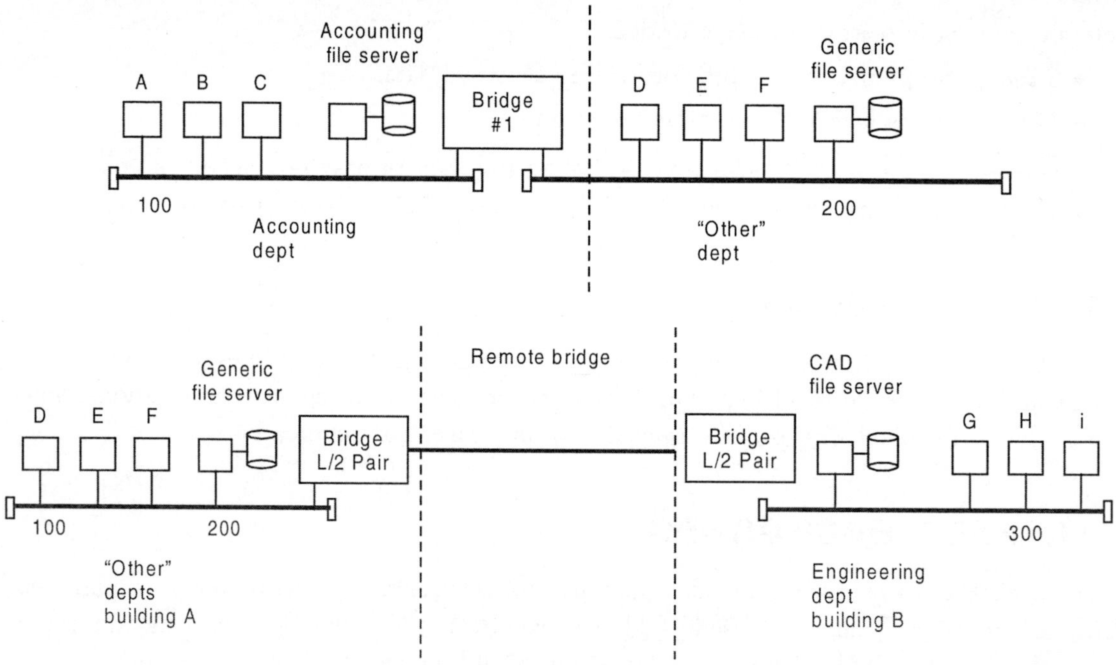

Figure 28.8 *Local and Remote Bridging.*

Remote bridging presents several unique internetworking challenges. One of these is the difference between LAN and Wide Area Network (WAN) speeds. Although several fast WAN technologies are now establishing a presence in geographically dispersed internet works, LAN speeds are often an order of magnitude faster than WAN speeds. Vastly different LAN and WAN speeds sometimes prevent users from running delay-sensitive LAN applications over the WAN.

Remte bridges cannot improve WAN speeds, but can compensate for speed discrepancies through sufficient buffering capability. If a LAN device capable of a 3-Mbps transmission rate wishes to communicate with a device on a remote LAN, the local bridge must regulate the 3-Mbps data stream so that it does not overwhelm the 64-kbps serial link. This is done by storing the incoming data in on-board buffers and sending it over the serial link at a rate the serial link can accommodate. This can be achieved only for short bursts of data that do not overwhelm the bridge's buffering capability.

The Institute of Electrical and Electronic Engineers (IEEE) has divided the OSI link layer into two separate sub-layers: the Media Access Control (MAC) sub-layer and the Logical Link Control (LLC) sub-layer. The MAC sub-layer permits and orchestrates media access (for example, contention, token passing, or others), while the LLC sub-layer is concerned with framing, flow control, error control, and MAC-sub-layer addressing.

Some bridges are MAC-layer bridges. These devices bridge between homogeneous networks (for example, IEEE 802.3 and IEEE 802.3). Other bridges can translate between different link-layer protocols (for example, IEEE 802.3 and IEEE 802.5). The basic mechanics of such a translation are shown in figure 28.9.

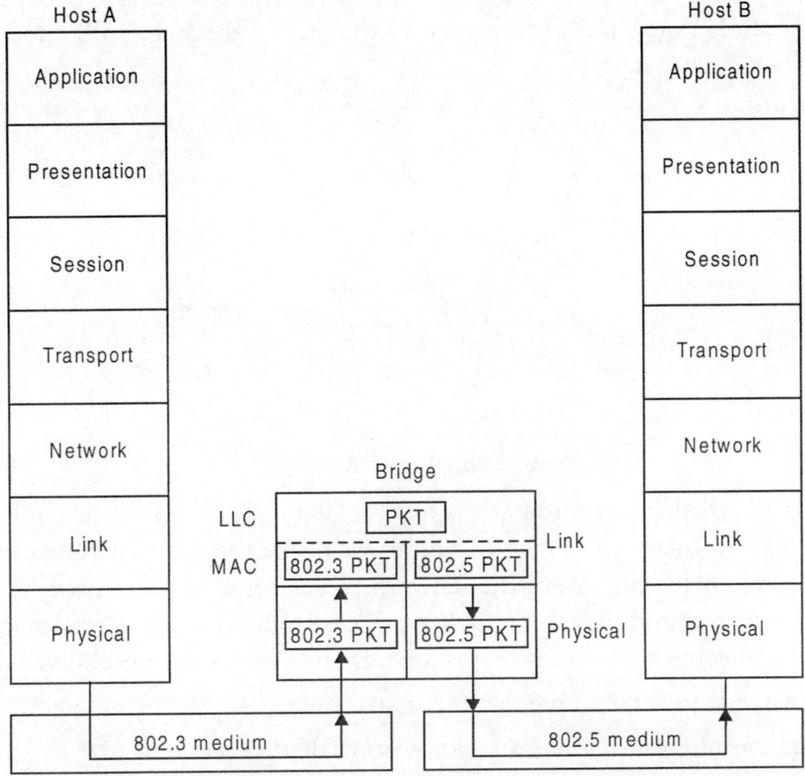

Figure 28.9 *IEEE 802.3/IEEE 802.5 Bridging.*

In the figure, the IEEE 802.3 host (host A) formulates a packet containing application information and encapsulates the packet in an IEEE 802.3-compatible frame for transit over the IEEE 802.3 medium to the bridge. At the bridge, the frame is stripped of its IEEE 802.3 header at the MAC sub-layer of the link layer and is subsequently passed up to the LLC sub-layer for further processing. After this processing, the packet is passed back down to an IEEE 802.5 implementation, which encapsulates the packet in an IEEE 802.5 header for transmission on the IEEE 802.5 network to the IEEE 802.5 host (host B).

HUBS

Hubs can also be called either multi port repeaters or concentrators. They are physical hardware devices. Some hubs are basic hubs with minimum intelligence (*i.e.*, no microprocessors). Intelligent hubs can perform basic diagnostics, and test the nodes to see if they are operating correctly. If they are not, the smart hubs (or intelligent hubs) will remove the node from the network. Some smart hubs can be polled and managed remotely.

Purpose of Hubs

Hubs are used to provide a physical star topology. The logical topology is dependent on the medium access control protocol. At the center of the star is the hub, with the network nodes located on the tips of the star.

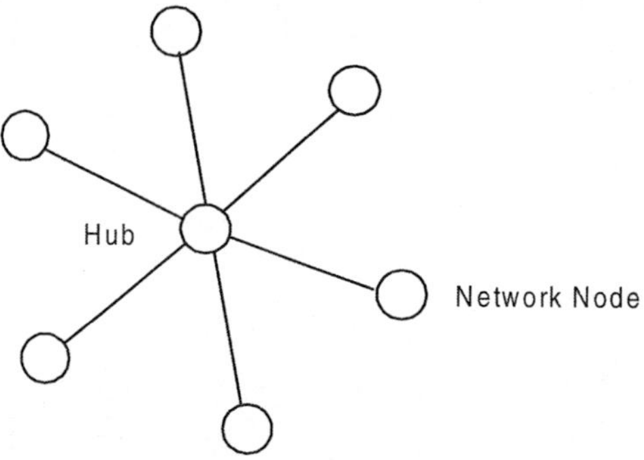

Figure 28.10 *Star Topology.*

The Hub is installed in a central wiring closet, with all the cables extending out to the network nodes. The advantage of having a central wiring location is that it's easier to maintain and troubleshoot large networks. All of the network cables come to the central hub. This way, it is especially easy to detect and fix cable problems. You can easily move a workstation in—a star topology—by changing the connection to the hub at the central wiring closet.

The disadvantages to a star topology are shown below:

- Failure of the hub can disable a major section of the network.
- The star topology requires more cabling than does the ring or the bus topology because all stations must be connected to the hub, not to the next station.

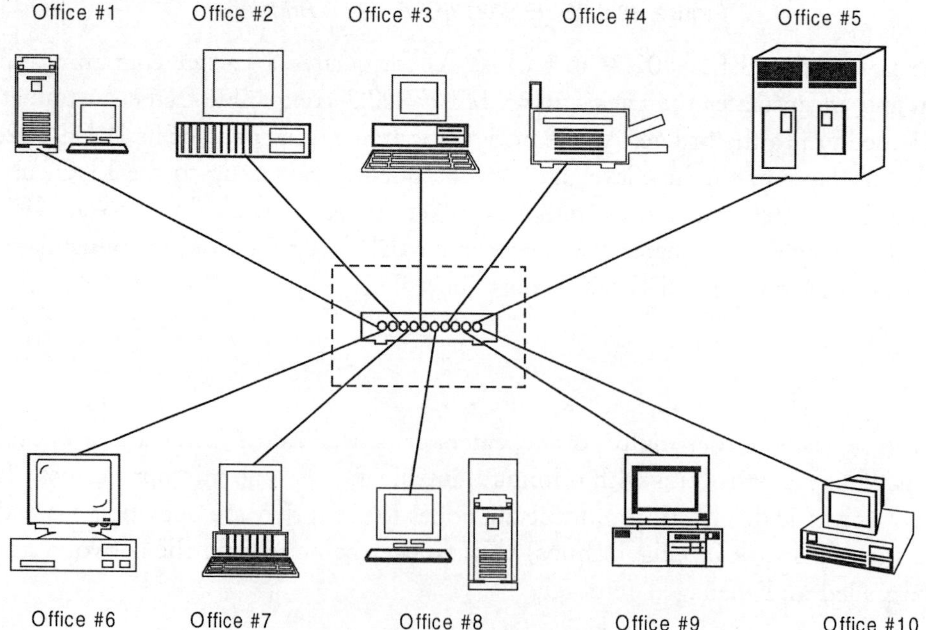

Figure 28.11 *Star Topology in Practical Life.*

Hub's OSI Operating Layer

Hubs are multi port repeaters, and as such they obey the same rules as repeaters (see previous section OSI operating layer). They operate at the OSI model physical layer.

Hub's Segment-to-Segment Characteristics

To understand the Ethernet segment-to-segment characteristics of a hub, determine how the Ethernet hubs operate. Logically, they appear as a bus topology, and physically as a star topology. Looking inside an Ethernet hub, we can see that it consists of an electronic printed circuit board (which doesn't tell us much). If we form a functional drawing, then we can clearly see how the physical and star topology appears:

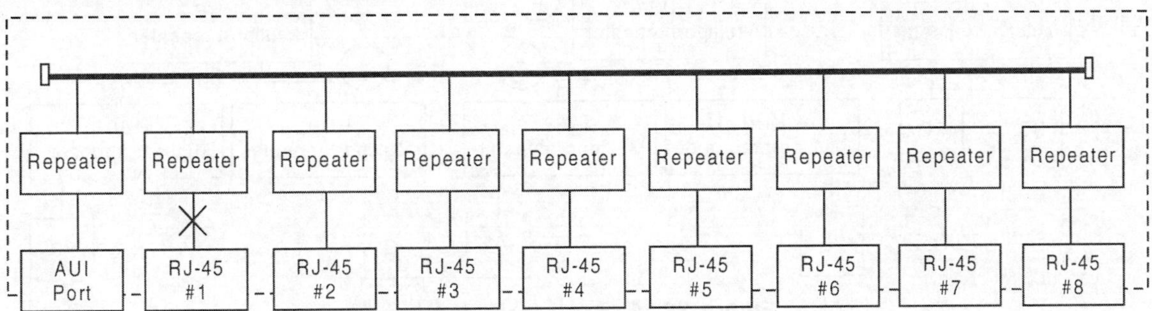

Figure 28.12 *Bus Topology in Practical Life.*

Understanding that inside the hub is only more repeaters, we can draw the conclusion that all connections attached to a hub are on the same segment (and have the same segment number). A single repeater is said to exist from any port to any port, even though it is indicated as a path of two repeaters.

Cascaded Hub Network

Connect hubs together through RJ45 ports creates cascading hubs. One master hub (level 1) is connected to many level 2 (slave) hubs, who are masters to level 3 (slave) hubs in a hierarchical tree (or clustered star). The maximum number of stations in a cascaded hub network is limited to 128.

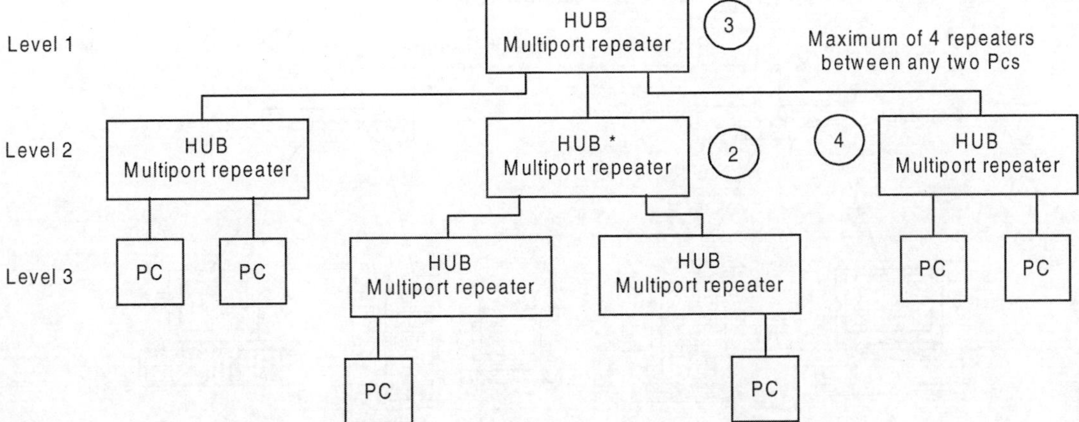

Figure 28.13 *Cascaded Hub Network.*

Backbone Networks

In a backbone network, there is no master hub. The level 1 hubs are connected through their AUI port to a coax backbone. For thin coax, up to 30 hubs can be connected together. For thick coax, up to 100 hubs can be connected to the backbone. The backbone is considered to be a populated segment.

Level 2 hubs are allowed to be connected to the level 1 hubs' 10BaseT ports. This connection between the two hubs is considered a UN populated segment, or link segment. Up to 1024 stations (or nodes) can be attached to the level 2 hubs' 10BaseT ports.

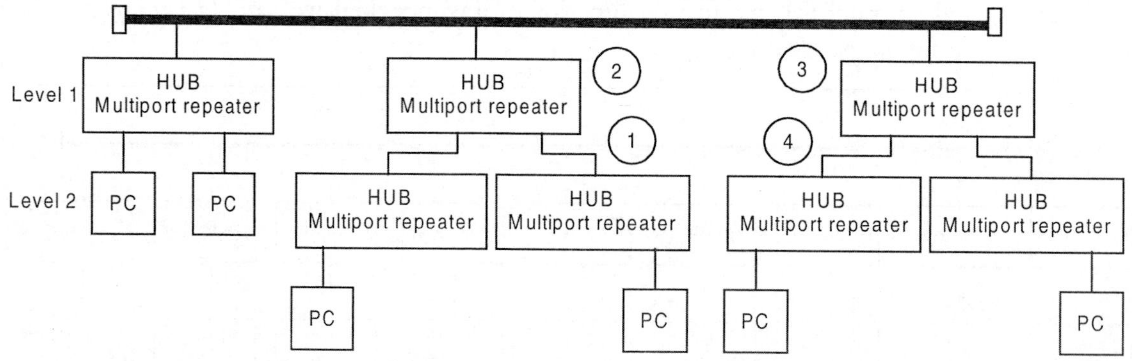

Figure 28.14 *Backbone Network.*

All stations and segments would appear as 1 logical segment, with 1 network number. In the real world, you would never attach 1024 stations to 1 segment; the resulting traffic would slow the network to a crawl.

Hub's Addressing

Again, because a hub is just many repeaters in the same box, any network traffic between nodes is heard over the complete network. As far as the stations are concerned, they are connected on 1 long logical bus (wire).

Half-Duplex and Full-Duplex Ethernet Hubs

Normal Ethernet operation is half-duplex: only 1 station or node is talking at a time. The stations take turns talking on the bus (CSMA/CD -bus arbitration).

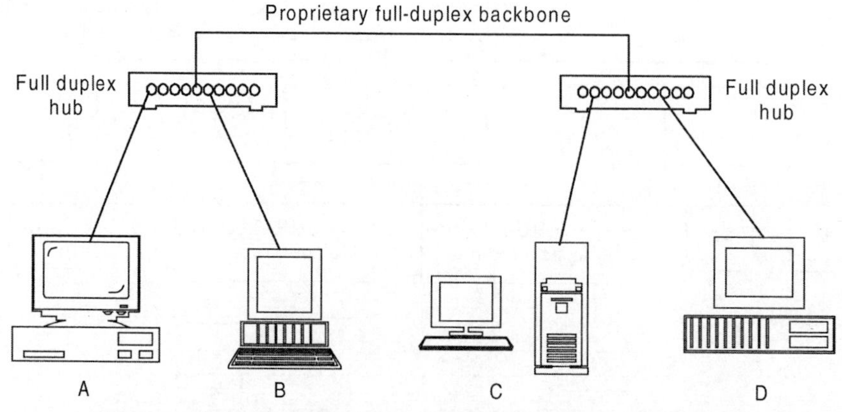

Figure 28.15 *Half-Duplex and Full-Duplex Ethernet Hubs.*

Full-duplex Ethernet hubs are hubs which allow two-way communication, thus doubling the available bandwidth from 10 Mbps to 20 Mbps. Full duplex hubs are proprietary products, and normally only work within their own manufacturer's line.

For example, if A wanted to talk to C, a direct 10 Mbps line would be connected through the two switching hubs. Simultaneously, if D wanted to talk to B, another direct 10 Mbps line (in the opposite direction) would be connected through the two switching hubs (doubling the available bandwidth to 20 Mbps). There are no official standards for full-duplex Ethernet.

Switching Hubs

Switching hubs are hubs that will directly switch ports to each other. They are similar to full duplex hubs, except that they allow dedicated 10 Mbps channels between ports.

If A wanted to communicate with B, a dedicated 10 Mbps connection would be established between the two. If C wanted to communicate with D, another dedicated 10 Mbps connection would be established.

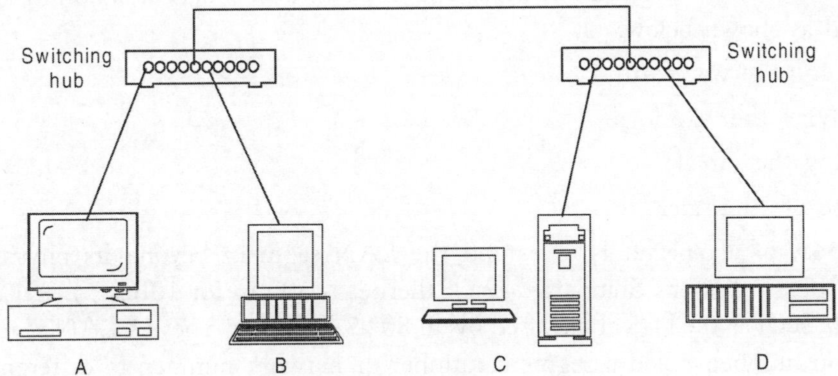

Figure 28.16 *Switching Hubs.*

Brouters

Brouters are protocol-dependent devices. When a brouter receives a frame to be forwarded to the remote segment, it checks to see if it recognizes the network layer protocol. If the brouter does, it acts like a router and finds the shortest path. If it doesn't recognize the network layer protocol, it acts like a bridge and forwards the frame to the next segment.

Figure 28.17 *Brouter.*

The key advantage to brouters is the ability to act as both a bridge and a router. It can replace separate bridges and routers, thus saving money. This is, of course, provided that the brouter can satisfactorily accomplish both functions.

Repeaters

Network **repeaters** regenerate incoming electrical, wireless or optical signals. With physical media like Ethernet or Wi-Fi, data transmissions can only span a limited distance before the quality of the signal degrades. Repeaters attempt to preserve signal integrity and extend the distance over which data can safely travel.

Actual network devices that serve as repeaters usually have some other name. **Active hubs,** for example, are repeaters. Active hubs are sometimes also called "multiport repeaters," but more commonly they are just "hubs." Other types of "passive hubs" are not repeaters. In Wi-Fi, access points function as repeaters only when operating in so-called "repeater mode."

Repeaters are physical hardware devices. That they have a primary function to regenerate the electrical signal as shown below:

- Reshaping the waveform
- Amplifying the waveform
- Retiming the signal
- Purpose of a repeater

The purpose of a repeater is to extend the LAN segment beyond its physical limits (as defined by the physical layer's Standards: *e.g.,* Ethernet is 500 m for 10Base5). A LAN segment is a logical path, such as the logical bus used by all 802.3 Ethernet types. A LAN segment is given an identification number, called a segment number or network number, to differentiate it from other segments.

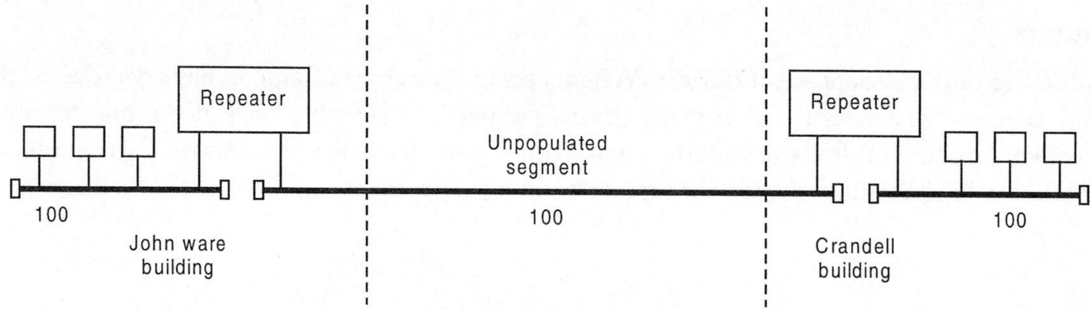

Figure 28.18 *Repeater.*

Typically, repeaters are used to connect two physically close buildings together (when they are too far apart to just extend the segment). They can be used to connect floors of a building that would normally surpass the maximum allowable segment length. Note: for large extensions, as in the above example, two repeaters are required. For shorter extensions, only one repeater may be required.

- Repeater's OSI Operating Layer
- Repeaters operate at the OSI Model Physical Layer.

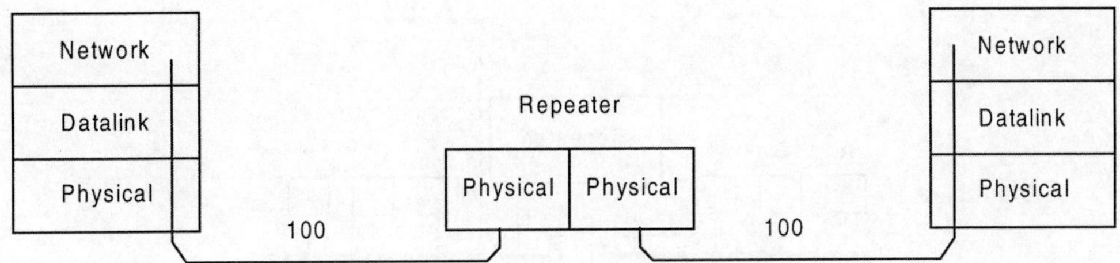

Figure 28.19 *Repeater's OSI Operating Layer.*

Repeater's Segment-to-Segment Characteristics

Repeaters do not "de-segment" a network. All traffic that appears on one side of the repeater appears on both sides. Repeaters handle only the electrical and physical characteristics of the signal.

Repeaters work only on the same type of physical layer: Ethernet-to-Ethernet, or token ring-to-token ring. They can connect 10Base5 to 10BaseT because they both use the same 802.3 MAC layer.

You can run into problems with the transfer rate (1 Mbps vs. 10 Mbps) when you connect 1Base5 to 10BaseT. A repeater cannot connect token ring to Ethernet because the physical layer is different for each network topology.

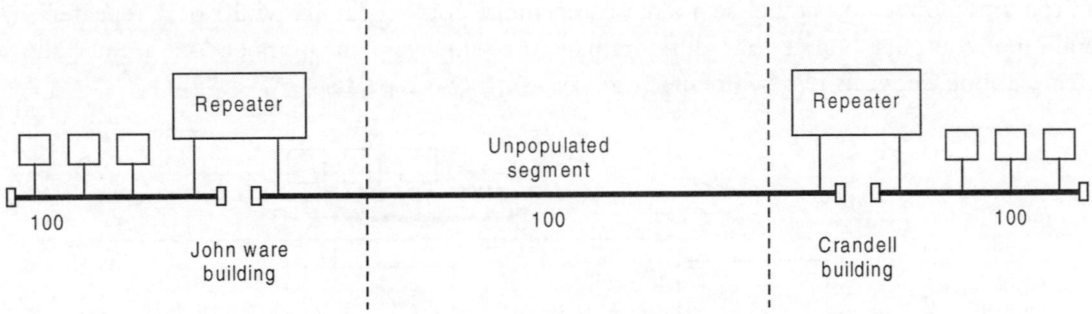

Figure 28.20 *Repeater's Segment-to-Segment.*

Repeater Addressing: MAC Layer and Network Segment

The MAC layer address is used to identify the network card to the network. The Repeater is transparent to both sides of the segment and both sides can "see" all the Mac addresses regardless of which side they are on. This means that any network traffic on floor 1 will also appear on floor 5, and vice versa.

Nodes A and B could be furiously being exchanging files; this network traffic would also appear on floor 1. Repeaters don't provide isolation between segments (there is only one collision domain).

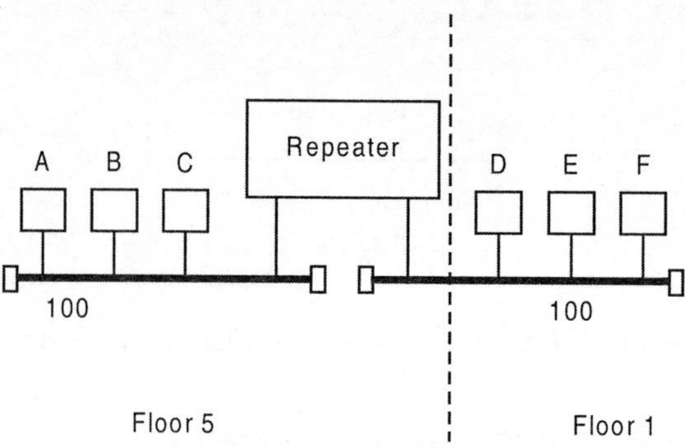

Figure 28.21 *Repeater Addressing.*

Because repeaters provide no isolation between segments, and the repeater is transparent to both sides of the segment, both sides of the repeater appear as 1 long segment. The network number, or segment number, is the same on both sides of the repeater.

When using repeaters, make sure that the overall propagation delay does not exceed the physical layer standard that is being used. Repeaters will also add a propagation delay to the signal that is being repeated. Check that rules, such as the 5-4-3 rule for IEEE 802.3, are not broken. For instance, check—for XNS Ethernet—that a maximum of only two repeaters are located between any two nodes.

You are allowed to parallel segments using multi port repeaters. Multi port repeaters have several inputs/outputs. Notice that all floors have the same segment number. You are not allowed to create a loop between two segments (*e.g.*, by using two repeaters).

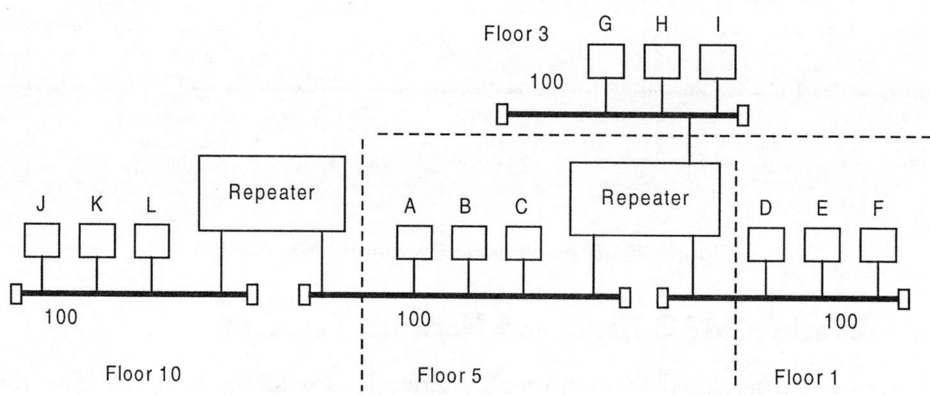

Figure 28.22 *Fiber Optic Repeaters.*

Fiber optic repeaters join two segments together with a fiber optic link. The transfer rate is not changed through the fiber. The advantages are noise immunity and longer distances. Segments can be joined up to 3000 m apart, and still be within the propagation delay specification for the physical layer. Two fiber optic repeaters are required (one at each end of the fiber).

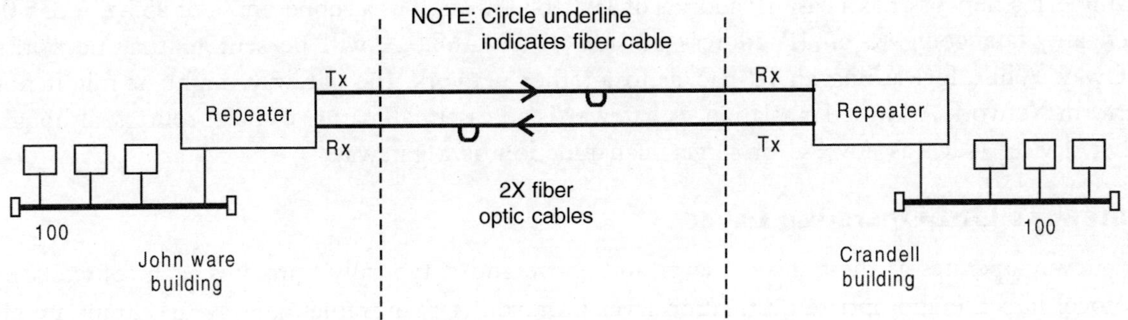

Figure 28.23 *Fiber Optic Repeater1.*

GATEWAYS

A gateway is the hardware/software device that is used to interconnect LANs and WANs using mainframe computers (such as DECnet and IBM's SNA).

Often, the router that is used to connect a LAN to the Internet will be called a gateway. It will have added capability to direct and filter higher layer protocols (layer 4 and up) to specific devices (such as web servers, FTP servers and e-mail servers).

In enterprises, the gateway node often acts as a proxy server and a firewall. The gateway is also associated with both a router, which use headers and forwarding tables to determine where packets are sent, and a switch, which provides the actual path for the packet in and out of the gateway.

Gateways work on all seven OSI layers. The main job of a gateway is to convert protocols among communications networks. A router by itself transfers, accepts and relays packets only across networks using similar protocols. A gateway on the other hand can accept a packet formatted for one protocol (*e.g.*, AppleTalk) and convert it to a packet formatted for another protocol (*e.g.*, TCP/IP) before forwarding it. A gateway can be implemented in hardware, software or both, but they are usually implemented by software installed within a router. A gateway must understand the protocols used by each network linked into the router. Gateways are slower than bridges, switches and (non-gateway) routers.

A gateway is a network point that acts as an entrance to another network. On the Internet, a node or stopping point can be either a gateway node or a host (end-point) node. Both the computers of Internet users and the computers that serve pages to users are host nodes, while the nodes that connect the networks in between are gateways. For example, the computers that control traffic between company networks or the computers used by internet service providers (ISPs) to connect users to the internet are gateway nodes.

In the network for an enterprise, a computer server acting as a gateway node is often also acting as a proxy server and a firewall server. A gateway is often associated with both a router, which knows where to direct a given packet of data that arrives at the gateway, and a switch, which furnishes the actual path in and out of the gateway for a given packet.

On an IP network, clients should automatically send IP packets with a destination outside a given subnet mask to a network gateway. A subnet mask defines the IP range of a network. For example, if a network has a base IP address of 192.168.0.0 and has a subnet mask of 255.255.255.0, then any data going to an IP address outside of 192.168.0.X will be sent to that network's gateway. While forwarding an IP packet to another network, the gateway might or might not perform Network Address Translation. A gateway is an essential feature of most routers, although other devices (such as any PC or server) can function as a gateway.

Gateway's OSI Operating Layer

A gateway operates at the transport layer and above and it typically translates each source layer protocol into the appropriate destination layer protocol. A mainframe gateway may translate all OSI model layers. For example, IBM's SNA (System Network Architecture) does not readily conform to the OSI model, and requires a gateway to translate between the two architectures.

OSI Model	SNA
Application	Transaction services
Presentation	Presentation services
Session	
Transport	Data flow control
Network	Transmission control
	Path control
Data Link	Data link control
Physical	Physical

Figure 28.24 *Gateway's OSI Operating Layer.*

Gateway Segment to Segment Characteristics

There can be major differences between "local" and "distance" segments. As shown in the above diagram, the two networks appear as if they are from other planets. Mainframes are based on a central number crunching CPU with terminals connected. All information displayed on the terminals is controlled by the central CPU.

LANs consist of distributed CPUs that share data and files. This leads to a unique problem (connecting the two architectures) that requires a gateway.

Gateway Addressing: The gateway addressing depends on which OSI layers are translated.

ADDRESS CLASSES

In the original Internet routing scheme developed in the 1970s, sites were assigned addresses from one of three classes: class A, class B and class C. The address classes differ in size and number.

Class A addresses are the largest, but there are few of them. Class Cs is the smallest, but they are numerous. Classes D and E are also defined, but not used in normal operation.

To say that class-based IP addressing in still used would be true only in the loosest sense. Many addressing designs are still class-based, but an increasing number can only be explained using the more general concept of CIDR, which is backwards compatible with address classes.

Suffice it to say that at one point in time, you could request the Internet NIC to assign you a class A, B or C address. To get the larger class B addresses, you might have to supply some justification, but only the class A was really tough to get. In any case, NIC would set the network bits, or n-bits, to some unique value and inform the local network engineer. It would then be up to the engineer to assign each of his hosts an IP address starting with the assigned n-bits, followed by host bits, or h-bits, to make the address unique.

A router receiving an IP packet extracted its destination address, which was classified (literally) by examining its first one to four bits. Once the address's class had been determined, it was broken down into network and host bits. Routers ignored the host bits, and only needed to match the network bits to find a route to the network. Once a packet reached its target network, its host field was examined for final delivery.

SUMMARY OF IP ADDRESS CLASSES

Class A—0nnnnnnn hhhhhhhh hhhhhhhh hhhhhhhh

- First bit 0; 7 network bits; 24 host bits
- Initial byte: 0–127
- 126 Class as exist (0 and 127 are reserved)
- 16,777, 214 hosts on each class A

Class B—10nnnnnn nnnnnnnn hhhhhhhh hhhhhhhh

- First two bits 10; 14 network bits; 16 host bits
- Initial byte: 128–191
- 16,384 class Bs exist
- 65,532 hosts on each class B

Class C—110nnnnn nnnnnnnn nnnnnnnn hhhhhhhh

- First three bits 110; 21 network bits; 8 host bits
- Initial byte: 192–223
- 2,097,152 class Cs exist
- 254 hosts on each Class C

Class D—1110mmmm mmmmmmmm mmmmmmmm mmmmmmmm

- First four bits 1110; 28 multicast address bits
- Initial byte: 224–247
- Class Ds are multicast addresses—see RFC 1112

Class E—1111rrrr rrrrrrrr rrrrrrrr rrrrrrrr

- First four bits 1111; 28 reserved address bits
- Initial byte: 248–255
- Reserved for experimental use.

SUB-NETTING

Sub-netting, documented in RFC 950, originally referred to the subdivision of a class-based network into sub-networks, but now refers more generally to the subdivision of a CIDR block into smaller CIDR blocks. Sub-netting allows single routing entries to refer either to the larger block or to its individual constituents. This permits a single, general routing entry to be used through most of the Internet, more specific routes only being required for routers in the sub-netted block.

A subnet mask is a 32-bit number that determines how an IP address is split into network and host portions, on a bitwise basis. For example, 255. 255. 0. 0 is a standard class B subnet mask, since the first two bytes are all ones (network), and the last two bytes are all zeros (host). In a sub-netted network, the network portion is extended. For example, a subnet mask of 255. 255. 255. 0 would subnet a class B address space using its third byte. Using this scheme, the first two bytes of an IP address would identify the class B network, the next byte would identify the subnet within that network, and the final byte would select an individual host. Since subnet masks are used on a bit-by-bit basis, masks like 255. 255. 240. 0 (4 bits of subnet; 12 bits of host) are perfectly normal.

In a traditional sub-netted network, several restrictions apply, which have been lifted by CIDR. However, if older, non-CIDR routing protocols (such as RIP version 1) are in use, these restrictions must still be observed.

1. **Identical subnet masks:** Since non-CIDR routing updates do not include subnet masks, a router must assume that the subnet mask it has been configured with is valid for all subnets. Therefore, a single mask must be used for all subnets with a network. Different masks can be used for different networks.

   Based on this assumption, a router can exchange subnet routes with other routers within the network. Since the subnet masks are identical across the network, the routers will interpret these routes in the same manner. However, routers not attached to the sub-netted network can't interpret these subnet routes, since they lack the subnet mask. Therefore, subnet routes are not relayed to routers on other networks. This leads to our second restriction.

2. **Contiguous subnets:** A sub-netted network can't be split into isolated portions. All the subnets must be contiguous, since routing information can't be passed to non-members. Within a network, all subnets must be able to reach all other subnets without passing traffic through other networks.

Variable Length Subnet Masks (VLSM)

VLSM, conceptually a stepping stone from sub-netting to CIDR, lifted the restrictions of subnetting by relaying subnet information through routing protocols. This idea leads us directly to CIDR.

GATEWAYS/ROUTERS

Can use terms interchangeably or think of routers as within a subnet (same network) versus gateways (between subnets). Text calls gateways multi-protocol routers.

Gateways are packet switches that operate at the network layer (level 3). Operating at the network level gives gateways increased flexibility compared to bridges in terms of:

1. Translating addresses between dissimilar networks.
2. Fragmenting large packets for transmission across networks that carry only small maximum packet lengths.
3. Selecting an appropriate path through the subnet.
4. Enforcing policies (*e.g.*, don't forward any local packets off of this network).

Because gateways do more work than bridges, they generally run slower than bridges.

GATEWAY OWNERSHIP

One issue that arises with gateways is who owns them. Typically, bridges connect LANs of one organization, and the issue does not arise there. The ownership question is important because someone has to be responsible for the gateway's operation and dual ownership frequently leads to finger pointing when something goes wrong.

One solution is to use half gateways. If two countries are involved, for instance, each country owns its half of the gateway, with a wire separating the two. A special protocol operates over the wire, and each half of the gateway is responsible for implementing the protocol. For example, the CCITT X.75 standard is used to connect half gateways in connection-oriented networks. Internetworking in a connection-oriented environment operates essentially as in the single network case:

1. The sending host opens a virtual circuit, but a circuit goes through gateway hops.
2. Any two neighboring gateways at the internetworking level must be connected to a common network.
3. Regular router-based virtual circuits connect neighboring gateways on the same physical network.
4. The end-to-end virtual circuit is a concatenation of individual virtual circuits through each of the networks along the path.

Connectionless internets operate just as connectionless networks. A host sends a packet to a neighboring gateway, which forwards it the next gateway, and so forth. Just as with connectionless networks, gateways make only a best-effort attempt at delivering the packet.

When a gateway receives a packet, it selects the interface to send the packet out on and encapsulates the packet using the local data link layer format. As a packet moves from gateway to gateway, it is repeatedly encapsulated and unencapsulated as it travels across each network.

Special case is tunneling between same type of networks across a foreign network(s).

REVIEW QUESTIONS

1. What do network bridge do?
2. How do network bridges differ from gateways?
3. What is the purpose of a router?
4. What is the primary purpose of servers?
5. How do DMAs improve performance?
6. Does a hub network always have to be a virtual ring?
7. How is a repeater different from an amplifier?
8. What is a transparent bridge?
9. How does a repeater extend the length of a LAN?
10. How is a hub related to a repeater?
11. What is the difference between a root bridge and a designated bridge?
12. What is the difference between a bus backbone and a star backbone?
13. What is the relationship between a switch and a bridge?
14. What are the advantages of dividing an Ethernet LAN with a bridge?

❑❑❑

PART 8

TRANSPORT LAYER

29

TRANSPORT LAYER PROTOCOLS

TRANSPORT LAYER

In order for the data to be sent across the network, the file must be broken up into usable small data segments (typically 512 - 18K bytes). The Transport layer breaks up the file into segments for transport to the network and combines incoming segments into a contiguous file. The transport layer does this logically not physically, it is done in software as opposed to hardware. The transport layer provides error checking at the segment level (frame control sequence). This checks that the datagrams are in the correct order and the Transport layer will correct out of order datagrams. The Transport layer guarantees an error-free host to host connection, it is not concerned with the path between machines.

Let's look at the specific functions often performed at the transport layer:

- **Process-Level Addressing:** Addressing at layer two deals with hardware devices on a local, and layer three addressing identifies devices on a logical internetwork. Addressing is also performed at the transport layer, where it is used to differentiate between software programs. This is part of what enables many different to use a network layer protocol simultaneously, as mentioned above. The best example of transport-layer process-level addressing is the TCP and UDP port mechanism used in TCP/IP, which allows to be individually referenced on any TCP/IP device.
- **Multiplexing and Demultiplexing:** Using the addresses I just mentioned, transport layer protocols on a sending device *multiplex* the data received from many application programs for transport, combining them into a single stream of data to be sent. The same protocols receive data and then *demultiplex* it from the incoming stream of datagram, and direct each package of data to the appropriate recipient application processes.
- **Segmentation, Packaging and Reassembly:** The transport layer segments the large amounts of data it sends over the network into smaller pieces on the source machine, and then reassemble them on the destination machine. This function is similar

conceptually to the fragmentation function of the network layer, just as the network layer fragments messages to fit the limits of the data link layer, the transport layer segments messages to suit the requirements of the underlying network layer.

- **Connection Establishment, Management and Termination:** Transport layer connection-oriented protocols are responsible for the series of communications required to establish a connection, maintain it as data is sent over it, and then terminate the connection when it is no longer required.
- **Acknowledgements and Retransmissions:** As mentioned above, the transport layer is where many protocols are implemented that guarantee reliable delivery of data. This is done using a variety of techniques, most commonly the combination of *acknowledgements* and *retransmission* timers. Each time data is sent a timer is started; if it is received, the recipient sends back an acknowledgement to the transmitter to indicate successful transmission. If no acknowledgement comes back before the timer expires, the data is retransmitted. Other algorithms and techniques are usually required to support this basic process.
- **Flow Control:** Transport layer protocols that offer reliable delivery also often implement *flow control* features. These features allow one device in a communication to specify to another that it must "throttle back" the rate at which it is sending data, to avoid bogging down the receiver with data. These allow mismatches in speed between sender and receiver to be detected and dealt with.

The transport layer of the TCP/IP protocol suite consists of two protocols, UDP and TCP. UDP provides an unreliable connectionless delivery service to send and receive messages. TCP adds reliable byte stream-delivery services on top of the IP datagram delivery service.

The ports numbered between 1 and 1,023 are well-known port numbers. For dynamically bound ports, an application requests that UDP assign a port to identify which port the process uses. The port must be in the range of 1,024 to 65,535.

UDP

UDP identifies applications through ports. The protocol defines two types of protocol ports: well-known port assignments and dynamically bound ports. For well-known port assignments, certain UDP port numbers are reserved for particular applications. Then the application can direct UDP datagrams to that port.

UDP enables multiple clients to use the same port number and different IP addresses. The arriving UDP data-grams are delivered to the client that matches both the destination port number and address. A socket consists of an IP address and the port number. If there is no matching client or if the ICMP destination is unreachable then a port unreachable message is sent and the packet is dropped.

The UDP datagram is encapsulated in an IP datagram that, in turn, is encapsulated in physical frames. Figure 29.1 shows a UDP datagram encapsulated in an IP datagram, which, in turn, is encapsulated in an Ethernet frame. This figure also illustrates how the concept of layering, discussed at the beginning of this section, affects the construction of packets sent across the network.

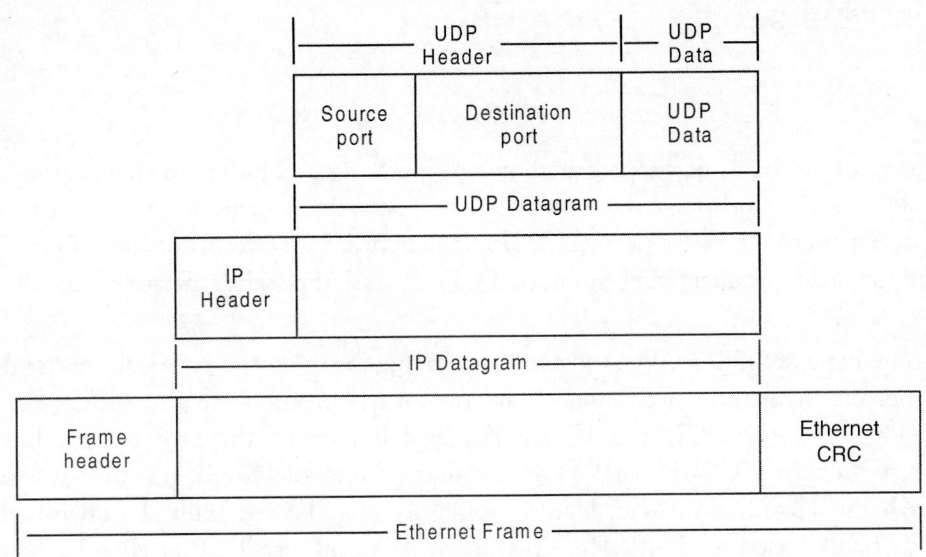

Figure 29.1 *UDP Datagram Encapsulation.*

TRANSPORT PROTOCOLS

A transport protocol is the lowest-layer protocol that defines what one station can say to another on behalf of the user. The three layers defines how a network operates; the transport layer is the first to define the end-user protocol. However, data link protocols defined communications between stations with physical connection. Connection-oriented transport protocols define communication between sites with a logical connection. There are also connectionless transport protocols.

The transport layer also provides the "connection" the user perceives. For example, users can log on to computers at remote sites, giving them the impression they are connected. But the connection is not the physical one as exists when connecting wires or making telephone calls. There is not necessarily a dedicated circuit devoted to transmitting information between user and computer. The transport layer can provide the perception of a connection by interfacing between the user and network protocols. It is similar to secretary whose function is to place calls on behalf of an executives. The secretary gets the executive's request, makes the call, and reaches the desired person, who may have been in an important meeting or any other place. When the executives has finished talking, the secretary may end the connection by getting additional important information such as a client's address, phone number etc.

Transport layer does more than make and break connections, however. The lowest three layers provide the means of connect separate devices, but the transport layer is the lowest layer that actually allows its users to communicate effectively and securely. Some transport layer functions are as follows:

Connection Management function defines the rules that allow two users to begin talking with one another as if they were connected directly. Defining and setting up the connection is also called handshaking.

TCP/IP

TCP/IP is a set of protocols developed to allow co-operating computers to share resources across a network. It was developed by a community of researchers centered around the Apranet. Certainly the Arpanet is the best- known TCP/IP network. However as of June, 87, at least 130 different vendors had products that support TCP/IP, and thousands of networks of all kinds use it.

First some basic definitions. The most accurate name for the set of protocols we are describing is the "Internet protocol suite". TCP and IP are two of the protocols in this suite. (They will be described below.) Because TCP and IP are the best known of the protocols, it has become common to use the term TCP/IP or IP/TCP to refer to the whole family. It is probably not worth fighting this habit. However this can lead to some oddities. For example, I find myself talking about NFS as being based on TCP/IP, even though it doesn't use TCP at all. The Internet is a collection of networks, including the Arpanet, NSFnet, regional networks such as NYsernet, local networks at a number of University and research institutions, and a number of military networks. The term "Internet" applies to this entire set of networks. The subset of them that is managed by the department of defense is referred to as the "DDN" (Defense Data Network). This includes some research-oriented networks, such as the Arpanet, as well as more strictly military ones. (Because much of the funding for Internet protocol developments is done via the DDN organization, the terms Internet and DDN can sometimes seem equivalent.) All of these networks are connected to each other. Users can send messages from any of them to any other, except where there are security or other policy restrictions on access. Officially speaking, the Internet protocol documents are simply standards adopted by the Internet community for its own use. More recently, the department of defense issued a MILSPEC definition of TCP/IP. This was intended to be a more formal definition, appropriate for use in purchasing specifications. However most of the TCP/IP community continues to use the Internet standards. The MILSPEC version is intended to be consistent with it.

Whatever it is called, TCP/IP is a family of protocols. A few provide "low- level" functions needed for many applications. These include IP, TCP, and UDP. (These will be described in a bit more detail later.) Others are protocols for doing specific tasks, *e.g.*, transferring files between computers, sending mail, or finding out who is logged in on another computer. Initially TCP/IP was used mostly between minicomputers or mainframes. These machines had their own disks, and generally were self- contained. Thus the most important "traditional" he TCP/IP protocol stack.

The TCP/IP protocols enable communication between pairs of hosts, or "peers", on a network. The TCP/IP protocol structure can be conceptualized as a series of layers, or "stack", between an application and the network. Each protocol layer on one peer has a corresponding layer on the other peer. To the application, it appears that it has a virtual connection to an application running on another host. In reality, data is passed over the network in the physical form that the network can handle. Each layer is required, by design, to handle communications in a predetermined fashion. Each protocol formats communicated data and appends information to or removes information from the data. Then the protocol passes the data to a lower layer on the sending host or a higher layer on the receiving host, as illustrated in "sender/receiver interaction".

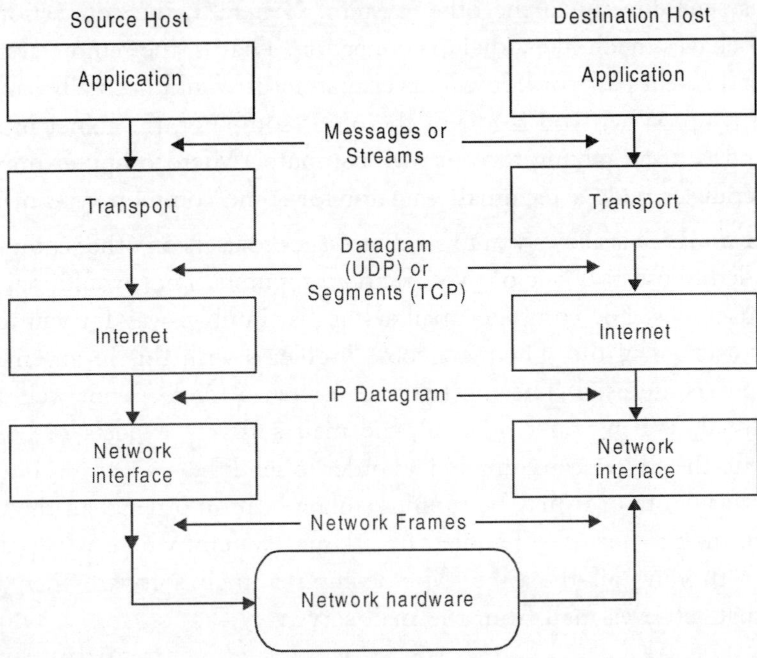

Figure 29.2 *TCP/IP Model.*

SENDER/RECEIVER INTERACTION

The interface between the application and the transport layers is termed a transport interface. Interfaces such as sockets and TLI/XTI eliminate the need for applications to know about the transport layer in detail. For more information about programming transport interfaces, see Using network programming interfaces.

The next sections briefly explain how each protocol layer handles messages, starting with the lowest layer. For more detailed information about each protocol, refer to the appropriate manual page. TCP/IP services are:

- **File transfer:** The File Transfer Protocol (FTP) allows a user on any computer to get files from another computer, or to send files to another computer. Security is handled by requiring the user to specify a user name and password for the other computer. Provisions are made for handling file transfer between machines with different character set, end of line conventions, etc. This is not quite the same thing as more recent "network file system" or "netbios" protocols, which will be described below. Rather, FTP is a utility that you run any time you want to access a file on another system. You use it to copy the file to your own system. You then work with the local copy. (See RFC 959 for specifications for FTP.)

- **Remote login:** The network terminal protocol (TELNET) allows a user to login on any other computer on the network. You start a remote session by specifying a computer to connect from that time until you finish the session, anything you type is sent to the other computer. Note that you are really still talking to your own computer. But the telnet program effectively makes your computer invisible while it is running. Every character you type is sent directly to the other system. Generally, the connection to the remote computer behaves much like a dialup connection. That is, the remote system will ask you to log in and give a password, in whatever manner it would normally ask a user who had just dialed it up. When you logoff of the other computer, the telnet program exits, and you will find yourself talking to your own computer. Microcomputer implementations of telnet generally include a terminal emulator for some common type of terminal.
- **Computer mail:** This allows you to send messages to users on other computers. Originally, people tended to use only one or two specific computers. They would maintain "mail files" on those machines. The computer mail system is simply a way for you to add a message to another user's mail file. There are some problems with this in an environment where microcomputers are used. The most serious is that a micro is not well suited to receive computer mail. When you send mail, the mail software expects to be able to open a connection to the addressee's computer, in order to send the mail. If this is a microcomputer, it may be turned off, or it may be running an application other than the mail system. For this reason, mail is normally handled by a larger system, where it is practical to have a mail server running all the time. Microcomputer mail software then becomes a user interface that retrieves mail from the mail server.

These services should be present in any implementation of TCP/IP, except that micro-oriented implementations may not support computer mail. These traditional applications still play a very important role in TCP/IP-based networks. However more recently, the way in which networks are used has been changing. The older model of a number of large, self-sufficient computers is beginning to change. Now many installations have several kinds of computers, including microcomputers, workstations, minicomputers, and mainframes. These computers are likely to be configured to perform specialized tasks. Although people are still likely to work with one specific computer, that computer will call on other systems on the net for specialized services. This has led to the "server/client" model of network services. A server is a system that provides a specific service for the rest of the network. A client is another system that uses that service. (Note that the server and client need not be on different computers. They could be different programs running on the same computer.) Here are the kinds of servers typically present in a modern computer setup.

This allows a system to access files on another computer in a somewhat more closely integrated fashion than FTP. A network file system provides the illusion that disks or other devices from one system are directly connected to other systems. There is no need to use a special network utility to access a file on another system. Your computer simply thinks it has some extra disk drives. These extra "virtual" drives refer to the other system's disks. This capability is useful for several different purposes. It lets you put large disks on a few computers, but still give others access to the disk space. Besides from the obvious economic benefits, this allows people working on several computers to share common files. It makes system maintenance and backup easier, because you don't have to worry about updating and backing up copies on lots of different machines. A number of vendors now offer high-performance diskless computers. These computers have no disk drives at all. They are entirely dependent upon disks attached to common "file servers". (see RFC's 1001 and 1002 for a description of PC-oriented NetBIOS over TCP. In the workstation and minicomputer area, sun's network file system is more likely to be used protocol specifications for it are available from Sun Microsystems.)

• **Remote printing:** This allows you to access printers on other computers as if they were directly attached to you.

This allows you to request that a particular program be run on a different computer. This is useful when you can do most of your work on a small computer, but a few tasks require the resources of a larger system. There are a number of different kinds of remote execution. Some operate on a command by command basis. That is, you request that a specific command or set of commands should run on some specific computer. (More sophisticated versions will choose a system that happens to be free.) However, there are also "remote procedure call" systems that allow a program to call a subroutine that will run on another computer. There are many protocols of this sort. Berkeley Unix contains two servers to execute commands remotely: rsh and rexec. The man pages describe the protocols that they use. The user-contributed software with Berkeley 4.3 contains a "distributed shell" that will distribute tasks among a set of systems, depending upon load. Remote procedure call mechanisms have been a topic for research for a number of years, so many organizations have implementations of such facilities. The most widespread commercially-supported remote procedure call protocols seem to be Xerox's courier and Sun's RPC. Protocol documents are available from Xerox and Sun. There is a public implementation of Courier over TCP as part of the user-contributed software with Berkeley 4.3. An implementation of RPC was posted to Usenet by Sun, and also appears as part of the user-contributed software with Berkeley 4.3.

• **Name servers:** In large installations, there are a number of different collections of names that have to be managed. This includes users and their passwords, names and network addresses for computers, and accounts. It becomes very tedious to keep this data up to date on all of the computers. Thus the databases are kept on a small number of systems. Other systems access the data over the network. RFC 822 and 823 describe the name server protocol used to keep track of host names and Internet addresses on the Internet. This is now a required part of any TCP/IP implementation. IEN 116 describes an older name server protocol that is used by a few terminal servers and other products to look up host names. Sun's yellow pages system is designed as a general mechanism to handle user names, file sharing groups, and other databases commonly used by Unix systems. It is widely available commercially. Its protocol definition is available from Sun.

• **Terminal servers:** Many installations no longer connect terminals directly to computers. Instead they connect them to terminal servers. A terminal server is simply a small computer that only knows how to run telnet (or some other protocol to do remote login). If your terminal is connected to one of these, you simply type the name of a computer, and you are connected to it. Generally it is possible to have active connections to more than one computer at the same time. The terminal server will have provisions to switch between connections rapidly, and to notify you when output is waiting for another connection. (Terminal servers use the telnet protocol, already mentioned. However, any real terminal server will also have to support name service and a number of other protocols.)

• **Network-oriented window systems:** Until recently, high-performance graphics programs had to execute on a computer that had a bit-mapped graphics screen directly attached to it. Network window systems allow a program to use a display on a different computer. Full-scale network window systems provide an interface that lets you distribute jobs to the systems that are best suited to handle them, but still give you a single graphically-based user interface. The most widely-implemented window system is X. A protocol description is available from MIT's project Athena. A reference implementation is publically available from MIT. A number of vendors are also supporting NeWS, a window system defined by Sun. Both of these systems are designed to use TCP/IP.

Note that some of the protocols described above were designed by Berkeley, Sun, or other organizations. Thus they are not officially part of the Internet protocol suite. However they are implemented using TCP/IP, just as normal TCP/IP application protocols are. Since the protocol definitions are not considered proprietary, and since commercially-support implementations are widely available, it is reasonable to think of these protocols as being effectively part of the Internet suite. Note that the list above is simply a sample of the sort of services available through TCP/IP. However it does contain the majority of the "major" applications. The other commonly-used protocols tend to be specialized facilities for getting information of various kinds, such as who is logged in, the time of day, etc. However if you need a facility that is not listed here, we encourage you to look through the current edition of Internet protocols (currently RFC 1011), which lists all of the available protocols, and also to look at some of the major TCP/IP implementations to see what various vendors have added.

GENERAL DESCRIPTION OF THE TCP/IP PROTOCOLS

TCP/IP is a layered set of protocols. In order to understand what this means, it is useful to look at an example. A typical situation is sending mail. First, there is a protocol for mail. This defines a set of commands which one machine sends to another, *e.g.*, commands to specify who the sender of the message is, who it is being sent to, and then the text of the message. However this protocol assumes that there is a way to communicate reliably between the two computers. Mail, like other application protocols, simply defines a set of commands and messages to be sent. It is designed to be used together with TCP and IP. TCP is responsible for making sure that the commands get through to the other end. It keeps track of what is sent, and retransmitts anything that did not get through. If any message is too large for one datagram, *e.g.*, the text of the mail, TCP will split it up into several datagrams, and make sure that they all arrive correctly. Since these functions are needed for many applications, they are put together into a separate protocol, rather than being part of the specifications for sending mail. You can think of TCP as forming a library of routines that applications can use when they need reliable network communications with another computer. Similarly, TCP calls on the services of IP. Although the services that TCP supplies are needed by many applications, there are still some kinds of applications that don't need them. However there are some services that every application needs. So these services are put together into IP. As with TCP, you can think of IP as a library of routines that TCP calls on, but which is also available to applications that don't use TCP. This strategy of building several levels of protocol is called "layering". We think of the applications programs such as mail, TCP, and IP, as being separate "layers", each of which calls on the services of the layer below it. Generally, TCP/IP applications use 4 layers:

- an application protocol such as mail.
- a protocol such as TCP that provides services need by many applications.
- IP, which provides the basic service of getting datagrams to their destination the protocols needed to manage a specific physical medium, such as Ethernet or a point to point line.

TCP/IP is based on the "catenet model". This model assumes that there are a large number of independent networks connected together by gateways. The user should be able to access computers or other resources on any of these networks. Datagrams will often pass through a dozen different networks before getting to their final destination. The routing needed to accomplish this should be completely invisible to the user. As far as the user is concerned, all he needs to know in order to access another system is an "Internet address". This is an address that looks like 128.6.4.194. It is actually a 32-bit number. However it is normally written as 4 decimal numbers, each representing 8 bits of the address. (The term "octet" is used by Internet documentation for such 8-bit chunks. The term "byte" is not used, because TCP/IP is supported by some computers that have byte sizes other than 8 bits.) Generally the structure of the address gives you some information about how to get to the system. For example, 128.6 is a network number assigned by a central authority to Rutgers University. Rutgers uses the next octet to indicate which of the campus Ethernets is involved. 128.6.4 happens to be an Ethernet used by the computer science department. The last octet allows for up to 254 systems on each Ethernet. (It is 254 because 0 and 255 are not allowed, for reasons that will be discussed later.) Note that 128.6.4.194 and 128.6.5.194 would be different systems. The structure of an Internet address is described in a bit more detail later.

Of course we normally refer to systems by name, rather than by Internet address. When we specify a name, the network software looks it up in a database, and comes up with the corresponding Internet address. Most of the network software deals strictly in terms of the address. (RFC 882 describes the name server technology used to handle this lookup.)

TCP/IP is built on "connectionless" technology. Information is transferred as a sequence of "data-grams". A datagram is a collection of data that is sent as a single message. Each of these data-grams is sent through the network individually. There are provisions to open connections (*i.e.,* to start a conversation that will continue for some time). However at some level, information from those connections is broken up into data-grams, and those data-grams are treated by the network as completely separate. For example, suppose you want to transfer a 15000 octet file. Most networks can't handle a 15000 octet datagram. So the protocols will break this up into something like 30,500 data grams. Each of these data-grams will be sent to the other end. At that point, they will be put back together into the 15000-octet file. However while those data-grams are in transit, the network doesn't know that there is any connection between them. It is perfectly possible that datagram 14 will actually arrive before datagram 13. It is also possible that somewhere in the network, an error will occur, and some datagram won't get through at all. In that case, that datagram has to be sent again.

Note by the way that the terms "datagram" and "packet" often seem to be nearly interchangable. Technically, datagram is the right word to use when describing TCP/IP. A datagram is a unit of data, which is what the protocols deal with. A packet is a physical thing, appearing on an Ethernet or some wire. In most cases a packet simply contains a datagram, so there is very little difference. However they can differ. When TCP/IP is used on top of X.25, the X.25 interface breaks the data-grams up into 128-byte packets. This is invisible to IP, because the packets are put back together into a single datagram at the other end before being processed by TCP/IP. So in this case, one IP datagram would be carried by several packets. However with most media, there are efficiency advantages to sending one datagram per packet, and so the distinction tends to vanish.

PROTOCOLS OTHER THAN TCP: UDP AND ICMP

So far, we have described only connections that use TCP. Recall that TCP is responsible for breaking up messages into datagrams, and reassembling them properly. However in many applications, we have messages that will always fit in a single datagram. An example is name lookup. When a user attempts to make a connection to another system, he will generally specify the system by name, rather than Internet address. His system has to translate that name to an address before it can do anything. Generally, only a few systems have the database used to translate names to addresses. So the user's system will want to send a query to one of the systems that has the database. This query is going to be very short. It will certainly fit in one datagram. So will the answer. Thus it seems silly to use TCP. Of course TCP does more than just break things up into datagrams. It also makes sure that the data arrives, resending data-grams where necessary. But for a question that fits in a single datagram, we don't need all the complexity of TCP to do this. If we don't get an answer after a few seconds, we can just ask again. For applications like this, there are alternatives to TCP.

The most common alternative is UDP ("user datagram protocol"). UDP is designed for applications where you don't need to put sequences of data-grams together. It fits into the system much like TCP. There is a UDP header. The network software puts the UDP header on the front of your data, just as it would put a TCP header on the front of your data. Then UDP sends the data to IP, which adds the IP header, putting UDP's protocol number in the protocol field instead of TCP's protocol number. However UDP doesn't do as much as TCP does. It doesn't split data into multiple datagrams. It doesn't keep track of what it has sent so it can resend if necessary. About all that UDP provides is port numbers, so that several programs can use UDP at once. UDP port numbers are used just like TCP port numbers. There are well-known port numbers for servers that use UDP. Note that the UDP header is shorter than a TCP header. It still has source and destination port numbers, and a checksum, but that's about it. No sequence number, since it is not needed. UDP is used by the protocols that handle name lookups and a number of similar protocols.

Another alternative protocol is ICMP ("Internet control message protocol"). ICMP is used for error messages, and other messages intended for the TCP/IP software itself, rather than any particular user program. For example, if you attempt to connect to a host, your system may get back an ICMP message saying "host unreachable". ICMP can also be used to find out some information about the network. ICMP is similar to UDP, in that it handles messages that fit in one datagram. However it is even simpler than UDP. It doesn't even have port numbers in its header. Since all ICMP messages are interpreted by the network software itself, no port numbers are needed to say where a ICMP message is supposed to go.

DOMAIN SYSTEM

As we indicated earlier, the network software generally needs a 32-bit Internet address in order to open a connection or send a datagram. However users prefer to deal with computer names rather than numbers. Thus there is a database that allows the software to look up a name and find the corresponding number. When the Internet was small, this was easy. Each system would have a file that listed all of the other systems, giving both their name and number. There are now too many computers for this approach to be practical. Thus these files have been replaced by a set of name servers that keep track of host names and the corresponding Internet addresses. (In fact these servers are somewhat more general than that. This is just one kind of information stored in the domain system. Note that a set of interlocking servers are used, rather than a single central one. There are now so many different institutions connected to the Internet that it would be impractical for them to notify a central authority whenever they installed or moved a computer. Thus naming authority is delegated to individual institutions. The name servers form a tree, corresponding to institutional structure. The names themselves follow a similar structure. A typical example is the name BORAX.LCS.MIT.EDU. This is a computer at the Laboratory for Computer Science (LCS) at MIT. In order to find its Internet address, you might potentially have to consult 4 different servers. First, you would ask a central server (called the root) where the EDU is a server that keeps track of educational institutions. The root server would give you the names and Internet addresses of several servers for EDU. (There are several servers at each level, to allow for the possibly that one might be down.) You would then ask EDU where the server for MIT is. Again, it would give you names and Internet addresses of several servers for MIT. Generally, not all of those servers would be at MIT, to allow for the possibility of a general power failure at MIT. Then you would ask MIT where the server for LCS is, and finally you would ask one of the LCS servers about BORAX. The final result would be the Internet address for BORAX.LCS.MIT.EDU. Each of these levels is referred to as a "domain". The entire name, BORAX.LCS.MIT.EDU, is called a "domain name". (So are the names of the higher-level domains, such as LCS.MIT.EDU, MIT.EDU, and EDU.)

Fortunately, you don't really have to go through all of this most of the time. First of all, the root name servers also happen to be the name servers for the top-level domains such as EDU. Thus a single query to a root server will get you to MIT. Second, software generally remembers answers that it got before. So once we look up a name at LCS.MIT.EDU, our software remembers where to find servers for LCS.MIT.EDU, MIT.EDU, and EDU. It also remembers the translation of BORAX.LCS.MIT.EDU. Each of these pieces of information has a "time to live" associated with it. Typically this is a few days. After that, the information expires and has to be looked up again. This allows institutions to change things.

The domain system is not limited to finding out Internet addresses. Each domain name is a node in a database. The node can have records that define a number of different properties. Examples are Internet address, computer type, and a list of services provided by a computer. A program can ask for a specific piece of information, or all information about a given name. It is possible for a node in the database to be marked as an "alias" (or nickname) for another node. It is also possible to use the domain system to store information about users, mailing lists, or other objects.

There is an Internet standard defining the operation of these databases, as well as the protocols used to make queries of them. Every network utility has to be able to make such queries, since this is now the official way to evaluate host names. Generally utilities will talk to a server on their own system. This server will take care of contacting the other servers for them. This keeps down the amount of code that has to be in each application program.

The domain system is particularly important for handling computer mail. There are entry types to define what computer handles mail for a given name, to specify where an individual is to receive mail, and to define mailing lists.

ADDRESS RESOLUTION PROTOCOL

ARP and RARP Address Translation

Address Resolution Protocol (ARP) provides a completely different function to the network than Reverse Address Resolution Protocol (RARP). ARP is used to resolve the Ethernet address of a NIC from an IP address in order to construct an Ethernet packet around an IP data packet. This must happen in order to send any data across the network. Reverse Address Resolution Protocol (RARP) is used for diskless computers to determine their IP address using the network.

Address Resolution Protocol (ARP)

In an earlier section, there was an example where a chat program was written to communicate between two servers. To send data, the user (Tom) would type text into a dialog box, hit send and the program passed Tom's typed text in a buffer, to the socket.

The data was put inside a TCP data packet with a TCP header added to the data. This header contained a source and destination port number along with some other information and a checksum. The TCP packet was be placed inside an IP data packet with a source and destination IP address along with some other data for network management. The IP data packet was placed inside an Ethernet data packet. This data packet includes the destination and source address of the Network Interface Cards (NIC) on the two computers. The address here is the hardware address of the respective cards and is called the MAC address. The Ethernet packet was transmitted over the network line.

With a direct connection between the two computers, the network interface card on the intended machine, recognized its address and grabbed the data. The IP data packet was extracted from the Ethernet data packet. The TCP data packet was extracted from the IP data packet.

The data was extracted from the TCP packet and the program displayed the retrieved data (text) in the text display window for the intended recipient to read.

In step 4 above, the IP data was going to be placed inside an Ethernet data packet, but the computer constructing the packet does not have the Ethernet address of the recipient's computer. The computer that is sending the data, in order to create the Ethernet part of the packet, must get the Ethernet hardware (MAC) address of the computer with the intended IP address. This must be accomplished before the Ethernet packet can be constructed. The Ethernet device driver software on the receiving computer is not programmed to look at IP addresses encased in the Ethernet packet. If it did, the protocols could not be independent and changes to one would affect the other. This is where address resolution protocol (ARP) is used. Tom's computer sends a network broadcast asking the computer that has the recipient's IP address to send it's ethernet address. This is done by broadcasting. The Ethernet destination is set with all bits on so all Ethernet cards on the network will receive the data packet. The ARP message consists of an Ethernet header and ARP packet. The Ethernet header contains:

- A 6 byte Ethernet destination address.
- A 6 byte Ethernet source address.
- A 2 byte frame type. The frame type is 0806 hexadecimal for ARP and 8035 for RARP.

The encapsulated ARP data packet contains the following:

- Type of hardware address (2 bytes).1= Ethernet.
- Type of protocol address being mapped (2 bytes).0800H (hexadecimal) = IP address.
- Byte size of the hardware address (1 byte).6
- Byte size of the protocol address (1 byte).4
- Type of operation. 1 = ARP request, 2 = ARP reply, 3 = RARP request, 4 = RARP reply.
- The sender's Ethernet address (6 bytes)
- The sender's IP address (4 bytes)
- The recipient's Ethernet address (6 bytes)
- The recipient's IP address (4 bytes).

When the ARP reply is sent, the recipient's Ethernet address is left blank. In order to increase the efficiency of the network and not tie up bandwidth doing ARP broadcasting, each computer keeps a table of IP addresses and matching Ethernet addresses in memory. This is called ARP cache. Before sending a broadcast, the sending computer will check to see if the information is in it's ARP cache. If it is it will complete the Ethernet data packet without an ARP broadcast. Each entry normally lasts 20 minutes after it is created. RFC 1122 specifies that it should be possible to configure the ARP cache timeout value on the host. To examine the cache on a Windows, UNIX, or Linux computer type "arp -a".

If the receiving host is on another network, the sending computer will go through its route table and determine the correct router (A router should be between two or more networks) to send to, and it will substitute the Ethernet address of the router in the Ethernet message. The encased IP address will still have the intended IP address. When the router gets the message, it looks at the IP data to tell where to send the data next. If the recipient is on a network the router is connected to, it will do the ARP resolution either using it's ARP buffer cache or broadcasting.

REVERSE ADDRESS RESOLUTION PROTOCOL (RARP)

As mentioned earlier, Reverse Address Resolution Protocol (RARP) is used for diskless computers to determine their IP address using the network. The RARP message format is very similar to the ARP format. When the booting computer sends the broadcast ARP request, it places its own hardware address in both the sending and receiving fields in the encapsulated ARP data packet. The RARP server will fill in the correct sending and receiving IP addresses in its response to the message. This way the booting computer will know its IP address when it gets the message from the RARP server.

Network Address

The network address is the first part of the IP address for every host in the network you manage. The network address identifies part of a total IP address as the network, and leaves the rest of the IP address to identify a particular host on that network.

The network information centers or NICs (including the original InterNIC) that assign network addresses for the Internet take into account the fact that different organizations manage different numbers of hosts. An NIC therefore assigns you a network ID belonging to one of the following three classes, based on how many hosts you have, or expect to have, on your network: class A, class B, or class C. Each class uses progressively more of the IP address to identify the network, and therefore leave you with fewer numbers to uniquely identify your hosts.

The following table shows the network classes available from an NIC. The portion of each IP address that is reserved for host and subnet addresses is shown by x's.

Class IP address range Description:

A 0.x.x.x—127.x.x.x Three bytes can be used for host and subnet addresses; addresses beginning with 0 or 127 are reserved for special use, such as 127.0.0.1 for the loop-back address

B 128.0.x.x—191.255.x.x Two bytes can be used for host and subnet addresses

C 192.0.0.x—223.255.255.x One byte can be used for host and subnet addresses

D 224.0.0.0—239.255.255.255 Multicast addresses

E 240.0.0.0—247.255.255.255 Reserved and experimental addresses

Ethernet Encapsulation: ARP

There was a brief discussion earlier about what IP datagrams look like on an Ethernet. The discussion showed the Ethernet header and checksum. However it left one hole: It didn't say how to figure out what Ethernet address to use when you want to talk to a given Internet address. In fact, there is a separate protocol for this, called ARP ("Address Resolution Protocol"). (note by the way that ARP is not an IP protocol. That is, the ARP datagrams do not have IP headers.)

Suppose you are on system 128.6.4.194 and you want to connect to system 128.6.4.7. Your system will first verify that 128.6.4.7 is on the same network, so it can talk directly via Ethernet. Then it will look up 128.6.4.7 in its ARP table, to see if it already knows the Ethernet address. If so, it will stick on an Ethernet header, and send the packet. But suppose this system is not in the ARP table. There is no way to send the packet, because you need the Ethernet address. So it uses the ARP protocol to send an ARP request. Essentially an ARP request says "I need the Ethernet address for 128.6.4.7". Every system listens to ARP requests. When a system sees an ARP request for itself, it is required to respond. So 128.6.4.7 will see the request, and will respond with an ARP reply saying in effect "128.6.4.7 is 8:0:20:1:56:34". (Recall that Ethernet addresses are 48 bits. This is 6 octets. Ethernet addresses are conventionally shown in hex, using the punctuation shown.) Your system will save this information in its ARP table, so future packets will go directly. Most systems treat the ARP table as a cache, and clear entries in it if they have not been used in a certain period of time.

Note by the way that ARP requests must be sent as "broadcasts". There is no way that an ARP request can be sent directly to the right system. After all, the whole reason for sending an ARP request is that you don't know the Ethernet address. So an Ethernet address of all ones is used, *i.e.,* ff:ff:ff:ff:ff:ff. By convention, every machine on the Ethernet is required to pay attention to packets with this as an address. So every system sees every ARP requests. They all look to see whether the request is for their own address. If so, they respond. If not, they could just ignore it. (Some hosts will use ARP requests to update their knowledge about other hosts on the network, even if the request isn't for them.) Note that packets whose IP address indicates broadcast (*e.g.,* 255.255.255.255 or 128.6.4.255) are also sent with an Ethernet address that is all ones.

For applications that must send or receive large volumes of data, unreliable datagram delivery can become burdensome. Application programmers might have to develop extensive error handling and status information modules to track the progress and state of data transfer for every application. The TCP/IP suite of protocols avoids this problem by using TCP, a reliable byte-stream delivery protocol. TCP establishes a connection between two applications and sends a stream of bytes to a destination in exactly the same order that they left the source. Before transmission begins, the applications at both ends of the transmission obtain a TCP port from their respective operating systems. These are analogous to the ports used by UDP. The application initiating the transfer, known as the client side, generally obtains a port dynamically. The application responding to the transfer request, known as the server side, generally uses a well-known TCP port. The client side is typically the active side and initiates the connection to the passive server side.

Like the UDP data-grams, TCP segments are encapsulated in an IP datagram. TCP buffers the stream by waiting for enough data to fill a large datagram before sending the datagram. The stream is unstructured, which means that before transmission of data, both the sending and receiving applications must agree on the meaning of the contents of the stream. The TCP protocol uses full-duplex transmission. Full duplex means that two data streams can flow in opposite directions simultaneously. Thus, the receiving application can send data or control information back to the sending application while the sending application continues to send data.

The TCP protocol gives each segment a sequence number. At the receiving end of the connection, TCP checks successive sequence numbers to ensure that all the segments are received and processed in the order of the sequence numbers. The receiving end sends an acknowledgement to the sender for the segments received. TCP enables the sender to have several outstanding segments before the receiver must return an acknowledgement. If the sending node does not receive an acknowledgement for a segment within a certain time, it retransmits that segment. This scheme, called positive acknowledgement with retransmission, ensures that the stream delivery is reliable.

TRANSPORT LAYER SERVICES AND PRINCIPLE

Residing between the application and network layers, the transport layer is in the core of the layered network architecture. It has the critical role of providing communication services directly to the application processes running on different hosts. In this chapter we'll examine the possible services provided by a transport layer protocol and the principles underlying various approaches towards providing these services. We'll also look at how these services are implemented and instantiated in existing protocols; as usual, particular emphasis will be given to the Internet protocols, namely, TCP and UDP transport layer protocols. In the previous two chapters we have touched on the role of the transport layer and the services that it provides. Let's quickly review what we have already learned about the transport layer:

A transport layer protocol provides for logical communication between application processes running on different hosts. By "logical" communication, we mean that although the communicating application processes are not *physically* connected to each other (indeed, they may be on different sides of the planet, connected via numerous routers and a wide range of link types), from the applications' viewpoint, it is as if they were physically connected. Application processes use the logical communication provided by the transport layer to send messages to each other, free for the worry of the details of the physical infrastructure used to carry these messages. Figure 29.3 illustrates the notion of logical communication.

As shown in figure, transport layer protocols are implemented in the end systems but not in network routers. Network routers only act on the network-layer fields of the layer-3 PDUs; they do not act on the transport-layer fields.

At the sending side, the transport layer converts the messages it receives from a sending application process into 4-PDUs (that is, transport-layer protocol data units). This is done by (possibly) breaking the application messages into smaller chunks and adding a transport-layer header to each chunk to create 4-PDUs. The transport layer then passes the 4-PDUs to the network layer, where each 4-PDU is encapsulated into a 3-PDU. At the receiving side, the transport layer receives the 4-PDUs from the network layer, removes the transport header from the 4-PDUs, reassembles the messages and passes them to a receiving application process.

A computer network can make more than one transport layer protocol available to network applications. For example, the Internet has two protocolsp—TCP and UDP. Each of these protocols provides a different set of transport layer services to the invoking application.

All transport layer protocols provide an application multiplexing/de-multiplexing service. In addition to multiplexing/de-multiplexing service, a transport protocol can possibly provide other services to invoking applications, including reliable data transfer, bandwidth guarantees, and delay guarantees.

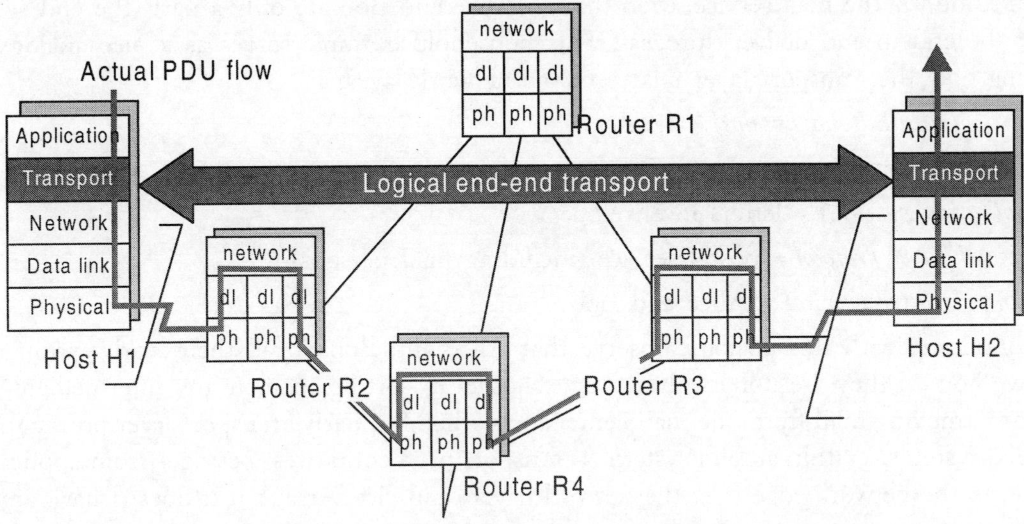

Figure 29.3 *The Transport Layer Provides Logical Rather than Physical Communication between Applications.*

RELATIONSHIP BETWEEN TRANSPORT AND NETWORK LAYERS

From the perspective of network applications, the transport layer *is* the underlying communication infrastructure. Of course, there is more to the communication infrastructure than just the transport layer. For example, the network layer lies just below the transport layer in the protocol stack. Whereas a transport layer protocol provides *logical communication between processes* running on different hosts, a network layer protocol provides *logical communication between hosts.* This distinction is subtle but important. Let's examine this distinction with the aid of a household analogy.

Consider two houses, one on the East coast and the other on the West coast, with each house being home to a dozen kids. The kids in the East coast household are cousins with the kids in the West coast households. The kids in the two households love to write each other—each kid writes each cousin every week, with each letter delivered by the traditional postal service in a separate envelope. Thus, each household sends 144 letters to the other household every week. In each of the households there is one kid—Alice in the West coast house and Bob in the East coast house—responsible for mail collection and mail distribution. Each week Alice visits all her brothers and sisters, collects the mail, and gives the mail to a postal-service mail person who makes daily visits to the house. When letters arrive to the West coast house, Alice also has the job of distributing the mail to her brothers and sisters. Bob has a similar job on the East coast.

In this example, the postal service provides logical communication between the two houses —the postal service moves mail from house to house, not from person to person. On the other hand, Alice and Bob provide logical communication between the cousins—Alice and Bob pick up mail from and deliver mail to, their brothers and sisters. Note that, from the cousins' perspective, Alice and Bob *are* the mail service, even though Alice and Bob are only a part (the end system part) of the end-to-end delivery process. This household example serves as a nice analogy for explaining how the transport layer relates to the network layer:

hosts (also called end systems) = houses

processes = cousins

application messages = letters in envelope

network layer protocol = postal service (including mail persons)

transport layer protocol = Alice and Bob

Continuing with this analogy, observe that Alice and Bob do all their work within their respective homes; they are not involved, for example, in sorting mail in any intermediate mail center or in moving mail from one mail center to another. Similarly, transport layer protocols live in the end systems. Within an end system, a transport protocol moves messages from application processes to the network edge (*i.e.*, the network layer) and vice versa; but it doesn't have any say about how the messages are moved within the network core. In fact, as illustrated in figure, intermediate routers neither act on, nor recognize, any information that the transport layer may have appended to the application messages.

Continuing with our family saga, suppose now that when Alice and Bob go on vacation, another cousin pair—say, Susan and Harvey—substitute for them and provide the household-internal collection and delivery of mail. Unfortunately for the two families, Susan and Harvey do not do the collection and delivery in exactly the same way as Alice and Bob. Being younger kids, Susan and Harvey pick up and drop off the mail less frequently and occasionally lose letters (which are sometimes chewed up by the family dog). Thus, the cousin-pair Susan and Harvey do not provide the same set of services (*i.e.*, the same service model) as Alice and Bob. In an analogous manner, a computer network may make available multiple transport protocols, with each protocol offering a different service model to applications.

The possible services that Alice and Bob can provide are clearly constrained by the possible services that the postal service provides. For example, if the postal service doesn't provide a maximum bound on how long it can take to deliver mail between the two houses (*e.g.*, three days), then there is no way that Alice and Bob can guarantee a maximum delay for mail delivery between any of the cousin pairs. In a similar manner, the services that a transport protocol can provide are often constrained by the service model of the underlying network-layer protocol. If the network layer protocol cannot provide delay or bandwidth guarantees for 4-PDUs sent between hosts, then the transport layer protocol can not provide delay or bandwidth guarantees for the messages sent between processes.

Nevertheless, certain services *can* be offered by a transport protocol even when the underlying network protocol doesn't offer the corresponding service at the network layer. For example, as we'll see in this chapter, a transport protocol can offer reliable data transfer service to an application even when the underlying network protocol is unreliable, that is, even when the network protocol loses, garbles and duplicates packets. As another example, a transport protocol can use encryption to guarantee that application messages are not read by intruders, even when the network layer cannot guarantee the secrecy of 4-PDUs.

OVERVIEW OF THE TRANSPORT LAYER IN THE INTERNET

The Internet, and more generally a TCP/IP network, makes available two distinct transport-layer protocols to the application layer. One of these protocols is UDP (User Datagram Protocol), which provides an unreliable, connectionless service to the invoking application. The second of the these protocols is TCP (Transmission Control Protocol), which provides a reliable, connection-oriented service to the invoking application. When designing a network application, the application developer must specify one of these two transport protocols. To simplify terminology, when in an Internet context, we refer to the 4-PDU as a *segment*. We mention, however, that the Internet literature (*e.g.*, the RFCs) also refers to the PDU for TCP as a segment but often refers to the PDU for UDP as a *datagram*. But this same Internet literature also uses the terminology datagram for the network-layer PDU! For an introductory book on computer networking such as this one, we believe that it is less confusing to refer to both TCP and UDP PDUs as segments, and reserve the terminology datagram for the network-layer PDU.

Before preceding with our brief introduction of UDP and TCP, it is useful to say a few words about the Internet's network layer. The Internet's network-layer protocol has a name—IP, which abbreviates "Internet protocol". IP provides logical communication between hosts. The IP service model is a *best-effort delivery service*. This means that IP makes its "best effort" to deliver segments between communicating hosts, *but it makes no guarantees*. In particular, it does not guarantee segment delivery, it does not guarantee orderly delivery of segments, and it does it guarantee the integrity of the data in the segments. For these reasons, IP is said to be an unreliable service. We also mention here that every host has an IP address. We will examine IP addressing in detail in chapter 4; for this chapter we need only keep in mind that each host has a *unique* IP address.

Having taken a glimpse at the IP service model, let's now summarize the service model of UDP and TCP. The most fundamental responsibility of UDP and TCP is to extend IP's delivery service between two end systems to a delivery service between two processes running on the end systems. Extending host-to-host delivery to process-to-process delivery is called application multiplexing and de-multiplexing. We'll discuss application multiplexing and de-multiplexing in the next section. UDP and TCP also provide integrity checking by including error detection fields in its header. These two minimal transport-layer services—host-to-host data delivery and error checking—are the only two services that UDP provides! In particular, like IP, UDP is an unreliable service—it does not guarantee data sent by one process will arrive in tact to the destination process. TCP, on the other hand, offers several additional services to applications.. First and foremost, it provides reliable data transfer. Using flow control, sequence numbers, acknowledgements and timers (techniques we'll explore in detail in this chapter), TCP's guarantee of reliable data transfer ensures that data is delivered from sending process to receiving process, correctly and in order. TCP thus converts IP's unreliable service between end systems into a reliable data transport service between processes. TCP also uses congestion control. Congestion control is not so much a service provided to the invoking application as it is a service for the Internet as a whole—a service for the general good. In loose terms, TCP congestion control prevents any one TCP connection from swamping the links and switches between communicating hosts with an excessive amount of traffic. In principle, TCP permits TCP connections traversing a congested network link to equally share that link's bandwidth. This is done by regulating the rate at which an the sending-side TCPs can send traffic into the network. UDP traffic, on the other hand, is unregulated. A an application using UDP transport can send traffic at any rate it pleases, for as long as it pleases.

A protocol that provides reliable data transfer and congestion control is necessarily complex. We will need several sections to cover the principles of reliable data transfer and congestion control, and additional sections to cover the TCP protocol itself. These topics are investigated in sections 3.4 through 3.8. The approach taken in this chapter is to alternative between the basic principles and the TCP protocol. For example, we first discuss reliable data transfer in a general setting and then discuss how TCP specifically provides reliable data transfer. Similarly, we first discuss congestion control in a general setting and then discuss how TCP uses congestion control.

ELEMENTS OF TRANSPORT PROTOCOL

The following issues are described, where appropriate to the discussion the above types have been separately considered.

- Addressing
- Multiplexing
- Flow Control
- Connection Establishment and Termination
- Crash Recovery
- Retransmission Strategy
- Duplicate Detection
- Sequencing.

Addressing

Addressing is one of the four main issues (others are multiplexing, flow control and connection establishment/termination) involved when considering the development of the simplest possible transport protocol. Two things must be known when addressing a TDPU:

Firstly, what is the protocol for addressing the item that is being sent ? How is the item addressed ?

Secondly, how does the user of the transport entity know the address of another specific transport user ? Where can the address be found ?

Addressing, as is expected, is there so that the user of one transport entity can establish a connection with or make a connectionless data transfer to a user of another transport entity. To do this, the destination transport entity must have an address. The address is made up of the following:

- User identification
- Transport entity identification
- End-system identification.
- A TSAP (Transport Service Access Point) represents the user identification. Each individual user of a transport layer accesses the services of the transport layer via a unique TSAP. A destination receipt of a TSAP; communicates it to the transport entity so that received data can be routed to the proper transport user.
- The transport entity identification is rarely needed due to there being only a single transport entity in each end system. A specific identification is not necessary here.

  An NSAP (Network Service Access Point) is the end-system identification. This identification is passed down to the network service where it is used in the end-system identification.

  How does the user of a transport entity know the address of another specific transport user ?

  There are four strategies to answer this question; two static and two dynamic strategies :
- The user must know the address it requires ahead of time. This is simply a system configuration function.

  A specific case:

  Certain processes may be only applicable to a certain number of transport users. For example, a process which collects statistics on performance in a station. A central network management routine may wish to connect to the process to obtain statistics. These processes should be well known only to that certain number of users to which they are applicable.
- Well-known addresses are given to common services.

  A specific case:

  Services such as word processing and time sharing would have addresses known to all.
- A name server exists which, when a user requests a service by a generic or global name; looks up its directory and returns an address.

  A specific case:

  Commonly used services may change their address occasionally. For example, a data entry process may be moved from one station to another on a local network to balance load. The names of these moving processes can be kept in the name server which updates addresses when they change.
- In certain cases, the destination user is to be a process which is spawned at request time. The initiating user can send a process request to a well known address. The user at that address is a privileged system process that will spawn the new process and return an address.

- **A specific case:**

  This might be applied where a user has a private application that will execute on a remote mainframe but be invoked from a local minicomputer. For example, an RJE-type request can be issued to a remote job-management process that spawns the simulator process.

TRANSPORT LAYER: MULTIPLEXING

The issue of multiplexing arises in the transport layer in two areas. These are discussed below.

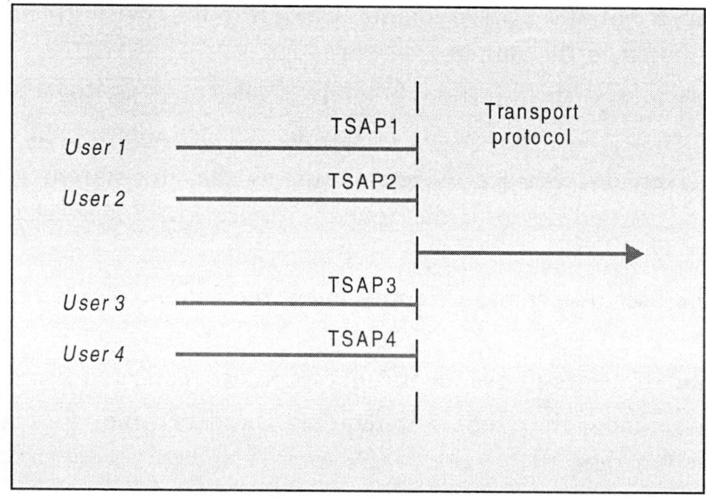

Figure 29.4 *Interface to Higher Level Protocols.*

The transport protocol performs a multiplexing/de-multiplexing function with respect to the interface between itself and higher level protocols such as the session layer. This means that multiple users an use the same transport protocol. These are then distinguished by having seperate transport service access points or TSAPs.

MULTIPLEXING IN TERMS OF NETWORK SERVICES

A transport entity may also perform multiplexing with respect to the network services that it uses. Both upward and downward multiplexing may be employed.

1. Uses of Upward Multiplexing

Upward multiplexing may be employed to reduce cost. Many networks base part of their charge on virtual circuit connect time, the reason being that each virtual circuit consumes node buffer resources. If several transport users can be serviced over a single virtual link via upward multiplexing, then this charge will be less.

2. Uses of Downward Multiplexing

Downward multiplexing may be employed to improve throughput. Data from a single transport user may be split and sent simultaneously through the network over several virtual circuits. Throughput can only be increased so far. If there is a single link over which all virtual circuits are multiplexed, the throughput of the transport connection cannot exceed the data rate of that link.

As can be seen from the above, there is a tradeoff between cost and throughput. Upward multiplexing allows the user to choose a lower cost and the expense of lower throughput. Likewise, downward multiplexing enables greater throughput at a higher cost.

FLOW CONTROL BASICS

Flow control is a function that prevents network congestion by ensuring that transmitting devices do not overwhelm receiving devices with data. A high-speed computer, for example, may generate traffic faster than the network can transfer it, or faster than the destination device can receive and process it. The three commonly used methods for handling network congestion are buffering, transmitting source-quench messages, and windowing.

Buffering is used by network devices to temporarily store bursts of excess data in memory until they can be processed. Occasional data bursts are easily handled by buffering. Excess data bursts can exhaust memory, however, forcing the device to discard any additional datagrams that arrive.

Source-quench messages are used by receiving devices to help prevent their buffers from overflowing. The receiving device sends source-quench messages to request that the source reduce its current rate of data transmission. First, the receiving device begins discarding received data due to overflowing buffers. Second, the receiving device begins sending source-quench messages to the transmitting device at the rate of one message for each packet dropped. The source device receives the source-quench messages and lowers the data rate until it stops receiving the messages. Finally, the source device then gradually increases the data rate as long as no further source-quench requests are received.

Windowing is a flow-control scheme in which the source device requires an acknowledgement from the destination after a certain number of packets have been transmitted. With a window size of 3, the source requires an acknowledgement after sending three packets, as follows. First, the source device sends three packets to the destination device. Then, after receiving the three packets, the destination device sends an acknowledgement to the source. The source receives the acknowledgement and sends three more packets. If the destination does not receive one or more of the packets for some reason, such as overflowing buffers, it does not receive enough packets to send an acknowledgement. The source then retransmits the packets at a reduced transmission rate.

- **Flow control:** It limits how much information one station can send to another without receiving some acknowledgement. To have flow control in transport layer may seem strange, first, but transport layer must operate independently of the lower layers. Lower layers may allows more or less (or no) flow control. In order to preserve this independence a transport layer may use its own flow control.

- **Error detection:** This is another case that seems to duplicate lower-layer features. Some errors, however, escape lower-layer error detection. This statement seem unusual because it means that even if data link error detection provides reliable transmission along each link there is still no guarantee of error-free transmission between the source and destination. Suppose it receives the IP packet intact, but an error that affects the packet's contents occurs during reformatting of the frame containing the packet. Any number of software or hardware errors can cause such a problem. Since the checksum is calculated after the new frame is created it includes the erroneous data. Strictly, it is not a transmission error because it occurred while the packet was in the possession of the router. But try telling that to the transport user, we saw his or her data changed while in transit. A transport-layer error detection mechanism would detect this error.
- **Response to users' requests:** Examples include sending and receiving data, as well as specific requests. For example, a user may request high throughput, low delays, or reliable service. The transport layer passes the request from the user to the IP.
- **Establishment of connectionless or connection-oriented communication:** A transport protocol must provide reliable communications between end users. This is especially important because IP does not guarantee reliable service. Transport protocols must provide acknowledgement and timers to make sure all of a user's data is sent and received. Two transport-layer protocols that the DOD designed specifically to run with its Arpanet IP are Transmission Control Protocol (TCP) and the User Datagram Protocol (UDP).

The transport layer is regarded as the highest of the lower layer protocols in the OSI protocol stack. It resides above the physical, data-link and network layers and just below the session layer and is concerned with the transmission of data between end systems across a communications facility. It provides a messaging service for the session layer and hides the underlying network from the upper layers. As such it may need to be very complex in order to deal with a variety of network characteristics and capabilities.

The transport layer provides the means to establish, maintain, and release transport connections on behalf of session entities. It provides reliable end-to-end data transport. Error checking and other reliability features are handled by the protocols in the transport layer if they are not handled by the underlying networks. This is the case, for example, with frame relay and Asynchronous Transfer Mode (ATM) networks, which do not perform error checks when delivering packets. Instead, error checking is assumed to be handled by transport layer protocols which examine information in the packet to make sure the information was delivered error-free.

The transport layer can provide a connection-oriented or connectionless service. In a connection-oriented session, a circuit is established through which packets flow to the destination. In this arrangement, packets arrive in order and do not require a full address or other information because the circuit guarantees their delivery to the proper destination. Connectionless session does not establish circuits or provide reliable data delivery. Packets are fully addressed and sent out over the network. The transport layer protocols at the destination can re-order the packets which arrive out of order and request retransmission of missing or defective packets.

FLOW CONTROL IN THE TRANSPORT LAYER

Flow control is a function for the control of the data flow within an OSI layer or between adjacent layers. In other words it limits the amount of data transmitted by the sending transport entity to a level, or rate, that the receiver can manage.

Flow control is a good example of a protocol function that must be implemented in several layers of the OSI architecture model. At the transport level flow control will allow the transport protocol entity in a host to restrict the flow of data over a logical connection from the transport protocol entity in another host. However, one of the services of the network level is to prevent congestion. Thus the network level also uses flow control to restrict the flow of Network Protocol Data Units (NPDUs).

The flow control mechanisms used in the transport layer vary for the different classes of service. Since the different classes of service are determined by the quality of service of the underlying data network which transports the Transport Protocol Data Units (TPDUs), it is these which influence the type of flow control used.

Thus flow control becomes a much more complex issue at the transport layer than at lower levels like the datalink level. Two reasons for this are:

- Flow control must interact with transport users, transport entities, and the network service.
- Long and variable transmission delays between transport entities.

Flow control causes Queuing amongst transport users, entities, and the network service. We take a look at the four possible queues that form and what control policies are at work here.

The transport entity is responsible for generating one or more Transport Protocol Data Units (TPDUs) for passing onto the network layer. The network layer delivers the TPDUs to the receiving transport entity which then takes out the data and passes it on to the destination user. There are two reasons why the receiving transport entity would want to control the flow of TPDUs:

- The receiving user cannot keep up with the flow of data
- The receiving transport entity itself cannot keep up with the flow of TPDUs

When we say that a user or transport entity cannot keep up with the data flow, we mean that the receiving buffers are filling too quickly and will overflow and lose data unless the rate of incoming data is slowed. Four possible ways to cope with the problem are:

- Let it be and do nothing
- Refuse any more TPDUs from the network service
- Use a fixed sliding-window protocol
- Use a credit scheme

There are different issues to be considered with transport flow control over different levels of network service. The more unreliable the network service provided the more complex flow control mechanism that may be needed to be used by the transport layer. The credit scheme works well with the different network services although specific issues need to be addressed as with a reliable non-sequencing network service and an unreliable network service.

The credit scheme seems most suited for flow control in the transport layer with all types of network service. It gives the receiver the best control over data flow and helps provide a smooth traffic flow. Sequence numbering of credit allocations handles the arrival of ACK/ CREDIT TPDUs out of order, and a window timer will ensure deadlock does not occur in a network environment where TPDUs can be lost.

Connection Establishment and Termination Issues. The issues involved here vary with the quality of network service available and are considered below.

- Reliable sequencing network service
- Reliable non-sequencing network service

Unreliable non-sequencing network service. Issues involved with a Reliable Sequencing Network Service.

A reliable sequencing network accepts messages of arbitrary length and delivers them with virtually 100% accuracy. TPDUs are guaranteed to arrive in sequence.

Connection establishment for a connection-oriented service has three main purposes :

- Assures each side of the connection that the other exists
- Negotiation of optional parameters *e.g.*, TPDU size
- Allocates transport entity resources.

Connection establishment is by mutual agreement and can be set up using a simple set of user commands (primitives) and control TPDUs.

To begin a user is in IDLE state w.r.t. the transport entity. The user can signal it will wait passively for a request with a LISTEN command. The user can send a CLOSE command to return to the IDLE state. If a RFC (Request For Connection) TPDU is received that specifies the listening user, then a connection is opened. The transport entity:

- Signals the user that a connection is open
- Sends an RFC to the remote transport entity as a confirmation
- Put the connection state to OPEN.

A user may open a connection by using an OPEN command. The transport entity will send a RFC. The return of a matching RFC establishes the connection. The connection is aborted if the user issues a CLOSE command or the remote transport entity refuses the connection by sending a CLS TPDU. If an RFC arrives while the user is IDLE then there are three options :

- The transport entity can reject the request by sending a CLS
- The request can be queued until the user LISTENs
- The transport entity can interrupt or otherwise signal the user.

Connection termination is handled similarly. To close a connection the transport entity sends a CLOSE. Either side or both sides of a connection may initiate a close. The connection is closed by mutual agreement. For a graceful termination a connection continues to receive data TPDUs until a CLS is received.

Issues involved with a Reliable Non-Sequencing Network Service. A reliable non-sequencing network service accepts messages of arbitrary length and delivers them with virtually 100% confidence. Howevere, some TPDUs may arrive out of sequence.

Connection establishment is now a little more tricky. After a transport entity has sent a RFC (Request For Connection), it expects to receive a CLS or RFC in reply. The entity receiving the RFC may reply with a RFC and some TPDUs. One or more of these TPDUs may arrive before the RFC. The solution is for the receiver to queue the TPDUs until the RFC arrives.

Likewise, data may arrive after the connection has closed. After the transport entity has sent its last data TPDU it sends a CLS. But the CLS may arrive before the last data TPDU. To avoid this problem the CLS TPDU could contain the sequence number after the last data TPDU. The receiving entity on receipt of a CLS would wait for the remaining data before closing the connection.

Issues involved with a Unreliable Non-Sequencing Network Service. For an unreliable network service TPDUs may be lost as well as arriving out of sequence. Suppose that transport entity A issues a RFC (Request For Connection) to B. A expects an RFC from B to confirm the connection. This is called two-way handshaking. Two things can go wrong—A's RFC can be lost or B's RFC can be lost. Both cases are handled by a re-transmitter timer. After the timer expires another RFC will be issued. This can give rise to the possibility of duplicate RFCs. The solution is simply to ignore duplicate RFCs once a connection is established.

Now consider the problem of a duplicate RFC arriving after the connection has closed *i.e.,* a duplicate RFC X (request for connection X, sequence number starts with X) arrives at B after the connection with B has closed. B thinking that a new connection has been requested sends and RFC Y to A. A decides to open the connection and sends a RFC Z as confirmation. B discards this as a duplicate and A initiates data transfer with a TPDU numbered Z. B rejects this TPDU as being out of sequence.

The solution now is that each side must acknowledge the other sides RFC and sequence number. This procedure is known as three-way handshaking.

CRASH RECOVERY

When the system using the transport entity crashes all connections are effectively left in a half-open state and the other other side does not realise the problem. The active side of the connection may still continue to send TPDUs and wait for their acknowledgement. Typically the sender will resend the TPDU a maximum number of times and then timeout after a certain 'give-up' time. The transport entity assumes the other transport entity has crashed, closses the connection and informs the user of the abnormal closure.

All these timeouts take time. If the crash system restarts fast enough it could send RST X in response to every TPDU X it receives. Thus the receiving transport entity performs an abnormal termination.

SEQUENCING PROBLEMS IN A NON-SEQUENCING NETWORK

When using a reliable non-sequencing network If you limit the size of a TPDU on your network then this is called a maximum TPDU size. We need to distinguish two types of data transfer required by the user: stream oriented and block oriented. A stream-oriented interface between transport and the user accepts data as if they were a continuous stream of bits and reproduces the stream at the other end without conveying any information about the breakpoints in the stream submitted by the sender. This interface might serve voice and real-time applications.

We need to distinguish two types of data transfer required by the user: stream oriented and block oriented. A stream-oriented interface between transport and user accepts data as if they were a continuous stream of bits and reproduces the stream at the other end without conveying any information about the breakpoints in the stream submitted by the sender. This interface might serve voice and real-time applications.

A more common occurrence is a transport user that sends data in blocks. For convenience, we refer to a block of data presented to transport as a letter. If a letter exceeds the maximum allowable TPDU size, the transport entity must segment the letter before transmission, to be reassembled at reception prior to delivery to the user. Because our network is non-sequencing, segments may arrive out of order. Worse, segments from different letters may be interchanged in route.

A simple solution to this problem is to number each letter sequentially and to number each segment sequentially within each letter. This, however, is an unnecessary duplication of TPDU sequence numbering function. All is required is an end of letter (EOL) flag. As TPDUs arrive at the destination transport entity, they are reordered.

Each sequential set of TPDUs, starting with the first TPDU after and EOL, and including all TPDUs through the next EOL, are treated as a unit. The data from this unit, stripped of transport headers, are delivered as a single letter to the user.

Internet Backbones, NAPs and ISPs

Our discussion of layering in the previous section has perhaps given the impression that the Internet is a carefully organized and highly intertwined structure. This is certainly true in the sense that all of the network entities (end systems, routers and bridges) use a common set of protocols, enabling the entities to communicate with each other. If one wanted to change, remove, or add a protocol, one would have to follow a long and arduous procedure to get approval from the IETF, which will (among other things) make sure that the changes are consistent with the highly intertwined structure. However, from a topological perspective, to many people the Internet seems to be growing in a chaotic manner, with new sections, branches and wings popping up in random places on a daily basis. Indeed, unlike the protocols, the Internet's topology can grow and evolve without approval from a central authority. Let us now try to a grip on the seemingly nebulous Internet topology.

As we mentioned at the beginning of this chapter, the topology of the Internet is loosely hierarchical. Roughly speaking, from bottom-to-top the hierarchy consists of end systems (PCs, workstations, etc.) connected to local Internet Service Providers (ISPs). The local ISPs are in turn connected to regional ISPs, which are in turn connected to national and international ISPs. The national and international ISPs are connected together at the highest tier in the hierarchy. New tiers and branches can be added just as a new piece of Lego can be attached to an existing Lego construction.

In this section we describe the topology of the Internet in the United States as of 1999. Let's begin at the top of the hierarchy and work our way down. Residing at the very top of the hierarchy are the national ISPs, which are called National Backbone Providers (NBPs). The NBPs form independent backbone networks that span North America (and typically abroad as well). Just as there are multiple long-distance telephone companies in the USA, there are multiple NBPs that compete with each other for traffic and customers. The existing NBPs include internetMCI, SprintLink, PSINet, UUNet Technologies, and AGIS. The NBPs typically have high-bandwidth transmission links, with bandwidths ranging from 1.5 Mbps to 622 Mbps and higher. Each NBP also has numerous hubs which interconnect its links and at which regional ISPs can tap into the NBP.

The NBPs themselves must be interconnected to each other. To see this, suppose one regional ISP, say MidWestnet, is connected to the MCI NBP and another regional ISP, say EastCoastnet, is connected to Sprint's NBP. How can traffic be sent from MidWestnet to EastCoastnet ? The solution is to introduce switching centers, called Network Access Points (NAPs), which interconnect the NBPs, thereby allowing each regional ISP to pass traffic to any other regional ISP. To keep us all confused, some of the NAPs are not referred to as NAPs but instead as MAEs (Metropolitan Area Exchanges). In the United States, many of the NAPs are run by RBOCs (Regional Bell Operating Companies); for example, PacBell has a NAP in San Francisco and Ameritech has a NAP in Chicago. For a list of major NBP's (those connected into at least three MAPs/MAE's),.

Because the NAPs relay and switch tremendous volumes of Internet traffic, they are typically in themselves complex high-speed switching networks concentrated in a small geographical area (for example, a single building). Often the NAPs use high-speed ATM switching technology in the heart of the NAP, with IP riding on top of ATM. The details of figures are unimportant for us now; it is worthwhile to note, however, that the NBP hubs can themselves be complex data networks.

The astute reader may have noticed that ATM technology, which uses virtual circuits, can be found at certain places within the Internet. But earlier we said that the "Internet is a datagram network and does not use virtual circuits". We admit now that this statement stretches the truth a little bit. We made this statement because it helps the reader to see the forest through the trees by not having the main issues obscured. The truth is that there are virtual circuits in the Internet, but they are in localized pockets of the Internet and they are buried deep down in the protocol stack, typically at layer 2. If you find this confusing, just pretend for now that the Internet does not employ any technology that uses virtual circuits. This is not too far from the truth.

Running an NBP is not cheap. In June 1996, the cost of leasing 45 Mbps fiber optics from coast-to-coast, as well as the additional hardware required, was approximately $150,000 per month. And the fees that an NBP pays the NAPs to connect to the NAPs can exceed $300,000 annually. NBPs and NAPs also have significant capital costs in equipment for high-speed networking. An NBP earns money by charging a monthly fee to the regional ISPs that connect to it. The fee that an NBP charges to a regional ISP typically depends on the bandwidth of the connection between the regional ISP and the NBP; clearly a 1.5 Mbps connection would be

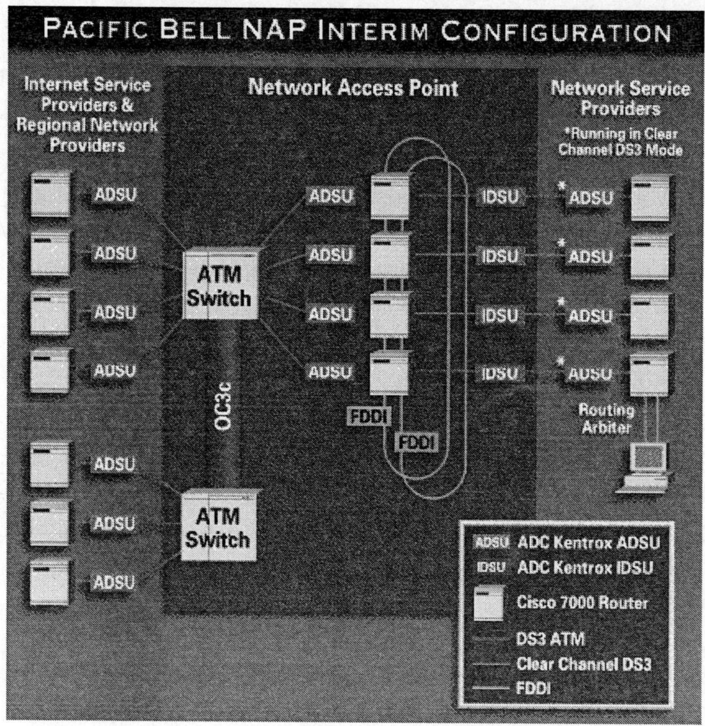

Figure 29.5 *The PacBell NAP Architecture.*

charged less than a 45 Mbps connection. Once the fixed-bandwidth connection is in place, the regional ISP can pump and receive as much data as it pleases, up to the bandwidth of the connection, at no additional cost. If an NBP has significant revenues from the regional ISPs that connect to it, it may be able to cover the high capital and monthly costs of setting up and maintaining an NBP.

A regional ISP is also a complex network, consisting of routers and transmission links with rates ranging from 64 Kbps upward. A regional ISP typically taps into an NBP (at an NBP hub), but it can also tap directly into an NAP, in which case the regional NBP pays a monthly fee to a NAP instead of to a NBP. A regional ISP can also tap into the Internet backbone at two or more distinct points (for example, at an NBP hub or at a NAP). How does a regional ISP cover its costs ? To answer this question, let's jump to the bottom of the hierarchy.

End systems gain access to the Internet by connecting to a local ISP. Universities and corporations can act as local ISPs, but backbone service providers can also serve as a local ISP. Many local ISPs are small "mom and pop" companies, however. A popular www site known simple as "the list" contains link to nearly 8000 local, regional, and backbone ISPs. The local ISPs tap into one of the regional ISPs in its region. Analogous to the fee structure between the regional ISP and the NBP, the local ISP pays a monthly fee to its regional ISP which depends on the bandwidth of the connection. Finally, the local ISP charges its customers (typically) a flat, monthly fee for Internet access: the higher the transmission rate of the connection, the higher the monthly fee.

CONNECTION-ORIENTED TRANSPORT-TCP

TCP/IP

The internet connects many networks, each of which runs a protocol known as TCP/IP (Transmission Control Protocol) and IP (Internet Protocol) correspond roughly to layers 4 and 3 of the OSI model, respectively, although they are not part of the OSI model. They were developed along with the ARPA project and have become DOD standards. TCP/IP is probably the most widely implemented protocol in the world and runs on almost anything from PCS to supercomputers.

The TCP/IP pair of protocols is part of a protocol collection called the TCP/IP protocol suite , TCP provides connection—oriented services for higher-layer applications and relies on IP to route packets, through the network in order to make those connections. These application, in turn, provide specific services for Internet users. For example, SMTP (simple mail transfer Protocol) defines the protocol used for the delivery of mail messages over the Internet. The telnet protocol allows users to log in to remote computers via the Internet. FTP (file transfer protocol) allows internet users to transfer files from remote computers. DSN (domain name system) provides a mapping of host names to addresses.

TCP is a connection-oriented transport protocol designed to provide communications over different network architectures. Its predecessor in the original Arpanet was NCP (network control protocol), which was designed to run on top of a reliable network. NCP, redesigned to run over unreliable networks, became TCP. UDP (user datagram protocol) provides a connectionless mode of communication over dissimilar networks.

The Internet protocol is a layer 3 protocol designed to provide a packet delivery service between two sites.

Overview of TCP/IP Protocol

Applications developed for TCP/IP generally use several of the protocols in the suite. The layers of the protocol suite is also known as the protocol stack. User applications communicate with the top layer of the protocol suite. The top-level protocol layer on the source computer passes information to the lower layers of the stack, which in turn pass it to the physical network. The physical network transfers the information to the destination computer. The lower layers of the protocol stack on the destination computer pass the information to higher layers, which in turn pass it to the destination application.

Each protocol layer within the TCP/IP suite has various functions; these functions are independent of the other layers. Each layer, however, expects to receive specific services from the layer beneath it, and each layer provides specific services to the layer above it.

Figure 29.6 shows the TCP/IP protocol layers. The layers at the same level on the source and destination computers are peers. For example, the application on the source computer and the application on the destination computer are peers. Each layer of the protocol stack on the source computer communicates with its peer layer on the destination computer. From the perspective of the software developer or user, the transfer takes place as if the peer layers sent their packets directly to one another.

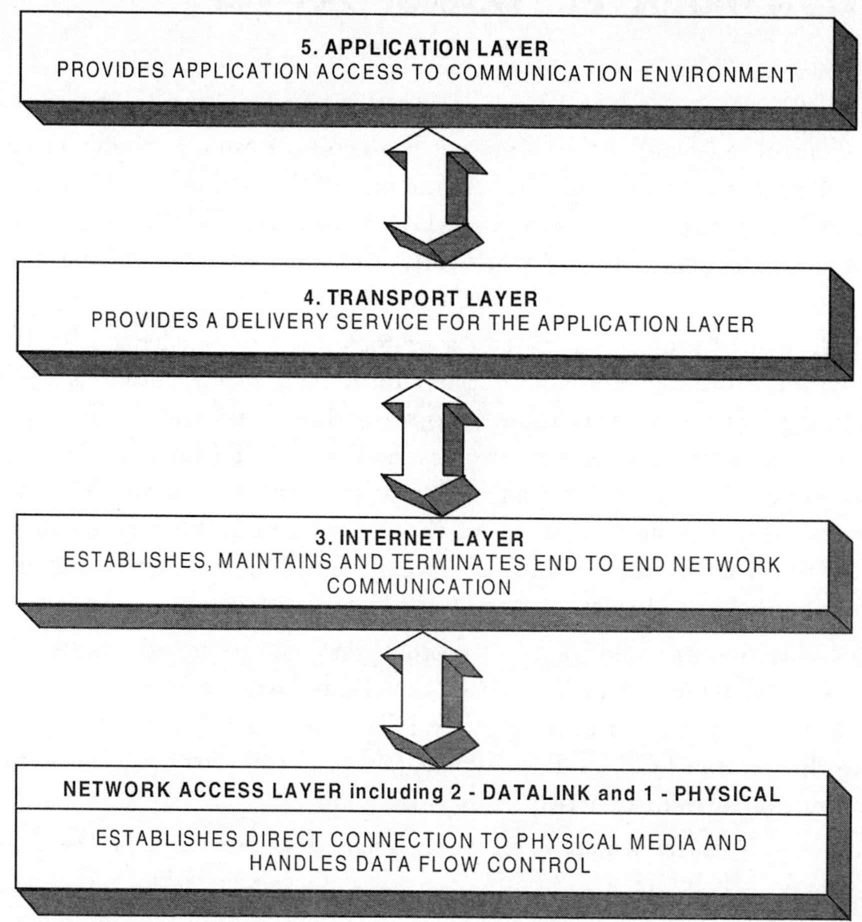

Figure 29.6 *TCP/IP Protocol Layers.*

TCP/IP Model

An application for transferring files with TCP, for instance, performs the following operations to send the file contents:

1. The application layer passes a stream of bytes to the transport layer on the source computer.
2. The transport layer divides the stream into TCP segments, adds a header with a sequence number for that segment, and passes the segment to the Internet (IP) layer. A checksum is computed over the TCP header and data.
3. The IP layer creates a packet with a data portion containing the TCP segment. The IP layer adds a packet header containing source and destination IP addresses.
4. The IP layer also determines the physical address of the destination computer or intermediate computer on the way to the destination host. It passes the packet and the physical address to the data-link layer. A checksum is computed on the IP header.

5. The data-link layer transmits the IP packet in the data portion of a data-link frame to the destination computer or an intermediate computer. If the packet is sent to an intermediate computer, steps 4 through 7 are repeated until the destination computer is reached.
6. At the destination computer, the data-link layer discards the data-link header and passes the IP packet to the IP layer.
7. The IP layer checks the IP packet header. If the checksum contained in the header does not match the checksum computed by the IP layer, it discards the packet.
8. If the checksums match, the IP layer passes the TCP segment to the TCP layer.
9. The TCP layer computes a checksum for the TCP header and data. If the computed checksum does not match the checksum transmitted in the header, the TCP layer discards the segment. If the checksum is correct and the segment is in the correct sequence, the TCP layer sends an acknowledgement to the source computer and passes the data to the application.
10. The application on the destination computer receives a stream of bytes, just as if it were directly connected to the application on the source computer.

The TCP Connection

TCP provides multiplexing, de-multiplexing, and error detection (but not recovery) in exactly the same manner as UDP. Nevertheless, TCP and UDP differ in many ways. The most fundamental difference is that UDP is connectionless, while TCP is connection-oriented. UDP is connectionless because it sends data without ever establishing a connection. TCP is connection-oriented because before one application process can begin to send data to another, the two processes must first "handshake" with each other—that is, they must send some preliminary segments to each other to establish the parameters of the ensuing data transfer. As part of the TCP connection establishment, both sides of the connection will initialize many TCP "state variables" associated with the TCP connection.

The TCP "connection" is not an end-to-end TDM or FDM circuit as in a circuit-switched network. Nor is it a virtual circuit (see Chapter 1), as the connection state resides entirely in the two end systems. Because the TCP protocol runs only in the end systems and not in the intermediate network elements (routers and bridges), the intermediate network elements do not maintain TCP connection state. In fact, the intermediate routers are completely oblivious to TCP connections; they see datagrams, not connections.

A TCP connection provides for full-duplex data transfer. That is, application-level data can be transferred in both directions between two hosts—if there is a TCP connection between process A on one host and process B on another host, then application-level data can flow from A to B at the same time as application-level data flows from B to A. TCP connection is also always point-to-point, *i.e.*, between a single sender and a single receiver. So called "multicasting", the transfer of data from one sender to many receivers in a single send operation—is not possible with TCP. With TCP, two hosts are company and three are a crowd.

Let us now take a look at how a TCP connection is established. Suppose a process running in one host wants to initiate a connection with another process in another host. Recall that the host that is initiating the connection is called the client host, while the other host is called the server host. The client application process first informs the client TCP that it wants to establish a connection to a process in the server. Recall from section 2.6, a Java client program does this by issuing the command:

Socket clientSocket = new socket ("hostname", "port number");

The TCP in the client then proceeds to establish a TCP connection with the TCP in the server. For now it suffices to know that the client first sends a special TCP segment; the server responds with a second special TCP segment; and finally the client responds again with a third special segment. The first two segments contain no "payload," *i.e.*, no application-layer data; the third of these segments may carry a payload. Because three segments are sent between the two hosts, this connection establishment procedure is often referred to as a three-way handshake.

Once a TCP connection is established, the two application processes can send data to each other; because TCP is full-duplex they can send data at the same time. Let us consider the sending of data from the client process to the server process. Once the data passes through the door, the data is now in the hands of TCP running in the client. As shown in figure 29.7, TCP directs this data to the connection's send buffer, which is one of the buffers that is set aside during the initial three-way handshake. From time to time, TCP will "grab" chunks of data from the send buffer. The maximum amount of data that can be grabbed and placed in a segment is limited by the Maximum Segment Size (MSS). The MSS depends on the TCP implementation (determined by the operating system) and can often be configured; common values are 1,500 bytes, 536 bytes and 512 bytes. (These segment sizes are often chosen in order to avoid IP fragmentation, which will be discussed in the next chapter.) Note that the MSS is the maximum amount of application-level data in the segment, not the maximum size of the TCP segment including headers. (This terminology is confusing, but we have to live with it, as it is well entrenched.)

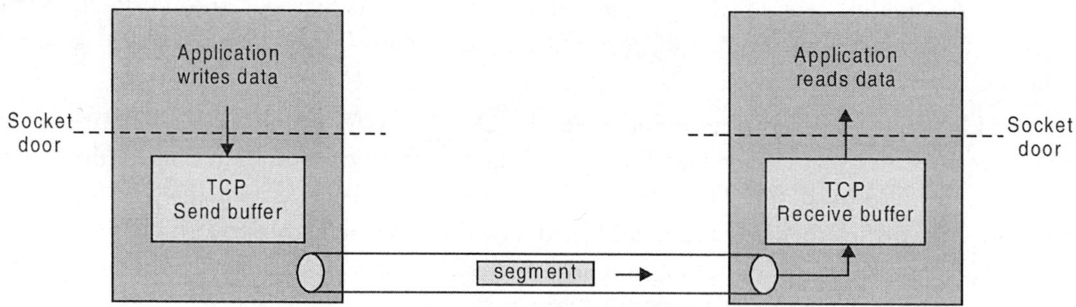

Figure 29.7 *TCP Send and Receive Buffers.*

TCP encapsulates each chunk of client data with TCP header, thereby forming TCP segments. The segments are passed down to the network layer, where they are separately encapsulated within network-layer IP data-grams. The IP data-grams are then sent into the network. When TCP receives a segment at the other end, the segment's data is placed in the TCP connection's receive buffer. The application reads the stream of data from this buffer. Each side of the connection has its own send buffer and its own receive buffer. The send and receive buffers for data flowing in one direction are shown in figure 29.7.

We see from this discussion that a TCP connection consists of buffers, variables and a socket connection to a process in one host, and another set of buffers, variables and a socket connection to a process in another host. As mentioned earlier, no buffers or variables are allocated to the connection in the network elements (routers, bridges and repeaters) between the hosts.

TCP Segment Structure

Having taken a brief look at the TCP connection, let's examine the TCP segment structure. The TCP segment consists of header fields and a data field. The data field contains a chunk of application data. As mentioned above, the MSS limits the maximum size of a segment's data field. When TCP sends a large file, such as an encoded image as part of a Web page, it typically breaks the file into chunks of size MSS (except for the last chunk, which will often be less than the MSS). Interactive applications, however, often transmit data chunks that are smaller than the MSS; for example, with remote login applications like Telnet, the data field in the TCP segment is often only one byte. Because the TCP header is typically 20 bytes (12 bytes more than the UDP header), segments sent by telnet may only be 21 bytes in length.

Figure 29.8 shows the structure of the TCP segment. As with UDP, the header includes source and destination port numbers, that are used for multiplexing/demultiplexing data from/to upper layer applications. Also as with UDP, the header includes a checksum field. A TCP segment header also contains the following fields:

The 32-bit sequence number field, and the 32-bit acknowledgement number field are used by the TCP sender and receiver in implementing a reliable data transfer service, as discussed below.

The 16-bit window size field is used for the purposes of flow control. We will see shortly that it is used to indicate the number of bytes that a receiver is willing to accept.

The 4-bit length field specifies the length of the TCP header in 32-bit words. The TCP header can be of variable length due to the TCP options field, discussed below. (Typically, the options field is empty, so that the length of the typical TCP header is 20 bytes.)

The optional and variable length options field is used when a sender and receiver negotiate the Maximum Segment Size (MSS) or as a window scaling factor for use in high-speed networks. A time-stamping option is also defined. The flag field contains 6 bits. The ACK bit is used to indicate that the value carried in the acknowledgement field is valid. The RST, SYN and FIN bits are used for connection setup and teardown, as we will discuss at the end of this section. When the PSH bit is set, this is an indication that the receiver should pass the data to the upper layer immediately. Finally, the URG bit is used to indicate there is data in this segment that the sending-side upper layer entity has marked as "urgent." The location of the last byte of this urgent data is indicated by the 16-bit urgent data pointer. TCP must inform the receiving-side upper layer entity when urgent data exists and pass it a pointer to the end of the urgent data. (In practice, the PSH, URG and pointer to urgent data are not used.

Two of the most important fields in the TCP segment header are the sequence number field and the acknowledgement number field. These fields are a critical part of TCP's reliable data transfer service. But before discussing how these fields are used to provide reliable data transfer, let us first explain what exactly TCP puts in these fields.

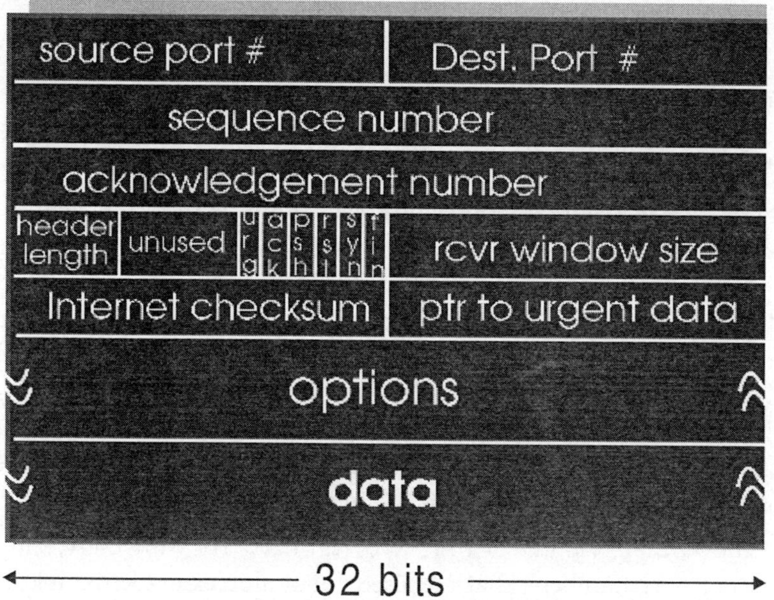

Figure 29.8 *TCP Segment Structure.*

TCP views data as an unstructured, but ordered, stream of bytes. TCP's use of sequence numbers reflects this view in that sequence numbers are over the stream of transmitted bytes and *not* over the series of transmitted segments. The sequence number for a segment is the byte-stream number of the first byte in the segment. Let's look at an example. Suppose that a process in host A wants to send a stream of data to a process in host B over a TCP connection. The TCP in host A will implicitly number each byte in the data stream. Suppose that the data stream consists of a file consisting of 500,000 bytes, that the MSS is 1,000 bytes, and that the first byte of the data stream is numbered zero. As shown in figure 29.9, TCP constructs 500 segments out

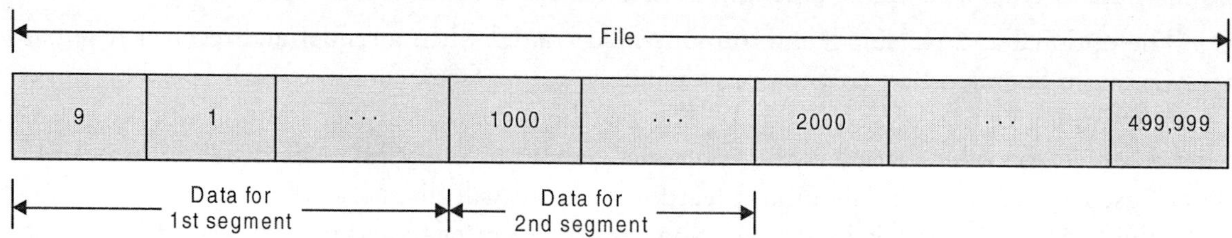

Figure 29.9 *Dividing File Data into TCP Segments.*

of the data stream. The first segment gets assigned sequence number 0, the second segment gets assigned sequence number 1000, the third segment gets assigned sequence number 2000, and so on. Each sequence number is inserted in the sequence number field in the header of the appropriate TCP segment.

Now let us consider acknowledgement numbers. These are a little trickier than sequence numbers. Recall that TCP is full duplex, so that host A may be receiving data from host B while it sends data to host B (as part of the same TCP connection). Each of the segments that arrive from host B have a sequence number for the data flowing from B to A. *The acknowledgement number that host A puts in its segment is sequence number of the next byte host A is expecting from host B*. It is good to look at a few examples to understand what is going on here. Suppose that host A has received all bytes numbered 0 through 535 from B and suppose that it is about to send a segment to host B. In other words, host A is waiting for byte 536 and all the subsequent bytes in host B's data stream. So host A puts 536 in the acknowledgement number field of the segment it sends to B.

As another example, suppose that host A has received one segment from host B containing bytes 0 through 535 and another segment containing bytes 900 through 1,000. For some reason host A has not yet received bytes 536 through 899. In this example, host A is still waiting for byte 536 (and beyond) in order to recreate B's data stream. Thus, A's next segment to B will contain 536 in the acknowledgement number field. Because TCP only acknowledges bytes up to the first missing byte in the stream, TCP is said to provide cumulative acknowledgements.

This last example also brings up an important but subtle issue. Host A received the third segment (bytes 900 through 1,000) before receiving the second segment (bytes 536 through 899). Thus, the third segment arrived out of order. The subtle issue is: What does a host do when it receives out of order segments in a TCP connection ? Interestingly, the TCP RFCs do not impose any rules here, and leave the decision up to the people programming a TCP implementation. There are basically two choices: either *(i)* the receiver immediately discards out-of-order bytes; or *(ii)* the receiver keeps the out-of-order bytes and waits for the missing bytes to fill in the gaps. Clearly, the latter choice is more efficient in terms of network bandwidth, whereas the former choice significantly simplifies the TCP code. Throughout the remainder of this introductory discussion of TCP, we focus on the former implementation, that is, we assume that the TCP receiver discards out-of-order segments.

In truth, both sides of a TCP connection randomly choose an initial sequence number. This is done to minimize the possibility a segment that is still present in the network from an earlier, already-terminated connection between two hosts is mistaken for a valid segment in a later connection between these same two hosts (who also happen to be using the same port numbers as the old connection) [Sunshine 78].

Telnet: A Case Study for Sequence and Acknowledgement Numbers

Telnet is a popular application-layer protocol used for remote login. It runs over TCP and is designed to work between any pair of hosts. Unlike the bulk-data transfer applications, telnet is an interactive application. We discuss a telnet example here, as it nicely illustrates TCP sequence and acknowledgement numbers.

Suppose one host, 88.88.88.88, initiates a telnet session with host 99.99.99.99. (anticipating our discussion on IP addressing in the next chapter, we take the liberty to use IP addresses to identify the hosts.) Because host 88.88.88.88 initiates the session, it is labeled the client and host 99.99.99.99 is labeled the server. Each character typed by the user (at the client) will be sent to the remote host; the remote host will send back a copy of each character, which will be displayed on the telnet user's screen. This "echo back" is used to ensure that characters seen by the telnet user have already been received and processed at the remote site. Each character thus traverses the network twice between when the user hits the key and when the character is displayed on the user's monitor.

Now suppose the user types a single letter, 'C', and then grabs a coffee. Let's examine the TCP segments that are sent between the client and server. As shown in figure 29.10, we suppose the starting sequence numbers are 42 and 79 for the client and server, respectively. Recall that the sequence number of a segment is the sequence number of first byte in the data field. Thus the first segment sent from the client will have sequence number 42; the first segment sent from the server will have sequence number 79. Recall that the acknowledgement number is the sequence number of the next byte of data that the host is waiting for. After the TCP connection is established but before any data is sent, the client is waiting for byte 79 and the server is waiting for byte 42.

As shown in figure, three segments are sent. The first segment is sent from the client to the server, containing the one-byte ASCII representation of the letter 'C' in its data field. This first segment also has 42 in its sequence number field, as we just described. Also, because the client has not yet received any data from the server, this first segment will have 79 in its acknowledgement number field.

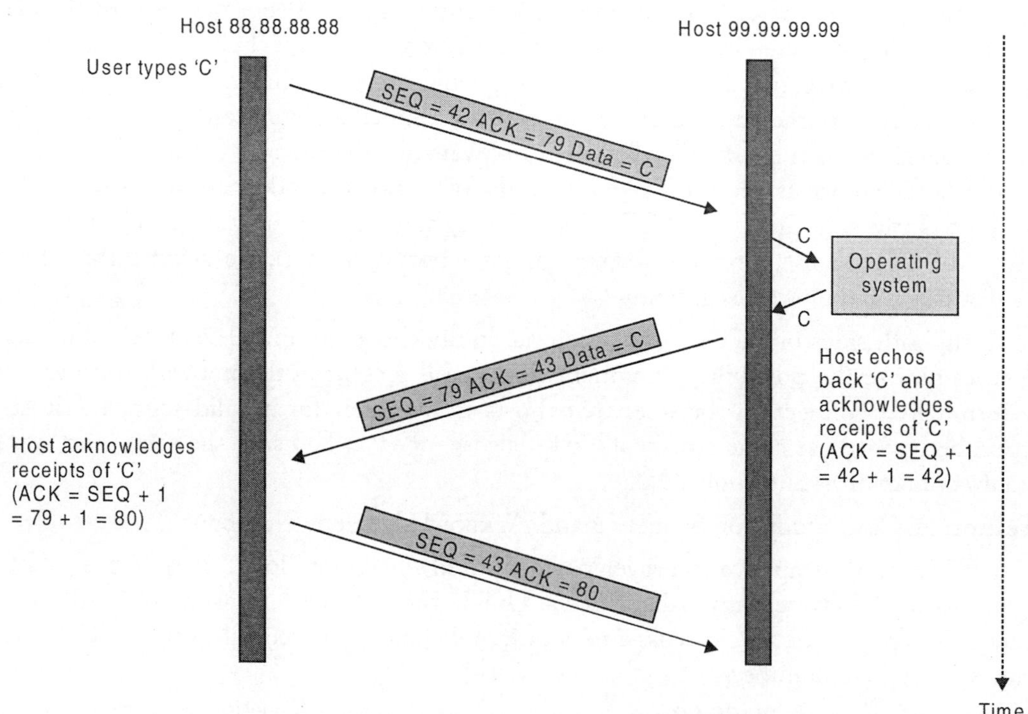

Figure 29.10 *Sequence and Acknowledgement Numbers for a Simple Telnet Application Over TCP.*

The second segment is sent from the server to the client. It serves a dual purpose. First it provides an acknowledgement for the data the client has received. By putting 43 in the acknowledgement field, the server is telling the client that it has successfully received everything up through byte 42 and is now waiting for bytes 43 onward. The second purpose of this segment is to echo back the letter 'C'. Thus, the second segment has the ASCII representation of 'C' in its data field. This second segment has the sequence number 79, the initial sequence number of the server-to-client data flow of this TCP connection, as this is the very first byte of data that the server is sending. Note that the acknowledgement for client-to-server data is carried in a segment carrying server-to-client data; this acknowledgement is said to be piggybacked on the server-to-client data segment.

The third segment is sent from the client to the server. Its sole purpose is to acknowledge the data it has received from the server. (Recall that the second segment contained data—the letter 'C'—from the server to the client.) This segment has an empty data field (*i.e.*, the acknowledgement is not being piggybacked with any cient-to-server data). The segment has 80 in the acknowledgement number field because the client has received the stream of bytes up through byte sequence number 79 and it is now waiting for bytes 80 onward. You might think it odd that this segment also has a sequence number since the segment contains no data. But because TCP has a sequence number field, the segment needs to have some sequence number.

Reliable Data Transfer

Recall that the Internet's network layer service (IP service) is unreliable. IP does not guarantee datagram delivery, does not guarantee in-order delivery of datagrams, and does not guarantee the integrity of the data in the datagrams. With IP service, datagrams can overflow router buffers and never reach their destination, data-grams can arrive out of order, and bits in the datagram can get corrupted (flipped from 0 to 1 and vice versa). Because transport-layer segments are carried across the network by IP datagrams, transport-layer segments can also suffer from these problems as well.

TCP creates a reliable data transfer service on top of IP's unreliable best-effort service. Many popular application protocols—including FTP, SMTP, NNTP, HTTP and telnet—use TCP rather than UDP primarily because TCP provides reliable data transfer service. TCP's reliable data transfer service ensures that the data stream that a process reads out of its TCP receive buffer is uncorrupted, without gaps, without duplication, and in sequence, *i.e.*, the byte stream is exactly the same byte stream that was sent by the end system on the other side of the connection. In this subsection we provide an informal overview of how TCP provides reliable data transfer.

Retransmissions

Retransmission of lost and corrupted data is crucial for providing reliable data transfer. TCP provides reliable data transfer by using positive acknowledgements and timers in much the same way as we studied in section 3.4. TCP acknowledges data that has been received correctly, and retransmits segments when segments or their corresponding acknowledgements are thought to be lost or corrupted. Just as in the case of our reliable data transfer protocol, RDT3.0, TCP can not itself tell for certain if a segment, or its ACK, is lost, corrupted, or overly delayed. In all cases, TCP's response will be the same: retransmit the segment in question.

TCP also uses pipelining, allowing the sender to have multiple transmitted but yet-to-be-acknowledged segments outstanding at any given time. We saw in the previous section that pipelining can greatly improve the throughput of a TCP connection when the ratio of the segment size to round trip delay is small. The specific number of outstanding unacknowledged segments that a sender can have is determined by TCP's flow control and congestion control mechanisms. TCP flow control is discussed at the end of this section; TCP congestion control is discussed in section 3.7. For the time being, we must simply be aware that the sender can have multiple transmitted, but unacknowledged, segments at any given time.

```
/*assume sender is not constrained by TCP flow or congestion control,
  that data from above is less than MSS in size, and that data transfer
  is in one direction only*/
sendbase = initial_sequence number
nextseqnum = initial_sequence number

loop(forever) {
  switch(event)
    event:data received from application above
      create TCP segment with sequence number nextseqnum
      start timer for segment nextseqnum
      pass segment to IP
      nextseqnum = nextseqnum + length(data)
    event: timer timeout for segment with sequence number y
      retransmit segment with sequence number y
      Compute new timeout interval for segment y
      restart timer for sequence number y

    event: ACK received, with ACK field value of y
      if(y>sendbase) { /*cumulative ACK of all data up to y*/
        cancel all timers for segments with sequence numbers < y
      sendbase = y
        }
      else { /*a duplicate ACK for already ACKed segment*/
        increment number of duplicate ACKs received for y
        if(number of duplicate ACKS received for y == 3) {
          /*TCP fast retransmit*/
          resend segment with sequence number y
          restart timer for segment y
        }
      }  /* end of loop forever */
```

Let us consider a TCP connection between host A and B and focus on the data stream being sent from host A to host B. At the sending host (A), TCP is passed application-layer data, which it frames into segments and then passes on to IP. The passing of data from the application to TCP and the subsequent framing and transmission of a segment is the first important event that the TCP sender must handle. Each time TCP releases a segment to IP, it starts a timer for that segment. If this timer expires, an interrupt event is generated at host A. TCP responds to the timeout event, the second major type of event that the TCP sender must handle, by retransmitting the segment that caused the timeout.

The third major event that must be handled by the TCP sender is the arrival of an acknowledgement segment (ACK) from the receiver (more specifically, a segment containing a valid ACK field value). Here, the sender's TCP must determine whether the ACK is a first-time ACK for a segment that the sender has yet to receive an acknowledgement for, or a so-called duplicate ACK that re-acknowledges a segment for which the sender has already received an earlier acknowledgement. In the case of the arrival of a first-time ACK, the sender now knows that *all* data up to the byte being acknowledged has been received correctly at the receiver. The sender can thus update its TCP state variable that tracks the sequence number of the last byte that is known to have been received correctly and in-order at the receiver.

To understand the sender's response to a duplicate ACK, we must look at why the receiver sends a duplicate ACK in the first place. Table 29.1 summarizes the TCP receiver's ACK generation policy. When a TCP receiver receives a segment with a sequence number that is larger than the next, expected, in-order sequence number, it detects a gap in the data stream— *i.e.,* a missing segment. Since TCP does not use negative acknowledgements, the receiver can not send an explicit negative acknowledgement back to the sender. Instead, it simply re-acknowledges (*i.e.,* generates a duplicate ACK for) the last in-order byte of data it has received. If the TCP sender receives three duplicate ACKs for the same data, it takes this as an indication that the segment following the segment that has been ACKed three times has been lost. In this case, TCP performs a fast retransmit, retransmitting the missing segment *before* that segment's timer expires.

Table 29.1 TCP ACK Generation Recommendations

Event	*TCP Receiver Action*
Arrival of in-order segment with expected sequence number. All data up to expected sequence number already acknowledged. No gaps in the received data.	Delayed ACK. Wait up to 500 ms for arrival of another in-order segment. If next in-order segment does not arrives in this interval, send an ACK.
Arrival of in-order segment with expected sequence number. One other in-order segment waiting for ACK transmission. No gaps in the received data.	Immediately send single cumulative ACK, ACKing both in-order segments.
Arrival of out-of-order segment with higher-than expected sequence number. Gap detected.	Immediately send duplicate ACK, indicating sequence number of next expected byte.
Arrival of segment that partially or completely fills in gap in received data.	Immediately send ACK, provided that segment starts at the lower end of gap.

Figure 29.11 depicts the scenario where host A sends one segment to host B. Suppose that this segment has sequence number 92 and contains 8 bytes of data. After sending this segment, host A waits for a segment from B with acknowledgement number 100. Although the segment from A is received at B, the acknowledgement from B to A gets lost. In this case, the timer expires, and host A retransmits the same segment. Of course, when host B receives the retransmission, it will observe that the bytes in the segment duplicate bytes it has already deposited in its receive buffer. Thus TCP in host B will discard the bytes in the retransmitted segment.

In a second scenario, host A sends two segments back to back. The first segment has sequence number 92 and 8 bytes of data, and the second segment has sequence number 100 and 20 bytes of data. Suppose that both segments arrive intact at B, and B sends two separate acknowledgements for each of these segments. The first of these acknowledgements has acknowledgement number 100; the second has acknowledgement number 120. Suppose now that neither of the acknowledgements arrive at host A before the timeout of the first segment. When the timer expires, host A resends the first segment with sequence number 92. Now, you may

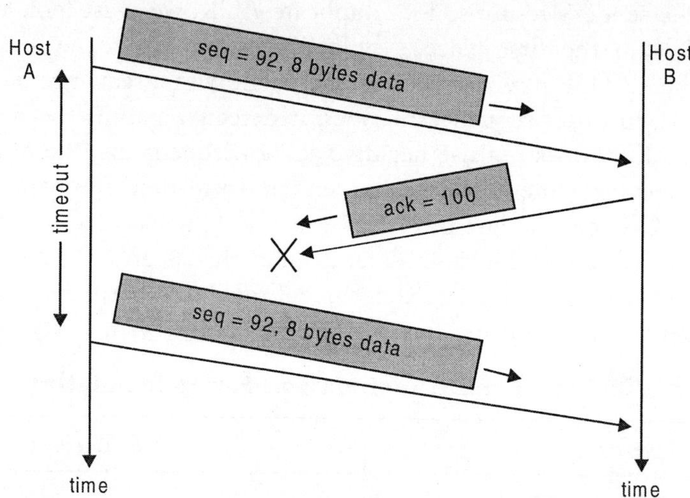

Figure 29.11 *Retransmission Due to a Lost Acknowledgement.*

ask, does A also resend second segment ? According to the rules described above, host A resends the segment only if the timer expires before the arrival of an acknowledgement with an acknowledgement number of 120 or greater. Thus, as shown in figure 29.12, if the second acknowledgement does not get lost and arrives before the timeout of the second segment, A does not resend the second segment.

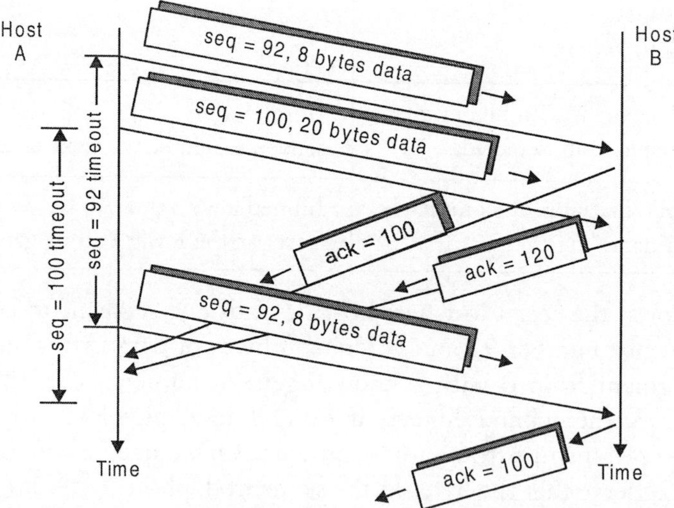

Figure 29.12 *Segment is not Retransmitted because its Acknowledgement Arrives before the Timeout.*

In a third and final scenario, suppose host A sends the two segments, exactly as in the second example. The acknowledgement of the first segment is lost in the network, but just before the timeout of the *first segment*, host A receives an acknowledgement with acknowledgement number 120. Host A therefore knows that host B has received *everything* up through byte 119; so host A does not resend either of the two segments. This scenario is illustrated in figure 29.13.

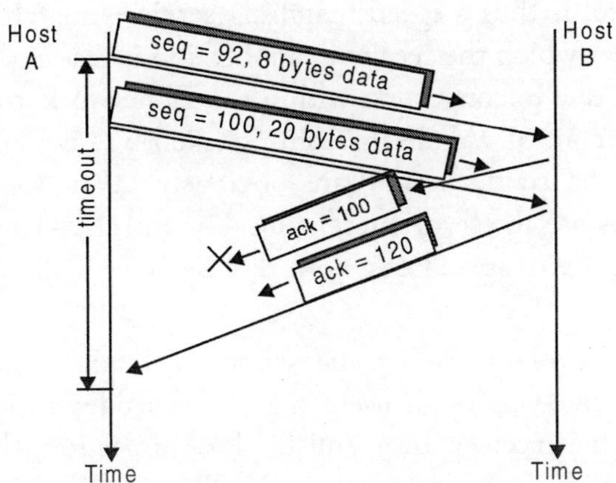

Figure 29.13 *A cumulative Acknowledgement Avoids Retransmission of First Segment.*

Recall that in the previous section we said that TCP is a go-back-N style protocol. This is because acknowledgements are cumulative and correctly-received but out-of-order segments are not individually ACKed by the receiver. Consequently, as shown in figure , the TCP sender need only maintain the smallest sequence number of a transmitted but unacknowledged byte *(sendbase)* and the sequence number of the next byte to be sent *(nextseqnum).* But the reader should keep in mind that although the reliable-data-transfer component of TCP resembles go-back-N, it is by no means a pure implementation of go-back-N. To see that there are some striking differences between TCP and go-back-N, consider what happens when the sender sends a sequence of segments *1, 2,..., N,* and all of the segments arrive in order without error at the receiver. Further suppose that the acknowledgement for packet $n < N$ gets lost, but the remaining *N-1* acknowledgements arrive at the sender before their respective timeouts. In this example, go-back-N would retransmit not only packet *n*, but also all the subsequent packets *n+1, n+2,...,N.* TCP, on the other hand, would retransmit at most one segment, namely, segment *n*. Moreover, TCP would not even retransmit segment *n* if the acknowledgement for segment *n+1* arrives before the timeout for segment *n*.

There have recently been several proposals to extend the TCP scheme to be more similar to a selective repeat protocol. The key idea in these proposals is to provide the sender with explicit information about which segments have been received correctly, and which are still missing at the receiver.

Flow Control

Recall that the hosts on each side of a TCP connection each set aside a receive buffer for the connection. When the TCP connection receives bytes that are correct and in sequence, it places the data in the receive buffer. The associated application process will read data from this buffer, but not necessarily at the instant the data arrives. Indeed, the receiving application may be busy with some other task and may not even attempt to read the data until long after it has arrived. If the application is relatively slow at reading the data, the sender can very easily overflow the connection's receive buffer by sending too much data too quickly. TCP thus provides a flow control service to its applications by eliminating the possibility of the sender overflowing the receiver's buffer. Flow control is thus a speed matching service—matching the rate at which the sender is seding to the rate at which the receiving application is reading. As noted earlier, a TCP sender can also be throttled due to congestion within the IP network; this form of sender control is referred to as congestion control. While the actions taken by flow and congestion control are similar (the throttling of the sender), they are obviously taken for very different reasons. Unfortunately, many authors use the term interchangeably, and the savvy reader would be careful to distinguish between the two cases. Let's now discuss how TCP provides its flow control service.

TCP provides flow control by having the sender maintain a variable called the receive window. Informally, the receive window is used to give the sender an idea about how much free buffer space is available at the receiver. In a full-duplex connection, the sender at each side of the connection maintains a distinct receive window. The receive window is dynamic, *i.e.*, it changes throughout a connection's lifetime. Let's investigate the receive window in the context of a file transfer. Suppose that host A is sending a large file to host B over a TCP connection. Host B allocates a receive buffer to this connection; denote its size by RcvBuffer. From time to time, the application process in host B reads from the buffer. Define the following variables:

LastByteRead = the number of the last byte in the data stream read from the buffer by the application process in B.

LastByteRcvd = the number of the last byte in the data stream that has arrived from the network and has been placed in the receive buffer at B.

Because TCP is not permitted to overflow the allocated buffer, we must have:

LastByteRcvd—LastByteRead <= RcvBuffer

The receive window, denoted RcvWindow, is set to the amount of spare room in the buffer :

RcvWindow = RcvBuffer—[LastByteRcvd - LastByteRead]

Because the spare room changes with time, RcvWindow is dynamic. The variable RcvWindow is illustrated in figure 29.14.

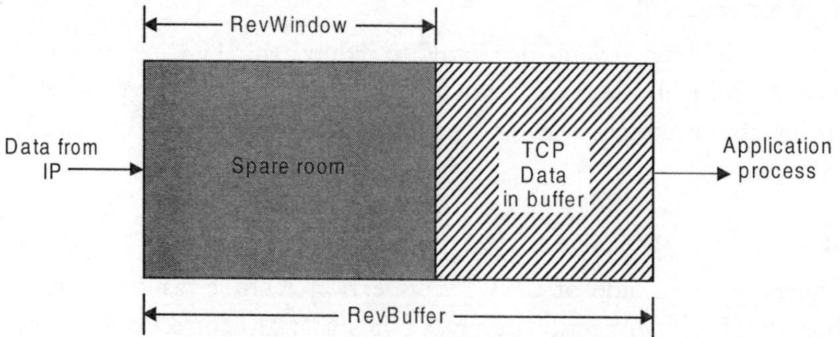

Figure 29.14 *The Receive Window (RcvWindow) and the Receive Buffer (RcvBuffer).*

How does the connection use the variable RcvWindow to provide the flow control service? Host B informs host A of how much spare room it has in the connection buffer by placing its current value of RcvWindow in the window field of every segment it sends to A. Initially host B sets RcvWindow = RcvBuffer. Note that to pull this off, host B must keep track of several connection-specific variables.

Host A in turn keeps track of two variables, LastByteSent and LastByteAcked, which have obvious meanings. Note that the difference between these two variables, LastByteSent - LastByteAcked, is the amount of unacknowledged data that A has sent into the connection. By keeping the amount of unacknowledged data less than the value of RcvWindow, host A is assured that it is not overflowing the receive buffer at host B. Thus host A makes sure throughout the connection's life that

LastByteSent – LastByteAcked <= RcvWindow.

There is one minor technical problem with this scheme. To see this, suppose host B's receive buffer becomes full so that RcvWindow = 0. After advertising RcvWindow = 0 to host A, also suppose that B has *nothing* to send to A. As the application process at B empties the buffer, TCP does not send new segments with new RcvWindows to host A – TCP will only send a segment to host A if it has data to send or if it has an acknowledgement to send. Therefore host A is never informed that some space has opened up in host B's receive buffer : host A is blocked and can transmit no more data! To solve this problem, the TCP specification requires host A to continue to send segments with one data byte when B's receive window is zero. These segments will be acknowledged by the receiver. Eventually the buffer will begin to empty and the acknowledgements will contain non-zero RcvWindow.

Having described TCP's flow control service, we briefly mention here that UDP does not provide flow control. To understand the issue here, consider sending a series of UDP segments from a process on host A to a process on host B. For a typical UDP implementation, UDP will append the segments (more precisely, the data in the segments) in a finite-size queue that "precedes" the corresponding socket (*i.e.,* the door to the process). The process reads one entire segment at a time from the queue. If the process does not read the segments fast enough from the queue, the queue will overflow and segments will get lost.

Following this section we provide an interactive Java applet which should provide significant insight into the TCP receive window.

Round Trip Time and Timeout

Recall that when a host sends a segment into a TCP connection, it starts a timer. If the timer expires before the host receives an acknowledgement for the data in the segment, the host retransmits the segment. The time from when the timer is started until when it expires is called the timeout of the timer. A natural question is, how large should timeout be ? Clearly, the timeout should be larger than the connection's round-trip time, *i.e.,* the time from when a segment is sent until it is acknowledged. Otherwise, unnecessary retransmissions would be sent. But the timeout should not be much larger than the round-trip time; otherwise, when a segment is lost, TCP would not quickly retransmit the segment, thereby introducing significant data transfer delays into the application. Before discussing the timeout interval in more detail, let us take a closer look at the round-trip time (RTT). Estimating the average round-trip time.

The sample RTT, denoted SampleRTT, for a segment is the time from when the segment is sent (*i.e.,* passed to IP) until an acknowledgement for the segment is received. Each segment sent will have its own associated SampleRTT. Obviously, the SampleRTT values will fluctuate from segment to segment due to congestion in the routers and to the varying load on the end systems. Because of this fluctuation, any given SampleRTT value may be a typical. In order to estimate a typical RTT, it is therefore natural to take some sort of average of the SampleRTT values. TCP maintains an average, called EstimatedRTT, of the SampleRTT values. Upon receiving an acknowledgement and obtaining a new SampleRTT, TCP updates EstimatedRTT according to the following formula:

EstimatedRTT = (1-x) EstimatedRTT + x SampleRTT.

The above formula is written in the form of a programming language statement — the new value of EstimatedRTT is a weighted combination of the previous value of Estimated RTT and the new value for SampleRTT. A typical value of x is x = .1, in which case the above formula becomes:

EstimatedRTT = .9 EstimatedRTT + .1 SampleRTT.

Note that EstimatedRTT is a weighted average of the SampleRTT values. As we will see in the homework, this weighted average puts more weight on recent samples than on old samples. This is natural, as the more recent samples better reflect the current congestion in the network. In statistics, such an average is called an Exponential Weighted Moving Average (EWMA). The word "exponential" appears in EWMA because the weight of a given SampleRTT decays exponentially fast as the updates proceed. In the homework problems you will be asked to derive the exponential term in EstimatedRTT.

Setting the Timeout

The timeout should be set so that a timer expires early (*i.e.*, before the delayed arrival of a segment's ACK) only on rare occasions. It is therefore natural to set the timeout equal to the EstimatedRTT plus some margin. The margin should be large when there is a lot of fluctuation in the SampleRTT values; it should be small when there is little fluctuation. TCP uses the following formula:

Timeout = EstimatedRTT + 4*Deviation,

where deviation is an estimate of how much SampleRTT typically deviates from EstimatedRTT:

Deviation = (1-x) Deviation + x | SampleRTT - EstimatedRTT |

Note that deviation is an EWMA of how much SampleRTT deviates from EstimatedRTT. If the SampleRTT values have little fluctuation, then deviation is small and timeout is hardly more than EstimatedRTT; on the other hand, if there is a lot of fluctuation, deviation will be large and timeout will be much larger than EstimatedRTT.

TCP Connection Management

In this subsection we take a closer look at how a TCP connection is established and torn down. Although this particular topic may not seem particularly exciting, it is important because TCP connection establishment can significantly add to perceived delays (for example, when surfing the web). Let's now take a look at how a TCP connection is established. Suppose a process running in one host wants to initiate a connection with another process in another host. The host that is initiating the connection is called the client host whereas the other host is called the server host.

The client application process first informs the client TCP that it wants to establish a connection to a process in the server. Recall from section 2.6, that a Java client program does this by issuing the command:

Socket clientSocket = new Socket ("hostname", "port number");

The TCP in the client then proceeds to establish a TCP connection with the TCP in the server in the following manner:

Step 1. The client-side TCP first sends a special TCP segment to the server-side TCP. This special segment contains no application-layer data. It does, however, have one of the flag bits in the segment's header, the so-called SYN bit, set to 1. For this reason, this special segment is referred to as a SYN segment. In addition, the client chooses an initial sequence number (*client_isn*) and puts this number in the sequence number field of the initial TCP SYN segment. This segment is encapsulated within an IP datagram and sent into the Internet.

Step 2. Once the IP datagram containing the TCP SYN segment arrives at the server host (assuming it does arrive!), the server extracts the TCP SYN segment from the datagram, allocates the TCP buffers and variables to the connection, and sends a connection-granted segment to client TCP. This connection-granted segment also contains no application-layer data. However, it does contain three important pieces of information in the segment header. First, the SYN bit is set to 1. Second, the acknowledgement field of the TCP segment header is set to *isn+1*. Finally, the server chooses its own initial sequence number (server_isn) and puts this value in the sequence number field of the TCP segment header. This connection granted segment is saying, in effect, "I received your SYN packet to start a connection with your initial sequence number, *client_isn*. I agree to establish this connection. My own initial sequence number is *server_isn*." The conenction-granted segment is sometimes referred to as a SYNACK segment.

Step 3. Upon receiving the connection-granted segment, the client also allocates buffers and variables to the connection. The client host then sends the server yet another segment; this last segment acknowledges the server's connection-granted segment (the client does so by putting the value *server_isn+1* in the acknowledgement field of the TCP segment header). The SYN bit is set to 0, since the connection is established.

Once the following three steps have been completed, the client and server hosts can send segments containing data to each other. In each of these future segments, the SYN bit will be set to zero. Note that in order to establish the connection, three packets are sent between the two hosts, as illustrated in figure 29.15. For this reason, this connection establishment procedure is often referred to as a three-way handshake. Several aspects of the TCP three-way handshake (Why are initial sequence numbers needed ? Why is a three-way handshake, as opposed to a two-way handshake, needed ?) are explored in the homework problems.

All good things must come to an end, and the same is true with a TCP connection. Either of the two processes participating in a TCP connection can end the connection. When a connection ends, the "resources" (*i.e.*, the buffers and variables) in the hosts are de-allocated. As an example, suppose the client decides to close the connection. The client application process issues a close command. This causes the client TCP to send a special TCP segment to the server process. This special segment has a flag bit in the segment's header, the so-called FIN bit , set to 1. When the server receives this segment, it sends the client an acknowledgement segment in return. The server then sends its own shut-down segment, which has the FIN bit set to 1. Finally, the client

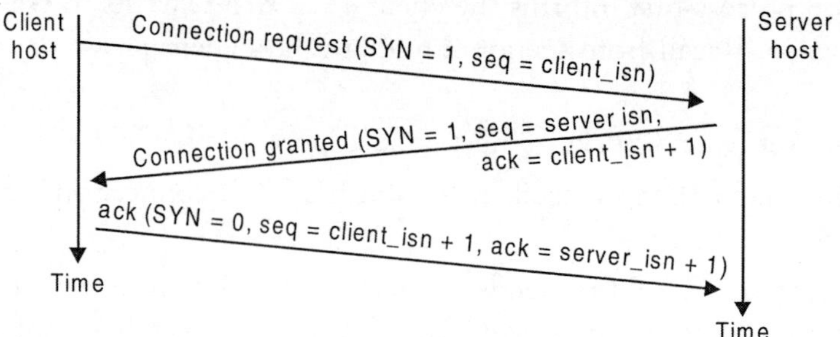

Figure 29.15 *TCP Three-Way Handshake: Segment Exchange.*

acknowledges the server's shut-down segment. At this point, all the resources in the two hosts are now de-allocated.

During the life of a TCP connection, the TCP protocol running in each host makes transitions through various TCP states. Figure 29.16 illustrates a typical sequence of TCP states that are visited by the *client* TCP. The client TCP begins in the closed state. The application on the client side initiates a new TCP connection (by creating a socket object in our Java examples). This causes TCP in the client to send a SYN segment to TCP in the server. After having sent the SYN segment, the client TCP enters the SYN_SENT sent. While in the SYN_STATE the

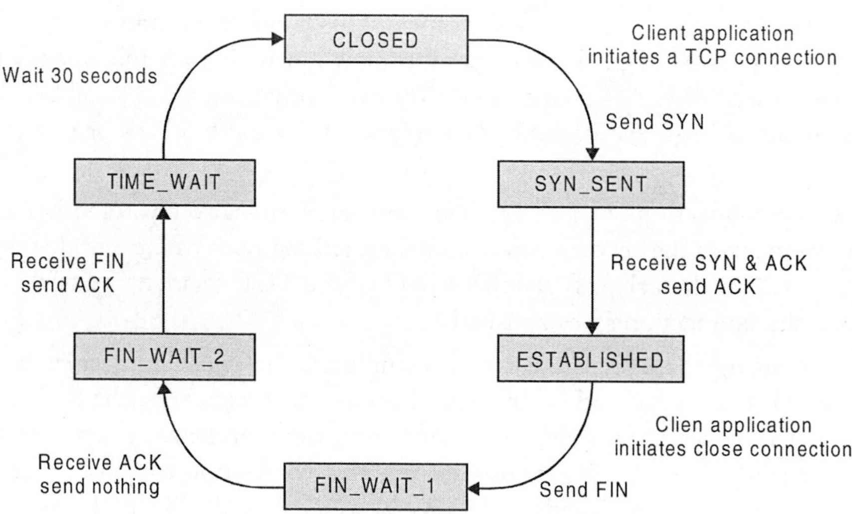

Figure 29.16 *A Typical Sequence of TCP States Visited by a Client TCP.*

client TCP waits for a segment from the server TCP that includes an acknowledgement for the client's previous segment as well as the SYN bit set to 1. Once having received such a segment, the client TCP enters the ESTABLISHED state. While in the ESTABLISHED state, the TCP client can send and receive TCP segments containing payload (*i.e.*, application-generated) data.

Suppose that the client application decides it wants to close the connection. This causes the client TCP to send a TCP segment with the FIN bit set to 1 and to enter the FIN_WAIT_1 state. While in the FIN_WAIT state, the client TCP waits for a TCP segment from the server with an acknowledgement. When it receives this segment, the client TCP enters the FIN_WAIT_2 state. While in the FIN_WAIT_2 state, the client waits for another segment from the server with the FIN bit set to 1; after receiving this segment, the client TCP acknowledges the server's segment and enters the TIME_WAIT state. The TIME_WAIT state lets the TCP client resend the final acknowledgement in the case the ACK is lost. The time spent in the TIME-WAIT state is implementation dependent, but typical values are 30 seconds, 1 minute and 2 minutes. After the wait, the connection formally closes and all resources on the client side (including port numbers) are released.

Figure 29.17 illustrates the series of states typically visited by the server-side TCP; the transitions are self-explanatory. In these two state transition diagrams, we have only shown how a TCP connection is *normally* established and shut down. We are not going to describe what happens in certain pathological scenarios, for example, when both sides of a connection want to shut down at the same time.

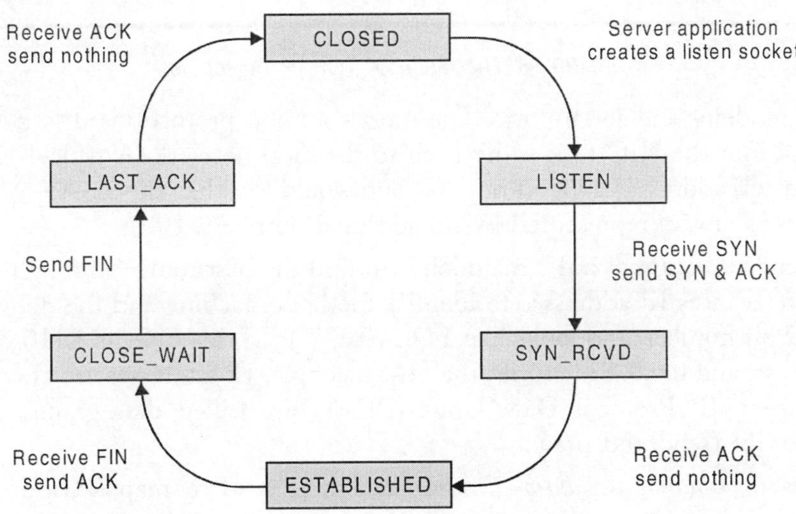

Figure 29.17 *A Typical Sequence of TCP States Visited by a Server-side TCP.*

The Suite of TCP/IP Protocols

Unix and the suite of TCP/IP protocols go hand in hand: it is not possible to separate the two. TCP/IP refers to a suite of protocols, not just the TCP and IP protocols. TCP/IP is the network portion of Unix. The following figure 29.18 relates the Dept. of Defense (DoD) model of TCP/IP with the OSI model. The DoD model is also called the ARPA model (Advanced Research Projects Agency).

OSI Model and the DoD Model of TCP/IP

It is not a perfect match between the OSI Model and the DoD model. However, it is close enough in principle. Note: Only a few of the major application layer protocols are displayed.

Network Devices are Network Interface Cards (NIC) and their software drivers. Typically, they are Ethernet cards, token ring cards, and WAN links (such as ISDN or frame relay), and

OSI Model	DoD Model	TCP/IP Suite of Protocols						
Application	Application (Port)	HTTP 80	SNMP 161 162	FTP 20 21	TFTP 69	SMTP 25	Telnet 23	NNTP 119
Presentation								
Session								
Transport	Host to Host	TCP			UDP			
Network	Internet	ICMP	IP			ARP		
Data Link	Network Access	Network Devices						
Physical								

Figure 29.18 *The Suite of TCP/IP Protocols.*

they can also be modems and serial ports. The most common protocol used is Ethernet. It uses an address burned into the NIC to identify itself to the local network. A typical Ethernet MAC (media access control) address is a 48 bit number, and would look like 00-02-AF-97-F2-03. Note: the MAC address is always represented by hexadecimal numbers.

IP stands for *Internet Protocol.* Its main job is to find the best route—through the Internet—to the destination. IP uses IP addresses to identify the host machine and the network. A typical IP address is a 32 bit number, and looks like 142.110.237.1. In this case, 142.110.237.0 identifies the network address, and 0.0.0.1 identifies the host machine. IP addresses are always represented by decimal numbers. IP Protocol Data Units (PDUs) are called data-grams, and provide a connectionless service (send and pray).

ARP stands for *Address Resolution Protocol* and it is used to map IP addresses to MAC addresses. This is needed because the network layer is not aware of the data link layer's addresses (and vice versa).

ICMP stands for *Internet Control Message Protocol*, and is used mainly for troubleshooting TCP/IP network connections. Two common programs, ping and trace-route, are part of ICMP.

TCP stands for *Transmission Control Protocol*, and is used to guarantee end to end delivery of segments of data, to put out of order segments in order, and to check for transmission errors. TCP is a connection-oriented service.

UDP stands for *User Datagram Protocol*, and is a connectionless service. This results in a low overhead and fast transfer service (relies on the upper layer protocols to provide error checking and delivery of data).

In the *application layer* lies many hundreds of network-aware programs and services such as the following:

HTTP (80)—Hyper Text Transport Protocol, which is used for transferring web pages.

SNMP (161/162)—Simple Network Management Protocol, which is used for managing network devices.

FTP (20/21)—File Transfer Protocol, which is used for transferring files across the network.

TFTP (69)—Trivial File Transfer Protocol, which is a low overhead fast transfer FTP protocol.

SMTP (25)—Simple Mail Transfer Protocol, which is used for transferring email across the Internet.

Telnet (23)—An application for remotely logging into a server across the network.

NNTP (119)—Network News Transfer Protocol, which is used for transferring news.

The numbers, shown in brackets next to the protocols, are called the *well-known port numbers.* TCP and UDP use these port numbers to indicate where the segments should be sent. For example, web servers use *port 80* to indicate that the HTTP protocol is used. A *socket* is another name for a well-known port.

Internet Protocol

The network layer protocol for TCP/IP is the Internet Protocol (IP). It uses IP addresses and the subnet mask to determine if the datagram is on a local or remote network. If it is on the remote network, the datagram is forwarded to the default gateway (which is a router that links to another network).

IP keeps track of the number of transverses through each router (that the datagram goes through to reach its destination). Each transvers is called a hop. If the hop count exceeds 255 hops, the datagram is removed, and the destination is considered unreachable. IP's name for the hop count is called Time to Live (TTL).

IP Addresses

IP addresses consist of a 32-bit number, and is represented by the dot-decimal format. For example: 142.110.237.1 is an IP address. There are 4 decimal digits separated by three dots. Each digit is allowed the range of 0 to 255. This range corresponds to 8 bits (one byte) of information.

A portion of an IP address represents the network address, and the remaining portion the host address. For example: 142.110.237.1 is the IP address of a firewall. The network that the firewall resides on is 142.110.237.0 (Note: IP addresses that end in a 0 represent network addresses). The host address of the firewall is 0.0.0.1 (Note: the network portion of the IP address is represented by 0s). Each host on the network—and Internet—must have a unique IP address. There are ways around having each host a unique IP address and they are discussed under firewalls.

The Network Information Center (NIC) assigns network addresses to the Internet. You must apply to receive a IP network address. Depending on the class of the IP address, you can then assign as many host IP addresses as are allowed (more on this later).

An alternative is to "rent" IP addresses from your local Internet Service Provider (ISP). They usually own the rights to a block of IP addresses, and will rent them out for a fee.

IP Address Classifications

There is a formal structure to the assignment of IP addresses. IP addresses are assigned by the Network Information Center (NIC), a central authority with the responsibility of assigning network addresses.

There are several classifications of IP addresses: they include network addresses and special purpose addresses.

Class A addresses:

IP address range 1.0.0.0 to 127.0.0.0 number of networks available:

125 (see special addresses below) number of hosts per network:16,777,214

Net Mask:255.0.0.0 (first 8 bits are ones) special addresses:

10.0.0.0 is used for networks not connected to the Internet

127.0.0.0 is the loop-back address for testing (see ping)

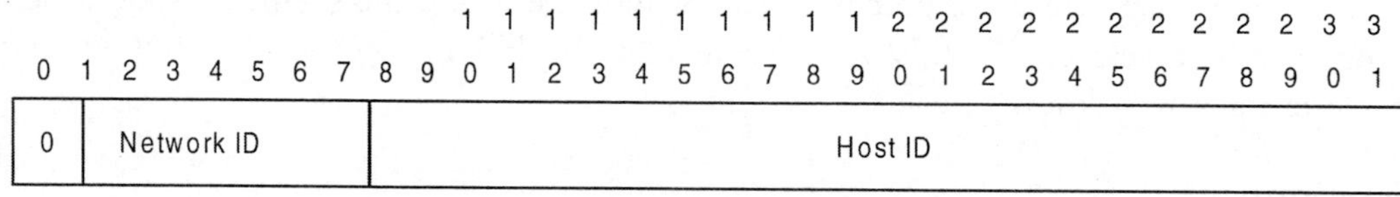

Figure 29.19 *Class A Addresses.*

Class A addresses always have bit 0 set to 0; bits 1–7 are used as the network ID; bits 8–31 are used as the host ID.

Class A networks are used by very large companies, such as IBM, US Dept. of Defense and AT and T. Appendix E: lists the IP addresses and the organizations that use them.

Class B addresses:

IP addresses range from 128.0.0.0 to 191.0.0.0

Number of networks available:16,382 (see special addresses below)

Number of hosts per network:65,534 Net Mask:255.255.0.0 (first 16 bits are ones)

Special Addresses: 172.16.0.0 to 172.31.0.0 are used for networks not connected to the Internet.

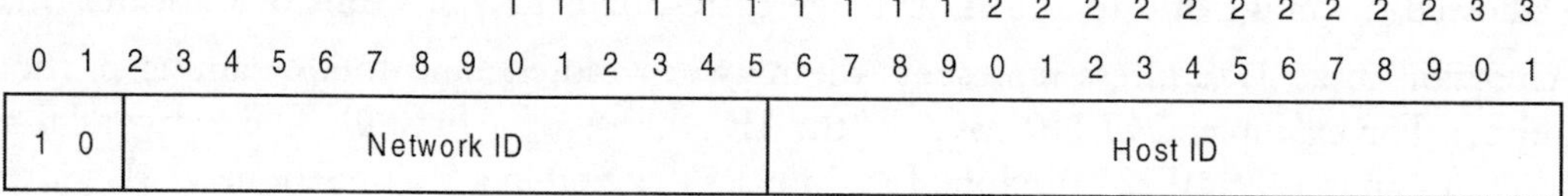

Figure 29.20 *Class B Addresses.*

Class B addresses always have bit 0 and 1 set to 10. Bits 2–15 are used as the network ID. Bits 16–31 are used as the host ID. Class B networks are assigned to large companies and universities.

Class C addresses:

IP address range 192.0.0.0 to 223.0.0.0

Number of networks available: 2,097,150 (see special addresses below)

Number of hosts per network: 254Net Mask:255.255.255.0 (first 24 bits are ones)

Special Addresses:192.168.1.0 to 192.168.255.0

are used for networks not connected to the Internet

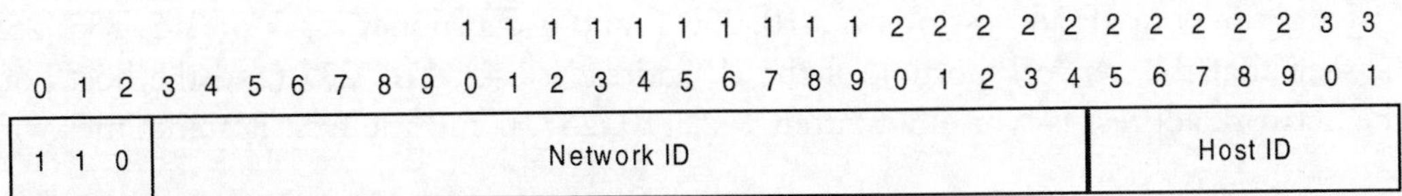

Figure 29.21 *Class C Addresses.*

Class C addresses always have bits 0–2 set to 110. Bits 3–24 are used as the network ID. Bits 25–31 are used as the host ID. Class C network addresses are assigned to small companies and local Internet providers.

Class D Addresses:

IP address range 224.0.0.0 to 239.0.0.0 Use:Multi-casting addresses

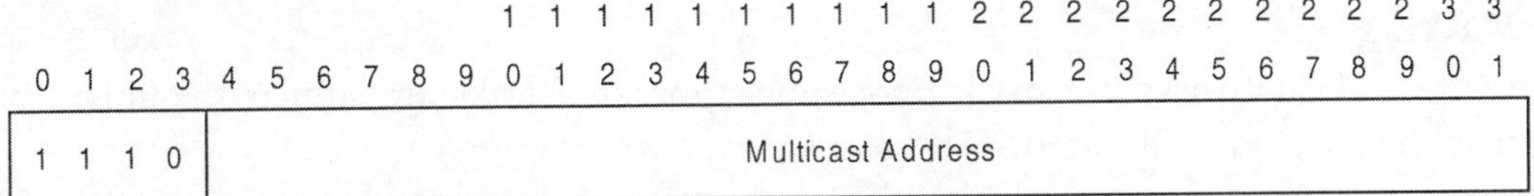

Figure 29.22 *Class D Addresses.*

Class D addresses always have bits 0–3 set to 1110, bits 4–31 are used as the multicast address.

Class D network addresses are used by multicasting. Multicasting is a method of reducing network traffic (rather than send a separate datagram to each host if multiple host require the same information). A special multicast address can be used where one datagram is read by many hosts. lists the assigned IP multicast address space.

Class E Addresses:

IP addresses range from 240.0.0.0 to 255.0.0.0

Use: Reserved by the Internet for its own use.

If you try to ping a class E address, you should get the error message that says it is an invalid IP address.

Reserved IP Addresses:

The following IP addresses are reserved.

- 127.0.0.0 network addresses used for local host mode (testing IP stack) 255. 255. 255. 255
- An IP address consisting of all 1s in binary (255). Broadcast address x.x.x.0
- An IP address with the host portion consisting of 0s. Used to indicate the network address.
- Newer routers have the option of allowing these addresses. 224.0.0.0 – 255.0.0.0 class D addresses.

Network Masking

The subnet mask is used to determine which portion of the IP address is the network address, and which is the host address. This means that the portions of network to host in an IP address can change. The most common subnet mask is 255. 255. 255. 0. The simple explanation is that wherever there is a 255, this indicates that it is the network portion. Wherever there is a 0, this indicates the host portion. Later on, subnet masking will be explained more thoroughly. For now, though, this explanation will have to suffice.

If we examine our IP address of 142.110. 237.1, and use a subnet mask of 255. 255. 255. 0, it can be seen that the network portion of the IP address is 142. 110. 237 (and the host portion is 1). The network address is typically written 142. 110. 237. 0 and the host is sometimes written 0.0.0.1.

Now if host 142.110. 237 .1 wanted to send a datagram to 142.110. 237 .21, it would look at the network portion of the IP address (of the destination), and determine that it is on the local network. It would then send out the datagram.

If host 142.110. 237 .1 wanted to send a datagram to 142.110.150.108, it would look at the network portion of the IP address (of the destination) and determine that it is not on the same network. It is on 142.110.150.0 network and it would send it to the default gateway. The default gateway is a router that knows how to reach the other networks.

Class Masking

Class A, B and C networks use masks, not subnet masks. Masks are similar to subnet masks, except that they are normally used in routers (not in workstations).

A class A network has a mask of 255.0.0.0, which allows approximately 16.7 million host addresses. Also, a class B network has a mask of 255. 255. 0.0, which allows approximately 65 thousand host addresses. Both classes of networks have too many hosts for one network to handle. Imagine 65,000 users trying to access a network service at the same time. The network would be swamped with requests, and would slow down to a crawl.

The solution is to divide the network up into smaller workable networks, called subnets. This is usually done by fooling the host machine into believing that it is on a class C network (only 254 hosts). The “fooling” occurs by using a class C mask 255. 255. 255. 0, called the subnet mask.

Thus, for a class A network using a subnet mask of 255. 255. 255. 0, you can have roughly 65 thousand subnets (of 254 hosts). On a class B network, using a subnet mask of 255. 255. 255. 0, you can have roughly 254 subnets of 254 hosts.

SUBNETTING A NETWORK

Subnet masks can divide networks into smaller networks (smaller than the 254 hosts discussed previously). In order to understand this process, a discussion on binary-to-decimal number conversion is required.

The typical subnet mask 255. 255. 255. 0 represents 4 bytes of data. Each number represents 1 byte, and is displayed as a decimal number. One byte of information can represent a range of 0–255. One byte consists of 8 bits, where 0000 0000 represents 0 (in decimal), and 1111 1111 represents 255 (in decimal).

The convention for displaying bits is to group in nibbles (4 bits): this makes it easier to read.

Each bit position has a weighting, where the weighting is equal to 2 to the power of the position (starting at position 0, on the right). The easiest way to determine the decimal weighting is to start on the right with the number 1 (which is 2^0), and double it at each bit position. The weighting for each position is follows:

Decimal Weighting	128	64	32	16	8	4	2	1
Bit Position	2^7	2^6	2^5	2^4	2^3	2^2	2^1	2^0

Figure 29.23 *Bits Position.*

Each position has its weighting multiplied by the binary bit value (0 or 1). For example, if bit position 23 had its bit set to 0, its decimal value would be 0 × 8 = 0. If bit position 25 had its bit set to 1, its decimal value would be 1 × 32 = 32.

To determine the decimal value of a binary number, add up all of the decimal weighting values (wherever there is a 1 in the binary number). For the following binary number 1111 1111, the decimal value would equal 255:

Decimal Weighting	128	64	32	16	8	4	2	1
Bits	1	1	1	1	1	1	1	1

Figure 29.24 *Bits Position1.*

For the binary number 0000 0000, the decimal value would equal 0:

Decimal Weighting	128	64	32	16	8	4	2	1
Bits	0	0	0	0	0	0	0	0

0 + 0 + 0 + 0 + 0 + 0 + 0 + 0 = 0

Figure 29.25 *Bits Position2.*

For the binary number 1010 1001, the decimal value would equal 169:

Decimal Weighting	128	64	32	16	8	4	2	1
Bits	1	0	1	0	1	0	0	1

128 + 0 + 32 + 0 + 8 + 0 + 0 + 1 = 169

Figure 29.26 *Bits Position3.*

The significance of the decimal weighting to network routing becomes more evident when the method of rolling over the binary count is examined. For example, the decimal number 63 compared to 64 in binary produces an interesting observation:

Decimal 63 = 0011 1111; Decimal 64 = 0100 0000

The decimal number 63 is represented by all 1s in the first 6 bit locations. The decimal number 64 is represented by only bit 6 being a logical 1. If the count was further increased, similar relationships would occur, as shown below:

Decimal 127 = 0111 1111; Decimal 128 = 1000 0000

and

Decimal 191 = 1011 1111; Decimal 192 = 1100 0000

and

Decimal 255 = 1111 1111; Decimal 0 = 0000 0000

Notice that bit 7 and 6 are the only bits that are changing from the initial example of 63 and 64. What this means is that the network can be subdivided into 4 logical networks (of 64 hosts each). In fact, the number is 62 hosts because address 0 is not allowed (network address), and address 63 is not allowed (broadcast address).

In the introduction to sub-netting, the portion of the IP address (that corresponded to the network portion) was easily identified as being the portion of the subnet mask (that corresponded to the decimal number 255). This is really only for the convenience of the dot decimal format (of the IP address). In fact, the IP address is a 32-bit address, and doesn't have byte "boundaries" (as implied by the dot decimal notation). For example :

192.168.1.0 = 1100 0000 1010 1000 0000 0001 0000 0000

This means that the portion of the subnet mask that corresponds to the network address can be further broken down on the host bit positions.

A class C network address of 192.168.1.0 has 254 hosts available to it. If your network consisted of 4 different physical locations, each with a maximum of 50 hosts, then sub-netting the network would be required. The locations could be different buildings or cities.

Bit 7 and bit 6 of the host portion can be used to describe the network portion of the subnet. The subnet masking would be:

1111 1111 1111 1111 1111 1111 1100 0000 = 255. 255. 255.192

The 4 subnets for class C address 192.168.1.0 would be 192.168.1.0, 192.168.1.64, 192.168.1.128 and 192.168.1.192 (with the following range of IP addresses):

Subnet Host Range Broadcast address 192.168.1.0192.168.1.1

to 192.168.1.62192.168.1.63192.168.1.64192.168.1.65

to 192.168.1.126192.168.1.127192.168.1.128192.168.1.129

to 192.168.1.190192.168.1.191192.168.1.192192.168.1.193

to 192.168.1.254192.168.1.255

In this manner, a router with 4 interfaces could be configured with subnet masks of 255. 255. 255.192. This would allow for subdividing of the class C network into 4 smaller networks.

Theoretically, all of the host bits—up to bit 1 and 0—can be used to make up to 64 subnets (of 2 hosts each). In this case, 128 IP addresses would be lost to the network IP address and the broadcast IP address. The following table lists the number of hosts and networks that can implemented using subnet masking (for a class C network):

Subnet maskNumber of subnetsNumber of hosts per subnet

255. 255. 255. 1282126255. 255. 255. 192462255. 255. 255. 224830

255. 255. 255. 2401614255. 255. 255. 248326255. 255. 255. 252642

The above example is based on sub-netting a class C network. Sub-netting can get extremely complicated if you are sub-netting assigned IP addresses that are in the middle of a class C network, such as when they are rented from an ISP. Fortunately, there are many subnet mask calculators that are available off the Internet. They are designed to determine the correct subnet mask for your network.

OVERVIEW OF TCP CONGESTION CONTROL

we saw that each side of a TCP connection consists of a receive buffer, a send buffer, and several variables (*LastByteRead, RcvWin*, etc.) The TCP congestion control mechanism has each side of the connection keep track of two additional variables: the congestion window and the threshold. The congestion window, denoted *CongWin*, imposes an additional constraint on how much traffic a host can send into a connection. Specifically, the amount of unacknowledged data that a host can have within a TCP connection may not exceed the minimum of *CongWin* and *RcvWin*, *i.e.*,

LastByteSent - LastByteAcked <= min{CongWin, RcvWin}.

The threshold, which we discuss in detail below, is a variable that effects how *CongWin* grows.

Let us now look at how the congestion window evolves throughout the lifetime of a TCP connection. In order to focus on congestion control (as opposed to flow control), let us assume that the TCP receive buffer is so large that the receive window constraint can be ignored. In this case, the amount of unacknowledged data hat a host can have within a TCP connection is solely limited by *CongWin*. Further let's assume that a sender has a very large amount of data to send to a receiver.

Once a TCP connection is established between the two end systems, the application process at the sender writes bytes to the sender's TCP send buffer. TCP grabs chunks of size MSS, encapsulates each chunk within a TCP segment, and passes the segments to the network layer for transmission across the network. The TCP congestion window regulates the times at which the segments are sent into the network (*i.e.*, passed to the network layer). Initially, the congestion window is equal to one MSS. TCP sends the first segment into the network and waits for an acknowledgement. If this segment is acknowledged before its timer times out, the sender increases the congestion window by one MSS and sends out two maximum-size segments. If these segments are acknowledged before their timeouts, the sender increases the congestion window by one MSS for each of the acknowledged segments, giving a congestion window of four MSS, and sends out four maximum-sized segments. This procedure continues as long as (1) the congestion window is below the threshold and (2) the acknowledgements arrive before their corresponding timeouts.

During this phase of the congestion control procedure, the congestion window increases exponentially fast, *i.e.*, the congestion window is initialized to one MSS, after one RTT the window is increased to two segments, after two round-trip times the window is increased to four segments, after three round-trip times the window is increased to eight segments, etc. This phase of the algorithm is called slow start because it begins with a small congestion window equal to one MSS. (The transmission rate of the connection starts slowly but accelerates rapidly.)

The slow start phase ends when the window size exceed the value of *threshold*. Once the congestion window is larger than the current value of *threshold*, the congestion window grows linearly rather than exponentially. Specifically, if w is the current value of the congestion window, and w is larger than *threshold*, then after w acknowledgements have arrived, TCP replaces w with $w + 1$. This has the effect of increasing the congestion window by one in each RTT for which an entire window's worth of acknowledgements arrives. This phase of the algorithm is called congestion avoidance.

The congestion avoidance phase continues as long as the acknowledgements arrive before their corresponding timeouts. But the window size, and hence the rate at which the TCP sender can send, cannot increase forever. Eventually, the TCP rate will be such that one of the links along the path becomes saturated, and which point loss (and a resulting timeout at the sender) will occur. When a timeout occurs, the value of *threshold* is set to half the value of the current congestion window, and the congestion window is reset to one MSS. The sender then again grows the congestion window exponentially fast using the slow start procedure until the congestion window hits the threshold. In short, following points are concluded:

- When the congestion window is below the threshold, the congestion window grows exponentially.
- When the congestion window is above the threshold, the congestion window grows linearly.
- Whenever there is a timeout, the threshold is set to one half of the current congestion window and the congestion window is then set to one.

If we ignore the slowstart phase, we see that TCP essentially increases its window size by 1 each RTT (and thus increases its transmission rate by an additive factor) when its network path is not congested, and decreases its window size by a factor of two each RTT when the path is congested. For this reason, TCP is often referred to as an additive-increase, multiplicative-decrease (AIMD) algorithm.

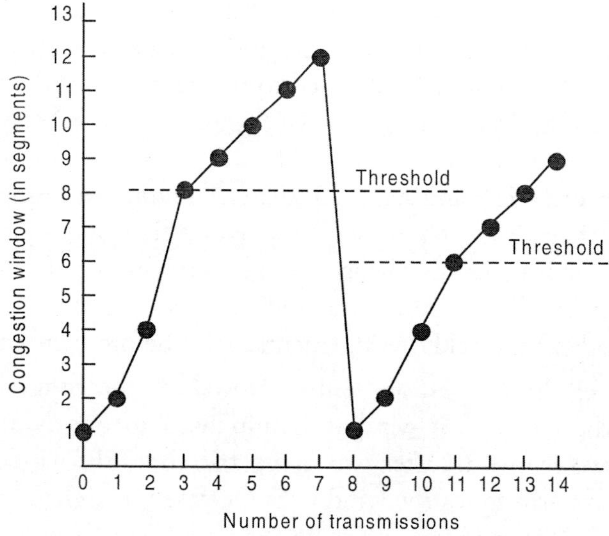

Figure 29.27 *Evolution of TCP's Congestion Window.*

The evolution of TCP's congestion window is illustrated in Figure. In this figure, the threshold is initially equal to 8*MSS. The congestion window climbs exponentially fast during slow start and hits the threshold at the third transmission. The congestion window then climbs linearly until loss occurs, just after transmission 7. Note that the congestion window is 12*MSS when loss occurs. The threshold is then set to .5**CongWin* = 6*MSS and the congestion window is set 1. And the process continues.

The TCP congestion control algorithm just described is often referred to as Tahoe. One problem with the Tahoe algorithm is that when a segment is lost the sender side of the application may have to wait a long period of time for the timeout. For this reason, a variant of Tahoe, called Reno, is implemented by most operating systems. Like Tahoe, Reno sets its congestion window to one segment upon the expiration of a timer. Recall that fast retransmit triggers the transmission of a dropped segment if three duplicate ACKs for a segment are received before the occurrence of the segment's timeout. Reno also employs a fast recovery mechanism, which essentially cancels the slow start phase after a fast retransmission. The interested reader is encouraged.

Most TCP implementations currently use the Reno algorithm. There is, however, another algorithm in the literature, the Vegas algorithm, that can improve Reno's performance. Whereas Tahoe and Reno react to congestion (*i.e.*, to overflowing router buffers), Vegas attempts to avoid congestion while maintaining good throughput. The basic idea of Vegas is to (1) detect congestion in the routers between source and destination *before* packet loss occurs, and (2) lower the rate linearly when this imminent packet loss is detected. Imminent packet loss is predicted by observing the round-trip times—the longer the round-trip times of the packets, the greater the congestion in the routers. We emphasize that TCP congestion control has evolved over the years, and is still evolving. What was good for the Internet when the bulk of the TCP connections carried SMTP, FTP and Telnet traffic is not necessarily good for today's Web-dominated Internet or for the Internet of the future, which will support who-knows-what kinds of services.

In the above discussion, we noted that the goal of TCP's congestion control mechanism is to share a bottleneck link's bandwidth evenly among the TCP connections traversing that link. But why should TCP's additive increase, multiplicative decrease algorithm achieve that goal, particularly given that different TCP connections may start at different times and thus may have different window sizes at a given point in time ? [Chiu 1989] provides an elegant and intuitive explanation of why TCP congestion control converges to provide an equal share of a bottleneck link's bandwidth among competing TCP connections.

Let's consider the simple case of two TCP connections sharing a single link with transmission rate R, as shown in figure 29.28. We'll assume that the two connections have the same MSS and RTT (so that if they have the same congestion window size, then they have the same throughput), that they have a large amount of data to send, and that no other TCP connections or UDP datagrams traverse this shared link. Also, we'll ignore the slow start phase of TCP, and assume the TCP connections are operating in congestion avoidance mode (additive increase, multiplicative decrease) at all times.

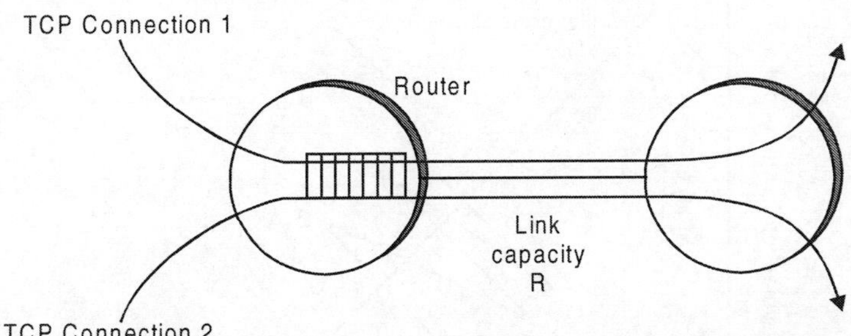

Figure 29.28 *Two TCP Connections Sharing a Single Bottleneck Link.*

Figure plots the throughput realized by the two TCP connections. If TCP is to equally share the link bandwidth between the two connections, then the realized throughput should fall along the 45 degree arrow ("equal bandwidth share") emanating from the origin. Ideally, the sum of the two throughputs should equal R (certainly, each connection receiving an equal, but zero, share of the link capacity is not a desirable situation!), so the goal should be to have the achieved throughputs fall somewhere near the intersection of the "equal bandwidth share" line and the "full bandwidth utilization" line in.

Suppose that the TCP window sizes are such that at a given point in time, connections 1 and 2 realize throughputs indicated by point A in figure 29.29. Because the amount of link bandwidth jointly consumed by the two connections is less than R, no loss will occur, and both connections will increase their window by 1 per RTT as a result of TCP's congestion avoidance algorithm. Thus, the joint throughput of the two connections proceeds along a 45 degree line (equal increase for both connections) starting from point A. Eventually, the link bandwidth jointly consumed by the two connections will be greater than R and eventually packet loss will occur. Suppose that connections 1 and 2 experience packet loss when they realize throughputs indicated by point B. Connections 1 and 2 then decrease their windows by a factor of two. The resulting throughputs realized are thus at point C, halfway along a vector starting at B and ending at the origin. Because the joint bandwidth use is less than R at point C, the two connections again increase their throughputs along a 45 degree line starting from C. Eventually, loss will again occur, *e.g.,* at point D, and the two connections again decrease their window sizes by a factor of two. And so on. You should convince yourself that the bandwidth realized by the two connections eventually fluctuates along the equal bandwidth share line. You should also convince yourself that the two connections will converge to this behavior regardless of where they being in the two-dimensional space! Although a number of idealized assumptions lay behind this scenario, it still provides an intuitive feel for why TCP results in an equal sharing of bandwidth among connections.

In our idealized scenario, we assumed that only TCP connections traverse the bottleneck link, and that only a single TCP connection is associated with a host-destination pair. In practice, these two conditions are typically not met, and client-server applications can thus obtain very unequal portions of link bandwidth.

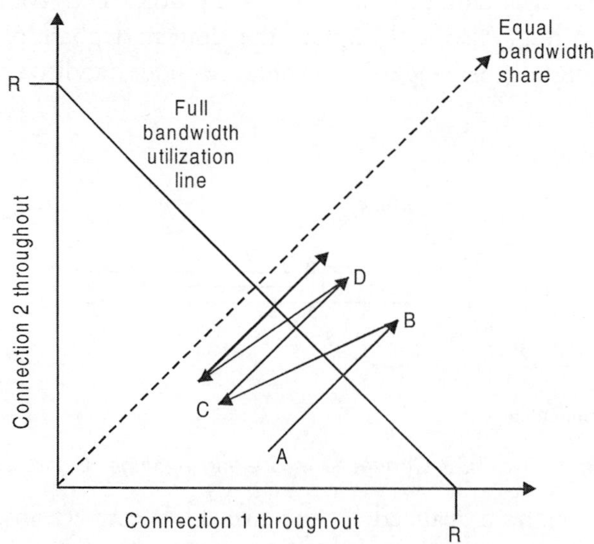

Figure 29.29 *Throughput Realized by TCP Connections 1 and 2.*

Many network applications run over TCP rather than UDP because they want to make use of TCP's reliable transport service. But an application developer choosing TCP gets not only reliable data transfer but also TCP congestion control. We have just seen how TCP congestion control regulates an application's transmission rate via the congestion window mechanism. Many multimedia applications do not run over TCP for this very reason—they do not want their transmission rate throttled, even if the network is very congested. In particular, many Internet telephone and Internet video conferencing applications typically run over UDP. These applications prefer to pump their audio and video into the network at a constant rate and occasionally lose packets, rather than reduce their rates to "fair" levels at times of congestion and not lose any packets. From the perspective of TCP, the multimedia applications running over UDP are not being fair—they do not co-operate with the other connections nor adjust their transmission rates appropriately. A major challenge in the upcoming years will be to develop congestion control mechanisms for the Internet that prevent UDP traffic from bringing the Internet's throughput to a grinding halt.

But even if we could force UDP traffic to behave fairly, the fairness problem would still not be completely solved. This is because there is nothing to stop an application running over TCP from using multiple parallel connections. For example, Web browsers often use multiple parallel TCP connections to transfer a web page. (The exact number of multiple connections is configurable in most browsers.) When an application uses multiple parallel connections, it gets a larger fraction of the bandwidth in a congested link. As an example consider a link of rate R supporting 9 on-going client-server applications, with each of the applications using one TCP connection. If a new application comes along and also uses one TCP connection, then each application approximately gets the same transmission rate of R/10. But if this new application instead uses 11 parallel TCP connections, then the new application gets an unfair allocation of R/2. Because web traffic is so pervasive in the Internet, multiple parallel connections are not uncommon.

Consider sending a very large file over a TCP connection. If we take a macroscopic view of the traffic sent by the source, we can ignore the slow start phase. Indeed, the connection is in the slow-start phase for a relatively short period of time because the connection grows out of the phase exponentially fast. When we ignore the slow-start phase, the congestion window grows linearly, gets chopped in half when loss occurs, grows linearly, gets chopped in half when loss occurs, etc. This gives rise to the saw-tooth behavior of TCP .

Given this saw-tooth behavior, what is the average through-put of a TCP connection ? During a particular round-trip interval, the rate at which TCP sends data is function of the congestion window and the current RTT: when the window size is w*MSS and the current round-trip time is RTT, then TCP's transmission rate is (w*MSS)/RTT. During the congestion avoidance phase, TCP probes for additional bandwidth by increasing w by one each RTT until loss occurs; denote by W the value of w at which loss occurs. Assuming that the RTT and W are approximately constant over the duration of the connection, the TCP transmission rate ranges from (W*MSS)/(2RTT) to (W*MSS)/RTT.

These assumptions lead to a highly-simplified macroscopic model for the steady-state behavior of TCP: the network drops a packet from the connection when the connection's window size increases to W*MSS; the congestion window is then cut in half and then increases by one MSS per round-trip time until it again reaches W. This process repeats itself over and over again. Because the TCP throughput increases linearly between the two extreme values, we have:

– average throughput of a connection = (.75*W*MSS)/RTT.

Using this highly idealized model for the steady-state dynamics of TCP, we can also derive an interesting expression that relates a connection's loss rate to its available bandwidth. This derivation is outlined in the homework problems.

MODELING LATENCY: STATIC CONGESTION WINDOW

Many TCP connections transport relatively small files from one host to another. For example, with HTTP/1.0 each object in a web page is transported over a separate TCP connection, and many of these objects are small text files or tiny icons. When transporting a small file, TCP connection establishment and slow start may have a significant impact on the latency. In this section we present an analytical model that quantifies the impact of connection establishment and slow start on latency. For a given object, we define the latency as the time from when the client initiates a TCP connection until when the client receives the requested object in its entirety.

The analysis presented here assumes that that the network is uncongested, *i.e.,* the TCP connection transporting the object does not have to share link bandwidth with other TCP or UDP traffic. Also, in order to not to obscure the central issues, we carry out the analysis in the context of the simple one-link network as shown in figure 29.30.

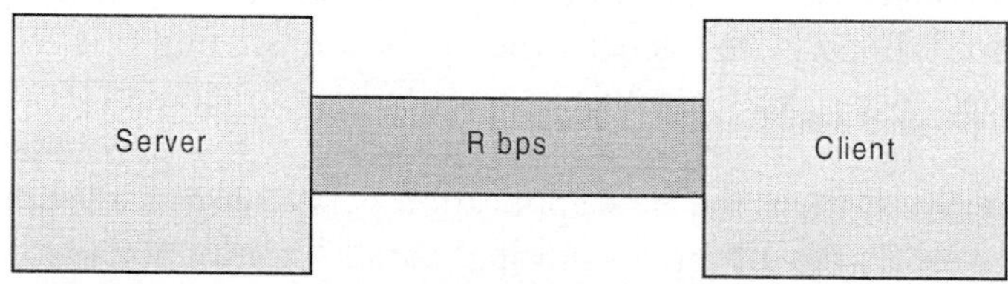

Figure 29.30 *A Simple One-link Network Connecting a Client and a Server.*

We also make the following simplifying assumptions:

- The amount of data that the sender can transmit is solely limited by the sender's congestion window. (Thus, the TCP receive buffers are large.)
- Packets are neither lost nor corrupted, so that there are no retransmissions.
- All protocol header overheads—including TCP, IP and link-layer headers—are negligible and ignored.
- The object (that is, file) to be transferred consists of an integer number of segments of size MSS (maximum segment size).
- The only packets that have non-negligible transmission times are packets that carry maximum-size TCP segments. Request packets, acknowledgements and TCP connection establishment packets are small and have negligible transmission times.
- The initial threshold in the TCP congestion control mechanism is a large value which is never attained by the congestion window.

We also introduce the following notation:

- The size of the object to be transferred is O bits.
- The MSS (maximum size segment) is S bits (*e.g.,* 536 bytes).
- The transmission rate of the link from the server to the client is R bps.
- The round-trip time is denoted by RTT.

In this section, we define the RTT to be the time elapsed for a small packet to travel from client to server and then back to the client, *excluding the transmission time of the packet*. It includes the two end-to-end propagation delays between the two end systems and the processing times at the two end systems. We shall assume that the RTT is also equal to the roundtrip time of a packet beginning at the server.

Although the analysis presented in this section assumes an uncongested network with a single TCP connection, it nevertheless sheds insight on the more realistic case of multi-link congested network. For a congested network, R roughly represents the amount of bandwidth received in steady state in the end-to-end network connection; and RTT represents a round-trip delay that includes queuing delays at the routers preceding the congested links. In the congested network case, we model each TCP connection as a constant-bit-rate connection of rate R bps preceded by a single slow-start phase. (This is roughly how TCP Tahoe behaves when losses are detected with triplicate acknowledgements.) In our numerical examples we use values of R and RTT that reflect typical values for a congested network.

Before beginning the formal analysis, let us try to gain some intuition. Let us consider what would be the latency if there were no congestion window constraint, that is, if the server were permitted to send segments back-to-back until the entire object is sent ? To answer this question, first note that one RTT is required to initiate the TCP connection. After one RTT the client sends a request for the object (which is piggybacked onto the third segment in the three-way TCP handshake). After a total of two RTTs the client begins to receive data from the server. The client receives data from the server for a period of time O/R, the time for the server to transmit the entire object. Thus, in the case of no congestion window constraint, the total latency is 2 RTT + O/R. This represents a lower bound; the slow start procedure, with its dynamic congestion window, will of course elongate this latency.

STATIC CONGESTION WINDOW

Although TCP uses a dynamic congestion window, it is instructive to first analyze the case of a static congestion window. Let W, a positive integer, denote a fixed-size static congestion window. For the static congestion window, the server is not permitted to have more than W unacknowledged outstanding segments. When the server receives the request from the client, the server immediately sends W segments back-to-back to the client. The server then sends one segment into the network for each acknowledgement it receives from the client. The server continues to send one segment for each acknowledgement until all of the segments of the object have been sent. There are two cases to consider:

$WS/R > RTT + S/R$. In this case, the server receives an acknowledgement for the first segment in the first window before the server completes the transmission of the first window.

$WS/R < RTT + S/R$. In this case, the server transmits the first window's worth of segments before the server receives an acknowledgement for the first segment in the window.

Let us first consider case 1, which is illustrated in figure 29.31. In this figure the window size is W = 4 segments.

One RTT is required to initiate the TCP connection. After one RTT the client sends a request for the object (which is piggybacked onto the third segment in the three-way TCP handshake). After a total of two RTTs the client begins to receive data from the server. Segments arrive periodically from the server every S/R seconds, and the client acknowledges every segment it receives from the server. Because the server receives the first acknowledgement before it completes sending a window's worth of segments, the server continues to transmit segments after

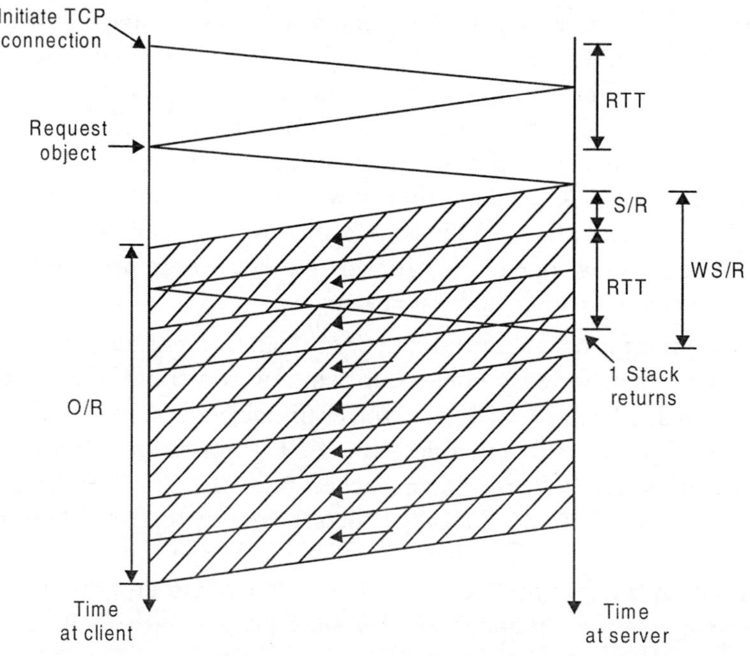

Figure 29.31 *The Case that WS -R Greater than RTT + S-R.*

having transmitted the first window's worth of segments. And because the acknowledgements arrive periodically at the server every S/R seconds from the time when the first acknowledgement arrives, the server transmits segments continuously until it has transmitted the entire object. Thus, once the server starts to transmit the object at rate R, it continues to transmit the object at rate R until the entire object is transmitted. The latency therefore is 2 RTT + O/R.

Now let us consider case 2, which is illustrated in figure 29.32. In this figure, the window size is W=2 segments.

Once again, after a total of two RTTs the client begins to receive segments from the server. These segments arrive periodically every S/R seconds, and the client acknowledges every segment it receives from the server. But now the server completes the transmission of the first window before the first acknowledgement arrives from the client. Therefore, after sending a window, the server must stall and wait for an acknowledgement before resuming transmission. When an acknowledgement finally arrives, the server sends a new segment to the client. Once the first acknowledgement arrives, a window's worth of acknowledgements arrive, with each successive acknowledgement spaced by S/R seconds. For each of these acknowledgements, the server sends exactly one segment. Thus, the server alternates between two states: a transmitting state, during which it transmits W segments; and a stalled state, during which it transmits nothing and waits for an acknowledgement. The latency is equal to 2 RTT plus the time required for the server to

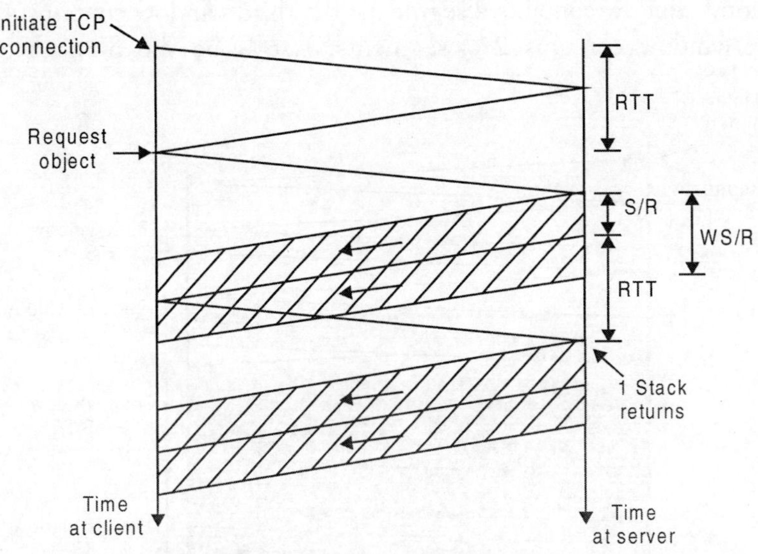

Figure 29.32 *The case that WS -R less than RTT + S-R.*

transmit the object, O/R, plus the amount of time that the server is in the stalled state. To determine the amount of time the server is in the stalled state, let K = O/WS; if O/WS is not an integer, then round K up to the nearest integer. Note that K is the number of windows of data there are in the object of size O. The server is in the stalled state between the transmission of each of the windows, that is, for K–1 periods of time, with each period lasting RTT- (W–1) S/R (see above diagram). Thus, for case 2,

$$\text{Latency} = 2\ RTT + O/R + (K-1)[S/R + RTT - W\ S/R]\ .$$

Combining the two cases, we obtain

$$\text{Latency} = 2\ RTT + O/R + (K-1)\ [S/R + RTT - W\ S/R]^{+}$$

where $[x]^{+} = \max(x,0)$.

This completes our analysis of static windows. The analysis below for dynamic windows is more complicated, but parallels the analysis for static windows.

MODELING LATENCY: DYNAMIC CONGESTION WINDOW

We now investigate the latency for a file transfer when TCP's dynamic congestion window is in force. Recall that the server first starts with a congestion window of one segment and sends one segment to the client. When it receives an acknowledgement for the segment, it increases its congestion window to two segments and sends two segments to the client (spaced apart by S/R seconds). As it receives the acknowledgements for the two segments, it increases the congestion window to four segments and sends four segments to the client (again spaced apart by S/R seconds). The process continues, with the congestion window doubling every RTT. A timing diagram for TCP is illustrated in figure 29.33.

Note that O/S is the number of segments in the object; in the above diagram, O/S =15. Consider the number of segments that are in each of the windows. The first window contains

1 segment; the second window contains 2 segments; the third window contains 4 segments. More generally, the kth window contains 2^{k-1} segments. Let K be the number of windows that

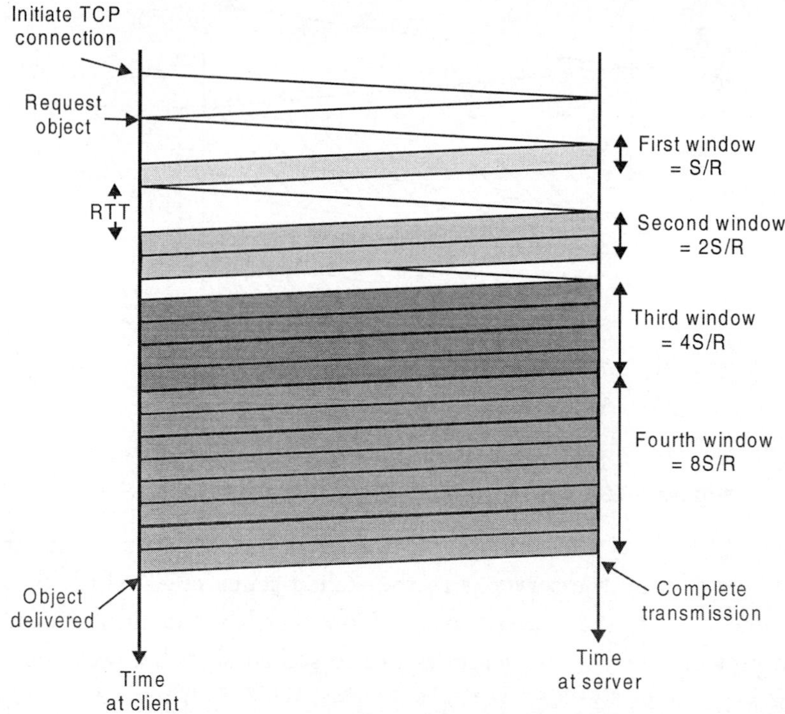

Figure 29.33 *TCP Timing During Slow Start.*

cover the object; in the preceding diagram K = 4. In general we can express K in terms of O/S as shown in figure 29.34:

$$K = \min \{k: 2^0 + 2^1 + \ldots\ldots + 2^{k-1} \geq \frac{O}{S}\}$$

$$= \min \{k: 2^k - 1 \geq \frac{O}{S})$$

$$= \min \{k: k \geq \log_2 (\frac{O}{S} + 1)\}$$

$$= \left\lceil \log_2 \left(\frac{O}{S} + 1\right) \right\rceil$$

Figure 29.34 *Calculation.*

After transmitting a window's worth of data, the server may stall (*i.e.*, stop transmitting) while it waits for an acknowledgement. In the preceding diagram, the server stalls after transmitting the first and second windows, but not after transmitting the third. Let us now calculate the amount of stall time after transmitting the kth window. The time from when the server begins to transmit the kth window until when the server receives an acknowledgement for the first segment in the window is S/R + RTT. The transmission time of the kth window is (S/R) 2^{k-1}. The stall time is the difference of these two quantities, that is,

$$[S/R + RTT - 2^{k-1}(S/R)]^+.$$

The server can potentially stall after the transmission of each of the first K–1 windows. (The server is done after the transmission of the Kth window.) We can now calculate the latency for transferring the file. The latency has three components: 2RTT for setting up the TCP connection and requesting the file; O/R, the transmission time of the object; and the sum of all the stalled times. Thus,

$$Latency = 2RTT + \frac{O}{R} + \sum_{K=1}^{K-1}\left[\frac{S}{R} + RTT - 2^{k-1}\frac{S}{R}\right]^{+}$$

Figure 29.35 *Latency Formula.*

The reader should compare the above equation for the latency equation for static congestion windows; all the terms are exactly the same except the term WS/R for static windows has been replaced by 2^{k-1} S/R for dynamic windows. To obtain a more compact expression for the latency, let Q be the number of times the server would stall if the object contained an infinite number of segments:

$$\begin{aligned} Q &= \max\{k\colon RTT + \frac{S}{R} - \frac{S}{R}2^{k-1} \geq 0\} \\ &= \max\{k\colon 2^{k-1} \leq 1 + \frac{RTT}{S/R}\} \\ &= \max\{k\colon k \leq \log_2(1 + \frac{RTT}{S/R}) + 1\} \\ &= [\log_2(1 + \frac{RTT}{S/R})] + 1. \end{aligned}$$

Figure 29.36 *Calculation2.*

The actual number of times the server stalls is P = min{Q, K-1}. In the preceding diagram P=Q=2. Combining the above two equations gives

$$Latency - \frac{O}{R} \mid 2RTT \mid \sum_{k=1}^{P}(RTT \mid \frac{S}{R})\ \frac{S}{R}2^{k-1}$$

Figure 29.37 *Formula1.*

We can further simplify the above formula for latency by noting.

$$\sum_{k=1}^{P} 2^{k-1} = 2^{P} - 1$$

Figure 29.38 *Formula2.*

Combining the above two equations gives the following closed-form expression for the latency:

$$Latency = 2RTT + \frac{O}{R} + P\left[RTT + \frac{S}{R}\right] - \left(2^{P} - 1\right)\frac{S}{R}$$

Figure 29.39 *Formula3.*

Thus to calculate the latency, we simple must calculate K and Q, set P = min{Q, K–1}, and plug P into the above formula.

It is interesting to compare the TCP latency to the latency that would occur if there were no congestion control (that is, no congestion window constraint). Without congestion control, the latency is 2RTT + O/R, which we define to be the *Minimum Latency*. It is simple exercise to show that

$$\frac{Latency}{Minimum\ Latency} \le 1 + \frac{P}{\lceil (O/R)/RTT \rceil + 2}$$

Figure 29.40 *Formula4.*

We see from the above formula that TCP slow start will not significantly increase latency if RTT << O/R, that is, if the round-trip time is much less than the transmission time of the object. Thus, if we are sending a relatively large object over an uncongested, high-speed link, then slow start has an insignificant affect on latency. However, with the Web we are often transmitting many small objects over congested links, in which case slow start can significantly increase latency.

Let us now take a look at some example scenarios. In all the scenarios we set S = 536 bytes, a common default value for TCP. We shall use a RTT of 100 msec, which is not an atypical value for a continental or inter-continental delay over moderately congested links. First consider sending a rather large object of size O = 100Kbytes. The number of windows that cover this object is K = 8. For a number of transmission rates, the following chart examines the affect of the the slow-start mechanism on the latency.

R	*O/R*	*P*	*Minimum Latency: O/R + 2RTT*	*Latency with Slow Start*
28 Kbps	28.6 sec	1	28.8 sec	28.9 sec
100 Kbps	8 sec	2	8.2 sec	8.4 sec
1 Mbps	800 msec	5	1 sec	1.5 sec
10 Mbps	80 msec	7	28 sec	98 sec

We see from the above chart that for a large object, slow-start adds appreciable delay only when the transmission rate is high. If the transmission rate is low, then acknowledgements come back relatively quickly, and TCP quickly ramps up to its maximum rate. For example, when R = 100 Kbps, the number of stall periods is P = 2 whereas the number of windows to transmit is K = 8; thus the server stalls only after the first two of eight windows. On one other-hand, when R = 10 Mbps, the server stalls between each window, which causes a significant increase in the delay.

Now consider sending a small object of size O = 5 Kbytes. The number of windows that cover this object is K = 4. For a number of transmission rates, the following chart examines the affect of the the slow-start mechanism.

R	*O/R*	*P*	*Minimum Latency: O/R + 2RTT*	*Latency with Slow Start*
28 Kbps	1.43 sec	1	1.63 sec	1.73 sec
100 Kbps	.4 sec	2	6 sec	.757 sec
1 Mbps	40 msec	3	24 sec	52 sec
10 Mbps	4 msec	3	20 sec	50 sec

Once again slow start adds an appreciable delay when the transmission rate is high. For example, when R = 1Mbps the server stalls between each window, which causes the latency to be more than twice that of the minimum latency.

For a larger RTT, the affect of slow start becomes significant for small objects for smaller transmission rates. The following chart examines the affect of slow start for RTT = 1 second and O = 5 Kbytes (K = 4).

R	*O/R*	*P*	*Minimum Latency: O/R + 2RTT*	*Latency with Slow Start*
28 Kbps	1.43 sec	3	3.4 sec	5.8 sec
100 Kbps	4 sec	3	2.4 sec	5.2 sec
1 Mbps	40 msec	3	2.0 sec	5.0 sec
10 Mbps	4 msec	3	2.0 sec	5.0 sec

In summary, slow start can significantly increase latency when the object size is relatively small and the RTT is relatively large. Unfortunately, this is often the scenario when sending of objects over the World Wide Web.

An Example: HTTP

As an application of the the latency analysis, let's now calculate the response time for a Web page sent over non-persistent HTTP. Suppose that the page consists of one base HTML page and M referenced images. To keep things simple, let us assume that each of the M+1 objects contains exactly O bits.

CONNECTIONLESS TRANSPORT: UDP

The Internet makes two transport protocols available to its applications, UDP and TCP. In this section we take a close look at UDP: how it works and what it does. The reader is encouraged to refer back to material in section 2.1, which includes an overview of the UDP service model, and to the material in section 2.7, which discusses socket programming over UDP.

To motivate our discussion about UDP, suppose you were interested in designing a no-frills, bare-bones transport protocol. How might you go about doing this ? You might first consider using a vacuous transport protocol. In particular, on the sending side, you might consider taking the messages from the application process and passing them directly to the network layer; and on the receiving side, you might consider taking the messages arriving from the network layer and passing them directly to the application process. But as we learned in the previous section, we have to do a little more than nothing. At the very least, the transport layer must provide a multiplexing/de-multiplexing service in order to pass data between the network layer and the correct application.

UDP, defined in, does just about as little as a transport protocol can. Aside from the multiplexing/de-multiplexing function and some light error checking, it adds nothing to IP. In fact, if the application developer chooses UDP instead of TCP, then the application is talking almost directly with IP. UDP takes messages from application process, attaches source and destination port number fields for the multiplexing/de-multiplexing service, adds two other fields of minor importance, and passes the resulting "segment" to the network layer. The network layer encapsulates the segment into an IP datagram and then makes a best-effort attempt to deliver the segment to the receiving host. If the segment arrives at the receiving host, UDP uses the port numbers and the IP source and destination addresses to deliver the data in the segment to the correct application process. Note that with UDP there is no handshaking between sending and receiving transport-layer entities before sending a segment. For this reason, UDP is said to be *connectionless.*

USER DATAGRAM PROTOCOL(UDP)

The User Datagram Protocol (UDP) is a host. UDP hosts service that operates at the transport layer of the OSI model. UDP relies on the upper layer protocol for both error correction and reliable service. The protocol is transaction oriented and delivery and duplicate protection are not guaranteed. The major uses of this protocol are DNS and TFTP.

UDP has a small header and for all intents and purposes it adds port addressing to the IP header. The IP header routes datagrams to the correct host on the network. UDP routes the datagram to the correct application.

UDP Header

0 1 2 3 4 5 6 7	8 9 10 11 12 13 14 15	16 17 18 19 20 21 22 23	24 25 26 27 28 29 30 31
Source Port (16 bits)	Destination Port (16 bits)		
Length (16 bits)	Checksum (16 bits)		
Data			

Source Port

The source port is a 16 bit number that indicates the upper level service (that the source is transmitting). UDP allows port numbers to be in the range from 0 to 65,535. The source port is optional, and if not used, a field of 0s is inserted. Clients will have a unique port number assigned to them by the server. Typically, the number will be above 8,000.

Destination Port

The destination port is a 16 bit number: it indicates the upper level service that the source wishes to communicate with at the destination.

Length

The length field is 16 bits long, indicates the length of the UDP datagram, and has a maximum value of 65, 535 bytes (and a minimum value of 8 bytes).

Checksum

The checksum field is 16 bits long: it calculates a checksum that is based on the UDP header, the Data field, and what is called the UDP Pseudo header. The UDP Pseudo header consists of the Source IP Address, Destination IP Address, Zero, IP Protocol field and UDP Length. For UDP, the IP Protocol field value is 17.

Data

The data field contains the IP header and data. The data field may be padded with zero octets at the end (if necessary) to make a multiple of two octets.

DNS is an example of an application-layer protocol that uses UDP. When the DNS application (see section 2.5) in a host wants to make a query, it constructs a DNS query message and passes the message to a UDP socket (see section 2.7). Without performing any handshaking, UDP adds a header fields to the message and passes the resulting segment to the network layer. The network layer encapsulates the UDP segment into a datagram and sends the datagram to a name server. The DNS application at the querying host then waits for a reply to its query. If it doesn't receive a reply (possibly because UDP lost the query or the reply), it either tries sending the query to another nameserver, or it informs the invoking application that it can't get a reply. We mention that the DNS specification permits DNS to run over TCP instead of UDP; in practice, however, DNS almost always runs over UDP.

Now you might be wondering why an application developer would ever choose to build an application over UDP rather than over TCP. Isn't TCP always preferable to UDP since TCP provides a reliable data transfer service and UDP does not ? The answer is no, as many applications are better suited for UDP for the following reasons:

TCP uses a three-way handshake before it starts to transfer data. UDP just blasts away without any formal preliminaries. Thus UDP does not introduce any delay to establish a connection. This is probably the principle reason why DNS runs over UDP rather than TCP – DNS would be much slower if it ran over TCP. HTTP uses TCP rather than UDP, since reliability is critical for Web pages with text. But, the TCP connection establishment delay in HTTP is an important contributor to the "world wide wait".

No connection state. TCP maintains connection state in the end systems. This connection state includes receive and send buffers, congestion control parameters, and sequence and acknowledgement number parameters. We will see that this state information is needed to implement TCP's reliable data transfer service and to provide congestion control. UDP, on the other hand, does not maintain connection state and does not track any of these parameters. For this reason, a server devoted to a particular application can typically support many more active clients when the application runs over UDP rather than TCP.

Small segment header overhead. The TCP segment has 20 bytes of header overhead in every segment, whereas UDP only has 8 bytes of overhead.

Unregulated send rate. TCP has a congestion control mechanism that throttles the sender when one or more links between sender and receiver becomes excessively congested. This throttling can have a severe impact on real-time applications, which can tolerate some packet loss but require a minimum send rate. On the other hand, the speed at which UDP sends data is only constrained by the rate at which the application generates data, the capabilities of the source (CPU, clock rate, etc.) and the access bandwidth to the Internet. We should keep in mind, however, that the receiving host does not necessarily receive all the data — when the network is congested, a significant fraction of the UDP-transmitted data could be lost due to router buffer overflow. Thus, the receive rate is limited by network congestion even if the sending rate is not constrained.

Table 29.2 lists popular Internet applications and the transport protocols that they use. As we expect, e-mail, remote terminal access, the Web and file transfer run over TCP—these applications need the reliable data transfer service of TCP. Nevertheless, many important applications run over UDP rather TCP. UDP is used for RIP routing table updates (see chapter 4 on the network layer), because the updates are sent periodically, so that lost updates are replaced by more up-to-date updates. UDP is used to carry network management (SNMP - see chapter 8) data. UDP is preferred to TCP in this case, since network management must often run when the network is in a stressed state - precisely when reliable, congestion-controlled data transfer is difficult to achieve. Also, as we mentioned earlier, DNS runs over UDP, thereby avoiding TCP's connection establishment delays.

Table 29.2 Popular Internet Applications and their Underlying Transport Protocols

Application	*Application-layer Protocol*	*Underlying Transport Protocol*
Electronic mail	SMTP	TCP
Remote terminal access	Telnet	TCP
Web	HTTP	TCP
File transfer	FTP	TCP
Remote file server	NFS	typically UDP
Streaming multimedia	proprietary	typically UDP
Internet telephony	proprietary	typically UDP
Network Management	SNMP	typically UDP
Routing Protocol	RIP	typically UDP
Name Translation	DNS	typically UDP

As shown in table, UDP is also commonly used today with multimedia applications, such as Internet phone, real-time video conferencing, and streaming of stored audio and video. We shall take a close look at these applications in chapter 6. We just mention now that all of these applications can tolerate a small fraction of packet loss, so that reliable data transfer is not absolutely critical for the success of the application. Furthermore, interactive real-time applications, such as Internet phone and video conferencing, react very poorly to TCP's congestion control. For these reasons, developers of multimedia applications often choose to run the applications over UDP instead of TCP. Finally, because TCP cannot be employed with multicast, multicast applications run over UDP.

Although commonly done today, running multimedia applications over UDP is controversial to say the least. As we mentioned above, UDP lacks any form of congestion control. But congestion control is needed to prevent the network from entering a congested state in which very little useful work is done. If everyone were to start streaming high bit-rate video without using any congestion control, there would be so much packet overflow at routers that no one would see anything. Thus, the lack of congestion control in UDP is a potentially serious problem. Many researchers have proposed new mechanisms to force all sources, including UDP sources, to perform adaptive congestion control.

Before discussing the UDP segment structure, we mention that it is possible for an application to have reliable data transfer when using UDP. This can be done if reliability is built into the application itself (*e.g.*, by adding acknowledgement and retransmission mechanisms, such as those we shall study in the next section). But this a non-trivial task that would keep an application developer busy debugging for a long time. Nevertheless, building reliability directly into the application allows the application to "have its cake and eat it too"—that is, application processes can communicate reliably without being constrained by the transmission rate constraints imposed by TCP's congestion control mechanism. Application-level reliability also allows an application to tailor its own application-specific form of error control. An interactive real-time may occasionally choose to retransmit a lost message, provided that round trip network delays are small enough to avoid adding significant playout delays.

Many of today's proprietary streaming applications do just this—they run over UDP, but they have built acknowledgements and retransmissions into the application in order reduce packet loss.

UDP Datagram Encapsulation

In this example, the IP address transmits the IP datagram to the node. At that destination, the IP software extracts the UDP datagram and delivers it to the UDP-layer software. The UDP-layer software delivers the UDP data through the destination port to the receiving application. The process at that port uses the data in the UDP datagram. The UDP datagram also contains a source port to ensure that the destination process can reply correctly.

UDP SEGMENT STRUCTURE

As figure 29.41 shows the UDP segment structure, in which the application data occupies the data field of the UDP datagram. For example, for DNS, the data field contains either a query

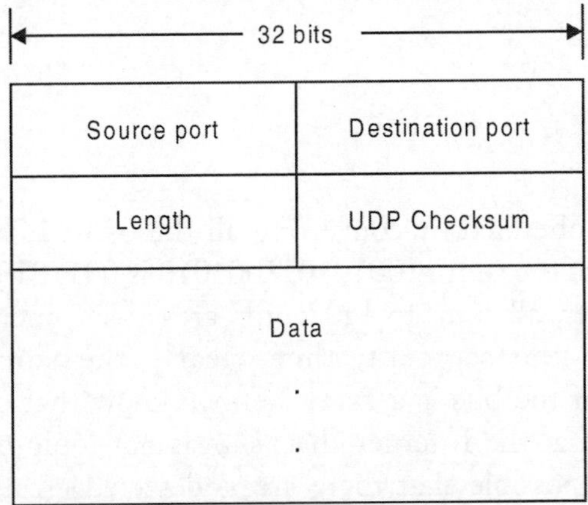

Figure 29.41 *UDP Segment Structure.*

message or a response message. For a streaming audio application, audio samples fill the data field. The UDP header has only four fields, each consisting of four bytes. As discussed in the previous section, the port numbers allow the destination host to pass the application data to the correct process running on that host (*i.e.,* perform the demultiplexing function). The checksum is used by the receiving host to check if errors have been introduced into the segment during the course of its transmission from source to destination.

UDP CHECKSUM

The UDP checksum provides for error detection. UDP at the sender side performs the one's complement of the sum of all the 16-bit words in the segment. This result is put in the checksum field of the UDP segment. (In truth, the checksum is also calculated over a few of the fields in the IP header in addition to the UDP segment. But we ignore this detail in order to see the forest through the trees.) When the segment arrives (if it arrives!) at the receiving host, all 16-bit words are added together, including the checksum. If this sum equals 1111111111111111, then the segment has no detected errors. If one of the bits is a zero, then we know that errors have been introduced into the segment.

Here we give a simple example of the checksum calculation. You can find details about efficient implementation of the calculation in the. As an example, suppose that we have the following three 16-bit words:

0110011001100110

0101010101010101

0000111100001111

The sum of first of these 16-bit words is:

0110011001100110

0101010101010101

1011101110111011

Adding the third word to the above sum gives

1011101110111011

0000111100001111

1100101011001010

The 1's complement is obtained by converting all the 0s to 1s and converting all the 1s to 0s. Thus the 1's complement of the sum 1100101011001010 is 0011010100110101, which becomes the checksum. At the receiver, all four 16-bit words are added, including the checksum. If no errors are introduced into the segment, then clearly the sum at the receiver will be 1111111111111111. If one of the bits is a zero, then we know that errors have been introduced into the segment. We'll see that the Internet checksum is not foolproof—even if the sum equals 111111111111111, it is still possible that there are undetected errors in the segment. For this reason, a number of protocols use more sophisticated error detection techniques than simple check summing.

You may wonder why UDP provides a checksum in the first place, as many link-layer protocols (including the popular Ethernet protocol) also provide error checking ? The reason is that there is no guarantee that all the links between source and destination provide error checking —one of the links may use a protocol that does not provide error checking. Because IP is supposed to run over just about any layer-2 protocol, it is useful for the transport layer to provide error checking as a safety measure. Although UDP provides error checking, it does not do anything to recover from an error. Some implementations of UDP simply discard the damaged segment; others pass the damaged segment to the application with a warning.

That wraps up our discussion of UDP. We will soon see that TCP offers reliable data transfer to its applications as well as other services that UDP doesn't offer. Naturally, TCP is also more complex than UDP. Before discussing TCP, however, it will be useful to step back and first discuss the underlying principles of reliable data transfer, which we do in the subsequent section.

REVIEW QUESTIONS

1. TCP/IP is one of them. What does the acronym TCP/IP stand for ?
2. What OSI model layers do IP and TCP operate at ?
3. What is the chief responsibility of the IP protocol ?
4. What type of packets was TCP designed to carry ?
5. Briefy describe each class of the TCP protocol.
6. What is the purpose of the sequence and acknowledge number fields in the TCP header ?
7. What parts of the TCP header is used to request and establish a connection ?
8. Besides address size change, what else does ipv6 address ?
9. What is the difference between a process-to-process delivery and a host-to-host delivery ?
10. When is a three way handshake used ?
11. Why would an application use UDP instead of TCP ?
12. What is a UDP packet called ? what is a TCP packet called ?
13. What is the purpose of sequence number in a TCP packet ?
14. What is the purpose of flow control ?
15. What is the purpose of the TCP push operation ?
16. Define UDP and explain why UDP is less complex and easiest to understand ? Discuss how UDP offers message-oriented interface ?

❑❑❑

PART 9

PRESENTATION AND APPLICATION LAYER

30

APPLICATION LAYER

The application layer provides to an application process the ability to communicate with another application process, to exchange information and interoperate in the accomplishment of a particular goal. Of all the seven layers of the structure of Network resources, only the application layer interacts directly with the other components of an application process. It is the only way available for an application to gain access to the resources needed for communication, and the only way for an application to determine the characteristics of that communication. Two concepts are key to the application layer and its relationship with an information processing task: application entity and abstract syntax.

This layer provides the interface to the communications environment which is used by the application process. It is responsible for communicating application process parameters. The following services may form part of the application layer. The first is information transfer and another is application entity.

1. Information Transfer. This covers the following points as detailed below:

1. Identification of intended communication partner. By name, address, or some other description.
2. Establishment of the authority of the application process to use the communication services.
3. Determination of the availability of intended communication partner.
4. Agreement of privacy mechanisms required for communication.
5. Authentication of intended communication partners.
6. Resource costing.
7. Determination of the adequacy of the resources available for intended communication.
8. Determination of service quality.
9. Synchronization between applications.
10. Selection of dialogue discipline. Including initiation and release procedures.
11. Agreement on who has responsibility for error recovery.
12. Agreement on procedures ensuring data integrity.

"When a specific instance of an application-process wishes to communicate with an instance of an AP in some other open system, it must invoke an instance of an AE in the Application Layer of its own open system. It then becomes the responsibility of this instance of the AE to establish an association with an instance of an appropriate AE in the destination open system. This process occurs by invocation of instances of entities in the lower layers. When the association between the two AEs has been established, the AP can communicate."

2. Application Entity. Application entities are those components of an application process that correspond to capabilities concerned with Open Systems Interconnection. That is, application entities are particular parts of an application process concerned with enabling communication and interaction with a corresponding application process in another open system.

NETWORK CATEGORIES

TDP/IP includes a wide range of protocols which are used for a variety of purposes on the network. The set of protocols that are a part of TCP/IP is called the TCP/IP protocol stack or the TCP/IP suite of protocols.

Considering the many protocols, message types, levels, and services that TCP/IP networking supports, I believe it would be very helpful to categorize the various protocols that support TCP/IP networking and define their respective contribution to the operation of networking. Unfortunately I have never seen this done to any real extent, but believe it would be worthwhile to help those learning networking understand it faster and better. I cannot guarantee that experts will agree with the categorizations that will be provided here, but they should help the reader get the big picture on the various protocols, and thus clarify what the reason or need is for each protocol.

As mentioned previously, there are four TCP/IP layers. They are link, network, transport, and application. The link layer is the hardware layer that provides ability to send messages between multiple locations. In the case of this document, Ethernet provides this capability. Below I define several categories some of which fit into the 4 layer protocol levels described earlier. I also define a relative fundamental importance to the ability of the network to function at all. Importance includes essential, critical, important, advanced, useful.

- **Essential:** Without this all other categories are irrelevant.
- **Critical:** The network, as designed, is useless without this ability.
- **Important:** The network could function, but would be difficult to use and manage.
- **Advanced:** Includes enhancements that make the network easier to use and manage.
- **Useful:** Functionality that you would like to be able to use as a network user. Applications or some functionality is supported here.

Table 30.1 Tabulization of N/W Categories

Name(layer)	*Importance*	*Names of Protocols*	*Description*
Hardware(link)	Essential	Ethernet, SLIP, PPP, Token Ring, ARCnet	Allows messages to be packaged and sent between physical locations.
Package management (network)	Essential	IP, ICMP	Manages movement of messages and reports errors. It uses message protocols and software to manage this process. (includes routing)
Inter layer communication	Essential	ARP	Communicates between layers to allow one layer to get information to support another layer. This includes broad-casting.
Service control (transport)	Critical	TCP, UDP	Controls the management of service between computers. Based on values in TCP and UDP messages a server knows what service is being requested.
Application and user support	Important	DNS, RPC	DNS provides address to name trans-lation for locations and network cards. RPC allows remote computer to per-form functions on other computers.
Network Management	Advanced	RARP, BOOTP, DHCP, IGMP, SNMP, RIP, OSPF, BGP, CIDR	Enhances network management and increases functionality.
Utility(Application)	Useful	FTP, TFTP, SMTP, Telnet, NFS, ping, Rlogin	Provides direct services to the user.

There are exceptions to my categorizations that don't fit into the normal layering scheme, such as IGMP is normally part of the link layer, but I have tried to list these categorizations according to network functions and their relative importance to the operation of the network. Also note that Ethernet, which is not really a protocol, but an IEEE standard along with PPP, SLIP, Token Ring, and Arc Net are not TCP/IP protocols but may support TCP/IP at the hardware or link layer, depending on the network topology. The list below gives a brief description of each protocol:

Ethernet: Provides for transport of information between physical locations on Ethernet cable. Data is passed in Ethernet packets.

SLIP: Serial Line IP (SLIP), a form of data encapsulation for serial lines.

PPP: Point to Point Protocol (PPP). A form of serial line data encapsulation that is an improvement over SLIP.

IP: Internet Protocol (IP). Except for ARP and RARP all protocols' data packets will be packaged into an IP data packet. Provides the mechanism to use software to address and manage data packets being sent to computers.

ICMP: Internet Control Message Protocol (ICMP) provides management and error reporting to help manage the process of sending data between computers.

ARP: Address Resolution Protocol (ARP) enables the packaging of IP data into Ethernet packages. It is the system and messaging protocol that is used to find the Ethernet (hardware) address from a specific IP number. Without this protocol, the Ethernet package could not be generated from the IP package, because the Ethernet address could not be determined.

TCP: A reliable connection oriented protocol used to control the management of application level services between computers.

UDP: An unreliable connection less protocol used to control the management of application level services between computers.

DNS: Domain Name Service (DNS) allows the network to determine IP addresses from names and vice versa.

RARP: Reverse Address Resolution Protocol (RARP) is used to allow a computer without a local permanent data storage media to determine its IP address from its Ethernet address.

Bootp: Bootstrap protocol is used to assign an IP address to diskless computers and tell it what server and file to load which will provide it with an operating system.

DHCP: Dynamic Host Configuration Protocol (DHCP) is a method of assigning and controlling the IP addresses of computers on a given network. It is a server based service that automatically assigns IP numbers when a computer boots. This way the IP address of a computer does not need to be assigned manually. This makes changing networks easier to manage. DHCP can perform all the functions of BOOTP.

IGMP: Internet Group Management Protocol (IGMP) used to support multicasting.

SNMP: Simple Network Management Protocol (SNMP). Used to manage all types of network elements based on various data sent and received.

RIP: Routing Information Protocol (RIP), used to dynamically update router tables on WANs or the Internet.

OSPF: Open Shortest Path First (OSPF) dynamic routing protocol.

BGP: Border Gateway Protocol (BGP). A dynamic router protocol to communicate between routers on different systems.

CIDR: Classless Inter-Domain Routing (CIDR).

FTP: File Transfer Protocol (FTP). Allows file transfer between two computers with login required.

TFTP: Trivial File Transfer Protocol (TFTP). Allows file transfer between two computers with no login required. It is limited, and is intended for diskless stations.

SMTP: Simple Mail Transfer Protocol (SMTP).

NFS: Network File System (NFS). A protocol that allows UNIX and Linux systems remotely mount each other's file systems.

Telnet: A method of opening a user session on a remote host.

Ping: A program that uses ICMP to send diagnostic messages to other computers to tell if they are reachable over the network.

Rlogin: Remote login between UNIX hosts. This is outdated and is replaced by Telnet.

Each protocol ultimately has it's data packets wrapped in an Ethernet, SLIP, or PPP packet (at the link level) in order to be sent over the ethernet cable. Some protocol data packets are wrapped sequentially multiple times before being sent. For example FTP data is wrapped in a TCP packet which is wrapped in a IP packet which is wrapped in a link packet (normally Ethernet).

INTERNET GROUP MANAGEMENT PROTOCOL

Internet Group Management Protocol (IGMP) is the protocol used to support multicasting. To use multicasting, a process on a host must be able to join and leave a group. A process is a user program that is using the network. Group access is identified by the group address and the interface (NIC). A host must keep track of the groups that at least one process belongs to and the number of processes that belong to the group. IGMP is defined in RFC 1112.

IGMP messages are used by multicast routers to track group memberships on each of its networks. It uses these rules:

1. The first time a process on a host joins a multicast group, the host will send an IGMP report. This means that every time the host needs to receive messages from a new group to support its processes, it will send a report.
2. Multicast routers will send IGMP queries regularly to determine whether any hosts are running processes that belong to any groups. The group address of the query is set to 0, the TTL field is set to 1, and the destination IP address is 224.0.0.1 which is the all hosts group address which address all the multicast capable routers and hosts on a network.
3. A host sends one IGMP response for each group that contains one or more processes. The router expects one response from each host for each group that one or more of its processes require access to.
4. A host does not send a report when its last process leaves a group (when the group access is no longer required by a process). The multicast router relies on query responses to update this information.

IGMP is defined in RFC 1112. Hosts and routers use IGMP to support multicasting. Multicast routers must know which hosts belong to what group at any given point of time. The IGMP message is 8 bytes. consisting of:

1. Bits 0 to 3 - IGMP version number
2. Bits 4 to 7 - IGMP type. 1 = query sent by a multicast router. 2 is a response sent by a host.
3. Bits 8 to 15 - unused
4. Bits 16 to 31 - Checksum
5. The last 4 bytes - 32 bit group address which is the same as the class D IP address.

IGMP message formats are encapsulated in an IP datagram which contain a time to live (TTL) field. The default is to set the TTL field to 1 which means the datagram will not leave its sub-network. an application can increase its TTL field in a message to locate a server distance in terms of hops.

Addresses from 224.0.0.0 to 224.0.0.255 are not forwarded by multicast routers since these addresses are intended for applications that do not need to communicate with other networks. Therefore these addresses can be used for group multicasting on private networks with no concern for addresses being used for multicasting on other networks.

The TCP Level

Two separate protocols are involved in handling TCP/IP data-grams. TCP (the "transmission control protocol") is responsible for breaking up the message into data-grams, reassembling them at the other end, resending anything that gets lost, and putting things back in the right order. IP (the "Internet protocol") is responsible for routing individual data-grams. It may seem like TCP is doing all the work. And in small networks that is true. However, in the Internet, simply getting a datagram to its destination can be a complex job. A connection may require the datagram to go through several networks at Rutgers, a serial line to the John von Neuman Supercomputer Center, a couple of Ethernets there, a series of 56Kbaud phone lines to another NSFnet site, and more Ethernets on another campus. Keeping track of the routes to all of the destinations and handling incompatibilities among different transport media turns out to be a complex job. Note that the interface between TCP and IP is fairly simple. TCP simply hands IP a datagram with a destination. IP doesn't know how this datagram relates to any datagram before it or after it.

We have talked about Internet addresses, but not about how you keep track of multiple connections to a given system. Clearly it isn't enough to get a datagram to the right destination. TCP has to know which connection this datagram is part of. This task is referred to as "de-multiplexing." In fact, there are several levels of de-multiplexing going on in TCP/IP. The information needed to do this de-multiplexing is contained in a series of "headers". A header is simply a few extra octets tacked onto the beginning of a datagram by some protocol in order to keep track of it. It's a lot like putting a letter into an envelope and putting an address on the outside of the envelope. Except with modern networks it happens several times. It's like you put the letter into a little envelope, your secretary puts that into a somewhat bigger envelope, the campus mail center puts that envelope into a still bigger one, etc. Here is an overview of the headers that get stuck on a message that passes through a typical TCP/IP network.

We start with a single data stream, say a file you are trying to send to some other computer.

TCP breaks it up into manageable chunks. (In order to do this, TCP has to know how large a datagram your network can handle. Actually, the TCP's at each end say how big a datagram they can handle, and then they pick the smallest size.)

TCP puts a header at the front of each datagram. This header actually contains at least 20 octets, but the most important ones are a source and destination "port number" and a "sequence number". The port numbers are used to keep track of different conversations. Suppose 3 different people are transferring files. Your TCP might allocate port numbers 1000, 1001, and 1002 to these transfers. When you are sending a datagram, this becomes the "source" port number, since you are the source of the datagram. Of course the TCP at the other end has assigned a port number of its own for the conversation. Your TCP has to know the port number used by the other end as well. (It finds out when the connection starts, as we will explain below.) It puts this in the "destination" port field. Of course if the other end sends a datagram back to you, the source and destination port numbers will be reversed, since then it will be the source and you will be the destination. Each datagram has a sequence number. This is used so that the other end can make sure that it gets the data-grams in the right order, and that it hasn't missed any. (See the TCP specification for details.) TCP doesn't number the data-grams, but the octets. So if there are 500 octets of data in each datagram, the first datagram might be numbered 0, the second 500, the next 1000, the next 1500, etc. Finally, I will mention the Checksum. This is a number that is computed by adding up all the octets in the datagram (more or less—see the TCP spec). The result is put in the header. TCP at the other end computes the checksum again. If they disagree, then something bad happened to the datagram in transmission, and it is thrown away. So here's what the datagram looks like now.

```
+-+-+-+-+-+-+-+-+-+-+-+-+-+-+-+-+-+-+-+-+-+-+-+-+-+-+-+-+-+-+-+-+
|     Source Port       |     Destination Port      |
+-+-+-+-+-+-+-+-+-+-+-+-+-+-+-+-+-+-+-+-+-+-+-+-+-+-+-+-+-+-+-+-+
|           Sequence Number            |
+-+-+-+-+-+-+-+-+-+-+-+-+-+-+-+-+-+-+-+-+-+-+-+-+-+-+-+-+-+-+-+-+
|         Acknowledgement Number           |
+-+-+-+-+-+-+-+-+-+-+-+-+-+-+-+-+-+-+-+-+-+-+-+-+-+-+-+-+-+-+-+-+
| Data |        |U|A|P|R|S|F|              |
| Offset| Reserved |R|C|S|S|Y|I|       Window       |
|    |        |G|K|H|T|N|N|             |
+-+-+-+-+-+-+-+-+-+-+-+-+-+-+-+-+-+-+-+-+-+-+-+-+-+-+-+-+-+-+-+-+
|      Checksum       |   Urgent Pointer     |
+-+-+-+-+-+-+-+-+-+-+-+-+-+-+-+-+-+-+-+-+-+-+-+-+-+-+-+-+-+-+-+-+
|  your data ... next 500 octets               |
|  ......                        |
```

If we abbreviate the TCP header as "T", the whole file now looks like this:

```
T....  T....  T....  T....  T....  T....  T....
```

You will note that there are items in the header that I have not described above. They are generally involved with managing the connection. In order to make sure the datagram has arrived at its destination, the recipient has to send back an "acknowledgement". This is a datagram whose "Acknowledgement number" field is filled in. For example, sending a packet with an acknowledgement of 1500 indicates that you have received all the data up to octet number 1500. If the sender doesn't get an acknowledgement within a reasonable amount of time, it sends the data again. The window is used to control how much data can be in transit at any one time. It is not practical to wait for each datagram to be acknowledged before sending the next one. That would slow things down too much. On the other hand, you can't just keep sending, or a fast computer might overrun the capacity of a slow one to absorb data. Thus each end indicates how much new data it is currently prepared to absorb by putting the number of octets in its "Window" field. As the computer receives data, the amount of space left in its window decreases. When it goes to zero, the sender has to stop. As the receiver processes the data, it increases its window, indicating that it is ready to accept more data. Often the same datagram can be used to acknowledge receipt of a set of data and to give permission for additional new data (by an updated window). The "Urgent" field allows one end to tell the other to skip ahead in its processing to a particular octet. This is often useful for handling asynchronous events, for example when you type a control character or other command that interrupts output. The other fields are beyond the scope of this document.

The IP Level

TCP sends each of these data-grams to IP. Of course it has to tell IP the Internet address of the computer at the other end. Note that this is all IP is concerned about. It doesn't care about what is in the datagram, or even in the TCP header. IP's job is simply to find a route for the datagram and get it to the other end. In order to allow gateways or other intermediate systems to forward the datagram, it adds its own header. The main things in this header are the source and destination Internet address (32-bit addresses, like 128.6.4.194), the protocol number, and another checksum. The source Internet address is simply the address of your machine. This is necessary so the other end knows where the datagram came from. The destination Internet address is the address of the other machine. This is necessary so any gateways in the middle know where you want the datagram to go. The protocol number tells IP at the other end to send the datagram to TCP. Although most IP traffic uses TCP, there are other protocols that can use IP, so you have to tell IP which protocol to send the datagram to. Finally, the checksum allows IP at the other end to verify that the header wasn't damaged in transit. Note that TCP and IP have separate checksums. IP needs to be able to verify that the header didn't get damaged in transit, or it could send a message to the wrong place. For reasons not worth discussing here, it is both more efficient and safer to have TCP compute a separate checksum for the TCP header and data. Once IP has tacked on its header, here's what the message looks like:

```
+-+-+-+-+-+-+-+-+-+-+-+-+-+-+-+-+-+-+-+-+-+-+-+-+-+-+-+-+-+-+-+-+
|Version| IHL |Type of Service|     Total Length      |
+-+-+-+-+-+-+-+-+-+-+-+-+-+-+-+-+-+-+-+-+-+-+-+-+-+-+-+-+-+-+-+-+
|     Identification     |Flags|  Fragment Offset  |
+-+-+-+-+-+-+-+-+-+-+-+-+-+-+-+-+-+-+-+-+-+-+-+-+-+-+-+-+-+-+-+-+
| Time to Live |  Protocol  |     Header Checksum    |
+-+-+-+-+-+-+-+-+-+-+-+-+-+-+-+-+-+-+-+-+-+-+-+-+-+-+-+-+-+-+-+-+
|           Source Address            |
+-+-+-+-+-+-+-+-+-+-+-+-+-+-+-+-+-+-+-+-+-+-+-+-+-+-+-+-+-+-+-+-+
|          Destination Address          |
+-+-+-+-+-+-+-+-+-+-+-+-+-+-+-+-+-+-+-+-+-+-+-+-+-+-+-+-+-+-+-+-+
| TCP header, then your data ......            |
|                 |
```

If we represent the IP header by an "I", your file now looks like this:

```
IT....  IT....  IT....  IT....  IT....  IT....  IT....
```

Again, the header contains some additional fields that have not been discussed. Most of them are beyond the scope of this document. The flags and fragment offset are used to keep track of the pieces when a datagram has to be split up. This can happen when datagrams are forwarded through a network for which they are too big. The time to live is a number that is decremented whenever the datagram passes through a system. When it goes to zero, the datagram is discarded. This is done in case a loop develops in the system somehow. Of course this should be impossible, but well-designed networks are built to cope with "impossible" conditions.

At this point, it's possible that no more headers are needed. If your computer happens to have a direct phone line connecting it to the destination computer, or to a gateway, it may simply send the data-grams out on the line.

THE ETHERNET LEVEL

However, most of our networks these days use Ethernet. So now we have to describe Ethernet's headers. Unfortunately, Ethernet has its own addresses. The people who designed Ethernet wanted to make sure that no two machines would end up with the same Ethernet address. Furthermore, they didn't want the user to have to worry about assigning addresses. So each Ethernet controller comes with an address builtin from the factory. In order to make sure that they would never have to reuse addresses, the Ethernet designers allocated 48 bits for the Ethernet address. People who make Ethernet equipment have to register with a central authority, to make sure that the numbers they assign don't overlap any other manufacturer. Ethernet is a "broadcast medium". That is, it is in effect like an old party line telephone. When you send a packet out on the Ethernet, every machine on the network sees the packet. So something is needed to make sure that the right machine gets it. As you might guess, this involves the Ethernet header. Every Ethernet packet has a 14-octet header that includes the source and destination Ethernet address, and a type code. Each machine is supposed to pay attention only to packets with its own Ethernet address in the destination field. Note that there is no connection between the Ethernet address and the Internet address. Each machine has to have a table of what Ethernet address corresponds to what Internet address. (We will describe how this table is constructed a bit later.) In addition to the addresses, the header contains a type code. The type code is to allow for several different protocol families to be used on the same network. So you can use TCP/IP, DECnet, Xerox NS, etc. at the same time. Each of them will put a different value in the type field. Finally, there is a checksum. The Ethernet controller computes a checksum of the entire packet. When the other end receives the packet, it recomputes the checksum, and throws the packet away if the answer disagrees with the original. The checksum is put on the end of the packet, not in the header. The final result is that your message looks like this:

```
+-+-+-+-+-+-+-+-+-+-+-+-+-+-+-+-+-+-+-+-+-+-+-+-+-+-+-+-+-+-+-+-+
|    Ethernet destination address (first 32 bits)     |
+-+-+-+-+-+-+-+-+-+-+-+-+-+-+-+-+-+-+-+-+-+-+-+-+-+-+-+-+-+-+-+-+
| Ethernet dest (last 16 bits) |Ethernet source (first 16 bits)|
+-+-+-+-+-+-+-+-+-+-+-+-+-+-+-+-+-+-+-+-+-+-+-+-+-+-+-+-+-+-+-+-+
|    Ethernet source address (last 32 bits)      |
+-+-+-+-+-+-+-+-+-+-+-+-+-+-+-+-+-+-+-+-+-+-+-+-+-+-+-+-+-+-+-+-+
|    Type code       |
+-+-+-+-+-+-+-+-+-+-+-+-+-+-+-+-+-+-+-+-+-+-+-+-+-+-+-+-+-+-+-+-+
| IP header, then TCP header, then your data         |
|                              |
...
|                              |
|  end of your data                   |
+-+-+-+-+-+-+-+-+-+-+-+-+-+-+-+-+-+-+-+-+-+-+-+-+-+-+-+-+-+-+-+-+
|            Ethernet Checksum          |
+-+-+-+-+-+-+-+-+-+-+-+-+-+-+-+-+-+-+-+-+-+-+-+-+-+-+-+-+-+-+-+-+
```

If we represent the Ethernet header with "E", and the Ethernet checksum with "C", your file now looks like this:

```
EIT....C  EIT....C  EIT....C  EIT....C  EIT....C
```

When these packets are received by the other end, of course all the headers are removed. The Ethernet interface removes the Ethernet header and the checksum. It looks at the type code. Since the type code is the one assigned to IP, the Ethernet device driver passes the datagram up to IP. IP removes the IP header. It looks at the IP protocol field. Since the protocol type is TCP, it passes the datagram up to TCP. TCP now looks at the sequence number. It uses the sequence numbers and other information to combine all the datagrams into the original file.

The ends our initial summary of TCP/IP. There are still some crucial concepts we haven't gotten to, so we'll now go back and add details in several areas.

WELL-KNOWN SOCKETS AND THE APPLICATIONS LAYER

So far, we have described how a stream of data is broken up into data-grams, sent to another computer, and put back together. However, something more is needed in order to accomplish anything useful. There has to be a way for you to open a connection to a specified computer, log into it, tell it what file you want, and control the transmission of the file. (If you have a different application in mind, *e.g.*, computer mail, some analogous protocol is needed.) This is done by "application protocols". The application protocols run "on top" of TCP/IP. That is, when they want to send a message, they give the message to TCP. TCP makes sure it gets delivered to the other end. Because TCP and IP take care of all the networking details, the applications protocols can treat a network connection as if it were a simple byte stream, like a terminal or phone line.

Before going into more details about applications programs, we have to describe how you find an application. Suppose you want to send a file to a computer whose Internet address is

128.6.4.7. To start the process, you need more than just the Internet address. You have to connect to the FTP server at the other end. In general, network programs are specialized for a specific set of tasks. Most systems have separate programs to handle file transfers, remote terminal logins, mail, etc. When you connect to 128.6.4.7, you have to specify that you want to talk to the FTP server. This is done by having "well-known sockets" for each server. Recall that TCP uses port numbers to keep track of individual conversations. User programs normally use more or less random port numbers. However, specific port numbers are assigned to the programs that sit waiting for requests. For example, if you want to send a file, you will start a program called "ftp". It will open a connection using some random number, say 1234, for the port number on its end. However, it will specify port number 21 for the other end. This is the official port number for the FTP server. Note that there are two different programs involved. You run ftp on your side. This is a program designed to accept commands from your terminal and pass them on to the other end. The program that you talk to on the other machine is the FTP server. It is designed to accept commands from the network connection, rather than an interactive terminal. There is no need for your program to use a well-known socket number for itself. Nobody is trying to find it. However, the servers have to have well-known numbers, so that people can open connections to them and start sending them commands. The official port numbers for each program are given in "Assigned Numbers".

Note that a connection is actually described by a set of 4 numbers: the Internet address at each end, and the TCP port number at each end. Every datagram has all four of those numbers in it. The Internet addresses are in the IP header, and the TCP port numbers are in the TCP header. In order to keep things straight, no two connections can have the same set of numbers. However, it is enough for any one number to be different. For example, it is perfectly possible for two different users on a machine to be sending files to the same other machine. This could result in connections with the following parameters:

	Internet addresses	*TCP ports*
connection 1	128.6.4.194, 128.6.4.7	1234, 21
connection 2	128.6.4.194, 128.6.4.7	1235, 21

Since the same machines are involved, the Internet addresses are the same. Since they are both doing file transfers, one end of the connection involves the well-known port number for FTP. The only thing that differs is the port number for the program that the users are running. That's enough of a difference. Generally, at least one end of the connection asks the network software to assign it a port number that is guaranteed to be unique. Normally, it's the user's end, since the server has to use a well-known number.

Now that we know how to open connections, let's get back to the applications programs. As mentioned earlier, once TCP has opened a connection, we have something that might as well be a simple wire. All the hard parts are handled by TCP and IP. However, we still need some agreement as to what we send over this connection. In effect this is simply an agreement on what set of commands the application will understand, and the format in which they are to be sent. Generally, what is sent is a combination of commands and data. They use context to differentiate. For example, the mail protocol works like this: Your mail program opens a connection to the mail server at the other end. Your program gives it your machine's name, the sender of the message, and the recipients you want it sent to. It then sends a command saying that it is starting the message. At that point, the other end stops treating what it sees as commands, and starts accepting the message. Your end then starts sending the text of the message. At the end of the message, a special mark is sent (a dot in the first column). After that, both ends understand that your program is again sending commands. This is the simplest way to do things, and the one that most applications use.

File transfer is somewhat more complex. The file transfer protocol involves two different connections. It starts out just like mail. The user's program sends commands like "log me in as this user", "here is my password", "send me the file with this name". However, once the command to send data is sent, a second connection is opened for the data itself. It would certainly be possible to send the data on the same connection, as mail does. However, file transfers often take a long time. The designers of the file transfer protocol wanted to allow the user to continue issuing commands while the transfer is going on. For example, the user might make an inquiry, or he might abort the transfer. Thus the designers felt it was best to use a separate connection for the data and leave the original command connection for commands. It is also possible to open command connections to two different computers, and tell them to send a file from one to the other. In that case, the data couldn't go over the command connection.

Remote terminal connections use another mechanism still. For remote logins, there is just one connection. It normally sends data. When it is necessary to send a command (*e.g.*, to set the terminal type or to change some mode), a special character is used to indicate that the next character is a command. If the user happens to type that special character as data, two of them are sent.

However, there are a couple of common conventions used by applications that will be described here. First, the common network representation: TCP/IP is intended to be usable on any computer. Unfortunately, not all computers agree on how data is represented. There are differences in character codes (ASCII vs. EBCDIC), in end of line conventions (carriage return, line feed, or a representation using counts), and in whether terminals expect characters to be sent individually or a line at a time. In order to allow computers of different kinds to communicate, each applications protocol defines a standard representation. Note that TCP and IP do not care about the representation. TCP simply sends octets. However, the programs at both ends have to agree on how the octets are to be interpreted. The RFC for each application specifies the standard representation for that application. Normally it is "net ASCII". This uses ASCII characters, with end of line denoted by a carriage return followed by a line feed. For remote login, there is also a definition of a "standard terminal", which turns out to be a half-duplex terminal with echoing happening on the local machine. Most applications also make provisions for the two computers to agree on other representations that they may find more convenient. For example, PDP-10's have 36-bit words. There is a way that two PDP-10's can agree to send a 36-bit binary file. Similarly, two systems that prefer full-duplex terminal conversations can agree on that. However, each application has a standard representation, which every machine must support.

AN EXAMPLE APPLICATION: SMTP

In order to give a bit better idea what is involved in the application protocols, I'm going to show an example of SMTP, which is the mail protocol. (SMTP is "simple mail transfer protocol".) We assume that a computer called TOPAZ.RUTGERS.EDU wants to send the following message.

First, note that the format of the message itself is described by an Internet standard (RFC 822). The standard specifies the fact that the message must be transmitted as net ASCII (*i.e.,* it must be ASCII, with carriage return/linefeed to delimit lines). It also describes the general structure, as a group of header lines, then a blank line, and then the body of the message. Finally, it describes the syntax of the header lines in detail. Generally they consist of a keyword and then a value.

Initially, addresses were simply "person at machine". However, recent standards have made things more flexible. There are now provisions for systems to handle other systems' mail. This can allow automatic forwarding on behalf of computers not connected to the Internet. It can be used to direct mail for a number of systems to one central mail server. Indeed there is no requirement that an actual computer by the name of RED.RUTGERS.EDU even exist. The name servers could be set up so that you mail to department names, and each department's mail is routed automatically to an appropriate computer. It is also possible that the part before the @ is something other than a user name. It is possible for programs to be set up to process mail. There are also provisions to handle mailing lists, and generic names such as "postmaster" or "operator".

The way the message is to be sent to another system is described by RFC's 821 and 974. The program that is going to be doing the sending asks the name server several queries to determine where to route the message. The first query is to find out which machines handle mail for the name RED.RUTGERS.EDU. In this case, the server replies that RED.RUTGERS.EDU handles its own mail. The program then asks for the address of RED.RUTGERS.EDU, which is 128.6.4.2. Then the mail program opens a TCP connection to port 25 on 128.6.4.2. Port 25 is the well-known socket used for receiving mail. Once this connection is established, the mail program starts sending commands. Here is a typical conversation. Each line is labelled as to whether it is from TOPAZ or RED. Note that TOPAZ initiated the connection:

- RED 220 RED.RUTGERS.EDU SMTP Service at 29 Jun 87 05:17:18 EDT
- TOPAZ HELO topaz.rutgers.edu
- RED 250 RED.RUTGERS.EDU - Hello, TOPAZ.RUTGERS.EDU
- TOPAZ MAIL From:
- RED 250 MAIL accepted
- TOPAZ RCPT To:
- RED 250 Recipient accepted
- TOPAZ DATA
- RED 354 Start mail input; end with.
- TOPAZ Date: Sat, 27 Jun 87 13:26:31 EDT
- TOPAZ From: hedrick@topaz.rutgers.edu

- TOPAZ To: levy@red.rutgers.edu
- TOPAZ Subject: meeting
- TOPAZ
- TOPAZ Let's get together Monday at 1pm.
- TOPAZ .
- RED 250 OK
- TOPAZ QUIT
- RED 221 RED.RUTGERS.EDU Service closing transmission channel.

First, note that commands all use normal text. This is typical of the Internet standards. Many of the protocols use standard ASCII commands. This makes it easy to watch what is going on and to diagnose problems. For example, the mail program keeps a log of each conversation. If something goes wrong, the log file can simply be mailed to the postmaster. Since it is normal text, he can see what was going on. It also allows a human to interact directly with the mail server, for testing. Some newer protocols are complex enough that this is not practical. The commands would have to have a syntax that would require a significant parser. Thus there is a tendency for newer protocols to use binary formats. Generally they are structured like C or Pascal record structures. Second, note that the responses all begin with numbers. This is also typical of Internet protocols. The allowable responses are defined in the protocol. The numbers allow the user program to respond unambiguously. The rest of the response is text, which is normally for use by any human who may be watching or looking at a log. It has no effect on the operation of the programs. However, there is one point at which the protocol uses part of the text of the response. The commands themselves simply allow the mail program on one end to tell the mail server the information it needs to know in order to deliver the message. In this case, the mail server could get the information by looking at the message itself. But for more complex cases, that would not be safe. Every session must begin with a HELO, which gives the name of the system that initiated the connection. Then the sender and recipients are specified. There can be more than one RCPT command, if there are several recipients. Finally the data itself is sent. Note that the text of the message is terminated by a line containing just a period. (If such a line appears in the message, the period is doubled.) After the message is accepted, the sender can send another message, or terminate the session as in the example above.

Generally, there is a pattern to the response numbers. The protocol defines the specific set of responses that can be sent as answers to any given command. However, programs that don't want to analyze them in detail can just look at the first digit. In general, responses that begin with a 2 indicate success. Those that begin with 3 indicate that some further action is needed, as shown above. 4 and 5 indicate errors. 4 is a "temporary" error, such as a disk filling. The message should be saved, and tried again later. 5 is a permanent error, such as a non-existent recipient. The message should be returned to the sender with an error message.

(For more details about the protocols mentioned in this section, see RFC's 821/822 for mail, RFC 959 for file transfer, and RFC's 854/855 for remote logins. For the well-known port numbers, see the current edition of assigned numbers, and possibly RFC 814.)

INTERNET HISTORY

1969—Birth of a Network

The Internet as we know it today, in the mid-1990s, traces it origins back to a defense department project in 1969. The subject of the project was wartime digital communications. At that time the telephone system was about the only theater-scale communications system in use. A major problem had been identified in its design - its dependence on switching stations that could be targeted during an attack. Would it be possible to design a network that could quickly reroute digital traffic around failed nodes ? A possible solution had been identified in theory. That was to build a "web" of datagram network, called an "catenet", and use dynamic routing protocols to constantly adjust the flow of traffic through the catenet. The Defense Advanced Research Projects Agency (DARPA) launched the DARPA Internet program.

1970s—Infancy

DARPA Internet, largely the plaything of academic and military researchers, spent more than a decade in relative obscurity. As Vietnam, Watergate, the Oil Crisis, and the Iranian Hostage Crisis rolled over the nation, several Internet research teams proceeded through a gradual evolution of protocols. In 1975, DARPA declared the project a success and handed its management over to the defense communications agency. Several of today's key protocols (including IP and TCP) were stable by 1980, and adopted throughout ARPANET by 1983.

On a cold war kind of day, in swinging 1969, work began on the ARPAnet, grandfather to the Internet. Designed as a computer version of the nuclear bomb shelter, ARPAnet protected the flow of information between military installations by creating a network of geographically separated computers that could exchange information via a newly developed protocol (rule for how computers interact) called NCP (Network Control Protocol).

One opposing view to ARPAnet's origins comes from Charles M. Herzfeld, the former director of ARPA. He claimed that ARPAnet was not created as a result of a military need, stating "it came out of our frustration that there were only a limited number of large, powerful research computers in the country and that many research investigators who should have access were geographically separated from them." ARPA stands for the advanced research projects agency, a branch of the military that developed top secret systems and weapons during the Cold War.

The first data exchange over this new network occurred between computers at UCLA and stanford research institute. On their first attempt to log into Stanford's computer by typing "log win", UCLA researchers crashed their computer when they typed the letter 'g'.

Four computers were the first connected in the original ARPAnet. They were located in the respective computer research labs of UCLA (Honeywell DDP 516 computer), stanford research institute (SDS-940 computer), UC Santa Barbara (IBM 360/75), and the University of Utah (DEC PDP-10). As the network expanded, different models of computers were connected, creating compatibility problems. The solution rested in a better set of protocols called TCP/IP (Transmission Control Protocol/Internet Protocol) designed in 1982.

To send a message on the network, a computer breaks its data into IP (Internet Protocol) packets, like individually addressed digital envelopes. TCP (Transmission Control Protocol) makes sure the packets are delivered from client to server and reassembled in the right order.

Under ARPAnet several major innovations occurred: e-mail (or electronic mail), the ability to send simple messages to another person across the network (1971); telnet, a remote connection service for controlling a computer (1972); and File Transfer Protocol (FTP), which allows information to be sent from one computer to another in bulk (1973).

As non-military uses for the network increased, more and more people had access, and it was no longer safe for military purposes. As a result, MILnet, a military only network, was started in 1983. Internet Protocol software was soon being placed on every type of computer, and universities and research groups also began using in-house networks known as Local Area Network or LAN's. These in-house networks then started using Internet Protocol software so one LAN could connect with other LAN's.

In 1986, one LAN branched out to form a new competing network, called NSFnet (National Science Foundation Network). NSFnet first linked together the five national supercomputer centers, then every major university, and it started to replace the slower ARPAnet (which was finally shutdown in 1990). NSFnet formed the backbone of what we call the Internet today.

"The Internet's pace of adoption eclipses all other technologies that preceded it. Radio was in existence 38 years before 50 million people tuned in; TV took 13 years to reach that benchmark. Sixteen years after the first PC kit came out, 50 million people were using one. Once it was opened to the general public, the Internet crossed that line in four years." - quote from the U.S. Department report "The Emerging Digital Economy".

Mid 1980s—The Research Net

Let's outline key features, circa-1983, of what was then called ARPANET. A small computer was a PDP-11/45, and a PDP-11/45 does not fit on your desk. Some sites had a hundred computers attached to the Internet. Most had a dozen or so, probably with something like a VAX doing most of the work - mail, news, EGP routing. Users did their work using DEC VT-100 terminals. FORTRAN was the word of the day. Few companies had Internet access, relying instead on SNA and IBM mainframes. Rather, the Internet community was dominated by universities and military research sites. It's most popular service was the rapid e-mail it made possible with distant colleagues. In August 1983, there were 562 registered ARPANET hosts (RFC 1296).

UNIX deserves at least an honorable mention, since almost all the initial Internet protocols were developed first for UNIX, largely due to the availability of kernel source (for a price) and the relative ease of implementation (relative to things like VMS or MVS). The University of California at Berkeley (UCB) deserves special mention, because their Computer Science Research Group (CSRG) developed the BSD variants of AT&T's UNIX operating system. BSD UNIX and its derivatives would become the most common Internet programming platform.

Many key features of the Internet were already in place, including the IP and TCP protocols. ARPANET was fundamentally unreliable in nature, as the Internet is still today. This principle of unreliable delivery means that the Internet only makes a best-effort attempt to deliver packets. The network can drop a packet without any notification to sender or receiver. Remember, the Internet was designed for military survivability. The software running on either end must be prepared to recognize data loss, retransmitting data as often as necessary to achieve its ultimate delivery.

Late 1980s—The PC Revolution

Driven largely by the development of the PC and LAN technology, sub-netting was standardized in 1985 when RFC 950 was released. LAN technology made the idea of a "catenet" feasible - an internet-work of networks. Sub-netting opened the possibilities of interconnecting LANs with WANs.

The National Science Foundation (NSF) started the supercomputer centers program in 1986. Until then, supercomputers such as Crays were largely the playthings of large, well-funded universities and military research centers. NSF's idea was to make supercomputer resources available to those of more modest means by constructing five supercomputer centers around the country and building a network linking them with potential users. NSF decided to base their network on the Internet protocols, and NSFNET was born. For the next decade, NSFNET would be the core of the U.S. Internet, until its privatization and ultimate retirement in 1995.

Domain naming was stable by 1987 when RFC 1034 was released. Until then, hostnames were mapped to IP address using static tables, but the Internet's exponential growth had made this practice infeasible.

In the late 1980s, important advances related poor network performance with poor TCP performance, and a string of papers by the likes of Nagle and Van Jacobson present key insights into TCP performance.

Early 1990s—Address Exhaustion and the Web

In the early 90s, the first address exhaustion crisis hit the Internet technical community. The present solution, CIDR, will sustain the Internet for a few more years by making more efficient use of IP's existing 32-bit address space. For a more lasting solution, IETF is looking at IPv6 and its 128-bit address space, but CIDR is here to stay.

Crisis aside, the World Wide Web (WWW) has been one of Internet's most exciting recent developments. The idea of hypertext has been around for more than a decade, but in 1989 a team at the European Center for Particle Research (CERN) in Switzerland developed a set of protocols for transferring hypertext via the Internet. In the early 1990s it was enhanced by a team at the National Center for Supercomputing Applications (NCSA) at the University of Illinois - one of NSF's supercomputer centers. The result was NCSA Mosaic, a graphical, point-and-click hypertext browser that made Internet easy. The resulting explosion in "Web sites" drove the Internet into the public eye.

Mid 1990s—The New Internet

Of at least as much interest as Internet's technical progress in the 1990s has been its sociological progress. It has already become part of the national vocabulary, and seems headed for even greater prominence. It has been accepted by the business community, with a resulting explosion of service providers, consultants, books, and TV coverage. It has given birth to the Free Software Movement.

The Free Software Movement owes much to bulletin board systems, but really came into its own on the Internet, due to a combination of forces. The public nature of the Internet's early funding ensured that much of its networking software was non-proprietary. The emergence of anonymous FTP sites provided a distribution mechanism that almost anyone could use. Network newsgroups and mailing lists offered an open communication medium. Last but not least were individualists like Richard Stallman, who wrote EMACS, launched the GNU project and founded the Free Software Foundation. In the 1990s, Linus Torvalds wrote Linux, the popular (and free) UNIX clone operating system.

The explosion of capitalist conservatism, combined with a growing awareness of Internet's business value, has led to major changes in the Internet community. Many of them have not been for the good.

First, there seems to be a growing departure from Internet's history of open protocols, published as RFCs. Many new protocols are being developed in an increasingly proprietary manner. IGRP, a trademark of Cisco systems, has the dubious distinction as the most successful proprietary Internet routing protocol, capable only of operation between Cisco routers. Other protocols, such as BGP, are published as RFCs, but with important operational details omitted. The notoriously mis-named Open Software Foundation has introduced a whole suite of "open" protocols whose specifications are available — for a price — and not on the net.

The very existence of the Free Software Movement is part of the Internet saga, because free software would not exist without the net. "Movements" tend to arise when progress offers us new freedoms and we find new ways to explore and, sometimes, to exploit them. The Free Software Movement has offered what would be unimaginable when the Internet was formed - games, editors, windowing systems, compilers, networking software, and even entire operating systems available for anyone who wants them, without licensing fees, with complete source code, and all you need is Internet access. It also offers challenges, forcing us to ask what changes are needed in our society to support these new freedoms that have touched so many people. And it offers chances at exploitation, from the businesses using free software development platforms for commercial code, to the Internet worm and the security risks of open systems.

People wonder whether progress is better served through government funding or private industry. The Internet defies the popular wisdom of "business is better". Both business and government tried to build large data communication networks in the 1980s. Business depended on good market decisions; the government researchers based their system on openness, imagination and freedom. Business failed; Internet succeeded. Our reward has been its commercialization.

For the next few years, the Internet will almost certainly be content-driven. Although new protocols are always under development, we have barely begun to explore the potential of just the existing ones. Chief among these is the World Wide Web, with its potential for simple on-line access to almost any information imaginable. Yet even as the Internet intrudes into society, remember that over the last two decades "The Net" has developed a culture of its own, one that may collide with society's. Already business is making its pitch to dominate the Internet. Already congress has deemed it necessary to regulate the Web. The big questions loom unanswered: How will society change the Internet... and how will the Internet change society ?

At the top of the TCP/IP protocol architecture is the application layer. This layer includes all processes that use the transport layer protocols to deliver data. There are many applications protocols. Most provide user services, and new services are always being added to this layer.

The most widely known and implemented applications protocols are:

- TELNET: The Network Terminal Protocol, which provides remote login over the network.
- FTP: The File Transfer Protocol, which is used for interactive file transfer.
- SMTP: The Simple Mail Transfer Protocol, which delivers electronic mail.
- HTTP: The Hypertext Transfer Protocol, which delivers Web pages over the network.

While HTTP, FTP, SMTP, and telnet are the most widely implemented TCP/IP applications, you will work with many others as both a user and a system administrator. Some other commonly used TCP/IP applications are:

Domain Name Service (DNS): Also called name service, this application maps IP addresses to the names assigned to network devices.

Open Shortest Path First (OSPF): Routing is central to the way TCP/IP works. OSPF is used by network devices to exchange routing information.

Network File System (NFS): This protocol allows files to be shared by various hosts on the network.

Some protocols, such as telnet and FTP, can only be used if the user has some knowledge of the network. Other protocols, like OSPF, run without the user even knowing that they exist. As system administrator, you are aware of all these applications and all the protocols in the other TCP/IP layers. And you're responsible for configuring them!

HTTP Features, Capabilities and Issues: The first four subsections of the large section covering the Hypertext Transfer Protocol were meant to give you a good understanding of the fundamental concepts and basic operation of the protocol. Modern HTTP, however, goes beyond the simple mechanics by which HTTP requests and responses are exchanged. It includes a number of features and capabilities that extend the basic protocol to improve performance and meet the various needs of organizations using modern.

HTTP CACHING FEATURES AND ISSUES

The explosive growth of the World Wide Web was a marvel for its users, but a nightmare for networking engineers. The biggest problem that the burgeoning Web created was an overloading of the internet-works over which it ran. Many of the features that were added to HTTP/1.1 were designed specifically to improve the efficiency of the protocol and reduce unnecessary bandwidth consumed by HTTP requests and responses. Arguably the most important of these is a set of features designed to support caching.

The subject of caching comes up again and again in discussions of computers and networking, because of a phenomenon that is widely observed in these technologies: whenever a user, hardware device or software process requests a particular piece of data, there is a good chance it will ask for it again in the near future. Thus, by storing recently-retrieved items in a cache, we can eliminate duplicated effort. This is why caching plays an important role in the efficiency of protocols such as ARP and DNS.

HTTP PROTOCOL OVERVIEW

The Hyper Text Transfer Protocol (HTTP) is the de facto standard for transferring World Wide Web documents, although it is designed to be extensible to almost any document format.

HTTP operates over TCP connections, usually to port 80, though this can be overridden and another port used. After a successful connection, the client transmits a request message to the server, which sends a reply message back. HTTP messages are human-readable, and an HTTP server can be manually operated with a command such as telnet server 80.

The simplest HTTP message is "GET url", to which the server replies by sending the named document. If the document doesn't exist, the server will probably send an HTML-encoded message stating this. It is said probably, because this simple method offers poor error handling and has been deprecated in favor of the more elaborate scheme outlined below.

A complete HTTP 1.0 message begins "GET url HTTP/1.0". The addition of the third field indicates that full headers are being used. The client may then send additional header fields, one per line, terminating the message with a blank link. The server replies in a similar vein, first with a series of header lines, then a blank line, then the document proper.

Here a sample HTTP 1.0 exchange:

```
GET / HTTP/1.0 >
        >
          < HTTP/1.0 200 OK
          < Date: Wed, 18 Sep 1996 20:18:59 GMT
          < Server: Apache/1.0.0
          < Content-type: text/html
          < Content-length: 1579
          < Last-modified: Mon, 22 Jul 1996 22:23:34 GMT
          <
          < HTML document
```

The use of full headers is preferred for several reasons:

- The first line of a server header includes a response code indicating the success or failure of the operation.

- One of the server header fields will be Content-type: which specifies a MIME type to describe how the document should be interpreted.
- If the document has moved, the server can specify its new location with a Location: field, allowing the client to transparently retry the request using the new URL.
- The Authorization: and WWW-Authenticate: fields allow access controls to be placed on Web documents.
- The Referer: field allows the client to tell the server the URL of the document that triggered this request, permitting savvy servers to trace clients through a series of requests.

In addition to GET requests, clients can also send HEAD and POST requests, of which POSTs are the most important. POSTs are used for HTML forms and other operations that require the client to transmit a block of data to the server. After sending the header and the blank line, the client transmits the data. The header must have included a Content-Length: field, which permits the server to determine when all the data has been received.

UNIFORM RESOURCE LOCATORS

Uniform Resource Locators (URLs) are strings that specify how to access network resources, such as HTML documents. They are part of the more general class of Universal Resource Identifiers (URIs). The most important use of URLs is in HTML documents to identify the targets of hyperlinks. When using a Web browser such as Netscape, every highlighted region has a URL associated with it, which is accessed when the link is activated by a mouse click. Relative URLs specify only a portion of the full URL—the missing information is inferred though the context of the source document. URLs are documented in RFC 1738. Relative URLs are documented in RFC 1808. URIs are documented in RFC 1630. The meaning of these fields is as follows:

THE SIGNIFICANCE OF CACHING TO HTTP

Caching is important to HTTP because Web users tend to request the same documents over and over again. For example, in writing this section on HTTP, I made reference to RFC 2616 many, many times. Each time, I loaded it from a particular Web server. Since the document never changes, it would be more efficient to just load it from a local cache rather than having to retrieve it from the distant Web server each time.

However, caching is even more essential to HTTP than to most other protocols or technologies where it used. The reason is that Web documents tend to be structured so that a request for one resource leads to a request for many others. Even if I load a number of different documents, they may each refer to common elements that do not change between user requests. Thus, caching can be of benefit in HTTP even if a user never asks for the same document twice, or if a single document changes over time so that caching the document itself would be of little value.

For example, suppose that each morning I load up CNN's Web site to see what is going on in the world. Obviously, the headlines will be different every day, so caching of the main CCN.com

Web home page won't be of much value. However, many of the graphical elements on the page (CNN's logo, dividing bars, perhaps a "breaking news" graphic) will be the same, every day, and these can be cached. Another example would be a set of discussion forums on a Web site. As I load up different topics to read, each one is different, but they have common elements (such as icons and other images) that would be wasteful to have to retrieve over and over again.

Caching in HTTP yields two main benefits. The first is reduced bandwidth use, by eliminating unneeded transfers of requests and responses. The second, equally important, is faster response time for the user loading a resource. Consider that on many Web pages today, the image files are much larger than the HTML page that references them. Caching these graphics will allow the entire page to load far more quickly. Figure 30.1 illustrates how caching reduces bandwidth and speeds up resource retrieval by "short-circuiting" the request/response chain.

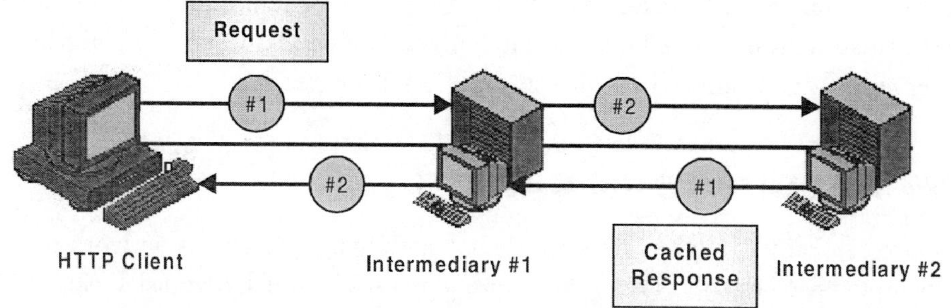

Figure 30.1 *Impact of Caching on HTTP Request/Response Chain.*

This diagram illustrates the impact of caching on the request/response chain of figure. In this example, intermediary #2 is able to satisfy the client's request from its cache. This "short-circuits" the communication chain after two transfers, which means the client gets its resource more quickly, and the HTTP server is spared the need to process the client's request.

The obvious advantages of caching have made it a part of the Web since pretty much the beginning. However, it was not until HTTP/1.1 that the importance of caching was really recognized in the protocol itself, and many features added to support it. Where the HTTP/1.0 standard makes passing mention of caching and some of the issues related to it, HTTP/1.1 devotes 26 full pages to caching (over 20% of the main body of the document!). I obviously cannot go into that level of detail here, but I will discuss HTTP caching in general terms to give you a feel for the subject.

HTTP PROXY SERVERS AND PROXYING

HTTP was designed to support not just communication between a client and server, but also the inclusion of intermediaries that may sit in the communication path between them. One of the most important types of intermediary is a device called a proxy server, or more simply, just a proxy.

A proxy is a "middleman" that acts as both a client and a server. It accepts requests from a client as if it were a server, then forwards them (possibly modifying them) to the real server, which sees the proxy as a client. The server responds back to the proxy, which forwards the reply back to the client. Proxies can be either transparent, meaning that they do not modify requests and responses, or non-transparent, if they do so in order to provide a particular service.

Benefits of Proxies

Since proxies have the ability to fully process all client requests and server responses, they can be extremely useful in a number of circumstances. They can be used to implement or enhance many important capabilities.

Security

Proxies can be set up to examine both outgoing requests and incoming responses, to address various security concerns. For example, filtering can be set up to prevent users from requesting "objectionable" content, or to screen out harmful replies such as files containing hidden viruses.

Caching

It can be advantageous to set up a "shared cache" that is implemented on an intermediary, so resources requested by one client can be made available to another. This can be done within a proxy server.

Performance

In some circumstances, the existence of a proxy server can significantly improve performance, particularly by reducing latency. An excellent example of this is the proxy server that is used by my own satellite Internet connection.

Due to the distance from the earth to the satellite, it takes over 500 milliseconds for a round trip request/response cycle between my PC and an Internet server. If I load a Web page containing images, I would have to wait 500+ milliseconds to get the HTML page, at which point my browser would then have to generate new requests for each graphical element, meaning another 500+ millisecond delay for each.

Instead, my ISP has a proxy server to which I send my requests for Web pages. It looks through the HTML of these pages and automatically requests any elements such as graphics for me. It then sends them straight back to my machine, cutting the time required to display a full Web page drastically.

Key Concept: One of the most important types of intermediary devices in HTTP is a proxy server, which acts as a middleman between the client and server, handling both requests and responses. A proxy server may either transport messages unchanged or may modify them to implement certain features and capabilities. Proxies are often used to increase the security and/or performance of Web access.

HTTP SECURITY AND PRIVACY

There are a number of different protocols in this Guide where I address security considerations. Usually, I start out by saying something to the effect that the protocol doesn't include much in the way of security, because when it was first developed, the Internet was small and used by a tight-knit group, so security wasn't a big concern. Today, the Internet is globe-spanning and used by millions of strangers, making security a big deal indeed.

Well, in the case of the World Wide Web this is true, but the issue is even more important due to the significance of the changes in the content of what HTTP messages carry. HTTP has become the vehicle for transporting any and every kind of information, including a large amount of personal data. HTTP was initially designed to carry academic documents such as memos about research projects, but today is more likely to carry someone's mortgage application, credit card details or medical details. Thus, not only does HTTP have the usual security issues such as preventing unauthorized access, it needs to deal with privacy concerns as well.

HTTP AUTHENTICATION METHODS

The main HTTP/1.1 standard, RFC 2616, also does not deal extensively with security matters. These are addressed in detail instead in the companion document, RFC 2617, which explains the two methods of HTTP authentication. Highly summarized, they are:

Basic Authentication: This is a conventional user/password type of authentication. When a client sends a request to a server that requires authentication to access a resource, the server sends a response to the client's initial request that contains a WWW-Authenticate header. The client then sends a new request containing the authorization header, which carries a base64-encoded username and password combination.

Digest Authentication: Basic authentication is not considered strong security because it sends credentials "in the clear", which means that they can be intercepted. Digest authentication uses the same headers as basic authentication, but employs more sophisticated techniques, including encryption, that protect against a malicious person "snooping" credentials information. Digest authentication is not considered as strong as public key encryption, but is a lot better than basic authentication.

HTTP State Management Using "Cookies"

Even though the modern Hypertext Transfer Protocol has a lot of capabilities and features, it is still, at its heart, a simple request/reply protocol. One of the unfortunate problems that results from this is that HTTP is entirely stateless. This means that each time a server receives a request from a client, it processes the request, sends a response, and then forgets about the request. The next request from the client is treated as independent of any previous ones.

Well, this is, yet again, another place where HTTP's behavior was well-suited to its original intended uses, but not to how the Web is used today. Sure, if all we want to do is to say "hey server, please give me that file over there", then the server doesn't have to care about whether or not it may have previously provided that client with any other files in the past. This is how HTTP was originally intended to be used.

Today, as most of us know, the Web is much more than a simple resource-retrieval protocol. If you go to an online store, you want to be able to select a number of items to put into a "shopping cart", and have the store's server remember them. You might also want to participate in a discussion forum, which requires you to provide a user name and password in order to post a message. Ideally, the server should let you log in once and then remember who you are so you can post many messages without having to enter your login information each and every time.

Cookies

Storing HTTP State Information. For other interactive applications, the stateless nature of HTTP is a serious problem. The solution was the addition of a new technology, called state management, that allows the state of a client session with a server to be maintained across a series of HTTP transactions. Initially developed by Netscape, this technique was later made a formal Internet standard in RFC 2109, later revised in RFC 2965 (HTTP State Management Mechanism). Note that this feature is actually not part of HTTP; it is an optional element but one that has been implemented in pretty much all Web browsers due to its usefulness.

The idea behind state management is very simple. When a server implements a function that requires state to be maintained across a set of transactions, it sends a small amount of data to the Web client called a "cookie". The cookie contains important information relevant to the particular Web application, such as a customer name, items in a shopping cart, or a user name and password. The client stores the information in the cookie, and then uses it in subsequent requests to the server that set the cookie. The server can then update the cookie based on the information in the new request and send it back to the client. In this manner, state information can be maintained indefinitely, allowing the client and server to have a "memory" that persists over a period of time.

HYPER TEXT TRANSFER PROTOCOL (HTTP)

The Hyper Text Transfer Protocol, or *HTTP*, must be the most widely used Application layer protocol in the world today. It forms the basis of what most people understand the Internet to be—the World Wide Web. Its purpose is to provide a lightweight protocol for the retrieval of HyperText Markup Language (*HTML*) and other documents from Web sites throughout the Internet. Each time you open a Web browser to surf the Internet, you are using *HTTP* over *TCP/IP*.

HTTP was first ratified in the early 1990s and has been through three main iterations:

- **HTTP/0.9:** A simplistic first implementation of the protocol that only supported the option to get a Web page.
- **HTTP/1.0:** Ratified by the *IETF* as RFC 1945 in 1996. This version added many supplemental data fields, known as *headers* to the specification. This allowed for other information passing between the client and server, alongside the request and consequent page.
- **HTTP/1.1:** Defined in RFC 2068 by the *IETF*, version 1.1 implemented a number of improvements over and above the 1.0 specification. One of the main improvements of 1.1 over 1.0 was the implementation of techniques such as persistent *TCP* connections, pipelining, and cache control to improve performance within *HTTP*-based applications.

Most browsers these days offer support for both 1.0 and 1.1 implementations, with new browsers using 1.1 as a default but supporting the ability to fall back to earlier versions if required. One thing the RFC definitions are clear to point out is that all implementations of the *HTTP* protocol should be backward compatible. That is to say that a browser implementing the *HTTP*/1.1 specification should be capable of receiving a 1.0 response from a server. Conversely, a 1.1 implementation on the server side should also be capable of responding to requests from a 1.0 browser.

It is well outside the bounds of this book to cover the *HTTP* protocols in huge detail, so let's concentrate on those elements most relevant to content switching.

BASIC HTTP PAGE RETRIEVAL

Let's start at the beginning and see how a basic browser retrieves a Web page from a Web server. The first important point to note is that a Web page is typically made up of many dozens of objects, ranging from the *HTML* base through to the images that are present on the page. The *HTML* can be thought of as the template for the page overall, instructing the browser on the layout of the text, font sizes and colors, background color of the page, and which other images need to be retrieved to make up the page. Think of the process, taking place in the following order:

Client sends a request for the required page to the Web server. The server analyzes the request and sends back an acknowledgement to the client along with the *HTML* code required to make the page. The client will begin interpreting the *HTML* and building the page. The client, in subsequent requests, will retrieve any embedded objects, such as images or other multimedia sources.

Once all elements of the page have been retrieved, the client browser will display the completed Web page. The order and timing of the process described previously depends largely on which implementation of *HTTP* is used—1.0 or 1.1—although all browsers work in this way of request and response.

HTTP Methods

HTTP does not only offer a mechanism for the client to receive data from the server, but also other communication types such as the passing of data from the client to the server. Such mechanisms are known within the *HTTP* specifications as a *method*. Table 30.2 shows the supported method types in *HTTP*/1.0 and 1.1.

Table 30.2 The HTTP Method Headers in HTTP/1.0 and HTTP/1.1

Method	*Description*	*HTTP/1.*	*HTTP/1.1*
GET	Retrieve the information specified.	□	□
HEAD	Identical to the GET request, but the server must not return any page content other than the *HTTP* headers.	□	□
POST	Allows the client to submit information to the server, used for submitting information from a form, etc.	□	□
PUT	Allows the client to place an item on the server in the location specified.		□
DELETE	Allows the client to delete the item specified in the request.		□
TRACE	Allows the client to see the request it made to the server. This acts as a loop-back in effect.		□
OPTIONS	Allows the client to determine the communications options available on the server.		□

In terms of general Web browsing, the GET and POST methods are by far the most commonly used. For a browser to build a standard Web page, the GET method is used to retrieve each object individually, whereas for transactional Web sites implementing shopping cart style applications, the POST method will also be used.

The HTTP URL

The *URL* is the most important piece of information that the client browser includes in any GET request. The *URL* is defined as being a combination of the host where the site is located, the scheme used to retrieve the page, and the full path and filename. Optionally, the *URL* may include information such as the *TCP* port number to be used or a unique reference point within a larger page.

The *URI* is also commonly used when referencing the location of documents within *HTTP*. The formal definition of the difference between a *URL* and a *URI* is simple: A *URI* is a *URL* without the scheme defined.

Persistent Connections in HTTP

One of the other major differences in operation between *HTTP*/1.0 and *HTTP*/1.1 is the handling of *TCP* connections required to retrieve a full Web page. Given that a client will typically have to retrieve multiple objects to make up a single Web page, it is often inefficient to open and close *TCP* sessions repeatedly when retrieving objects from the same server. To improve the overall performance of *HTTP* in this instance, the protocol defines the Connection : header that communicates to the server whether the *TCP* session should be closed or remain open once the object has been retrieved. The Connection: header has two options:

Connection: *Closed:* The default for *HTTP*/1.0

Connection: *Keep-Alive:* The default for *HTTP*/1.1

The Closed state indicates that the server should close the *TCP* connection once the request has been fulfilled. The Keep-Alive state indicates that the server should keep the *TCP* connection open after the request has been fulfilled. Along with an obvious performance increase from removing the need to open and close *TCP* connections, the Keep-Alive state also allows the implementation of *pipelining*. Pipelining allows a client to send multiple *HTTP* GET requests over the same *TCP* connection without needing to wait for individual responses after each.

The final piece in the puzzle of interaction between client and server is in opening multiple *TCP* connections. We've already seen that a client can open a persistent *TCP* connection to the server and pipeline *HTTP* requests. To further improve performance of the *HTTP* operation, many browsers will open several simultaneous connections.

Other HTTP Headers

The *HTTP* protocol includes definitions for dozens of headers that can be included in the client-to-server and server-to-client requests and responses. We will not attempt to list and describe all those available here; for a full description, the RFC for *HTTP*/1.0 and *HTTP*/1.1 offers a better source. The RFCs define a series of standard headers, which can be complemented by adding user-defined headers from either the client or server side.

As headers are ASCII readable text in every *HTTP* request and response pair, they can prove very useful in the implementation of content switching. Let's look at some of the *HTTP* headers most commonly used in content switching.

The "Accept:" Header

The client browser uses the "Accept:" header to indicate to the server which content and media types can be accepted. Examples of the "Accept:" header include:

Table 30.3

Accept: */*	Accept anything
Accept: text/plain; text/html	Accept plain text and *HTML*
Accept: text/html; image/jpeg; image/bmp	Accept *HTML* and JPEG and bitmap images

The "Accept:" header is useful in the context of content switching to be able to determine the capabilities of a particular client. If the client browser cannot accept images, for example, the request can be directed to a server optimized to deliver text-only versions of the Web pages.

The "Host:" Header

One of the main problems in the original *HTTP*/1.0 specification was that a user's request as typed into the browser would not contain the host element in the GET request sent to the server. This represents a problem if virtual hosting is used within a Web server farm, where the server is potentially hosting multiple Web sites and needs to use this host information to determine which path and page the user is requesting.

Within the *HTTP*/1.1 specification, and subsequently in many new *HTTP*/1.0 browsers, support was added for the "Host:" header. This allows the user's requested *URL*, typed into the browser, to be converted into a GET request containing the full path and filename along with the host from which the content is being fetched. The following is an example of translating a full *URL* into its component parts.

URL : http://www.foocorp.com/directory/somewhere/page.html

GET /directory/somewhere/page.html HTTP/1.0\r\n

Host: wwwfoocorp.com

The "Host:" header has many uses within content switching, examples of which are shown in previous chapter, *Content-Aware Server Load Balancing*.

The "User-Agent:" Header

The "User-Agent:" header indicates to the server the type of browser being used by the client. The "User-Agent:" header is useful in the context of content switching as it can be used to determine the browser type used by the client and direct the request to a resource offering content optimized for such a browser. The following is an example of the "User-Agent:".

User-Agent: Mozilla/4.0(Compatible; MSIE 6.0; Windows NT 5.0)

Cookies—The HTTP State Management Mechanism

As we'll see, one of the biggest challenges in *HTTP* environments, whether content switched or not, is maintaining some form of client-side state that enables Web servers and intermediary devices to recognize the client session and understand the current status of the user session. This issue was tackled in RFC 2109, which defined the use of the Set-Cookie and Cookie *HTTP* headers used to set and use the cookies, respectively. In *HTTP*, cookies take the form of a small piece of text information that is implanted into the user's browser either permanently or temporarily. The term *cookie* is commonly used in computing to describe an opaque piece of information held during a session and, unfortunately, seems to have no more interesting origin than that. Once the backend server has implanted the cookie into the user's browser, the information can be used for a number of different applications ranging from content personalization, user session persistence for online shopping, and the collection of demographic and statistical information on Web site usage.

The server issuing a Set-Cookie header in any *HTTP* response can post a cookie to the client at anytime during an *HTTP* session. This Set-Cookie header has the following syntax :

Set-Cookie: <name>=<value>; expires=<date>; path=<path>; domain=<domain>; secure

The name and value fields are the only ones that are mandatory when issuing a cookie. As the name suggests, these define the name of the cookie and its value, such as UserID=Phil, for example. The expires field identifies, down to the second, the date and time on which a cookie will expire and be deleted from the client computer. The path and domain fields indicate the domain, such as *www.foocorp.com*, and the *URL*, such as /home/brochures/, for which the cookie should be used. Both of these options can effectively be wild-carded by specifying foocorp.com to match *www.foocorp.com* and *intranet.foocorp.com*, for example. Finally, the secure field indicates to the client that the cookie should only be used when a secure connection (*SSL* secured *HTTP* or HTTPS) is used between the client and server.

The following code shows the *HTTP* responses from the server in more detail. Note that the second cookie includes the Path field, which will limit the use of the cookie to URLs requested by the user that include the string /docs.

- **Hypertext Transfer Protocol**

  HTTP/1.1 200 OK\r\n

  Set-Cookie: UserID=Phil

  Connection: Keep-Alive\r\n

  Content-Type: text/html\r\n

  \r\n

- **Hypertext Transfer Protocol**

  HTTP/1.1 200 OK\r\n

  Set-Cookie: UserType=Gold; Path=/docs

  Connection: Keep-Alive\r\n

  Content-Type: text/html\r\n

  \r\n

The mechanism that governs whether a cookie is permanent (*i.e.*, stored on the hard disk of the user's machine) or temporary (*i.e.*, removed once the user closes the browser application) is the Expires field in the Set-Cookie header. If the server does not issue an Expires directive when implanting the cookie, it is considered temporary, whereas if the Expires directive is used, then the cookie will be stored on the client machine until the expiry date has passed.

Cookies are by far one of the most useful additions made to the *HTTP* specifications, and as we'll see in later chapters can be used in conjunction with content switching to enable a whole host of new experience-enhancing services.

FILE TRANSFER PROTOCOL (FTP)

In Internet terms, The File Transfer Protocol, or *FTP*, has been around for a long time. First defined in RFC 172 written in June 1971, the protocol has been through several changes through to the current specification, which is defined in RFC 959. Again, while it's not the purpose of this book to describe every detail about *FTP*, it's worth looking at its basic operation to get a better understanding of how content switching can improve performance and reliability in *FTP* environments.

FTP Basics

FTP exists primarily for the transfer of data between two end points. The RFC itself actually states that two of the objectives of the protocol are to "promote the sharing of files" and "transfer data reliably and efficiently." *FTP* differs from *HTTP* fundamentally as it is an application made up of two distinct *TCP* connections:

- **Control connection:** This *TCP*-based connection is used to provide a communications channel for the delivery of commands and replies. This is effectively the mechanism that enables the user to tell the server which file is being requested, which directory it is in, and so forth.
- **Data connection:** The second *TCP*-based connection is used for the actual transfer of user data. Once the Control connection has been used to exchange information on which file is required, the Data connection is used to transfer the file between the client and server.

Using these two communication connections, two distinct modes of operation determine in which direction the connections are established: Active mode and Passive mode.

Active Mode FTP

Within an Active *FTP* session, the Control connection is established from the client to the server, with the Data connection established back from the server to the client. In order to do this, the client issues a PORT command to the server that contains the *IP* address and source and destination *TCP* ports that should be used during the Data connection.

Once the user has logged on with a valid username and password, the very first "data" that is passed—in this case, a directory listing—is carried using a separate data channel. The format for communicating the *IP* and *TCP* information of the data channel is as follows:

PORT [Octet 1], [Octet 2], [Octet 3], [Octet 4], [TCP Port 8 Bytes], [TCP Port 8 Bytes]

Therefore, in the preceding example, the PORT command of PORT 10,10,10,10,15,199 equates to *IP* address 10.10.10.10 and *TCP* port 4039 [15 × 256 + 199 × 1].

In some instances, Active *FTP* can be considered a security risk mainly because there is often little control over the contents of the PORT command. Under normal usage, this information *should* be the *IP* address and listening *TCP* port of the client waiting for the Data connection. When used maliciously, however, the client could issue PORT commands with *IP* addresses and *TCP* ports of other machines either within the same network as the server or remotely. Many Application layer firewalls and proxies, or firewalls with support for *FTP* command parsing can be used to reduce the effectiveness of such attacks. One alternative is to implement the second method of *FTP*—Passive mode *FTP*.

Passive Mode FTP

Passive mode *FTP* works similarly to Active mode *FTP* with one major exception: both the Control and Data connections within a Passive mode *FTP* session are established from the client to the server. To implement this, rather than use the PORT command, Passive mode *FTP* implements the PASV command, which instructs the server that *it* should listen for the incoming Data connection.

We can see that rather than the client dictating the parameters of the Data connection, it simply requests this information from the server. Similarly to the PORT command in Active mode, the server's RESPONSE to the PASV request from the client can be interpreted as follows :

RESPONSE 227 (10, 10, 10, 10, 41, 38)

which means open from client to server on *IP* address 10.10.10.10 and *TCP* port 10534 [41 × 256 + 38 × 1].

More recently, *wireless Internet service providers* or WISPs have emerged that offer Internet access through wireless LAN or wireless broadband networks. In addition to basic connectivity, many ISPs also offer related Internet services like e-mail, Web hosting and access to software tools.

A few companies also offer *free ISP* service to those who need occasional Internet connectivity. These free offerings feature limited connect time and are often bundled with some other product or service.

Communication between Servers

The message formats used for exchange of queries and responses between hosts and DNS servers is specified in RFC 1035. Queries and responses can be transferred either via TCP or via UDP. There are "well-known" port numbers for DNS service using either protocol. The format of a DNS query and response is as shown in the given table 30.4.

Table 30.4 The Format of a DNS Query and Response

Bits 0-15	*Bits 16-31*
Identification	Flags
Number of questions	Number of answer RRs
Number of authority RRs	Number of additional RRs
Questions	
Answers (RRs)	
Authority (RRs)	
Additional information	

- **RR**s are Resource Records

  The 16 flag bits provide further information about the query
- **QR** bit.

  A single indicating a query (0) or a response (1)
- **opcode**

  4 bits whose value means

Table 30.5 Value with its Meaning

Value	*Meaning*
0	Standard Query
1	Inverse Query
2	Server status request

- **AA** bit.
  If set, this means that the server is authoritative for the domain in question.
- **TC** bit.
  If set this means that the reply size exceeded 512 bytes and only the first 512 bytes were actually returned. This will only be used if the response is being returend via UDP.
- **RD** bit.
  If this bit is not set then recursion is denied. This means that if the responding server cannot resolve the query itself rather than passing it on to "higher authority" and returning the result it eventually receives, it will simply return a list of other servers to try.
- **RA** bit.
  If this bit is set by a responding server then that server is indicating that it can handle queries recusively.
- **3 unused** bits.
  These must be zero.
- **4 rcode** bits.
  This indicates the status

Table 30.6 Values with its Meanings

Value	*Meaning*
0	No error
1	Malformed query
2	Server failed
3	Name does not Exist
4	Query type unsupported by server
5	Server refused to answer

After the 12 byte header the DNS query message consists of a block of questions which in turn consist of query name, query type and query class.

Typically the query name is the name of site, each component of the name is sent a sequence of characters preceded by a byte holding the binary count of the number of characters in the component. The name is terminated by a zero byte. The query type indicates the type of information required encoded in a 16 bit field. Common values are as in table 30.7.

Table 30.7 Representation of Values with its Description

Name	*Value*	*Description*
A	1	IPv4 Address (32 bits)
NS	2	Name Server
CNAME	5	Canonical Name
PTR	12	Pointer Record
HINFO	13	Host Information
MX	15	Mail Exchange Record
TXT	16	Text String
AAAA	28	IPv6 Address (128 bits)
AXFR	252	Request for Zone Transfer
ANY	255	Request for All Records

Query class is usually 1 meaning an Internet domain query, other values could be used for different addressing domains.

Response Records known as RRs form the body of the reply to a DNS query. They are used for the answers, authority and additional information fields.

Table 30.8 Tabulization of Distribution of Bits

Bits 0–15	*Bits 16–31*
Domain Name	
Type	Class
Time to live	
Resource Data length	Resource Data
Resource data (continued)	

The *domain name* is the query name from the query. The *type* is the query type. The *class* is 1 for the Internet domain. The *time to live* is the time for which the information can be cached by the client, typically two days, expressed in seconds. The *resource data length* specifies the number of bytes of resource data.

It is important to note that queries can be made for information relating to both individual hosts and for zones/domains. Most of the query types are fairly obvious. The MX query is used specifically for mail handling and can return information about hosts not directly or regularly connected to the Internet. The result of an MX query for such a host is the address of an Internet host that will receive mail for such a host and make its own arrangements for forwarding the mail via non-Internet means or when the host does connect. An MX query response for a domain provides the address of the host that will handle mail for that domain allowing e-mail addresses of the form User@domain_name. The NS query can be used to identify the name servers for a particular domain.

User Interfaces

On Unix systems the normal user interface is the program /use/sbin/nslookup. *[The actual path may be different on some hosts]*. This can be used to perform almost any DNS function and display the results to the user.

Here is an example of its use on *scitsc.wlv.ac.uk*. This example was prepared before the scit.wlv.ac.uk zone was delegated, *scitsc* is now known as *sunc* although the old name still works.

bash$ /usr/etc/nslookup

- Default Server: scitsc.wlv.ac.uk
  Address: 134.220.4.1

  > set q=A
  > ccub.wlv.ac.uk.

- Server: scitsc.wlv.ac.uk
  Address: 134.220.4.1

  Name: ccub.wlv.ac.uk
  Address: 134.220.1.20

  > set q=CNAME
  > www.wlv.ac.uk.

- Server: scitsc.wlv.ac.uk
  Address: 134.220.4.1
  www.wlv.ac.uk canonical name = ccuf.wlv.ac.uk
  > set q=MX
  > wlv.ac.uk.

- Server: scitsc.wlv.ac.uk
  Address: 134.220.4.1

  wlv.ac.uk preference = 1, mail exchanger = wlv.ac.uk
  wlv.ac.uk inet address = 134.220.1.12
  > set q=HINFO
  > ccub.wlv.ac.uk.

- Server: scitsc.wlv.ac.uk
  Address: 134.220.4.1

ccub.wlv.ac.uk CPU=SUN 690MP OS=Solaris 2.4

> set q=PTR

> 12.1.220.134.in-addr.arpa

- Server: scitsc.wlv.ac.uk

  Address: 134.220.4.1

  12.1.220.134.in-addr.arpa host name = ccug.wlv.ac.uk

Here it shows that *sunc* was providing DNS service. A number of queries were made. The query type was specified using nslookup's set q = command.

- **Type A:** A simple query for the IP address corresponding to ccub.wlv.ac.uk.
- **Type CNAME:** A given host can have several DNS names. One of these is the canonical or reference name. This query reveals that www.wlv.ac.uk is really ccuf.wlv.ac.uk.
- **Type MX:** A mail exchanger query, this time for the domain wlv.ac.uk which reveals that mail sent to user@wlv.ac.uk is actually sent to 134.220.1.12 which is really ccug.wlv.ac.uk. (see below).
- **Type HINFO:** An HINFO query. This is only useful if the DNS domain administrator has bothered to create the relevant records and keep them up to date.
- **Type PTR:** A PTR query. This shows "inverse" or "reverse" resolution. Notice the very clumsy way the query has to be entered, this is partly because IP addresses have the most significant part first whereas DNS addresses have the most significant part last. There are plenty of pieces of software that do reverse resolution without this clumsy interface.

Program Interface

The commonest program interface to DNS uses the library functions gethostbyname() and gethostbyaddr()..

Exploring a Zone

The nslookup program can be used to obtain a listing of all the hosts in a zone. To do this it is first necessary to identify the name server for the zone. This is done using an NS query, setting the server parameter to one or other of the identified name servers and then using nslookup's ls command. Note that in this example the user was careful to include the final dot on the domain name, this prevented nslookup from trying to append the local default domain name (scit.wlv.ac.uk.) to the required domain name. For large domains the ls command has an option to write its results to a file.

bash$ /usr/sbin/nslookup

- Default Server: sunc.scit.wlv.ac.uk

  Address: 134.220.4.1

  +1L#

```
> set q=NS
> bilston.ac.uk.
• Server: sunc.scit.wlv.ac.uk
  Address: 134.220.4.1

  Non-authoritative answer:
  bilston.ac.uk  nameserver = unad1.wlv.ac.uk
  bilston.ac.uk  nameserver = ccua.wlv.ac.uk
  bilston.ac.uk  nameserver = ccub.wlv.ac.uk
  Authoritative answers can be found from:
  unad1.wlv.ac.uk internet address = 134.220.192.26
  ccua.wlv.ac.uk internet address = 134.220.1.39
  ccub.wlv.ac.uk internet address = 134.220.1.20
  > server ccub.wlv.ac.uk
• Default Server: ccub.wlv.ac.uk
  Address: 134.220.1.20

  > ls bilston.ac.uk.
  [ccub.wlv.ac.uk]
  bilston.ac.uk.        server = ccub.wlv.ac.uk
  bilston.ac.uk.        server = unad1.wlv.ac.uk
  bilston.ac.uk.        server = ccua.wlv.ac.uk
  gw                194.62.148.1
  novix1            195.188.205.2
  www               194.62.148.4
  fc                194.62.148.5
  student1          195.18.205.3
```

The session above was logged in March 1998. It reveals 5 hosts in the bilston.ac.uk domain. Surprisingly three different class C IP network addresses appear in the output. This was because the organisation was in the process of changing its Internet service provider accounting for two of the network addresses, the third (195.18.205) is, apparently, a typographical error for 195.188.205.

Further information on identifying the ownership of an IP network and, implicitly, a DNS domain can be found in the notes on IP routing.

Alternative DNS Hierarchies

With the rapid commercialization of the Internet in the late 1990's disputes over DNS names arose from time to time and suggestions have been made for the creation of extra top level domains. The root of the current DNS hierarchy is maintained by the Network Information Center on a contract from the government of the United States of America. There have been several attempts to set up alternative hierarchies. To use the Alternic DNS service you need to know the address of their root servers, one of these is mx.alternic.net. Here's an example showing that it does work for DNS resolution of www.alternic.nic.

bash$ /usr/sbin/nslookup

- Default Server: sunc.scit.wlv.ac.uk
  Address: 134.220.4.1

  > server mx.alternic.net
- Default Server: mx.alternic.net
  Address: 206.191.128.47

  > www.alternic.nic.
- Server: mx.alternic.net
  Address: 206.191.128.47

- Name: www.alternic.nic
  Address: 206.191.128.47

Alternic uses three letter top level domains for countries (such as jpn and ger) and has a large number of commercially oriented top level domains. At the time of writing the only domains with significant populations are porno and xxx.

A normal name server can only resolve Alternic addresses if they're already in its cache. Most DNS implementations with a list of root servers consult them in random order or consistently consult the first one in the list. Including one of the Alternic servers in amongst the list of root servers will not provide consistent resolution of addresses in both hierarchies.

Zones of Convenience

It is tempting to think that an Internet host with a name ending in ".uk" is actually located in the United Kingdom. There is no requirement that this should be so. For example the well known host www.yahoo.co.uk is actually located in southern Germany. In the case of the United Kingdom it is simply necessary to present the organization that runs the ".co.uk" domain with an IP address (and a suitable sum of money !) and the DNS address will be registered. The top-level administration of the ".uk" domain will only delegate to specifically UK based organizations.

Some administrations are distinctly less fussy and a number of "zones of convenience" along the same lines as "flags of convenience" have come into fairly common usage. These are mostly poor third world countries or tiny groups of islands desperate for some hard cash, they also tend to sell un-necessary sets of stamps and coins to guillible collectors.

The most common ones seem to be ".cc" (the Cocos-Keeling Islands), ".to" (Tonga) and ".nu" (Niue). At one time both ".is" (Iceland) and ".tm" (Turkmenistan) allowed their top level domains to be used in this fashion, but they now seem to adopt a more rational approach.

Some of the blame must attach to Internic who have created some pretty unlikely top-level domains. It is difficult to imagine anybody using ".bv", the allocated top-level domain for Bouvet Island, an uninhabited.

OVERVIEW OF PRESENTATION LAYER

The presentation layer is concerned with the representation (syntax) of data during transfer between two communicating application processes.

To achieve true open systems interconnection, a number of common abstract data syntax forms have been defined. ISO defined a general abstract syntax suitable for the definition of data types associated with most distributed applications, known as abstract syntax notation number one or ASN.1. The data types associated with ASN.1 are abstract data types and an associated transfer syntax has been defined.

At present, only one transfer syntax notation exists in OSI - the Basic Encoding Rules (BER) of ASN.1. As experience with applications using BER grows, new transfer syntax notations, such as those including data compression or encryption, will no doubt be defined.

Syntax conversion may be the major role of the presentation layer, because it performs processing operations on all data prior to transfer and on all data that is received. It is also a good idea to perform data encryption and if required data compression in the presentation layer.

PRESENTATION LAYER

The presentation layer performs certain functions that are requested sufficiently often to warrant finding a general solution for them, rather than letting each user solve the problems. In particular, unlike all the lower layers, which are just interested in moving bits reliably from here to there, the presentation layer is concerned with the syntax and semantics of the information transmitted.

A typical example of a presentation service is encoding data in a standard, agreed upon way. Most user programs do not exchange random binary bit strings. They exchange things such as people's names, dates, amounts of money, and invoices. These items are represented as character strings, integers, floating point numbers, and data structures composed of several simpler items. Different computers have different codes for representing character strings, integers and so on. In order to make it possible for computers with different representation to communicate, the data structures to be exchanged can be defined in an abstract way, along with a standard encoding to be used "on the wire". The job of managing these abstract data structures and converting from the representation used inside the computer to the network standard representation is handled by the presentation layer.

The presentation layer is also concerned with other aspects of information representation. For example, data compression can be used here to reduce the number of bits that have to be transmitted and cryptography is frequently required for privacy and authentication.

Abstract Syntax/ASN.1

The task of an abstract language is to describe data types in a machine-independent fashion. This means that the abstract syntax language is freed from machine-oriented restrictions.

The abstract syntax (ISO ASN.1, CCITT standard notation) is based on the concept of data type. This concept is used in many programming languages. ASN.1 and X.409 refer to four classes of types:

- *Universal:* Application-independent types and construction mechanisms.
- *Application-Wide:* Relevant to a particular application, defined in other standards.
- *Context-Specific:* Relevant to a particular application, but applicable in a limited context.
- *Private:* Types defined by users and covered by any standard.

Each type is distinguished by a tag, which specifies the class of type and identifies a particular type. For example, UNIVERSAL 4 refers to OctetString, which is of class UNIVERSAL and has ID 4 within that class. The syntax is used to define data types and to specify data values.

Formally, a type definition has the form: <type name> ::= <type definition>

A simple example, Employee Number ::= [APPLICATION 2] IMPLICIT INTEGER

This uses the built-in type Integer, but the user has decided to give the type a new tag. The use of [APPLICATION 2] gives the tag (class and ID) for this new type. The designator IMPLICIT means that values of this type will be encoded only with the tag APPLICATION 2. By omission of the term IMPLICIT explicit tagging is used.

- In ASN.1 there are types Sequence and Set. Three forms of Sequence are allowed.
- A variable number of elements, all of one type (the designation SEQUENCE OF is used).
- A fixed number of elements, possibly of more than one type.
- A fixed number of elements, some of which are optional; all elements, including optional ones, must be of distinct types.
- A Set is similar to a Sequence, except that the order of the elements is not significant.

  The most important types in the syntax are:

  - *BitString:* An ordered set of zero or more bits.
  - *OctetString:* An ordered set of zero or more octets.
  - *External:* Used for presentation service user data in the ISO presentation protocol.
  - *Object identifier:* Used to name abstract and transfer syntaxes.
  - *Object descriptor:* A human-readable text providing a brief description of an object designated by an object identifier.

Abstract Syntax

Abstract syntax is specification of data or control information independent of the encoding technique used to represent them.

An application entity is the conceptual embodiment of all aspects of an application process that have to do with communication with another system. In the application example of section an application entity must establish contact between the inventory programs running on separate systems, must access the inventory files to determine stock availability, and must provide that information to the application process for use in answering the salesperson's query. These several functions that make up an application entity for this example may be further grouped into application objects for efficiency or convenience in developing the application.

Abstract syntax corresponds to type declarations in programming languages such as Pascal or C. For example, declaration of a variable as an integer implies properties of values the variable may hold and operations allowed on it, but does not determine how the value will be represented (2's complement, perhaps, or a specific number of bits). In the office supplies unlimited inventory example, consider the problem of exchanging inventory information. The application may call for the transfer of an inventory record consisting of an item number, an item description, and count of the item in stock at that site. Using ASN.1, for example, we can imagine something similar to the following specification of the inventory information:

```
inventory_record::=
  {item:    character string, length 5;
  description: character string, length 30;
  item_count: integer;
  }
```

An application entity belongs to only one application process, though another identical application entity may exist for another process simultaneously. A number of application entities may belong to one application process. These application entities may be of the same or different types. For example, a given application may consist of a number of complementary activities requiring communications activity of very different descriptions. Activities requiring interactive exchange of information could occur concurrently with activities requiring bulk transfer of large volumes of data. These might be designed and implemented as separate, but co-existing, application entities.

Application entities communicate by using application protocols between themselves and by using the services of the presentation layer to transmit the messages required by the application protocols. Communication between application entities occurs in either connection-oriented or connectionless mode.

In both modes of operation, in addition to the transfer of information, the application entities may support the identification of intended partners in the communication, determination of acceptable quality of service (including acceptable probability of error occurrence, cost, time requirements, etc.) and identification of abstract syntaxes. In connectionless mode, the data unit transferred may include an indication of authority to send the data and to enter communication with the destination. In connection-oriented mode, the Services provided by application entities may also include synchronization of the cooperating application, negotiation of responsibility for error control and for various security aspects of the communication. Because the application layer is the only contact between the application process and the requirements for communication with another system, all choices must be made, all specifications of service requirements must be completed in the invocation of application entities.

Though the World Wide Web is built on Internet (TCP/IP) protocols that do not conform precisely to the OSI Reference Model, it does include an example of an application entity: http. Web applications have many components; http provides those aspects of the application that are related to its communications requirements. Other aspects, such as the browser used and the viewers available to display various resource file formats are local issues. http encapsulates all aspects of communication with a remote system and all the steps needed to invoke lower layer network services.

ASN.1

Abstract Syntax Notation One (ANS.1) is a language that defines the way data is sent across dissimilar communication systems. ASN.1 ensures that the data received is the same as the data transmitted by providing a common syntax for specifying application layer (program-to-program communications) protocols.

Each communications system contains a similar ASN.1 encoding/decoding scheme written in the language used on that particular system. When one system wants to send data to another, the first system encodes the data into ASN.1, sends the data, and the second system receives and decodes the data using the decoder written in the language used on that system.

ASN.1 is an ISO/ITU standard based on the OSI model. It was first defined in 1984 as part of CCITT X.409; revised in 1995; then became its own standard, X.208, in 1998.

MIB—MANAGEMENT INFORMATION BASE

SNMP also consists of an extensible Management Information Base (MIB) that runs on each agent's workstation. Each MIB contains the configuration data for that device. The MIB structure is defined by the Structure of Management Information (SMI) language.

Basically, the MIB details what information is stored for any specific type of agent, how it is stored and how storage is to be structured.

RMON—Remote Network Monitoring

RMON is a MIB definition that provides for remote network monitoring and manager-to-manager communications. This standard defines the information that a device must collect to provide an accurate picture of a network's health. The information that the RMON MIB provides is divided into the following 9 groups:

1. **Segment statistics:** Statistics on the attached segment: packets, octets, collisions...
2. **History:** Data collected by the statistics group for future retrieval and analysis.
3. **Alarms:** Thresholds can be set for a certain alarm condition. (Collisions/sec).
4. **Events:** Thresholds can be set for certain event conditions to trigger certain activities.
5. **Host:** Statistics can be gathered on individual nodes or hosts on the LAN.
6. **Host top N:** Statistics can be gathered on individual nodes over a user-specified time.
7. **Traffic matrix:** Shows the amount of traffic and number of errors between any host pair.
8. **Packet capture:** Allows the capturing of entire packets or individual slices indicating protocols used.
9. **Filters:** The filter group specifies the criteria by which the packet is captured.

SNMP allows you to monitor and control a TCP/IP Network using SNMP Managers. All nodes (Agents) on a network, regardless of whether or not they are SNMP compliant, should show up on the Network map. The SNMP non-compliant nodes typically show up as being present (but not accessible).

SNMP-Compliant nodes allow information to be displayed that indicates how the node is configured. Machine Type, Ethernet Address, DOS Ver, IP Address, Name, and so on.

The Simple Network Management Protocol (SNMP) forms part of the internet protocol suite as defined by the Internet Engineering Task Force. The protocol serves to monitor any network-attached devices for any conditions that warrant it.

The first RFCs for SNMP appeared in 1988:

- RFC 1065—Structure and Identification of Management Information for TCP/IP-based Internets
- RFC 1066—Management Information Base for Network Management of TCP/IP-based Internets
- RFC 1067—A Simple Network Management Protocol

A clean separation of the protocol from the structure of management information has made it easy to use SNMP to monitor hundreds of different types of subsystems within a network, across all layers of the OSI reference model and extending into applications such as databases, e-mail, and the J2EE reference model.

Architecturally, the SNMP framework has three fundamental components:

1. Master agents
2. Subagents
3. Management stations

Each Internet Protocol (IP) addressable system in a network, such as a node or a router, hosts a master agent for that system. A master agent typically limits its activity to parsing and formatting of the protocol. If system has multiple manageable subsystems present, the master agent passes on the requests it receives to one or more subagents. These subagents model objects of interest within a subsystem and interface to that subsystem for monitoring and management operations. The role of the master agent and subagent can merge, in which case it is simply referred to as an agent.

The manager or management station provides the third component. It functions as the equivalent of a client in a client-server architecture. It issues requests for management operations on behalf of an administrator or application, and receives traps from agents as well.

The SNMP protocol operates at the application layer (layer 7) of the OSI model. It specified (in version 1) four core protocol data units (PDUs):

1. GET, used to retrieve a piece of management information.
2. GETNEXT, used iteratively to retrieve sequences of management information.
3. SET, used to make a change to a managed subsystem.
4. TRAP, used to report an alert or other asynchronous event about a managed subsystem.

Simple network management protocol version 2 revises version 1 and includes improvements in the areas of performance, security, confidentiality, and manager-to-manager communications.

NETWORK MANAGEMENT

The early 1980s saw tremendous expansion in the area of network deployment. As companies realized the cost benefits and productivity gains created by network technology, they began adding networks and expanding existing networks almost as rapidly as new network technologies and products were introduced. By the mid-1980s, growing pains from this expansion were being felt, especially by those companies that had deployed many different (and incompatible) network technologies.

The primary problems associated with network expansion are day-to-day network operation management and strategic network growth planning. Specifically, each new network technology requires its own set of experts to operate and maintain. In the early 1980s, strategic planning for the growth of these networks became a nightmare. The staffing requirements alone for managing large, heterogeneous networks created a crisis for many organizations. Automated network management (including what is typically called network capacity planning), integrated across diverse environments, became an urgent need.

This chapter describes technical features common to most network management architectures and protocols. It also presents the five functional areas of management as defined by the International Standardization for Organization (ISO).

NETWORK MANAGEMENT ARCHITECTURE

Most network management architectures use the same basic structure and set of relationships. End stations (managed devices) such as computer systems and other network devices run software allowing them to send alerts when they recognize problems. Problems are recognized when one or more user-determined thresholds are exceeded. Upon receiving these alerts, management entities are programmed to react by executing one, several, or all of a group of actions, including :

- Operator notification
- Event logging
- System shutdown
- Automatic attempts at system repair

Management entities can also poll end stations to check the values of certain variables. Polling can be automatic or user initiated. Agents in the managed devices respond to these polls. Agents are software modules that compile information about the managed devices in which they reside, store this information in a management database, and provide it (proactively or reactively) to management entities within Network Management Systems (NMSs) via a network management protocol. Well-known network management protocols include the Simple Network Management Protocol (SNMP) and Common Management Information Protocol (CMIP). Management proxies are entities that provide management information on behalf of other entities. A typical network management architecture is shown in figure 30.2.

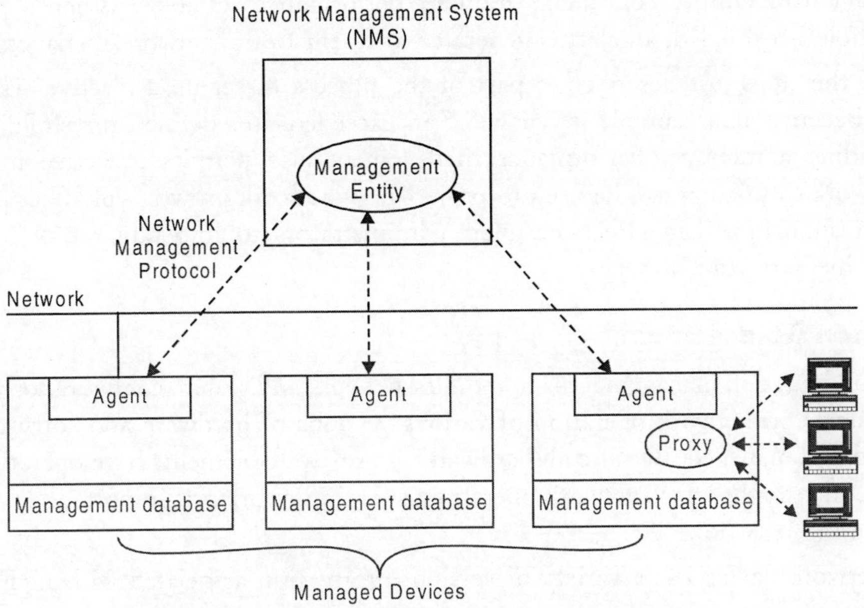

Figure 30.2 *Typical Network Management Architecture.*

ISO NETWORK MANAGEMENT MODEL

The ISO has contributed a great deal to network standardization. Their network management model is the primary means for understanding the major functions of network management systems. This model consists of five conceptual areas:

- Performance management
- Configuration management
- Accounting management
- Fault management
- Security management

Performance Management

The goal of performance management is to measure and make available various aspects of network performance so that internetwork performance can be maintained at an acceptable level. Examples of performance variables that might be provided include network throughput, user response times, and line utilization.

Performance management involves several steps:

- Gather performance data on those variables of interest to network administrators.
- Analyze the data to determine normal (baseline) levels.
- Determine appropriate performance thresholds for each important variable such that exceeding of these thresholds indicates a network problem worthy of attention.

- Management entities continually monitor performance variables. When a performance threshold is exceeded, an alert is generated and sent to the network management system.

Each of the steps just described is part of the process to set up a reactive system. When performance becomes unacceptable by virtue of an exceeded user-defined threshold, the system reacts by sending a message. Performance management also permits proactive methods. For example, network simulation can be used to project how network growth will affect performance metrics. Such simulation can effectively alert administrators to impending problems, so that counteractive measures can be taken.

Configuration Management

The goal of configuration management is to monitor network and system configuration information so that the effects on network operation of various versions of hardware and software elements can be tracked and managed. Because all hardware and software elements have operational quirks, flaws, or both that might affect network operation, such information is important to maintaining a smooth-running network.

Each network device has a variety of version information associated with it. For example, an engineering workstation might be configured as follows:

- Operating system, Version 3.2
- Ethernet interface, Version 5.4
- TCP/IP software, Version 2.0
- NetWare software, Version 4.1
- NFS software, Version 5.1
- Serial communications controller, Version 1.1
- X.25 software, Version 1.0
- SNMP software, Version 3.1

Configuration management subsystems store this information in a database for easy access. When a problem occurs, this database can be searched for clues that might help solve the problem.

Accounting Management

The goal of accounting management is to measure network utilization parameters so that individual or group uses of the network can be regulated appropriately. Such regulation minimizes network problems (because network resources can be apportioned out based on resource capacities) and maximizes the fairness of network access across all users.

As with performance management, the first step toward appropriate accounting management is to measure utilization of all important network resources. Analysis of the results provides insight into current usage patterns. Usage quotas can be set at this point. Some correction will be required to reach optimal access practices. From that point on, ongoing measurement of resource use can yield billing information as well as information used to retrieve continued fair and optimal resource utilization.

Fault Management

The goal of fault management is to detect, log, notify users of, and (to the extent possible) automatically fix network problems in order to keep the network running effectively. Because faults can cause downtime or unacceptable network degradation, fault management is perhaps the most widely implemented of the ISO network management elements.

Fault management involves several steps:

- Determine problem symptoms.
- Isolate the problem.
- Fix the problem.
- Test the fix on all important subsystems.
- Record the problem's detection and resolution.

Security Management

The goal of security management is to control access to network resources according to local guidelines so that the network cannot be sabotaged (intentionally or unintentionally) and sensitive information cannot be accessed by those without appropriate authorization. For example, a security management subsystem can monitor users logging on to a network resource, refusing access to those who enter inappropriate access codes.

Security management subsystems work by partitioning network resources into authorized and unauthorized areas. For some users, access to any network resources is inappropriate. Such users are usually company outsiders. For other (internal) network users, access to information originating from a particular department is inappropriate. For example, access to human resource files is inappropriate for most users outside the human resource department.

Security management subsystems perform several functions:

- Identify sensitive network resources (including systems, files, and other entities).
- Determine mappings between sensitive network resources and user sets.
- Monitor access points to sensitive network resources.
- Log inappropriate access to sensitive network resources.

Network management stems from the realization that hosts, routers, and other networking devices often require maintenance operations, and the network is a communications medium, so why not use the network to perform the maintenance ?

The oldest and simplest form of network management is the remote login. In fact, most fancy routers support TELNET access to some sort of command prompt. Many operations can be performed in no other way.

However, more sophisticated network management tools have been developed, for a variety of reasons. Remote logins are designed for human interaction, and use command style and syntax that varies between different hardware and software platforms. A more specialized and standardized approach allows automated software tools to easily perform management operations on a variety of platforms. Also useful is a standard method of reporting network failures and error conditions to a centralized location.

For Internet engineers, the SNMP protocol is currently the most popular vehicle for network management.

SNMP PROTOCOL OVERVIEW

The Simple Network Management Protocol (SNMP) is essentially a request-reply protocol running over UDP (ports 161 and 162), though TCP operation is possible. SNMP is an asymmetric protocol, operating between a management station (smart) and an agent (dumb). The agent is the device being managed - all its software has to do is implement a few simple packet types and a generic get-or-set function on its MIB variables. The management station presents the user interface. Simple management stations can be built with UNIX command-line utilities. More complex (and expensive) ones collect MIB data over time and use GUIs to draw network maps.

SNMP Version 1 is documented in RFC 1157. SNMP Version 2 is documented in several RFCs:

- RFC 1902 (MIB Structure)
- RFC 1903 (Textual Conventions)
- RFC 1904 (Conformance Statements)
- RFC 1905 (Protocol Operations)
- RFC 1906 (Transport Mappings)
- RFC 1907 (MIB)

SNMP's packet formats are described using Abstract Syntax Notation 1 (ASN.1), one of ISO's "Open" protocols. ASN.1 basically fills the role of XDR, but does so differently. ASN.1, like all OSI standard documents, is not freely available on-line.

An SNMP operation takes the form of a Protocol Data Unit (PDU), basically a fancy word for packet. Version 1 SNMP supports five possible PDUs:

- GetRequest / SetRequest supplies a list of objects and, possibly, values they are to be set to (SetRequest). In either case, the agent returns a GetResponse.
- GetResponse informs the management station of the results of a GetRequest or SetRequest by returning an error indication and a list of variable/value bindings.
- GetNextRequest is used to perform table transversal, and in other cases where the management station does not know the exact MIB name of the object it desires. GetNextRequest does not require an exact name to be specified; if no object exists of the specified name, the next object in the MIB is returned. Note that to support this, MIBs must be strictly ordered sets (and are).
- Trap is the only PDU sent by an agent on its own initiative. It is used to notify the management station of an unusual event that may demand further attention (like a link going down). In version 2, traps are named in MIB space. Newer MIBs specify management objects that control how traps are sent.

SIMPLE NETWORK MANAGEMENT PROTOCOL (SNMP)

SNMP is not actually a protocol: it's a client server application that runs on the UDP (User Datagram Protocol) service of the TCP/IP protocol suite. It was developed to be an efficient means of sending network management information over UDP, using Ports 161(SNMP) and 162 (SNMPTRAP).

SNMP consists of three parts: messages, agents and managers.

- SNMP messages (such as Get and GetResponse) communicate the management information.
- SNMP managers asks the questions (polls) and manages the agents approximately every 15 minutes to see if anything has changed.
- SNMP agents are resources to be managed such as hosts, servers, routers, hubs, etc.

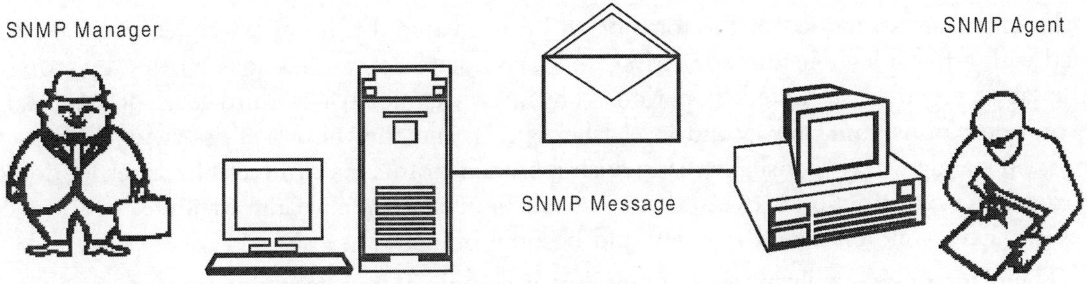

Figure 30.3 *SNMP.*

There are only 5 PDUs (Protocol Data Units) associated with SNMP.

- GetRequest allows the SNMP manager to access info stored in the Agent.
- GetNextRequest allows the SNMP manager to obtain multiple values.
- GetResponse is a response from the SNMP Agent to GetRequest, GetNextRequest and SetRequest.
- SetRequest is used by the SNMP manager when configuring agents.
- Trap reports that an event has occurred by the SNMP agent. (Error or status has changed)

Efficiency suffers because UDP restricts the amount of information that will fit into a single UDP packet. For example, at least 1 GetNextRequest is required for each row in a routing table. There may be hundreds of rows in a routing table (hundreds of packets can be generated).

UDP is a connectionless protocol. Agents have no method of confirming that the events reported using trap have actually been received. This is considered to be a "safety" issue.

Security is also a problem. The only mechanism for determining if an authorized network manager is requesting management action is a clear text community name, located in the packet header. There is no method of providing privacy for management information. Due to these security faults, most SNMP implementation is used for monitoring, and no "strong" management functions are defined.

SNMPv2 to the Rescue

SNMPv2 combined the RMON (Remote Network Monitoring) MIB definition and Secure SNMP. Secure SNMP provides strong authentication and privacy mechanisms that are suitable for network management in a generally open environment. These two independent evolutions of SNMP were brought together in a new version of SNMP called SNMPv2.

In addition, SNMPv2 was extended to address the concerns over protocol efficiency and safety (acknowledgments of trap). Two new protocol functions (PDUs) were added (GetBulk and inform request) to allow efficient reading of tables, and provide reliable communications.

DOMAIN NAMES

Internet domains form the basis of the common Internet naming scheme. For example, www.cnn.com is a domain name, and cnn.com is a domain.

Domains are structured in the form of an inverted tree. Each branch or leaf on the tree is labeled with an simple alphanumeric string, and a complete domain name is written by stringing all the labels together, separated by periods. Thus, www.cnn.com is a third-level domain name. The root domain is com, the second level label is cnn, and the third level is www. Incidentally, there is no standard way to visually distinguish a branch from a leaf. In fact, the Internet domain system makes no distinction between the two, since branches can have any attributes of a leaf, and leaves can have children added to them and become branches.

The diagram below illustrates the novell.com domain. The interpretation of domain names ending in novell.com is solely at the discretion of novell. They manage the shaded area of the domain name space.

First, they can be generic domains, all of which are populated by predominately American domains. Alternately, a top-level domain can be a UN two-digit country code, listed in ISO-3166, the most common form for non-American domains.

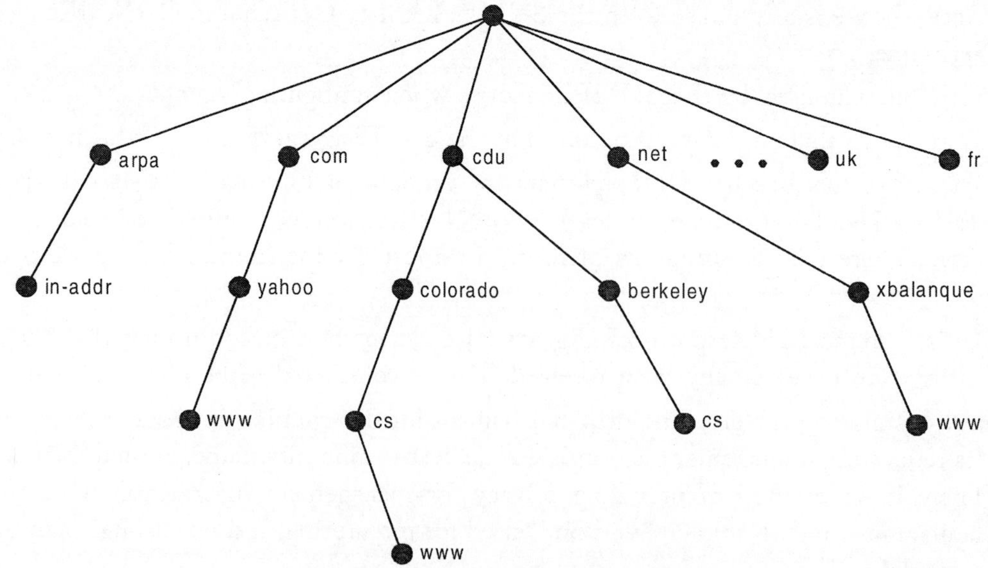

Figure 30.4 *Domain Name Space.*

Generic Domains	**Country Domains**
(partial list)	
com - Commercial	uk - United Kingdom
edu - Educational	fr - France
org - Non-profit Organizations	de - Germany
net - Networking Providers	nl - Netherlands
mil - US Military	us - United States
gov - US Government	au - Australia
int - International Organizations	ax - Antarctica

To make use of domain names, they must be converted into 32-bit IP addresses. This is done using the DNS protocol.

Domain name registrations are handled by InterNIC in North America, RIPE in Europe, and APNIC in Asia. Domain name assignment is completely distinct from IP address assignment.

AUTHENTICATION-PROTOCOL

On some links it may be desirable to require a peer to authenticate itself before allowing network-layer protocol packets to be exchanged. This configuration option provides a method to negotiate the use of a specific protocol for authentication. By default, authentication is not required.

An implementation MUST NOT include multiple authentication-protocol configuration options in its configure-request packets. Instead, it SHOULD attempt to configure the most desirable protocol first. If that protocol is configure-Nak'd, then the implementation SHOULD attempt the next most desirable protocol in the next configure-request.

The implementation sending the configure-request is indicating that it expects authentication from its peer. If an implementation sends a configure-ack, then it is agreeing to authenticate with the specified protocol. An implementation receiving a configure-ack SHOULD expect the peer to authenticate with the acknowledged protocol.

There is no requirement that authentication be full-duplex or that the same protocol be used in both directions. It is perfectly acceptable for different protocols to be used in each direction. This will, of course, depend on the specific protocols negotiated.

A summary of the authentication-protocol configuration option format is shown below. The fields are transmitted from left to right.

```
0                   1                   2                   3
0 1 2 3 4 5 6 7 8 9 0 1 2 3 4 5 6 7 8 9 0 1 2 3 4 5 6 7 8 9 0 1
+-+-+-+-+-+-+-+-+-+-+-+-+-+-+-+-+-+-+-+-+-+-+-+-+-+-+-+-+-+-+-+-+
| Type  |   Length  | Authentication-Protocol | Data
+-+-+-+-+-+-+-+-+-+-+-+-+-+-+-+-+-+-+-+-+-+-+-+-+-+-+-+-+-+-+-+-+
```

```
Type
  3
```

```
Length
  >= 4
```

The authentication-protocol field is two octets, and indicates the authentication-protocol desired. Values for this field are always the same as the PPP protocol field values for that same authentication-protocol.

Up-to-date values of the authentication-protocol field are specified in the most recent "Assigned Numbers" RFC. Current values are assigned as follows:

Value (in hex)	Protocol
c023	Password Authentication-Protocol
c223	Challenge Handshake Authentication-Protocol

Data

The data field is zero or more octets, and contains additional data as determined by the particular protocol.

IP addresses are difficult for humans to remember: they're great for PCs! Domain names were invented to make it easier to navigate the Internet. A domain name is a vaguely descriptive name that's separated by dots. For example: www.Linuxhq.org

Every machine that runs TCP/IP has a text file called hosts. It is a simple lookup table that the network stack (IP) checks: it looks to see if it has a match between a domain name and an IP address. It is easily modified with a text editor, and the contents look like the following:

- 127.0.0.1localhost142.110.237.1e237
- -firewall.tech.el.sait.ab.ca142.110.237.2e237
- -bridge.tech.el.sait.ab.ca142.110.237.3ashley.tech.el.sait.ab.ca
- 142.110.237.4mariah mariah.tech.el.sait.ab.ca

The IP address is listed on the left, and the domain name is listed on the right. The actual registered domain name is sait.ab.ca (Southern Alberta Institute of Technology). The domain name el.sait.ab.ca (electronics dept.) is a subnet of sait.ab.ca. The domain name tech.el.sait.ab.ca (technical) is a subnet of el.sait.ab.ca.

The machine names are e237-firewall, e237-bridge, ashley and mariah. Mariah's entry is unique in that both the domain name mariah and mariah.tech.el.sait.ab.ca would be recognized by the IP stack as 142.110.237.4.

The problem with the hosts file is that each machine must have a current up to date copy of the network. For a small network (25 or less) that is not connected to the Internet, this is not a problem to manage. If the network is larger, then problems can occur when trying to keep everyone updated.

Another solution is Unix's Network Information Service (NIS) (formerly called yellow pages until there was a copyright conflict with the telcos). A central NIS server shares a master hosts file to all the clients. In this way, only one file exists (and is updated). This works well for a network that's not connected to the Internet.

If you are connected to the Internet, then a Domain Name Server (DNS) is used. A DNS is a special server that communicates with other servers, and keeps an up-to-date look-up table.

This table matches IP addresses to domain names for the complete Internet. It is a hierarchical system, where each DNS is authorative for the domain underneath it. This means that each server knows the domain name to IP address mapping of the network underneath it.

DOMAIN NAME STRUCTURE

Domain names tend to follow a loose structure (giving a description of the network). For example, sait.ab.ca uses the Canada extension ca, preceded by the province of Alberta extension ab, and then the abbreviation SAIT (for the Southern Alberta Institute of Technology). This is a geographically-designed domain name that follows the ISO-3166 country code structure examples of country codes are shown below:

- brBrazilcaCanadafiFinlandgbUnited Kingdomna
- NambianzNew ZealandtwTaiwanusUnited States

There are top level domain (TLD) names extensions that attempt to describe the purpose of the domain. It is broken down into these seven basic categories:

com- Commercial domains that are a business.edu- Educational institutesnet-

This is for computers of network providers such as Internet Service Providersorg-Standard organizations or non profit organizationsint organizations that have been established by international treaties.gov-Municipal, federal, provincial, state governments.mil-United States military.

All in all, it is often quite difficult to establish where a domain is physically located (or what it actually does) from just the domain name itself. But it makes remembering locations easier than attempting to remembering an IP address.

DOMAIN NAME LOOK-UP PROCEDURE

The look-up order is as follows:

- The IP stack checks the hosts file to see if there is a domain name match to IP address. If there is, the IP address is used.
- If there is no match, the IP stack will look for a NIS server with its host file shared. If this service is not installed, the IP stack will jump to the next step.
- If there is still no match, the IP stack will send out a request to the domain name server configured during the network configuration to see if it knows whose IP address belongs to the domain name.
- If the domain name server doesn't know, it may make an enquiry to the next level up domain name server to see if it knows whose IP address belongs to the domain name and so on.

On the Internet, there are 13 top level root domain name servers. The current addresses and domain names are found at ftp://internic.net/domain/named.cache (also called named.ca and named.root).

- Domain NameIP AddressDescription A.ROOT-SERVERS.NET198.41.0.4
- formerly NS.INTERNIC.NETB.ROOT-SERVERS.NET128.9.0.107
- formerly NS1.ISI.EDUC.ROOT-SERVERS.NET192.33.4.12
- formerly C.PSI.NETD.ROOT-SERVERS.NET128.8.10.90
- formerly TERP.UMD.EDUE.ROOT-SERVERS.NET192.203.230.10
- formerly NS.NASA.GOVF.ROOT-SERVERS.NET192.5.5.241
- formerly NS.ISC.ORGG.ROOT-SERVERS.NET192.112.36.4
- formerly NS.NIC.DDN.MILH.ROOT-SERVERS.NET128.63.2.53
- formerly AOS.ARL.ARMY.MILI.ROOT-SERVERS.NET192.36.148.17
- formerly NIC.NORDU.NETJ.ROOT-SERVERS.NET198.41.0.10
- temporarily housed at NSI (InterNIC)K.ROOT-SERVERS.NET193.0.14.129
- housed in LINX, operated by RIPE NCC L.ROOT-SERVERS.NET198.32.64.12
- temporarily housed at ISI (IANA)M.ROOT-SERVERS.NET202.12.27.33
- housed in Japan, operated by WIDE

These are controlled by InterNIC, which is the primary agency responsible for registering domain names. At the time of this writing, there are several new agencies that are taking over the domain registration process for different parts of the world.

IP Header

The IP datagram is traditional represented by many rows of 32 bits (4 octets or bytes). Each 32 bit word is stacked on top of each other as per the following diagram for the IP header:

<table>
<tr><td>Version
(4 bits)</td><td>IHL
(4 bits)</td><td>Type of Service
(8 bits)</td><td colspan="2">Total Length
(16 bits)</td></tr>
<tr><td colspan="3">Identification
(16 bits)</td><td>Flags
(3 bits)</td><td>Flags
(3 bits)</td></tr>
<tr><td colspan="2">Time to Live
(8 bits)</td><td>Protocol
(8 bits)</td><td colspan="2">Header Checksum
(16 bits)</td></tr>
<tr><td colspan="5">Source Address
(32 bits)</td></tr>
<tr><td colspan="5">Destination Address
(32 bits)</td></tr>
<tr><td colspan="5">Options and Padding
(multiples of 32 bits)</td></tr>
</table>

Figure 30.5 *IP Header.*

Field description version (4 bits) the IP version, currently it is version 4.

0 Reserved

1–3 Unassigned

4	IP	Internet Protocol
5	STST	Datagram Mode
6	SIP	Simple Internet Protocol
7	TP/IXTP/IX: The Next Internet	
8	PIP	The P Internet Protocol
9	TUBA	TUBA
10–14	Unassigned	
15	Reserved	IHL (4 bits) Internet Header Length, the length of the IP header in 32 bit words.
		Type of ServiceFlags to indicate precedence, delay, throughput and (8 bits) reliability parameters.

Bit 0-2: Precedence000 - Routine001 - Priority010 - Immediate011 - Flash100 - Flash override101 - CRITIC / ECP110 - Internet control111 - Network controlBit 3:0 = Normal delay, 1 = Low delay Bit 4:0 = Normal throughput, 1 = High throughputBit 5:0 = Normal reliability, 1 = High reliabilityBit 6–7:Reserved for future use.Total LengthTotal length in bytes of the IP datagram (IP header and data) (16 bits) Minimum length = 576, Maximum length = 65,535 IdentificationUnique identifying number for this datagram (16 bits) Flags (3 bits) Options that indicate if fragmentation s permitted and/or usedBit 0:Reserved, allways set to 0 Bit 1:0 = May fragment, 1 = Don't fragmentBit 2:0 = Last fragment, 1 = More fragmentsFragment OffsetIndicates where in the entire datagram, this particular fragment (13 bits) belongs. Measured in 64 bit units from the beginning of the initial datagram. Time to live (TTL) Measured in hop counts or seconds. Every transverse through (8 bits) a router or gateway will decrement the hop count. When the TTL equals 0, the datagram is discarded. This stops datagrams from circulating the network forever. Starts at TTL = 255.Protocol Identifies the next protocol that follows the IP header (8 bits).

E-MAIL

E-mail is a familiar way of transferring messages between two Internet users. e-mail was one of the earliest applications to be developed on the Internet, the first e-mail was, reputedly, sent in 1973.

The Internet e-mail system is associated with the RFC822 protocol commonly (and incorrectly) known as Simple Mail Transfer Protocol (SMTP) although as these notes will show there are several other protocols involved in the actual transfer of e-mail.

Historically there have been several other e-mail protocols including the failed ISO-CCITT X.400 protocol, the retired UK-JANET coloured book protocol and numerous proprietary protocols for use under proprietary operating systems and environments. All non-SMTP systems still operational have gateways to the Internet SMTP e-mail system.

The e-mail services, you can install components on your computer to configure it as a

With e-mail services, you can install components on your computer to configure it as a mail server. e-mail services includes the Post Office Protocol 3 (POP3) service and the Simple Mail Transfer Protocol (SMTP) service, which retrieve and transfer e-mail, respectively. To provide e-mail services to users, such as sending and receiving e-mail, administrators can create mailboxes on the server.

- Simple Mail Transfer Protocol (SMTP) service
- POP3 service

E-mail Addresses

An e-mail address such as has two parts known as the local part and the domain part separated by the @ symbol. The domain part identifies directly or indirectly an Internet host for receipt of the message. This host will run mail server software that will examine the local part and take whatever action is appropriate to deliver the message to the end user.

User and Transfer Agents

There are two sorts of software functionality involved in the transfer of e-mail. These are as:

(1) Mail Transfer Agents (MTAs)

These are permanently running programs on hosts with permanent Internet connections. An MTA listens for incoming e-mail from both local users and remote MTAs, examines the e-mail and either saves it locally (in a mail spool) for retrieval by the destination user or identifies and contacts a remote MTA and transfers the e-mail to the remote MTA. Several MTAs may be involved in the transfer of e-mail from originator to destination, the intermediate MTAs are known as mail relays. Typical MTAs are programs such as send mail and exim. A different type of MTA will listen for requests from users for any e-mail saved for them and will transfer the e-mail to the user. Host computers running MTA software are commonly known as mail servers.

(2) Mail User Agents (MUAs)

An MUA is a program that a user runs when he or she wishes to send or receive e-mail. It provides a user interface for composition and local storage of mail messages and also has facilities to communicate with MTAs.

There are numerous MUAs available under modern windows based environments. Typical examples include Eudora and Microsoft Outlook. On Unix based systems character based (non-windows) based programs such as elm and mail may be encountered. World Wide Web browsers such as netscape also commonly incorporate MUA functions.

The Protocols

There are number of protocols involved in the transfer of e-mail. Such as:

- **RFC 821:** Simple Mail Transfer Protocol (SMTP)

  This protocol defines the mechanism by which MTAs communicate with each other and with MUAs.

- **RFC 822:** Internet Message Format

  This protocol defines the actual format of e-mail messages, especially the headers that are used by MTAs and MUAs to determine destinations and reply addresses.

- **RFC 1939:** Post Office Protocol 3 (POP3)

  This protocol defines how a end user interacts with a POP MTA to retrieve incoming e-mail.

- **RFC 2046:** Multimedia Internet Mail Extensions (MIME)

  The basic message format defined in RFC 822 does not allow messages to include anything other than normal printing ASCII characters. This protocol defines a standard method for encoding data in other formats such as graphical images, binary files, word processed documents etc.

The Mechanism

The transfer of an e-mail from a local user to a remote user will typically involve the following steps assuming both users are using personal computers with dial-up Internet connections.

Local User Set Up

The local user starts his MUA program ensuring that it is configured with the Internet address of a host running an SMTP server MTA. Theoretically he could use any MTA anywhere on the Internet, however, mail server administrators normally configure MTAs so they will only accept such requests from or for users in the same domain as the server. See notes on open relaying.

Local User Sends E-mail

The local user composes the e-mail message possibly attaching files and then tells the MUA to send the e-mail to the MTA using SMTP. He may, of course, have prepared several items of mail "off-line" and send them all once a connection is established with the MTA. The MUA autommically includes the required headers in the e-mail message based on information supplied by the user either as part of the MUA configuration or entered interactively during mail composition.

E-mail Transmission

The MTA analyses the headers of the incoming message to identify the destination mail server. The MTA then attempts to communicate with the destination mail server and transfers the message using SMTP. If the message cannot be transferred it is queued in the mail spool for further attempts.

It is common that a single mail server host provides services for a large group of machines. The Internet DNS mechanism provides the facility for identifying a **mail exchanger** or **MX** host for a DNS domain so that e-mail can, apparently, be sent to a domain (such as *wlv.ac.uk*) rather than a specific host within that domain.

E-mail Receipt

The destination mail server examines the incoming message to identify the local part of the address from the headers. This may be a nick-name (or **alias**) for an actual user, group of users or even a file or a program input. The server will usually store the incoming e-mail in the mail spool.

Remote User Receives E-mail

The remote user starts his MUA program ensuring that it is configured with the Internet address of a host running a POP server MTA. This may well be the same host as he uses for outgoing e-mail although this is not essential. He establishes his bona-fides to the POP server by quoting a user identification code and password and the POP server examines the mail spool and responds with details of the number of incoming e-mail messages. The user can then instruct his MUA to transfer or copy the e-mail messages to his personal computer.

If the destination mail server host is a general purpose computer into which users may login, there is no need for the use of POP, user programs can directly manipulate the mail spool. This used to be standard practice and is still widely used.

The following diagram illustrates the process. The dashed lines show possible dial-up connections, the solid lines show permanent connections.

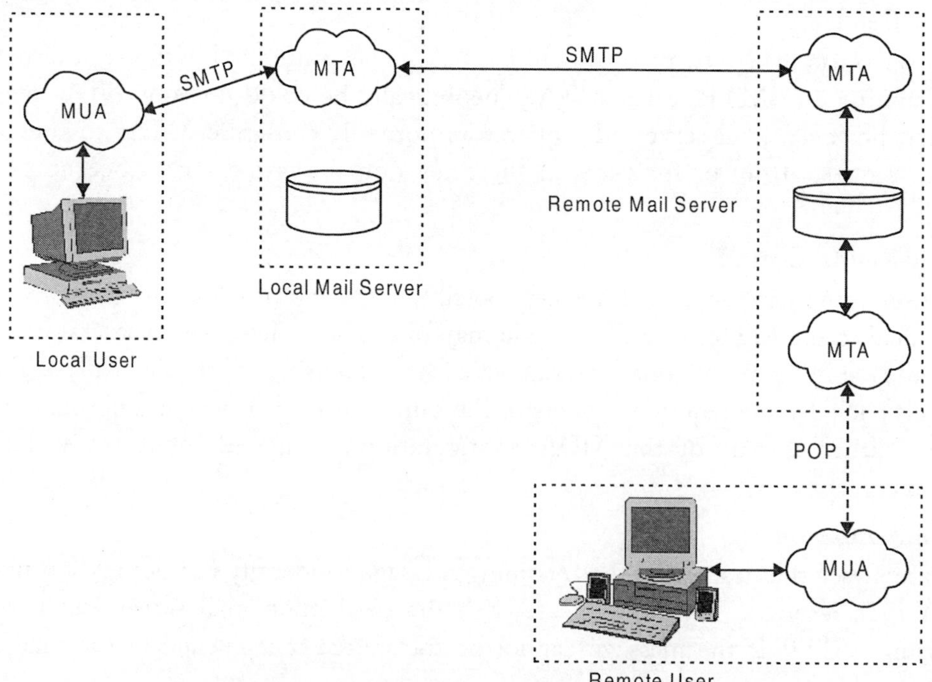

Figure 30.6 *MUA to Transfer or Copy the e-mail Messages.*

RFC 821-SIMPLE MAIL TRANSFER PROTOCOL (SMTP)

This protocol is used for communication between MTAs and between MUAs and MTAs. Like many Internet protocols it runs on top of TCP and the basic structure consists of ASCII messages starting with a four letter code indicating the function of the message. Responses messages start with a three digit numeric code. All messages have a single space after the function code and are terminated with a carriage return and line feed pair. [Known as <CRLF>]. SMTP servers are expected to listen on port 23.

It is possible to send e-mail without using an MUA by running a telnet session to port 23 on the mail server host although administrators are likely to discourage the practice as it by-passes any checks on the validity of the RFC 822 headers. The RFC defines 13 standard messages.

Table 30.9 13 Standard Messages

Code	*Meaning*
DATA	Body of message follows. The body is terminated by the sequence <CRLF>.<CRLF>
EXPN	Reply will give expansion of group alias. The RFC also suggests that mailing lists will be expanded, however, it seems probable that the meaning associated with "mailing list" is not that currently associated with the phrase.
HELO	Establish connection between hosts.
HELP	Send helpful information. This would really only be useful if the protocol were being driven directly by a human user.
MAIL	Start of messages relevant to individual item of e-mail.
NOOP	do nothing (!)
QUIT	Terminate connection.
RCPT	Identify recipient of e-mail.
SAML	e-mail is both to user's mailbox and direct display on his terminal screen if he is logged in.
SEND	e-mail is direct to user's terminal screen.
SOML	e-mail is direct to user's terminal screen or if he isn't logged in to his mailbox.
TURN	Reverse direction of data flow.
VRFY	Confirm that the address refers to a real user.

RFC 822—INTERNET MESSAGE FORMAT

This protocol defines the actual format of an e-mail message, particularly the *headers* that appear at the start of a message. All headers are required to consist of a *name part* and *value part.* The two parts are separated by a colon followed immediately by a space. The list of headers is terminated by a null line. Here is a fairly typical example taken pretty much at random from the author's mailbox,

- Return-path: <nothemba.mrwetyana@continuing-education.oxford.ac.uk>
- Envelope-to: jphb@scitsc.wlv.ac.uk
- Delivery-date: Sat, 13 Feb 1999 11:53:38 +0000
- Received: from oxmail1.ox.ac.uk [129.67.1.1] by sunc.scit.wlv.ac.uk with esmtp (Exim 1.73 #4) id 10Bddh-0002Cc-00; Sat, 13 Feb 1999 11:53:37 +0000
- Received: from scf-6.conted.ox.ac.uk ([163.1.150.85] by oxmail.ox.ac.uk with esmtp (Exim 2.10 #1) id 10BddW-0002RP-00 for jphb@scitsc.wlv.ac.uk; Sat, 13 Feb 1999 11:53:26 +0000
- From: "Nothemba Mrwetyana" <nothemba.mrwetyana@continuing-education.oxford.ac.uk>
- To: <jphb@scitsc.wlv.ac.uk>
- Subject: aberystwyth university
- Date: Sat, 13 Feb 1999 12:01:44 -0000
- X-MSMail-Priority: Normal
- X-Priority: 3
- X-Mailer: Microsoft Internet Mail 4.70.1161
- MIME-Version: 1.0
- Content-Type: text/plain; charset=ISO-8859-1
- Content-Transfer-Encoding: 7bit
- Message-ID: <E10BddW-0002RP-00@oxmail.ox.ac.uk>
- X-Mozilla-Status: 8003
- X-Mozilla-Status2: 00000000
- X-UIDL: d43a35866570e8b68b804abe596ab77b

The headers beginning with the letter **x** are not defined in RFC 822 and have been generated by the various transfer and user agents for various purposes specific to those agents. The 'MIME' and 'content' headers are also not part of RFC 822.

RFC 822 imposes no limits on the length of headers and allows headers to be **folded** by inserting the sequence <CRLF> SPACE into the header at a suitable point.

There are a significant number of headers defined in RFC 822. The ones indicated in bold are the most common.

Table 30.10

Header	*Meaning*
bcc:	'blind' other recipients. I.e the "bcc" recipients won't be aware of each other.
cc:	Other recipients. Literally "Carbon Copy" referring to an obsolete method of duplicating documents using special paper impregnated with carbon.
Date:	Date of origination. These are often spectacularly wrong, especially when the originating MUA is on PC that hasn't been set up correctly. The value associated with this header often determines the order in which messages appear in the recipient's MUA list of incoming mail items.
Delivery-Date:	Date of delivery to recipient's mailbox.
Envelope-To:	This header, if present, is the actual address the message is destined for, it over-rides any setting of the **To:** header, although it usually has the same value.
From:	Sender's name (in a quoted string) and e-mail address. The name part is likely to be displayed by the recipient's MUA. The quoted e-mail address will be used for any reply, for some reason spammers seem rather fond of setting this as a blank.
Message-ID:	Unique message identification created by originator so that possible multiple copies of the message can be discarded.
Received:	"Trace" information recording the messages transit through intermediate MTAs.
Return-path:	This, if present, is the route back to the originator for tracing purposes. It is often the same as the **From:** address.
Sender:	The sender
Subject:	Filled in by the sender and likely to be displayed by the recipient's MUA.
To:	Destination address, as entered by sender.

There are many other less widely used headers both defined in RFC 822 and, inevitably, devised by individual software vendors.

It is now possible to discover several facts about the e-mail whose headers are shown above.

- *From the second Received:* header, the e-mail was originated on the host scf-6.conted.ox.ac.uk and was transferred to the host oxmail.ox.ac.uk (presumably Oxford University's main mail handling system or *mail hub*) which was running version 2.10 of the 'Exim' software. The Oxford machine then contacted the SCIT mail system (sunc.scit.wlv.ac.uk) which runs version 1.73 of Exim.
- *From the X-Mailer:* header it is cellar that the sender was using microsoft internet mail 4.70.1161
- *From the Received:* headers and the *Delivery-Date*: header the message was received by the Oxford mail hub at 11:53:26, received by the SCIT hub at 11:53:37 (11 seconds later) and delivered to the recipient's mailbox at 11:53:38. The recipient's mailbox is part of the SCIT hub's file system.

- *From the Date:* header it will be seen that the originator's computer clock was running about 8 minutes fast.

THE MAIL SERVER—RFC822

Here's an example of a typical dialogue between an MUA and an MTA. In this example a simple telnet client is used to talk to the mail server.

bash$ telnet mail.scit.wlv.ac.uk 25

Trying 134.220.4.1...

Connected to sunc.scit.wlv.ac.uk.

Escape character is '^]'.

- 220 sunc.scit.wlv.ac.uk ESMTP Exim 1.73 #4 Fri, 12 Mar 1999 10:06:58 +0000
  HELO It's me
- 250 sunc.scit.wlv.ac.uk: Hello sund.scit.wlv.ac.uk [134.220.4.205]
  MAIL FROM: jphb@scit.wlv.ac.uk
- 250 <jphb@scit.wlv.ac.uk> is syntactically correct
  RCPT TO: jphb@scit.wlv.ac.uk
- 250 <jphb@scit.wlv.ac.uk> is syntactically correct
  DATA
  354 Enter message, ending with "." on a line by itself
- To: cm1901@wlv.ac.uk
- From: James Q.Hacker
- Subject: Testing

  Hi There !

  .

- 250 OK id=10LOqx-00044U-00
  QUIT
- 221 sunc.scit.wlv.ac.uk closing connection
  Connection closed by foreign host.

The lines starting with 3 digit numbers are replies from the mail server program, the remaining lines, after the initial establishment of connection are direct user input in this case. The mail was duly delivered.

MAILING LISTS AND GROUP ALIASES

The address of an e-mail message includes a local part. The local part is the subject of processing by the receiving mail server which may simply assume that the local part is the name of a user with a login account on the mail server host or a related machine. Unfortunately such login codes are usually rather unfriendly and many MTAs allow the use of *aliases* whereby a more friendly name can be used as the local part and the MTA will translate this to the actual login code by consulting a local database. On Unix systems this database is almost invariably stored in a file called /etc/aliases although more elaborate mail handling systems may also use other databases.

An alias may expand to several real addresses rather than a single real address in which case it is known as a *group alias.*

Such aliases can, normally, only be created by the system administrator who has the necessary privileges to modify the database. As well as being a real user login code and alias can also be a further e-mail address possibly on a completely different system. This would typically allow a university to provide e-mail forwarding to former students who could continue to receive e-mail sent to their student e-mail addresses.

An alternative to a group alias that has superficially similar behaviour is the fully fledged *mailing list.* The similarity is that e-mail sent to the list address is copied to the every member of the list. Such mechanisms are sometimes called *mail reflectors* or *mail exploders.*

The actual method of operation is quite different from a group alias. The list address is actually associated with a group of programs which as well as reflecting the e-mail also provide facilities for users to join and leave the list automatically by sending messages to special addresses. The best known mailing list programs are "majordomo" and "listserv".

Mailing lists come in a variety of flavours such as:

- *moderated* which means all postings are vetted by the human moderator before being sent to list members
- *open* which means anybody can subscribe themselves without human intervention
- *closed* which means either that people requesting to join the list have to be approved by the list maintainer/owner or that only members of the list can post messages to the list.

SPAM AND UNSOLICITED COMMERCIAL E-MAIL (UCE)

Since there are now many millions of people with the facility to send and receive e-mail, it is now an attractive medium to people who want to sell something. Given the very low costs compared with other communication media and the comparatively unregulated nature of the Internet, e-mail promoting various dubious get-rich-quick schemes and sources of sexually explicit material has become a widespread nuisance, especially as users have to pay to receive the stuff before throwing it away.

It is simple to develop programs that will send e-mail to thousands of unsuspecting recipients. There is also software that will trawl newsgroups and WWW pages looking for new e-mail addresses. Lists of millions of e-mail addresses are available commercially for a few dollars.

Such material is known as *Unsolicited Commercial e-mail (UCE)* or, more usually *spam*. The later term reflects a famous Monty Python TV sketch of a rather dysfunctional cafe that sold spam (tinned processed pork) with everything even to the extent of having a menu item labelled "Spam, spam, spam and spam". The term spam also refers to posting irrelevant messages to large numbers of newsgroups.

There does not seem to be any really effective remedy although most more responsible Internet Service Providers cancel the accounts of persistent offenders. As anybody reading these notes will have realised it is easy to forge *all* the headers to an e-mail message and many spammers do just that so that a simple reply is destined for a non-existent host and will just clutter the mail spool of the local mail host.

It is also unwise to reply to those messages saying a reply will ensure that you won't receive any more e-mail from this source. These just ensure that your e-mail address is added to one of the commercial lists.

Mail Bombing

This refers to the practice of sending large numbers of large e-mail messages to a particular individual or organisation in an attempt to overwhelm their mail handling facilities.

Telnet

The telnet protocol enables terminals and terminal-oriented processes to communicate on a network running TCP/IP. It is implemented as the program telnet on the local machine and the daemon telnetd on the remote machine. telnet provides a user interface through which two hosts can open communications with each other, then send information on a character-by-character or line-by-line basis. The application includes a series of commands, which are documented on the telnet(1tcp) manual page. The telnetd daemon on the remote host handles requests from the telnet command. For more information about telnetd, see the telnetd(1Mtcp) manual page.

RFC 2046-Multimedia Internet Mail Extensions (MIME)

The basic message format defined in RFC 822 does not allow messages to include anything other than normal printing ASCII characters. This protocol defines a standard method for encoding data in other formats such as graphical images, binary files, word processed documents etc.

The transfer of an e-mail from a local user to a remote user will typically involve the following steps assuming both users are using personal computers with dial-up Internet connections.

Local User Set Up

The local user starts his MUA program ensuring that it is configured with the Internet address of a host running an SMTP server MTA. Theoretically he could use any MTA anywhere on the Internet, however, mail server administrators normally configure MTAs so they will only accept such requests from or for users in the same domain as the server. See notes on open relaying.

Local User Sends E-mail

The local user composes the e-mail message possibly attaching files and then tells the MUA to send the e-mail to the MTA using SMTP. He may, of course, have prepared several items of mail "off-line" and send them all once a connection is established with the MTA. The MUA automatically includes the required headers in the e-mail message based on information supplied by the user either as part of the MUA configuration or entered interactively during mail composition.

E-mail Transmission

The MTA analyses the headers of the incoming message to identify the destination mail server. The MTA then attempts to communicate with the destination mail server and transfers the message using SMTP. If the message cannot be transferred it is queued in the mail spool for further attempts.

It is common that a single mail server host provides services for a large group of machines. The Internet DNS mechanism provides the facility for identifying a mail exchanger or MX host for a DNS domain so that e-mail can, apparently, be sent to a domain (such as wlv.ac.uk) rather than a specific host within that domain.

E-mail Receipt

The destination mail server examines the incoming message to identify the local part of the address from the headers. This may be a nick-name (or alias) for an actual user, group of users or even a file or a program input. The server will usually store the incoming e-mail in the mail spool.

Remote User Receives E-mail

The remote user starts his MUA program ensuring that it is configured with the Internet address of a host running a POP server MTA. This may well be the same host as he uses for outgoing e-mail although this is not essential. He establishes his bona-fides to the POP server by quoting a user identification code and password and the POP server examines the mail spool and responds with details of the number of incoming e-mail messages. The user can then instruct his MUA to transfer or copy the e-mail messages to his personal computer.

If the destination mail server host is a general purpose computer into which users may login, there is no need for the use of POP, user programs can directly manipulate the mail spool. This used to be standard practice and is still widely used.

E-mail Design-E-mail Addresses

Each internet domain has an associated e-mail server that manages all addresses at that domain. Each e-mail address is expressed in the form "name@domain", and is unique at that domain.

The key to this elegant architecture is its simple structure—each domain has an associated e-mail server (or logical group of servers) that maintains the accounts for all users with addresses at that domain. Therefore, any e-mail server can use the Internet's standard domain name service to find the IP address of any other e-mail server, connect to that server, and transfer e-mail to recipients at that domain using the standard SMTP protocol.

Usually your best course is to include the entire domain specification exactly as received whenever replying to a user with a multi-level address. However, if that doesn't work, then you can try dropping the left-most levels and send the e-mail to the second-level domain, as in jack@twenty.net, which sometimes lets the top-level server figure out the correct address from there.

E-mail Design–Servers

E-mail servers exchange e-mail with the SMTP protocol. Each Internet domain has a corresponding e-mail server. When you send an e-mail to someone, your e-mail client first sends it to your e-mail server, which then contacts the addressee's e-mail server and carries out conversation according to the rules defined by the Simple Mail Transfer Protocol (SMTP). Your server asks the other server if the user name is valid, and, if it is, transfers the e-mail, where the receiving server stores it until the addressee logs on and downloads it.

By far the most common SMTP server in use is the venerable sendmail system, first distributed for free with the Unix operating system.

The list of commands that can be exchanged during an SMTP session between two e-mail servers are listed below. The first command of an SMTP conversation must be the HELO command. A mail transaction is begun with the MAIL command. The last command in a session must be the QUIT command.

E-mail Design–Clients

Your e-mail client communicates with a server to login, get mail status, and send and receive e-mail. The most common client connection protocols are described in the following sections:

- Post Office Protocol 3
- Internet Message Application Protocol
- Messaging Application Programming Interface.

E-mail Clients—Post Office Protocol 3

POP3 has become the most common e-mail client connection protocol. Your e-mail client talks to your e-mail server to send it commands to login, get mail status, and send and receive e-mail. The most common protocol used by e-mail clients to communicate with e-mail servers is the post office protocol first defined in RFC 918, with version 2 published as RFC 937, and POP Version 3 published as RFC 1725.

The POP3 protocol enables any e-mail program anywhere on the Internet to connect to any e-mail server to perform the usual e-mail functions, such as reading and sending, as long as they have a valid account and password.

POP3 is an open Internet standard. The common POP3 commands and responses are listed in the following table:

Table 30.11 The Common POP3 Commands and Responses

Command	*Responses*
getwelcome ()	Gets the greeting from the server.
user (username)	Login with a username. If valid username, server will respond with request for password.
pass_(password)	Send password. If valid, server response will be two numbers, message count and mailbox size.
stat ()	Get the mailbox status. Response is two numbers, message count and mailbox size.
list([message])	Get list of messages. An option "message" gets information on a specific message.
retr (message)	Get message number "message".
dele (message)	Delete message number "message".
rset ()	Remove all deleted message markings.
noop ()	No operation. Do nothing. Really. Needed in unusual programming situations.
quit ()	Quit. Commits call changes, unlocks the mailbox, and ends the server connection.
top (message, lines)	Gets just the first "lines" number of lines of message number "message". Useful on low bandwidth lines to get just the first part of long messages.
uidl ([message])	Gets a unique id list—a message digest including unique ids. The option gets the unique id for the specific message "message".

You can telnet into your e-mail provider on port 110 and exchange POP3 commands with your server just as though you were an e-mail application.

Resources. The following resources provide more information about POP3:

- Google—POP3 Directory
- Yahoo—POP3 Directory
- Santovec, Michael—Using Telnet with a POP3 Mail Server.

E-mail Clients–Internet Message Access Protocol

The Internet Message Access Protocol (IMAP) is a more modern protocol than POP3, first developed at Stanford University in 1986. The current version is IMAP4, providing similar services to the POP3 protocol, but with additional features such as the ability to keep your e-mail on the server after downloading a copy to read locally.

The IMAP features can be useful in several situations, for example when you are traveling and don't want to download your e-mail onto a laptop, because then you won't have them on your home computer. It can also be useful for use on low-bandwidth devices like personal digital assistants, enabling you to select a few e-mail from a list of subject headers before downloading just the ones you want.

The Messaging Application Programming Interface (MAPI) is a standardized set of C functions originally developed by microsoft and supported by many third party vendors for Windows platforms.

REVIEW QUESTIONS

1. Which network was the foundation for the internet ?
2. What type of switching is used by ARPANET ?
3. What is the internet ?
4. What is the name of the group that oversees the internet ? What subgroups are under that group and what are their responsibilities ?
5. Define datagram.
6. What is the main advantage and disadvantage of using data-grams ?
7. Which suite of protocols are used to handle internet traffic ?
8. Which protocol was added to handle news and mail servers on the ARPANET network ?
9. What is the name of the first internet graphical browser ?
10. Name four basic applications the internet is used for.
11. List four search engines and note what each one searches for.
12. List the causes for undeliverable e-mail messages.
13. Name two e-mail protocols and one e-mail specification.
14. Which portion of the X.400 specification addresses service authorization ?
15. Which X.400 portion applies to routing messages to dissimilar mail systems ?
16. What is the purpose of X.500 ?
17. What is the purpose of newsgroups ?
18. Which protocol is used for downloading files from the internet ?
19. What is the first page of a web site called ?
20. What function does a hyper-link perform ?
21. What term applies to the most frequently asked questions about the internet ?
22. What is the formal term for an internet address ?
23. Which protocol translates internet addresses associated with web sites ?
24. What are the main sections of the user internet address ?
25. What is meant by a domain top in an internet address ?
26. What does a domain top identify ? Give four examples of a domain top ?
27. Give a purpose for a sub-network masked address.
28. How do the three classes of internet addresses differ ?

29. How are internet broadcast messages identified ?
30. What is the purpose of an IP multicast ? How does an IP router reduce multicast traffic ?
31. Which protocol defines multicast-type packets ?
32. Name the two basic methods for securing internet messages.
33. What is the difference between a primary server and a secondary server ?
34. What are the three domains of the domain name space ?
35. What is the purpose of the inverse domain ?
36. How does caching increase the efficiency of name resolution ?
37. What are the two main categories of DNS messages ?
38. What is the name of the protocol used for electronic mail over the internet ?
39. What are the two main parts of an e-mail ?
40. Describe the addressing system used by SMTP.
41. What is a user agent ?
42. What are the two types of user agents ?
43. What is MIME ?
44. What are the three mail transfer phases ?
45. Name two mail access protocols.
46. What is the purpose of FTP ?
47. Describe the functions of the two FTP connections.
48. What kinds of file types can FTP transfer ?
49. What are the three FTP transmission modes ?
50. How does storing a file differ from retrieving a file ?
51. What is anonymous FTP ?
52. How is HTTP relates to WWW ?
53. How is HTTP similar to SMTP ?
54. How is HTTP similar to FTP ?
55. What is a URL and what are its components ?
56. What is a proxy server and how is it related to HTTP ?
57. What is a homepage ?
58. Name the common three components of a browser.
59. What are the three types of web documents ?
60. What does HTML stand for and what is its function ?
61. What is the difference between an active document and a dynamic document ?
62. What is a VPN and why is it needed ?
63. What is the name of the protocol that provides security for e-mail ?
64. What is DNS ? Explain the function of DNS and different sections of the DNS. *(IV-BCA (4.1)-DCCN)*
65. Explain the components of the SNMP management model. *(IV-BCA (4.1)-DCCN)*

❑❑❑

APPENDIX A

IEEE ETHERNET STANDARDS

Here is the Listing of some IEEE Standards:

1. IEEE 802.1.
2. 802.1D (1993) MAC Layer Bridges(ISO 10038).
3. 802.1p Quality of Service and Multicast support.
4. 802.1Q VLAN processing.
5. 802.1G Remote Bridges.

List of most useful Supplements to the IEEE 802 Standards:

1. 802.3 (1985) Base Standard (10B5).
2. 802.3a (1992) 10B2 Ethernet over thin coaxial cable.
3. 802.3b (1985) Broadband Ethernet (using coaxial TV cable, now seldom used).
4. 802.3c (1985) Improved definition of a Repeater 802.3d (1987) Definition of Ethernet for Fiber (10BFOIRL) (now seldom used).
5. 802.3e (1987) 1Base5 or StarLAN (now seldom used).
6. 802.3h (1991) Layer Management.
7. 802.3i (1990) 10BaseT, Ethernet over CAT-5 Unshielded Twisted Pair(UTP).
8. 802.3j (1993) defines Ethernet over Fiber (10BF).
9. 802.3p/q (1993) Definition of managed objects.
10. 802.3u (1995) Definition of Fast Ethernet (100BTX, 100BT4, 100BFX).
11. 802.3x (1998) Definition of Full Duplex operation in a switched LAN.
12. 802.3y (1998) Definition of Fast Ethernet (100BT2 over low quality UTP).
13. 802.3z Definition of Gigabit Ethernet (over Fiber).
14. 802.3aa Definition of Gigabit Ethernet Maintenance.
15. 802.3ab Definition of Gigabit Ethernet (over UTP CAT-5).
16. 802.3ac Definition of Ethernet VLANs.
17. 802.3ad Definition of Ethernet VLAN Trunking.

Appendix B

ASCII-AMERICAN STANDARD CODE FOR INFORMATION INTERCHANGE

ASCII is the most popular code and is used by the majority of the computing world. ASCII itself is a 7 bit code which allows only 128 characters (27). Most applications follow IBM's Extended ASCII code which uses 8 bits and allows an addition 128 graphic characters for a total of 256 characters (28). We will be concentrating on 7 bit ASCII codes.

Format Effectors

Format effectors control the movement of the cursor on the screen and the print head in a printer. The format effectors are:

BS Backspace
HT Horizontal Tab
LF Line Feed
CR Carriage Return
FF Form Feed
VT Vertical Tab

Communication Controls

Communication controls are used in controlling data transmission over a communication network. They are used in both Asynchronous and Synchronous Transmissions. They are used in "handshaking".

STX Start of Text
ETX End of Text
EOT End of Transmission
ENQ End of Inquiry
ACK Acknowledge
NAK Negative Acknowledge
EXT Interrupt
SYN Synchronous idle
ETB End of Block
EOF End of File

Information Separators

Information separators are used to separate database enquiries and files:

FS File Separator (in a PC - used as cursor R, L, U, D)
GS Group Separator
RS Record Separator
US Unit Separator

Additional Control Codes

Of the remaining codes used by the computer, the most important ones are:

NUL Nothing character
BEL Rings the bell!
DC1 - 4 Device Control 1 - 4
ESC Escape - used for formatting printers & terminals
DEL Delete - deletes characters under cursor

DC1 & DC2 are used in the Xon/Xoff software handshaking to control data transfer.

Displaying ASCII Codes Directly to the Screen

You can type in the ASCII codes directly to the screen on IBM capatible computers. You press the "ALT" key and a 3 digit number on the numeric keypad. The 3 digit number is the ASCII decimal code for the character. You must use the numeric keypad, the QWERTY numbers will NOT work.

For example, the character "A" corresponds to the ASCII decimal code 65. To access the ASCII code directly, hold down the ALT key and type in 065 on the numeric keypad. On releasing the ALT key, the letter A will appear on the screen.

Table B.1 shows the ASCII codes according to decimal numbers and hexadecimal numbers. If a network sniffer or analyzer is used, it will show raw data in decimal or hexadecimal formats. You may have to perform a manual translation using table B.1.

Table B.1 ASCII Code

Dec	*Hex*	*Name*	*Dec*	*Hex*	*Name*	*Dec*	*Hex*	*Name*	*Dec*	*Hex*	*Name*
0	0	NUL	32	20	Space	64	40	@	96	60	‘
1	1	SOH	33	21	!	65	41	A	97	61	a
2	2	STX	34	22	"	66	42	B	98	62	b
3	3	ETX	35	23	#	67	43	C	99	63	c
4	4	EOT	36	24	$	68	44	D	100	64	d
5	5	ENQ	37	25	%	69	45	E	101	65	e
6	6	ACK	38	26	&	70	46	F	102	66	f

7	7	BEL	39	27	¢	71	47	G	103	67	g
8	8	BS	40	28	(	72	48	H	104	68	h
9	9	HT	41	29	)	73	49	I	105	69	i
10	A	LF	42	2A	*	74	4A	J	106	6A	j
11	B	VT	43	2B	+	75	4B	K	107	6B	k
12	C	FF	44	2C	,	76	4C	L	108	6C	l
13	D	CR	45	2D	-	77	4D	M	109	6D	m
14	E	S0	46	2E	.	78	4E	N	110	6E	n
15	F	S1	47	2F	/	79	4F	O	111	6F	o
16	10	DLE	48	30	0	80	50	P	112	70	p
17	11	DC1	49	31	1	81	51	Q	113	71	q
18	12	DC2	50	32	2	82	52	R	114	72	r
19	13	DC3	51	33	3	83	53	S	115	73	s
20	14	DC4	52	34	4	84	54	T	116	74	t
21	15	NAK	53	35	5	85	55	U	117	75	u
22	16	SYN	54	36	6	86	56	V	118	76	v
23	17	ETB	55	37	7	87	57	W	119	77	w
24	18	CAN	56	38	8	88	58	X	120	78	x
25	19	EM	57	39	9	89	59	Y	121	79	y
26	1A	SUB	58	3A	:	90	5A	Z	122	7A	z
27	1B	ESC	59	3B	;	91	5B	[	123	7B	{
28	1C	FS	60	3C	<	92	5C	\	124	7C	|
29	1D	GS	61	3D	=	93	5D	]	125	7D	}
30	1E	RS	62	3E	>	94	5E	^	126	7E	~
31	1F	US	63	3F	?	95	5F	_	127	7F	DEL

APPENDIX C

BRIEF HISTORY OF NETWORKING

The following is a brief history of computers, networking and telecommunication milestones:

1. CRT (Cathode Ray Tube) credited to Braun in 1897
2. Teletype (telegraph 5 bit) during WW1
3. ARQ (Automatic Repeat reQuest) credited to Van Duuren during WWII
   - error checking and auto request for retransmission
4. ENIAC credited to DOD / MIT during WWII
   - Electronic Numerical Integrator And Calculator
   - Used for decoding enemy messages
   - 1st generation computer: used vacuum tubes
   - Programmed with jumpers and switches
   - MTBF (Mean Time Between Failure): 7 minutes
   - 337 multiplications per second
5. SAGE (Semi-Automatic Ground Environment) MIT 1950s
   - 23 centres for ground/air enemy detection systems
   - error checking, keyboard & CRT terminals
   - duplexed computers, voice grade (300-4KHz)
   - 300 baud, light pens, multi-user system
   - magnetic core memory
   - Ground to air data Tx
   - 1st commercial use was Sabre Reservation System
6. Jacquard's Loom
   - First programmable machine
7. Transistorized Computers - 2nd Generation 1960s
   - One of the 1st inventors: Cray
   - Batch programming: 1 pgm @ a time
   - Punch cards
   - Stored programs: held in memory
   - 50K instructions/second
   - ex. IBM 7905

8. CTSS (Compatible Time Sharing System) credited to Cobato/MIT in 1961
   - time slices multi-users
9. Synchronous Orbit Communication Satellites. Idea by Arthur C. Clarke in 1945
   - Geo-stationary orbit around equator by Rose/Hughes Aerospace in1963
   - 36,000 miles altitude
10. LASER credited to Maiman in 1960
    - A narrow band source of optical radiation suitable for use as a carrier of info.
    - Light Amplification by Stimulated Emission of Radiation
11. T-1 Carrier System credited to Bell Labs in 1961
    - TDM (Time Domain Multiplexing)
    - 24 channels = 64 Kbps ea.
    - 1.544 Mbps (mega bits per sec)
12. RS232 developed in 1960 and revised since.
    - Standard plug and "protocol" convention between modems and machines: 25 pin
    - Europe uses V.24 compatible standard
13. Auto Equalization Techniques of Phone lines credited to Lucky et al. in 1965
    - adapt to characteristics of telephone line to increase speed
14. Fibre Glass credited to Kao & Hockman in 1966
    - proposed "fibre glass " optics developed at Standard Telecom Labs
15. Integrated Circuits Computers - 3rd Generation - 1967
    - SSI/MSI (Small Scale Integration/Medium Scale Integration)
    - 10 transistors/chip and 100 transistors/chip
    - Multi-user systems
    - Multitasking
16. Carterfone—FCC Decision in 1968
    - FCC decision allows other manufacturer's to use phone lines
    - opens up competition among phone systems
17. Low-loss Fibre credited to Kapron in 1970
    - speeds: 45-90 Mbps developed at Corning Glass Works
    - 1984: attained 405-565 Mbps in single mode
    - Early 1990s: attained 1.7 Gbps
18. ARPA Network (ARPANET) developed by the DOD in the 1970s
    - Advanced Research Projects Agency of the Department of Defence - US
    - 1st use of Packet Switching, layered protocols
    - Beginning of the Internet
19. VLSI Integration - 4th Generation Computers developed by Intel in 1971
    - Very large scale integration: 20,000+ transistors/chip

- Intel 4004 microprocessor - 4 bit
- Grandparent of processors today

20. Layered Network Architecture
    - SNA: System Network Architecture IBM Mainframe
    - DNA: Digital Network Architecture DEC for DECNET
21. Ethernet developed by Xerox in 1974
    - Ether is the mysterious invisible fluid that transfers heat
    - Originally based on the ALOHA radio protocol
22. Videotex developed by Teletel (France) in the 1980s
    - Interactive video Minitel
23. Reference Model for Open Systems Interconnect developed by the ISO in 1983
    - Continuously evolving model for layering network protocols
24. AT&T Divestiture in 1984
    - Break-up of AT&T monopoly into Baby Bells
25. ISDN developed in 1984
    - Integrated Services Digital Network
    - Strong in Europe
    - A network evolving from a telephony integrated digital network supporting: voice, teletex, videotex, fax, slowscan video, etc.
26. Linux Version 0.01 released Sept 17, 1991

APPENDIX D

STANDARD DIGITAL CODES

Computers process information in digital form. Characters are assigned a 7 or 8 bit code to indicate which character it is. This 7 or 8 bit code becomes a number (usually hexadecimal) that the computer can work with. The characters stored in a computer include:

Lower case letters	:	a - z
Upper case letters	:	.A - Z
Digits	:	0 - 9
Punctuation Marks	:	. , ;: ! ? etc...
Unit Symbols	:	# $ % & * etc...
Control Codes	:	EOF, etc..

There are 2 major codes existing today: ASCII (pronounced ah-skee) and EBCDIC (pronounced eb-ce-dic).

APPENDIX E

EBCDIC-EXTENDED BINARY CODED DECIMAL INTERCHANGE CODE

EBCDIC is used mainly by IBM mainframes and compatibles. It is not common in the PC LAN world unless you are connecting to the IBM mainframe world. In order to connect, you would require either an IBM 3270 terminal emulation program or a device called a gateway.

Table E.1 shows the EBCDIC translation table. Computers speak in binary code which is 1s and 0s. The computers do not know what the letter "A" is. Instead they speak of the letter "A" as the binary number 1100 0001. It is not easy for humans to remember binary numbers such as 1100 0001 but it is easier to remember the hexadecimal number C1. The hexadecimal number C1 is equal to the binary number 1100 0001.

The hexadecimal number C1 is equal to the decimal number 193. The table shows both the decimal (dec) number and the hexadecimal (hex) number for the capital letter "A". Lower case "A" is represented by the EBCDIC decimal code 129 or hexadecimal code 81.

Besides character codes such as the previous letter "A", the EBCDIC code also defines control characters. These are characters that have special meaning. For example, the control character FF stands for Form Feed and is used by printers to advance one page or to eject a page. The decimal code for FF is 12 and the hexadecimal code is C.

Both hexadecimal and decimal codes are indicated because many times, a program or interface will report the EBCDIC code in one or the other formats. You may have to use Table to translate from the numerical code to the actual character.

Note: Some EBCDIC codes are not defined and have no name.

Table E.1 EBCDIC Code

Dec	*Hex*	*Name*	*Dec*	*Hex*	*Name*	*Dec*	*Hex*	*Name*	*Dec*	*Hex*	*Name*
0	0	NUL	32	20	DS	64	40	RSP	96	60	-
1	1	SOH	33	21	SOS	65	41		97	61	/
2	2	STX	34	22	FS	66	42		98	62	
3	3	ETX	35	23	WUS	67	43		99	63	
4	4	SEL	36	24	BYP	68	44		100	64	
5	5	HT	37	25	LF	69	45		101	65	

6	6	RNL	38	26	ETB	70	46		102	66	
7	7	DEL	39	27	ESC	71	47		103	67	
8	8	GE	40	28	SA	72	48		104	68	
9	9	SPS	41	29	SFE	73	49		105	69	
10	A	RPT	42	2A	SM	74	4A	¢	106	6A	|
11	B	VT	43	2B	CSP	75	4B	.	107	6B	,
12	C	FF	44	2C	MFA	76	4C	<	108	6C	%
13	D	CR	45	2D	ENQ	77	4D	(	109	6D	-
14	E	SO	46	2E	ACK	78	4E	+	110	6E	>
15	F	SI	47	2F	BEL	79	4F	ê	111	6F	?
16	10	DLE	48	30		80	50	&	112	70	
17	11	DC1	49	31		81	51		113	71	
18	12	DC2	50	32	SYN	82	52		114	72	
19	13	DC3	51	33	IR	83	53		115	73	
20	14	RES	52	34	PP	84	54		116	74	
21	15	NL	53	35	TRN	85	55		117	75	
22	16	BS	54	36	NBS	86	56		118	76	
23	17	POC	55	37	EOT	87	57		119	77	
24	18	CAN	56	38	SBS	88	58		120	78	
25	19	EM	57	39	IT	89	59		121	79	‘
26	1A	UBS	58	3A	RFF	90	5A	!	122	7A	:
27	1B	CU1	59	3B	CU3	91	5B	$	123	7B	#
28	1C	IFS	60	3C	NAK	92	5C	*	124	7C	@
29	1D	IGS	61	3D		93	5D	)	125	7D	‘
30	1E	IRS	62	3E	SUB	94	5E	;	126	7E	=
31	1F	IUS	63	3F	SP	95	5F	ù	127	7F	“
128	80		160	A0		192	C0	{	224	E0	\
129	81	a	161	A1	~	193	C1	A	225	E1	NSP
130	82	b	162	A2	s	194	C2	B	226	E2	S

131	83	c	163	A3	t	195	C3	C	227	E3	T
132	84	d	164	A4	u	196	C4	D	228	E4	U
133	85	e	165	A5	v	197	C5	E	229	E5	V
134	86	f	166	A6	w	198	C6	F	230	E6	W
135	87	g	167	A7	x	199	C7	G	231	E7	X
136	88	h	168	A8	y	200	C8	H	232	E8	Y
137	89	i	169	A9	z	201	C9	I	233	E9	Z
138	8A		170	AA		202	CA	SHY	234	EA	
139	8B		171	AB		203	CB		235	EB	
140	8C		172	AC		204	CC		236	EC	
141	8D		173	AD		205	CD		237	ED	
142	8E		174	AE		206	CE		238	EE	
143	8F		175	AF		207	CF		239	EF	
144	90		176	B0		208	D0	}	240	F0	0
145	91	j	177	B1		209	D1	J	241	F1	1
146	92	k	178	B2		210	D2	K	242	F2	2
147	93	l	179	B3		211	D3	L	243	F3	3
148	94	m	180	B4		212	D4	M	244	F4	4
149	95	n	181	B5		213	D5	N	245	F5	5
150	96	o	182	B6		214	D6	O	246	F6	6
151	97	p	183	B7		215	D7	P	247	F7	7
152	98	q	184	B8		216	D8	Q	248	F8	8
153	99	r	185	B9		217	D9	R	249	F9	9
154	9A		186	BA		218	DA		250	FA	
155	9B		187	BB		219	DB		251	FB	
156	9C		188	BC		220	DC		252	FC	
157	9D		189	BD		221	DD		253	FD	
158	9E		190	BE		222	DE		254	FE	
159	9F		191	BF		223	DF		255	FF	EO

NETWORK TERMINOLOGY

Access Point—AP

An Access Point (AP) is a specially configured node on a Wireless Local Area Network (WLAN). Access points act as a central transmitter and receiver of WLAN radio signals.

APs used in home or small business networks are generally small, dedicated hardware devices featuring a built-in network adapter, antenna, radio transmitter, and adapter.

A network adapter interfaces a computer to a network. The term "adapter" was popularized originally by Ethernet add-in cards for PCs. Nowadays, network adapters refer in a broader sense to include PCMCIA devices (also know as credit card or PC card adapters) and analogous wireless devices.

Address

A network address serves as a unique identifier for a computer on a network. Computers can determine the addresses of other computers on the network and use these addresses to send messages to each other. One of the best known form of network addressing is the Internet Protocol (IP) address. IP addresses consist of four bytes (32 bits) that uniquely identify all computers on the public Internet. Another popular form of address is the Media Access Control or MAC address. MAC addresses are six bytes (48 bits) that manufacturers of network adapters burn into their products to uniquely identify them. Also Known As: Network Address.

ARP

ARP converts an IP address to its corresponding physical network address. It is a low-level protocol (at layer 2 in the OSI model) usually implemented in the device drivers of network operating systems. ARP is most commonly seen on Ethernet networks, but ARP has also been implemented for ATM, Token Ring, and other physical networks. The first RFC discussing ARP (for Ethernet) was RFC 826.

Ethernet network adapters are produced with a physical address (called the Media Access Control or MAC address) embedded in the hardware. Manufacturers take care to ensure these 6-byte addresses are unique, and Ethernet relies on these unique identifiers for frame delivery. When an IP packet arrives at a network gateway, the gateway needs to convert the destination IP address to the appropriate MAC address so that it can be delivered over Ethernet. Some IP-to-MAC address mappings are maintained in an ARP cache, but if the given IP address does not appear there, the gateway will send an ARP request that is broadcast on the local subnet. The host with the given IP address sends an ARP reply to the gateway, who in turn delivers the packet (and updates its cache). Also Known As: Address Resolution Protocol.

ATM

ATM is a high-speed networking standard designed to support both voice and data communications. ATM can support speeds ATM operates at the data link layer over either fiber or twisted-pair cable.

ATM differs from more common data link technologies like Ethernet in several ways. ATM does not involve routing for example. Hardware devices known as ATM switches establish point-to-point connections between endpoints and data flows directly from source to destination. Instead of using variable-length packets, ATM utilizes fixed-sized cells. ATM cells are 53 bytes in length, that includes 48 bytes of data and 5 bytes of header information.

The performance of ATM is often expressed in the form of OC (Optical Carrier) levels, written as "OC-xxx." Performance levels as high as 10 Gbps (OC-192) are technically feasible with ATM. More common performance levels for ATM are 155 Mbps (OC-3) and 622 Mbps (OC-2).

ATM is designed to support easier bandwidth management. Without routing and with fixed-size cells, one can much more easily monitor and control bandwidth under ATM than under Ethernet, for example. The high cost of ATM relative to Ethernet is one factor that has limited its adoption to "backbone" and other high-performance applications.

Examples: Also Known As: Asynchronous Transfer Mode.

Address

A character or sequence of characters designating the terminal equipment which is the origin or destination of data being transmitted. Alternate routing A method for varying the route of the traffic in a network in The event of circuit failure or to optimise loading and use of channels.

ANSI

The American National Standards Institute is the national clearing house and coordinating organisation for voluntary. Standards in the USA. ANSI does not directly develop standards hut accredits other groups to do so.

Application layer, Top layer of the OSI reference model.

This name is misleading since the ultimate application processes do not reside in this layer. The application layer provide services to applications and a window for applications to gain access to the OSI environment.

ASCII

Pronounced "asky". The American Standard Code for Information Interchange. The US version of the ISO 7-bit data code usually transmitted in bit characters, the additional bit often being an (odd or even) parity bit.

Asynchronous

A communications channel capable of transmitting data hut not timing is called "asynchronous" strictly speaking, the correct terminology is "asynchronous".

Asynchronous Transfer Mode ATM

The term Asynchronous Transfer Mode (ATM) strictly speaking refers to a generic mode of data transfer in which units of data arc not time related to each other. ATM has now he come closely identified with a fast packet switching technology called "cell relay" in which information is handled in fixed length cells of 53 octets.

Bandwidth

Bandwidth in computer networking refers to the data rate supported by a network connection or interface. One most commonly expresses bandwidth in terms of bytes per second (bps). The term comes from the field of electrical engineering, where bandwidth represents the total distance or range between the highest and lowest signals on the communication channel (band).

Bandwidth represents the capacity of the connection. The greater the capacity, the more likely that greater performance will follow, though overall performance also depends on other factors, such as latency.

Examples: A V.90 modem supports a maximum theoretical bandwidth of 56 Kbps. Fast Ethernet supports a theoretical maximum bandwidth of 100 Mbps.

Also Known As: Throughput.

Baud

A baud is a unit of measure for analog signaling. At a minimum, one baud corresponds to one bit per second (bps) although at higher signaling speeds, multiple bits can be transfered in a single baud. The term baud was popular in the early days of modems, but it is no longer relevant in mainstream computer networking terminology.

Bit

A bit is the smallest unit of data transfer on a computer network. Bits represent the two binary values "on" or "off". Bits are often stored on computers as the digital numbers '1' and '0', but in networking, bits can also be "encoded" by electrical signals and pulses of light. In computer networking, some network protocols send and receive data in the form of bit sequences.

Bluetooth

Bluetooth is a specification for using low-power radio to link phones and computers over short distances without wires. The name is borrowed from Harald Bluetooth, who was a king in Denmark more than 1,000 years ago.

Bluetooth networks use a dynamic topology called a piconet or PAN. Piconets contain a minimum of two and a maximum of eight Bluctooth peer devices.

Bluetooth technology uses low power and signals over a relatively short distance, typically no more than 30 feet (10 meters). Bluetooth devices generally communicate at less than 1 Mbps. The Bluetooth specification, developed by an industry consortium, uses radio signalling in the 2.4 Ghz range, the same range used by 802.11b.

As is true for many wireless technologies today, concerns with Bluetooth include security and interoperability with other standards. Practical adoption of the technology has not yet lived up to the initial industry hype around Bluetooth.

bps/Bps

Network performance has traditionally been measured in units of bits per second (bps). Not too many years ago, dialup network connections routinely performed at 9600 bps. As networks have greatly improved in performance, rates are now specified in Kbps (thousands of bps) or Mbps (millions of bps). Bps (with uppercase 'B') represents bytes per second.

Bridge—network bridges

A bridge device filters data traffic at a network boundary. Bridges reduce the amount of traffic on a LAN by dividing it into two segments. Bridges operate at the data link layer (Layer 2) of the OSI model. Bridges inspect incoming traffic and decide whether to forward or discard it.

Broadband

The term broadband refers to any type of transmission technique that carries several data channels over a common wire. DSL services, for example, combine separate voice and data channels over a single telephone line – voice fills the low end of the frequency spectrum and data fills the high end.

Examples: Both cable TV and DSL service rely on broadband transmission techniques.

Related Resources: Introduction to DSL.

Byte (In Computer Networking)

A byte is a sequence of bits. In computer networking, some network protocols send and receive data in the form of byte sequences. These are called byte-oriented protocols. Examples of byte-oriented protocols include TCP/IP and telnet.

The order in which bytes are sequenced in a byte-oriented network protocol is called the network byte order.

Bit

Binary digit which can be in a state of either "0" or "1".

Broadband

Broadband is a term applied to coaxial cable LAN systems which employ multiple radio frequency channels Nowadays, broadband is being used to describe the generation of high speed digit services beyond the currently planned ISDN.

Byte (In Computer Technology)

A digital unit of information comprising eight binary digits (bits). In computer technology usually used to encode an alphanumeric character.

Cable Modem

A cable modem connects a home computer (or network of home computers) to residential cable TV service. Like the television "set top" box, cable modems are usually supplied by the service provider and not a piece of equipment individuals need to shop for on their own.

Most cable modems supply a 10 Mbps Ethernet connection for the home LAN, although cable modem service rarely if ever performs at those speeds. The performance of a cable modem Internet connection can vary depending on the utilization of the shared cable line in that neighborhood, but typical data rates range from 300 Kbps to 1500 Kbps. Also Known As: Broadband Modem.

CGI

Common Gateway Interface. CGI usually means the program that is run on the server to add dynamic actions to the Web site.

Cluster

The word "cluster" is used broadly in computer networking to refer to a number of different implementations of shared computing resources. Typically, a cluster integrates the resources of two or more computing devices (that could otherwise function separately) together for some common purpose.

A Web server farm (a collection of networked Web servers, each with access to content on the same site) function as a cluster conceptually. However, purists may debate the classification of a server farm as a cluster, depending on the details of the hardware and software configuration. It is important to recognize that network clustering involves a long past history of research and development with many ofshoots and variations.

Crash

The term "crash" refers to a critical failure in a computer, network device, or software running on these (such as a network operating system or application). Crashes often occur with little or no warning. As evidenced by the number of different synonyms employed over the years, crashes have a long and colorful history in computer networking.

A crash can manifest itself in many different ways. The computer may "freeze" or "hang" indefinitely when a crash occurs, or it may display any number of obscure error messages. In Windows operating systems, a crash usually causes the infamous "blue screen of death" to appear. To recover from a crash, often a person must power down and restart their computer (as in the case of blue screens) or their network device(s).

Also Known As: crash and burn, fatal error, bomb, blow-up, core dump, blue screen of death (BSOD), ABEND.

CCITT

The International Telegraph and Telephone Consultative Committee, which is part of the International Telecommunications Union, an agency of the United Nations. The principal members of CCITT are the world's public communication authorities (TOs).

CEN/CENELEC

CEN (comite europeen de normalisation) and CENELEC (Comite european de normalisation electrotechnique) are the two official European standards organisations responsible for standardisation in the field of information technology. CEN and CENELEC are effectively the European subsets of the members of ISO and the International Electro Technical Committee (ISO) respectively.

CEPT

The European Conference of Posts and Telecommunication Administrations CEPT is an association of European PTTs (Postal Telephone and Telegraph Administrations) and network operators from 18 countries.

Circuit-Switching

A type of network whereby a circuit is established and maintained between the communicating parties for the duration of the "call".

Codec Short for Coder-Decoder

A device for digitising analogue voice or video signals Connectionless service. In a connectionless service, no circuit is set up between sender and recipient. Every unit of data that is exchanged is totally self contained and contains within it all of the necessary control information (*e.g.*, addresses of destination and sender) to ensure correct delivery.

Connection-Oriented Service

In a connection-oriented service, a dedicated circuit (real or virtual) is set up between two points and maintained for as long as the connection is required. A connection-oriented service has three phases; establishment, data transfer, release.

CSMA/CD Carrier Sense Multiple Access/Collision Detection

One of the major classes of media access technology, used in LANs, particularly Ethernet. It is specified in 0SI Standard ISO 8802/3, based upon the work of IEEE committee 802.3.

Data link layer, Second layer of the OSI Reference Model.

The second layer of the OSI reference model at which blocks of data are reliably transmitted over a transmission link.

Dialup

The term dialup relates to network client access to a LAN or WAN via telephone lines. Types of dialup include V.34 and V.90 modem dialup as well as Integrated Services Digital Network (ISDN). Dialup uses special-purpose network protocols like Point-to-Point Protocol (PPP). As the popularity of the Internet exploded in the 1990s, dialup remained the most common form of Internet access due mainly to its low cost. However, the performance of dialup networking is relatively poor due to the limitations of traditional modem technology. V.90 modem dialup handles less than 56 Kbps bandwidth and ISDN handles approximately 128 Kbps. In the future, dialup access to the Internet will gradually be phased out in favor of relatively faster and more modern broadband technology.

DNS

The DNS translates Internet domain and host names to IP addresses. DNS implements a distributed database to store name and address information for all public hosts on the Net. DNS assumes IP addresses do not change (*i.e.*, are statically assigned rather than dynamically assigned). The DNS database resides on a hierarchy of special-purpose servers. When visiting a Web site or other device on the Net, a piece of software called the DNS resolver (usually built into the network operating system) first contacts a DNS server to determine the server's IP address. If the DNS server does not contain the needed mapping, it will in turn forward the request to a DNS server at the next higher level in the hierarchy. After potentially several forwarding and delegation messages are sent within the DNS hierarchy, the IP address for the given host eventually is delivered to the resolver. DNS also includes support for caching requests and for redundancy. Most network operating systems allow one to enter the IP addresses of primary, secondary, and tertiary DNS servers, each of which can service initial requests from clients. Many ISPs maintain their own DNS servers and use DHCP to automatically assign the addresses of these servers to dial-in clients, so most home users need not be aware of the details behind DNS configuration. Registered domain names and addresses must be renewed periodically, and should a dispute occur between two parties over ownership of a given name, such as in trademarking, ICANN's Uniform Domain-Name Dispute-Resolution Policy can be invoked.

Download/Upload

A download involves the receipt of a file copied from a remote network location. Often, a person downloads files to their personal computer from a remote server computer. In Microsoft e-mail networks, for example, people download their email from an exchange server to their Outlook client. An upload involves sending a copy of a file to a remote network location. For example, Web publishers upload files to their Web server. Sending files across a computer network does not necessarily constitute an upload or a download. The terms are more commonly used in client/server networking than in peer-to-peer networking.

DSL

DSL provides high-speed networking over ordinary phone lines using digital modem technology. It integrates voice and data functionality, bringing the "always on" feature of the telephone to the computer network. The technology theoretically supports data rates of 8,448 Kbps (8.448 Mbps), although typical rates vary from 1,544 Kbps to 512 Kbps and sometimes as low as 90 Kbps.

DSL services target home and small business customers. However, the service only works over a limited physical distance and remains unavailable in many residential areas. The term "xDSL" generally refers to the complete family of related DSL technologies—ADSL, SDSL, VDSL, and so on—rather than any one specific implementation.

DCE

Data Circuit Termination Equipment. In a communications link, equipment which is an access point to the network, a network node or equipment at which a network circuit terminates.

DTE

Data Terminal Equipment. CCITT terminology for the data terminal devices themselves, a category which includes the computer.

Ethernet

Ethernet is a physical and data link layer technology for Local Area Networks (LANs). Ethernet was invented by engineer Robert Metcalfe. When first widely deployed in the 1980s, Ethernet supported a maximum theoretical data rate of 10 megabits per second (Mbps).

Extranet

An extranet is a computer network that allows controlled access from the outside for specific business or educational purposes. Extranets are extensions to, or segments of, private intranet networks that have been built in many corporations for information sharing and ecommerce.

Most extranets use the Internet as the entry point for outsiders, a firewall configuration to limit access, and a secure protocol for authenticating users.

ECMA

The European Computer Manufacturers Association is an association of the major computer vendors of Europe plus some North American companies. ECMA is active in many areas particularly in the development of higher layer protocols in OSI.

EIA

The Electronic Industries Association is an Accredited Standards Committee of ANSI responsible for some Physical Layer standards. *e.g.*, RS232.

Ethernet

A type of local area network based upon CSMA/CD technology—originally developed by Xerox.

ETSI

The European Telecommunications Standards Institute (ETSI) is an autonomous body within CERT and was formed to undertake the standards writing activities of CERT. The membership of ETSI is open and there are currently 135 member organisations including national administrations public network operators, manufacturers, users and research bodies.

Fast Packet Switching

A term used to describe a generic mode of packet switching distinguished by switching in hardware at layers 1 or 2 in order to achieve high speed and low delay across the network.

Fast Ethernet

Fast Ethernet supports a maximum data rate of 100 Mbps. It is so named because original Ethernet technology supported only 10 Mbps. Fast Ethernet began to be widely deployed in the mid-1990s as the need for greater LAN performance became critical to universities and businesses.

A key element of Fast Ethernet's success was its ability to coexist with existing network installations. Today, many network adapters support both traditional and Fast Ethernet. These so-called "10/100" adapters can usually sense the speed of the line automatically and adjust accordingly. Just as Fast Ethernet improved on traditional Ethernet, Gigabit Ethernet improves on Fast Ethernet, offering rates up to 1000 Mbps instead of 100 Mbps.

FAQ

The FAQ is a time-honored tradition on the Internet. It explains the sometimes boring details of technology in an easy-to-read question and answer format. FAQs are written by individuals, volunteer groups, and corporations. FAQs exist for nearly all basic computer networking technologies.

A typical FAQ entry will appear as follows:

Q : Who created Napster, the MP3 music sharing system ?

A : Shawn Fanning conceived and implemented Napster while a college student in Massachusetts. The name "Napster" was a nickname his friends gave him because of his hair style.

FDDI

FDDI is a high speed LAN standard being developed by an ANSI committee employs a token passing on dual 100 Mbps fibre optic ring.

Frame

A group of bits exchanged between data link layer entities that contains its own control information for addressing and error checking in addition to user data. As used in HDLC also the repeating sequence of time slots in a time division multiplex.

Frame Relay

A standardised form of fast packet switching in which packets are switched in hardware and at the data link layer. Basically dead and gone as far the Internet is concerned. Especially with the bandwidth requirements the way they are. Frame relay runs around 64 kbps to 1.5 Mbps [64,000 bits per second to 1.5 million bits per second]. Frame relay is shared line with other people and your bandwidth depends on the current utilization of the line.

FireWire

FireWire is a high performance networking standard based on a serial bus architecture. The industry created the IEEE 1394 FireWire standard in 1995. Adoption of FireWire has been slow to materialize, but many people use FireWire today to network their digital video cameras with their computers. FireWire theoretically supports networking of any computer peripherals and does not require a central computer be present on the network.

FireWire is known for its low cost and also ease of setup and use. FireWire competes with and is technically similar to the Universal Serial Bus (USB) standard. FireWire supports a theoretical maximum data rate of 400 Mbps, that is roughly equivalent to the performance of USB 2.0.

FTP

FTP allows one to transfer files between computers on the Internet. Technically, FTP is a simple network protocol based on IP, but many also use the term "FTP" to refer to this type of file sharing service. The FTP service is based on a client/server architecture. An FTP client program initiates a connection to a remote computer running FTP server software. After the connection is established, the client can choose to send and/or receive copies of files, singly or in groups. To connect to an FTP server, a client generally requires a username and password as set by the administrator of the server. Many public FTP archives follow a special convention for that accepts a username of "anonymous".

Gateway

A network gateway is an internetworking system, a system that joins two networks together. A network gateway can be implemented completely in software, completely in hardware, or as a combination of the two. Depending on their implementation, network gateways can operate at any level of the OSI model from application protocols to low-level signaling.

Because a network gateway by definition appears at the edge of a network, related functionality like firewalling tends to be installed on the network gateway.

Kbps/kbps, Mbps, Gbps

One kilobit per second (Kbps) equals 1000 bits per second (bps). Kbps is also written as "kbps" that carries the same meaning. Likewise, one megabit per second (Mbps) equals one million bps and one Gigabit equals one billion bps. Network performance is best measured in bps, but sometimes numbers are given in bytes per second (Bps). Then, one KBps equals one kilobyte per second, one MBps equals one megabyte per second, and GBps equals one gigabyte per second. Many times people write KBps, for example, when they mean Kbps, and it is important to be clear on this distinction.

Examples: V.90 modems support data rates up to 56 Kbps. Traditional Ethernet supports data rates up to 10 Mbps and Fast Ethernet 100 Mbps. Gigabit Ethernet supports 1000 Mbps or 1 Gbps.

Kilobyte, Megabyte, Gigabyte

A kilobyte equals 1024 (or 210) bytes. Likewise, a megabyte (MB) equals 1024 KB or 220 bytes and a gigabyte 30 bytes.

The meaning of the words kilobyte, megabyte, and gigabyte change when they are used in the context of network data rates. A rate of one kilobyte per second (KBps) equals 1000 (not 1024) bytes per second. One megabyte per second (MBps) equals one million (106, not 220) bytes per second. One gigabyte per second (GBps) equals one billion (109, not 230) bytes per second. To avoid some of this confusion, networkers typically measure data rates in bits per second (bps) rather than bytes per second (Bps) and use the terms kilobyte, megabyte, and gigabyte only when referring to disk space.

Examples: "This eight gigabyte disk only has 200 megabytes of free space left". Also Known As: K, KB, M, MB, "meg", G, GB, "gig".

HDSL

HDSL technology was developed in the early 1990s, making it one of the oldest forms of DSL. HDSL service provides equal bandwidth for both downloads and uploads, offering data rates up to 2,048 Kbps. Note that HDSL requires multiple phone lines to accomplish this. Like other forms of DSL, HDSL features "always on" combined voice and data services. HDSL enjoyed some popularity in years past, but the technology has effectively been replaced by alternatives like SDSL that only require one phone line and offer similar performance and reach. Also Known As: High-data-rate DSL, High-speed DSL.

Hop

In computer networking, a hop represents one portion of the path between source and destination. When communicating over the Internet, for example, data passes through a number of intermediate devices (like routers) rather than flowing directly over a single wire. Each such device causes data to "hop" between one point-to-point network connection and another. In networking, the hop count represents the total number of devices a given piece of data (packet) passes through. Generally speaking, the more hops data must traverse to reach their destination, the greater the transmission delay incurred. Network utilities like ping can be used to determine the hop count to a specific destination. Ping generates packets that include a field reserved for the hop count. Each time a capable device receives these packets, that device modifies the packet, incrementing the hop count by one. In addition, the device compares the hop count against a predetermined limit and discards the packet if its hop count is too high. This prevents packets from endlessly bouncing around the network due to routing errors. Both routers and bridges are capable of managing hop counts, but other types of intermediate devices (like hubs) are not.

HTTP

HTTP is an application layer network protocol built on top of TCP. HTTP allows Web browsers and Web servers to communicate.

HTTP clients and servers communicate via request and response messages. The three main HTTP message types are GET, POST, and HEAD. HTTP utilizes TCP port 80 by default, though other ports such as 8080 are also used. The current version of HTTP in widespread use - HTTP version 1.1 - was developed to address some of the performance limitations of the original version - HTTP 1.0. HTTP 1.1 is documented in RFC 2068. Also Known As: Hyper Text Transfer Protocol.

Hub

A hub is a small, simple, inexpensive device that joins multiple computers together at a low-level network protocol layer.

Most hubs manufactured today support the Ethernet standard. A person plugs one end of an Ethernet cable (that has an RJ-45 connector attached) into the hub, while the other end of the cable runs to the computer's network interface card (NIC). Non-Ethernet hubs (Token Ring, for example) also exist. One good way to differentiate between Ethernet hubs is by the speed (data rate) they support. The most basic Ethernet hubs support 10 Mbps speeds. Newer hubs support 100 Mbps Ethernet. Some hubs, to help users move ahead to the newer technology while still supporting the old, support both 10 Mbps and 100 Mbps data rates. These are so-called "dual-speed" hubs. Another common differentiator in hubs is the number of ports they support. Four- and five-port hubs are most common in home networks, but eight- and 16-port hubs can be found in some home and small office environments.

ICMP

ICMP is a network protocol useful in Internet Protocol (IP) network management and administration. ICMP is a required element of IP implementations.

ICMP is a control protocol, meaning that it does not carry application data, but rather information about the status of the network itself. ICMP can be used to report.

- errors in the underlying communications of network applications.
- availability of remote hosts.
- network congestion.

Perhaps the best known example of ICMP in practice is the ping utility, that uses ICMP to probe remote hosts for responsiveness and overall round-trip time of the probe messages. ICMP also supports trace route, that can identify intermediate "hops" between a given source and destination.

ICQ

ICQ is a software system for instant messaging originally developed in 1996 at a small company named Mirabilis. ICQ allows any two registered people on the Internet to interact either "live" (like a person-to-person chat) or disconnected (like email).

Any Internet user may download ICQ and install the free client program. To register with the ICQ system, a person chooses their public username (handle) and private password. To use ICQ , a person simply logs in to the client program with that information. ICQ keep track of all the registered users logged in to the system at any given time.

Therefore, people can keep buddy lists of their friends and be notified when these people log on to the system. The ICQ client software works by connecting to an ICQ server on the Internet. When the program is launched, it initially finds and connects to a server using UDP port 4000. This allows clients to discover other online clients. For person-to-person communications, ICQ sets up and tears down point-to-point TCP connections as needed.

ICS

ICS allows a local network of Windows computers to share a single Internet connection. Microsoft developed ICS as part of Windows 98 Second Edition. The feature has been included as part of all subsequent Windows releases, but it is not available as a separate installable program. ICS follows a client/server model. To set up ICS, one computer must be chosen as the "server." This computer must support two network interfaces, one directly connected to the Internet and the other connected to the remainder of the LAN. In a traditional home dial-up network, for example, the server computer is directly connected to the modem.

IIS

IIS is Microsoft's business-class Web server. Although apache boasts more total worldwide installations than IIS, many corporations choose IIS as their Web server because it is supported by a commercial organization. Some have criticized IIS in the past, though, for its alleged security weaknesses.

IIS has improved over the years, supports many Web standards including SSL, and integrates well with other Microsoft Web technologies such as FrontPage. An admininstrator can manage IIS through a graphical console, the Internet Services Manager.

Internet

The term Internet today refers to the global network of public computers running Internet protocol. The Internet supports the public WWW and many special-purpose client/server software systems. Internet technology also supports many private corporate intranets and private home LANs.

The term "Internet" was originally coined in the 1970s. At that time, only the very meager beginnings of a public global network were in place. Throughout the 1970s, 1980s, and 1990s, a number of smaller national networks like ARPANET, BITNET, CSNET, and NSFNET evolved, merged, or dissolved, then finally joined with non-US networks to form the global Internet. Also Known As: The Net.

IP

IP is probably the world's single most popular network protocol. Data travels over an IP-based network in the form of packets; each IP packet includes both a header (that specifies source, destination, and other information about the data) and the message data itself. IP supports the notion of unique addressing for computers on a network. Current IP (IPv4) addresses contain four bytes (32 bits) that is sufficient to address most computers on the Internet. IP supports protocol layering as defined in the OSI reference model.

Popular higher-level protocols like HTTP, TCP, and UDP are built directly on top of IP. Likewise, IP can travel over several different lower-level data link interfaces like Ethernet and ATM. IP originated with UNIX® networking in the 1970s.

Intranet

An intranet is the generic term for a collection of private computer networks within an organization. Intranets generally use standard network technologies like Ethernet, TCP/IP, Web browsers and Web servers. An organization's intranet often enjoys Internet access but is firewalled so that its computers cannot be reached directly from the public Net. A common extension to an intranet, an extranet opens holes in this firewall to provide controlled access to outsiders. Many schools and non-profit groups have deployed intranets, but an intranet is still seen primarily as a corporate productivity tool. Besides email and groupware applications, intranets generally offer internal Web sites to disseminate information.

IP Address

An IP address is the logical address of a network adapter. The IP address uniquely identifies computers on a network.

An IP address can be private, for use on a LAN, or public, for use on the Internet or other WAN. IP addresses can be determined statically (assigned to a computer by a system administrator) or dynamically (assigned by another device on the network on demand).

IP addresses consist of four bytes (32 bits). Each byte of an IP address is known as an octet. Octets can take any value between 0 and 255, but various rules exist for ensuring IP addresses are valid.

Also Known As: Network Address.

ISDN

ISDN is a network technology that supports transfer of simultaneous voice and data traffic. Similar to DSL in this respect, an ISDN Internet service works over ordinary telephone lines. ISDN Internet service generally supports data rates of 128 Kbps.

ISDN emerged as an alternative to traditional dial-up networking during the 1990s. The relatively high cost of service, though, limited its popularity with home users. The much higher speeds supports by newer cable and DSL technologies diminish the importance of ISDN for home networking, but ISDN technology may still have application in other areas of business. Also Known As: Integrated Services Digital Network.

ISP

An ISP is a company that provides Internet connectivity to home and business customers. ISPs choose what forms of access to provide customers, ranging from traditional modem dial-up to DSL and cable modem to T1/T3 lines. Recently, ISP companies have begun to diversify and offer additional services besides Net access. These include email, Web site and database hosting, and Web site development services and tools.

Also Known As: Internet Service Provider, Internet Access Provider (IAP).

IEEE, US Institute of Electrical and Electronic Engineers.

An Accredited Standards Committee of ANSI active in standards making, mainly in LANs.

ISDN Integrated Services Digital Network.

ISDN an internationally Agreed public network offering switched end-to-end digital services for voice and data.

ISO

The International Organisation for Standardisation is a voluntary activity of the national standardisation organisations of each member country. ISO has been the primary force in developing the OSI architecture ISO work closely with CCITT in the development of standards.

IT

Information Technology A catch-all term used to describe the techniques used for the automation of information handling and retrieval, including computing, telecommunications and office systems.

LAN-Local Area Network

A network which spans a limited geographical area (usually within one building or site) and interconnects a variety of computers and terminals.

Layer

In the OSI Reference Model, refers to a collection of related functions within a communications system with a defined service interface to layers above and below.

Local Loop

The name for the local analogue circuit (usually copper wires) which connects a subscriber to a local telephone exchange.

LDAP

LDAP is a standard technology for network directories. Network directories are specialized databases that store information about devices, applications, people and other aspects of a computer network. LDAP is both a network protocol and a standard architecture for organizing the directory data. LDAP was created in 1995 as an academic university project, then commercialized by Netscape in the late 1990s. As a protocol, LDAP is a simplified version of the Data Access Protocol (DAP) used in the earlier standard X.500. LDAP's chief advantage over its predecessor is the ability to run over TCP/IP. As an architecture, LDAP utilizes a distributed tree structure similar to X.500. Prior to standards like X.500 and LDAP being adopted, most business networks used priopgietary network directory technology, chiefly Banyan VINES or Novell NDS. LDAP has gradually replaced all of these others as a universal standard "building block." Today's popular directory technologies like microsoft active directory can use LDAP as a standard foundation to improve their performance and their maintainability.

Also Known As: Lightweight Directory Access Protocol, Lightweight DAP.

Leased Line

A leased line connects two locations for private voice or data telecommunication service. Not a dedicated cable, a leased line is really just a reserved circuit between two points that can be near to each other or separated by a long distance. Traditional telephone service reuses the same lines for many different conversations through a process called "switching," but leased lines maintain a single open circuit at all times. Leased lines most commonly are rented by businesses to connect branch offices, because these lines guarantee bandwidth for network traffic. So-called T1 leased lines are common and offer the performance of symmetric DSL (1.544 Mbps). Individuals can also rent leased lines for high-speed Internet access, but their high cost (sometimes more than $2000 USD per month) deters some organizations. Fractional T1 lines, starting at 128 Kbps, reduce this cost somewhat and have been installed in some apartment buildings and hotels.

Also Known As: Dedicated Line.

Modem

"Modem" is an acronym for "Modulator Demodulator." Traditionally, a modem converts data between the analog form used on telephone lines and the digital form used on computers for the purpose of computer-to-computer communication. Standard modems can transmit data at a maximum rate of 56,000 bits per second (bps) or 56 kbps. However, inherent limitations of the phone system translate to modem speeds of 33.6 kbps or lower in practice.

More recently, modems for cable and DSL service have come to be known as digital modems and those used for traditional dial-up networking as analog modems. The terminology is somewhat misleading as modems all involve analog signaling; "digital" actually refers to improved digital support at the access provider's location and not within the modem itself. Nonetheless, cable and DSL modems use broadband signaling techniques to achieve dramatically higher network speeds than traditional modems.

MTU

The MTU is a limit, expressed in bytes, on the size of data sent over a network. It is the maximum size of a single unit (*e.g.*, an Ethernet frame) of digital communications.

MTU sizes are properties of physical network interfaces. The MTU for Ethernet, for instance, is 1500 bytes. Some types of networks (like Token Ring) have larger MTUs, and some types have smaller MTUs. Higher-level network protocols like TCP/IP can be configured with a maximum packet size, but this setting is distinct from the physical MTU. The MTU of a network has important implications on the performance of computer communications as explained below.

In Microsoft Windows, the maximum packet size for protocols like TCP can be set in the Registry. If this value is set too low, streams of network traffic will be broken up into a relatively large number of small packets that adversely affects performance. If the maximum TCP packet size is set too high, it will exceed the network's MTU and also degrade performance by requiring that each packet be subdivided into at least two smaller ones (a process known as fragmentation). Setting an optimal TCP packet size on home computers can be tricky. For communications within the home LAN, a setting of 1500 bytes to match the Ethernet MTU is optimal. Windows 95 uses a default of 1500 bytes for this reason. However, for communications over a dial-up connection to the Internet, the recommended MTU size is only 576 bytes. Windows 98 uses 576 bytes as its default for this reason. But high-speed connections (including DSL or cable service and home LANs) usually perform better at the higher value. Tuning the maximum packet size of TCP/IP also depends in important ways on two other related parameters named MSS and RWIN. Also Known As: Maximum Transmission Unit.

MAN

A Metropolitan Area Network is a geographically extended high speed LAN designed to interconnect users within a city or metropolitan area.

Medium

Any material substance that can be used for the propagation of signals in the form of electrons, modulated radio, light or acoustic waves from one point to another such as optical fibre, cable, wire, air or free space.

Modem

A contraction of the term "modulator-demodulator" A modem converts the serial digital data from a transmitting terminal into a form suitable for transmission over the analogue telephone channel A second unit re converts this signal to serial digital data for acceptance by the receiving terminal.

Multiplexing

The function of transporting more than one stream of data over a single circuit (real or virtual) apparently simultaneously. Multiplexing can be either in the frequency domain (EDM) or the time domain (TDM).

NAT

NAT allows an IP-based network to manage its public (Internet) addresses separately from its private (intranet) addresses. It is a popular technology for Net connection sharing on DSL or cable LANs. With NAT, each private IP address can be translated to a different public address, or multiple private addresses can be aliased to a single public one. To accomplish this, NAT software snoops both incoming and outgoing packets on the network. It modifies the source or destination address in the IP header (and the affected checksums) to reflect the mapping between internal and external addressing for that network. NAT functionality appears on routers and other gateway devices with low-level access to packets at the network boundary. Several variations on NAT have also been implemented to provide additional support for application-level protocols. NAT for the Internet is defined in RFC 1631. Also Known As: Network Address Translation.

NetWare

The NetWare operating system was one of the first software products built for the networking of personal computers (PCs). NetWare emphasizes file and print serving capabilities, and the predominant use of NetWare is as a LAN server. Early version of

NetWare appeared in the late 1980s, and today NetWare enjoys an installed base of millions of computers. NetWare is just one of many networking software products and services developed by Novell, Inc. Despite stiff competition from Microsoft and various other companies, Novell continues to offer strong network technology. Also Known As : Novell NetWare.

Network Firewall

A network firewall protects a computer network from unauthorized access. Network firewalls may be hardware devices, software programs, or a combination of the two. A network firewall typically guards an internal computer network (intranet) against malicious access from the outside; however, network firewalls may also be configured to limit access to the outside from internal users.

Perhaps the most common form of network firewall is a proxy server. Proxy servers act as an intermediary between intranet and Internet computers by receiving and selectively blocking data packets at the network boundary. These network firewalls also provide an extra measure of safety by hiding internal LAN addresses from the outside Internet. In a proxy server firewall environment, network requests from multiple clients appear to the outsider as all coming from the same proxy server address.

Network Switch

A network switch is a small device that joins multiple computers together at a low-level network protocol layer. Technically, network switches operate at layer two (Data Link Layer) of the OSI model. Network switches look nearly identical to hubs, but a switch generally contains more "intelligence" (and a slightly higher price tag) than a hub. Unlike hubs, network switches are capable of inspecting the data packets as they are received, determining the source and destination device of that packet, and forwarding that packet appropriately. By delivering messages only to the connected device that it was intended for, network switches conserve network bandwidth and offer generally better performance than hubs. As with hubs, Ethernet network switches are the most common. A network switch offers differing port configurations starting with the four- and five-port models, and support 10 Mbps Ethernet, 100 Mbps Ethernet, or both.

NIC

In computer networking, NIC provides a hardware interface between a computer and a network. The term NIC most commonly refers to network adapter hardware in the form factor of an add-in card; for example, a PCI or PCMCIA card. These devices plug into the system bus of the PC and include jacks for network cables. NICs are usually Ethernet adapters, but some NICs support alternate physical layer protocols like ATM. Several vendors manufacture Ethernet NICs. Many of these products come pre-installed as part of a total computer system configuration. The primary consideration with Ethernet NICs is the speed they support - 10 Mbps traditional, 100 Mbps Fast Ethernet, or both (dual-speed). Some Ethernet NICs include a built-in dial-up modem on the card.

Also Known As: Network Interface Card.

Node

A node is any device connected to a computer network. Nodes can be computers, personal digital assistants (PDAs), cell phones, or various other network appliances. On an IP network, a node is any device with an IP address. Also Known As: Device

NOS—Network Operating System

A NOS is a network operating system. A network operating system implements protocol stacks as well as device drivers for networking hardware. Some network operating systems, like Windows 98 Second Edition, also add custom networking features like Internet Connection Sharing (ICS). Network operating systems have existed for more than thirty years. The UNIX® operating system was designed from the beginning to support networking. In its early forms, Windows did not support networking, so Novell NetWare became the first popular network operating system for the personal computer (Windows 95 and Windows for Workgroups were Microsoft's first network operating system products). Today, nearly any consumer operating system qualifies as a NOS due to the popularity of the Internet and the obvious need to support Internet Protocol (IP) networking at a minimum. Also Known As: Network Operating System.

Octet

Technically, an octet represents any eight bit quantity. By definition, an octet ranges in mathematical value from zero to 255. Typically an octet is also a byte, but the term octet came into existence because historically some computer systems did not represent a byte as eight bits.

In networking, an octet most commonly refers to any of the four bytes of an IPv4 address. In dotted-decimal notation, an IP address appears as follows -

[octet] . [octet] . [octet] . [octet]

For example, 192 . 168 . 0. 1. Also Known As: Byte.

OSI Model—Open Systems Interconnection Mode

The OSI model defines internetworking in terms of a vertical stack of seven layers. The upper layers of the OSI model represent software that implements network services like encryption and connection management. The lower layers of the OSI model implement more primitive, hardware-oriented functions like routing, addressing, and flow control.

P2P

P2P technically stands for "peer-to-peer". A peer-to-peer architecture allows hardware or software to function on a network without the need for central servers. Peer-to-peer is commonly used in configuring home computer networks where the cost of a server can be difficult to justify. The approach has also been popularized by some Net software applications such as Groove and Napster.

The P2P acronym has acquired a non-technical meaning as well. Some people have described this second meaning as "people-to-people." From this angle, P2P is a model for developing software and growing businesses that help individuals on the Net to meet each other and share common interests.

Also Known As: Peer-to-Peer.

Packet

A packet is one unit of binary data capable of being routed through a computer network. To improve communication performance and reliability, each message sent between two network devices is often subdivided into packets by the underlying hardware and software. Depending on the protocol(s) they need to support, packets are constructed in some standard packet format. Packet formats generally include a header, the body containing the message data (also known as the payload), and sometimes a footer (also known as the trailer). The packet header lists the destination of the packet (in IP packets, the destination IP address) and often indicates the length of the message data. The packet footer contains data that signifies the end of the packet, such as a special sequence of bits known as a magic number. Both the packet header and footer may contain error-checking information. The eceiving device is responsible for re-assembling individual packets into the original message, by stripping off the headers and footers and concatenating packets in the correct sequence. Also Known As: Datagram.

Ping

Ping is the name of a standard network utility packaged with popular network operating systems. The utility can be used to determine if a remote device (such as Web or game server) can be reached on the network and, if so, roughly how fast the current connection is. Traditional pings are implemented with the Internet Control Message Protocol (ICMP), although it is possible to achieve a similar effect with UDP or other protocols. Ping utilities send requests to the designated computer at periodic intervals and measure the time it takes for a respone packet to arrive. A number of popular "ping tools" that add features to the operating system commands are available on the Net today. By manipulating the contents of ICMP packets, hackers have also used ping utilties to take down servers in the so-called "Ping of Death" attack.

Also Known As: Packet Internet Gopher.

Port Number

A port number represents an endpoint or "channel" for network communications. Port numbers allow different applications on the same computer to utilize network resources without interfering with each other. Port numbers most commonly appear in network programming, particularly socket programming. Sometimes, though, port numbers are made visible to the casual user. For example, some Web sites a person visits on the Internet use a URL like the following:

http://www.mairie-metz.fr:8080/

In this example, the number 8080 refers to the port number used by the Web browser to connect to the Web server. Normally, a Web site uses port number 80 and this number need not be included with the URL (although it can be). In IP networking, port numbers can theoretically range from 0 to 65535. Most popular network applications, though, use port numbers at the low end of the range (such as 80 for HTTP). The port number is included as a field within the header of each IP packet. Note: The term port also refers to several other aspects of network technology. A port can refer to a physical connection point for peripheral devices such as serial, parallel, and USB ports. The term port also refers to certain Ethernet connection points, such as those on a hub, switch, or router. Also Known As: Port Number, Protocol Number.

Portal

A portal is a kind of Web site. The term originated with large, well-known Internet search engine sites that expanded their features to include email, news, stock quotes, and an array of other functionality. Some corporations took a similar approach in implementing their intranet sites, that then became known as enterprise information or corporate portals. Technically speaking, a portal site includes a start page with rich navigation, a collection of loosely-integrated features (some of which may be provided by partners or other third parties), and a diverse, large target audience. Also Known As: Web Site.

PPPoE

PPPoE technology is being adopted by some providers of DSL service. PPPoE combines the Ethernet and Point-to-Point Protocol (PPP) standards specifically for use with modems capable of broadband connectivity. PPPoE itself is documented in RFC 2516.

When used with DSL, PPPoE can require additional software that establishes a network session via dial-up. Some DSL routers, though, include built-in PPPoE support to eliminate the need for software.

Also Known As: Point to Point Protocol over Ethernet (PPPoE).

Protocol

A network protocol defines a "language" of rules and conventions for communication between devices. A protocol includes formatting rules that specify how data is packaged into messages. It also may include conventions like message acknowledgement or data compression to support reliable and/or high-performance communication. Many protocols exist in computer networking ranging from high level (like SOAP) to low level (like ARP). The Internet protocol family includes IP and all higher-level network protocols built on top of it, such as TCP, UDP, HTTP, and FTP. Modern operating systems include services or daemons that implement support for specific protocols. Some protocols, like TCP/IP, have also been implemented in silicon hardware for optimized performance.

Also Known As: Network Protocol.

QoS

The term QoS refers to a broad collection of networking technologies and techniques. The goal of QoS is to provide guarantees on the ability of a network to deliver predictable results. Elements of network performance within the scope of QoS often include availability (uptime), bandwidth (throughput), latency (delay), and error rate. QoS generally involves prioritization of network traffic. QoS can defined in terms of the total network "pipe," in terms of a given server's or router's performance, or in terms of specific applications. A network monitoring system must typically be deployed as part of QoS, to insure that networks are performing at the desired level. QoS is an increasingly important area of research and development in computer networking. It is especially important for the new generation of Internet applications such as video-on-demand and other consumer services. Some core Internet technologies like Ethernet were not designed to support prioritized traffic or guaranteed performance levels, making it much more difficult to implement QoS solutions. One of the most attractive features of ATM is its built-in support for QoS. Also Known As: Quality of Service.

RADSL

RADSL is an implementation of ADSL that automatically adjusts the connection speed to adjust for the quality of the telephone line. This feature allows RADSL service to function over longer distances than does ordinary ADSL, an important feature in suburban neighborhoods. In RADSL, the broadband modem is configured at startup to test the phone line and adjust the data rate. RADSL typically operates at a lower date rate than regular ADSL. Like ADSL, RADSL provides relatively more bandwidth for downloads and less for uploads. Also Known As: Rate-Adaptive Asymmetric Digital.

Repeater

Network repeaters regenerate incoming signals. On physical media like Ethernet, data transmissions can only span a limited distance before the quality of the signal degrades. Repeaters attempt to preserve signal integrity and extend the distance over which data can safely travel.

The actual network devices that serve as repeaters are usually referred to by another name. Active hubs, for example, are sometimes called "multiport repeaters" but usually these are simply referred to as hubs. Not all hubs are repeaters, though. So-called passive hubs retransmit signals but do not regenerate them, thus they do not perform the service of a repeater.

Higher-level devices in the OSI model, like switches and routers, generally do not incorporate the functions of a repeater. Technically, a repeater is a physical layer device.

Router

A router is a physical device that joins multiple wired or wireless networks together. Technically, a wired or wireless router is a Layer 3 gateway, meaning that it connects networks (as gateways do), and that it operates at the network layer of the OSI model.

The home networker typically uses an Internet Protocol (IP) wired or wireless router, IP being the most common OSI network layer protocol. An IP router such as a DSL or cable modem router joins the home's local area network (LAN) to the wide-area network (WAN) of the Internet. By maintaining configuration information in a piece of storage called the "routing table", wired or wireless routers also have the ability to filter traffic, either incoming or outgoing, based on the IP addresses of senders and receivers. Some routers allow the home networker to update the routing table from a Web browser interface.

DSL routers and cable modem routers typically combine the functions of a router with those of a switch in a single unit.

RPC—Remote Procedure Call

RPC is a network programming model for point-to-point communication within or between software applications.

In RPC, the sender makes a request in the form of a procedure, function, or method call. RPC translates these calls into requests sent over the network to the intended destination.

SONET

SONET is a physical layer network technology designed to carry large volumes of traffic over relatively long distances on fiber optic cabling. SONET was originally designed by ANSI for the public telephone network in the mid-1980s. SONET possesses several characteristics that make it appealing on the Internet today. SONET defines clear interoperability standards between different vendors' products, SONET can carry nearly any higher-level protocol (including IP), and it includes built-in support for ease of management and maintenance. SONET performs at high speeds at a cost competitive with alternatives like ATM and Gigabit Ethernet.

Also Known As: Synchronous Optical Network, Synchronous Digital Hierarchy (SDH).

SDSL

SDSL is a form of Digital Subscriber Line (DSL) service that provides equal bandwidth for both uploads and downloads. Originally developed in Europe, SDSL was one of the earliest forms of DSL to not require multiple telephone lines.

SDSL possesses all of the common characteristics of DSL, including an "always on" combination of voice and data services, availability limited by physical distance, and high speed access compared to analog modems. SDSL supports data rates up to 3,088 Kbps.

Also Known As: Symmetric Digital Subscriber Line, Single-line DSL.

Segment

A segment is a specially-configured subset of a larger network. The boundaries of a network segment are established by devices capable of regulating the flow of packets into and out of the segment, including routers, switches, hubs, bridges, or multi-homed gateways (but not simple repeaters). Network designers create segments to physically separate related computers into groups. This grouping can improve network performance and security. In Ethernet networks, for example, computers send many broadcast packets onto the network, but only other computers on the same segment receive them. Network segments and subnets serve similar purposes; both create a grouping of computers. The difference between a segment and a subnet is as follows: a segment is a physical network construction, whereas a subnet is simply a higher-level software configuration. In particular, one cannot define a single IP subnet that functions correctly across multiple segments. Also Known As: Network Segment.

Socket

A socket represents a single connection between two network applications. These two applications nominally run on different computers, but sockets can also be used for interprocess communication on a single computer. Applications can create multiple sockets for communicating with each other. Sockets are bidirectional, meaning that either side of the connection is capable of both sending and receiving data. Programmers often use sockets in network programming, albeit indirectly. Programming libraries like Winsock hide many of the low-level details of socket programming. Sockets have been in widespread use since the early 1980s.

Also Known As: Software Object.

SSL—Secure Sockets Layer

SSL security technology helps to improve the safety of Internet communications. SSL is a standard for encrypted client/server communication between network devices.

A network protocol, SSL runs on top of TCP/IP. SSL utilizes several standard network security techniques including public keys, symmetric keys, and certificates.

Subnet

A subnet is a logical grouping of connected network devices. Nodes on a subnet tend to be located in close physical proximity to each other on a LAN. Network designers employ subnets as a way to partition networks into logical segments for greater ease of administration. When subnets are properly implemented, both the performance and security of networks can be improved.

In IP networking, nodes on a subnet share a contiguous range of IP address numbers. A mask (known as the subnet mask or network mask) defines the boundaries of an IP subnet.

Symmetric/Asymmetric

In a symmetric network, all devices can transmit and receive data at equal rates. Asymmetric networks support more bandwidth in one direction than the other. For example, symmetric DSL offers customers identical bandwidth for both downloads and uploads. Asymmetric DSL offers more bandwidth for customer downloads at the cost of less bandwidth for uploads.

A more general but less common definition of network symmetry involves access to resources. In this sense, all devices on a symmetric network share equal access to resources or the same capabilities. Asymmetric networks divide at least some resources unequally between devices. Examples: Pure peer-to-peer networks like Gnutella implement perfect symmetry: all computers on the Gnutella network have equal opportunity to discover, publish, or receive content. A hybrid peer-to-peer network like Napster is technically asymmetric because it utilizes central servers for user registration and file catalogs. However, from the point of view of clients, Napster is effectively symmetric because all customers share equivalent functionality.

TCP/IP

Technically, Transmission Control Protocol (TCP) and Internet Protocol (IP) are two distinct network protocols. TCP and IP are so commonly used together, though, that TCP/IP has become standard terminology to refer to either *or* both of the protocols.

IP roughly corresponds to the Network layer (layer 3) in the OSI model, whereas TCP corresponds to the Transport layer (layer 4) in OSI. In other words, the term TCP/IP refers to network communications where the TCP transport is used to deliver data across IP networks. The average person on the Internet works in a predominately TCP/IP environment. Web browsers, for example, use TCP/IP to communicate with Web servers.

Also Known As: Transmission Control Protocol/Internet Protocol.

UDP

UDP is a lightweight transport built on top of IP. UDP squeezes extra performance from IP by not implementing some of the features a more heavyweight protocol like TCP offers. Specifically, UDP allows individual packets to be dropped (with no retries) and UDP packets to be received in a different order than they were sent.

UDP is often used in videoconferencing applications or games where optimal performance is preferred over guaranteed message delivery. UDP is one of the oldest network protocols, introduced in 1980 in RFC document 768. Also Known As: User Datagram Protocol.

UNC

UNC provides a naming convention for identifying network resources. UNC names consist of three parts, a server name, a share name, and an optional file path, that are combined using backslashes as follows: \\server\share\file_path.

The server portion of a UNC path refers to names maintained by a network naming service such as DNS or WINS. Share names can be defined by a system administrator or, in some cases, exist automatically within the local operating system.

For example, in Windows 2000 and earlier versions of Windows, the built-in share name admin$ refers to the root directory of the operating system installation (usually C :\WINNT or C:\WINDOWS). (Predefined share names in Windows generally end with a $, but this convention is not required for any new shares an administrator defines.) Using Windows Explorer or the DOS command prompt, a person can map to the \\computer-name\admin$ UNC share and (with proper security credentials) can remotely access the directory tree under C:\WINNT or equivalent on that computer.

A person can also connect to subdirectories beneath admin$ by specifying the optional portion of the UNC name. For example, \\computer-name\admin$\system32 is the UNC name referring to C:\WINNT\system32 or equivalent on that computer.

UNC notation is used primarily for mapping network drives in the Microsoft Windows family of operating systems, although support for UNC appears in related technologies like Samba. UNC names are most commonly used to reach file servers or printers on a LAN.

Also Known As: Universal Naming Convention, Uniform Naming Convention.

URI

A URI is a standard global identifier for an Internet resource that may be local or remotely-accessible. URIs follow the same general syntax as URLs; in fact, URLs are one type of URI.

Whereas URLs always refer to network addresses (including a protocol specification, host name or address, and local path), a URI does not necessarily refer to a remote resource. For example, the URI file:///c:/ specifies a local directory. Because file does not refer to any specific network protocol, this URI is not also a URL.

Also Known As: Uniform Resource Identifier.

URL

A URL is a specially-formatted text string that defines a location on the Internet. URL strings contain three parts or substrings:

1. network protocol, 2. host name or address, 3. file location.

The network protocol substring determines the underlying Internet protocol to be used in reaching the location. These strings consist of a standard protocol name followed by the :// characters. Typical protocols found in URLs include http://, ftp://, and mailto ://.

The host substring immediately follows the protocol defintion. Hosts may be defined by Internet-standard naming (DNS) or by IP address. For example, a URL of http://compnetworking.about.com or, equivalently, http://209.143.212.20 contains the protocol and host information needed to access this Web site.

The file location portion of a URL defines the location of a network resource. Resources are files that can be plain text files, documents, graphics, or programs, and resource names are relative to a local root directory. Technically, a URL like http://compnetworking.about.com contains an implied file location of /, that Web servers like Apache automatically translate to a specific file name like index.htm.

When creating HTML pages, the author can choose to use either the relative file locations or complete URLs. A user of the Internet generally works with complete URLs. Also Known As: Uniform Resource Locator.

USB

USB is a high-performance networking standard based on a serial bus architecture. Most new computers and associated periperhal devices like printers and scanners support USB. USB hubs for file and printer sharing also exist.

To build a USB network, one connects special USB cables to the USB ports on those devices.

VDSL

VDSL was developed to support exceptionally high-bandwidth applications such as High-Definition Television (HDTV). VDSL is not as widely deployed as other forms of DSL service. However, VDSL can achieve data rates up to approximately 51,840 Kbps, making it the fastest available form of DSL.

To perform at this speed, VDSL relies on fiber optic cabling. VDSL is designed to work more as a business service that uses ATM internetworking rather than as a consumer service that utilizes IP. VDSL supports both voice and data communication on the same line, like other forms of DSL. Also like most DSL technology, the performance of VDSL depends significantly on the physical distance traversed by wires: Shorter distances mean faster networking. The technology was originally named VADSL ('A' for asymmetric), but VDSL has now been improved and can operate in either symmetric and asymmetric modes.

Vortal

A vortal is a specialized form of portal. The term "portal" was associated first with large public search engine sites, then with corporate intranet sites. Both of these types of portals offered a breadth of functionality intended to capture as much of the available readership as possible. Later, a different form of Web site attracted the attention of analysts—a portal geared toward a specific niche audience with focused content. The buzzword "vortal" (for "vertical portal") was applied to this category of site to distinguish it from the others. By targeting a very focused audience, vortals in theory can provide easier-to-understand navigation, deeper content, and a place for people with common interests to meet each other. Also Known As: Vertical Portal.

VPN

A VPN utilizes public networks to conduct private communications. Most VPN implementations today use the Internet as the public infrastructure and a variety of specialized protocols to support private communications within the Internet. VPN follows a client and server approach. VPN clients authenticate users, encrypt data, and otherwise manage sessions with VPN servers utilizing a technique called tunneling. VPN clients and VPN servers are typically used in these three scenarios:

1. to support remote access to an intranet,
2. to support connections between multiple intranets within the same organization, and
3. to join networks between two organizations, forming an extranet.

The main benefit of a VPN compared to alternatives is lower cost.

Users typically interact with simple graphical VPN client programs. These applications support creating tunnels, setting configuration parameters, and connecting to and disconnecting from the VPN server. VPN solutions utilize several different network protocols including PPTP, L2TP, IPsec, and SOCKS.

VPN servers can also connect directly to other VPN servers. A VPN server to server connection extends the intranet or extranet to span multiple networks.

Many vendors have developed VPN hardware and software products, though some of these do not inter-operate due to the immaturity of some VPN standards. Still, VPNs offer a viable alternative to traditional leased lines or remote access servers.

Also Known As: Virtual Private Networks.

WAN

A WAN spans a large geographic area, such as a state, province or country. WANs often connect multiple smaller networks, such as LANs or MANs. The most popular WAN in the world today is the Internet. Many smaller portions of the Internet, such as extranets, are also WANs. WANs generally utilize different and much more expensive networking equipment than do LANs. Technologies sometimes found in WANs include SONET, frame relay, and ATM.

Also Known As: Wide Area Network.

WAP

WAP defines a network architecture for content delivery over wireless networks. Central to WAP's design is a network stack based on the OSI model. WAP implements several new networking protocols that perform functions similar to the well-known Web protocols HTTP, TCP, and SSL.WAP includes the concepts of browsers, servers, URLs, and gateways. WAP browsers are intended to be implemented on small mobile devices such as cell phones, pagers, and PDAs. Instead of developing content in HTML and JavaScript, WAP developers use WML and WMLScript.

WAP-enabled devices exist today, although their capability is generally limited to news feeds, stock quotes, and similar basic applications. WAP is in the very early stages of development relative to other networking technologies, and its future viability remains unclear. Also Known As: Wireless Application Protocol.

WINS—Windows Internet Naming Service

The Windows Internet Naming Service (WINS) supports name resolution, the automated conversion of computer names to network addresses, for Windows networks. Specifically, WINS converts NetBIOS names to IP addresses on a LAN or WAN.

Like DNS, the Windows Internet Naming Service employs a distributed client/server system to maintain the mapping of computer names to addresses.

WinSock—Windows Sockets

WinSock is the standard socket programming API for the Windows operating system. WinSock has been a standard feature shipped with all versions of Windows starting with Windows 95.

WinSock was created to allow different microsoft windows TCP/IP software applications to communicate with each other.

Wireless

Wireless networks utilize radio waves and/or microwaves to maintain communication channels between computers. Wireless networking is a more modern alternative to wired networking that relies on copper and/or fiber optic cabling between network devices.

A wireless network offers advantages and disadvantages compared to a wired network.

WLAN—Wireless LAN

WLANs provide wireless network communication over short distances using radio or infrared signals instead of traditional network cabling. A WLAN typically extends an existing wired local area network. WLANs are built by attaching a device called the access point (AP) to the edge of the wired network.

WML—Wireless Markup Language

WML is a tag-based markup language designed after the model of HTML for Web content. The designers of WML (and its companion scripting language, WMLScript) created an environment that demands less memory and processing power from browsers than HTML and JavaScript.

Workgroup—A collection of workstations and servers on a LAN that are designated to communicate and exchange data with one another.

Workstation—A computer connected to a network at which users interact with software stored on the network.

WWW—World Wide Web

The term WWW refers to the open development phase of the Internet that occured in the 1990s. The WWW consists of all the global public Web sites hosted on server computers and the client devices (computers, cell phones, etc.) that access their Web content.

Technically, the WWW is constructed using the following set of technologies:

- HTML—Hypertext Markup Language
- HTTP—Hypertext Transfer Protocol
- Web servers and Web browsers

Researcher Tim Berners-Lee led the development of the original WWW in 1992.

X.25

X.25 is a standard suite of protocols used for packet switching across computer networks. The X.25 protocols works at the physical, data link, and network layers (Layers 1 to 3) of the OSI model. Each X.25 packets contains up to 128 bytes of data.

XML-RPC

XML-RPC is a network programming technique for making procedure calls to software running on remote devices. XML-RPC uses XML coding for calls and sends messages using the Hypertext Transfer Protocol (HTTP). Developers commonly use XML-RPC to develop Web services.

ZoneAlarm—ZoneAlarm Pro

ZoneAlarm is a popular network security software utility created by Zone Labs. ZoneAlarm is a free download, and ZoneAlarm Pro is an enhanced version with a low purchase price.

Primarily, ZoneAlarm acts as a firewall when installed on a LAN.

802.11a

802.11a is a WLAN communication standard. 802.11a is one of the wireless Ethernet standards in the 802.11 series.

802.11a wireless networks support a maximum theoretical bandwidth of 54 Mbps.

802.11b

802.11b is a WLAN communication standard. 802.11b is one of the wireless Ethernet standards in the 802.11 series.

Compared to alternatives like 802.11a and 802.11g, 802.11b network equipment costs less.

802.11g

802.11g was ratified in 2003 as the latest in the series of IEEE 802.11 standards for wireless LAN (WLAN) communications. 802.11g extends and improves on the earlier 802.11b standard.

802.11g supports a maximum bandwidth of 54 Mbps compared to the 11 Mbps of 802.11b.

10Base2

Ethernet specification for thin coaxial cable, transmits signals at 10 Mbps (megabits per second) with a distance limit of 185 meters per segment.

10Base5

Ethernet specification for thick coaxial cable, transmits signals at 10 Mbps (megabits per second) with a distance limit of 500 meters per segment.

10BaseF

Ethernet specification for fiber optic cable, transmits signals at 10 Mbps (megabits per second) with a distance limit of 2000 meters per segment.

10BaseT

Ethernet specification for unshielded twisted pair cable (category 3, 4, or 5), transmits signals at 10 Mbps (megabits per second) with a distance limit of 100 meters per segment.

100BaseT

Ethernet specification for unshielded twisted pair cabling that is used to transmit data at 100 Mbps (megabits per second) with a distance limit of 100 meters per segment.

1000BaseTX

Ethernet specification for unshielded twisted pair cabling that is used to trasmit data at 1 Gbps (gigabits per second) with a distance limitation of 220 meters per segment.

GLOSSARY

Accuracy: Closeness of a reading or indication of a measurement device to the actual value of the quantity being measured.

ActiveX Control (OLE Control): Custom control applet based on Microsoft's OLE architecture. Can run in any OLE-enabled container application or web browser. Address **:** Label or number identifying the memory location of a unit of information.

Alias: A false lower frequency component that appears in sampled data acquired at too low a sampling rate.

Alternating Current (ac): An electric current that reverses its direction at regularly recurring intervals.

Ambient Compensation: The design of an instrument such that changes in ambient temperature do not affect the readings of the instrument.

Amplitude: A measurement of the distance from highest to lowest excursion of a variable or physical motion. Often used with reference to waveforms.

Analog Trigger: A trigger that occurs at a user-selected point on an incoming analog signal. Can be set to occur at a specific level on either an increasing or a decreasing signal (positive or negative slope).

Analog-to-Digital (A/D): Generic term referring to the conversion of analog information to the digital language of computers.

Analog-to-Digital Converter (ADC): An electronic device that converts analog signals to an equivalent digital form.

ARCnet: Token-passing network technology in which nodes Òtake turnsÓ talking according to which node has the token.

Asynchronous: An event that occurs at an arbitrary time, without synchronization to a reference clock. May refer to network messaging, in which a node sends a message without waiting for the receiver to signal that it is ready to receive.

B

Backbone: High capacity network designed to provide high bandwidth for corporate communication requirements.

Backplane: Multi-conductor assembly into which computer-based boards are inserted. Typically supplies power and allows boards to communicate at high speeds.

Bolometer: Infrared thermometer detector consisting of a resistance thermometer arranged for response to radiation.

Baud Rate: Serial communications data transmission rate expressed in bits per second (bps).

Bipolar: A signal range that includes both positive and negative values (*i.e.,* -10 to +10 V).

Block: A high-speed data transfer in which the address of the data is sent followed by a specified number of back-to-back data words.

Breakdown Voltage: Threshold voltage at which circuit components begin to be damaged. See also "working voltage."

Burst Mode: High-speed data acquisition mode in which data points are measured as quickly as possible then held for subsequent conversion. Helps reduce skew.

Bus Master: A type of a plug-in board or controller with the ability to read and write to devices on the computer bus.

Bus: Group of conductors that interconnect individual circuitry in a computer. Examples of PC buses include ISA, EISA, and PCI.

Byte (B): Eight related bits of data, an eight-bit binary number. Also used to denote the amount of memory required to store one byte of data.

Cache: High-speed processor memory that buffers commonly used instructions or data to increase processing throughput.

Calibration: The process of adjusting an instrument or compiling a deviation chart so that its reading can be correlated to the actual value being measured.

Central Processing Unit (CPU): Microprocessor that functions as the primary computational ÒbrainÓ of a PC or other computer-based device.

Code Width: Smallest voltage an A/D converter can detect; a function of resolution, gain, and range.

Cold Junction Compensation (CJC): The referencing of thermocouple voltage outputs to ambient temperature in a thermocouple measurement circuit.

Common-Mode Range: Input range over which a circuit can handle a common-mode signal.

Common-Mode Rejection Ratio (CMRR): Measure of an instrument's ability to reject interference from a common-mode signal, usually expressed in decibels (dB).

Common-Mode Signal: Mathematical average voltage, relative to a computer's ground, of the signals from a differential input.

Controller Area Network (CAN): A serial bus developed by Bosch for use in automotive in-vehicle communications. With added communication layers, is the foundation of DeviceNet industrial automation protocol.

Conversion Time: Time required to convert an analog or digital signal into its converse.

Crosstalk: Unwanted signal on one channel due to interference from another channel.

Data Acquisition (DAQ): The activity of measuring, transmitting, and recording electrical signals from sensors, switches, and transducers. Often implies the conversion of these signals into computer-compatible digital information.

Data Communications Equipment (DCE): Generic telecommunications term referring to the equipment used to actually communicate messages among data terminal equipment (DTE).

Data Terminal Equipment (DTE): Generic telecommunications term referring to a computer-based device that needs to communicate, also referred to as a generator or receiver. See also Data communications equipment.

Decibel (dB): Unit for expressing a logarithmic measure of the ratio of two signal levels.

DeviceNet: Non-proprietary device-level networking protocol for industrial automation. Developed by Allen-Bradley based on Bosch's CAN chips, now the province of the non-profit Open DeviceNet Vendors Association. (ODVA).

Differential Input: Analog input consisting of the voltage difference between two terminals, both of which are different from computer ground.

Digital Input/Output (DIO): Input or output points allowed only two discrete states, typically on or off, 1 or 0.

Digital Signal Processing (DSP): The manipulation of signal information while it exists in digital rather than analog form.

Digital-to-Analog Converter (D/A): Electronic device, often an integrated circuit, that converts a digital number into a corresponding analog voltage or current.

Distributed Control System (DCS): Typically a large-scale process control system characterized by a distributed network of processors and I/O subsystems that encompass the functions of control, user interface, data collection, and system management. DCSs are commonly used in large industrial facilities, such as chemical plants, petroleum refineries, and paper mills.

Electromagnetic Interference (EMI): electrical noise induced upon signal wires with the possible effect of obscuring the instrument signal.

Encoder: Device that converts linear or rotary displacement into digital or pulse signals.

Error: The difference between the correct or desired value and the actual read or value taken.

External Trigger: Voltage pulse from an external source that triggers an event such as A/D conversion.

Fieldbus: All-digital communication network used to connect process instrumentation and control systems. Designed to replace existing 4-20 mA analog signals with bidirectional, multivariable data communications capability.

First-In First-Out (FIFO): Memory buffer in which the first data stored is the first data sent.

Flash ADC: High-speed ADC whose output code is determined in a single step by a bank of comparators and encoding logic.

Frequency: The number of cycles over a specified time period over which an event occurs. Normally expressed in cycles per second (hertz, Hz).

Function: A set of software instructions executed by a single line of code that may have input and/or output parameters and returns a value when executed.

G

Gain Accuracy: Measure of deviation of the gain of an amplifier from the ideal gain.

General Purpose Interface Bus (GPIB): Synonymous with HP-IB (for Hewlett-Packard), the standard bus used for controlling electronic instruments with a computer. Also called IEEE 488 in reference to defining ANSI/IEEE standards.

Graphical User Interface (GUI): An intuitive, graphical means of communicating information between computer-based devices and human users. GUIs can resemble the front panels of instruments or other objects associated with a computer program.

Ground: The electrical neutral line having the same potential as the surrounding earth; the negative side of a direct current power system; the reference point for an electrical system.

Hertz (Hz): Unit of frequency, defined as one cycle per second. Hierarchical: Method of organizing computer programs with a series of levels, each with further subdivisions.

Human-Machine Interface (HMI): The means by which a human operator interacts with an industrial machine or other piece of equipment. See also graphical user interface.

IEEE 488: See general purpose interface bus.

Impedance: The total opposition to electrical flow in an electrical circuit. Input bias current **:** Current that flows into circuit inputs.

Input Impedance: The measured resistance and capacitance between the input terminals of a circuit.

Input/Output (I/O): The transfer of data to and from a computer system involving communications channels, operator interface devices, and/or data acquisition and control interfaces.

Institute of Electrical and Electronic Engineers (IEEE): Professional and standards-writing organization of electrical and computer-related professionals.

Integral Nonlinearity (INL): A measure in LSB of the worst-case deviation from the ideal A/D or D/A transfer characteristic of analog I/O circuitry.

Integrating ADC: ADC that works by integrating an unknown voltage over time. Time required is compared to the time required to integrate a known reference voltage.

J

Joint Time-Frequency Analysis (JTFA): Technique for spectral analysis of rapidly changing waveforms.

L

Linearity: The deviation of an instrument's response from a straight line.

Logical Address: Digital number that uniquely identifies each device in a system.

Loop Resistance: The total resistance of a complete electrical circuit.

Least Significant Bit (LSB): Refers to the smallest increment of resolution in an A/D or D/A conversion.

M

Media Access Control (MAC): Networking layer that determines which node can access the physical media.

Million Floating-Point Operations Per Second (MFLOPS): Unit for expressing the computational power of a processor.

Million Instructions Per Second (MIPS): Unit for expressing the speed of processor execution of machine code instructions.

Module: A board assembly and its associated mechanical parts. A module contains everything required to occupy one or more slots in a mainframe chassis.

Multiplexer (Mux): A switching device that sequentially connects multiple inputs or outputs in order to process several signal channels with a single A/D or D/A converter.

Multitasking: Property of an operating system in which several processes can be run simultaneously.

N

Noise: Any undesirable electrical signal, from external sources such as ac power lines, motors, electrical storms, and radio transmitters, as well as internal sources such as electrical components.

Normal-Mode Rejection Ratio: The ability of an instrument to reject electrical interference across its input terminals, normally of line frequency (50–60 Hz).

Nyquist Theorem: Law of sampling theory stating that data sampling frequency should be at least twice that of the highest frequency variations in the signal of interest. Must be observed to preserve patterns in data and to not introduce artificial, lower frequency patterns.

Personal Computer Memory Card International Association (PCMCIA): An expansion card form factor popular in laptop and notebook computers.

Peripheral Component Interconnect (PCI): High-performance expansion bus architecture common in modern desktop PCs.

Phase: A time-based relationship between a periodic function and a reference.

Polarity: In electricity, the quality of having two charged poles, one positive and one negative.

Port: A communications connection on a computer-based device.

Postriggering: The acquisition of a programmed number of samples by a data acquisition board after trigger conditions are met.

Power Supply: A separate unit or part of a circuit that provides power to the rest of a circuit.

Pretriggering: A data acquisition board that maintains a continuous buffer of data, so that when trigger conditions are met, data generated before the condition occurred can be acquired.

Protocol: Defined sequence of bits, characters, and control codes used to transfer data among computer-based devices.

Quantization Error: Inherent uncertainty in an A/D conversion due to the finite resolution of the conversion process.

Radio Frequency Interference (RFI): Noise induced upon signal wires by ambient radio-frequency electromagnetic radiation with the effect of obscuring the instrument signal.

Range: An area between two limits within which a quantity is measured, stated in terms of a lower and upper limit.

Relative Accuracy: Measure in LSB of the accuracy of an ADC. It includes all non-linearity and quantization errors.

Remote Terminal Unit: Industrial control and data collection device similar to a PLC, but designed for remote communication via wire-based or radio telemetry. Repeatability: The ability of an instrument to give the same output or reading under repeated, identical conditions.

Sample-and-Hold (S/H): Circuit that acquires and stores an analog voltage on a capacitor for subsequent conversion.

Self-Calibrating: Data acquisition board that calibrates its own A/D and D/A circuits with reference to a stable onboard reference.

Sensitivity: The minimum change in a physical variable to which an instrument can respond.

Sequenced Packet Exchange/Internetwork Packet Exchange (SPE/IPE): Novell implementation of network addressing scheme.

Signal-to-Noise Ratio (SNR): The ratio of the overall rms signal level to the rms noise level, expressed in dB.

Simultaneous Sampling (SS): System in which each input or output channel is digitized or updated at the same time.

Successive-Approximation ADC: ADC that sequentially compares a series of binary-weighted values with an analog input to produce an output digital word in *n* steps, where *n* is the bit resolution of the ADC.

Synchronous: An event or action that is synchronized to a reference clock.

System Noise: Measure of the amount of noise seen by an analog circuit or an ADC when the analog inputs are grounded.

Throughput Rate: Speed of execution, in samples or bits per second, for a given continuous operation, calculated to include software overhead.

Transfer Rate: Rate at which data is moved from source to destination.

Unipolar: A signal range that is always positive (for example, 1 to 5 V).

Unshielded Twisted Pair (UTP): Cable construction consisting of pairs of wires twisted at regular intervals (called the pitch) in order to reduce electrical noise interferences.

Volt (V): The electrical potential difference between two points in a circuit. One volt is the potential needed to move one coulomb of charge between two points while using one joule of energy.

Word: Standard number of bits that a processor or memory manipulates at one time. Microprocessors typically use 8, 16, or 32-bit words.

Zero Offset: The non-zero output of an instrument, expressed in units of measure, under conditions of true zero.

Index

A

B

H

I

L

M

N

❑❑❑